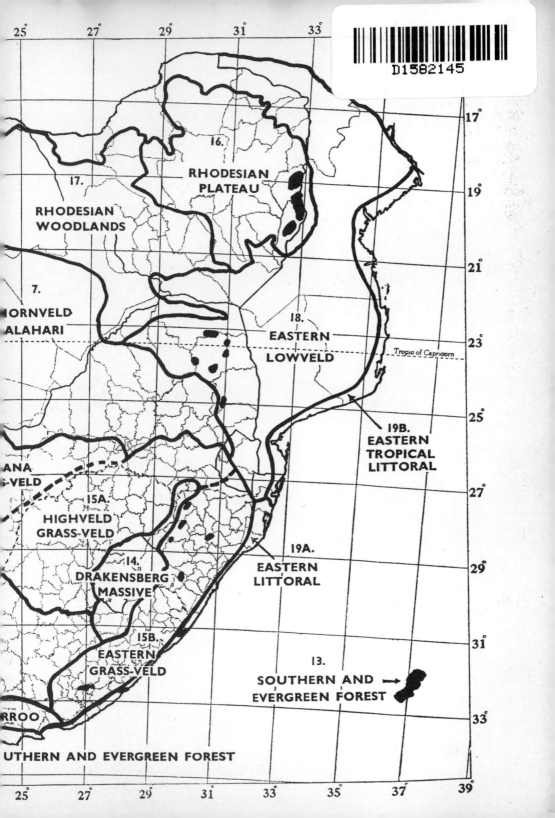

25°   27°   29°   31°   33°

17°

16.
RHODESIAN
PLATEAU

19°

17.
RHODESIAN
WOODLANDS

21°

7.
HORNVELD
ALAHARI

18.
EASTERN
LOWVELD

Tropic of Capricorn

23°

25°

19B.
EASTERN
TROPICAL
LITTORAL

ANA
S-VELD

27°

15A.
HIGHVELD
GRASS-VELD

14.
DRAKENSBERG
MASSIVE

19A.
EASTERN
LITTORAL

29°

15B.
EASTERN
GRASS-VELD

31°

13.
SOUTHERN AND →
EVERGREEN FOREST

RROO

33°

UTHERN AND EVERGREEN FOREST

25°   27°   29°   31°   33°   35°   37°   39°

430. Ground Hornbill

1. Ostrich

K B NEWMAN '76

ROBERTS BIRDS
of South Africa

Revised by
G. R. McLACHLAN Ph.D. (Cantab)
and
R. LIVERSIDGE Ph.D. (U.C.T.)

Plates in colour by
NORMAN C. K. LIGHTON
and
KENNETH NEWMAN

Black and White Illustrations by
J. Adams and H. Grönvold

Published by
The Trustees of the John Voelcker Bird Book Fund

Distributed by C. Struik (Pty) Ltd.

The John Voelcker Bird Book Fund
5 Church Square, Cape Town

First published 8th June 1940
Second Impression 17th December 1940
Third Impression (revised) 1942
Fourth Impression 1944
Fifth Impression 1946
Sixth Impression 1948
Seventh Impression 1949
Eighth Impression 1951
Ninth Impression 1953
Second Edition—First Impression 1957
Second Impression 1958
Third Impression 1961
Fourth Impression 1963
Fifth Impression 1965
Sixth Impression 1966
Seventh Impression 1969
Third Edition—First Impression 1970
Second Impression 1971
Third Impression 1972
Fourth Impression 1975
Fourth Edition—First Impression 1978
Second Impression 1978
Third Impression 1980
Fourth Impression 1981
Fifth Impression 1981

ISBN 0 620 03118 2

PRINTED IN SOUTH AFRICA BY
CAPE & TRANSVAAL PRINTERS (PTY.) LTD., CAPE TOWN

BD9801

Foreword

by Field-Marshal J. C. Smuts

ALTHOUGH the bird life of South Africa forms one of its outstanding glories there has so far—apart from the handy little volume by Dr Leonard Gill—not been available a comprehensive guide for the use of bird-lovers. This need has at last been met, and I am happy to be able to introduce this valuable work to the public of South Africa. It represents a lifetime of study by the Author both at the Transvaal Museum and in the field.

The South African Bird Book Fund was formed in 1935 for the express purpose of producing the book in collaboration with the South African Ornithological Society. The Trustees of the Fund were supported by subscriptions from many private individuals and bodies, and after five years' work this scientific and practical handbook has resulted. It reflects great credit on both the Author and Artist, together with all who have been concerned and worked together for its production.

The book is bound to be not only of great educational value and suitable for school use, but of interest both to the student ornithologist and to those members of the general public who would like to know more of the nature and habits of the immense variety of bird life to be seen in South Africa.

Whilst the text is necessarily condensed, to be confined conveniently to one volume, it covers the whole of the species and varieties to be found in South Africa south of the Cunene and Zambesi rivers, and the majority are illustrated in colour.

The reader will find that the book contains the common names of all our birds in English, Afrikaans, and Eastern Bantu and Native languages, their distribution, habits, and the general characters by which they can be recognized.

The system of indexing is novel, and simplifies reference both to the text and illustration of any particular species.

The book should remain a standard work of reference for many years.

The Author in his introduction sets out many lines of possible future research into the scientific problems which arise in the study of ornithology, and a helpful guide is given to those anxious to go further into this interesting subject.

1938

[signature]

Contents

vii

FAMILY (cont.)   *Page*

List of Colour Plates

Preface to the Fourth Edition

IT IS over thirty-five years since *Birds of South Africa* was first published, and during this period some 100 000 copies of the various editions have been sold.

However, as mentioned in my preface to the Third Edition, the Trustees have had it in mind for some time to revise the original plates. The passage of time has meant that many new birds have been admitted to the list for southern Africa. While these birds have been incorporated in the text from time to time, it was not possible to add them to the plates because of the expense of making new letterpress blocks. Further, it was felt that Lighton's original paintings suffered from over-reduction and could with advantage be enlarged by removing the broad white margins surrounding the plates. However, it was not possible to effect this without new artwork, as four of the originals were lost, due in the main to enemy action in the last war. In addition, some plates, notably the difficult waders and birds of prey, had attracted criticism in the light of modern knowledge.

The Trustees therefore decided to invite Mr Kenneth Newman in collaboration with the editors, to rearrange the entire set of illustrations, retaining as many as possible, adding the new birds and making any regroupings which might aid field identification.

Dr G. R. McLachlan and Dr R. Liversidge are to be congratulated for continuing their excellent work as editors, and we are particularly grateful to Mr Ken Newman for the vast amount of research and hard work he has put into the new plates—the results speak for themselves. Our thanks are also due to our very able and energetic secretary Mr Richard Knight, and also to Mr R. M. Hodgson and Mr J. B. Leitch of Cape & Transvaal Printers.

All these changes have taken several years and I should like to thank the Trustees for their encouragement and support in making what are, after all, somewhat revolutionary changes in the old-established Roberts format. We trust that this completely changed edition will be even more successful than its predecessors in promoting the study of birds in southern Africa.

February 1978

C. S. BARLOW

Editors' Preface to the Fourth Edition

THE MAIN feature of this new edition is the complete rearrangement of the colour plates. There are thirty-one new plates by Ken Newman. In some of the others odd birds have been changed or new ones added, or the positions have been rearranged. No alterations have been made to the remainder except to enlarge the figures by deleting the original white border. The value of these enlargements will be immediately apparent by comparing the waxbills on Plate 70 with the same birds on the old Plates 54 and 55. The old black-and-white plates have been redrawn in colour, making a total of 72 colour plates instead of 56 in colour and 8 black and white as in previous editions. Most important, the plates are reproduced by lithography, and this means that they can be kept up-to-date—unlike the letterpress blocks of the old editions which were too expensive to alter.

Small marginal sketches have been added; some of these are taken from Stark and Sclater, *Fauna of South Africa: Birds*, Vols. 1, 3 and 4. Others have been drawn especially for this edition by Jill Adams.

Very few changes have been made in the English names, and as few as possible in the scientific list. Unfortunately there is still lamentably little agreement among taxonomists, and as always, this has made the attainment of a stable nomenclature very difficult. Distribution maps have been altered where necessary in the light of recent records, and old single records have been omitted.

Adding new birds to the plates has accentuated the difficulty of deciding which birds merit inclusion and which do not. Obviously every aviary escapee or storm-driven sea bird cannot be included, but our approach in the past has been somewhat inconsistent. As a guide-line in the future we have decided to admit a species on the basis of five specimens *except* for birds which occur normally just across the border, in which case fewer are acceptable.

We must acknowledge the help given us in the past and listed in earlier editions. Shortage of space precludes our repeating all the names here.

Together with Ken Newman we should like to thank the following for the loan of specimens and for assistance in various other ways: The Directors of the Durban, Transvaal and South African museums; A. Bannister, G. Bennett, H. H. Berry, W. Bloomfield, W. B. Boshoff, R. K. Brooke, P. A. Clancey, C. F. Clinning, T. Crowe, G. Currie, N. Elwell, L. Gillard, V. Hards, M. Jankowitz, R. A. C. Jensen, P. G. Johnson, A. C. Kemp, Mrs M. Kemp, J. Kieser, C. Loubscher, G. L. Maclean, J. Mendelsohn, G. Mills, P. le S. Milstein, G. Nichols, S. Pringle, D. Prout-Jones, R. Siegfried, I. Sinclair, P. Steyn, M. P. Stuart-Irwin, S. P. van Nierop, F. Weber, J. M. Winterbottom, S. Wolff, K. Wood, C. J. Uys and N. Zaloumis.

We wish to thank Ken Newman for his enthusiastic co-operation in the preparation of the new plates, and for his patience and tolerance when asked to make changes. We are also grateful to the Trustees of the South African Museum for allowing us to use the original drawings which appear in Stark and Sclater Volume 4.

R. LIVERSIDGE,
MacGregor Museum,
Kimberley

G. R. McLACHLAN,
South African Museum,
Cape Town
1978

Subscribers to the Fourth Edition

De luxe Edition

1 McMurtry, Douglas M.
2 Conradie, W. S.
3 Johnson, Peter George
4 Burton, Mrs J.
5 Herbert, G. B.
6 Westcott, T. N.
7 Schroder, Lionel
8 Brooke, P. M.
9 Wolhuter, Joan B.
10 McCormick, N. S. R.
11 Schöning, Haydée
12 Crawford, J. L.
13 Meredith, Courtney D.
14 Perrin, Trevor
15 Twaddle, Ian Gordon
16 Abbot, J. H.
17 Chalkley, Irene
18 Fabian, D. T.
19 Shapland, Pam
20 Poole, Mr and Mrs K. R.
21 More, Mr and Mrs John
22 Roche, Wilson
23 Durham, Dr F. J.
24 Cornish, John Burchell
25 Stannard, Mrs June
26 Smith, G. H. Vivian
27 Bennett, Joan M.
28 Bell, Shellagh M.
29 Reed, R. A.
30 Steyn, Peter
31 Ellis, P.
32 Lambie, A. A.
33 Cantrell, Mr and Mrs A. C.
34 Hosken, J. H.
35 Hall, Mrs D. G.

36 Davidson, Ian H.
37 Plug, Professor C.
38 Grobler, Professor N. J.
39 Pirow, Peter C.
40 Wilkins, Barrie
41 Baines, C. J. R.
42 Brodie, Len
43 Sweatman, Michael
44 Hayes, F. G.
45 Stainer, D. J.
46 Ferrett, Peter B.
47 Johnson, Geoffrey A. L.
48 Davies, Dr John B.
49 Weaving, Alan
50 Hurry, Simon Boyd
51 Livingstone, Brian and Dawn
52 Wilson, Derric Harmen
53 Hosken, F. W.
54 Loraine-Grews, Michael D.
55 Lyons, Eliot
56 Hancock, Mr and Mrs N.
57 Perry, Ronald Edward
58 Greig, Italia
59 Egan, Mr and Mrs D. M. and A. M.
60 Rowsell, P. H.
61 Anderson, D. I. E.
62 McClean, Mr and Mrs A. G.
63 Jeffery, R. G.
64 Lund, Desmond Hotspur
65 Glanvill, André
66 Line, John
67 Tregoning, Tina

68 Witney, Peter
69 Pringle, J. S.
70 Mullins, A. R.
71 Lightfoot, C. J.
72 Brodie, Raynor
73 Noakes, M. W.
74 Bullen, J. W.
75 Van Jaarsveldt, H. S. M.
76 Gawith, Toby
77 Gasson, Dr Reg
78 Saunders, Dr Colin
79 Mockford, H. H.
80 Pringle, V. L.
81 Crozier, Dr Robert and Irene
82 Stewart, Mrs Ronald
83 Scheepers, Jack
84 Fannin, The Hon. D. G.
85 Lucke, Eric
86 Campbell, John and Peta
87 Levitt, Robert E.
88 Humphrey, R. W. H.
89 Bateman, E. Laurence
90 Sturrock, I. L. B.
91 Latham, Mr and Mrs P.
92 Lomberg, Mrs Anna C. E.
93 Berry, M. P. S.
94 Robson, Thomas William
95 Reed, Derrick H.
96 Main, Vivienne G. (Paddy)
97 Morris, Phil
98 Fannin, Dr John
99 Johnson, Miles Robert
100 Moore, A. E.

Subscribers to the Fourth Edition

Subscribers' Edition

Abbott, Loide
Aird, Mr and Mrs R. A.
Aitken, Mrs L. H.
Ambler-Smith, B.
Anderson, Jeremy
Antelme, Henri
Attwell, R. I. G.

Baer, Christine
Balderson, Colin
Balderson, Guy
Barker, Dorothy Jean (2)
Barlow, Pamela
Barnes, Catherine Scott
Barnes, Ian Scott
Barnes, Monica Mary Agnes
Bartlett, Beryl E.
Bashall, F. J.
Bateman, E. Laurence
Bathgate, H. T.
Baxter, Darryl L.
Baxter, Mike
Beadle, Lady
Beaumont, Mrs P. M.
Bell, Mrs Eve
Bensimon, I. A.
Bentley, F. W. P.
Bérard, Dr and Mrs R. M. F.
Berry, G. F.
Bezuidenhout, John
Bligh, G. P.
Boddam-Whetham, A. D.
Bolitho, D.
Bolton, Brian R.
Bophuthatswana Government
    Nature Conservation Division
Borsook, Sheila
Bosch, Dr H. W.
Bosman, P. B.
Böttger, H. A.
Böttger, H. W. P.
Böttger, M.
Böttger, W. A.

Bowyer, H. L.
Bradley, A. J.
Brandt, Dr H. D.
Brebner, Miss Betty
Brenchley, P. D.
Brenthurst Library
Brett, Maurice
Brink, Jeanita
Britten, Stephen Philip
Brodie, B. E. M.
Brodie, Len
Brodie, Raynor
Bromley-Gans, J. M.
Brooker, C. J.
Brossy, Dr J. J.
Brown, Mrs A. I. D.
Brown, D. M. V.
Anonymous

Bryant, A. J.
Buchanan, D. A.
Bullock, D. M.
Bunning, L. John
Burgess, Mrs B. E.
Burnett, D.
Burrows, Mrs H. G.
Busby, Muriel
Buss, A. Martin
Butcher, Alan R.
Butlin, Dr John L.
Buys, Linda, (Greytown)

Anonymous (2)
Cairns, W. W. P.
Calder, D. R.
Carruthers, Heather
Cawood, Clive
Chalkley, Irene
Champken, Captain R. M.
Channing, Alan and Jenny
Charlton, R. W.
Chenaux-Repond, Rolf
Christopher, B.

Cleghorn, Mr and Mrs W. B.
Clinning, C. F.
Coaker, Quentin
Coe, W. A., M.B., F.R.C.S.E.
Collett, Lionel H.
Connan, A. P.
Conradie, H. D.
Cope, Mrs G. C.
Corrie, Mrs H. T.
Coulson, Dr P. P.
Coxwells, Louis Trichardt
Craig, Desmond Alexander
Craven, Dan and Pat
Creasy, Charles Quinton
Crewe-Brown, Dr Geoffrey F.
Cullinan, Wendy
Cunliffe, Mrs C. J. M.

Davey, Dr J. K. A.
Davies, Dr John B.
Deitch, B. G.
De Lange, C. J. A.
Denman, E. B.
De Ujfalussy, Philippa
de Villiers, Dr J. S.
de Villiers, Noel N.
de Villiers, Elise
de Villiers, Kevin
de Villiers, S. W. L.
Van Wyk de Vries, Anton
Dicey, A. M.
Dichmont, E. V.
Dickens, Mr and Mrs C. J.
Doepel, W. R.
Doidge, Mr and Mrs A. H.
Doyle, Gerald
Dreboldt, William C.
Durban Museum
Du Toit, Mr and Mrs G. J.

Eades, Mrs M. L.
Egerton, F. M. G., Pr. Eng.

xiii

Eichbaum, H. A.
Elley, Eloi
Elphinstone, Mrs C. I.
Elwell, N. H.
Emerson, John
Espie, Ian W.
Evans, Chris

Fannin, Craig
Fannin, Glenn
Farrant, John C.
Faurie, W. H.
Feely, Jim
Fenn, J. L.
Ferguson, W. T.
Ferreira, P. J.
Ferreira, P. J. (2)
Ferri, Dario and Bircher,
  Sheryl
Fisons Agrochemicals (Pty)
  Ltd (4)
Foggin, B. J. M.
Folker, N. P. L.
Forbes, Dr A. T. and Mrs J.
Forsyth, Beryl
Forsyth, Robin
Foster, James
Fourie, Hilgard
Fourie, S. R.
France, C. R. B.
Francioso Family Trust
Franklin, Deryk E.
Frean, J. M.
Freemantle, James, (In Mem.)
Fry, John
Frylinck, Ruth

Gamsu, Robert
Gans, Miss M. S.
Garnett, M. N.
Gartrell Family, F. R.
Geekie, J. K.
Gilfillan, Mrs N. H.
Gillatt, I. F. G.
Gilston, Harvey
Ginn, Peter J.
Girdwood, R. J.
Gladstone, Shelley and John
Goldswain, Mary
Gordon, P. S. L.
Gorfinkel, Val
Gosling, D. C.
Goulding, Mr and Mrs A. K.
Goulding, Dr and Mrs K. C.
Graaff, J. de V. (2)

Graham, A. W.
Gregorowski, W. R.
Gregory, Neil and Pam
Grieve, G. R. H.
Grobler, Professor N. J. (2)
Gush, R. O. and P. J.
Guy, Jeff

Haagner, Clem
Haagner, Hal K.
Haerlen, Ernst
Haig, W. R.
Hall, Jean
Hall, R. S.
Harper, Colin and Hazel
Harris, Edwin
Harrison, E. R.
Hartley, David (2)
Harwin, Dr and Mrs R. M.
Hathorn, K.
Haugland, N. P. J.
Haupt, P. B.
Hellman, Margaret W.
Hepburn, A. I. M.
Hepburn, S. K.
Hetherington, Ian J.
Hickman, Mr and Mrs M. H.
  (2)
Hill, Mrs F. G.
Hobsy,
Hobson, B. N.
Hodge, E. M.
Hodge Family, N. M.
Anonymous
Hoets, Mrs D. A.
Hofmeyr, Mr and Mrs A. H.
Hofmeyr, Dr P. K.
Hogg, W. D.
Hollmann, Lex
Horne, Mr and Mrs P. J.
Hosken, J. H.
Hotson, A. J.
Houston, Mr and Mrs N.
Houston, Mr and Mrs W.
Howcroft, Wendy
Howell, G. H.
Hudson, John
Hulett, Cameron
Hulett, Miles
Hulett, Sean
Hundleby, C. J. B.
Hurry, Burford
Hutchison, Harry M.
Hutchison, Ian
Hutton, J. M.

Ingram, F. A.
Irish, Shirley

Jankowitz, Dr Mike
Jantzen, G.
Jeffery, R. G.
Jensen, Jorn Vestergaard
Jerome, Charles H.
Johnson, Geoffrey C.
Jones, E. Roy
Anonymous
Josselsohn, Dr and Mrs E. Q.
Joubert, Dr Eugene
Junod, Mrs S. M.

Karg, R.
Keen, Ian W.
Keenan-Smith, Denis
Keogan, Mrs N. A.
Kerr and Family, C. W. P.
Kieser, Dr and Mrs Julius A.
Kinsey, H. W.
Kirk, Craig John
Klugman, Dr and Mrs Leon
Knorr, D. I. R.
Knox-Shaw, P. H.
Kockott, Claude
Kretzmar, D. L.
Kruger, Hazel and Jan
Kruger, J. J.

Laburn, Beryl and Bob
Lamont, Gavin T.
Lamont Smith, D.
Lane, A. W.
Lane, J. B.
Laschinger, E. F.
Laubscher, Cyril
Leathern, Margot and Mike
Ledger, John and Amy
Lee, Molly and Derek
Le May, B. C.
Le Riche, E. A. N.
Le Roux, Peter Alfred
Lessing, Alice A.
Levitt, Mrs Rosamond
Levy-Strauss, Andre L.
Lewis, Mr and Mrs O. G.
Little, B.
Livingstone, Mark
Livingstone, Peter
Lloyd, D. Allden

Lockhart, Patrick S.
Loock, Johannes Jacobus
Lowry, A. V.
Loxton, Sam and Anna
Lüderitz-Museum, Lüderitz-
  bucht SWA
Luke, I.
Lund, Desmond Hotspur
Lund, S. M.
Lyttelton Manor High School

Macduff, Alastair Robert
MacGillivray, Donald
MacKenzie, D. L.
Mackintosh, Bernys
Maggs, C. O'C.
Malan, Mr and Mrs F. D.
Mansell, M. W.
Marchand, M. F. H.
Markus, Dr M. B.
Marsh, Major W. D.
Marshall, Brian
McCallum, R. W.
McCullough, M. W.
McEwan, The Hon. Mr Justice
  W. S. and Mrs
McGregor, Mrs L. C.
McIlleron, Geoff
McIntosh, Bruce M.
McIntosh, P. D. D. (2)
McKechnie, Dr J. K.
McKenzie, Colin A.
McLaren, Dr James D. M.
McMurtry, Roddy
Medway, B. M.
Meijer, Lambertus
Meikle, Arthur James
Meldrum, Sheila M.
Melville, P. S.
Meredith, Philip G.
Merryne Watson, J.
Michler, Mr and Mrs John
Middelmann, Mrs J. D.
Millar, Jack and Stella
Mills, Mr and Mrs M. G. L.
Mills, Veronica
Mitchell, Michael and Esther
Mitchell-Innes, E. F.
Mockford, G. E.
Molteno, C. B.
Morgan, H. K.
Morris, Dr and Mrs B. D.
Morris, Dr D. R.

Morris, Phil
Mortimer, Mr and Mrs J. H.
Muir, Dr and Mrs M. S.
Mullins, Mrs D. M.
Mumby, M. A. I.
Mun-Gavin, Mr and Mrs C. I.
Murdoch, D. S.
Murray, Dr C. E.
Murray, P. J.
Murrell, Clive

Natal Bird Club
Natal Parks, Game and Fish
  Preservation Board
Nathan, Chief Justice and Mrs
  C. J. M.
National Archives of Rhodesia
Naylor, S. P.
Neethling, C.
Nevill, H. M. D.
Newman, Mr and Mrs Noggs
Nichols, G. R.
Nielsen, Leon
Nightingale, Ron
Noyce, Michael
Nutt, Eric Eugene

Odquist, Gustaf
Oliver, Mr and Mrs Frank
Olivier, A.
Orford, J. L.

Parker, E. M.
Patterson, P. M.
Patz, Dr and Mrs D. M.
Patz, Dr and Mrs I. M.
Pauw, Samuel
Pearse, Mr and Mrs W. E.
Perry, E. M.
Perryer, J. N.
Peverett, Wayne
Pickard, Mr and Mrs F. R.
Pitt, Aubrey
Pocock, V. F. T.
Potgieter, F. J.
Pretorius, Mev M. J.
Pringle, J. M.
Pullen, Elma and Roy

Quinton-Smith, O. (2)

Rabie, Dr C. J.
Rae, John
Randall, Mr and Mrs Rod
Ranger, Gordon
Ranger, Mr and Mrs Gray
Ratcliffe, Brian W. Stansfield
Ratcliffe, G. H.
Rauch, Dr and Mrs R. N. L.
Raw, John C.
Reabow, Charles
Reid, Dr M. B. S.
Reilly, Ted and Liz
Renaud, Delphine
Renny, A. T.
Resnik, Harold
Richards, Charles E. C.
Richardson-Berl, M. L.
Rickaby, Fred
Rissik, Diane
Ritchie, J. B.
Ritson, Bill
Robb, D. A.
Roberts, Mrs C.
Roberts, Simon
Robertson, Kevin
Robertson, S. H.
Robin, Geoff
Robinson, L. S.
Rogers, Edgar H.
Ross, Mrs D. H.
Rothgiesser, Hazel K.
Roux, P. F.
Royston, M. G.
Rudolf, Mrs Anita
Russell, Dr and Mrs John T.

Sacerdote, Mr and Mrs F.
  (Phil)
Savage, I.
Savage, P.
Scheepers, Mrs Joy
Scheepers, V.
Schmidt, R. K.
Schneider-Waterberg, H. R.
Schoeman, Daan W.
Schoon, Phyl
Schulze, Susan
Schütte, Marc
Searle, Ronald
Sentefol, U.
Shearer, Mrs A. V.
Shuker, Dr G. W.

Simms, Mr and Mrs R. G.
Sinclair, Ann C.
Slogrove, A. E.
Smale, Mr and Mrs S. E.
Smeenk, C.
Smith, Mr and Mrs A. Clement
Smith, Mary
Smithyman, J. H.
Sonderegger, H. N.
Spavins, A. W.
Spearpoint, Mrs J. A.
Spethmann, Klaus
Stacey, B. M.
Starling, Mrs P. M. (Jill)
Statham, S. A. H.
Stead, Colin
Stein, Eleanor
Stewart, Mrs Ronald
Steyn, C. E.
Steyn, Mr and Mrs H.
Stidolph, Mr and Mrs P.
Stocken, Dr C. G.
Stretton, Sandy

Taylor, Jean E.
Theiler, Gertrud
Thesen, A. R.
Thoele, S.
Thompson, Grace Noreen
Thorpe, K. M.
Thurlow, M. R.
Tilch, M.
Toms, B. O'R.
Toms, T. B.

Tonkin, Peter A.
Tooley, M. W. R.
Towers, Peter
Traill, J. C.
Troughton, M. E.
Turner, J. J.
Turner, John R.
Turner, Roger P.
Twaddle, Mrs L. E.
Tweedie, Anthony

Underhill, G. D.
Uphill-Brown, G. A.
Uys, Professor C. J.
Uys, W. P. en C. E.

Van Assen, B. J.
Van den Berg, H. D.
Van der Heever, Leo
Van der Merwe, Carel and Ingrid
Van der Merwe, Dr H. P.
Van Nierop, P. A.
Van Reenen, Archie
Van Veen, Willem P.
Venning, Spencer
Verwayen, Dr J. C.
Viljoen, Dr R. E.
Von Maltitz, E. F.
Anonymous
Vos, W. J. (2)

Walker, Eric and Ann
Walmsley, W. C.

Walter, G. H.
Ward, David
Warnes, W. E. J.
Watt, Dr J. S.
Watt, M. C.
Webster, Mrs B. H. S.
Wemyss, Lieut.-Colonel J. R. M.C.
Wheeler, Gillian and Patrick
Wilkes, B. J.
Wilkin, E. W. S.
Wilkins, Barrie
Williams, Peter
Williamson, Dr Graham
Williamson, Dr M. L.
Wilson, Hardy E.
Wilson, Dr J. H.
Winchester-Gould, G. A. (2)
Wise, R. O.
Witwatersrand Bird Club
Wolhuter, Joan B.
Wolters, Dr Hans Edmund Bonn, W. Germany
Wood, A. D.
Wood, C. H.
Wright, Dr Michael
Wylde, Dr R. B.

Yarrow Africa Maritime Consultancy (3)

Zaloumis, Alec
Zaloumis, George
Zaloumis, Nolly

Introduction

THIS book is intended to be a simple guide to the species of birds found in South Africa, and, as such, cannot be expected to furnish all the details that go to the make-up of the life-history of the species. Complete accounts could be given only in a set of volumes that would have to be retained on library shelves for use in the home, whereas the present single-volume work can be conveniently carried into the field where the birds can be seen and studied in their natural setting. Identification of the species in the field is most easily effected by sight and the great majority have, therefore, been illustrated in colour, by Norman C. K. Lighton and Ken Newman. These colour plates cover most of the species found on land and along the sea-shore, the sea-birds being less completely illustrated. In the majority of cases in which the sexes differ in appearance, both have been illustrated; but it has not been possible in this condensed volume to show also the immature and juvenile plumages, except in a few cases amongst the conspicuous birds of prey in which immature birds may look very different from the adults. Nor has it been possible in this small compass to illustrate all the resident subspecies; but a few subspecies have been illustrated to show how some of them change in appearance under different geographical physical conditions—some subspecies looking more unlike at geographical extremes than other related but distinct species which may occur side by side with them.

The text has been condensed to contain information about the families, under special brief paragraphs, followed by accounts of the species, which are numbered from 1 to 875 as a guide to the species shown on the colour plates and bearing the same number.

Nomenclature and Classification

While the primary need in all branches of human interests is the use of suitable terms with which to express oneself, the nomenclature of animals takes three forms: the vernacular, the literary, and the scientific. To the layman a single name in the vernacular, such as "Toppie", "Willie", "Fiskaal", is all that is needed to indicate a certain species of bird; but to others the use of single names such as these is insufficient in a country like South Africa, where we have not only two introduced European languages to consider, but also in the background a number of Native tribal names, some of which are in common use amongst Europeans, such as "Mahem".

Vernacular names always vary, even in the same districts in the most advanced civilized countries, and on account of this authors in the countries concerned have endeavoured to fix upon one name only to avoid confusion in literature. Perhaps the most successful in this respect have been the American settlers, who have developed much upon their own lines and have stabilized the literary names for the species of birds, with great benefit to American literature on, and general knowledge of, birds. In South Africa the choice of single names for certain species remains to be made in the case of many, and we have had to search for appropriate ones amongst those in use with an eye to causing as little disturbance of current usage as possible. The desire has not been to force the use of any of these names upon anyone, but to conform as nearly to common practice as seems consistent with clarity.

The scientific system of nomenclature was started by Carl Linnaeus, a Swedish naturalist, during the eighteenth century, as a result of careful study of the need for an *international* system of nomenclature that would meet with general approval. After producing nine editions of his work *Systema Naturae*, in which he dealt with the various forms of Nature, he definitely decided in his 10th edition, in 1758, upon the use of only two Latin names for each species; the first name was for the genus—or group of species—and the second for the individual species within that group. The British school of ornithologists dated the start of the system from the final, 12th, edition of 1766 of Linnaeus's work, as being the best he had produced, and it was not until the year 1910 that it was decided to fall into line with other national schools and adopt the 10th edition as the starting-point. This change has meant a few alterations in Latin nomenclature, in addition to many other alterations arising from a definite adoption at the same time of the first name to be applied and elimination of choice, upon various grounds, at the whim of some systematists; much work has been done since 1910 to ascertain the exact dates of publication of names, and a number of changes have been found to be necessary as a result. Linnaeus also sometimes used a third name under the term "variety" for less important divisions of the species, but as the term was loosely applied it was not made use of in zoology until more than a century later, when it became adopted exclusively for geographical varieties, now styled "subspecies" in birds. His system covered the whole field of biology as conceived at that time, and was divided into major groups named Classes, such as *Aves* for birds, *Mammalia* for mammals, *Insecta* for insects, etc. The Classes were split up into major groups known as Orders, and the Orders were again split up into Families. After this came the lower divisions of Genera and Species, the names for which were used in common practice. The original concept of the system has been continued ever since, but with modifications found necessary to accord with the advance of knowledge in the various branches of biological science. Many thousands of systematists have been engaged upon the classification of animals since the days of Linnaeus and the subject has been reduced to a considerable degree of refinement. The whole basis of the system is that of the relationship of species—that is, upon the characters of structure of living species, plus the evidence adduced from the study of fossils. Careful comparison of the characters of species has often shown that while two species may look much alike to the layman, actually they may have a widely different origin, which is shown by small, but important, differences, such as between Swifts and Swallows, or Larks and Pipits. Linnaeus placed the Herons, Storks, and Cranes all in the same genus *Ardea*, yet today they are recognized to represent three distinct Orders of birds. Our knowledge of existing species has increased enormously since the days of Linnaeus and it is to be expected that great changes have had to be effected. Some recent comprehensive works have shown the advisability of subdivision of the major groups into Subclasses, Superorders, Suborders, Superfamilies, Subfamilies, and Supergenera; and even in ordinary usage we find Subgenera sometimes recognized and placed in brackets between the genus and species names. Whenever a species varies geographically and names are applied to signify this, a third (subspecies) name is used, such as will be seen in numerous cases when the species are being dealt with hereafter. This system takes no account of fortuitous individual variations, nor differences of sexual or seasonal plumages, but deals only with the characters that are perpetuated from generation to generation in Nature. Thus the differences seen in domesticated animals cannot be compared with those found in Nature, as they are the result of artificial and not natural selection.

The basic unit of Linnaeus' system was the species. As is to be expected, when relationships of one species or one group to another are considered by different workers there are bound to be different conclusions. Workers who show a tendency to unite genera or subspecies are often referred to as lumpers, whilst others who show the opposite inclination to divide genera or to recognize many subspecies are known as splitters. In time there will be more agreement with an increase in knowledge. Until this stage is reached, or even approached, there will continue to be disagreement and its accompanying swing from one extreme to the other.

Reverting to the basic unit—a species—we find that it is usually denoted by two names.

Thus the scientific name of a bird appears as follows:

Aquila rapax (Temminck), 1828: *South Africa.*

Aquila is the generic name and is borne by several related eagles; *rapax* is the specific name and tells us which sort of eagle it is; Temminck is the name of the author who published the first scientific description of this bird. His name is placed in parenthesis because he originally called the bird *Falco rapax*. That is to say, he considered all the eagles and falcons as belonging to one big genus. Today such a genus would be considered much too large and it is now split up into several smaller ones such as *Aquila, Falco, Kaupifalco*, etc. If Temminck *had* used the genus *Aquila* his name would appear without brackets; 1828 is of course the year in which the original description was published and in some scientific works the publication itself may be mentioned; *South Africa* is known as the type locality, and is the locality from which the first described specimen was collected.

The example quoted above is described as a binomial because the name consists of only two parts. Where a species shows geographical variation and has been divided into named races (also known as subspecies), the scientific names of these races consist of three parts and are known as trinomials.

Aquila rapax raptor Brehm, 1855: *Blue and White Nile.*

One of these races will have to have the same sub-specific name as the original binomial, in our example, *Aquila rapax rapax* (Temminck), 1828: *South Africa*. This race is described as the typical or nominate race. Notice that in the race, *raptor* and the author's name are not contained in brackets because he used the genus *Aquila* when describing the new race.

Many workers of the last decade have so stressed the importance of races that to many the trinomial name has unfortunately become the unit. Students of bird life who are not trained scientists often find difficulty in understanding the difference between the species and the subspecies. The species unit is difficult to define, but to all intents and purposes may be considered as a population of animals (living organisms) which breed freely among themselves but which are separated from other breeding populations by some barrier. This barrier may take the form of a difference in appearance or structure, spatial separation, difference in behaviour, habits, biology and so on. Fortunately, most species are easily separable. Where there is close similarity, the usual point to consider first is interbreeding; whether the two populations would, under natural conditions interbreed if they were in the same locality. If they are considered unlikely to interbreed then they should be taken as separate species.

The subspecies is a unit within the species. Birds or other animals which occur over a wide area, particularly if they do not move about much, tend to develop local peculiarities of plumage, song or habits which make them slightly different from examples of the species from other areas. If these populations differ appreciably they are given names as explained below. If the population is continuous throughout an area, every gradation between subspecies may be found. Sometimes, however, a desert, ocean or mountain range may separate one subspecies from another. These separated populations are not considered to be species if they appear so similar that it must be presumed that they would interbreed quite naturally if they came into contact with one another. Of course this introduces a subjective element and one worker may consider two separated populations as different species, while another may argue that they are only one species differentiated into subspecies by isolation. Detailed study of such cases will usually reveal the true state of affairs. In general it will be obvious that birds which move about a great deal—vultures, eagles and migratory birds—tend to differentiate into subspecies less than sedentary species because they may breed and interbreed with other individuals born many hundreds of miles away. Thus any peculiarities developed tend to get lost by interbreeding. On the other hand, some larks and other species which never move far tend to form isolated populations and develop distinctive characters.

Bibliography

The following more important books dealing with South African Birds, or of a more general nature, are in common use:

HOESCH und NIETHAMMER, *Die Vögelwelt Deutsch–Südwest Afrikas*, 1940
PRIEST, C. D., revised by Winterbottom, J. M., *The Eggs of Birds Breeding in Southern Africa*
CLANCEY, P. A. *A Check List of the Birds of Natal and Zululand*, 1953
HOESCH, W. *Die Vögelwelt Südwestafrikas*, 1955
SMITHERS, R. H. N., STUART IRWIN, M. P. and PATERSON, M. L. *A Check List of the Birds of Southern Rhodesia*, 1957
MACKWORTH-PRAED, C. W. and GRANT, C. H. B. *Birds of Eastern and North Eastern Africa*, 2 vols., 1952 and 1955
MACKWORTH-PRAED, C. W. and GRANT, C. H. B. *Birds of the Southern third of Africa*, 2 vols., 1962 and 1963
MACKWORTH-PRAED, C. W. and GRANT, C. H. B. *Birds of West Central and Western Africa*, 2 vols. 1970 and 1973
BANNERMAN, D. *The Birds of West and Equatorial Africa*, 2 vols., 1953
CAVE, F. O. and MACDONALD, J. D. *The Birds of Sudan*, 1955
BENSON, C. W., BROOKE, R. K., DOWSETT, R. J. and IRWIN, M. P. S. *The Birds of Zambia*, Collins 1971.

Of books dealing with South African birds in particular in a more popular form we have the following:

WOODWARD, R. B. and J. D. S. *Natal Birds*, 1899
HAAGNER, A. K. and IVY, R. H. *Sketches of South African Bird Life*, 1908
SKEAD, C. J. (ed) *The Canaries, Seed-eaters and Buntings of Southern Africa*, Johannesburg C.N.A., 1960
SKEAD, C. J. *The Sunbirds of Southern Africa*, Balkema, Cape Town, 1967
CLANCEY, P. A. *The Birds of Natal*, Oliver and Boyd, Edinburgh, 1964
SMITHERS, R. H. N. *Checklist of the birds of the Bechuanaland Protectorate and the Caprivi Strip*, Nat. Museums of Southern Rhodesia, 1964
CLANCEY, P. A. *Game Birds of Southern Africa*, Purnell, Cape Town, 1967
S.A. ORNITHOLOGICAL SOCIETY LIST COMMITTEE. *Check List of the Birds of South Africa*, 1969
PRIEST, C. D. *Birds of Southern Rhodesia*, 4 vols. 1933 to 1935
GILL, E. L. *A First Guide to South African Birds*, 1937
HEY, Dr. D. H. *Protected Birds of the Cape*, 2 vols. 1955
BROEKHUYSEN, G. J. *The Birds around us: The commoner birds of Southern Africa*, H. Timmins, Cape Town, 1966
BROEKHUYSEN, G. J. *Fieldguide to the Birds of the South African Seashore*, H. Timmins, Cape Town, 1969

NEWMAN, K. *Garden Birds of South Africa*, Hortors, Johannesburg, 1967
WINTERBOTTOM, J. M. and UYS, C. J. *Some birds of the Cape*, Purnell, 1969
NEWMAN, K. (ed) *Bird Life in Southern Africa*, Purnell, 1971
NEWMAN, K. *Roadside Birds*, 1969
KEMP, A. C. "The Distribution and Status of the Birds of the Kruger National Park", Koedoe Monograph, 1974.

There are also a great number of articles on birds in scientific journals, too numerous to quote here; but special attention must be drawn to two ornithological journals published in South Africa, which ornithologists abroad have been apt to overlook—namely, *The Journal of the South African Ornithological Union*, of which twelve volumes were published from 1905 to 1916, when the Union amalgamated with the South African Biological Society; thereafter various articles on birds appeared in the organs of the S.A. Biological Society, the *South African Journal of Natural History, Bulletin of the S.A. Biological Society*, and latterly "Pamphlets" of the S.A. Biological Society. The second journal is *The Ostrich*, the medium of records of the South African Ornithological Society, started in 1929 and publishing two or three parts to a volume each year since 1930. *The Bokmakierie* and *African Wild Life*, more general magazines produced by the S.A.O.S. and Wild Life Society respectively, contain much information. It has been entirely due to the initiative and enthusiasm of a member of the former society, Mr John Voelcker, assisted by a Board of Trustees, who interested others and obtained contributions in funds, that preparation for this book was made possible. The combined efforts to sponsor the publication of this book have been supported strongly by the S.A. Ornithological Society and it is hoped that all who can do so will enrol as members and thereby help to promote the aims of the Society. The Hon. Secretary's address is P.O. Box 87234, Houghton, 2041.

Physical Conditions of South Africa
The limits of South Africa as understood in this book are bounded by a line drawn from the Cunene River on the west to the Zambesi River on the east, and between them by the southern political boundaries of Angola and Zambia. Its greatest width from east to west is about 2 500 kilometres and its length from north to south in the same parallel about 2 000 km. Within this comparatively small area the most diverse conditions of environment of birds are to be found, for we have not only tropical conditions in the north and temperate conditions in the south and at higher levels, but have winter rains from the south in the south and south-west and the other extreme of summer rains from the Indian Ocean in the east and north; moreover, the heaviest winter rains are in the south and they decrease rapidly northwards until hardly any rains occur from the Orange River northwards; and in the east the heaviest rains occur in the mountains, foothills, or interior plateaux, decreasing westwards, so that the average rainfall varies from 2 000 mm per annum on the Great Escarpment to less than 125 mm in the extremely dry areas of Bushmanland, Great Namaqualand, and the Namib Desert. If these rains were regular, probably there would be more uniformity than there is in the flora and fauna but they are so irregular, and droughts of several years' duration so often upset the normal conditions, that the vegetation and fauna have long ago become adapted to the worst. We see the effect of uniformity of rainfall in the Knysna forests, where there is a regular rainfall of from two to three inches for every month in the year, whereas towards the west the forests gradually disappear with the change-over to a purely winter rainfall season, and to the east these forests occur only where mists as well as rain reach them for about nine months in the year. The summer-rain region of the east and tropics is characterized by a covering of grass, whereas in western parts of the Republic,

for the greater part, the vegetation is of a succulent or sclerophytic nature that is able to withstand long periods of dryness; but the close covering of grass brings with it a great drawback, as its ignition by lightning or human agency tends to burn out all the vegetation not adapted to withstand it. It is a notable fact that most of the evergreen forests of the east are situated on the sheltered side of mountains away from the strong north-westerly winds that prevail during the end of the dry season. Where soil conditions permit on the east the trees often form such dense evergreen and non-inflammable growths that grass cannot gain a foothold and they do not become destroyed; but very often farmers have thinned out such growths to make use of the richer soil for cultivation of crops, and grass subsequently taking the place of the crops, when the soil is no longer planted, grass fires prevent a re-growth of the trees. The farmers are notoriously shortsighted in respect of such forests, and within historic times have been known to cause the complete denudation of trees near their settlements; this still goes on in the wilder parts where there is no supervision to check it.

The rains of the southern and south-western districts are precipitated mostly on the mountains and, coming as they do from the south, the plains to the north of the ranges get even less than the coastal flats. The interior plateaux on the west secure less rain the farther north they are situated. Even the mountainous area of Little Namaqualand, where the rainfall is lower than in the south, has a heavier rainfall about Garies than about Klipfontein, a little farther to the north, while the mountains along the Orange River indicate by their barrenness that they seldom receive any rain. In this southern and western region the majority of small birds breed in July and August, whereas in eastern parts of the Republic related forms breed during midsummer. Since the winter rains do not often penetrate beyond the escarpment that cuts across the Karoo, and the summer rains from the eastern Cape Province also do not often do so, though usually taking a north-westerly direction, the area to the north of the escarpment is often subject to droughts and Bushmanland and Great Namaqualand are very arid; linking up with the somewhat similar Namib situated to the west of the plateau area of Damaraland. This mountainous area of Damaraland has a greater rainfall than Great Namaqualand to the south and Kalahari to the east, which lie at lower levels; but the Kaokoveld plateau to the north-west of Damaraland has a lesser rainfall, while Ovamboland to the north of Damaraland is not only inundated by floods from Angola, but also has a heavier rainfall. The Kalahari is a large sandy tract that extends from the Molopo River northwards to the Makarikari Lakes region on the east, Ngamiland in the centre, and links up more or less through the Etosha Pan area (between Damaraland and Ovamboland) with Benguella in Angola; north of the Molopo River it effectually cuts off the hilly and mountainous country lying to the east and west, and rains are sporadic and local, but on account of the absorbent nature of the sand, sustain a covering of tufted grasses, low bushes, and occasional thorn-trees of higher stature, but with no running streams and only "pans" here and there to hold surface water. Since precipitation of rain is greater on higher ground than in the flats and wide valleys below them, a Kalahari-like type of flora and fauna extends eastwards in the Limpopo River valley and thence southwards to Swaziland, northern Zululand, and even to the east of the Lebombo range in Zululand and Mozambique. Likewise in Rhodesia, Kalahari-like conditions prevail in the western and lower-lying ground towards, but not apparently east of, the escarpment. Breaks in the eastern escarpment are marked in both the Limpopo and Zambesi River valleys, forming the limits of southward radiation of some montane species; but to the east of the escarpment, in the low-lying country, there are no such obvious barriers and yet some species have radiated farther south than others, some tropical species extending to Lake St Lucia, others to Durban, and even the eastern Cape Province.

The following regions, which are illustrated by the map inside the front cover, may be regarded as the main geographical subdivisions which arise as a result of the factors already discussed. They may be regarded as small regions in which one or more endemic species or races of birds may occur, as indicated, though some of them extend slightly beyond the limits of the regions and the areas are seldom clearly defined. The boundaries of these districts have been derived by considering the distribution of all our birds, each of which may inhabit one or several of these regions:

1. Kaokoveld, a dry, more or less hilly type of veld, situated south of the Cunene River, containing birds such as the Bare-cheeked Babbler (No. 537), the Damara Rock-jumper (No. 539) and Hartlaub's Francolin (No. 184), which also occur in Southern Angola, some of them extending to Damaraland as well.

2. Namib Desert, the coastal strip of South West Africa, characterized by mist, wind-borne sand and light-coloured soil, so far only partly explored ornithologically, extending from west of the Kaokoveld southwards to Orange River and west of the higher ground of Damaraland and Great Namaqualand. It contains very pallid types of ground birds such as Rüppell's Korhaan (No. 220 (e)), various pallid races of the larks and chats which occur farther inland, such as the Sicklewing Chat (No. 572), the Karoo Lark (No. 461 race (h)) and Gray's Lark (No. 483).

3. Ovamboland, the flooded area of mopane forests, palms and open plains, bordering southern Angola and north of Etosha Pan, containing some remarkably pale forms related to those of Angola or the Kalahari. Closely related to No. 17.

4. Damaraland, a more or less mountainous region, varying from east to west and north to south. Contains characteristic birds such as Monteiro's Hornbill (No. 429), Bradfield's Hornbill (No. 428), Rüppell's Parrot (No. 329) and particularly the peculiar White-tailed Shrike (No. 726).

5. Ngamiland, the southern border of an area inundated by the Okavango River, from Angola and the Zambesi River from north-western Rhodesia. Contains a number of intrusive types from the north such as White-rumped Babbler (No. 535), the West African Boubou (No. 710) and the Sharp-tailed Glossy Starling (No. 741).

6. Sandveld Kalahari, a very dry area of red sandveld poorly covered with vegetation except along the dry river beds where Camelthorn trees occur, extending from Ovamboland south-eastwards to the Orange River, containing such characteristic types as the Social Weaver (No. 783), the Red-headed Finch (No. 820) and Sandgrouse (Nos 307, 308, 310).

7. Thornveld Kalahari characterized by sand, low scrub and scattered trees, especially acacia species. Typical birds are the Pied Babbler (No. 536), the Crimson-breasted Shrike (No. 711), the Fawn-coloured Lark (No. 459) and the Kalahari Scrub Robin (No. 586).

8. Great Namaqualand and Bushmanland, a very dry area situated south of Damaraland and Kalahari and extending south of the Orange River. Contains such characteristic types as Sclater's Lark (No. 491), the Red Lark (No. 479) and the Social Weaver (No. 783).

9. Little Namaqualand from the coast to the hilly edge of the escarpment covered with scrub and remarkable for its show of flowers after the winter rains. It has intrusive rather than endemic types, mainly like those from the south but some characteristic forms such as the pale race (b) of the Karoo Lark (No. 461).

10. Southern and south-western Cape, mainly bleak with protea and other trees and scrub in the sheltered places on the mountains and *Restio* type reeds dominating the flats. Contains characteristic avifauna in the Cape Sugarbird (No. 749), the Rock-jumper (No. 540), Protea Seed-eater (No. 869) and the Orange-breasted Sunbird (No. 753).

11. Little Karoo, the dry plains north of the southern mountain ranges with xerophytic and succulent low vegetation containing no real endemic forms except perhaps the Black Harrier (No. 169).
12. Karoo, situated north of the escarpment range, Stormberg, etc., for the most part sparsely covered with xerophytic scrub. Containing distinct types such as the Rufous-eared Warbler (No. 619), Layard's Tit-babbler (No. 659), the Karoo Green Warbler (No. 626) and the Namaqua Prinia (No. 653).
13. Southern and eastern evergreen forests, such as Knysna, between the escarpment and the coast farther east to Natal and thence northwards to Swaziland, Woodbush, Transvaal, and the Eastern Districts of Rhodesia. Contains such typical species as the Knysna Loerie (No. 336), the Brown-necked Parrot (No. 326), the Olive Bush-shrike (No. 717), the Terrestrial Bulbul (No. 546), the Cinnamon Dove (No. 322), the Knysna Woodpecker (No. 448), the Bush Blackcap (No. 542) and the Forest Prinia (No. 649X).
14. Drakensberg massive, rugged high-level mountains, rather bleak and similar to western Cape vegetation, containing such distinct types as the Buff-streaked Chat (No. 569), the Rock Pipit (No. 697), the Bald Ibis (No. 82) and the Lammergeyer (No. 150).
15. A. Highveld grass-veld, characterized by level grass-land with distinct species such as Rudd's Lark (No. 473), Botha's Lark (No. 472) and the Short-tailed Pipit (No. 700).
    B. Eastern grass-veld, undulating grass-covered country with well-wooded river valleys containing no real endemic forms but allied in part to the highveld species and in part to the eastern lowveld species.
    C. Botswana grass-veld, mixed grass and flat-crowned acacia, rather Kalahari-like but with hard soil, containing a distinct species of lark, the Short-clawed Lark (No. 465).
16. Rhodesia plateau of the higher central portions of the territory typically covered with *Brachystegia* type woodland. Closely allied to a similar area north of the Zambesi in Malawi.
17. Rhodesian woodlands, typically with mopane and to the west with acacia, having such species as Bradfield's Hornbill (No. 428).
18. Eastern Lowveld, between the escarpment and the littoral, savanna country consisting of open grass-lands and more or less tangled bush or scattered trees, containing such types as the Yellow-throated Long-claw (No. 704), the Gorgeous Bush Shrike (No. 721), the Brown-headed Parrot (No. 328), the Purple-crested Loerie (No. 337) and other tropical intruders.
19. A. Eastern littoral, comprising grassy sand dunes and coastal bush, containing such types as the Pink-throated Longclaw (No. 705), the Black-bellied Glossy Starling (No. 740), the Grey Waxbill (No. 842), and the Olive Sunbird (No. 766).
    B. Eastern tropical littoral, somewhat like the littoral to the south but with more tropical bush and containing more tropical types of birds. Many birds of the southern littoral keep west of the Lebombo mountains north of Zululand rather than in southern Mozambique. Birds characteristic of the eastern tropical littoral are the Green Twinspot (No. 827), Pink-throated Twinspot (No. 831), Neergaard's Sunbird (No. 761) and Woodward's Batis (No. 676).

In addition to these smaller areas in which some endemic species occur, there are wider areas covered by certain less local types, the avifauna of the west being distinct from that of the east in the Republic, and the eastern species being sometimes limited to south of the Zoutpansberg, which lies on the Tropic of Capricorn. The tropical forms extend farther south on the east than the west.

A few notes on some of the earlier ornithologists, especially those who gave names to some of our birds, may be of interest.

Among the earliest visitors to the Cape who commented on the birds was the artist, probably Hendrik Claudius, who accompanied Simon van der Stel's famous expedition to Little Namaqualand in 1685. He depicted the Pied Barbet, Sacred Ibis, Namaqua Sandgrouse, Pied and Redwing Starlings, European Bee-eater and many others with considerable fidelity.

Kolbe, after whom the Cape Vulture is sometimes called Kolbe's Vulture, was a German who wrote a fanciful account of the Cape in 1719.

Sparrman was a Swedish scientist who sailed round the world with Captain Cook. On his return he stopped off at the Cape, describing many new species of birds and publishing a valuable account of his travels in the Cape Province. His name is perpetuated in Sparrman's Honeyguide, No. 440, now usually known as the Greater Honeyguide.

Francois le Vaillant, born in French Guiana, was the first ornithologist to visit the country. He made two important expeditions—the first as far east as the Fish River and the second to Little Namaqualand. These were described in a quaint and often bombastic series of volumes. He described a great number of our birds for the first time but unfortunately was not a believer in the Linnean system and only gave them French names, for example the Bataleur and Chanteur (Chanting Goshawk). However, other workers gave scientific names to his material and we often find names such as *Trachyphonus vaillantii* or *Francolinus levaillantii*. Le Vaillant was a great admirer of the Hottentots and the beautiful Narina Trogon is named after a Hottentot girl whom he admired. Klaas's Cuckoo is also in honour of one of his servants.

Burchell was an English botanist of particular brilliance who conducted a four-year journey through Southern Africa. He collected an incredible number of natural history specimens, among them many birds. Thus we have Burchell's Coucal, Burchell's Courser and Burchell's Glossy Starling. The account of his travels is one of the most sought-after pieces of Africana.

In 1817 an apothecary, Ludwig Krebs, landed at the Cape. He later moved to the Eastern Cape where he died in 1844. During his stay here he collected some 6 000 bird skins which were sent to the Berlin Museum; twelve of these were new to science.

In 1820 there came to the Cape a remarkable young Scots medical doctor, by name Andrew Smith. He made several journeys into the interior and discovered great numbers of new birds, reptiles and mammals. Reptiles were undoubtedly his greatest interest and he has been described as the father of herpetology in South Africa. He is also credited with having the finest collection of reptiles in England. In addition to this he made an outstanding contribution to the classification of South African birds and probably described more *species* than any one before or since. The Cape Town Museum had Smith as its first Director in 1825. He was knighted for his work during the Crimean War as Inspector-General of Army Hospitals. He died in 1872.

Many other names crop up in the older literature; Verreaux was an early Director of the Cape Town Museum (Verreaux's Twinspot and the Black Eagle *Aquila verreauxi*); Layard, another Director of the South African Museum (*Pycnonotus b. layardi*, Layard's Tit-babbler); Andersson was a Swede who travelled extensively in South West Africa, enduring incredible hardships, ultimately meeting his death on the Cunene River. His ornithological notes were later edited by Gurney, who worked at the British Museum. Exton was the first president of the Geological Society of South Africa (Exton's Barbet), while Mennell was another geologist remembered in Mennell's Seed-eater. Wahlberg, another Swede, made journeys through Natal, Transvaal and Ngamiland collecting birds extensively. He, too, met his death near Lake Ngami in an encounter with an elephant in 1856 (Wahlberg's Eagle, No. 137).

Thomas Ayres, who lived in Natal and at Potchefstroom, corresponded widely and wrote many valuable articles in the 1870s (Ayres' Hawk Eagle, *Cisticola ayresii* and the Flufftail *Sarothrura ayresi*).

Stark, another medical doctor, who began the series of volumes known affectionately as Stark and Sclater, was killed by a shell during the siege of Ladysmith. W. L. Sclater, Director of the Cape Town Museum, had to finish the work and he, too, strangely enough, fell victim to enemy action during the Second World War while working at the British Museum.

Since the turn of the century, many ornithologists have worked in Southern Africa but they are too numerous to mention here and their works may be found in contemporary journals.

Field Equipment

The amateur bird watcher and the serious ornithologist must rely to a great extent on accurate field identification of birds. Obviously, bird watchers cannot shoot every bird they wish to identify nor can serious field studies be carried out unless the bird is identified with absolute certainty.

The first essential for field work is a suitable pair of binoculars. Of course any pair of glasses is better than none; as an American ornithologist put it "after all, 2-power just about doubles one's potentialities". Generally speaking, binoculars should not be too powerful, better a small bright image than a large shaking one. The more powerful the glass the more difficult it is to keep steady, particularly when walking or climbing, when the slightest fatigue causes shake which is magnified by the glasses.

Popular and suitable glasses are the 7×50, 8×30, 8×40, 9×35 and perhaps 10×50. Of these the 7×50 and 8×30 are very popular and there is also a 9×35 on the market, which is probably ideal for African conditions. In these specifications, the first figure is the linear magnification while the second is the diameter of the front lens expressed in millimetres. The latter is therefore a rough index of the amount of light admitted and also an approximate indication of the field of view. Thus, the larger the front lens the brighter the image and the wider the field of view. An 8×40 will give a brighter image than an 8×30 although the magnification will be exactly the same. The width of the eye-piece also influences the brightness; the wider the better.

Field glasses which focus by means of a central milled knob are preferable to those in which the eye-pieces focus separately because they can be focused quicker, an important factor when watching a small agile bird, although many experienced workers still prefer individual focusing. Watchers who normally wear spectacles can, and should, obtain special field glasses which obviate the necessity for removing their spectacles. Seconds wasted while raising spectacles may be precious and there is also less strain on the eyes when using these special binoculars. The only snag is that they are more expensive, but this is undoubtedly money well spent.

Prospective buyers of glasses should also apply the following simple test. Examine the edge of a white building which is in full sunlight through the instrument. Then move the image towards the edge of the field. If coloured fringes appear on the edge of the wall the glass suffers from chromatic aberration. If the wall appears to bend or become blurred spherical aberration is present. A good instrument should show neither of these effects.

In the field binoculars should be worn "at the ready" suspended on a short strap at chest level.

The second essential for field observations is a note-book. In this all observations made during the day should be entered. On returning home, these may be put into some more permanent reference system. Filing cards, loose-leaf note-books or large ledgers may be used. Quite a good system is to use a very cheap note-book in the field and write on one side of the page only. At home these pages can be torn out and pasted on to larger sheets and filed under their respective species.

A camera is a valuable adjunct to field work, and in particular the single lens reflex type is to be recommended in bird work for the following reasons: In close-up work there are no parallax difficulties and the depth of focus can be seen and evaluated in the view-finder; any reasonably good lens may be used as a supplementary lens for close-up work without expensive accessories: no supplementary rangefinders are necessary when using telephoto lenses of whatever size; lastly, the picture taken may be composed better than with any other camera because what is seen in the viewfinder is *exactly* what appears on the negative, neither smaller, larger or more out of focus. Some modern reflex cameras even combine the accurate split-image rangefinder with the panoramic focusing screen.

Field identification

It has been said that if one cannot see the colour of the eye of a bird one cannot expect to identify it. This may be an exaggeration, but it does indicate that one should have a good view of a bird and be able to see detailed characters before a correct identification can be made, at any rate of a bird unfamiliar to the observer.

To identify a bird it is important to note:
(1)   the relative size and proportions of body, i.e., long neck or legs or bill;
(2)   colour; whether patterned, where bright colours are or where white patches, collars or bars etc. occur;
(3)   where the bird is seen—on the ground, in a bush, wading in water, flying in a certain way, etc.;
(4)   obvious characters—sings a. lot, perches on reeds, clambers on tree trunks, etc.

From a combination of this type of information it should be possible to work out a bird's identity.

DIAGRAMS OF PARTS OF A BIRD

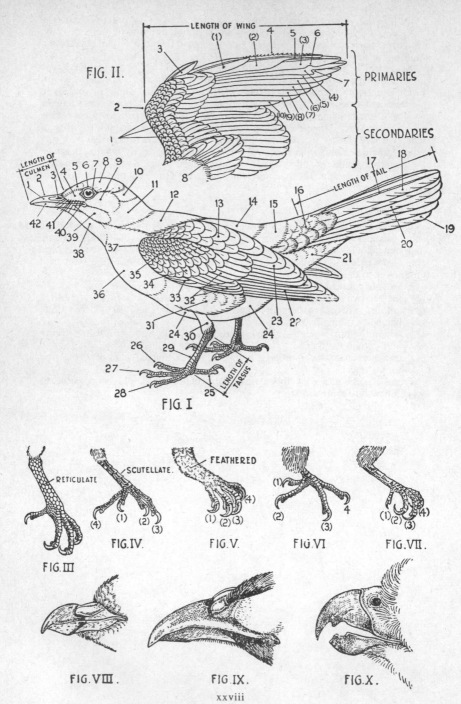

FIG. II.

LENGTH OF WING

PRIMARIES

SECONDARIES

LENGTH OF CULMEN

LENGTH OF TAIL

FIG. I

RETICULATE

SCUTELLATE.

FEATHERED

FIG. III

FIG. IV.

FIG. V.

FIG. VI

FIG. VII.

FIG. VIII.

FIG. IX.

FIG. X.

LENGTH OF TARSUS

Descriptive terms
used in ornithology

1. Maxilla
2. Culmen
3. Nostril
4. Lores
5. Forehead
6. Eyelid
7. Iris
8. Crown
9. Ear-coverts
10. Nape
11. Neck
12. Mantle
13. Scapulars
14. Back
15. Rump
16. Upper tail-coverts
17. Shaft of feather
18. Central tail-feather
19. Outer tail-feather
20. Tail (rectrices)
21. Under tail-coverts
22. Primaries ⎫
23. Secondaries ⎬(remiges)
24. Abdomen ⎭
25–28. 1st to 4th toes
29. Tarsus
30. Thigh (tibia)
31. Flank
32. Primary- and greater wing-coverts
33. Bastard-wing (alula)
34. Median wing-coverts
35. Lesser wing-coverts
36. Breast
37. Shoulder
38. Throat
39. Cheek
40. Gape
41. Rictal bristles
42. Mandible (lower)

Figure II
1. Under wing-coverts
2. Elbow, bend of wing
3. Bastard-wing (alula)
4. Serrated primary (e.g. *Psalidoprocne*)
5. Sickle emargination (e.g. *Turtur*)
6. Nicked emargination (e.g. *Lamprotornis*)
7. Notched emargination (e.g. *Falco*)
8. Axillaries

(1) to (10). 1st to 10th primaries

Figure III   Normal type of foot, 1st toe behind, 2nd to 4th in front; naked tarsus with reticulate scales.

Figure IV   1st and 4th toes behind, 2nd and 3rd toes in front, zygodactylous (e.g. *Picidae*); front of tarsus with scutellate scales.

Figure V   1st to 4th toes normally all in front, pamprodactylous; tarsus feathered (e.g. *Micropodidae*).

Figure VI   1st and 2nd toes behind, 3rd and 4th toes in front, syndactylous (e.g. *Trogonidae*).

Figure VII   1st toes reversible to back or front, pamprodactylous (e.g. *Coliidae*).

Figure VIII   Fore part of bill (detrum) hardened, hinder part soft (e.g. *Treron*).

Figure IX   Whole bill hardened, but with a hardened cere at base of culmen and an operculum over the nostrils (e.g. *Pternistis* and *Francolinus*); cutting edge of bill (tomium) plain.

Figure X   Bill hardened, but with a soft cere over the base; nostrils exposed and situated within the cere; bill toothed on cutting edge (e.g. *Falco*).

Signs and Abbreviations

♂ = Male
♀ = Female
Ad. = Adult
Br. = Breeding
Juv. = Juvenile
Imm. = Immature
N-Br. = Non-breeding
S. = Summer plumage
W. = Winter plumage
opp. p. = opposite page
pl. p. = plate page

(X)	Xhosa	(D)	Chindao
(Z)	Zulu	(G)	Singuni
(S)	Sotho (Sesutu)	(P)	Pondomese
(Ch)	Chuana	(Sh)	Shona
(Zw)	Chizwina	(T)	Sintabele

Arrows on the distribution maps indicate isolated records outside the species' normal range.

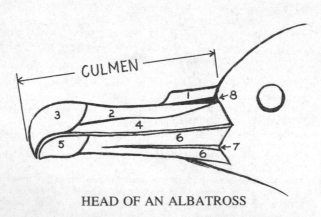

HEAD OF AN ALBATROSS

1. Nostrils
3. Maxillary unguis
5. Mandibular unguis
7. Sulcus

2. Culminicorn
4. Latericorn
6. Ramicorn
8. Naricorn

xxx

LIST OF DOUBTFUL SPECIES

17. White-headed Petrel *Pterodroma lessonii* (Garnot)
A large (44 cm length, wing span 110 cm) white and grey petrel, dark underwings contrasting with white head and underparts. A black patch through eye. Recorded from Cape Seas. One record Fish River Mouth, Eastern Cape (ECWBS Checklist). Also Kleinmond, R., Bathhurst, October 1945.

32. Madeiran Fork-tailed Petrel *Oceanodroma castro* Harcourt
Distinguished from No. 31 by having the tips of the upper tail coverts brown and outer tail feathers white at base. Not recorded from our area at all.

34. White-faced Storm Petrel *Pelagodroma marina* (Latham)
White underparts and underwing coverts. A narrow black subocular eye stripe contrasting with white forehead, superciliary and cheek. Dark tail and remiges. A sight record of five birds off Bazaruto Is. Mozambique, June 1950. Possible after a stormy period.

35. Grey-backed Storm Petrel *Garrodia nereis* (Gould)
Differs from previous species by its dark head and chest, grey tail with dark terminal band and dark leading edge to under wing. No positive records better than an old specimen from "Cape Seas".

38. Diving Petrel *Pelecanoides urinatrix* Gaimard
About 20 cm. Shiny black above, white below with a band across chest. No known record other than an old specimen labelled "Cape Seas".

43. White pelican. When Roberts 1940 appeared *Pelecanus roseus* was considered to be a separate species. Now considered the same as No. 42.

45. Masked Booby. *Sula dactylatra* Lesson
Smaller than No. 44; with white head. Immature similar to No. 46 but differs from adult and immature 46 by having white speckled effect on back and wing coverts. An old specimen from "Cape Seas". A sight record in Mozambique Channel.

XXX. European Shelduck *Tadorna tadorna* (Linnaeus)
Unmistakeable with black head, white neck, rufous chest and back, black and white wing with white tail. Recorded at Port Elizabeth, June 1974. Known to have escaped from captivity.

XXX. American Black Duck *Anas rubripes* Brewster
A dark duck similar to Nos. 95 and 96; feet red or brown, bill yellowish or greenish. Speculum metallic violet. Sexes alike. One recorded Durban Bay, March 1975. Probably an escaped bird.

XXX. Merlin *Falco columbarius* Turnstall
Similar in size to Hobby but has cheek uniform brown. Tail is broadly barred. Thighs streaked. A single specimen Durban, February 1891.

166. European Marsh Harrier *Circus aeruginosus* (Linnaeus)
Differs from No. 167 by having in female and immature birds whitish head with dark eye and ear covert patch. Males have black wing tips contrasting with grey wing. Ayres collected one at Potchefstroom, last century. Two modern sight records in Rhodesia.

252. Bairds Sandpiper *Calidris bairdii* (Coues)
Similar to No. 253 in all respects except that back markings are transverse and appear like scales. The chest is more heavily marked in summer plumage. Collected by Andersson at Walvis Bay, October 1863.

XXX. Long-toed stint *Calidris subminuta* (Middendorff)
The size of No. 253 but has greenish legs and back with longitudinal stripes patterned like a snipe. Note short bill. Recorded photographically July 1968, Benoni, Transvaal. There are recent specimens from East Africa.

XXX. Least Sandpiper *Calidris minutilla* (Viellot)
Sometimes considered as a race of No. 251X from which it differs only by a slightly more pronounced wing bar. Reputedly netted and ringed Bathhurst, January 1967. More probably misidentified for 251X.

XXX. Temminck's Stint *Calidris temminckii* (Leisler)
Similar to the Little Stint but legs are greenish brown to yellow. Darker upper parts less patterned. Has a decided dusky breast. In the hand only outer primary has white shaft and outer tail feathers are pure white. Usually avoids salt water. Sight records from Swakopmund, December 1964 and Wankie, Rhodesia, November 1972. Needs confirmation.

260. Spotted Redshank *Tringa erythropus*. (Pallas)
Distinguished from 261 by its longer thinner bill, longer legs and spotted back. No wingbar and legs extend well beyond tail in flight. Layard (1867) collected a specimen from Knysna. Description of sight record from Port Alfred unacceptable. Salisbury sight record needs confirmation.

XXX. Franklin's Gull *Larus pipixcan* Wagler
Fractionally smaller than No. 289. Breeding plumage black head is lost in non breeding state where a dark patch from eye extends round nape. Note black tips to primaries separated by white from grey of upper wing. A bird was photographed at Langebaan, April 1973. Identity not fully resolved.

XXX. Sooty Gull *Larus hemprichii* (Bruch)
There are several "black headed" gulls other than 288x. Most difficult to distinguish from each other. Important characters are the amount of black and white on primaries, the relative length and depth of bill as well as colour. Colour of eye. Size. This bird has bill green, eye brown. Sight record from Beira needs confirmation. Known down east coast as far as Zanzibar.

XXX. Black-naped Tern *Sterna sumatra* Raffles
Fractionally smaller than No. 291. Distinguished by black band commencing in front of eye encircling the sides of head and nape. Tail deeply forked. Adult has leading edge of first primary black; immature primaries dark grey. A specimen collected from a group of 4 Umvoti River Natal, March 1976. Further sight recorded from Inhaca Is. Mozambique.

XXX. White cheeked Tern *Sterna repressa* Hartert
Distinguished from No. 292 by its slightly smaller size and grey rump and tail. Sight recorded once Umvoti Estuary, Natal, November 1975.

XXX. Royal Tern *Sterna maxima* Boddaert
Differs from No. 298 in being fractionally larger. The black of crown and forehead extends to bill in this species and is separated by a white band in No. 298. Sight record at mouth of Cunene needs confirmation. Specimens recently from Angola.

301. White-capped Noddy *Anous minutus* Boie
Distinguished from No. 303 with difficulty. This species is smaller and has a longer more slender bill. Sooty black rather than brownish black of No. 303. One specimen from Alexandria district, Eastern Cape.

302. White Tern *Gygis alba* Sparrman
A wholly white tern. The wings appear translucent from below. Black ring around eye. An old specimen labelled "Cape Seas" doubtfully from our region.

XXX. European Turtle Dove *Streptopelia turtur* Linnaeus
About the size of No. 316 but has two patches on either side of neck of black and white markings. Back scaly in appearance, rust edges to dark feathers. Reputedly wild caught by an aviculturalist at Oranjemund and on the Okavango. Needs confirmation.

XXX. Lady Ross's Turaco *Musophaga rossae* Gould. A violet species with crimson crown. Recorded once from the Okavango.

469. Namaqualand Clapper lark *Corypha rufipilea* Le Vaillant
An excellent picture of a Clapper lark in Le Vaillant's bird plates but nothing like it has been obtained since. Considered indeterminate.

487. Calandra Lark *Melanocorypha bimaculata* Ménétriés
A largish lark with a very heavy and large bill and characterized by large black patches on sides of upper chest. One specimen collected at Swakopmund, September 1930.

XXX. Red-rumped Swallow *Cecropis daurica* (Linnaeus)
A smaller edition of No. 500 but has chestnut nape and ear coverts which latter distinguish it from No. 501. Two sight records near Salisbury, February 1966. Needs confirmation.

XXX. Redstart *Phoenicurus phoenicurus* (Linnaeus)
Male unmistakable with black face, white forehead, rufous chest. Female greyish brown with rufous tail and rump. Smaller than No. 593x. Sight records of four in northern South-West Africa unacceptable.

XXX. Wood Warbler *Phylloscopus sibilatrix* Bechstein
Slightly larger than No. 599. Yellow about head and neck only and wing coverts. Bill thin and slender where as No. 596 has wider bill and orange gape. Call very different. Sight and ringing records from Grootfontein and Erongo Mountains need confirmation. (Probably confused with No. 596.)

604X. European Reed Warbler *Acrocephalus scirpaceus* Herman
Practically indistinguishable from Nos. 606 and 607—legs distinctly darker. Slightly more rufous upper parts. Specimen from Colenso Natal, February 1959. Recorded from Botswana and Hartebeestpoort Dam.

691. Black headed Wagtail. *Motacilla flava feldegg*
Considered a race of the Yellow Wagtail.

702. Golden Pipit *Tmetothylacus tenellus* (Cabanis)
Similar to No. 704 but male has broad black chest band and not a rounded bib. Both male and female have flight feathers and outer tail feathers yellow. Collected originally at Irene (Verwoerdburg), January 1906. Another collected at Wankie, March 1972.

782. Red-backed Sparrow Weaver *Plocepasser rufoscapulatus* Büttikofer
Similar to No. 780 but eyebrow not white and back rufous. Occurs only in Miombo Woodland in Zambia. Extralimital—no known records.

795. Bar-winged Weaver *Notiospiza angolensis* Bocage
Blackish mottled upperparts, white belly and yellow rump distinguish this easily identified weaver. No record from within our limits—occurs in Angola and Zambia.

807. Cardinal Quelea *Quelea cardinalis* (Hartlaub)
Similar to No. 806 but with crimson head, nape and upper chest. Female like No. 806. Not yet recorded within our limits.

848. Purple widowbird
Now considered to be a hybrid. Similar birds have been produced in captivity by crossing various Whydahs and Widow-finches.

Family STRUTHIONIDAE

The largest living birds, primitive and distantly related to the Rheas of South America and more distantly still to the Emu and Cassowary of Australia. A member of the sub-class Ratitae: primitive, flightless birds without any keel to the sternum, small wings, no stiff contour feathers or oil gland but with long powerful legs which aid them in defending themselves or escaping from enemies by running. Characterized also by having only two toes (the third and fourth), the larger with a nail. The feathers are not oiled and consequently the birds become wet if exposed to rain.

The family contains only one genus, with one or two species, according to the authority consulted, with several recognizable forms from the Cape to Iraq. The southern form is the heaviest (up to 156,8 kg), with bluish-grey neck and with breeding cocks showing red skutes along the full length of the tarsus. Selective breeding for plumes produced many thousands of birds which became feral after the ostrich plume slump. Most of the birds in the Southern Cape and Karoo are derived from these farming activities. In 1912 the Government imported 132 birds from Nigeria and breeding experiments were carried out at Grootfontein Agricultural College.

1 Ostrich   Volstruis

Struthio camelus Linnaeus, 1758: *North Africa*

Native Names: Inciniba (X); 'Ntje (Z); 'Nche (Sh); Mpse (S)

FRONTISPIECE
Height of ♂ up to 2 metres; tarsus ♂ 45 cm, ♀ 37 cm. Iris hazel; bill horn-coloured; legs lead-grey with front scales red in breeding season.

Identification: Male largely black-and-white as illustrated. Female is a pale brown with wing feathers dirty white. Young: head and neck fawn with longitudinal black streaks. The back is hedgehog-like with black-and-white bristles. Heaviest weight recorded 156,8 kg.

Distribution: General in Africa, Syria and Arabia. Formerly widespread in Southern Africa but not now occurring in settled areas except where domesticated birds have gone wild.

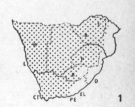

Habits: A common resident species in the drier areas of the west. Usually found in small scattered parties, though often singly. They can run at a surprising speed, with their wings held free, but not as an aid to speed. It is said their speed is not less than 70 kilometres an hour.

Food: Succulent and other plants, berries and seeds. Hard objects such as pebbles are swallowed to assist in crushing the harder parts of its food.

Voice: The male utters a dull kind of roar, like a lion at a distance, usually at night.

Breeding: Normally monogamous, but instances are known where two or three females accompany a single male, and the females may lay in the same nest, which is a mere hollow scraped in the ground. Nest is constructed by

1

1

both sexes. The conspicuous black-and-white cocks incubate the eggs at night, the inconspicuous hens during daylight, but this rule is not invariable. Eggs 15—20, laid every other day, are cream coloured with smooth glossy surface heavily pitted. Average (51) 148,1 × 121,6 (135—158 × 110—130). Their capacity is about equal to that of two dozen fowl eggs. Incubation: 40 days, starts at completion of clutch. Nests February to November.

LOCAL RACE
S.c. australis Gurney, 1868: *Naarip Plain near Walvis Bay*. Confined to the area south of the Zambezi and Cunene rivers.

Family SPHENISCIDAE

Flightless birds of the southern hemisphere. Wings flipper-like, with no quill-feathers differentiated from the others, hence the name of the group—Impennes. The flippers are used to "fly" under water, steering with the feet. Body-feathers short and furry, fitting closely. The three metatarsal bones separated by deep grooves and not fused into one as in all other birds. A tufted oil gland is present. Legs short, toes long, the front three connected by webbing, a short one behind, all with strong claws; the feet are adapted to swimming and when the birds are on land they stand upright and waddle along with a peculiar gait. Six genera are recognized with 15 species living (36 fossil). Two genera occur on our mainland—one has a crest and a deep groove down the mandible, the other has neither.

2 Jackass Penguin   Pikkewyn

Spheniscus demersus   (Linnaeus), 1758: *Cape of Good Hope*
Native Name: Inguza

PLATE 4 (OPP. P. 32).
Length 60 cm (Flippers 165, leg 25; culmen 55). Iris hazel, with flesh-pink skin over eye; bill black with grey subterminal band; legs black.

Identification: The *black chin and facial patch*, separated by a broad white line from the black upper parts distinguishes this from the next species. Sexes alike. There is also a narrow black line forming an inverted horseshoe on the chest. Tail has 18 feathers. Immature sooty black, except chest and belly which is white, the lower chin later becomes white.
Distribution: A sea-bird found from the Cunene River mouth on the west coast extending around the Cape to Maputo, from the Transkei north, mainly in winter.
Habits: A common resident of the coastal islands, wandering to the mainland irregularly. An aquatic bird, capable of swimming rapidly under water with the aid of its feet and flippers.

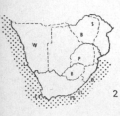

2

Food: Small fish of the Clupeidae family, i.e. pilchards, harder etc., small crayfish.
Voice: A loud bray similar to that of a donkey, uttered mainly at night.
Breeding: Usually in colonies. Eggs can be found throughout the year but mainly in summer. The nest is either a burrow dug out of hard sand or a protected site between boulders, usually well lined with old feather quills, bits of dried seaweed or other rubbish. Eggs 1—3, usually 2, white. Average (58) 67,0 × 52,3 (62,8—76,4 × 48,3—55,9).

3 Rockhopper Penguin   Geelkuif-pikkewyn

Eudyptes crestatus   (Miller), 1784: *Falkland Islands*

PLATE 4 (OPP. P. 32).
Length about 56 cm. (Flippers 155—190; bill 38—51; plumes 63—83. 8 specimens).
Iris dull rosy pink; bill dull pink; feet reddish, darker on the webs—non-breeding condition.

Identification: Differs from the previous species in that it has long *pale yellow plumes* and black plumes projecting behind the eyes forming side crests. The belly is plain white. The bill contains a single deep groove sloping forward in the middle of the upper mandible. The tail has 16 or less feathers.
Distribution: Southern oceans, occurring on the South African coast as a summer vagrant. Recorded from Verloren Vallei, south of Lamberts Bay to Port Shepstone and Pondoland.
Habits: On the rare occasions that this bird is seen it is quite indifferent to the presence of human beings.

LOCAL RACE
E.c. crestatus (Miller), 1784: *Falkland Islands*

Family PODICIPIDAE

A cosmopolitan group of swimming and diving birds, distinguished from all others by the absence of ordinary tail-feathers (only short plumes) and by the lobed toes, with nails instead of claws. Three or four living genera and twenty-two species are recognized by most authorities. In our region one genus has a crest and the other does not. The separation of Tachybaptus and Podiceps is based on differences in behaviour which have resulted in skeletal changes. When alarmed, these birds, which live entirely on the water, dive or may swim away with their bodies almost completely submerged. When undisturbed they float on the surface. They are poor fliers taking off with a long run beating their comparatively short, pointed wings very rapidly. The moult of the secondaries and primaries is simultaneous, leaving the birds flightless for a short period.

4 Great Crested Grebe   Kuifkop-duikertjie

Podiceps cristatus   (Linnaeus), 1758: *Sweden*

PLATE 6 (OPP. P. 48).
Length about 50 cm (wing 173—176,3—182; tarsus 56,5—59,6—64; culmen 43—47,9—51,6. 8 specimens). Iris crimson; bill reddish brown; legs dusky.

Identification: Immediately separated from the ducks by its long thin neck, topped by the large head. *The crest on either side of the head is conspicuous.* General upper coloration brown, under parts silky white. In flight the secondaries show as a white bar across base of wing. Nestling with bare patch on crown. Young, head and neck marked with longitudinal brown stripes. This pattern is retained for several months.
Distribution: Over the greater part of Old World and Africa south of the Sahara. Absent from Rhodesia, Botswana and inland South West Africa; irregular in Natal.

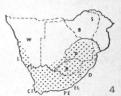

4

3

Habits: A sparingly distributed resident on the larger vleis. Occurs singly, in pairs or small family parties, where there is shelter in the water plants and reeds—although not necessarily found in this shelter. The courtship is elaborate, the birds swim towards each other, with bill just skimming the water, the crest is raised and displayed by head-jerking movements.

Food: Small fish, water-beetles and their larvae, crustacea, molluscs and *Zostera*.

Breeding: Builds a floating nest of dead reeds, situated within shelter of reeds. When the parent leaves the nest the eggs are always covered with some wet vegetation. Breeds from August to September in the Cape, May and June in the Transvaal. Eggs 2—3, chalky white with greenish tinge when fresh becoming discoloured and brownish later. Average (14) 53,4 × 36,1 (48,8 − 58,6 × 34,3—38,2). Incubation 25 days.

LOCAL RACE
P.c. infuscatus Salvadori, 1884: *Lago Kilola, S. Abyssinia,* Less white on head than in nominate race. Africa south of the Sahara.

5 Black-necked Grebe   Swartnek-duikertjie

Podiceps nigricollis (Brehm), 1831: *Germany*

PLATE 6 (OPP. P. 48).
Length 28 cm (wing 117—125,4—137; tarsus 35,5—38,7—44; culmen 19,1—21,7—25,7. 12 specimens). Iris crimson with an inner white band, bill and legs blackish.

Identification: Black neck and golden ear tufts distinguish this species in its breeding plumage. In non-breeding plumage it is separated from the next species No. 6, by its larger size and by *silky white flanks and belly*. See habits. Also, the head, though it may lack side crests, is large compared to the next species. Flight pattern as No. 6. Nestling has no bald patch on head; the young has streaked head, neck and body.

Distribution: Europe, Asia, North America and Africa. Recorded from Transvaal, Orange Free State, Botswana, Cape Province and along the coast of South West Africa.

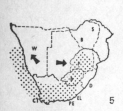

5

Habits: Not common, a migrant, occurring during summer on large sheets of water, usually in flocks. Along the sea coast of S.W.A. these flocks reach considerable numbers in winter, and form dense rafts of closely packed birds. Has characteristic habit of preening, floating on its side, thus exposing the silky-white under parts—a conspicuous character.

Food: Small water animals.

Voice: A quiet poo-eep and a rapid clatter.

Breeding: An irregular breeder in season or locality, more widely recorded in wet seasons. A colonial nester from six nests to twenty-five in one area, sometimes even on a small temporary vlei. Nests are similar to those of the next species. Recorded breeding October to April. Eggs 2—3, round at both ends, yellowish brown; (23) 43,1 × 29,5 (39,8—46 × 27,7—31,3). Incubation: 20—21 days by both sexes.

LOCAL RACE
P.n. gurneyi (Roberts), 1919: *Lamberts Bay.* South Africa and Botswana.

6 Dabchick

Klein Duikertjie

Tachybaptus ruficollis (Pallas), 1764: *Holland*

Native Names: le Fuli (S); Unolwilwilwi (X)

PLATE 6 (OPP. P. 48).
Length 20 cm (wing 93—102; tarsus 29—35; culmen 18—23, 19 specimens). Iris brown; bill black, greenish at base; legs black.

Identification: Breeding plumage (illustrated) has rufous sides to neck and the *light spot at gape* is conspicuous. In non-breeding plumage there is no rufous on the head. The small size and the light spot at base of bill, smoky grey neck and sides distinguish this species from the last, No. 5. There is a line of contrast between the dark crown and light face and chin. See also habits. In flight the white secondaries are conspicuous. Nestling has no bald patch on head. Young is streaked on head and sides of neck and back.

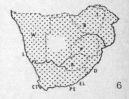

Distribution: Throughout the greater part of Europe, Asia and Africa. Widely distributed throughout Southern Africa.

Habits: A common resident frequenting open sheets of water and often also quiet streams and pools. Usually occurs in pairs or small family parties, but may occur in large loose flocks. Has a characteristic habit of "standing" on the water whilst flapping its wings vigorously, shaking its whole body when settling back onto the water, flapping wings in partial flight and "running" along the surface with its feet, finally skidding along the surface to a stop, accompanied in most instances by its call, a descending laughing trill.

Food: Small frogs, especially platannas, Daphnia and water insects.

Voice: See above. Alarm note is a sharp loud "chick".

Breeding: The floating nest is placed near open vegetation, constructed of a pile of wet weeds built about one inch above the water on the perimeter, whilst the hollow is at water-level. Breeds August to February in the Cape; January to March and June to August in Rhodesia. Eggs 3—6, pale powdery blue when fresh but turning ivory after a few days. Average (69) 36,7 × 25,2 (33—40 × 22—27). Incubation: 18—25 days. Nestlings leave the nest immediately. Often carried on parent's back at this early stage, even when the parent dives. Chicks are capable of swimming and diving on the first day.

LOCAL RACE
T.r. capensis (Salvadori), 1884: *Shoa, Abyssinia.* Throughout Africa.

Family DIOMEDEIDAE

The largest members of the order *Procellariiformes*, distinguished by nostrils which extend on either side of the culmen in short tubes. One genus, sometimes two, is recognized with twelve or thirteen living species. The three front toes are completely connected by webbing and the hind toe is absent. Distributed mainly in the southern oceans and breed on small uninhabited islands. All lay a single egg in an open nest.

In our waters these birds may be seen gliding as only masters of the wind and sea can. Though they may follow boats for offal they are not dependent upon them. They gather about trawlers in large numbers. Food is primarily cephalopods (squid) which are taken at night.

7 Wandering Albatross   Groot Albatros

Diomedea exulans   Linnaeus, 1758: *Cape of Good Hope*
PLATE 2 (OPP. P. 16), AD. ♂ AND ♀. IMM. B AND C.
Length about 130 cm (wing 585—645—679; tail 177—194,5—205; tarsus 111—120—168—177. 24 specimens). Iris brown; bill whitish with pink tinge; legs white with blue tinge.

Identification: Adult male totally white except for *black tips to wing*. Female often *has a dark cap*, with black speckling on back and upper-wing. Juvenile totally brown except for white under wings and a conspicuous white face mask. Immatures grade from the brown juvenile to the speckled female plumage. Wingspan from 280—350 cm. The adult is the only Albatross with white mantle and back.

Distribution: Antarctic and neighbouring seas. Recorded off the coast of South West Africa to Inhambane and Malagasy in the east.

Habits: A fairly common pelagic species recorded throughout the year but commoner from October to December. Frequently follows ships to within sight of shore, but seldom seen from the shore except in stormy weather. Feeds mainly at night taking small fish and squid which come to the surface. A bird ringed on Crozet Island was recovered at Fish River mouth.

LOCAL RACE
D.e. exulans Linnaeus, 1758: *Cape of Good Hope*

8 Black-browed Albatross   Malmok

Diomedea melanophris   Temminck, 1828: *Cape of Good Hope*
PLATE 2 (OPP. P. 16), AD. AND IMM.
Length 85—95 cm (wing 478—503—544; tail 172—189—201; tarsus 81—85,6—92; culmen 111—118,8—124. 38 specimens). Iris brown; bill pale yellow, pink at tip (see immature); legs pinky white to yellow.

Identification: Yellow bill, *dark line through the eye*, slate black on wings, tail and back, are diagnostic; sexes alike. Plain yellow bill separates this from all smaller albatross except the Shy Albatross. No. 11, from which it can be distinguished by its *white head* and underwing pattern. Pattern of underwing in adult has a broader dark leading edge than is found in the Shy Albatross—see also No. 10. The immature has a grey head and neck but bill is dusky olive with dark tip. Underwing of immature dark with lighter centre line. Wingspan 215—240 cm.

Distribution: Southern Oceans. Occurs along the west coast as far as Walvis Bay along the east coast to Zululand, recently recorded off Mombasa.

Habits: Common pelagic species, more numerous than the last, No. 7, and often coming close inshore particularly following ships into bays. Present throughout the year, but many more from October to December. Quite often trail their wing tips in water. Large numbers congregate on the trawling grounds off Cape Town where they feed extensively on the fish offal from the trawlers. Birds ringed in South Georgia have been recovered in Table Bay and Algoa Bay.

Food: Surface fish, squid and offal.

LOCAL RACE
D.m. melanophris Temminck, 1828: *Cape of Good Hope*

9 Grey-headed Albatross   Gryskop-malmok

Diomedea chrysostoma Forster, 1785: *Isla de los Estados, off Tierra del Fuego*

PLATE 2 (OPP. P. 16), AD. AND IMM.
Length about 82 cm (wing 473—508,4—555; tail 175—193,4—205; tarsus 79—85,3—91; culmen 106—114,4—122. 19 specimens). Iris brown; bill black at sides, yellow nose-ridge from feathers to tip and along lower margin of mandible; legs bluish-flesh.

Identification: Head and neck slate-grey, with dark patch in front of eye. Wings blackish-brown above, back and tail dark grey. See bill above. Immature similar to No. 8, but with a grey chin, bill bluish. Wingspan 215 cm.
Distribution: Antarctic oceans, as far north as the Cape.
Habits: A rare species recorded from the western Cape and Algoa Bay. Only recorded off the continental shelf and farther out to sea. A banding recovery 56 km from Cape Point was from South Georgia.
Food: Cephalopods.

10 Yellow-nosed Albatross   Geelbek-malmok

Diomedea chlororhynchos Gmelin, 1789: *Cape of Good Hope*

PLATE 2 (OPP. P. 16), AD.
Length about 75 cm (wing 456—480—499; tail 177—185—199; tarsus 74—75,7—84; culmen 105—115—124. 30 specimens). Iris brown; bill black with yellow nose-ridge reddish at tip; legs bluish, with pink tinge.

Identification: Head and neck white, nape grey. Otherwise as for previous species, distinguished by lack of yellow on bottom edge of mandible. The bill is more slender than Nos 8, 9 and 11, and in the adult the pink tip is conspicuous. Narrow black margins of underwing distinguish this species from the Black-browed, No. 8. Immature has uniformly black bill, otherwise as adult. Wingspan 175—205 cm.
Distribution: Southern Oceans extending to Mossamedes in the west and recorded from north of Durban and south of Malagasy.
Habits: A common pelagic species in the Cape where it occurs throughout the year, though more plentiful in summer. Not usually observed from near the shore, common on trawling grounds. This species is not as common as the Black-browed Albatross, No. 8.
Food: Mostly cephalopods and large shrimps; offal.

11 Shy Albatross   Bloubek-malmok

Diomedea cauta Gould, 1840: *Bass Straits*

PLATE 2 (OPP. P. 16), AD. AND IMM.
Length about 100 cm (wing 523—556—585; tail 188—205—220; tarsus 86—88—95; culmen 117—128—135. 32 specimens). Iris brown; bill bluish with dark tip to lower mandible; legs bluish.

Identification: Capped effect produced by pale-grey face, nape and sides of neck of adult birds. *Dark mark in front of eye* extending back over it. Back dark. Upper wing and mantle dark but not as black as Nos 8 and 10. Immature bird has darker patch on forehead and crown; bill uniform dark grey. Appearance of a short-bodied bulky albatross. Wingspan 170—240 cm.

7

ALBATROSSES

Distribution: Southern seas, extending to Lamberts Bay on the west coast and to Durban on the east coast to south of Malagasy.
Habits: Not uncommon offshore throughout the year, commonest October to December and on the south-east coast. Birds ringed off Cape Campbell, N.Z. recovered from Port Nolloth to Jeffrey's Bay.

LOCAL RACES
(a) D.c. salvini Rothschild, 1893: *New Zealand.* Ranges from New Zealand east to South America and west to the South Atlantic. Bill grey with ivory culminicorn and greyer head.
(b) D.c. cauta Gould, 1840: *Bass Strait.* The bill of this race is greenish or yellowish and without dark tip.

12 Sooty Albatross   Bruin Malmok

Phoebetria fusca   (Hilsenberg), 1822: *Mozambique Channel*
PLATE 2 (OPP. P. 16).
Length 85 cm (wing 481—502—516; tail 237—253—265; tarsus 75,5—81,7—85; culmen 110—113—116. 13 specimens). Iris brown; bill black with yellow or orange line along middle lower mandible lacking in young birds; legs grey.

Identification: Dark brown, slightly lighter on back and belly; incomplete *white ring around the eye* and *long wedge-shaped tail* distinguish this and next species, No. 12X, from other albatrosses. Wingspan 180—240 cm.
Distribution: Southern Oceans; recorded from Dassen Island area on the west, up to Mozambique Channel (type locality) in the east.
Habits: Uncommon winter species from Cape Agulhas area, recorded also at Cape Point in August and near Dassen Island in May and June. This species has a diagnostically more graceful flight which is accentuated by its thin wings. It may be confused with No. 13, but flight, wedge-shaped tail and dark bill distinguish it. Sometimes follows ships.

12X Light-mantled Sooty Albatross

Phoebetria palpebrata   (Forster), 1785: *64° S., 38° E.*
PLATE 2 (OPP. P. 16).
Length 75—90 cm (wing 507—528—545; tail 236—262—274; tarsus 77—80,3—86; culmen 99—103,1—110. 10 specimens). Iris brown; bill black with bluish line along middle of mandible.

Identification: Distinguished from No. 12 by its lighter, almost off-white back and chest. Also by lack of any yellow on bill, but this is not an easy field character. In the hand the bill of this species is concave along the top while in No. 12 the line is straight.
Distribution: Southern Oceans; recorded from Algoa Bay (and Dassen Island).
Habits: As for No. 12.

Family PROCELLARIIDAE

Small to fairly large marine birds, with more than twelve secondaries; tarsus, which has hexagonal scales in front, is slightly shorter than the middle toe; leg bones shorter than the wing bones, front toes completely webbed; basipterygoid process of skull present.

The structure of the external nostrils varies with each genus in the family but in all cases the two tubes run side by side on top of the bill. There are about fifty or sixty species which fall into four groups:

The Fulmars: Nasal tube with one opening (Macronectes, Daption, Fulmarus and Thalassoica). Chunky birds with narrow pointed wings. Capable of swooping down between crests but attracted to ships where they settle on the sea.

The Prions: Nasal tubes short and separate: Palate with lamellae (Pachyptila and Halobaena). Small compact groups of birds which appear out of nowhere and disappear again.

The Shearwaters: Bill slender, as long as head. Nasal tubes separate and short (Puffinus, Calonectris and Procellaria). Named from their habit of swooping along troughs of giant waves on motionless wings, often towering high then diving down again. Do not normally take much interest in ships.

The Gadfly Petrels: Bill strongly hooked, shorter than head. Nasal tubes short and separate. Bill always black (Pterodroma and Bulweria). Usually light-coloured birds from tropical and sub-tropical waters. Flight more erratic and flapping.

13 Giant Petrel   Nellie

Macronectes giganteus   (Gmelin), 1789: *near Staten Island,*
Cape Horn

PLATE 2 (OPP. P. 16).
Length 85—100 cm (Male wing 512—528—544; tail 160—178—192,3; tarsus 89—94—99,6; culmen 94,3—99—105. 12 specimens. Female wing 490—504—520; tail 160—168,4—176,4; tarsus 79—85,4—90; culmen 83,5—87—91,5. 19 specimens). Iris grey to brown; bill yellowish—or greenish—horn to brown. Feet blackish-grey or flesh.

Identification: Dark form: Chocolate brown, slightly paler below. Light form: Wholly white or sparingly marked with black feathers in irregular manner; note that albatrosses are symmetrically marked. See also below. The bill appears heavy owing to the large tubular nostrils. Wingspan 180—200 cm.

Distribution: Southern Oceans; extending as far as Mossamedes in the west and Maputo in the east.

Habits: Common species near the coast, recorded throughout the year but not frequently from December to April. Known to fishermen as the "Stinker". The dark phase is usually seen but several records of the white form are published. The species may be found close inshore and near harbours, usually occurs singly. The habit of alighting near food and swimming up to it is characteristic. The ungainly "stiff" flight, exaggerated by comparatively small wings, slightly hunchbacked appearance, large body and heavy bill easily separate this bird from any albatross.

Food: Scraps, carrion and even small sea-birds.

14 Cape Pigeon   Seeduif

Daption capense   (Linnaeus), 1758: *Cape of Good Hope*
PLATE 3 (OPP. P. 17).
Length 40 cm (wing 249—261,7—273; tail 89—95—103; tarsus 34—44—47; culmen 28—30,8—34. 35 specimens). Iris brown; bill black; legs black.

Identification: The mottled upper parts are a characteristic feature; *remiges patterned black and white*. The amount of black on secondaries is variable.

The black head and neck and *black edge to tail* are also diagnostic. Sexes alike. Also called Pintado. Wingspan 80—90 cm.
Distribution: Southern Oceans, extending to Angola on the west coast and Beira on the east.
Habits: A common winter visitor to our coast from May to November. A single December record. Not often recorded from the shore but freely approaches boats. Often settles on the sea and is quite a capable diver. Usually gregarious.
Food: Fish larvae and young fish; also offal from the trawlers.

LOCAL RACE
D.c. capense (Linnaeus), 1758: *Cape of Good Hope.*

15 Silver-grey Fulmar   Silwer Stormvoël

Fulmarus glacialoides   (A. Smith), 1840: *Cape of Good Hope*
PLATE 3 (OPP. P. 17).
Length 50 cm (wing 325—340—351; tail 114—123—136; tarsus 46—49—52; culmen 39—43—47. 20 specimens). Iris brown; bill pink, dark at base and tip; legs flesh.

Identification: General colour pearly grey, forepart of head and neck, underparts of body and *underwing pure white*. Primaries blackish on outer and white on inner webs. Wingspan 115 cm.
Distribution: Southern Oceans, rare within Cape territorial waters.
Habits: Recorded (in May) off Agulhas and Cape Point, Eastern Cape and off Durban in September. Agile in flight, capable of alighting and taking off with great ease. Often follows boats. Alternates fast wingbeats and long glides with a light rocking motion. Gregarious at sea.

15X Antarctic Petrel   Antarkties-stormvoël

Thalassoica antarctica   (Gmelin), 1789: *Latitude 36° S—61° S.*
PLATE 3 (OPP. P. 17).
Length 45 cm (wing 305—315—338; tail 101—112—125; tarsus 41,6—44,5—46,5; culmen 33—36,4—40. 12 specimens). Iris brown; bill dark horn; legs and feet bluish or flesh grey.

Identification: Upper parts dull greyish or slaty brown, more or less mottled on nape. White below with mottled chin and sides of chest. White tail dark tipped. Extensive white on primaries and secondaries. In flight, conspicuous white trailing edge to wing; underwing coverts and axillaries white with brown margin.
Distribution: Southern Oceans. A single specimen collected south of Bird Island off Algoa Bay, September 1965.
Habits: A pelagic species rarely recorded in our latitudes; occurs within the limits of the pack-ice. Flight usually high over the water.
Food: Euphausids, cephalopods, fish. Not recorded taking refuse.

16 Great-winged Petrel   Langvlerk-stormvoël

Pterodroma macroptera (A. Smith), 1840: *Seas off Cape of Good Hope*
PLATE 3 (OPP. P. 17).
Length 40 cm (wing 300—306—312; tail 116—123—129; tarsus 40—41—44; culmen 34—37—39. 6 specimens). Iris brown; bill and feet black.

Identification: Distinguished from other wholly dark brown sea-birds (Nos 26X and 29) by its very much shorter, stubby beak. In flight wings are held somewhat bent and it towers higher into the sky compared to others. Note feet are black. Juveniles have palish face and chin. Wingspan 100 cm.
Distribution: Southern Oceans, recorded from Lambert's Bay in the west, rarely from Pondoland and Durban roadstead, and as far north as the mouth of the Limpopo River.
Habits: Fairly common in the southern part of its range throughout the year. This swift-flying petrel ranges widely, and is not attracted by boats.
Food: Mainly cephalopods.

LOCAL RACE
P.m. macroptera (A. Smith), 1840: *Seas off the Cape of Good Hope.* Southern Oceans between 50° S. and 30° S.; other races in Australian and New Zealand waters.

17 See page xxxi

18 Schlegel's Petrel

Pterodroma incerta   (Schlegel), 1863: *"Mers australes"*, *restricted to Cape of Good Hope*
PLATE 3 (OPP. P. 17).
Length 45 cm (wing 313—323—335; tail 121—131—138; tarsus 43—45—47; culmen 35—37—39. 12 specimens). Iris brown; bill black; legs flesh.

Identification: Brown above. Light brown on throat and under tail-coverts, *white breast and belly* and *dark underwing* separates this from other brown petrels. In worn plumage the throat may also be white.
Distribution: Sub-tropical and sub-antarctic regions of the Atlantic and western Indian Oceans. Recorded from the Western Cape and off Natal.
Habits: Fairly common. This bird with its powerful flight often passes near boats but is not diverted from its course by them.

19 Soft-plumaged Petrel   Donsveer-stormvoël

Petrodroma mollis   (Gould), 1844: *South Atlantic Ocean*
PLATE 3 (OPP. P. 17).
Length 35 cm (wing 247—256—268; tail 106—110,6—117; tarsus 34—35—36; culmen 26,8—28,3—29,2. 9 specimens). Iris brown; bill black; legs flesh; dark brown tips to feet.

Identification: Light form: Slate-grey above, white below except for a narrow slate-grey chest band. *Broad sooty stripe extends through eye* onto ear coverts. Dark form: Sooty grey instead of slate-grey and chest band broad. Distin-

11

guished from other petrels by uniform upper parts, white breast and *dark grey under wing-coverts*. Some have dark patches on side of breast. The dark wing coverts form an M on back of open wings. Wingspan 85 cm.

Distribution: Southern Oceans. Recorded usually far from land but occasionally storm-blown to the shore between the Cape and Maputo.

Habits: An uncommon off-shore pelagic species. Recorded throughout the year. Rapid and graceful in flight, usually solitary and does not follow boats. The flight is typically in zigzag progression, flying high at the turns.

20   Blue Petrel   Blou Stormvoël

Halobaena caerulea   (Gmelin), 1789: *Southern Ocean 47° S to 58° S. lat.*

PLATE 3 (OPP. P. 17).
Length 30 cm (wing 205—213—221; tail 77—87—91; tarsus 29—31—33; culmen 25—26,5—28. 23 specimens). Iris brown; bill blue; legs blue.

Identification: Separable from other whale birds Nos 21—22 by the *white tip to tail which is also squared* in this species. General colour above is blue, slightly *darker on crown* and bend of wing, primaries darker. *Distinct white forehead* but no white stripe above eye. See also No. 21. Longer winged than other whale birds of the same size. Wingspan 58 cm.

Distribution: Southern Oceans, rarely found within our limits, recorded from East London and Western Cape.

Habits: Often occurs in company with prions and also follows ships. The flight of this species is less agile, or erratic than prions.

21   Broad-billed Prion

Pachyptila vittata   (Forster), 1777: *South Island, New Zealand*
Length 30 cm (wing 199—205—213; tail 92—101—113; tarsus 33—35—36; culmen 32—34—37; width of bill 20—21—23. 10 specimens). Iris brown; bill light blue; legs pale blue.

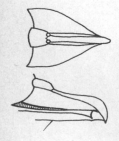

Identification: These birds (21—22) cannot be differentiated easily in the field. Dark blue-grey above, browner along the front edge of the wing and with a *darker broad terminal band on the tail* which in this group is tapered. The dark dorsal markings form a conspicuous V in flight. The bill is very broad two-thirds of its length. There is a dark stripe through the eye with a *white line above it*. See below. Tail-band narrower than other prions.

Distribution: Southern Oceans, not uncommon but mainly beyond our limits.

Habits: A pelagic species occasionally driven landwards during stormy weather while dead specimens are not infrequently washed up on the shore. Occurs usually from May to August and like the previous species follows boats. The flight is rapid, flapping and dove-like.

LOCAL RACE
P.v. vittata (Forster), 1777: *South Island, New Zealand*

21X Medium-billed Prion

Pachyptila salvini (Mathews), 1912: *Marion Island*

Length 25—30 cm (wing 185—200; tail 83—100; culmen 28—33; tarsus 30—34; width of bill 13—17).

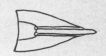

Identification: Similar to No. 21 but having a smaller bill. The length of the bill is twice the width while in No. 21 the ratio width to length is greater than two and up to three times the length. Tail-band narrow.

Distribution: Southern Oceans recorded from the Cape, eastwards as far as Natal and the Mozambique Channel. Uncommon.

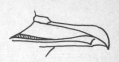

22 Dove Prion

Pachyptila desolata (Gmelin), 1789: *Kerguelen Island*

PLATE 3 (OPP. P. 17).
Length 27 cm (wing 182—188,9—194; tail 87,5—92,7—97,6; tarsus 31,6—32,9—34,3; culmen 26,7—27,8—29,6; culmen width 13,6—14,4—15,4. 10 specimens from South Georgia). Iris brown, bill and legs blue.

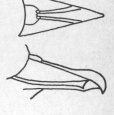

Identification: This species can only be separated from No. 21 in the hand, by its narrower bill. The prominent subocular eye-stripe is sooty black. Tail-band narrow.

Distribution: Southern Oceans. As in the previous species it is often blown inshore or ashore during storms.

Habits: Recorded from Walvis Bay to Durban. A pelagic species, generally met with in flocks. Though the whale birds may follow ships they do not feed on refuse. Flocks of birds often perish in storms and may be found on the shore in wrecks of up to 20 birds or more.

LOCAL RACES
(a) P.d. desolata (Gmelin), 1789: *Kerguelen Island.*
(b) P.d. banksi A. Smith, 1840: *Cape of Good Hope*. Bill longer and broader than nominate. South Georgia, South Orkneys and Heard Island.

22X Fairy Prion

Pachyptila turtur (Kuhl), 1820: *Bass Strait*

PLATE 3 (OPP. P. 17).
Length 28 cm (wing 174—180—187; tail 81—86—93; tarsus 29—31—32; culmen 22—23—24; width of bill 10—10,9—11,8. 10 specimens). Iris brown; bill and legs blue.

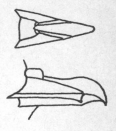

Identification: This prion has a narrower and shorter bill than Nos 21 or 22. The black tail-band is broader than in the other species, more than one-third of the length of the tail.

Distribution: Seldom reaching the latitudes of the southern extremities of Australia, Africa and America. Nothing is recorded about this species but specimens exist in local museums from Algoa Bay and off Natal. Found along the convergence of the sub-tropical and sub-Antarctic waters.

22Y Slender-billed Prion

Pachyptila belcheri (Mathews), 1912: *Geelong, Victoria, Australia*
Length 28 cm (wing 180—186,5—191; tail 86,2—92,1—96,5; tarsus 31—32,6—34; culmen 23,7—25,9—28,3; width of bill 9,8—10,6—11,4. 10 specimens). Iris brown; bill and legs blue.

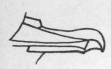

Identification: Distinguished from No. 22X by its longer bill and narrow tail-band. The palest prion with distinct head pattern; the white lores and broad eyebrows contrasting with narrow bluish-grey stripe below and behind the eye.
Distribution: More southerly distributed in the sub-Antarctic zone than other Prions. Records from the Natal coast, and Western Cape.
Habits: Erratic rapid weaving flight low over the water in small flocks.

23 White-chinned Petrel   Bassiaan

Procellaria aequinoctialis Linnaeus, 1758: *Cape of Good Hope*
PLATE 3 (OPP. P. 17).
Length 51—58 cm (wing 367—375—382; tail 117—123,9—130; tarsus 60—64,9—68,2; culmen 48—51,2—55. 6 specimens). Iris brown; bill pale yellowish to greenish horn; legs black.

Identification: A large dark petrel with contrasting pale bill and white chin patch. The amount of white varies from practically none to an extensive white chin and may rarely form white spots on the crown. (See Races.) Flies less stiff-winged than other Petrels; known as the Cape Hen or Shoemaker. Wingspan 140 cm.
Distribution: Southern Oceans, extending to Angola on the west, Bazaruto and South of Malagasy on the east.
Habits: A common and fearless petrel found throughout the year. This species is a scavenger which follows boats to feed on the offal thrown overboard. It may even come into harbours. Known to fishermen as "stinker" but this is more truly applied to No. 13. It is a capable diver and on occasions will duck under like a cormorant and swim actively after young fish. Occurs sometimes in hundreds when scavenging.
Food: Includes squid, crabs and euphausids.

LOCAL RACES
(a) P.a. aequinoctialis Linnaeus, 1758: *Cape of Good Hope.* Specimens of this race have been collected in our area.
(b) P.a. conspicillata Gould, 1844: *Tristan da Cunha.* This race which has a distinct ring of white over the crown, is recorded very rarely from territorial waters. Very abundant in the Atlantic and Pacific Oceans. The ring-eyed shoemaker.

24 Great Grey Shearwater   Pediunker

Procellaria cinerea Gmelin, 1789: *within the Antarctic Circle*
PLATE 3 (OPP. P. 17).
Length 50 cm (wing 340—346,5—355; tail 110—115,9—124; tarsus 57—59,8—64; culmen 45—46,8—49. 11 specimens). Iris brown; bill greenish yellow, nostrils and culmen black; legs fleshy grey, webs yellow.

Identification: From below the dark underwing and undertail-coverts contrast with the white belly. Above the wings, tail rump and back are uniform and dark. The dark crown merges with a paler collar. No white on rump. Note

SHEARWATERS

relatively longish beak. Appears brownish in worn plumage. Glides much like an albatross and beats its wings with a rapid paddling motion. Wingspan 117 cm.
Distribution: Southern Oceans, recorded from "Cape Seas" as far north as Port Nolloth, and the Mozambique Channel.
Habits: This pelagic species ranges well out to sea and has only been recorded more than 65 km off shore from an area west of Agulhas. Follows boats and dives for its food more frequently than most other petrels and shearwaters.
Food: Cephalopods, fish, offal and refuse.

25 Great Shearwater   Groot Pylstormvoël

Puffinus gravis (O'Reilly), 1818: *Cape Farewell, Greenland*
PLATE 3 (OPP. P. 17).
Length 45 cm (wing 309—324—337; tail 105—111—116; tarsus 53—58,2—62; culmen 41,8—45,4—48,5. 23 specimens). Iris brown; bill dark-horn; legs flesh with outer edge brownish-black.

Identification: Similar to No. 24, but general colour above brown; separated from it by *white on upper tail-coverts* and *white underwing-coverts*. Differs from No. 26 by capped effect of dark crown and dark bill. Juvenile greyish and with pale feather edging. Bill bluish-grey. Flight is low and skimming—a flap and a glide with quick wing-beats.
Distribution: Atlantic Ocean from Cape Seas and Cape Horn to the Arctic Circle.
Habits: A pelagic species common off shore from October to January; during this period it has even been recorded from Cape Town docks. For the rest of the year stragglers may be recorded off shore. In winter large rafts of this species are a feature on the trawling grounds. Completely indifferent to boats.

26 Mediterranean Shearwater   Bruin Pylstormvoël

Calonectris diomedea (Scopoli), 1769: *Tremiti Is., Adriatic Sea*
PLATE 3 (OPP. P. 17).
Length 45 cm (wing 325—360; tail 118—140; tarsus 51—57; culmen 46—55). Bill yellow with black tip; legs yellow.

Identification: Similar in appearance to No. 25, differs mainly by having *cheeks and side of neck mottled grey* so that the brown crown which is lighter than No. 25 does not appear such a conspicuous cap. *Note yellow bill.* Underwing-coverts are white. Some white may be present at base of tail. Sometimes called Cory's Shearwater.
Distribution: The Mediterranean, Atlantic and Indian Oceans.
Habits: Not uncommon off the coast from November to March with a few records in other months. Rare off Durban. Similar in habits to No. 25.

LOCAL RACE
Uncertain—too few specimens.

PLATE 2

7. *Diomedea exulans.* Wandering Albatross. Groot Albatros.

A ♂ and ♀. B and C Imm.

8. *Diomedea melanophris* Black-browed Albatross. Malmok. Ad. and Imm.

9. *Diomedea chrysostoma.* Grey-headed Albatross. Gryskop-malmok.

Ad. and Imm.

10. *Diomedea chlororhynchos.* Yellow-nosed Albatross. Geelbek-malmok. Ad.

11. *Diomedea cauta.* Shy Albatross. Bloubek-malmok. Ad. and Imm.

12. *Phoebetria fusca.* Sooty Albatross. Bruin-malmok.

12X. *Phoebetria palpebrata.* Light-mantled Sooty Albatross.

13. *Macronectes giganteus.* Giant Petrel. Nellie. Dark and White forms.

ALBATROSSES & GIANT PETREL

Wandering
7
A
♀
7 Imm
B
C
♂

8
8 Imm
Black-browed

9
Grey-headed
9
Imm
10
Yellow-nosed
Imm

11
Shy
Imm

12
Sooty
12 X
Light-mantled Sooty

13
Giant Petrel
13
(White form)

K. NEWMAN '76

PETRELS, PRIONS & SHEARWATERS

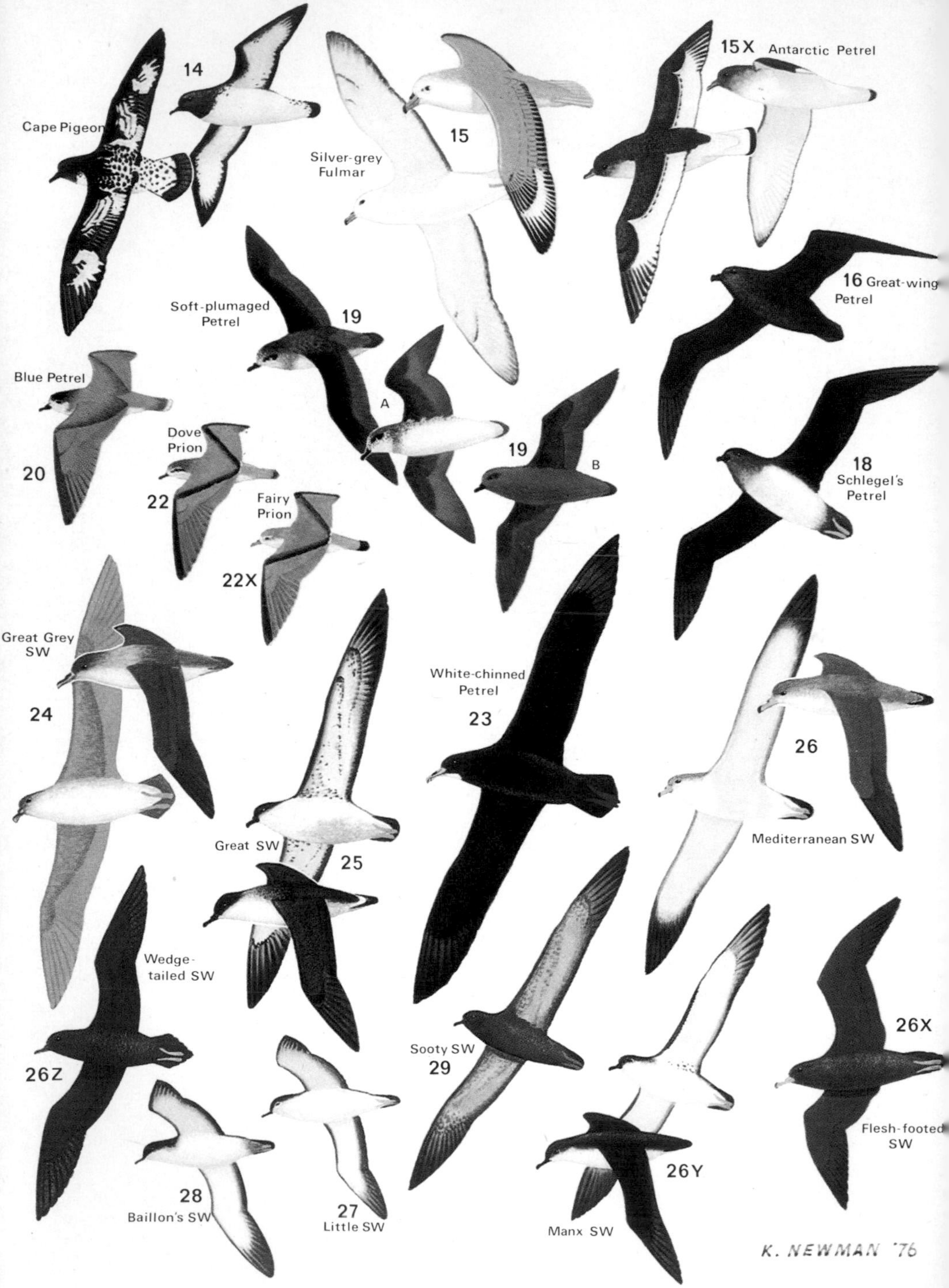

Cape Pigeon

14

15

15 X Antarctic Petrel

Silver-grey
Fulmar

16 Great-wing
Petrel

Soft-plumaged
Petrel

19

Blue Petrel

A

18
Schlegel's
Petrel

20

Dove
Prion

22

19

B

Fairy
Prion

22X

Great Grey
SW

24

White-chinned
Petrel

23

26

Great SW

25

Mediterranean SW

Wedge-
tailed SW

26Z

Sooty SW
29

26X

28
Baillon's SW

27
Little SW

26Y

Manx SW

Flesh-footed
SW

K. NEWMAN '76

PLATE 3

14. *Daption capense.* Cape Pigeon. Seeduif.
15. *Fulmarus glacialoides.* Silver-grey Fulmar. Silwer Stormvoël.
15X. *Thalassoica antarctica.* Antarctic Petrel. Antarkties-stormvoël.
16. *Pterodroma macroptera.* Great-winged Petrel. Langvlerk-stormvoël.
18. *Pterodroma incerta.* Schlegel's Petrel.
19. *Pterodroma mollis.* Soft-plumaged Petrel. Donsveer-stormvoël.
Phases A and B.
20. *Halobaena caerulea.* Blue Petrel. Blou Stormvoël.
22. *Pachyptila desolata.* Dove Prion.
22X. *Pachyptila turtur.* Fairy Prion.
23. *Procellaria aequinoctialis.* White-chinned Petrel. Bassiaan.
24. *Procellaria cinerea.* Great Grey Shearwater. Pediunker.
25. *Puffinus gravis.* Great Shearwater. Groot Pylstormvoël.
26. *Calonectris diomedea.* Mediterranean Shearwater. Bruin Pylstormvoël.
26X. *Puffinus carneipes.* Flesh-footed Shearwater.
26Y. *Puffinus puffinus.* Manx Shearwater.
26Z. *Puffinus pacificus.* Wedge-tailed Shearwater.
27. *Puffinus assimilis.* Little Shearwater.
28. *Puffinus lherminieri.* Baillon's Shearwater.
29. *Puffinus griseus.* Sooty Shearwater. Malbaatjie.

17

26X   Flesh-footed Shearwater

Puffinus carneipes   Gould, 1844: *off Cape Leeuwin, Australia*
PLATE 3 (OPP. P. 17).
Length 45 cm (wing 294—309—317; tail 102—107—112; tarsus 49—51—54; culmen 39—42—44. 12 ex Serventy). Bill fleshy pink with dark tip. Iris brown. Legs flesh-pink.

Identification: A dark heavily built shearwater with pale bill and feet, *dark underwing*, bill stouter and nasal tubes more raised than others. Tail fan-shaped (rounded). Flutters heavily and glides on stiff wings in corkscrew motion low over the waves. Wing-beats less rapid than No. 29. Pale edges to feathers become prominent with wear.
Distribution: Eastern Indian Ocean and westwards. Specimens from Algoa Bay and Natal. Several seen on Pilchard runs.

26Y   Manx Shearwater

Puffinus puffinus   (Brunnich), 1764: *Faroe Islands*
PLATE 3 (OPP. P. 17).
Length 37 cm (wing 232—239—246; tail 72—75—89; tarsus 44—46—49; culmen 34,2—35,9—38,5. 12 sp. ex Serventy). Iris brown. Bill slate-black. Legs pink.

Identification: The black cap extends below eye-level. Outer tail-coverts edged black. Flight mainly gliding and far less flapping in gaining height than in No. 27 and 28. Undertail-coverts white.
Distribution: Atlantic and Mediterranean, south of South America. A single record of a bird in Algoa Bay.

26Z   Wedge-Tailed Shearwater

Puffinus pacificus   (Gmelin), 1789: *Pacific Ocean.*

PLATE 3 (OPP. P. 17).
Length 41—46 cm (wing 280—290—308; tail 119—126—138; culmen 36—38—41; tarsus 42—46—48. 20 specimens). Iris brown; bill lead-grey; legs white-flesh to black.

Identification: A large entirely all dark shearwater similar in size and colour to Nos. 16, 26X and 29. Not easily separable from Sooty (29) unless a good view is obtained. Tail normally folded giving body a long slim appearance. Tail shape can only be confirmed during quick flight manoeuvres. In the hand white toe-nails are a reliable diagnostic feature. Often seen singly at sea.
Distribution: Oceanic in sub-tropical and tropical waters. Sight records off Natal need confirmation.

27   Little Shearwater

Puffinus assimilis   Gould, 1838: *"New South Wales", Norfolk Islands*
PLATE 3 (OPP. P. 17).
Length 28—30 cm (wing 182—190,5—196; tail 64—66,8—69; tarsus 39—40,3—41,5; culmen 24—25,8—27,5. 6 specimens). Iris brown; bill dull blue-grey; legs blue with webs yellowish or pinkish.

Identification: Another small black-and-white shearwater. The black cap is above eye-level. Undertail-coverts white. See No. 28.

Distribution: Recorded from the South Atlantic. One record of a washed-up specimen from the Cape Peninsula.

Habits: This species rarely ranges beyond its breeding ground, the Tristan group of islands being the nearest breeding locality to South Africa. This is a fast flyer with rapid-flattering wing-beats. Swims and dives—gregarious.

28 Baillon's Shearwater

Puffinus lherminieri Lesson, 1839: *"Ad ripas Antillarum"*, *West Indies*

PLATE 3 (OPP. P. 17).

Length 30 cm (wing 200—208—216; tail 82—87—94; tarsus 39—40—43; culmen 26—30—32. 26 specimens). Iris brown; bill black; legs flesh with outer side blackish.

Identification: *Brownish black* above, white below; *undertail-coverts black* sometimes with a few central feathers white. Separated from the Little Shearwater with great difficulty, the latter is "blue-black" above, the undertail-coverts are more white and the feet are bluish. Black cap below eye-level. Known also as Audubon's Shearwater.

Distribution: Tropical oceans. Recorded from near East London and Durban.

Habits: This very rare species does not normally range far from its breeding areas. It is said to glide less than other shearwaters. Recorded in November, December and March.

LOCAL RACES

P.l. bailloni Bonaparte, 1857: *Isle of France*, i.e. Mauritius. Occurs on Mauritius and Seychelles Islands.

29 Sooty Shearwater   Malbaatjie

Puffinus griseus (Gmelin), 1789: *New Zealand*

PLATE 3 (OPP. P. 17).

Length 45 cm (wing 280—293—309; tail 84—89—99; tarsus 52—55—60; culmen 38—42—45. 40 specimens). Iris brown; bill black; legs slate-grey, outer toe blackish.

Identification: Greyish-brown with contrasting *under wing-coverts* which are *greyish-white* in the center. Dark legs and bill distinguish this species from the other brown petrels except No. 16. Distinguishable from No. 16 by the bill which is much more slender. See also No. 26X. A few birds may have dark underwings and older birds have more white underwing.

Distribution: Southern Atlantic and Pacific oceans to the Arctic Circle. Recorded from western Cape coast to Durban.

Habits: Common inshore bird especially during the winter months. Often found in fair-sized flocks and tends to follow boats. Flies low over the surface and may dive for food. Rests in close-packed rafts on the sea. The stiff-winged rising-and-falling flight is both fast and graceful.

Family OCEANITIDAE

These small, delicate petrels known as "Mother Carey's chickens" are the subject of sailors' legends. They occur in all oceans and typically fly close to the water with erratic, fluttering wing-beats; sometimes solitary, often in company and occasionally in thousands. They snatch their food from the water without landing.

There are some twenty-one species in two sub-families:

The Oceanitinae of the southern oceans (10 primaries and square tail).

Bouncing along, with wings held high they "walk" on the water—hence the vernacular name "petrel" from the legend of St Peter walking the waves.

The Hydrobatinae of northern oceans (12 primaries, rounded or forked tail). Their flight is swooping, skimming the water's surface to feed.

30 Storm Petrel   Stormvoël

Hydrobates pelagicus (Linnaeus), 1758: *"in albo Oceano"*, *coast of Sweden*

Length 16 cm (wing 116—123; tail 52—55; tarsus 20—24; culmen 10—12. 12 males measured). Iris brown, bill and legs black.

Identification: Sooty black with white tail-coverts. Note square tail and black feet. In flight the legs do not extend beyond the end of the tail. Underwing-coverts light.

Distribution: Southern Atlantic extending as far as the Zambezi mouth in the Indian Ocean.

Habits: Common summer (November to May) visitor often found close inshore. Incessant wing action not rapid but gliding for only short periods between its erratic flight. Often paddles with its feet in the water while flying low, occasionally settling on the water.

Food: Euphausiacea.

31 Leach's Storm Petrel   Swawelstert-stormvoël

Oceanodroma leucorhoa (Vieillot), 1817: *Picardy, France*

Length 22 cm (wing 153—156,8—164; tail 76—80,4—85; tarsus 23—24,4—26; culmen 16—17—17,8. 13 specimens). Iris, bill and legs dark brown.

Identification: Sooty black with white tail-coverts. The tail is deeply forked and in flight the feet extend to the base of the fork. In flight the lighter secondary coverts show as a lightish wing-bar above.

Distribution: Apparently wanders to the "Cape Seas". Dassen and Bird Islands.

Habits: Little positive information regarding this species is obtainable. Their "springy" butterfly-like fluttering flight is said to distinguish them from Wilson's Storm Petrel. Further, this species settles more frequently on the water, holding the tips of their wings high while they swim about. The nominate race is said to occur in Cape Seas, but recorded only some distance from territorial waters. Does not follow ships.

32 See page xxxi

33 Wilson's Storm Petrel   Stormswawel

Oceanites oceanicus (Kuhl), 1820: *South Georgia*
Length about 19 cm (wing 136—144,9—155,5; tail 56,5—63,7—73; tarsus 31—34,6—37; culmen 11,1—12,6—13,2. 97 specimens). Iris dark brown; bill black; legs black with webs between toes yellow.

Identification: Sooty black with white tail-coverts. The tail is square. The feet, which in flight extend beyond the end of the tail, have yellow webs (see below for flight). A pale band across inner end of each wing. Juvenile has light spot on lores; white tips to secondaries, scapulars and belly feathers.
Distribution: South Atlantic extending into the Indian Ocean up the coastal waters as far as Bazaruto Island.
Habits: The commonest storm petrel from our seas, occurring throughout the year. The flight—"consists of an alternate gliding and fluttering, producing a forward movement of very different appearance from the 'leaping' strokes of Leach's Storm Petrel". In flight often carries its legs forward tucked against its belly so that feet may not necessarily be seen beyond tail. They will follow boats and take scraps, often flying so close to the water that they lower their legs and feet, trailing them on the surface.

LOCAL RACES
O.o. oceanicus (Kuhl), 1820: no locality given: *South Georgia* designated by Murphy. North and south Atlantic Ocean.

34 See page xxxi

35 See page xxxi

36 Black-bellied Storm Petrel   Swartpens-stormswawel

Fregetta tropica (Gould), 1844: *Lat. 6° 33' N., Long. 18° 6' W.,*
Atlantic Ocean
Length 21 cm (wing 160—167; tail 73—77; tarsus 39—41; culmen 15—16. 6 specimens). Iris brown; bill and legs black.

Identification: Sooty black above with white upper tail-coverts. Tail square and legs not beyond end of tail. Chin light. White sides to belly, axillaries and centrally on the underwing-coverts. Usually with a black irregular mid-ventral line.
Distribution: Southern Oceans; Recorded from Algoa Bay, East London and off Durban.
Habits: Recorded June to November. Does not follow ships as readily as other Storm Petrels—often flying ahead of ships.

37 White-bellied Storm Petrel

Fregetta grallaria (Vieillot), 1817: *"Nouvelle Hollande": West Coast*
of South America
Length 20 cm (wing 156—170; tail 71—82; tarsus 36—42,3; culmen 14—15,6. 6 specimens). Iris brown; bill and legs black.

Identification: Sooty black above except upper tail-coverts which are white. Sooty head and chest; lower chest and belly white. Tail square and legs not

21

extending beyond tail. The large triangular white underwing patch is conspicuous at a distance.

Distribution: South Atlantic and "Cape Seas".

Habits: Very rarely recorded from our territorial waters; no records nearer than 65 km from Cape Town. Race not determined.

38 See page xxxi

Family PHAETHONTIDAE

Marine birds of the tropical seas, with long wings and tail, the longer feathers of the latter as long as the head and body; about the size of small Cormorants, but the bill pointed and not hooked. Front toes completely webbed; hind toe very small. Nostrils as open linear slits, situated high up near the base of the culmen. The tropic birds are quick, strong flyers, resembling the flight of pigeons. Usually they fly high and plunge into the water from some height. Inquisitive birds which will inspect ships or lighthouses.

Three species are recognized.

39 Red-tailed Tropic Bird   Rooi Pylstert-seevoël

Phaethon rubricauda Boddaert, 1783: *Mauritius*

PLATE 4 (OPP. P. 32).

Length 50 cm (wing 322—349; tail 206—384; tarsus 28—32; culmen 59—70. 3 sp. ex Serventy). Bill orange-red; legs pale blue with ends of toes and webs black.

Identification: Pinky white, with black marks over and behind eye, flanks and bar on wing black. Long wedge-shaped tail has two centre feathers red. Wingspan 104 cm.

Distribution: Recorded as far south as Natal, Algoa Bay, Mossel Bay and Dyers Island.

Habits: Very rare vagrant. Usually collected in exhausted condition on the shore though reported in flocks by lighthouse keepers. An extraordinary record is from the Orange Free State.

LOCAL RACE

P.r. rubricauda Boddaert, 1783: *Mauritius*. This Indian Ocean race recorded from Durban in November.

40 White-tailed Tropic Bird   Wit Pylstert-seevoël

Phaethon lepturus Lacépède and Daudin, 1802: *Mauritius*

PLATE 4 (OPP. P. 32).

Length 43 cm (wing 273—285; tail 355—524; tarsus 23—25; culmen 46—50,6. 9 sp. ex Serventy). Iris white, bill red, legs yellow, ends of toes black.

Identification: All white except black stripe in front of and over eye and black band in wing. Tail pure white.

Distribution: Recorded as far south as Umgeni River, Durban, Natal.

Habits: Very rare vagrant with fewer records than the previous species No. 39.

LOCAL RACE

P.l. lepturus Lacépède and Daudin, 1802: *Mauritius*.

Family PELECANIDAE

Large, white aquatic birds of the coast or inland waters characterized by their large bodies, short legs, webbed toes, fairly long necks, long bills, and a naked pouch suspended from the mandible and upper part of the throat. Subsist on fish, which are captured by large flocks foregathering, forming into line and driving the fish into shallow water, where they are deftly scooped up and collected in the pouch. Construct flat nests of sticks in trees, or of rushes and other plants in marshes or on rocky islands near the coasts, and lay one or two oblong eggs, white with a greenish-blue shell that shows up through the chalk when held to the light.

Six species are living and 10 fossil species are known.

41   Pink-backed Pelican   Klein Pelikaan

Pelecanus rufescens   Gmelin, 1789: *West Africa*

Native Name: Inegwangube (X)

PLATE 4, BR. (OPP. P. 32).
Length 135 cm (wing 570—620; tail 176—195; tarsus 80—105; culmen 300—360). Iris red or yellow; bill and pouch yellow flesh; legs orange or yellow.

Identification: General colour greyish except interscapulars, back and rump which are pink tinged. Feathers of chest elongated and pointed. Feathers of the forehead meet base of maxilla in a broad arc, extending further forward at the sides than the centre. In flight, the primaries are slightly darker than rest of plumage; not black as in the next species, No. 42. Young brownish above with head and neck greyish-white, the underparts, rump and back are white.
Distribution: Confined to Africa and Malagasy. This species is distributed down the east coast, rare in the Cape Peninsula. Recorded from Salisbury, Rhodesia.

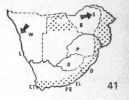

41

Habits: Not a very common species, resident in Natal and farther north. These birds frequent the bays and river mouths along the coast; found less often on large rivers and inland sheets of water. They are gregarious and may associate with the next species. Feed more actively early or late in the day.
Food: Fish. Feeds close inshore mainly on fry.
Breeding: Colonial breeders, they nest on Mimosa trees near water, St Lucia, Zululand and Zambezi River delta. The nest is a platform of large sticks, recorded in December and January. Eggs 2—4, chalky white in colour. Average (5) 92,4 × 60,3 (88—95 × 57—64). Incubation unrecorded.

42   White Pelican   Wit Pelikaan

Pelecanus onocrotalus   Linnaeus, 1758: *Africa*

Native Name: Ingcwangube (X)

PLATE 4, ♂ BR. (OPP. P. 32).
Length male about 180 cm; female 148 cm (male wing 630—710; tail about 200; tarsus 127—142; culmen 413—450). Iris red, bill purplish-white at base, edges yellowish, pouch yellow, legs pinkish straw-yellow.

Identification: General colour white, which in breeding season is tinged pink. The primary coverts and primaries are black. The feathers of the forehead converge to a point at the base of the culmen. In breeding condition both sexes

23

have a longer crest and the naked patch between eye and bill becomes more swollen, orange in female, pink in male. Young brownish, including head and neck, except for back rump and underparts which are white or mottled brown and white.

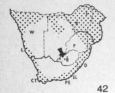

Distribution: Southern Europe, Asia and Africa. Mozambique, Natal and Cape Province usually near the seaboard. Recorded from Walvis Bay, Sandwich Harbour, South West Africa; Lake Ngami; Wankie, the Zambezi Valley and Salisbury in Rhodesia. Occasional inland records.

Habits: Fairly common resident in breeding areas, local movements elsewhere. Similar in habits to the preceding species though more often found on stretches of fresh water. Also fishes in deeper water and eats larger fish.

Breeding: Colonial breeders nesting on several islands off the S.W. Cape, St Lucia, Zululand, at Etosha Pan, and on Lake Ngami. The nest is a shallow scrape or a dirty built-up ring of seawead and feathers. Eggs in June-July at Etosha, September Walvis Bay, January in Cape. Eggs 2—3, chalky white, discoloured by guano. Average (54) 93,9 × 60,1 (84,4—107 × 52,7—67,5). Incubation between 38 and 45 days.

43 See page xxxi

Family SULIDAE

Fairly large white or brown marine birds, with long wings, completely webbed toes and pointed bills; nostrils not visible; tail feathers not so stiff as in Cormorants and Pelicans. Subsist upon fish captured by diving from a height above the water, often following shoals of fish in great hosts. Breed in large colonies on rocky islands off the coast.

Nine species are recognized in two genera.

44 Cape Gannet   Malgas

Morus capensis (Lichtenstein), 1823: *Cape of Good Hope*

Native Name: Umkholonjane (X)

PLATE 4, AD. AND IMM. (OPP. P. 32).

Length about 90 cm (wing 360—450—478; tail 160—178—190; tarsus 56—62,8—73; culmen 91—93,2—97. 8 specimens). Iris whitish; bill pale bluish; legs black with turquoise-blue line down front of tarsus dividing to run along top of each toe.

Identification: Naked skin around eye and lores, black except for light blue ring around the eye. Black line of naked skin extends from mandible about 15 cm down the front of the neck. In flight the wings appear pointed, head is stretched forward and wing motion is unbending. Immature birds are dark brown flecked with white spots at the tips of the feathers. Nestlings are black-skinned, covered with white down feathers. Albinos recorded.

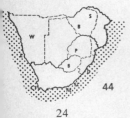

Distribution: Islands off the South African coast. Recorded up the west coast as far as Port Harcourt, East Nigeria and as far as Mombasa, Kenya on the east coast.

Habits: A common off-shore species resident throughout the year on the west and southern coasts. Young birds seen from December to May migrate during the winter months up the east and west coasts. Large numbers frequently accompany the ''sardine'' run up the east coast to Natal and Zululand during

June and July each year. Social in habit, these birds may be picked up at some distance by their conspicuous whiteness and mode of flight which is characterized by frequent gliding up in an arc and down again. When feeding dive from considerable height into the sea.

Food: Surface fish such as pilchard, maasbanker, mackerel, and mullet, also cephalopods.

Voice: A loud, raucous "kara-kara-kara-kara".

Breeding: September to March. Colonial breeding birds on many of our coastal islands from Algoa Bay to S.W.A. Many thousands nest close together on the ground; the nest is a mound of guano-covered debris built up in a small hollow-topped cone. Eggs incubated by the birds' feet. Eggs 1, initially bluish-white later becoming trodden and guano covered. Average (500) 82,5 × 47,6 (73—84 × 45,6—49,0). Incubation 40—43 days. Nestling period 12—16 weeks.

45 See page xxxi

46 Brown Booby   Bruin Malgas

Sula leucogaster (Boddaert), 1783: *Cayenne ex Daubenton*

PLATE 4 (OPP. P. 32).
Length 70 cm (wing 380; tail 195; tarsus 46; culmen 101). Iris silvery-white; bill greenish-white, flesh-coloured base; legs greenish.

Identification: Smaller than the Cape Gannet, sooty-brown, lower breast to undertail-coverts white. No naked line on throat; naked skin of throat yellow-greenish or bluish.

Distribution: Ascension Island in the Atlantic, the Red Sea and eastern seaboard of Kenya. One record of a dead bird from Beira after a storm in 1954. Also a record from last century "at sea off the Cape of Good Hope". Rare vagrant seen at sea after storms.

Family PHALACROCORACIDAE

More or less black aquatic birds with short legs, all the toes webbed, stiff tail feathers. Bodies more slender than Gannets and Pelicans, with fairly long necks, sleek heads, often with a small crest and rather slender bills hooked at the tip. In flight the neck is stretched forward, the wings beat rapidly with stiff unbending motion—rather ungainly birds in the air. Cormorants' feathers,  unlike those of wholly aquatic birds, get slightly wet if they are in contact with water for long; it is a characteristic of the family to see them drying the outstretched wings in the sun. Expert swimmers and divers. Subsist on fish caught by pursuing them under the water and not by diving. Freshwater species also take frogs. Inhabit inland waters and the coasts. Commonly observed perched conspicuously on rocks or snags in the water, or dead trees overhanging the water, otherwise swimming or diving. Nest in colonies, the nest made of twigs or weeds, either on branches of trees, in reed beds, or on the exposed rocks of islets. Eggs greenish, more or less covered with chalk, usually three or four to the clutch. The young have naked crown and throat usually red or yellow. Both sexes share incubation and feeding, the young being fed by regurgitation.

   Twenty-nine or thirty living species are recognized and 21 fossil species are known.

CORMORANTS

47   White-breasted Cormorant   Witbors-duiker

Phalacrocorax carbo   (Linnaeus), 1758: *Europe—Sweden*

Native Name: Ugwidi (X)

PLATE 4, BR., N-BR. AND IMM. (OPP. P. 32).
Length about 90 cm (wing 304—325—350; tail 125—139,4—148; tarsus 48—53,3—
61; culmen 60—65,5—70. 10 specimens). Iris green; bill grey; lores naked yellow,
pouch dark green; legs black.

Identification: The largest cormorant, short-tailed and always showing white
on breast. In breeding condition the white is conspicuous against its glossy
green-black plumage. Non-breeding birds are brownish, and lack white
patches on upper thigh; not all breeding birds show these white patches.
Immature birds are off-white below, extending to a varying amount to belly.
Nestling is sooty-brown.

Distribution: World-wide. Throughout Africa.

Habits: Common resident along the coast and inland where it occurs on dams
and large stretches of water. Usually social in habits and return to the same
perch over long periods thus whitening the dead tree or other roost.

Food: Klipfish, mullet and molluscs.

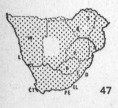

47

Breeding: Colonial nesters, building on islands around the coast, occasionally
on coastal cliffs; on trees and islands in inland areas. Nest built of coarse
sticks becoming covered in guano as the season passes; frequently use old
nests which are subsequently built up a little each year, usually lined with a
little seaweed or green vegetable matter. Breed throughout the year, August or
January peak periods in the Cape; recorded from March to October inland.
Eggs 3—4, occasionally 5, chalky white with greenish-blue tinge when fresh.
Average (112) 62,5 × 39,7 (55,5—70,7 × 37,7—42,2). Incubation 26—29
days (Europe). Nestling period more than four weeks (Europe).

LOCAL RACE
P.c. lucidus (Lichtenstein), 1823: *Cape of Good Hope.* Recorded from west coast (Cape
Verde), South West Africa, the Republic, Rhodesia, Zambia and north on the east coast
to Tana River. Separated principally by size of bill. Size as given above.

48   Cape Cormorant   Trekduiker

Phalacrocorax capensis (Sparrman), 1788: *False Bay, Cape of Good*
Hope

Native Name: Ugwidi (X)

PLATE 4, AD. AND IMM. (OPP. P. 32).
Length 64 cm (wing 245—253,5—275; tail 86—95,3—100; tarsus 56—58,7—63;
culmen 50,4—53,8—56,4. 10 specimens). Iris green; bill black; naked lores and pouch
yellow; legs black.

Identification: Uniform black in breeding plumage. Immature and non-
breeding birds are brown, with lighter-brown throat and breast. *Naked yellow
lores* and *short-tailed* appearance, distinguish this from other marine cormorants.

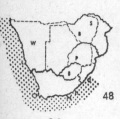

48

Distribution: Coastal, from the Congo River mouth southwards to the Cape
and eastwards as far as Durban.

26

Habits: Marine birds showing definite migratory tendencies although single birds are found at all seasons throughout its range. Abundant on the South West coast, otherwise not uncommon but found singly or in small numbers. "Trekking" is commonly seen during the summer months in the Cape when hundreds, sometimes thousands of birds following in long lines, cross the water, now low, now rising higher in a ripple that runs down the line as the front ones return to near the surface. When a flock finds a shoal of fish they settle, dive and surface in great activity.

Food: Pelagic surface fish including pilchards etc., also rock lobster.

Breeding: Colonial breeding bird on islands off the west coast and artificial platforms in S.W.A. The nest is made up of sticks and seaweeds. Large colonies of nests may be deserted for no apparent reason. Breeding from September to February. Eggs 2—3, occasionally 4 or 5; chalky white. Average (18) 54,1 × 35,8 (53—59,9 × 32—38,8).

49 Bank Cormorant   Bankduiker

Phalacrocorax neglectus (Wahlberg), 1855: *Islands off the S.W. coast of Africa*

PLATE 4 (OPP. P. 32).

Length about 75 cm (wing 260—288; tail 112—132; tarsus 62—70; culmen 53,7—56,5. 3 specimens). Iris brown above, green below; bill black, lores feathered and pouch black; legs black.

Identification: A *totally black* cormorant, large in size and heavy in body; short-tailed; generally "woolly" in appearance, not so sleek as the previous species. Only occasionally having white on the rump; the amount of white is variable. Albinistic birds occasionally seen. Bill comparatively shorter than in previous two species, Nos 47 and 48.

Distribution: Confined to the south-western seaboard from Swakopmund in the north to Agulhas in the south.

Habits: Local resident species usually occurring near the coast in widely dispersed flocks or small groups. Nearly all the islands have a small resident population of these cormorants.

Food: Inshore invertebrates and fishes (blennies and klipfish) often from kelp.

Breeding: Social breeding birds which build in small groups on the same large boulders year after year. The nest is constructed of red algae collected from the sublittoral off-shore areas. Unguarded nests are often torn to bits by neighbours, the material being used for their own nests. Breeding recorded for all months except April, August and November. Eggs 2—3, chalky white. Average (88) 59,5 × 38,8 (51,1—67 × 33,4—40,4).

49

50 Reed Cormorant   Rietduiker

Phalacrocorax africanus (Gmelin), 1789: *River Nile, Egypt*

Native Names: um-Pishamanzi (Z); i-Nyaopetana (D)

PLATE 4, ♂ AND ♀ BR. AND N-BR. (OPP. P. 32).

Length 60 cm (wing 200—210,9—234; tail 142—155,3—174; tarsus 33—35,6—38; culmen 28—31—35. 71 specimens). Iris ruby red; bill black, lores naked and yellow; legs black.

Identification: A long-tailed cormorant separated from the Darter, No. 52, by its shorter neck and cormorant's bill which is hooked at the tip. Crest is longer

27

in the breeding season, and almost absent the rest of the year. See No. 51. Immature birds have off-white breast, light-brown throat and belly. Bill is comparatively shorter than in other cormorants. Nestling covered in black down.

Distribution: Throughout Africa south of the Sahara.

Habits: A common inland resident. May be found on dams, lakes and rivers. Social in habit but not usually in very large numbers. May be seen flying high in the sky between different fishing waters, usually in loose formation.

Food: Fish and frogs.

Breeding: Colonial nesters, constructing a light platform of sticks and/or reeds. Nest may be situated on rocky ledges, trees or on reeds over water. Breeds in the Cape from July to April, but throughout the year inland. Eggs 2—4, occasionally 5, elongated bluish-white when fresh. Average (107) 45,3 × 30,3 (40,5—53,9 × 26,9—36,1). Incubation 23—25 days.

LOCAL RACE
(a) P.a. africanus (Gmelin), 1789: *River Nile, Egypt.* Africa except Malagasi.

51 Crowned Cormorant   Kuifkop-duiker

Phalacrocorax coronatus (Wahlberg), 1855: *Possession Island, S.W.A.*

PLATE 4 (OPP. P. 32).
Length 54 cm (wing 198—210—223; tail 115—135,2—168; tarsus 37—39,3—42; culmen 27—30,6—34. 8 specimens). Iris ruby red; bill yellow to orange; lore naked, yellow; legs black.

Identification: This marine species is distinguished from other coastal forms by red eye, yellow gape and longer tail. Distinguished from No. 50 by slightly smaller size, comparatively shorter tail and longer legs. Always has a crest. Immature, much browner than No. 50.

Distribution: Along the south-west coastal area of cold water from Cape Agulhas to Benguela.

Habits: Confined to coastal islands and rocky shorelines, this is a social species but numbers are never very high. Sometimes found in lagoons after storms.

Food: Clinid rockfish, pipefish, soles, shrimps and isopods.

Breeding: Colonial nesters, usually near other species. Usually on rocky ledges, rarely on bushes; the nests are used from year to year and are thus substantial platforms. Breeds throughout the year with spring and autumn peaks. Eggs 2—3, occasionally 4, white and elongate. Average (134) 46,7 × 30,9 (41,0—57,6 × 29,0—34,5).

Family ANHINGIDAE

Resemble Cormorants in habits and habitat, but have pointed bills, longer stiff tail-feathers, longer and more slender necks, slender heads, but the same webbed feet and short legs adapted to swimming. Inhabit inland waters rather than the coasts, though found in the coastal lagoons, and nest in colonies in the branches of trees. Only one genus and species inhabits this continent, but other species are found in all the other continents.

52 Darter   Slanghalsvoël

Anhinga rufa   (Lacépède et Daudin), 1802: *Senegal*

Native Name: Ivusi (X)

PLATE 4, ♂ BR. AND N-BR. (OPP. P. 32).
Length 79 cm (wing 320—341,4—363; tail 220—238,9—264; tarsus 36—40,2—45; culmen 69—77,6—84. 15 specimens). Iris golden yellow; bill yellowish; legs brown.

Identification: Sharp *pointed bill* separates this species from the cormorants. Long-tailed and long-necked bird of rather graceful proportions. The male in breeding condition has black crown and hind neck, white chin and sides of upper neck, chestnut throat. Except for longitudinal white streaks on back the bird is otherwise black. Female, non-breeding males and immature are brown instead of black and the underparts are fawn. Nestling birds are downy white, changing to light chestnut later.

Distribution: Throughout Africa south of the Sahara.

Habits: Not an uncommon resident in suitable localities such as the larger rivers and stretches of water. Usually social but quite frequently solitary birds may be met with perched on a stump or dead tree overhanging quiet stretches of river. Sometimes rest on a bank near to water but they slide off and dive silently so that their presence is not always noticed. These birds swim with their bodies almost completely submerged so that the head, waving to and fro may be all that is seen. Frequently roost and breed near cormorants.

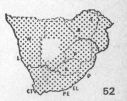

52

Food: Frogs and fish.

Breeding: Usually colonial, nesting on a dead tree or on reeds; the nest is a largish structure up to 46 cm across built of twigs and reeds scantily lined with green reeds. Breeds from September to January. Eggs 3—5; white, smooth and elongate. Average (39) 53,8 × 34,4 (47,3—58,3 × 29,2—38). Incubation 21—28 days.

LOCAL RACE:
A.r. rufa (Lacépède et Daudin), 1802: *Senegal*. Throughout Africa except Malagasy.

Family FREGATIDAE

Oceanic birds related to the Cormorants in respect of their hooked bill, short legs, webbed toes and black plumage, but differ in respect of their long wings and forked tail (of 12 feathers), having a small pouch on the throat and in their larger size. They catch their prey on the surface of the sea and not by diving like the Cormorants, and also deprive other birds of their prey by pursuing them until it is disgorged and dropped when they swoop down and deftly catch it before it reaches the water.

53 Frigate Bird   Roofduiker

Fregata minor   (Gmelin), 1789: *Jamaica*

PLATE 4, ♂ AND ♀. (OPP. P. 32).
Length about 100 cm (wing 555; tail 355; tarsus 17,5; culmen 100. 1 specimen). Iris brown; bill grey; pouch red; legs reddish.

Identification: Long wings, long forked tail and large size distinguish them from other seabirds. Male bird entirely black except for red pouch. Female and immature birds have underparts white.

29

Distribution: Sub-tropical seas; found in both the Atlantic and Indian oceans. One specimen collected inland, Grabouw, Cape, in 1907. Off Natal sight records.
Habits: Vagrant. A marine bird, usually flies higher than other marine birds. These it pursues boldly to obtain food, which is released by its victim. Several observations, after storms, have been noted by Natal workers from 1970 onwards.

LOCAL RACE
F.m. aldabrensis Mathews, 1914: *Aldabra.* Western Indian Ocean.

Family ARDEIDAE

Tall and slender wading birds, with long, lax plumage, long and pointed bill, long and slender toes with long, curved claws. Frequent shallow water, marshes and sometimes grassy flats and cultivated lands in search of their prey, which consists of fish, water animals of all sorts, insects and even mice in some cases. Nests are platforms of sticks or weeds, often in large colonies, placed in trees, reed beds or rank marshy vegetation. In most species the eggs are green, but in a few cases are white or olive, three to five eggs forming the usual clutch. All species utter some kind of croaking note when alarmed, the Bittern, however, uttering a booming note. The family is cosmopolitan and contains some 15 genera and 62 living species (34 fossil species are known). The living species are separated by their powder down as the important taxonomic character. All herons are four toed.

54 Grey Heron   Blou Reier

Ardea cinerea Linnaeus, 1758: *Europe = Sweden.*
Native Names: Ukhwalimanzi (X), Kokolofitoe (S)
PLATE 5 (OPP. P. 33).
Length about 100 cm (wing 433—449,7—475; tail 173—178,2—190; tarsus 136—152—165; culmen 104—118—128. 9 specimens). Iris yellow; bill yellowish green; legs greenish yellow. Bill and legs have been recorded reddish.

Identification: Grey in colour with *white* neck. In flight the underwing pattern is a uniform grey. Sexes alike. Immature birds have bill and legs dull greenish grey and they are generally more uniform grey colour—the white of adult is replaced by grey though the pattern is similar to the adult. In flight wing-flaps about 125 per minute.
Distribution: Europe, Asia and Africa. Throughout Southern Africa.
Habits: Nowhere plentiful and rather solitary in habits; resident. Rather shy. Commonly found in shallow water or near water, much less frequently in open grassland. When feeding stands motionless for long periods; occasionally moving forward stealthily and alert for the movement of its food. Occasionally swims, rarely plunging to catch fish. These birds sometimes gather in the evening at communal roosts. Occasionally feed at night by moonlight. When returning to roost or the nest they drop down in long spiral flights. On the nest there is mutual greeting where the birds call vociferously and raise their crests and plumes in display. Longevity record 152 months from ringed bird.
Food: Varied; fish, frogs, crabs, insects and on land both small rodents and moles, as well as small birds.

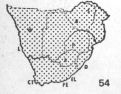

54

Voice: A guttural "frank" or "kraak". Chicks carry on a continuous "kak kak kak".
Breeding: July to February to April and May in Natal. Solitary or more commonly colonial with other herons. Building either in high trees or in extensive reed beds, rarely on cliffs. The nest is a large structure of sticks. Eggs 2—4, pale blue. Average (94) 60,9 × 43,4 (56,4—71,8 × 39,3—48,8). Both sexes build the nest. Incubation 23—28 days (Europe). Nestling period 50—55 days (Europe).

LOCAL RACE:
A.c. cinerea Linnaeus, 1758: *Sweden.* Another race occurs in Malagasy.

55 Black-headed Heron   Swartkopreier

Ardea melanocephala   Vigors & Children, 1826: *Near Lake Chad.*

Native Names: Ukhwalimanzi (X), Kokolofitoe (S)

PLATE 5, AD. AND IMM. (OPP. P. 33).
Length 96,5 cm (wing 387—401,3—410; tail 142—157—160; tarsus 118—136—180; culmen 85—99,9—105. 9 specimens). Iris yellow; bill slaty brown; legs black.

Identification: Differs from the Grey Heron No. 54 by having a black head and neck; chin is white with light streaks on neck. The bill is dark. In flight the underwing is black and white—remiges black, under-coverts white. Sexes alike. Immature is grey instead of black on head and neck—below pinkish, but shows same pattern as adult. In flight wing-flaps about 175 per minute.
Distribution: The whole Ethiopian region.
Habits: Like the Grey Heron nowhere plentiful and rather solitary in habits. This species is more frequently observed on open grassland where it occurs to the same extent as it does near water. It is also stealthy in its hunting habits, but not as shy as the Grey Heron. Longevity record 147 months.
Food: As varied as the previous species; perhaps taking moles more frequently, also passerine birds.
Voice: Guttural "kwaak".
Breeding: Usually colonial, similar to the previous species. Recorded July—January in the Cape, throughout the year in the Transvaal. Eggs 2—4, pale blue. Average (100) 60,5 × 43,3 (55,4—67,8 × 39,8—46,1). Incubation 23—27 days (Priest).

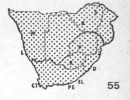

56 Goliath Heron   Reuse Reier

Ardea goliath   Cretzschmar, 1826: *Bahhar Abiad, i.e. White Nile.*

PLATE 5 (OPP. P. 33).
Length about 140 cm (wing 546—583,2—605; tail 200—226—235; tarsus 225—231—238; culmen 173—185—189. 5 specimens). Iris bright yellow; bill black immature pale below, legs black.

Identification: Huge size distinguishes this heron from all others; flight even slower than other herons, with slow ponderous wing beats. The legs tend to sag below the horizontal in flight. Sexes alike as illustrated. Immature birds browner above; below dirty white streaked with blackish-brown.

PLATE 4

2. *Spheniscus demursus.* Jackass Penguin. Pikkewyn.
3. *Eudyptes crestatus.* Rockhopper Penguin. Geelkuif-pikkewyn.
39. *Phaethon rubricauda.* Red-tailed Tropic Bird. Rooi Pylstert-seevoël.
40. *Phaethon lepturus.* White-tailed Tropic Bird. Wit Pylstert-seevoël.
41. *Pelecanus rufescens.* Pink-backed Pelican. Klein Pelikaan.
42. *Pelecanus onocrotalus.* White Pelican. Wit Pelikaan.
44. *Morus capensis.* Cape Gannet. Malgas.
46. *Sula leucogaster.* Brown Booby. Bruin Malgas.
47. *Phalacrocorax carbo lucidus.* White-breasted Cormorant. Witbors-duiker.
Br., N-Br. and Imm.
48. *Phalacrocorax capensis.* Cape Cormorant. Trekduiker. Ad. and Imm.
49. *Phalacrocorax neglectus.* Bank Cormorant. Bankduiker.
50. *Phalacrocorax africanus africanus.* Reed Cormorant. Rietduiker.
♂ and ♀ Br. and N-Br.
51. *Phalacrocorax coronatus.* Crowned Cormorant.
52. *Anhinga rufa.* Darter. Slanghalsvoël. ♂ Br. and N-Br.
53. *Fregata minor.* Frigate Bird. Roofduiker.

40

39

53

♀

♂

44

Imm

46

47

N-Br

Imm

Br

49

48

Imm

51

50

N-Br

Br ♀

Br ♂

52

Br ♂

N-Br

42

41

2

3

Br ♂

Br

K. NEWMAN '76

71

69

Im

70

Br

58

N-Br

N-Br

61

Br

59

60

Imm

57

56

54

55

Imm

K B NEWMAN '73

PLATE 5

54. *Ardea cinerea cinerea.* Grey Heron. Blou Reier.
55. *Ardea melanocephala.* Black-headed Heron. Swartkopreier.
56. *Ardea goliath.* Goliath Heron. Reuse Reier.
57. *Ardea purpurea purpurea.* Purple Heron. Rooi Reier.
58. *Casmerodius albus melanorhynchus.* Great White Egret. Groot Witreier.
Br. and N-Br.
59. *Egretta garzetta garzetta.* Little Egret. Klein Witreier.
60. *Egretta intermedia brachyrhyncha.* Yellow-billed Egret.
Geelbek-witreier.
61. *Bubulcus ibis.* Cattle Egret. Bosluisvoël. Br., N-Br. and Imm.
69. *Nycticorax nycticorax nycticorax.* Night Heron. Nagreier. Ad. and Imm.
70. *Gorsachius leuconotus.* White-backed Night Heron. Witrug-nagreier.
71. *Botaurus stellaris capensis.* Bittern. Roerdomp.

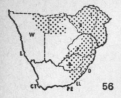

Distribution: The greater part of Africa, Malagasy, Srilanka and India. Recorded from Damaraland, Rhodesia, Transvaal and Natal. Rarely recorded from O.F.S. and down the east coast as far as Port Elizabeth, the Vaal River to the Orange River.

Habits: Resident, rather scarce and usually occurring singly or in pairs. Rather shy and generally haunts quieter areas of rivers, estuaries and large inland vleis. Always occurs near water, usually wading and hunting for fish.

56

Food: Mainly fish including mullet, catfish, carp and eels.

Voice: Deep hoarse "kraak".

Breeding: Usually solitary but also recorded from mixed heronries. Nests on large trees on the banks of rivers in September, and has also been found to use submerged trees in big rivers and large marshes. The nest is constructed of strong sticks lined with smaller twigs, and is at least three feet in diameter. September to January. Later in Rhodesia, December to October. Eggs 3, chalky pastel blue. Average (8) 73,4 × 52,8 (68,6—77,4 × 50—58,9). Incubation 24 and 30 days. Nestling period less than six weeks.

57 Purple Heron   Rooi Reier

Ardea purpurea Linnaeus, 1766: *"in Oriente"* = River Danube.

PLATE 5 (OPP. P. 33).

Length 89 cm (wing 310—335,9—363; tail 111—122—133; tarsus 105—115,5—125; culmen 112—124—138. 29 specimens). Iris yellow; bill brown above with yellow base, horn below with yellow tip; legs brown, yellow behind.

Identification: Non-breeding and immature birds have less bright colouring than illustrated, being rufous brown; the neck purplish grey although the markings are the same as in the adult. Has noticeably large feet.

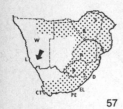

Distribution: Widely distributed over Africa, Malagasy, Southern Europe to Turkestan and Persia. Throughout our area, except dry west.

Habits: A resident species not frequently seen due to its shy and skulking nature. Somewhat crepuscular in habit and during the day resorts to cover of large reed beds where its colour blends remarkably well with the surroundings. When alarmed it may stand bolt upright, with bill pointing upwards, or it may fly up in a comical, undignified and indignant manner. Normally feeds along the water's edge.

57

Food: Fish, frogs, insects; also recorded are lizards, snakes, young birds including chickens and ducklings and rodents.

Voice: Hoarse "kwaak".

Breeding: As a rule in the midst of dense reed beds and not often in communities. September to October in the Cape; May to January in Transvaal; September, December to February and April in Rhodesia. The nest is a large platform of twigs and lined with reeds. Eggs 2—5, greenish blue. Average (73) 55,4 × 39,5 (49,7—59,7 × 38,7—43,0). Incubation, both sexes, 23—27 days. Nestling period about seven weeks. May be double brooded.

LOCAL RACES:
A.p. purpurea Linnaeus, 1766: *"in Oriente"* = River Danube. Another race occurs in Malagasy.

58 Great White Egret Groot Witreier

Casmerodius albus (Linnaeus), 1758: *Europe = Sweden.*

Native Name: i-Ntechana (G).

PLATE 5 BR. AND N-BR. (OPP. P. 33).
Length 95 cm (wing 343—383—396; tail 131—147—163; tarsus 134—149—170;
culmen 104—108—115. 8 specimens). Iris pale yellow, bill black in breeding condition,
orange-yellow in non-breeding condition; legs black.

Identification: The largest of the white herons, but not quite as big as the
Grey Heron. Distinguished from other egrets by large size, wholly black legs
and feet (see No. 59), and long slender neck with long bill. Sexes alike.
Nestling covered in white down.

Distribution: Africa and Europe. Although recorded from all parts of
Southern Africa it is a vagrant in the Cape Province.

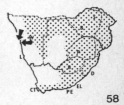

58

Habits: Relatively scarce, shy and solitary, as a rule; rather local in habitat
and apparently restless appearing irregularly in non-breeding areas. Usually to
be seen feeding along the margins of vleis or rivers; rests on the ground or in
reeds near water. Tends to keep its long neck stretched out, leaning at a
slightly forward angle.

Food: Fish, frogs, aquatic animals and insects.

Voice: A very low guttural "aahrr".

Breeding: In communities with other herons, January in Free State. Nests in
large trees on river bank. Eggs 2—4, pale blue and of rather coarse texture.
Sizes given by Jackson from a clutch taken at Kisumu in June are 56—57 ×
39—40. Incubation 25—26 days (Europe). Nestling about 6 weeks (Europe).

LOCAL RACE:
C.a. melanorhynchus Wagler, 1827: *Senegambia.* The Tropical African race occurring
right down to the Cape.

59 Little Egret Klein Witreier

Egretta garzetta (Linnaeus), 1766: *"in Oriente" = Malabergo, N. Italy.*

PLATE 5 (OPP. P. 33).
Length 64 cm (wing 255—272—296; tail 92—100,6—112; tarsus 90—113,6—114;
culmen 83—88—96. 22 specimens). Iris pale yellow; bill black; legs black with yellow
feet.

Identification: Distinguished from No. 58 by the slender bill, yellow feet and
smaller size. Breeding birds have long white plumes on head, neck and back.
Nestling birds differ from Nos. 60 and 61 by grey eye, black upper mandible
(light below), and green legs. The melanistic form has been recorded on the
Kafue River swamps.

Distribution: General over Africa and Southern Asia. Throughout Southern
Africa in suitable localities.

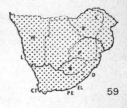

59

Habits: Resident, not uncommon on marshy rivers, dams, estuaries, mangroves, and along the sea shore. This species is usually solitary when feeding,
gregarious when roosting at night. It hunts with a characteristic alertness,
making lightning movements here and there, twisting and turning with
wonderful agility. The yellow feet become conspicuous in its careful high
stepping gait as it wades through the water. Like the Hamerkop No. 72, this
species often stirs the bottom of a pool by shuffling its foot back and forth to
frighten any aquatic life into movement. Longevity from ringing 119 months
and longest distance 1 840 kms N.E. from Rondevlei.

Food: Dragonflies, spiders, grasshoppers, water beetles, shrimps, molluscs and frogs, small fish and lizards.

Voice: Hoarse "kraak", usually uttered in flight.

Breeding: Gregarious in mixed heronries either in trees or reeds in water or on islands. Nests are built up of a platform of sticks, with a shallow cup. Recorded from August to February in the Cape, October to February in Transvaal. Eggs 2—4, greenish blue. Average (44) 49,3 × 35,2 (42,9—58,1 × 31,2—43,4). Incubation by both parents, 21—27 days.

LOCAL RACE:
E.g. garzetta (Linnaeus) 1766: *"in Oriente"* = *Malalbergo, N. Italy.* Another race from India and Australia exists.

60 Yellow-billed Egret   Geelbek-witreier

Egretta intermedia   (Wagler), 1829: *Java.*

PLATE 5 (OPP. P. 33).
Length 68,5 cm (wing 300—315; tail 125—136; tarsus 100—112; culmen 70—76). Iris pale yellow; bill yellow; legs yellow at base (tibia) otherwise black.

Identification: A medium sized egret with long slender neck and yellow bill. The neck has the S bend typical of the larger herons. The yellow at the base of legs and smaller size separates this species from No. 58; the dark tarsus and feet and long slender neck separate it from No. 61. Nestlings separated from No. 59 and 61 by the bright yellow bill, biscuit coloured eye and greenish grey legs.

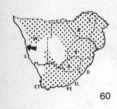

Distribution: Found throughout Southern Africa except dry west; general in Africa south and east of the Sahara. Also Asia and Australia.

Habits: A not uncommon resident in most areas where water is to be found but numbers occasionally fluctuate markedly, indicating some local movements. This species does not normally hunt away from water.

Food: Fish and small animals.

60 **Voice:** Not usually heard except during the breeding season—hoarse "kwaak".

Breeding: In mixed communities on trees, reed beds or rocks. Nest as previous species. August to November in the Cape; up to March in the Transvaal. Eggs 2—4, light greenish blue. Average (23) 48,3 × 35,1 (43,8—53,5 × 33,2—37,0). Incubation, 24—27 days (Priest).

LOCAL RACE:
E.i. brachyrhyncha (Brehm), 1854: *Blue Nile.* Eastern and Southern Africa.

61 Cattle Egret   Bosluisvoël

Bubulcus ibis   (Linnaeus), 1758: *Egypt.*

Native Names: Tsoelientane (S); Bebele, Chifudsangombe (Zw).

PLATE 5 AD. BR., N.BR. AND IMM. (OPP. P. 33).
Length 54 cm (wing 228—242—257; tail 80—91,5—98; tarsus 68—74,8—81; culmen 47,5—50,9—58. 19 specimens). Iris yellow; bill ad. yellow with dark tip in non-breeding season, often red early breeding. imm see below; legs yellowish brown to red, dark during non-breeding period.

Identification: Distinguished by yellow bill and legs. The smallest of the white egrets, short-necked, the bill short and thick compared to the other species. The legs are usually yellowish although mud and dirt may discolour them. Sexes alike. Nestlings distinguished from No. 59 and No. 60 by having dark blackish bill with distinct light tip. Eye and legs as No. 60.

Distribution: Widely distributed over Africa, Southern Europe and south-western Asia and Malagasy. Found throughout the Republic, though before 1930 it was very rare in the southern provinces.

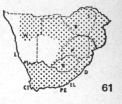

61

Habits: A common resident, gregarious in habit particularly in roosting when it foregathers in very large numbers. This bird, as its common name "Tick-bird" infers, is usually found in association with domestic or wild beasts which it follows to collect the insects that these animals disturb. Not infrequently it settles on an animal's back to pick ticks and flies off it; this service is also performed on resting animals, around which it stalks. Like other egrets, this species also fishes in shallow water. Flocks travel in formation, especially when going long distances to roost. Against strong winds the skeins battle low over the ground, soaring briefly to skim over any obstructions in their path such as windbreaks. Longevity record 162 months—movements, no true migration but move north; Ficksburg to Uganda 3 440 km; Tvl to Republic French Africa 3 520 km.

Food: Insects, especially renowned for its destruction of hoppers; spiders, ticks, water beetles, dragonflies, shrimps, molluscs, frogs, fish, rodents and young birds.

Voice: Harsh "kraak" or "kraak-kraak", also a deep shorter note "krok".

Breeding: Colonial nesters, usually in company with other herons and not infrequently with other reed or tree nesting water birds such as cormorant, ibis, etc. The nest is a platform of sticks or reeds. June to December in the Cape, October to February in the Transvaal. Eggs 3—4, rarely 5, pale chalky blue. Average (100) 45,8 × 33,5 (40,0—52,1 × 29,8—35,5). Incubation 21—24 days.

LOCAL RACE:
Bubulcus ibis ibis (Linnaeus), 1758: *Egypt*. The Ethiopian Region.

62 Squacco Heron   Ralreier

Ardeola ralloides (Scopoli), 1769: *Carniola, River Danube*.

Native Name: Chipugwapugwa (D).

PLATE 6 (OPP. P. 48).
Length 43 cm (male wing 201—217—227; tail 67—79,3—83; tarsus 55—58,5—63; culmen 63—65—67. 6 specimens. Female wing 194—203,5—213; tail 68—72,5—81; tarsus 50—54,5—58; culmen 59—60,7—64. 10 specimens). Iris pale yellow; bill dark tinged bluish at base in breeding and yellowish in non-breeding times; legs pinky-yellow in breeding, greenish otherwise. Weight 345 g (4).

Identification: The illustration shows the breeding plumage. The female in breeding plumage has less of a crest than the male. The immature has an earth-brown mantle rather like the non-breeding plumage. In flight it appears on rising to be startlingly white due to white wings, rump and tail, but is separable from the egrets in flight by its more rapid wingbeat and less frequent gliding. Nestling with white down, buff tinge on shoulders and coarse buff down on crown. See 62X.

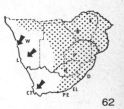

Distribution: In the moister parts of Africa, Southern Europe, south-western Asia, Malagasy and South West Africa. A vagrant in the rest of the Republic, extending rarely as far south as Colesberg and Uitenhage in the east.

62

Habits: Resident; not uncommon but its solitary disposition leads one to think it rare. Seldom occurs in flocks. On the ground when feeding blends well with its surroundings, especially since it spends the greater part of its time in one position. Frequents only sluggish streams and lakes with an abundance of reeds and other marsh vegetation.

Food: Very large aquatic insects; small fish, frogs, grasshoppers, beetles and small crabs.

Voice: Low soft staccato "kok".

Breeding: Colonial breeder in low bushes or reeds over water. Nest is made of dry rushes and reeds, a tidy structure for a heron. Recorded in December. Eggs 2—4, greenish blue. Average (8) 37,4 × 28,2 (35,8—39 × 27,9—29,4).

62X   Madagascar Squacco Heron   Malgassiese Ralreier

Ardeola idae   (Hartlaub), 1860: *E. coast Madagascar.*

PLATE 6 (OPP. P. 48).
Length 47 cm (wing 210—262; tail 77—101). Iris yellow; bill yellow grey with black tip; legs pink or greenish yellow.

Identification: Slightly larger than No. 62; in non-breeding dress is browner than the Squacco, breast streaking much broader. Bill heavier than No. 62.

Distribution: Breeds on Malagasy from October to December but in non-breeding season crosses to East Africa. A specimen recently discovered from Mount Selinda collected in September, 1923. There is an October record from Zambia.

Habits: Apparently much as for No. 62. Probably overlooked because it is a regular migrant to east Africa.

63   Green-backed Heron   Groenrug-reier

Butorides striatus   (Linnaeus), 1758: *Surinam.*

PLATE 6 AD. AND IMM. (OPP. P. 48).
Length 41 cm (wing 168—178—188; tail 56—62,2—69; tarsus 42—47,3—53; culmen 54—61,3—66. 24 specimens). Iris yellow; bill dusky with yellow on the lower mandible; legs dusky blending to orange yellow feet, bright orange-red during breeding season.

Identification: A small dull-coloured heron with glossy dark green crown, ornamental back plumes and tail. Chin is white, blending to a buff line down lower neck. Light-edged feathers of back and wing-coverts aid identification. Immature, brown above with washed green crown and back, the feathers of the upper parts tipped with white. Underparts with longitudinal stripes along central line of neck, fine near the chin but increasing and merging along the lower neck. Nestling with black skin and white hairs on the head. In flight the protruding orange-yellow legs are conspicuous.

Distribution: Over the moister parts of Africa, islands of the Indian Ocean and eastwards to Asia. Extends southwards to the Okavango in the west, Barberspan in the centre, King William's Town and East London in the east.

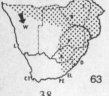

63

Habits: Resident of solitary disposition, frequenting reed and bush bound streams, rivers and mangrove swamps; also small pools quite far from any open water. Largely nocturnal. Crouches motionless, sometimes darting here and there after food; moves about with a typical hunched attitude and is adept at climbing over mangrove roots and similar obstructions.
Food: Dragonflies, water-beetles, locusts, spiders, penaeid prawns, mud prawns (*Upogebia*), small crabs, frogs, molluscs, and fish—mainly mud-skippers.
Voice: A monosyllabic "chuck". Also a trill, "kek-kek-kek-kek".
Breeding: Usually singly, though small colonies are recorded. The nest is made up loosely of sticks and is so transparent the eggs can be seen from below; it is situated in low bushes or branches over water. October—February. Eggs 2—4, bluish green. Average (14) 37,1 × 27,8 (35,2—40,1 × 26,1—30,0). Incubation about 24 days (Priest).

LOCAL RACE:
B.s. atricapillus (Afzelius) 1804: *Sierra Leone*. From Tropical Africa and southwards. Other races on Malagasy and adjacent Indian Ocean islands.

64 Black Egret   Swart Reier

Egretta ardesiaca (Wagler), 1827: *Senegambia*.

PLATE 6 (OPP. P. 48).
Length 66 cm (wing 241—268; tail 90—101; tarsus 79,5—90; culmen 66—71). Iris bright yellow; bill black; legs black with *yellow* feet.

Identification: Unmistakable, both sexes and immature being wholly black; perhaps more brown-black in immature. The yellow feet confirm identification. Wing-beats are rapid and the flight is swift for a heron. The bill is long and thin like that of the Little Egret, No. 59, but the crest is more heavily feathered.
Distribution: West Africa east to Ethiopia, down the eastern half of the continent to Kimberley and Port Elizabeth. Also recorded from Lakeside and Rondevlei in the Cape.
Habits: Apparently resident, rare and solitary in the southern extremities of its range though not regularly recorded. Gregarious in flocks of up to 30 or 40 north of the Zambesi. Inhabits the edges of lakes and rivers where it can remain concealed in reeds or vegetation. Its fishing is performed standing in shallow water with wings stretched out and forward, forming an umbrella-like canopy which casts a shadow on the water. See plate 6. In this way its food can be seen. This manner of fishing may be observed on sunny or dull days. Has a characteristic habit of erecting all its plumage, shaking itself vigorously and then allowing the feathers to return to normal.

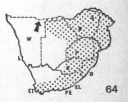

Food: Small fish.
Voice: A low cluck.
Breeding: In mixed heronries; the nest is the usual heron structure of sticks and reeds. Eggs 3—4, pale blue-green, darker than other small herons' eggs. Average (14) 45,5 × 32,8 (42,0—48,0 × 32,0—33,5).

64 X   Slaty Egret

Egretta vinaeceigula   Sharpe, 1895: *Potchefstroom.*

PLATE 6 (OPP. P. 48).
Length 60 cm (wing 229—242; tarsus 83—86; culmen 53—57,5. 3 specimens.) Iris brown, bill black and pale base to lower mandible; legs dull greenish yellow to yellow.

Identification: Similar in shape to No. 59 but smaller. Similar in colour to No. 64 but has a vinous throat. The belly is variable and may be black or pale grey.

Distribution: Although originally described from Potchefstroom, this species is now found only in the Okavango swamps, the Chobe River, Kafue Flats and south-western Zambia.

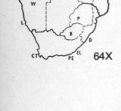

64X

Habits: An inhabitant of marshes and flood plains. Subject to local movements but found regularly from April to October in the Moremi Reserve. Tends to feed in shallow water covered by vegetation rather than open waters. Sometimes the vegetation is tall enough to conceal birds until they stretch their necks or fly up. Recorded perching on trees. Usually a solitary species but often feeds in dispersed assemblies of a variety of aquatic feeders. Feeding by a quick walk and darting for food rather than waiting.
Food: Unrecorded.
Voice: Unrecorded.
Breeding: Recorded breeding in a colony in dense reeds on Chobe River in May. About eight pairs breeding together in nests sited about 1 metre above water level.

65   Rufous-bellied Heron   Rooipens-reier

Ardeola rufiventris (Sundevall), 1850: *"Caffraria superior"* = *Mooi River, near Potchefstroom.*
Native Name: i-Nyakola-encani (G).
PLATE 6 (OPP. P. 48).
Length 58 cm (wing 198—216—231; tail 70—74,7—83; tarsus 51—57,4—66; culmen 56—61,5—75. 17 specimens). Iris yellow with an orange outer ring; skin about eye yellow; bill yellow below, dark brown above; legs yellow.

Identification: Male illustrated; note flight feathers black whilst rump and tail are maroon. The female is sooty brown where the male is black; also there is a narrow buff-white line from the chin petering out at the base of neck. Immature similar to female but streaked buff-brown on neck, upper chest and side of head. Appears all blackish in flight when the maroon of the wing-coverts and belly is not obvious.

Distribution: Africa south of Uganda and Angola. Recorded from northern South West Africa, Okavango and Ngami areas; the Zambesi River, down Mozambique, eastern Transvaal, Natal and eastern Cape as far as King William's Town.

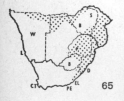

65

Habits: Not common anywhere, rare in the Republic. Peculiar to larger rivers where there is an abundance of marshy shallows. In habits very like the Squacco Heron, No. 62, in that it remains stationary and hidden along margins of swamps. When flushed it flies only a short distance before dropping back into hiding.
Food: Frogs, water-insects, beetles, worms and small fish.
Voice: A muffled, almost crow-like "kar", repeated several times.

Breeding: In colonies of up to 30 nests in company with other species (No. 62 and 69). Recorded in February, Transvaal; March, Zambia, and August in Rhodesia. The nest situated in a tree four to five feet from the water, constructed of dry reeds and rushes on a slight foundation of a few twigs (Jackson). Eggs 2—3, pale blue. Average (13) 38,5 × 29,4 (36,1—41,6 × 28,2—30,7).

66 Dwarf Bittern   Dwerg-reier

Ardeirallus sturmii (Wagler), 1827: *Senegambia*.

PLATE 6 AD. AND IMM. (OPP. P. 48).
Length 25 cm (wing 154—162—169; tail 48—52,8—56; tarsus 44—48,7—51; culmen 39—40—42. 6 specimens). Iris red brown; bill horn shading to bluish green at the base and on skin around eye; legs yellow, slightly brownish in front.

Identification: The male has dark line down the centre of chin; under-wing and axillaries also slaty black, but there is a narrow buff line along the coverts on the leading edge of the wing. Sexes similar. Immature has feathers of upper-part with sandy-buff. Flight is slow and heavy, with hanging legs and often outstretched neck.

Distribution: Widely distributed over Africa. Recorded from Damaraland, and as far south as East London on the east with a single record from Uitenhage, also Bloemhof and Hopetown. There were two records from the Cape Peninsula last century. Subject to migration; here in summer.

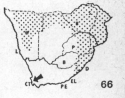

66

Habits: Not uncommon, especially on reed-bound rivers; somewhat solitary though not very shy. Not so frequently met with in grassy or reedy swamps, being apparently more partial to trees and bushes. Largely nocturnal in habit. Has been observed to take up the protective stance typical of the Bittern.

Food: Water beetles, grasshoppers, aquatic crustacea, crabs, small frogs and fishes.

Voice: A croaking cry.

Breeding: Andersson found its nest on small palms partly immersed by flood waters; Hoesch found nests in a thorn bush in the water. Usually solitary, the nest is placed near the water; it is built of small twigs or coarse grass constructed loosely as in the Green-backed Heron, No. 63. Recorded September to December and in April. Eggs 2—5, a bluish white. Average (27) 36,8 × 27,9 (35—39,1 × 26—31). Incubation 14—15 days (Priest).

67 Little Bittern   Woudapie

Ixobrychus minutus (Linnaeus), 1766: *Switzerland*.

Native Name: Ihashe (X).

PLATE 6 AD. AND IMM. (OPP. P. 48).
Length 36 cm (wing 144—149—156; tail 41—44,9—49; tarsus 41—43,2—46; culmen 46—47,5—51. 11 specimens). Iris yellow to orange; bill pale chrome, darker above and towards base; legs greenish yellow.

Identification: This little bittern is dark green above except for light wing-coverts and hind-neck. Male illustrated. Female generally brown, feathers edged with pale buff, whilst wing, tail and head are similar to male. Under wing-coverts white. Immature more heavily streaked on neck than female and under wing-coverts buff. Nestling reddish buff above, whitish below. In flight, which is heavy, the white wing-coverts contrast strongly with blackish flight feathers—see plate.

Distribution: Occurs in central and southern Europe, eastward to India and Australia, Africa and Malagasy. See details under races.

Habits: Occurs on reed beds along streams and rivers. Mainly nocturnal. Cunning in hiding themselves by perching on the side of a reed stem, pointing the bill upwards parallel with the stem, the plumage stripes matching the light and shade of the reeds to a remarkable degree. Difficult to flush since they readily assume the above-mentioned posture.

Food: Grasshoppers, caterpillars, mole crickets, spiders, shrimps, molluscs, fish, frogs and lizards.

Voice: When alarmed they utter a "squawking" note. They do not boom at night but utter a peculiar frog-like croak "crick" which has been recorded during the day as well.

Breeding: Not usually colonial. Nests are made in August and September among the reeds, near the ground or water, a small platform of twigs and roots, like a dove's nest. Eggs 2 or 3, white. Both sexes feed young (Europe). Two in the Bell Marley collection measure 36,5 × 27,6 and 36,0 × 27,9 although Reichenow records Ghana eggs as 31—32,5 × 24—25. Incubation 16—19 days (Europe). Nestling: Young leave the nest 7—14 days but able to fly at 30 days (Europe).

LOCAL RACES:

(a) *I.m. minutus* (Linnaeus), 1766: *Switzerland*. Size as given above. The outermost primary is about the longest and thus more or less equal to 2nd and 3rd. Appears to come to South Africa as a migrant. Recorded from Bulawayo district, Rhodesia; Potchefstroom; Exelsior, O.F.S. and as far south as Port St. Johns on the east coast.

(b) *I.m. payesii* (Hartlaub), 1858: *Casamans, Senegal*. (Wing 130—143,1—150; tail 36—45,3—50; tarsus 40—43,0—46; culmen 43—47,9—54,5. 28 specimens). Similar to nominate race, but smaller; and the male has a paler neck. As illustrated. The outermost primary shorter than the 2nd or 3rd, about equal to the 4th or 5th primaries. Resident, though nowhere very common. Extending from the north, as far south as Lake Ngami; through to the Transvaal, Ladysmith, Natal and Port Elizabeth in the Eastern Cape, and in the Western Cape. Recorded breeding from the Cape Peninsula. Previously considered a separate species, No. 68.

69   Night Heron   Nagreier

Nycticorax nycticorax   (Linnaeus), 1758: *South Europe*.

PLATE 5 AD. AND IMM. (OPP. P. 33).

Length 56 cm (wing 276—287—298; tail 103—110,6—119; tarsus 69—73,5—78; culmen 65—70,3—74. 16 specimens). Iris crimson, with the skin around eye pale green; bill uniform grey in breeding; slaty black above, flesh coloured below merging to greenish at base non-breeding; legs pale yellow. (See immature.)

Identification: Breeding plumage illustrated; sexes alike. In non-breeding dress there are no plumes on the nape. Immature birds have orange eye, legs greenish yellow; pale brown general colouration streaked with darker brown, upper feathers tipped with white spots, more white below. Immature plumage is retained for about 14 months. Separable from the Bittern, No. 71, by colour of eye, broad streaks below and white spots to tips of feathers on upper parts.

67

See also No. 70. In flight this species shows very broad rounded wings which give it a squat appearance and buoyant flight.
Distribution: Africa, Southern Europe and Asia. A migrant within Africa.
Habits: Common resident in the Republic but apparently partial migration does occur since a nestling ringed at Rondevlei, Cape, was recovered within a few months in Mozambique. Gregarious as well as solitary. Comes out flying towards dusk. Hunts by waiting, sitting on a branch or reed, more so than by stalking in the reeds. Recorded also to swim. Longevity record of 123 months.
Food: Frogs, fish, aquatic insects and young birds in heronries.
Voice: Sharp "kok" or "kwok" when disturbed and when arriving or departing from the roost.
Breeding: August—January. Gregarious, usually in mixed heronries. Nest, built either in trees or reed beds, a large structure of sticks and reeds. Eggs 2 to 4, very pale greenish. Average (26) 48,8 × 34,6 (45,0—52,6 × 32,0—36,7). Incubation 21 days (Europe), 24—26 days (Priest). Nestling: When almost fully grown, 3—4 weeks, young leave the nest and take refuge in the reeds.

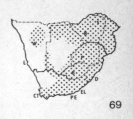

69

LOCAL RACE:

N.n. nycticorax (Linnaeus), 1758: *South Europe*. Europe, Asia and Africa; another race occurs in South America.

70   White-backed Night Heron   Witrug-nagreier

Gorsachius leuconotus (Wagler), 1827: *Senegambia*.

PLATE 5 (OPP. P. 33).

Length 53 cm (wing 262—267—274; tail 109—112—120; tarsus 68—72—79; culmen 57—59,9—61. 6 specimens). Iris brownish in breeding, yellow non-breeding; skin around eye greenish yellow; bill blackish, yellowish towards base; feet yellowish.

Identification: Sexes alike. The dark head and large light "eye" render identification easy. In flight the white triangular patch on back is conspicuous. Immature bird develops white back before moulting from the spotted phase. Differs from immature Night Heron, No. 69, by having a darker, unstreaked forehead and crown, and less streaking on the side of face.
Distribution: Found only in Africa. Recorded from the Okavango, Victoria Falls, Lundi River in Rhodesia and down the eastern areas as far south as Nature's Valley. One old record for Rustenburg, Transvaal.
Habits: Rather a rare species frequenting quiet, tree-fringed streams, rivers and dams, either solitary or in pairs. During daylight hides in the lower branches of thickly foliaged trees, feeding at dusk and night.
Food: Fish, flying ants and flies.
Voice: Usually silent. When alarmed gives a toad-like "kraak".
Breeding: Nests on low projecting branches of trees (including Euphorbias) or on snags just above the water, from September to January; April records from Transvaal and Rhodesia. Nest usually a substantial structure of twigs and reeds. Eggs 2—3, very pale greenish white. Average (17) 45,7 × 35,1 (44—48 × 33—37,2). Incubation 24—26 days.

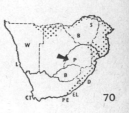

70

71 Bittern   Roerdomp

Botaurus stellaris (Linnaeus), 1758: *Europe=Sweden.*

Native Name: Khoiti-mohlaka (S).

PLATE 5 (OPP. P. 33).

Length 64 cm (wing 280—310; tail 92—95; tarsus 80—90; culmen 57—60,2—64. 6 specimens). Iris yellow to hazel, with bare skin around eye ashy fulvous; bill light green-grey; legs pale green.

Identification: Black crown, nape and malar stripe separate this species from the somewhat similar immature-plumaged night herons. Markings are very fine vermiculations in immature and adult which also separate this species at all stages from any other species in our area. Both sexes and immature alike; immature does not have such a definite head pattern as the adult. Nestling covered with long vinous down; legs and feet pale pink; bill pinkish yellow; eye dark brown.

Distribution: Europe, Asia and Australia. Southern Africa from Zambia, not yet recorded from Rhodesia but otherwise recorded from every territory and province except S.W.A.

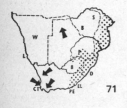

71

Habits: Found only in the permanent marshes and nowhere plentiful (see below under race). Its presence is usually disclosed by its booming notes, in the breeding season, uttered from the depths of the marshes and usually regarded with fear by Natives, and by others ignorant of their origin. When alarmed takes up the typical bittern stance pointing bill upwards, remaining perfectly motionless and thus merging with the background. Difficult to put up and then flies only a short distance before re-settling.

Voice: When disturbed utters a "Squark". During breeding season utters a deep booming throughout the night, even recorded during the daytime too. If close to the bird there are 2 or 3 introductory notes sharper and with much less volume before the big effort.

Food: Fish and frogs.

Breeding: Nest formed of a mass of rushes in the marshes. Breeding October to January. Eggs 3—4, pale olive green, smooth and greasy to the touch. 51 × 38,3; 49,5 × 38,7; 50 × 38 and 49,6 × 40,3. Incubation 25—26 days (Europe). Nestling young leave the nest at 2—3 weeks, fly at about 8 weeks (Europe).

LOCAL RACE:

B.s. capensis (Schlegel), 1863: *South Africa = Wynberg, Cape.* Smaller than nominate race (which is only recorded as far south as Zaïre) and remiges more narrowly and irregularly barred. Status of this bird in recent times is not fully known. Apparently much rarer than it used to be, especially in the south and south-west Cape. Modern records from the Cape Province needed.

Family SCOPIDAE

Containing only one genus with one species, peculiar to Africa, southern Arabia and Malagasy and characterized by its singular appearance, structure and habits. On anatomical grounds it is placed between the Herons and Storks and yet obviously belonging to neither. In colour a sombre brown, faintly banded on the tail, with a slight bronzy sheen, the legs and neck rather short for a wader; a large crest lying backwards in line with the bill: and the bill deep but narrow, the culminicorn extending as a narrow ridge for the whole length of the bill and hooked at the tip, and the deep latericorn separated from it by a thin groove in which the nostrils are not visible; the mandible also peculiar in trending upwards and thin, bladelike, for the terminal half; the tibia naked for the lower half. In habits it is a wader, subsisting mainly upon frogs caught in the shallows, but unlike any other waders, and in fact any other birds, builds a large closed oven-like nest of sticks and rubbish, with a small circular entrance below. It is one of Nature's curiosities, whose affinities are obscure.

72   Hamerkop

Scopus umbretta   Gmelin, 1789: *Africa = Senegal.*

Native Names: i-Tekwane (Z); Uthekwane (X); Masianoke (S); Masilanukwe (Ch).

PLATE 7 (OPP. P. 49).
Length 56 cm (wing 297—305—316; tail 152—156—158; tarsus 69—70,2—73; culmen 80—81,8—85. 5 specimens). Iris dark brown; bill and legs black.

Identification: Sepia brown all over with a large crest on head which, coupled with its large bill, gives the illusion of a hammer shape, hence the name. The bill is laterally compressed and appears thin from the front. There are traces of a purplish gloss on the back. The wings appear large; the neck only slightly curved; flight is light and buoyant. Chick has head, neck, back and wings white, otherwise brown; bill slightly compressed. Young attain brown plumage and crest before leaving nest.

Distribution: Throughout southern and central Africa.

Habits: Generally solitary and fairly common. A familiar bird where there is open shallow water in the vicinity of trees or low cliffs where it can construct its nest; it may be found either wading in the shallows or standing about near water, when alarmed flying off with a peculiar squeaky whistling cry which is also sometimes uttered during times of excitement when on the ground. The appearance, reedy call and wisdom of the bird in its nest building causes natives always to regard it with superstitious awe—even to the removal of their huts when a Hamerkop flies over them and calls. Its method of feeding is to shuffle one foot or stamp in the mud and feed on what it disturbs in this way.

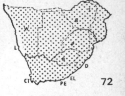

72

Food: Insects, shrimps, crustacea, worms, fishes, tadpoles and frogs, as well as small mammals.

Voice: See above. Courtship flight is typically accompanied by a monotonous croak.

Breeding: Its nest is an accumulation of sticks, reed stems and any sort of rubbish it fancies—such as old clothing, bits of leather, skin, bone and a fair quantity of grass upon occasion—formed into a hollow dome, with an entrance situated below in such a way that it cannot be reached by human and other marauders. The only way marauders can gain access is by breaking away the top of the dome, and this is so strongly made of sticks and reeds laid crossways, with other material interlaid and thickly overlaid, that attempts to rob the nest are discouraged. This nest takes about 6 months to construct, and as it becomes the haunt of Barn Owls and wild honey bees when not in use, new nests are frequently made especially when other suitable nesting sites are available. Breeds July to January. Eggs 3—6, white becoming mudstained as incubation proceeds. Average (78) 46,0 × 34,8 (41,3—52,0 × 32,0—36,8). Incubation is about 21 days; fledgling period about 7 weeks.

LOCAL RACE:
S.u. umbretta Gmelin, 1789:*Africa=Senegal.* Africa south of the Sahara, except Sierra Leone to Cameroon.

Family CICONIIDAE

Tall birds, frequently confused with Herons and Cranes on that account, but unlike Cranes in having a long bill and unlike Herons in having robuster bodies and legs. They are cosmopolitan, some species local but the majority to a greater or lesser extent migratory. The bill is always longer than the head, usually straight, but varies in shape in different genera; the nostrils are situated high up nearer the base than the middle of the bill; the toes are stout, webbed at the base with strong blunt claws, more like nails than bird claws. One of their peculiarities is that they have no voice, but clap their bills instead. Their diet consists of frogs and other water animals captured in the marshes, and large insects, such as locusts, of which they consume great quantities and are protected for that reason: but one is a carrion bird. Their eggs are white and their nests are made of sticks placed on ledges of precipices, on trees or even on housetops in the case of the favourite White Stork. There are 10 living and 9 fossil genera and 17 species are recognized. Three toes with the fourth reduced and high.

73 Marabou   Maraboe

Leptoptilos crumeniferus   (Lesson), 1831: *Senegal.*

Native Name: Igababa (Z).

PLATE 7 (OPP. P. 49).
Length 152 cm (wing 620—673—720; tail 250—276—295; tarsus 215—242—270; culmen 226—244—280. 10 specimens). Iris brown; bill dirty light green to dirty horn yellow; bare skin of head and neck dirty yellowish flesh; legs black covered with a fine ashy powder and thus appearing white.

Identification: Its huge size and repulsive appearance leave no doubt as to the bird's identity. The naked head and neck bear sparse woolly down which, in the immature bird, is thicker. When sitting or walking, has a very upright stance. In flight the white body shows up well against the contrasting black wings.

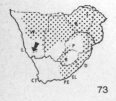

Distribution: Not uncommon in the tropics of Africa but rare in the southern part of the Republic. Recorded in fair numbers from Damaraland, southern Botswana, Rhodesia and Zululand. Rare records extend to the Eastern Province as far south as Graaff-Reinet, Cradock, Port Elizabeth and Somerset West. Also Bloemhof, Transvaal and Jacobsdal and Odendaalsrus, O.F.S.

73

Habits: This stork has adopted to a large extent the habits of the vultures. It is frequently found in association with vultures, attracted to the carcasses of animals. Vultures stand in awe of it, on account of its powerful bill. Like vultures also it may rest for long periods on trees but may also be seen stalking across grass veld, feeding on insects, occasionally in loose association with European storks. In Ngamiland it is not uncommon when cattle have been

STORKS

slaughtered by natives, who do not disturb it, either from a feeling of repugnance or superstition.
Food: Carrion, termites, locusts, fish, frogs, lizards, snakes and rats.
Voice: Guttural croak on alarm. Clatter their bills normally.
Breeding: A single nest recorded in Stegi district, Swaziland, situated in *Acacia nigrescens*. Nests in very large trees, singly or in small communities; reported to nest on ledges of cliffs. A large structure of sticks with shallow cup lined with grass and rushes. Clutch 2—4. Eggs dull white average (18) 79,2 × 56,3 (72,5—86,2 × 52,3—58,5).

74 Openbill   Oopbek-ooievaar

Anastomus lamelligerus Temminck, 1823: *Senegal.*

PLATE 7 (OPP. P. 49).
Length 94 cm (wing 435; tail 200; tarsus 155; culmen 200). Iris brown, inner rim golden yellow; bare patch around eye and lores blue; bill dusky, basal half lighter; legs black.

Identification: General brownish black colour and large bill are the first impressions. The open space in centre of bill is easily observed. Birds in breeding condition have a greenish gloss on back and these feathers as well as those on neck and chest are broadened and flattened. It has a sailing flight and the rounded tail and projecting legs are characteristic. Well grown young are duller and browner than adults, bill shorter and lacking any space between mandibles.
Distribution: A rare migrant to the Republic from the tropics of Africa and from Malagasy. Recorded from Rhodesia, Chobe, Okavango and Ovamboland, a single record from Swakopmund and as far south as the Incomati flats on the east. Vagrant in Natal and the Eastern Cape, but common in north Zululand. A single record from Tsolo, Transkei.

74

Habits: Gregarious except when feeding and partially nocturnal. Often perches on trees. Feeds wading in still water, deep or shallow, picking food off the surface or immersing head completely. Its peculiarly shaped bill seems to be adapted to its main diet of fresh-water mussels (*Ampullaria*) which may be carried from the water to dry ground and laid in the hot sun until they open (Roberts), or crushed under water to remove shell before swallowing (Jackson), or swallowed whole (White).
Food: Mainly fresh-water molluscs; crabs, fish and frogs also recorded.
Voice: No record.
Breeding: Recorded from Gwaai River, Rhodesia; also in the marshes of the Upper Zambesi (Livingstone). More recently in South West Africa near Tsumeb, the extreme north of Kruger National Park and Zululand. Colonially, in trees or reed beds. The nest is a platform of sticks and reeds. Eggs 2—4, in July; dull white, smooth with white pores. Average (12) 55,9 × 39,5 (51,0—61,4 × 38—41,3).

LOCAL RACE:
A.l. lamelligerus Temminck, 1823: *Senegal.* Eastern and southern Africa except Malagasy, where another race occurs.

PLATE 6

4. *Podiceps cristatus infuscatus.* Great Crested Grebe.
Kuifkop-duikertjie.
5. *Podiceps nigricollis gurneyi.* Black-necked Grebe. Swartnek-duikertjie.
6. *Tachybaptus ruficollis capensis.* Dabchick. Klein Duikertjie.
62. *Ardeola ralloides.* Squacco Heron. Ralreier. S. and W.
62X. *Ardeola idae.* Madagascar Squacco Heron. Malgassiese Ralreier.
63. *Butorides striatus atricapillus.* Green-backed Heron. Groenrug-reier.
Ad. and Imm.
64. *Egretta ardesiaca.* Black Egret. Swart Reier.
64X. *Egretta vinaceigula.* Slaty Egret.
65. *Ardeola rufiventris.* Rufous-bellied Heron. Rooipens-reier.
66. *Ardeirallus sturmii.* Dwarf Bittern. Dwerg Reier. Ad. and Imm.
67. *Ixobrychus minutus payesii.* Little Bittern. Woudapie. Ad. and Imm.

Imm.

67

67

63

Imm.

66

62

62X

62

Imm.

64

64X

65

6

4

4

5

B NEWMAN '73

86

87

72

81

84

83

82

79

74

78

77

80

75

73

85

76

K B NEWMAN '72

PLATE 7

72. *Scopus umbretta umbretta.* Hamerkop.
73. *Leptoptilos crumeniferus.* Marabou. Maraboe.
74. *Anastomus lamelligerus lamelligerus.* Openbill. Oopbek-ooievaar.
75. *Ephippiorhynchus senegalensis.* Saddlebill. Saalbek-ooievaar.
76. *Mycteria ibis.* Yellow-billed Stork. Nimmersat.
77. *Ciconia episcopus microscelis.* Woolly-necked Stork. Wolnek-ooievaar.
78. *Ciconia abdimii.* White-bellied Stork. Swart Sprinkaanvoël.
79. *Ciconia nigra.* Black Stork. Swart Ooievaar.
80. *Ciconia ciconia ciconia.* White Stork. Wit Sprinkaanvoël.
81. *Threskiornis aethiopicus aethiopicus.* Sacred Ibis. Skoorsteenveër.
82. *Geronticus calvus.* Bald Ibis. Wilde-kalkoen.
83. *Plegadis falcinellus falcinellus.* Glossy Ibis. Glansende Ibis.
84. *Hagedashia hagedash hagedash.* Hadeda.
85. *Platalea alba.* African Spoonbill. Lepelaar.
86. *Phoenicopterus ruber roseus.* Greater Flamingo. Groot Flamink.
87. *Phoeniconaias minor.* Lesser Flamingo. Klein Flamink.

75 Saddlebill   Saalbek-ooievaar

Ephippiorhynchus senegalensis   (Shaw), 1800: *Senegal.*

Native Names: Kololoane (Ch.); Nyamantando (S).

PLATE 7 (OPP. P. 49).

Length 145 cm (wing 620—670; tail 257—272; tarsus 293—353; culmen 282—334. 4 specimens). Iris brown in male, bright yellow in female. Flesh around eye and under bill, including lappets, bright crimson in male; female has yellow eye ring and no wattle. Bill from base to nostril and distal half bright crimson with black central patch, frontal shield yellow. Legs black, tarsal joint (knee) and feet red.

Identification: An unmistakable species with sexes similar (see above) and immature bird differing only in having dull grey instead of black markings, the white back and remiges (and thus flight pattern) mottled with sooty black; bill darkish grey, legs dullish green but with pink knee joint. This species has a naked spot on breast which is crimson. In flight shows a very distinctive pattern in black and white; the flight feathers, shoulder, back and rump white, otherwise all black. Flight ponderous, legs trailing beyond tail.

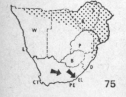

Distribution: Confined to tropical Africa, but rare in the Republic. Generally distributed in Rhodesia, Damaraland and Caprivi Strip; recorded from Lake Chrissie, Kruger National Park, Bloemhof and Sand River in Transvaal; Mtunzini, Zululand; East London and Beaufort West in the Cape.

75

Habits: Usually in pairs or small parties except in the south of its range when it becomes a solitary vagrant. Usually seen in marshy areas or water, stalking about with measured stride. When feeding often tosses prey into the air before re-catching and devouring it.

Food: Crabs, shrimps, fish and frogs, mammals and young birds.

Voice: The only noise recorded is a clapping of the bill.

Breeding: Recorded from Northern Transvaal in June and Rhodesia January to April on the larger rivers, nesting in high trees on the river banks, rarely on cliffs. Eggs 3, dull white, slightly glossy, coarse in texture; 78,5 × 56,2; 77,3 × 56; 76,1 × 56,2.

76 Yellow-billed Stork   Nimmersat

Mycteria ibis   (Linnaeus), 1766: *Egypt.*

Native Name: Levlosyane (S).

PLATE 7 (OPP. P. 49).

Length 97 cm (wing 455—517; tail 170—190; tarsus 195—218; culmen 203—243). Iris brown; bill golden yellow; bare parts of the face red with narrow orange borders; legs brownish pink, waxy orange at base.

Identification: Distinguished from the European stork by the yellow bill, red facial patch and black tail. The immature lacks the light pink tinge on upper wing-coverts. Younger birds have head, neck and upper wing-coverts brown. Nestlings covered in white down, bill yellow. Flight is stork-like with projecting neck and feet, upper and under wing-coverts deep pink.

Distribution: Comes to South Africa only as a migrant from the northern tropics of Africa and Malagasy. Le Vaillant saw it at Verloren Vlei and Dr Stark found it at Knysna. Recorded everywhere, but rare in south-western Cape.

76

Habits: Resident all the year in Rhodesia; arrives October in the south and departs northwards in April. A single winter record. Commonly occurs near water, along rivers, streams, dams and estuaries, usually in small parties. Comparatively tame and when not feeding may rest on islands or protected sand banks in company with herons, spoonbills and other large wading birds. Seeks food whilst walking through shallow or deep water, probing with its long bill, often with its head under water.

Food: Aquatic insects, crabs, fish, frogs and small mammals.

Voice: A long loud nasal sound like a squeaky hinge—although not recorded in the south.

Breeding: Nests on large trees or cliffs, often in company with other species. A large structure of sticks with a shallow cup lined with fine grass and rushes. Recorded breeding in Zululand June and August. Eggs 2—3, dull white. Average (15) 66,7 × 45,3 (62,1—71,1 × 42,3—47,6).

77 Woolly-necked Stork   Wolnek-ooievaar

Ciconia episcopus (Boddaert), 1783: *Coromandel coast*
PLATE 7 (OPP. P. 49).
Length 86 cm (wing 440; tail 177; tarsus 152; culmen 140). Iris dark red; bill black with culmen and tip red; legs blackish red showing in places.

Identification: A generally glossy black bird with *white woolly head and neck*, black crown and orbits and white belly. In flight under wing-coverts black; the white under tail-coverts project beyond the black tail feathers in the centre. Immature birds differ in that the white line across the forehead of the adult bird is black streaked with white. Nestling down generally brown except white on neck and abdomen; iris dark green, eyelid and lores black; bill black with reddish brown tip; feet dark grey.

Distribution: A tropical African and Asian species that extends on the east as far south as Port St. Johns and Umtata River mouth. Normally scarce in Rhodesia. Kalahari National Park.

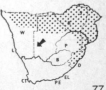

Habits: Very local and resident in Zululand where they breed. Rare, and usually seen in pairs or small parties, though known to migrate in flocks. Not very shy. Usually occur near water, banks of rivers and lagoons where they wade about feeding, also on open grassland. Seldom settle on trees outside the breeding season and frequently seen standing about apparently in meditation. Attracted to burned areas, although they do not catch insects in flight.

77

Food: Fibres of palm nuts found in stomach, grasshoppers, mantises, insect larvae, crabs, molluscs, fish and lizards.

Voice: A harsh raucous call.

Breeding: Recorded breeding in Zululand since 1953 (I. Garland) and now Rhodesia. Solitary breeders. The nest, a platform of sticks is placed on a forked branch 40—50 feet up in a swamp forest. Young in November. Eggs 2—4, white, mud-stained. (3) 60—61,3 × 41,2—43,3 (Uganda). Incubation 30—31 days. Fledgling period 55—65 days.

LOCAL RACE:
C.e. microscelis Gray, 1848:*Africa*. The nominate race occurs in Asia.

51

78 White-bellied Stork Swart Sprinkaanvoël

Ciconia abdimii (Lichtenstein), 1823: *near Dongola, Sudan.*

Native Name: Lekololoane (S).

PLATE 7 (OPP. P. 49).

Length 76 cm (wing 400—475; tarsus 117—136; culmen 103—127). Iris greyish brown; bill horny green with crimson tip, cheeks bright lead colour with crimson around ears, front of eye, nostril and throat. Legs dull olive with crimson feet and knees.

Identification: The black head and neck distinguish this from the previous species; the horny green bill and white back separate it from the following one, for which it is not infrequently mistaken. Immature is similar to adult but has down on throat; the bill dull red. In flight the white back is obvious and the under-wing is black except for a basal central strip which is white.

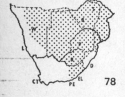

Distribution: A migrant from North Africa. Recorded as far south as Rehoboth, S.W.A.; Colesberg, central Cape; and Keiskama River on the east; irregular in Natal.

78

Habits: A non-breeding migrant arriving in October and departing north towards the end of March. A very common gregarious bird recorded in flocks often of several hundred; quite often in association with White and other Storks. Usually seen scattered over the open veld during the greater part of the day, congregating when satiated at water-pools, and on trees (especially blue gums), to roost. These birds have the habit of soaring and circling high in the air, often becoming mere specks in the sky. The birds are constantly on the move and follow wherever food is available.

Food: A great insect consumer, especially of locusts, and protected for that reason. Also millipedes, crabs and vegetable matter, molluscs, frogs and lizards.

Voice: Usually silent here. A rather feeble "peep-peep-peep".

79 Black Stork Swart Ooievaar

Ciconia nigra (Linnaeus), 1758: *North Europe = Sweden.*

Native Name: Unocofu (X).

PLATE 7 (OPP. P. 49).

Length 122 cm (wing 520—600; tail 190—240; tarsus 180—200; culmen 160—190. 9 specimens). Iris brown; bill coral red as is also naked skin around orbit and pouch; legs coral red.

Identification: Glossy brownish-black except white abdomen and under tail-coverts; bill red. Has been mistaken for previous species. The immature bird has a yellowish bill with orange tip, appears streaked on the neck and is generally sooty brown. The nestling is greyish white.

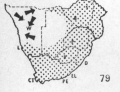

Distribution: Widely distributed in Europe and Asia, coming to Africa during the northern winter. Recorded throughout Southern Africa.

Habits: Locally resident where it breeds, not common; it appears that the northern-breeding migrants are nowhere numerous if indeed their presence is certain south of the Zambesi. Normally shy and has a preference for aquatic habitats, marshes, dams, rivers and estuaries. Usually singly or in small numbers, but flocks of up to 15 birds have been recorded.

79

Food: Grasshoppers, crabs, fish (including trout), tadpoles and frogs.

Voice: A quiet, throaty croak.

Breeding: Recorded from all areas. Apparently always on ledges of precipices, using the same nest year after year. One record of a nest on top of a hammerkop's nest. The nest is a loose platform of sticks. Eggs from May to October, 2—4, dull greyish white colour. Average (21) 69,4 × 48,8 (63—74 × 45—56).

80 White Stork   Wit Sprinkaanvoël

Ciconia ciconia (Linnaeus), 1758: *Sweden*

Native Names: u-Nowanbu, u-Mowanga, in-Gwangwane, in-Godomza, in-Gwanza, in-Golantete (Z); Ingwamza, Undwanga (X); Mokotatsie, le Akapula (S).

PLATE 7 (OPP. P. 49).
Length 117 cm (male wing 530—630; tail 215—240; tarsus 195—240; bill 150—190. 9 specimens. Female wing 530—590; bill 140—170. Iris brown; bill dark red, skin of pouch black anteriorly, red posteriorly; legs and feet reddish pink (see below).

Identification: This large white stork with red bill and black flight feathers is one of our best-known birds. It may be mistaken for the Yellow-billed Stork, but has a white tail and bill colour is diagnostic. The immature has a duller red bill, and legs and the flight feathers are browner. Many birds appear to have white legs with red showing through, but this is due to their own droppings.
Distribution: Common and familiar in Europe and Asia, migrating to Africa for the northern winter, it occurs right to the most southerly tip of the continent. Commonest on the dry Karroo and grassveld of the Orange Free State and Transvaal.

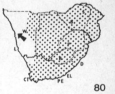

80

Habits: Common migrant, breeding recorded. Arrives in great flocks of three or four hundred, gyrating in thermals up and up then gliding off in the direction of migration. At the end of the southern summer it foregathers in great flocks, to migrate northwards, the signal to foregather being repeated flights in a spiral formation to a great height, until all have arrived. Generally arrive mid-November and leave towards the end of March. Wintering birds are not uncommon, but vary in number from year to year. Occasionally summer flocks are killed by hailstorms, one such flock was of thousands scattered over an area three-quarters of a mile long and 100 yards wide, visible from 20 miles away. Usually found on open veld and grassland, appearing in large numbers sporadically where there are locusts or caterpillar pests in abundance in the open veld, and consequently protected both by law and common sentiment. Known to live 19 years 2 months.
Food: Locusts and hoppers, army worms and other gregarious insect pests, also rodents.
Breeding: A single record by Roberts of a pair which apparently bred for at least seven successive years near Oudtshoorn in 1940. Nest placed high in a dead tree, made of large sticks and twigs. Three young recorded in November. Several nests recorded from the early 60s along southern Cape Province, one nest near Bredasdorp used in several successive years. One young from this nest was recovered on Zambia/Tanzania border.

LOCAL RACE:
C.c. ciconia (Linnaeus) 1758, *Sweden*. Europe, Western Asia and Northern Africa.

53

Family THRESKIORNITHIDAE

A cosmopolitan family of wading birds, fairly large, with rather short legs for waders, fairly long toes, robust bodies, moderately long necks and long, slightly down-curved bills. Their diet consists of small aquatic and other animals, such as lower vertebrates and large insects, captured in shallow water or in open ground, open forests or elsewhere near their haunts on rivers; also offal and carrion. They are often gregarious and may nest in communities or singly, normally laying three or four eggs with very handsome markings. Nests are platforms of sticks or other material, such as pads of grass, placed on branches of trees, ledges of precipices or rocks on islets on the coast or inland lakes. Twenty genera are recognized and 28—30 species. The family is sometimes united with the Plataleidae.

81 Sacred Ibis   Skoorsteenveër

Threskiornis aethiopicus   (Latham), 1790: *Æthiopia = Egypt.*

Native Names: Lehalangone (S); um-Xwagele (Z).

PLATE 7 (OPP. P. 49).

Length 89 cm (wing 348—376—395; tail 130—141—155; tarsus 92—100,7—103,9; culmen 131—170—184. 7 specimens). Iris dark brown; bill very dark brown; legs blackish tinged dark red.

Identification: Cannot be confused with any other bird. In flight the glossy green-black tips to all the flight feathers form a margin around the wing; there is also a red stripe on the under-wing where naked skin is exposed at the base of the wing.

Distribution: Widely distributed over Africa, eastwards to Western Asia. Found throughout southern Africa except Bushmanland.

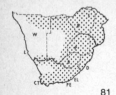

81

Habits: Restless but not a regular migrant. Ringing results show Transvaal birds recorded hundreds of kilometres to the north as far as Zambia. Usually gregarious, but stray ones are sometimes seen away from their normal haunts. Found on the coast, especially south-west Cape, and on inland waters; most common at Pietermaritzburg and on the Rand. Nearly always feed near water but may go on to farm lands in search of snails, etc. In flight usually flies in formation, each to the side and slightly behind the bird in front. Ringing indicates age of 122 months and movement from Orange Free State to Zambia, 1 488 km.

Food: Mainly crickets, grasshoppers, water beetles, molluscs, frogs and small reptiles. They also eat young birds from the nests of neighbouring colonial breeders such as cormorants, egrets, etc.; also carrion.

Voice: Harsh croak.

Breeding: Colonial with other species in trees, bushes, in reed beds and on rocks. The nest is of sticks or reeds padded with grass or other vegetable matter. July to March. Eggs 2—4, rarely 5, chalky white blotched with red brown spots. Average (60) 66,7 × 43,6 (60,2—70,5 × 39,7—51,2). Incubation 21 days.

LOCAL RACE:

T.a. aethiopicus (Latham), 1790: *Egypt.* Another race occurs on Malagasy and Aldabra Island.

82 Bald Ibis   Wilde-Kalkoen

Geronticus calvus   (Boddaert), 1783: *Cape of Good Hope*.

Native Names: Lekhoatlo, mo-Khootlo (S); Umcwangele (X); umXwagele (Z)

PLATE 7 (OPP. P. 49).
Length 79 cm (wing 369—386—403; tail 175—191—200; tarsus 66—70,4—73; Culmen 140—146—151. 7 specimens). Iris red; bill and legs red.

Identification: Generally green with conspicuous red on head. In flight shows pointed wings and carries its bill directly ahead unlike the Hadeda No. 84; has a graceful and bouyant flight, interspersed with much gliding. Immature lacks coppery patch on wing; the naked part of head and neck thinly covered with greyish feathers leaving only a small bare blue patch around the eye and a little red on the forepart of the crown.
Distribution: Peculiar to the Republic and Lesotho. Was more widespread.
Habits: Very local and resident where it breeds, which is in mountainous territory especially near the Drakensberg. Wanders during the non-breeding season to the vleis and lakes of neighbouring lower areas. A rather shy, wild bird. It is a restless forager, turning dung or leaves or probing here and there in open grassland and burnt veld.

82

Food: Worms, grasshoppers, caterpillars, also carrion.
Voice: A high-pitched "keeauw-klaup-klaup".
Breeding: Nests from July to October in the mountains in crevices of precipices or bushes growing on ledges. The nest which is a flat platform of sticks lined with grass, and the nest site, are much fouled by their own droppings. Eggs 2—3, rarely 1, dirty pale blue, spotted red-brown, mostly at thicker end. Average (24) 64,2 × 42,8 (57—71 × 38—49).

83 Glossy Ibis   Glansende Ibis

Plegadis falcinellus   (Linnaeus), 1766: *Austria*
Native Name: in-Kankane (Z).

PLATE 7 (OPP. P. 49).
Length about 71 cm (wing 280; tail 101; tarsus 101; culmen 127). Iris brown; bill and legs dark brownish olive.

Identification: The illustration shows breeding plumage. The non-breeding plumage has head, neck, back and top of head glossy green, greyer below. Immature birds similar to non-breeding dress. Nestling black with pinkish patch on back of crown; bill black with two vertical pinkish stripes. The small size and colour of bill separate this species from the Hadeda, No. 84; in flight much lighter and buoyant, occasionally sailing— usually silent; *the legs project slightly beyond tail*.
Distribution: Wide distribution over Southern Europe and Asia to Australia and also the eastern United States of America. Sparsely distributed in southern Africa being recorded from Caprivi Strip; rarely in Rhodesia and South West Africa; Welkom, Transvaal, Natal and Zululand, Pondoland and the Cape Peninsula.
Habits: Until recently considered a rare, non-breeding migrant from the northern hemisphere, but now known to breed here. A shy bird which occurs irregularly and inhabits boggy meadows and edges of quiet waters. It appears blackish from a distance, and walks with its comparatively long legs in a

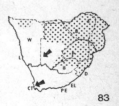

83

55

graceful manner—which has made several authors compare this species to a curlew. Perches freely on trees. Usually seen singly but flocks of over 40 are occasionally recorded.

Food: Worms, insects, crustaceans and molluscs.

Voice: A gull-like "keeauw-klaup-klaup" seldom heard. "Kwuk-kwuk-kwuk-kwuk" recorded from bird at breeding colony.

Breeding: Colonial breeders in mixed colonies in reed beds. Recorded breeding regularly on the Rand, also at Rondevlei and Berg River, Cape. The nest, placed on mud or in reeds just over water, is constructed of shredded rushes and placed in thick reed beds. September to January. Eggs 2—3, bright blue to dark blue-green, slightly glossed. Average (13) 51,9 × 36,5 (48,9—54,7 × 35,5—37,3).

LOCAL RACE:
P.f. falcinellus (Linnaeus), 1766: *Austria.* Southern Europe, Asia and Africa.

84   Hadeda

Hagedashia hagedash   (Latham), 1790: *Cape of Good Hope.*

Native Names: in-Kankane (Z); i-Han (P); Ing'ang'ane (X).

PLATE 7 (OPP. P. 49).
Length 76 cm (wing 334—353—370; tail 137—154—170; tarsus 63—67,9—73; culmen 117—134—153. 17 specimens). Iris dark brown; bill black with crimson along the top (culmen); legs dull red.

Identification: At a distance appears dull olive-grey, but metallic reflections on back and wing-coverts may be seen. It is a larger bird with a heavier build and shorter legs than the Glossy Ibis, No. 83, and is usually found on open veld—not so much alongside water. The flight is heavy with broad rounded wings and the bill points downwards. *In flight the feet do not extend beyond the tail.* Usually heard calling when flying—see below.

Distribution: Africa south of the Sahara and along the southern and eastern moist belt as far as De Hoop and Somerset West; in the northern Transvaal extending west of the Limpopo River, the Upper Vaal River, occasional in the eastern Orange Free State. Recorded from northern Botswana and Caprivi Strip.

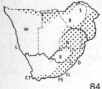

84

Habits: Common resident over most of its range. Occur in small parties or flocks of up to thirty in number, in plantations and open bush near streams and rivers and on open veld. When disturbed they rise with loud cries that startle everything in the neighbourhood. Settle readily on trees. In the breeding season usually occur in pairs but out of breeding season, although they forage in pairs or small parties, they often congregate to roost on trees at a regular time, returning over the same route day after day.

Voice: A well-known raucous call rendered variously from "ah-a-a-a" to "ha-ha-ha-ha-dahah" from which the species gets its name. Heard most frequently at dawn and dusk when flying to or from roost.

Food: 60% animal matter. Mole crickets, green locusts, fly larvae, beetles, snails and worms, etc.

Breeding: Solitary; nests are platforms of sticks, with a thin padding of grass, placed in the branches of trees, usually on the banks of streams and rivers. Also recorded nesting on telephone poles. Normally September to December but recorded from June to March. Eggs 3—4, pale olive greenish much marked with reddish streaks and smudges. Average (90) 61,3 × 42,7 (57—65,1 × 38,5—46,8). Incubation by both sexes 25—28 days. Nestling period about 33 days.

LOCAL RACES:
(a) *H.h. hagedash* (Latham), 1790: *Cape of Good Hope*. Measurements as given above. Cape Province to the lower Zambesi River.
(b) *H.h. erlangeri* Neumann, 1909: *Dogge, South Somaliland*. Smaller size but longer bill and darker colouration below. Culmen 126—163. Average 140,6. East Africa as far south as lower Zambesi River valley.
(c) *H.h. brevirostris* Reichenow, 1907: *Alen, Spanish Guinea*. Size similar to nominate but bill longer and even darker below than *H.h. erlangeri*. Upper Zambesi valley to West Africa.

Family PLATALEIDAE

Although placed by some authorities with the Ibises *(Threskiornithidae)* the Spoonbills are widely different in the shape of the bill which is flattened, spatular and not down-curved. The legs are also relatively longer and they are less sociable in habits than are the Ibises.

85 African Spoonbill   Lepelaar

Platalea alba Scopoli, 1786: *Luzon; probably the Cape of Good Hope.*

Native Names: in-Kenkane, in-Xulamasele (Z).

PLATE 7 (OPP. P. 49).
Length 91 cm (wing 365—384—414; tail 105—124—152; tarsus 131—144—157; culmen 172—193—230 (11); greatest width 45—50,6—56 (11). 15 specimens). Iris white to pearly-grey; bill, upper mandible red, lower mandible slaty-black with yellow spots and edges; legs bright red.

Identification: From a distance may be overlooked as one of the white egret group, but bill shape and colour are easily discernable. Young birds have brown outer primaries, covert shafts brown, and head streaked with blackish brown; bill dusky yellow and feet blackish. The flight is strong but moderately slow with head and neck extended.
Distribution: Over most of Africa south of the Sahara; also found in Malagasy. Widespread in southern Africa but absent in the dry west.
Habits: Not common; a vagrant except near breeding localities where it is resident; general throughout the dry interior and Zululand. Movements not fully known but a Transvaal bird has been recovered from Zambia. Single or in small parties, always found at water, marshes, lagoons and dams. Rather shy. Regularly sleeps standing on one leg with head and bill tucked back into scapulars. Walks with deliberate tread and feeds either by probing the bill into soft mud or sweeping it from side to side. Ringing indicates an age of 137 months and random movements up to 680 km.
Food: Water insects and locusts.
Voice: Sometimes emits a ''kor'' in flight. A guttural grunt at the nest. Alarm note ''wark-wark''.
Breeding: Though in communities with herons and other water birds, it still keeps apart. Breeds rather earlier than most water birds, April to December, making a flat nest of water plants in marshes or pans, preferring reeds. Eggs 2—3, white, beautifully blotched and spotted in a mass at the obtuse end with olive red-brown. Average (33) 66,4 × 44,2 61—71,4 × 39,7—47,8).

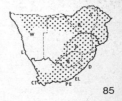

85

FLAMINGOS

Family PHOENICOPTERIDAE

With extremely long legs and necks, and the bill bent downwards in the middle to enable the bird to wade in fairly deep water and still rake the mud below by a front to back sweep of the bill; the toes are webbed, enabling them to swim in deeper water. Highly gregarious and a most beautiful sight with their white and scarlet plumage displayed, especially when in flight. Nests are made in large colonies in muddy, unfrequented flats, the nests being mounds of mud with a hollow at the top for the clutch of two eggs, which are white, oblong in shape, rough in texture. Their food seems to consist largely of algae, as well as small animals associated with it.

Three living genera are recognized with five living species two of which are numbered in the 14 fossil species known.

86 Greater Flamingo   Groot Flamink

Phoenicopterus ruber   Linnaeus, 1758: *Africa. America = Bahamas.*

PLATE 7 (OPP. P. 49).
Length 140 cm (wing 355—470; tail 125—157; tarsus 240—265; culmen 120—135. 12 specimens). Iris pale straw; bill flesh pink with terminal third black; legs pink.

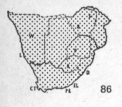

86

Identification: Differentiated from the next species, No, 87, by its greater size and whiter appearance, and by the pink bill with black tip. The bill, when seen from very close quarters, can be seen to show upper and lower mandibles—see No. 87. Unmistakable in flight, with neck and legs held straight out and showing beautiful red and black wings; when taking off the legs often hang at an angle. Immature lack pink on wings, bill similar in pattern to adult but white, tipped black, legs dark.
Distribution: Widely distributed over southern Europe, Asia, the greater part of Africa and America. Recorded from all areas in southern Africa.
Habits: Resident in some areas but for the most part a summer migrant, October to April. Also subject to annual fluctuations, being very numerous some years, with the next species, in flocks of up to a million, whilst in other years hardly any birds are to be seen. Large numbers are mainly recorded from the Cape, Free State, Transvaal, Zululand and the South West Africa coast; elsewhere numbers are more restricted or even irregular. Frequents only suitable shallow coastal lagoons or large sheets of shallow water in the interior, especially temporary waters and saltpans. These birds may swim if the water is deep, and if feeding in deep water head and neck are immersed. Usually feed in shallow water, the head bent down and forward so that the upper mandible is beneath the lower. In this way they may move forward zig-zagging head from side to side. More often they stand in one place and rotate while stamping up and down, thus forming a circular mound of mud.
Food: Principally animal matter: chironomid larvae, other insect larvae, shrimps and small molluscs which are strained through the bill.
Voice: A goose-like ''honk-honk'', often mixed with lower honking from a calling flock.
Breeding: Breeds regularly in East Africa but irregularly in southern Africa. Recorded nesting at Etosha Pan, Welkom and Bredasdorp with individual records from several widely spread sites. Normally nest in colonies of up to 30 000 (Etosha) in inundated areas; the nests are mounds of mud with a

58

shallow depression on top, about 33 cm in diameter. Eggs reported from November to January and small young to July. Eggs 1 normally, 2 rarely, white (95) 88,3 × 53,9 (79,0—103,0 × 48,9—58,6). Young fly 85 days after hatching.

LOCAL RACE:
P.r. roseus Pallas, 1811: *Mouth of the River Volga, Caspian Sea, Southern Russia,* Southern Europe, Asia and Africa.

87 Lesser Flamingo   Klein Flamink

Phoeniconaias minor Geoffroy, 1798: *Senegal.*

PLATE 7 (OPP. P. 49).
Length 102 cm (wing 317—333—346; tail 87—95,5—100; tarsus 151—179,1—198 (220); culmen 99—102,6—104. 6 specimens). Iris red or orange; bill dark lake red; legs red.

Identification: Smaller than the preceding species, No. 86, with a *dark red bill* appearing black from a distance and a much deeper red-pink general colour. Quite often beautifully-coloured birds with entire plumage bright red-pink may be seen in flocks of this species. Immature has a dark brown bill; lacks the pink of the adult and is capable of flight at a small size—even when still having downy feathers on the neck.

Distribution: Over the eastern parts of Africa to north-west India; also Cameroon in West Africa, and Malagasy. Found over most of southern Africa, although rather rarer than the preceding species, particularly in the eastern Cape and Transkei.

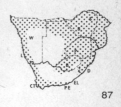

87

Habits: As for previous species, with which it frequently occurs. Usually found in more permanent waters, whilst the Greater Flamingo shows a preference for temporary vleis. The feeding habits do not include the circling and stamping as found in the previous species.

Food: Largely vegetable matter, especially unicellular algae.

Voice: Similar to No. 86.

Breeding: A very young specimen collected last century at Saldanha Bay was the first breeding record. The nest is a mound of mud, made in shallow water which frequently dries up, leaving the nest on dry land. An unsuccessful nesting attempt was made at Welkom; 60 nests were flooded. Nest mounds also recorded from Port Elizabeth. About 50 000 bred at Etosha (1971).

(The Makarikari breeding records were of Pelican according to Austin Roberts field notes, not this species as published.)

Family ANATIDAE

Ducks, Geese and Swans constitute a well-known family owing to some of them having been domesticated. They are aquatic birds with webbed toes and short legs adapted to swimming, robust bodies, rather short wings and tails, close-set feathers, and bills adapted in most cases to sifting the food taken in water or mud by an arrangement of lamellae inside the edge of the bill. They are gregarious in habits, but do not nest in communities, and usually lay large clutches of white or yellowish eggs, most species plucking down from their bodies to line the nest. Most species are of wide distribution, restless or migratory in adaption to the fluctuation of water in which they procure their food, and the characters of the species are usually well defined, with the result that the proportion of genera to species is large. All members of the family undergo a moult which leaves most flightless for a short period when all the flight feathers are discarded at once. This moult usually occurs after breeding has been completed. Recent classification based largely on behavioural characteristics has reduced the recognized living genera to 41 with some 145 or 146 species.

87X   Mute Swan   Swaan

Cygnus olor   (Gmelin), 1789: *Russia.*

PLATE 9 (OPP. P. 65).

Length 102 cm Iris dark brown; bill orange with black knob and base, immature greyish-pink; feet black, grey in immature.

Identification: This large well-known species needs no description. Entirely white.

Distribution: Confined originally as a feral breeding species to Kromme River Valley, Humansdorp district. Range extends from Gamtoos River mouth to the Kromme River. Also introduced to Groenvlei near Knysna.

Habits: A beautiful species which swims with neck curved gracefully and bill pointing downwards. Social except when breeding. A population of about 60 birds usually congregate to moult on the Seekoei River estuary—January to February.

Food: Water weeds and aquatic insects.

Voice: A defiant explosive grunt defending nest. Soft low notes in breeding season.

Breeding: Solitary pairs breed on islands near water edge, a large nest forming a mound of vegetable matter. Either along river islands or on dams in the district. Eggs recorded in September and October. Clutch, 5—8, white eggs.

88   Spur-winged Goose   Wildemakou

Plectropterus gambensis   (Linnaeus), 1766: *Gambia.*

Native Names: i-Hoye (Z); mo-Salamotlaka, Letsikhui (S); i-Sikwi (G); Ihoye (X).

PLATE 9 (OPP. P. 65).

Length 102 cm (wing ♂ 530—533; ♀ 500—503; tail ♂ 230—235; ♀ 193—195; tarsus 105—115; culmen 70—76; spur ♂ 20 ♀ 16—18. 2 ♂ and 2 ♀ specimens). Iris hazel; bill, including bare skin at top of the head, red with nail whitish; bare skin around eye and sides of face grey; feet flesh pink.

Identification: Large size and long neck separate this species from other geese. The amount of white on neck and on shoulder varies between individuals, northern birds tend to show more white. Older birds have more prominent carbuncles on bill. Sexes alike. Young birds have face entirely feathered. Gosling pale yellow with pale brown upper parts, two yellow spots on the back at the base of the wings and two others on sides of rump. In flight the wing shows a white front edge.

Distribution: Throughout Africa and Malagasy, absent from the drier areas.

Habits: Gregarious and common on larger stretches of water, also on streams and rivers, where there are mixed open grassy flats adjacent with grasses and

88

water weeds to shelter in. Notoriously wary. Found at certain places for the greater part of the year but after rains they make for flooded areas. Often congregate on the grassy banks or in shorter vegetation in the water and when fired at fly off and settle in open water out of range; hard to shoot and tough to eat. Usually rest during the middle of the day, flying at dawn and dusk to feeding haunts and normally feeding at night.

Food: Vegetable matter including young grasses, lucerne, grain shoots, young potatoes, and fallen figs.

Voice: High-pitched bubbling "cherwit" while flying.

Breeding: The nest is placed in dense beds of grass, or in holes, or even on the top of old nests including those of the Hamerkop, No. 72. The nest, made of reeds and vegetation, is a fairly large structure. August through to May, mainly September and January. Eggs 6—12, glossy ivory. Average (50) 74,5 × 55,3 (68—86,2 × 51—58,8). Incubation about four weeks.

89 Egyptian Goose   Kolgans

Alopochen aegyptiacus (Linnaeus), 1766: *Egypt.*

Native Names: Ildwe (X); le-Faloa (S).

PLATE 9 (OPP. P. 65).
Length 71 cm (wing ♂ 403; ♀ 350—380; tail ♂ 145; ♀ 133—142; tarsus ♂ 80; ♀ 68—72; culmen ♂ 48; ♀ 48—54. One male and 5 female specimens). Iris orange-brown to crimson; bill light pink, darker on the top, margins and base; legs pinkish-red.

Identification: May be confused with the Shelduck, No. 90, but separable at some distance by the brown "inverted horseshoe" patch on its chest. There is also a broad brown rim around the eye. In flight the dark chest mark is the easiest character to separate the two species; otherwise the wing patterns are very similar, with white shoulder and black flight feathers. Sexes alike. Young lacks brown around eye and on chest; also the wing is not so pure white. Gosling sooty brown above; forehead, the streak over eye and under parts white.

Distribution: Widely distributed over Africa and southern Europe; not uncommon in southern Africa.

Habits: Resident, though restless when the western districts become dry. Usually found in pairs but vast flocks may be met with especially in wheat producing areas, e.g., Berg River, south-western Cape. Frequently seen near water, even the smallest of dams, but may feed in open lands away from water; diurnal feeders returning to roost on sandbanks or in trees at night. The only goose which occurs in large enough numbers to become a pest to grain farmers, doing as much damage trampling down shooting plants as eating them. Irregular movements up to 1 100 km recorded.

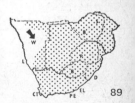

89

Food: Soft vegetable substances, especially young grass and wheat.

Voice: "Honk-haah-haah-haah". Female calls a long rapid series of honks ending with a long drawn out note. Male utters loud hiss.

Breeding: Nests in various situations, such as in matted vegetation near water, in hollow trees, on the top of old Hamerkop nests, or even on ledges of precipices; most frequently in old nests of other species. A few feathers and down in nest lining, which hide the eggs. July to March, with a peak in the south in September—October. April to December in Rhodesia. Eggs 7—9, white to cream colour, smooth and rather glossy. Average (79) 68,6 × 50,6 (68,3—76,0 × 45,8—53,8). Incubation 4 weeks by female; chicks come down from high nests by falling out.

90 South African Shelduck   Bergeend

Tadorna cana   (Gmelin), 1789: *Cape of Good Hope.*

PLATE 9 ♂ AND ♀ (OPP. P. 65).
Length 64 cm (wing ♂ 354—360; ♀ 315—335; tail ♂ 130—136; ♀ 120—139; tarsus ♂ 56—58; ♀ 52—56; culmen ♂ 45—48; ♀ 39,5—42. 4 ♂ and 3 ♀ specimens). Iris pale yellow; bill and legs black.

Identification: Sexes illustrated. The female is often wrongly identified as the White-faced Duck, No. 100; she has a white head of variable pattern, often similar to that species, but is a larger bird with white wing-coverts. Furthermore, grey-headed males are usually present to assist identification. Goslings light brown above, creamy white below, with white line down back of "wing" and around the tail; white patches on side of back and rump.

Distribution: A species restricted to the Republic and South West Africa. Widespread in the Cape Province, Free State and southern Transvaal; recorded from Durban, Mooi River and Underberg District in Natal, Ndumu Game Reserve in Zululand. Also Moremi Reserve, Botswana.

90

Habits: Gregarious when not breeding, occurring in flocks of up to several hundred, occasionally in sufficient numbers to become a pest. Usually more females than males, sometimes two to one. Partial to dams or vleis with shallow water and wet mud. They congregate on islands or mud banks where they seem to spend much of the day sleeping or preening. Rather shy, put to flight very easily. Moult November to January. Subject to local movements, not yet understood. Known age 10 years.

Food: Vegetable matter; *zostera, spirogyra* and *brachiopoda* recorded.

Voice: Male utters a deeper "Hoogh" or "how" or "honk" at intervals. Often the female alternates with a harsher "hark". Both may hiss.

Breeding: Breeds away from water in holes such as antbear burrows and consequently observed on open veld. Johnson records a nest at a depth of 27 feet from the entrance. July to November. Eggs 10, white with a matt surface and averaging 71 × 57.

91 Knob-billed Duck   Knobbel-eend

Sarkidiornis melanotos   (Pennant), 1769: *Ceylon.*

Native Names: i-Sebwi (G).

PLATE 9 ♂ AND ♀ (OPP. P. 65).
Length ♂ 79 cm, ♀ 64 cm (wing ♂ 349—359—370; ♀ 263—286—293; tail ♂ 130—137,3—150, ♀ 100—110—120; tarsus ♂ 56—59,8—67, ♀ 42—47—50; culmen and knob ♂ 45—51—60; culmen ♀ 42,5—44—48). Iris dark brown; bill black with an erect compressed semi-circular elevation in the male; legs dark plumbeous.

Identification: A conspicuous black and white duck at a distance. Sometimes the male has a row of black-tipped feathers across the sides of breast forming an incomplete bar. The knob or comb varies in size, being largest in breeding season. The young are similar to the female but have more speckling on the side of chest and flanks. In flight wings are dark above and below. Note difference in size of sexes.

Distribution: Widely distributed all over Africa, Malagasy and southern Asia Rare south of the Orange River and in the north-eastern Cape, though recorded regularly in Lesotho.

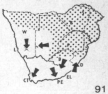

Habits: Not uncommon in good "duck country", where there is abundant water in shallows and marshes. Subject to considerable fluctuations, movements are not understood; in Central Africa stated to be a definite migrant as well as having local fluctuations. During an influx they may form flocks of a hundred, but normally observed in small groups or singly. Seems to spend much of its time resting on a sand bank or islet feeding more actively early and late. Somewhat shy. In flight the wings move rather slowly giving a false impression of being a slow bird. A bird ringed at Que Que (Rhodesia) was recovered at Chad 3 879 km north. Others from Zaire and the Sudan.

91

Voice: Generally silent, but heard to utter a hoarse, whistled sound in flight.

Food: Partial to grass seeds, water lily seeds and has been recorded a pest on cultivated fields. Also aquatic insect larvae and locusts.

Breeding: There is no evidence regarding polygamy *in southern Africa*. Recorded breeding in long grass and amongst stones near water, but more usually breed in holes of dead trees or suitable holes in trees sometimes as much as a mile from water. Nest in same tree in successive years. No down in the nest. March to December in Rhodesia. Eggs 5—8, pale yellowish and glossy. Average (7) 63,3 × 43,9 (56—71 × 41,5—46). Incubation about 4 weeks.

92 Pygmy Goose   Dwerg-gans

Nettapus auritus   (Boddaert), 1783: *Madagascar*.

PLATE 9 ♂ AND ♀ (OPP. P. 65).
Length 33 cm (wing 156—159—165; tail 52—66,4—73; tarsus 22—23—24; culmen 23,5—25—26. 8 specimens). Iris dark brown, bluish; bill bright yellow with a dark brown nail; legs and feet bluish black shading to the back to yellowish.

Identification: Its small size separates it from other geese and duck; from a distance the orange and white under-parts are conspicuous. In flight the wing has a conspicuous white line down the centre (see also below). Young birds are similar to the female. Gosling black on crown, nape and upperparts, a black line through eye, white below with white markings at base of nape, wing and sides of rump.

Distribution: Over the greater part of tropical Africa and Malagasy. Extends down the eastern tropical belt as far as Port Elizabeth and Humansdorp district. Recorded from Potchefstroom, Transvaal, Grootfontein in South West Africa, and not uncommon in Rhodesia and northern Botswana.

Habits: Resident, usually observed in small parties or pairs swimming on quiet back waters of streams, rivers and open sheets of water where there is much surface vegetation such as lilies, etc.; also in estuaries. Show a preference for deep water. Seldom leave the water as other geese do, in fact their habits are more like those of the diving ducks since they are capable divers and often feed in this manner. May settle or even roost on trees. When put to flight they rise straight out of the water and fly off rapidly, low over the

92

PLATE 8

93. *Anas clypeata.* European Shoveler. Europese Slopeend. ♂ and ♀.
94. *Anas smithii.* Cape Shoveler. Kaapse Slopeend. ♂ and ♀.
95. *Anas sparsa sparsa.* Black Duck. Swart Eend.
96. *Anas undulata undulata.* Yellow-billed Duck. Geelbek.
97. *Anas erythrorhyncha.* Red-billed Teal. Rooibek-eendjie.
97X. *Anas querquedula.* Garganey. ♂ and ♀.
98. *Anas capensis.* Cape Teal. Teeleendjie.
99. *Anas hottentota.* Hottentot Teal. Gevlekte Eendjie.
99X. *Anas acuta.* Pintail. ♂ and ♀.
102. *Netta erythrophthalma.* Red-eyed Pochard. Bruin Eend. ♂ and ♀.
103. *Oxyura punctata.* Maccoa Duck. Makou-eend. ♂ and ♀.

94

93

♂

♀

96

97

95

98

97x

♂

♀

99x

♂

♀

99

102

♀

♂

103

♂

♀

K B NEWMAN 1972

100

101

104

91

92 ♂ ♀

♂

90 ♀

89

88

87X

K B NEWMAN 19

PLATE 9

87X. *Cygnus olor*. Mute Swan. Swaan.
88. *Plectropterus gambensis*. Spur-winged Goose. Wildemakou.
89. *Alopochen aegyptiacus*. Egyptian Goose. Kolgans.
90. *Tadorna cana*. South African Shelduck. Bergeend. ♂ and ♀.
91. *Sarkidiornis melanotos*. Knob-billed Duck. Knobbel-eend. ♂ and ♀.
92. *Nettapus auritus*. Pygmy Goose. Dwerg-gans. ♂ and ♀.
100. *Dendrocygna viduata*. White-faced Whistling Duck. Nonnetjie-eend.
101. *Dendrocygna bicolor*. Fulvous Whistling Duck. Fluit-eend.
104. *Thalassornis leuconotus*. White-backed Duck. Witrug-eend.

DUCKS

surface, usually to settle a short way off since they are not shy unless disturbed by regular shooting.

Food: Aquatic vegetation which they gather on the surface or dive for; also aquatic insects. Mainly Nymphaea seed.

Voice: Male has a soft whistle. Also a whistled "choo-choo, pee-wee".

Breeding: Recorded from a hole in a mopane tree "1 metre up, 190 metres from river" and also "in a heavy clump of grass on river bank". (H. W. Bell-Marley). The nest is made of grass and lined with any material including leaves, but no down. October to December. January to April in Rhodesia. Eggs 6—7, creamy white. Average (14) 43,3 × 32,9 (41,6—44,8 × 31,7—35,2).

93 European Shoveler   Europese Slopeend

Anas clypeata (Linnaeus), 1758: *Europe = Sweden.*

PLATE 8 ♂ AND ♀ (OPP. P. 64).
Length 53 cm (wing 253; tail 81; tarsus 33; culmen 76). Iris yellow; bill lead colour; feet reddish orange. Female has brown iris.

Identification: Breeding male illustrated. The female is noticeably paler than the next species when seen in company with it, but otherwise very similar. In the hand, this species has white shafts to its primaries whilst the next species, No. 94, has brown shafts.

Distribution: Widely dispersed in the whole of the northern hemisphere, migrating southwards to Tanzania. One specimen from near Cape Town; three sight records at the same locality and single records from Knysna, Kleinsee and Transvaal.

Habits: A very rare migrant. All records are from July to November except the Benoni record by Daniels, who records a pair from November to February. 93 Other habits are similar to the next species.

94 Cape Shoveler   Kaapse Slopeend

Anas smithii (Hartert), 1891: *Cape Province.*

PLATE 8 ♂ AND ♀ (OPP. P. 64).
Length 53 cm (wing ♂ 230—241—250, ♀ 230—236—248; tail ♂ 74—76,1—80, ♀ 79—80,7—83; tarsus ♂ 34—38,4—38, ♀ 33—36—39; culmen ♂ 54,5—59,4—60, ♀ 55—57,3—64; width of bill ♂ 25,5—27,8—30, ♀ 24—26—27,5. 7 specimens, 4 ♂ 3 ♀). Iris ♂ light yellow, ♀ dark sepia; bill deep reddish brown to black in ♂; horn coloured in ♀, legs yellow-ochre, both sexes, to bright orange in ♂ breeding condition.

Identification: The bill is dark as illustrated. The male has a lighter coloured head and eye than the female and is blacker on the back. The female has the back mottled brown; blue of wings very dull and not conspicuous as in male. Sexual difference is present when first able to fly. In flight the blue shoulder, green speculum with white edge are conspicuous; the wings are placed so far back that they appear to push the bird along. Large heavy-looking beak merging with forehead gives a distinctive shape to head. Ducklings have lemon-yellow underparts; soft brown upper parts with yellow spots at base of wing and sides of rump.

66

Distribution: Found mainly in the Cape Province, Fee State and Transvaal. A single record from Rhodesia (32 kilometres N.W. of Bulawayo), rarely from Natal, once from St. Lucia, Zululand. Common in Botswana and scarce in South West Africa as far north as Okavango River and Damaraland. Records north of the Zambesi are confusing.

Habits: A common resident with local movements possibly coupled with the occurrence of rains. Occurs mostly in shallow waters, especially those rich in aquatic insects and vegetation, including temporary vleis. Mixes freely with other species of duck, occurring in pairs during the breeding season, otherwise in small flocks, occasionally large flocks of up to 600 birds. When disturbed take off straight from the water, rising vertically at first and then flying forward. The flight is very rapid—probably the swiftest of our local ducks. Often rest on islands and mud banks in company with other duck. In feeding usually "shovel" around in shallow water, with head well forward and bill kept more or less horizontal: also known to "upend". A bird ringed at Rondevlei (Cape) recovered Ondongwa (S.W.A.)—1 680 kms.

Food: Not recorded. Probably aquatic insects, unicellular plants and small floating plants as European Shoveller.

Voice: Male has a low rather guttural call; the female calls a "quack" not unlike the Yellowbill, No. 96.

Breeding: Nest in lush grass, reed clumps and other ground sites, usually near water but may be 21 metres away from water. The nest is made of fine grass and a ring of down is formed around the eggs, used for covering them when parent leaves the nest. No down under the eggs. Breeds throughout the year, mainly August to October. Eggs, 6—11, pale cream. Average (200) 53,3 × 38,7 (48,4—57,5 × 34,0—43,4). Incubation 27—28 days.

95 Black Duck   Swart Eend

Anas sparsa   Eyton, 1838: *South Africa.*

Native Names: Idada (Z and X): le-Tata (S).

PLATE 8 (OPP. P. 64).
Length 56 cm (wing 241—255—275; tail 105—114—120; tarsus 36—38—40; culmen 44—45,7—47,5. 8 specimens). Iris dark brown; bill slate with black patches and centre line, yellow at base of lower mandible; legs yellow to orange-yellow.

Identification: Occasionally with white on neck in front. Distinguished from the Yellowbill, No. 96, by its uniform slate bill, white markings on back, and *yellow feet.* In flight the green speculum shows a white edge above and below; the under-wing is white at the base, whilst in the next species, No. 96, it is brown. If in company with the Yellowbill, this species appears plumper in flight. Duckling is sooty brown above, with streaks above and below the eye and underparts buff cream; black collar at base of neck.

Distribution: Africa as far north as Ethiopia and Cameroon. Not recorded from the central and northern areas of South West Africa; otherwise throughout the southern continent.

Habits. A very local species, found in pairs or family parties on streams and rivers, practically always where there is running water. Active at dawn and dusk, usually resting up during the day, when they lie hidden and well camouflaged on a regular site. Rely on their camouflage and will remain absolutely stationary whilst one is passing within metres of them. When put to

94

95

flight they take off upwards from the water and then fly off with rapid flight; if not obstructed by vegetation they fly very low over the water with wing tips practically touching the surface. Feed by immersing the whole head under water, also upend and are capable divers.

Food: Aquatic insects, crabs, seeds and grain crops.

Voice: A noisy "Quack" by female in flight. Male utters a quiet, almost inaudible, wheezy "peep", also in flight.

Breeding: Often a permanent nest site if placed above flood level; they also nest on the top of driftwood caught in trees along river banks or in matted grass on the ground, thickly lining the hollow with down. The eggs are covered with down during bird's absence. July to February in the South; May to August in Rhodesia. Eggs 5—7, light cream to buff yellow. Average (27) 63,5 × 45 (57,3—65,5 × 40,2—48,8). Incubation 32 days plus.

LOCAL RACE:
A.s. sparsa. Eyton, 1838: *South Africa.* Differs from the Central African race by having a darker bill and greener speculum.

96 Yellow-billed Duck   Geelbek

Anas undulata Dubois, 1837: *Cape of Good Hope = near Piquet-berg.*

Native Name: Idada (X).

PLATE 8 (OPP. P. 64).

Length 51—58 cm (wing 235—248—256; tail 73—91,3—100; tarsus 34—37,5—44; culmen 54—58,1—61. 10 specimens). Iris hazel; bill yellow with black along the centre and at tip; legs black.

Identification: Perhaps our best-known duck, which can only be confused with the preceding species, No. 95, but the yellow bill with its black central patch distinguishes it. In flight shows a green speculum with white edges above and below; also carries its head high, silhouette exaggerated by its high forehead. Duckling sooty brown above, darker on back and rump; under-parts yellowish white with light forehead and streak over eye.

Distribution: From the Cape northwards to Central Africa and Ethiopia. Absent from most of South West Africa, northern Namaqualand, central Botswana and sparse in Rhodesia.

Habits: A very common and highly gregarious species, restless owing to the drying up of its haunts. Usually found in large flocks, except when breeding. Found in all open waters, rivers, estuaries and rarely along the coast; active during the day and sometimes wandering on to dry land in the vicinity of water. Swims high in the water, feeding by upending or putting head under water. Flight is rapid and usually when put up, flies high. Rather shy and wary and not often seen at close quarters. When disturbed from the nest or young they readily resort to the "broken wing" display to attract attention away from the nest. The flightless period of moult lasts about 36 days. Ringing results show ages up to 156 months and erratic movements up to 1 080 kms. Hybrids with Red-bill and Pochard recorded in the wild.

Food: Grass and monocotyledon seeds.

Voice: The male utters a loud "Queerk-queerk", the female a coarse "quark".

96

Breeding: Breed in lush grass, reeds or thick vegetation, usually well hidden. Nest is often many metres from water, though it may be placed on vegetation which is quite saturated just over water. The nest is constructed of fine grass, the eggs laid on consecutive days and the down (which is not always present) is added over a few days when the clutch is completed. Breeds throughout the year in the south, mainly July to October; August to May further north. Eggs 6—12, yellowish ivory. Average (100) 53,7 × 41,5 (51—59,3 × 37—46). Incubation 28—30 days.

LOCAL RACE:
A.u. undulata. Dubois, 1837: *Cape of Good Hope = near Piquetberg.* Differs from the other race which occurs in Ethiopia and northern Kenya by being lighter below and having a greener speculum.

97   Red-billed Teal   Rooibek-eendjie

Anas erythrorhyncha   Gmelin, 1789: *Cape of Good Hope.*

PLATE 8 (OPP. P. 64).
Length 48 cm (wing 190—212,5—222; tail 70—79,8—90; tarsus 30—31,5—35; culmen 45—48,8—53. 14 specimens). Iris hazel; bill pink with a brownish stripe down the centre; legs dirty grey.

Identification: This species may be confused with the Hottentot Teal, No. 99, but the pink bill, conspicuously lighter cheek and the speculum separate them fairly easily in the field. See also No 98. This is also a much larger bird. In flight the speculum is light chestnut colour, with a narrow dark brown line along it near the leading edge; the under-wing is grey. Sexes alike, bill of male brighter. Albino recorded. Duckling golden brown above; stripe over eye and patches at base of wing and sides of rump; buffy cream below.
Distribution: Occurs over the whole of South Africa, north-eastwards towards Ethiopia and also in Malagasy. Most abundant in the drier regions of the Karoo and South West Africa and Rhodesia.
Habits: A highly gregarious species, abundant at times in flocks of mixed species with Yellowbill and Wigeon. Subject to local fluctuations. Common in the flooded pans of the Kalahari and its borders, favouring shallow temporary water and flooded grasslands. An active species that is not very shy. Feeds usually with only the bill under the water, but frequently upends or puts its head under. Also displays the "broken wing" act.
Food: Aquatic plants and insects, small frogs and fish. Sacciolepis seeds preferred.
Voice: Male, a soft swizzling "whizzzt", female, loud "quaaaak".
Breeding: Builds a nest of fine grass placed in reeds or lush grass usually near water or slightly awash, but may be some metres from the water. Down is usually placed after the clutch is completed, though some nests have no down at all. August to May; early in the Cape, mainly the later months in the Transvaal and Rhodesia. Eggs 5—12, creamy yellow. Average (55) 49,3 × 37,1 (44,2—54,6 × 32—41,7). Ringing has given an age of 103 months and movements up to 1 539 kms (Barberspan to Angola). Hybrid with yellowbill recorded in wild.

97X Garganey

Anas querquedula Linnaeus, 1758: *Europe = Sweden.*

PLATE 8 (OPP. P. 64), ♂ AND ♀.
Length 38 cm (wing ♂ 187—198, ♀ 175—194; tail 62—70; tarsus 26—30; bill ♂ 36,5—40, ♀ 34—39. 12 specimens measured). Iris umber-brown; bill black or grey; legs lead-grey. Weight 357 g.

Identification: A small duck. The male in breeding plumage has a conspicuous *white line over eye*, generally, mottled brown with *brown breast sharply demarcated* from white belly and vermiculated greyish flanks. The lesser wing-coverts are blue. Male in eclipse plumage has the blue wing, otherwise similar to female. The female is mottled brown, with light stripe over eye, light chin and belly; green speculum dull and lesser wing-coverts grey. Could only be mistaken for female Pochard, No. 102, or female Maccoa duck, No. 103, both of which have light lines above the eye; but both lack the green speculum, and are darker, more uniformly brown birds.
Distribution: Europe and Asia to the Philippines. Migrates to Central Africa. Recently recorded from Botswana (May) and now recorded from Rhodesia from December to March.
Habits: Possibly a regular migrant in small numbers (Smithers). In East Africa show a strong preference for sheltered, shallow water where aquatic vegetation is plentiful. Usually seen in small flocks but gather in large numbers for migration. The flight is strong and swift.
Food: Seeds and leaves of aquatic vegetation, insect larvae, crustacea and small molluscs; also small tadpoles and fish.
Voice: "Ka-nak".

98 Cape Teal   Teeleendjie

Anas capensis Gmelin, 1789: *Cape of Good Hope.*

PLATE 8 (OPP. P. 64).
Length 46 cm (wing 191—195—199; tail 63—70,3—81; tarsus 27—30,3—32; culmen 45—47,5—49. 6 specimens). Iris light hazel to deep orange; bill waxed semi-transparent pink, base and edge of upper mandible black; legs dirty yellow.

Identification: This bird has a light pinkish bill but is easily separated from the Redbill, No. 97, by its uniform light-coloured head. Field impression is that of a very light grey bird speckled on sides, side of chest and on head. In flight the easiest duck to identify, because the speculum is mainly white surrounding a central glossy green square; underwing dark. Sexes alike. Duckling ash-brown above, with white line from bill over eye and white patch on side of rump.
Distribution: Fairly widely dispersed over South Africa and northwards on the east to Ethiopia, thence westwards to Lake Chad. Generally scarce in Natal, Mozambique and the Mashonaland plateau.
Habits: Common in the western Cape; not uncommon elsewhere. Resident, usually found in small flocks in shallow waters, temporary vleis, saltpans, estuaries and even coastal waters. When put to flight usually fly around and settle a little way off. Feed by diving or upending. Not very shy, but seem to remain at a safe distance.
Food: Aquatic vegetation, seeds, insects and small molluscs.

98

Voice: The male utters a high-pitched whistle, frequently heard in flight. The female a nasal "quurk".
Breeding: Under bushes or rushes on islands and in lush grass, sometimes in old goose nests. Down in nest. Throughout the year in the Cape, mainly August to November; March to September in Karoo; April to August in the Transvaal. Eggs 6—10, pale cream coloured. Average (62) 49,8 × 35,2 (46,9—56,8 × 31—41,3). Incubation by female only, 26—27 days.

99 Hottentot Teal   Gevlekte Eendjie

Anas hottentota   Eyton, 1838: *Orange River, W. Cape Province.*

PLATE 8 (OPP. P. 64).
Length 35,5 cm (wing 147—149,3—153; tail 56—60,2—66; tarsus 22—23,4—25; culmen 39—40,4—42. 10 specimens). Iris black; bill turquoise with black along the centre down to the tip, lead coloured lower mandible; legs turquoise to leaden.

Identification: Can be mistaken for the Redbill, No. 97, because of similar pattern of contrasting dark crown and white "cheeks", but is much smaller. Distinguished easily by "notch" of wing below speculum of sitting duck. This species has speckling on sides of neck and a *blue bill*. Also, most of the wing and lower back are dark, or glossy green. In flight the speculum is green with a white bar along the edge below; the *under-wing is black and white*. In the folded wing, the visible secondaries are metallic green in the male and brown in the female.
Distribution: Widely distributed over South Africa and north-eastwards to Ethiopia. Does not occur in Central and Western Cape except for type locality and an old record from Verloren Vlei. Recorded from Uitenhage northwards on the east, the northern Free State and from Great Namaqualand on the west.
Habits: A comparatively uncommon duck, resident, usually found in pairs or small parties in flooded marshy ground, and sheltered waterways with plenty of floating vegetation. Retiring and unobtrusive, frequently remaining stationary on water whilst shooting is going on, and are thus overlooked. Difficult to put up and usually do not fly far before settling again. Surface feeders, usually around the edges of pools mainly at dusk or nocternally.

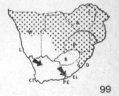

99

Food: Seeds, especially sacciolepis seeds, corms, insects and especially ostracods.
Voice: A whistle uttered in flight.
Breeding: Shallow nest placed not far from water, built of reeds and rushes among reeds. April and May in Rhodesia. Eggs 6—8, dark cream coloured. Average (19) 44,1 × 32,3 (41,7—46,9 × 31—35,5).

99X Pintail

Anas acuta   Linnaeus, 1758: *Sweden.*

PLATE 8 ♂ AND ♀ (OPP. P. 64).
Length 47 cm. Iris dark, bill in both sexes grey.

Identification: A slender-necked, pointed-tailed duck generally slimmer in appearance than the Yellowbill, sitting higher in the water. In flight both sexes have a thin white border on trailing edge of wing and pointed tail. The male

71

PLATE 10

105. *Sagittarius serpentarius*. Secretary Bird. Sekretarisvoël.
106. *Gyps coprotheres*. Cape Vulture. Krans-aasvoël.
107. *Gyps africanus*. White-backed Vulture. Witrug-aasvoël. Adult and Imm.
108. *Torgos tracheliotus*. Lappet-faced Vulture. Swart Aasvoël.
109. *Trigonoceps occipitalis*. White-headed Vulture. Witkop-aasvoël.
110. *Necrosyrtes monachus pileatus*. Hooded Vulture. Monnik-aasvoël.
Adult and Imm.
111. *Neophron percnopterus percnopterus*. Egyptian Vulture.
Egiptiese Aasvoël. Adult and Imm.
112. *Gypohierax angolensis*. Palm-nut Vulture. Wit Aasvoël.
150. *Gypaetus barbatus meridionalis*. Bearded Vulture. Lammergeyer.

Plate 11

VULTURES & SNAKE EAGLES

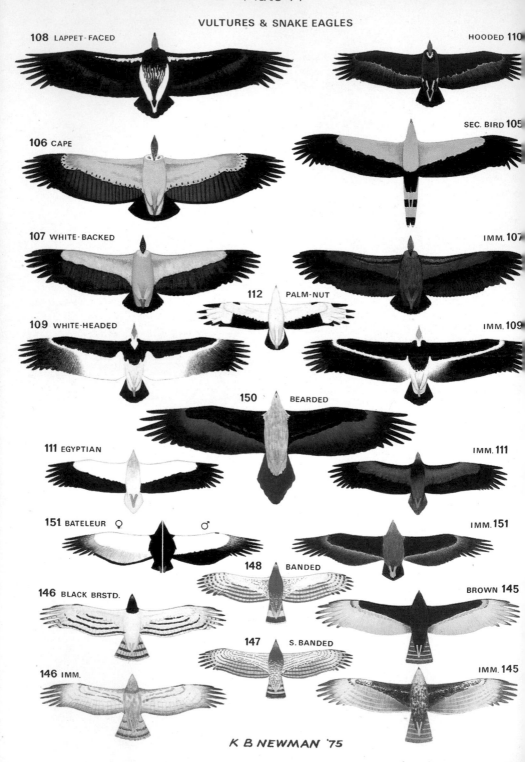

108 LAPPET-FACED

HOODED 110

106 CAPE

SEC. BIRD 105

107 WHITE-BACKED

IMM. 107

112 PALM-NUT

109 WHITE-HEADED

IMM. 109

150 BEARDED

111 EGYPTIAN

IMM. 111

151 BATELEUR ♀ ♂

IMM. 151

148 BANDED

146 BLACK BRSTD.

BROWN 145

147 S. BANDED

146 IMM.

IMM. 145

K B NEWMAN '75

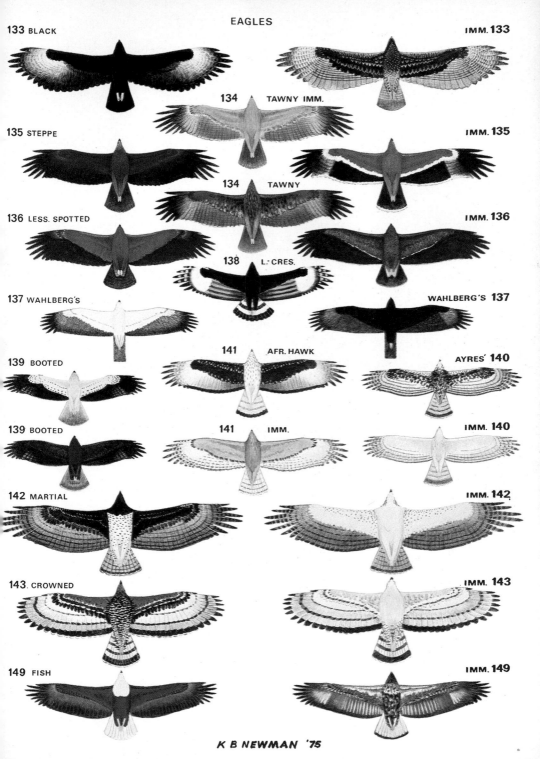

Plate 12

EAGLES

133 BLACK

IMM. 133

134 TAWNY IMM.

135 STEPPE

IMM. 135

134 TAWNY

136 LESS. SPOTTED

IMM. 136

138 L. CRES.

137 WAHLBERG'S

WAHLBERG'S 137

141 AFR. HAWK

139 BOOTED

AYRES' 140

139 BOOTED

141 IMM.

IMM. 140

142 MARTIAL

IMM. 142

143 CROWNED

IMM. 143

149 FISH

IMM. 149

K B NEWMAN '75

K. NEWMAN

PLATE 13

113 *(a). Falco peregrinus minor.* Peregrine. Slegvalk. Ad. and Imm.
113 *(b). Falco peregrinus calidus.* Peregrine. Slegvalk.
114. *Falco biarmicus biarmicus.* Lanner. Edelvalk. A and B.
115. *Falco subbuteo subbuteo.* Hobby. Europese Boomvalk. Ad. and Imm.
116. *Falco cuvieri.* African Hobby. Afrikaanse Boomvalk. Ad. and Imm.
116X. *Falco fasciinucha.* Teita Falcon.
116Y. *Falco concolor.* Sooty Falcon. Ad. and Imm.
117. *Falco chicquera.* Red-necked Falcon. Rooinek-valkie. Ad. and Imm.
119. *Falco amurensis.* Eastern Red-footed Kestrel.
Oostelike Rooipoot-valkie. ♂ and ♀, Imm.
120. *Falco vespertinus.* Western Red-footed Kestrel.
Westelike Rooipoot-valkie. ♂ and ♀, Imm.
121. *Falco dickinsoni.* Dickinson's Kestrel. Dickinsonse Valk.
121X. *Falco ardosiacus.* Grey Kestrel. Grysvalkie.
122. *Falco rupicoloides.* Greater Kestrel. Groot Rooivalk.
123. *Falco tinninculus rupicolus.* Rock Kestrel. Rooivalkie. ♂, ♀ and Imm.
125. *Falco naumanni naumanni.* Lesser Kestrel. Klein Rooivalkie. ♂ and ♀.
126. *Poliohierax semitorquatus semitorquatus.* Pygmy Falcon.
Dwergvalk. ♂ and ♀ and Imm.
127. *Aviceda cuculoides.* Cuckoo Falcon. Koekoekvalk. Ad. and Imm.

has chocolate brown head and neck with conspicuous white streak from white of breast towards ear-coverts; green speculum even in eclipse plumage. The female differs in having no metallic speculum and grey bill. Male in eclipse resembles female.

Distribution: Northern hemisphere migrating to central Africa and Asia during the northern winter. Specimens recorded from Zambia and Rhodesia, sight records from Barberspan, Transvaal.

Habits: Recorded in November in Rhodesia, February in Zambia and January in Transvaal. This bird swims high in the water and buoyant and more slender bird than say, the yellowbill. Feeds by upending and may rest on the bank. The pair seen in Rhodesia associated with other duck, flew with them and always kept together.

100   White-faced Whistling Duck   Nonnetjie-eend

Dendrocygna viduata (Linnaeus), 1766: *Cartagena Colombia.*

Native Name: i-Yabakene (G).

PLATE 9 (OPP. P. 65).
Length 48 cm (wing 223—230,1—240; tail 59—65,4—71; tarsus 47—50,8—52; culmen 45—49,3—53. 7 specimens). Iris hazel; bill black with a leaden blue bar at tip; legs leaden coloured.

Identification: The only other species with such conspicuous white on the "face" is the Shelduck, No. 90. Easily separated from that species by lack of any white on the wing. The sexes are alike. In flight the rounded wings and rump are blackish. (See also No. 101.) Immature not so pure white on head and neck. Duckling olive-brown to greenish black above, pale yellowish cream below, with cream patches at base of wing and sides of rump. White face variable and becomes discoloured before moult.

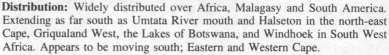

100

Distribution: Widely distributed over Africa, Malagasy and South America. Extending as far south as Umtata River mouth and Halseton in the north-east Cape, Griqualand West, the Lakes of Botswana, and Windhoek in South West Africa. Appears to be moving south; Eastern and Western Cape.

Habits: Except at its southern limits it is a common, highly gregarious species, usually occurring on open waters in flocks of a dozen to twenty birds, but sometimes in vast numbers. Subject to local movements. Seen most of the day sleeping or preening on some promontory, but active feeding and flying at night. Although they are capable swimmers they spend much of their time wading in shallow water, and when alarmed have a very upright stance, due to their long legs and necks. Somewhat wary, and when put to flight they circle around calling. The flight is slow and heavy. Sometimes perch in trees. Hybrids with 101 recorded.

Food: Principally seeds and corms; also molluscs and crustaceans.

Voice: Very characteristic clear whistle of three notes rendered as "mai-wi-wi" or "sip-sip-sieu".

Breeding: Nest is a shallow depression of a few wisps of dry grass well concealed in rank vegetation. Occasionally placed more in the open, the nest is usually near marsh or water but may be several hundred yards away. Down is present but not often recorded. October to November, in Rhodesia. December to February in Natal, March to April in Transvaal. Eggs 5—12, white tinged with cream becoming nest stained yellowish; surface smooth, chalky and soft. Average (48) 49,5 × 37,9 (44,4—57,6 × 35—40,1). Incubation 28—30 days.

101 Fulvous Whistling Duck   Fluit-eend

Dendrocygna bicolor (Viellot), 1816: *Paraguay.*

PLATE 9 (OPP. P. 65).
Length 46 cm (wing 216; tail 47; tarsus 46; culmen 45. One specimen). Iris dark brown; bill bluish black; legs slaty blue.

Identification: The dark line down the hind neck and nape, as well as the speckled white throat-patch and white markings on the flank, are good field characters. In flight, similar to the preceding species in that it has rounded wings, long thin neck and feet extending beyond the tail. Easily separated in flight by white tail coverts, above and below.

Distribution: A widely dispersed species of the north, occurring in southern North America, South America, southern Asia, Malagasy and eastern Africa between the Sahara and Zambesi, but rarer in South Africa. Recorded from the Cape Peninsula, where it has bred: Natal, extending as far south as Peddie on the east; common on the Rand where it breeds, but generally rare in the Transvaal and Rhodesia though stated to be more common during the rains. Also Ondangua and Namutoni in South West Africa.

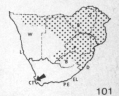

101

Habits: What has been recorded for the previous species, could be repeated for this species. Associates freely with Yellow-billed Duck.

Food: Primarily seeds and corms.

Voice: In flight a clear but soft whistle "tsii-ee, tsoo-ee". A quacking note is recorded during breeding.

Breeding: The nest is usually constructed in reeds or sedge over water. Bell Marley has recorded a nest beautifully concealed among bracken and tall grass some distance from water. The reeds are bent down to give the base, on top of which are piled reeds and rushes up to almost a foot. Both the presence and absence of down are recorded for the nest. July (young) in the Cape, June (eggs) in Natal and eggs in March and April in the Transvaal. Eggs 6-12, rarely 13, creamy buff. Average (33) 53,9 × 40,6 (49—55 × 39—41,9).

102 Red-eyed Pochard   Bruin Eend

Netta erythrophthalma (Weid), 1833: *Lagoa do Braco, near Villa de Belmonte, Bahia.*

PLATE 8 ♂ AND ♀ (OPP. P. 64).
Length 51 cm (wing 207, 213; tail 57, 58; tarsus 32, 36; culmen 41,5, 43,5, one male and one female). Iris, male orange-yellow to blood-red; female umber; bill leaden blue with black tip; legs blackish.

Identification: Sexes illustrated. The female is generally much paler, being light buff below but with quite different markings on the head; there is a white line through the eye, which extends back behind ear coverts and curves round to meet a white line extending from the white throat, thus forming a light ring. Thus distinguished from the female Maccoa, No. 103, by this ringed effect; also by wing pattern. In flight appears generally dark, whilst the wing has a conspicuous white line down the speculum. See below. Immature male similar to the female. Duckling dark brown above, sulphur yellow on underparts; male has chrome-yellow lores, the female has sulphur-yellow lores.

75

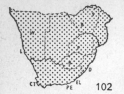

102

Distribution: South Africa, extending to Ethopia; also recorded from southern Brazil and Peru. Widely distributed throughout.

Habits: A common duck in open flooded marshes and deep waters, possibly migratory. Usually occurs in small flocks but numbers of up to 300 have been recorded; pairs off during the breeding season. A diving duck, thus more partial to deeper areas and centre of vleis. Sits fairly low in the water, with the tail submerged. Not very bold, diving and swimming away from danger. When put to flight takes a run along the water before being able to fly off; flight swift and in silhouette, the high forehead and thin neck are characteristic. Moult recorded in September-October, Cape; but flying birds occur at the same time.

Food: Principally seeds, corms and shoots of aquatic vegetation; crustacea and aquatic molluscs. Nymphae seed is 50% of food.

Voice: Male, a nasal, whirring "whrreeooorrr" or "par-ah-ah" especially in flight; female, a short "quarrrk".

Breeding: The nest is built in reeds over water and is constructed of reeds and rushes, more or less dry. "No down" and "practically no down" recorded. August to December and May in the Cape; February, July and August in the Transvaal; February to July and September in Rhodesia. Eggs 6—13, are creamy buff, well pitted. Average (49) 56,2 × 43,9 (53,2—58,5 × 41,0—45,9).

LOCAL RACE:
N.e. brunnea (Eyton), 1838: Southern Africa. As above.

103 Maccoa Duck   Makou-eend

Oxyura maccoa (Eyton), 1838: *South Africa = Verlorenvlei.*

PLATE 8 ♂ AND ♀ (OPP. P. 64).
Length 46 cm (wing ♂ 165, 173, ♀ 155; tail ♂ 72, 73, ♀ 66; tarsus ♂ 34, 34, ♀ 31; culmen ♂ 40, 42, ♀ 36. 3 specimens, 2 ♂, 1 ♀). Iris dark hazel; bill, male blue to black; female brown. Legs lead blue.

Identification: Sits very low in the water and when alarmed it sticks the tail up perpendicularly to the water. The flight is rapid, very low over the water, the wings appearing short. The male assumes eclipse plumage and is indistinguishable from female May to mid-September though odd males in breeding plumage can be seen in these times. Ducklings, black-brown above. Ducklings assume pattern of female with first feathers.

Distribution: Widely distributed over South Africa and northwards to Ethopia. Generally sparse and local.

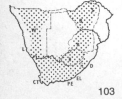

103

Habits: For the most part resident, found on small dams, lakes, quiet waters; but always in the vicinity of reeds. Recorded in pairs or family parties. A diving duck, very difficult to put to flight because of its diving abilities. When put up takes a little while to rise, splashing along with its feet before becoming airborne. Swims low in the water but when suspicious may lie with its body almost wholly submerged, only the head, short thick neck and top of the back visible.

Food: Sub-aquatic seeds, roots, algae, insect larvae, water beetles and molluscs.

Voice: A soft snoring note "purrr-rrr-rrr".

Breeding: This species may use other birds' nests, e.g., Coot, Great-crested Grebe, but usually constructs its own nest. It is placed on top of trampled reeds, constructed of reeds and rushes and sometimes floats. No down is present though "a little down" has been recorded. Breeds throughout the year, with peaks in November-December, starting a little earlier in the Transvaal. Eggs 4—12, pale bluish white when fresh, rough, pitted and very large for the size of bird. Average (65) 67,7 × 50,3 (63,7—72,8 × 45,8—52,7). Incubation 25—27 days.

104   White-backed Duck   Witrug-eend

Thalassornis leuconotus Eyton, 1838: *South Africa = Verlorenvlei, Piquetberg, C.P.*

PLATE 9 (OPP. P. 65).
Length 43 cm (wing ♂ 163—170, ♀ 160; tail ♂ 43—52, ♀ 44; tarsus 34—37,5, ♀ 35; culmen ♂ 36,5—39 ♀ 37; 4 specimens, 3 ♂, one ♀). Iris dark brown; bill blue and slate; lower mandible yellow; legs dark brown.

Identification: This rounded-backed, low-sitting duck is easily distinguished by the light spot at base of bill. Sexes alike. In flight shows no speculum; the white line down back is conspicuous and separates it easily from the other swift, low-flying, diving duck, No. 103. Duckling dark brown above, buff below, more russet on neck.
Distribution: South Africa, northwards to Ethiopia and Malagasy.
Habits: Uncommon, resident on open sheets of water in pairs or family parties only. Subject to local movements. Sparsely distributed, retiring, keeping like the previous species, to reeds and vegetation for cover. Difficult to put up and when taking to flight needs a run along the water. A capable diving bird, somewhat like a Grebe in habits and appearance.

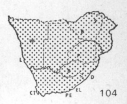

Food: A mixture of Paspalidium and Nymphaea seeds.
Voice: Described as a soft musical chuckle or weak whistle "curwee-curwee".
Breeding: What has been recorded for the preceding species may be repeated for this bird. Recorded all months. Eggs 6—10, rarely 14, yellow ochre or yellow-brown in colour and *smooth*. Average (42) 61,6 × 48,5 (55,0—66 × 44,9—51).

LOCAL RACE:
T.l. leuconotus Eyton, 1838: *South Africa = Verlorenvlei, Piquetberg, C.P.* Larger than and not so brightly coloured as the other race from Malagasy.

Family SAGITTARIIDAE

Only one species and genus is found in this family, characterized by its terrestrial habits, in adaptation to which it has long legs and short toes; it has the usual Eagle type of bill and a long crest of feathers, the middle ones projecting from the back of the head and reminding people of a hundred years ago of the quill pens inserted over the ear by secretaries or scribes of the era, whence the name. The tail feathers are also long, the longest projecting straight out gracefully, which, together with its stately walk and conspicuousness, constitute a great attraction to those who are interested in nature in the wilds. It is peculiar to the savanna veld of Africa south of the Sahara Desert, and subsists upon small animals, particularly snakes, which it discovers by striding over the veld. Although terrestrial in habits, it is a strong flier and still nests on the tops of low trees.

105 Secretary Bird   Sekretarisvoël

Sagittarius serpentarius   (Miller), 1779: *Cape of Good Hope.*
Native Names: Ingxangxosi (X); i-Ntungonono (Z); Mamalangoane, Lekheloha,
Kotochi-peli (S); Mokolokute, Same, Thlame (T); Wata (Sh).
PLATE 10 (OPP. P. 72), PLATE 11.
Length about 125—150 cm (wing ♂ 630—670, ♀ 610—660; tail ♂ 670—854, ♀ 570—705;
tarsus 295—320 (2); culmen 45—54, 10 specimens, 5 ♂, 5 ♀). Iris hazel, grey in young;
bill bluish white; cere greenish yellow; bare face orange; legs flesh.

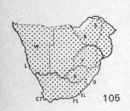

105

Identification: Adults unmistakable, sexes alike, males slightly larger. Young
birds duller with face coloured as the cere.
Distribution: Africa south of the Sahara except mountainous and forested
regions.
Habits: Widely but locally dispersed over the savanna and open veld of the
continent. Usually seen striding majestically over the veld, either alone or with
its mate not far off. When pursued relies on its running powers, perhaps with
wings half spread. If hard pressed takes off and flies strongly. After landing,
runs for some distance with wings open. Snakes are attacked with violent
blows from the feet while the wings are held outspread as a shield. Great care
is taken to make certain the snake is dead before it is swallowed, whole if
small. Roosts in the nest at night even when not breeding.
Food: Insects including termites, wasps and their larvae, snakes, lizards,
tortoises, young birds and any small animals it can kill.
Voice: A deep frog-like croak and a high-pitch note uttered on the wing.
Breeding: The nest is a large platform of sticks placed just below the top of a
small, often isolated, tree or bush and is difficult to see. Thorn trees are
favoured in the north of our area. Height 2—6 metres. Eggs, usually 2 but quite
often 3, are laid in spring (Cape) or summer (Transvaal and Rhodesia) as late
as March, white, sometimes blood-stained. Average (100) 77,0 × 56,3
(72—87 × 51,2—62,5, one 92 × 59). Incubation by both sexes, female far
more than male, 42—46 days (3). Nestling period 83—100 days (4) in South
Africa.

Family AEGYPIIDAE

Vultures are well known as scavenging birds of prey, mostly of large size and
with the head more or less bare of feathers. Their claws are not adapted to
holding their prey as in most birds of prey, as they subsist upon the carcasses
of animals for the greater part; but the bill is powerful and suited to
rending the skin and flesh from the carcasses. Most of the species soar at great
heights to search for dead animals, and when these are discovered they float
down towards them in such a way that others on similar bent observe them
from afar and make for the same spot. They have wonderful eyesight, and
when once a Vulture has discovered a carcass, many more gather to the spot.
To devour the animal the stomach is torn open and the head inserted inside to
get at the softer parts, the rest of the body being soon consumed when the host
of others arrive. The large species lay only one egg, but the smaller Egyptian
Vulture lays two. Nests are made of sticks in trees, or merely on the bare
ground on ledges or precipices.

106 Cape Vulture

Krans-aasvoël

Gyps coprotheres (Forster), 1798: *South Africa*.

Native Names: Rantsoe, Semanana, le-Nong, le-Noayane, le-Tlaka (S); i-Xadanga, i-Hlanga (X); Inqe (Z).

PLATE 10 (OPP. P. 72), PLATE 11.
Length 105—115 cm. (wing 650—683—702; tail 300—345; tarsus 90—105; culmen 51—60. 7 specimens). Iris reddish brown; bill horn; cere, bare skin of face and neck, legs blue.

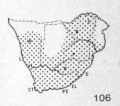

106

Identification: Adults very pale, almost white, paler than any other vulture of similar size. Young birds are browner and streaked below and the ruff consists of lanceolate *feathers*, not down. Young resemble young of White-backed Vulture No. 107 but are larger and paler about the shoulders.

Distribution: General north to Damaraland and south-western Rhodesia. Absent from central Kalahari.

Habits: The commonest vulture in South Africa, though not in such numbers as formerly. This is due, partly to carcasses of domestic animals (which have displaced the game) being buried, and partly on account of their attacking sheep and having been poisoned off in retaliation. Also electrocution on power lines and drowning in cement reservoirs. Still occurs in fair numbers in and near mountain fastnesses of the south and east. Has been known to attack sheep but this is a rare occurrence and the sheep are often sick. At a carcass the birds fight by bounding at each other with great hops, wings held outspread.

Food: Carrion, offal, and small bones.

Voice: A dry grating cry while feeding.

Breeding: Nests in communities on ledges of precipices, often inaccessible but usually visible from miles away due to the sheets of white droppings on the rocks below the nests. The nest may be an elaborate structure lined with vegetable matter but the eggs may also be laid on the bare ledges. Breeding colonies may be destroyed by blizzards. May to November in all areas. Eggs, one pure white, rarely with red markings. Average (50) 90,8 × 68,8 (83,2—98 × 63,2—72,5). Incubation 53 days by both sexes. Nestling 150 days.

107 White-backed Vulture

Witrug-aasvoël

Gyps africanus Salvadori, 1865: *Sennar Sudan*

Native Name: le-Aka (S).

PLATE 10 (OPP. P. 72), AD. AND IMM. PLATE 11 AD. AND IMM.
Length 90—98 cm (wing 585—620—640; tail 250—261—275; tarsus 86—94—101; culmen 46—48—50. 10 specimens). Iris dark brown; bare skin of head dark grey; bill blackish, culmen horn; legs black.

Identification: Adults distinguishable by white backs and darker upper wing-coverts than Cape Vulture No. 106. Female much paler than male. Young lack white back and have white down on neck; also have almost no contrast

79

between upper wing coverts and flight feathers whereas young Cape Vulture has coverts paler than flights. In flight, from below, adults show white coverts; young show uniform dark wings, with light streaks on coverts. Young birds breed while still in dark plumage.

Distribution: From Zululand, Transvaal and the Kalahari northwards through East Africa to Ethiopia and west to Senegal.

Habits: The common vulture of the tropical savanna bushveld. Gathers in numbers at carcasses, the birds struggling and fighting to get at the meat. The eyes and mouth are attacked first, then flesh is extracted through holes torn in the skin by the bird inserting its whole head and neck.

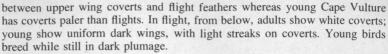

107 **Food:** Carrion and offal.

Voice: Squeals and hisses when fighting.

Breeding: Nests in trees, mainly *Acacias,* in scattered communities, usually only one or two nests to a tree. Lays in winter, May and June. Eggs, 1 pure white with blotches of red, or plain. Average (23) 89,2 × 67,2 (84,3—96 × 63,2—74,5). Incubation by both sexes, 56—58 days. Nestling period 4½ months.

108   Lappet-faced Vulture   Swart Aasvoël

Torgos tracheliotus   (Forster), 1791: *Cape Colony.*

Native Names: Isilwangangubo (X); le-Tlakapipi (S).

PLATE 10 (OPP. P. 72), PLATE 11.
Length 98—105 cm (wing 715—733—755; tail 340—380; tarsus 125—135; culmen 68—71, 6 specimens). Iris dark brown; bill greenish brown, tip yellow; cere blue; bare head livid red; legs bluish.

Identification: Huge size and dark, lanceolate feathers on breast overlying white down are characteristic. Sexes alike, females larger. Young birds similar but with some white down on head. In flight, if size not apparent, very like Hooded Vulture, which, however, shows grey flight feathers and dark brown coverts from below, whereas this species is uniform dark brown. Wingspan over 2,7 metres.

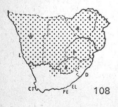

Distribution: General but now rare in Cape Province and unknown in the south-west Cape to-day. The commonest vulture in southern South West Africa. From our area north to Cairo and West Africa.

Habits: A less sociable species than the other large vultures, more than two or three seldom seen at a carcass among scores of others. Held in awe by the

108 common species, hence the old name "King Vulture", usually driving off the others until it has had its fill and then standing aloof. Does not feed quite as grossly as the commoner types.

Food: Carrion, mainly skin.

Voice: A sharp yelp.

Breeding: In winter (May to July) builds a large nest about 2 metres across, of sticks, in a tree, well away from the communities of other species. Placed on top of flat trees as a rule about 6 metres up. Egg, 1 white, often marked quite heavily with reddish brown and underlying lilac. Average (32) 92,1 × 68,5 (83—94,7 × 65,5—72,8). Nestling 120±days.

109 White-headed Vulture   Witkop-aasvoël

Trigonoceps occipitalis (Burchell), 1824: *Makkwari River, near Kuruman.*

PLATE 10 (OPP. P. 72), PLATE 11.
Length 78—82 cm (wing 610—626—643; tail 265—295; tarsus 95—110; culmen 48—54. 8 specimens). Iris umber-brown; bill and bare skin of head red; cere bluish, legs pale flesh.

Identification: The white head, red bill and white secondaries make the adult unmistakable. Flight pattern very distinctive, see Plate 11. Sexes alike, male slightly smaller. The young rather resembles the young White-backed Vulture, No. 107, but is darker, unstreaked, with head brown and bill red.

Distribution: The savanna bushveld from Orange River on the west and Zululand on the east, northwards to the Sudan and across to West Africa.

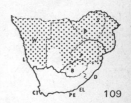

Habits: This striking and, for a vulture, almost beautiful bird is not uncommon in the tropical savanna, coming to carcasses together with other vultures in fair numbers. Otherwise seen singly or in pairs and in flight and habits rather eagle-like, even recorded as killing fair-sized prey on its own.

Food: Carrion and occasionally live birds and mammals.

Voice: A shrill chittering.

109

Breeding: Breeds normally in trees but in Kenya sometimes on cliffs. Nest very large, solitary. Eggs, laid in July and August, one only, white plain or marked with underlying slate and overlying light brown. Average (22) 85 × 64 (82,5 × 100 × 59,5—67). Incubation 43 days. Nestling about 4 months.

110 Hooded Vulture   Monnik-aasvoël

Necrosyrtes monachus (Temminck), 1823: *Senegal.*

Native Name: Khonyaito (S).

PLATE 10 (OPP. P. 72), AD. AND IMM. N.B. The *upper* figure is the adult. PLATE 11.
Length 65—75 cm (wing 510—522—542; tail 235—262—285; tarsus 78—83—90; culmen 29,5—31—33,5. 15 specimens). Iris dark brown; bill greenish black, brown tip; legs bluish flesh; bare skin of face pinkish to purplish.

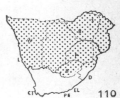

Identification: The down on the neck is whitish in adults and brown in young birds. The latter might be confused with young Egyptian or Palm-nut Vultures but both these have *feathers,* not down, on head and neck.

Distribution: From the Orange River and Transvaal northwards to the Sudan and across to Senegal.

Habits: With its slender beak this vulture is more of an offal eater than the larger species. Frequently haunts native villages where it is not molested. At a carcass tends to hang around the outside and sneak what pieces it can from the bigger birds. Frequently perches inside the bigger trees instead of on top. It also soars less than the large vultures but notices their flight and follows them to the feast. Prefers to loiter round villages and slaughter-houses.

110

Food: Carrion, offal, excrement, termites, locusts and small reptiles.

Voice: Female recorded as going "fee-oo, fee-oo".

Breeding: The nest is built in trees, on branches close to the trunk instead of on top of the tree. Occasionally on cliffs. One nest per tree. Eggs: one, white, sometimes plain, usually blotched with rusty-brown at the larger end. Shell rough. Few in collections. Recorded August in Rhodesia. Average (100, both races) 71,9 × 54,9 (66,4—82,1 × 50—59,1). The eggs of East and West African birds appear to be similar in size although birds from West Africa are shorter-winged. Incubation 46—51 days. Nestling 3—4 months.

LOCAL RACE:
N.m. pileatus (Burchell), 1824: *Hopetown District, C.P.* The nominate race occurs in West Africa and has wing less than 500.

111 Egyptian Vulture   Egiptiese Aasvoël

Neophron percnopterus   (Linnaeus), 1758: *Egypt.*

Native Names: Inkqo (X); Tlakatsoana (S).

PLATE 10 (OPP. P. 72), AD. AND IMM. PLATE 11 AD. AND IMM.

Length 64—71 cm (wing 460—520; tail 220—260; tarsus 75—88; culmen 31—34. 14 specimens Europe). Iris orange-brown in young; bill dark horn, tip black; cere, bare skin of face yellow, blue grey in young; legs grey to yellowish.

Identification: Sexes alike. The young resemble young Hooded Vultures, No. 110, but have feathered necks. Also resemble young Palm-nut Vultures, No. 112, but have slender, less aquiline bills. In flight adults and young show pointed tails. See Plate 11.

Distribution: Southern Europe, India and Africa. Now very rare in our area; recent sight records required.

Habits: Nowhere common in our area but once nested in the Cape Province. A scavenger, haunting native villages, slaughter yards, refuse dumps and even the foreshore, rather like the Hooded Vulture. Usually single or in pairs.

Food: Carrion, offal, excrement, dates, palm-nut husks and any small animals they can catch. Breaks ostrich eggs by dropping stones on them.

Voice: A whining mew (India).

Breeding: Nest on cliffs, sometimes on trees or palms. Nest of sticks lined with hair, wool, rags, dung, etc. Eggs, creamy or dirty white, richly blotched and mottled with reddish brown. Clutch normally two. Average (100) 66,2 × 50 (58,2—76.4 × 43—56,1 Europe). Three South African eggs measure 66,9 × 54,6, 68,6 × 54,5 and 67,1 × 52,2. Incubation by both sexes, begins with first egg, about 42 days (Europe).

LOCAL RACE:
N.p. percnopterus (Linnaeus), 1758: *Egypt.* Africa and Europe. Another race occurs in India.

112 Palm-nut Vulture   Wit Aasvoël

Gypohierax angolensis   (Gmelin), 1788: *Luanda, Angola.*

PLATE 10 (OPP. P. 72). PLATE 11.

Length about 60 cm (wing 397—445; tail 188—210; tarsus 75—85; culmen 40—45. 15 specimens ex Bannerman). Iris golden yellow; bill whitish horn; cere greenish; skin round eye orange, pale yellow in young; legs pinkish yellow.

Identification: Might be mistaken for Egyptian Vulture No. 111 but has more aquiline beak, black on tail and back. Young resembles young Egyptian Vulture but is less whitish on back and has no ruff, distinguished from Hooded Vulture No. 110 by having neck and head *feathered* not down-covered. In flight shows black secondaries, Egyptian Vulture shows white. Tail shape and colour also different, see Plate 11.

Distribution: Tropical Africa southwards to Ngamiland and Zululand. Odd birds recorded in Orange Free State, Transvaal and Eastern Cape Province. None yet from Rhodesia.

112

Habits: A peculiar bird which has commonly been placed with the eagles. From its bare face, vulturine habits and internal anatomy it is better placed among the vultures. Most commonly found where oil-palms grow. Usually seen circling overhead, sitting on trees or walking along the shores of rivers and lakes. Very inquisitive.

Food: Very varied. Largely the husks of the oil-palm *(Elaeis guineensis)* and the raffia palm *(Raphia vinifera)*. In addition fish, carrion, lizards, crabs and crayfish.

Voice: A bark followed by a prolonged guttural growl. Also a cawing "kwa-kwa-kwa" when two birds maintain contact.

Breeding: A large nest is built by both sexes, in a high tree (at 10 to 60 metres) during the early summer months. It is lined with leaves, grass and dung. Eggs: one only is laid, white usually heavily marked with chocolate and purple. Average (12) 70,7 × 54 (67—78,3 × 52—57). The female only appears to feed the young, mainly with palm husks. Incubation 44 days. Nestling period approximately 47 days, and the young is fed for about a month after leaving the nest.

Family FALCONIDAE

An artificial group of diurnal birds of prey, comprising the Falcons and Kestrels, characterized by the notched condition of the cutting edge of the maxilla behind the hooked, down-curved tip, with a projection behind the notch commonly spoken of as the "tooth". The group is cosmopolitan, with many species and much difference in their habits. The true Falcons "stoop" at their prey, while the Kestrels "hover" over and drop on it; but there are others which neither stoop nor hover, and opinions have been divided upon the generic status of the species. Nests are made on ledges of precipices, in holes in rocks, banks or old trees, broad forks of large trees and even amongst the thinner branches: in one instance the nests of Social Weavers are used. Clutches vary from two to six eggs, which are always white or yellowish in ground-colour, to a great or lesser extent marked with red, except in *Poliohierax*, in which the egg is pure white. They usually occur in pairs, or together with their young, but some species of Kestrels and small Falcons become highly gregarious during the period of migration and in—to them—foreign countries.

113   Peregrine   Slegvalk

Falco peregrinus   Tunstall, 1771: *Great Britain*

Native Names: Phaloe (S); Ukhetshe (X).

PLATE 13 (OPP. P. 73) AD. A AND B IMM. PLATE 17.
Length 34—38 cm. (wing ♂ 265—311; tail 127—150; tarsus 17—23; culmen 35—43; wing ♀ 297—318; tail 148—160; tarsus 21—23; culmen 39—42. 12 specimens 6 ♂, 6 ♀). Iris dark brown; bill blue-grey; cere and legs yellow.

Identification: The birds figured in Plate 13 are of races *(a)* and *(b)*. Distinguishable from the Lanner No. 114 by the blackish crown and heavier barring below. Young birds streaked below. Sexes alike, female larger.

113

Distribution: Almost world-wide in suitable localities.
Habits: Not a common bird in our area, usually found in mountains or hilly country. May also enter large towns to prey on pigeons. The boldest and most dashing of the falcons, killing by swooping down in a curve from above (stooping) and striking the victim with the claws without stopping, the hind claw severing the victim's head from the body. Sometimes holds onto the prey in the air, known as "binding" to it. The stoop is very spectacular, the bird descending at terrific speed with wings almost folded. After striking the prey, "throws up" in a steep climb and either stoops again, if unsuccessful, or descends to its kill.
Food: Mainly birds, particularly pigeons and doves.
Voice: A shrill, chattering "kek-kek-kek-kek-kek" and a hoarser "kwaahk-kwaahk-kwaahk". Also a plaintive drawn-out "weeeeee" as recognition note.
Breeding: Nests normally on cliffs, sometimes inaccessibly but also on low kopjes if nothing better available. Also in old nests of other birds in trees. Nest on cliff very slight, a mere scrape. Eggs, normally 3, white, heavily marked with reddish, are laid from July to October. Average (12) 50,6 × 40,2 (47,9—52,6 × 38—41,2). Incubation 28—29. Nestling 35—42.

LOCAL RACES:
(a) F.p. minor Bonaparte, 1850: *Cape of Good Hope*. Smaller and darker below than race *(c)*, often with some rufous on nape. The resident race in Africa south of the Sahara and Sudan. Size given above.
(b) F.p. calidus Latham, 1790: *India*. Described as having a narrower moustache stripe and a larger white cheek patch. Size the same. This race has been recorded from South Africa and Angola.
(c) F.p. peregrinus Tunstall, 1771: *Great Britain*. This race, resident in Europe and Asia, visits Southern Africa as a migrant during the summer months, leaving again in April. It is larger and has no rufous on the nape. Paler below. (Wing ♂ 295—322, ♀ 344—370; tail 130—158; tarsus 34—50; culmen ♂ 18—22, ♀ 22—26. 31 specimens ex Handbk. Brit. Birds).

114 Lanner   Edelvalk

Falco biarmicus   Temminck, 1825: *Peddie District, Cape Province.*

Native Names: Ukhetshe (X); u-Geja P); Phakoe, Pekoa (S).

PLATE 13 (OPP. P. 73) AD. A AND B IMM. PLATE 17.
Length 40—45 cm (♂ wing 308—317—332; tail 160—178; tarsus 46—55; culmen 18—20; ♀ wing 340—350—360; tail 185—210; tarsus 45—53; culmen 20—23. 16 specimens, 9 ♂, 7 ♀). Iris brown; bill horn, blue tip; cere, skin round eye and legs, yellow.

Identification: Rufous crown distinctive at all ages. Young birds browner above, broadly and heavily streaked below. Adults have only a few narrow pear-shaped marks on flanks. In flight appears longer in body and broader-winged than Peregrine. Sexes alike, female much larger and pinker.
Distribution: Africa, Italy and Greece eastwards to Mesopotamia.
Habits: Fairly common in rather drier mountainous or open country; less dependent on cliffs than Peregrine. A true falcon, stooping at its prey, but not quite as dashing as the Peregrine and takes prey from the ground more often. Also trained for falconry. Recorded as using trains to flush its prey. Follows quail hunts and whips injured birds away. May come into small towns.

114

Food: Birds, especially Rock Pigeons No. 311, doves, waders, ducks, francolins and finches. Queleas in particular. Also reptiles and insects. Very fond of locusts.

Voice: A loud metallic "chack-chack-chack". A piercing scream and a plaintive "kweeep" recognition note. Subdued "kekking" near nest.

Breeding: Nest placed on ledge of a cliff, often easily accessible, sometimes in old crow or vulture nests. Eggs, 3 to 4. White, almost covered with blotches of brick red, yellowish and purplish brown; beautiful objects. Average (23) 52,3 × 40,7 (49—55 × 38,5—42,9). Incubation by both sexes.

LOCAL RACE:
F.b. biarmicus Temminck, 1825: *Peddie Dist., C.P.* From our area north to Kenya. Replaced by other races in Northern Africa.

115 Hobby   Europese Boomvalk

Falco subbuteo   Linnaeus, 1758: *Sweden.*

PLATE 13 (OPP. P. 73) ♂ AND ♀. PLATE 17.
Length 30—35 cm (♂ wing 247—272; tail 130—140; tarsus 34—37; culmen 12,5—14. 12 specimens: ♀ wing 265—280. Ex Handbk. Brit. Birds). Iris dark brown; bill blue-grey; cere yellow, grey in young; legs yellow.

Identification: Very similar to next species but has chestnut restricted to thighs and under tail-coverts. Young birds are darker above, the feathers edged with buff. In flight wings appear very long, almost swift-like.

Distribution: A non-breeding migrant from Europe recorded occasionally throughout our area, except the south-west Cape.

Habits: Sometimes seen in company with migratory kestrels. Extremely fast and agile in the air, even able to catch swifts and bats.

Food: In this country mainly insects, particularly flying ants which are caught in the feet and eaten on the wing. Also beetles, small birds and bats. Often seen to take swallows settling in a roost.

Voice: A clear "kew-kew-kew-kew" or "wer-wer-wee-wee-wee" in Europe.

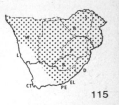

115

LOCAL RACE:
The nominate race, *F.s. subbuteo*, Linnaeus, 1758: *Sweden.* Visits Africa.

116 African Hobby   Afrikaanse Boomvalk

Falco cuvieri   A. Smith, 1830: *Kei River, Cape Province.*

PLATE 13 (OPP. P. 73). PLATE 17.
Length 28—30 cm (♂ wing 208—243; ♀ wing 230—254; tail 108—125; tarsus 30—35; culmen 12—14. 14 specimens). Iris dark brown; bill bluish horn; cere and legs yellow.

Identification: Chestnut below from chest to under tail-coverts, thus differing from the Hobby, No. 115. Some birds, probably fully adult, only faintly streaked on flanks. Young broadly streaked as in Plate 13 but may breed in this plumage.

Distribution: Eastern Cape Province northwards to Ethiopia and across to Ghana.

Habits: A rare bird of which very little has been recorded and certainly more restricted than indicated by the distribution map. Probably migratory to some

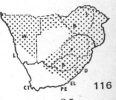

116

85

FALCONS

extent. In Kenya is reported to frequent the outskirts of forests. Very fast and dashing.
Food: Recorded as small birds, cicadas, grasshoppers, termites.
Voice: ''A shrill cry of three or four notes kik, kik, kik, not unlike mewing of a seagull but shriller and uttered more quickly.'' Calls on the wing.
Breeding: Utilizes the old nests of larger birds of prey. Usually high up, 70 feet or so. Relines the nest with smaller sticks and a little grass. Eggs: normally 3, cream, almost entirely obscured by red-brown mottling with darker cap at broad end. Average (11) 39,2 × 31,5 (36—40,8 × 29,0—33,2).

116X   Teita Falcon

Falco fasciinucha   Reichenow and Neumann, 1895: *Teita, Kenya Colony.*
PLATE 13 (OPP. P. 73). PLATE 17.
Length about 28 cm (wing 202—237; tail about 80). Iris brown; bill horn-blue; cere and legs yellow.

Identification: In colour very similar to the African Hobby No. 116 but with a chestnut mark on the nape and *back* of the black crown, rather like the Lanner No. 114. Note black under eye. The tail is short, folded wings extend beyond tail, and the bird appears thicker set than the African Hobby.
Distribution: A rare East African species recorded from the gorges of the Zambesi and near Livingstone; Lake Kariba, Mozambique and eastern highlands of Rhodesia.
Habits: A powerful and very swift flier. Associated with cliffs.
Food: Birds as large as pigeons.
Voice: A high-pitched scream; also ''kek, kek, kek.''
Breeding: August and September in Rhodesia. The nest is situated in a cave on a cliff. Eggs, 3—4, pale yellowish buff with small spots or blotches of yellowish brown. 42—45,2 × 34,1—34,7.

116Y   Sooty Falcon

Falco concolor   Temminck, 1825: *Barakan Island, Red Sea.*
PLATE 13 (OPP. P. 73) AD. AND IMM. PLATE 17.
Length about 31 cm (wing 276; tail 128—134. 2 specimens). Iris dark brown; bill yellow-green base, black tip; legs orange-yellow, cere and bare skin around eye straw-coloured.

Identification: Adult slate-grey above and below, with dark primaries. Wings extend beyond tail. Juvenile can be confused with No. 115 but upper parts light grey, feathers fringed fulvous; underparts pale fulvous streaked with grey not black.
Distribution: Egypt down eastern Africa, apparently wintering on Malagasy from November to April. Recently identified from five specimens in Natal; Tongaat, Durban, Umzimkulu and Umvoti.
Habits: Crepuscular and thus easily overlooked. Feeding on bats and insects, it sallies out at dusk. Apparently not very afraid of man.

117 Red-necked Falcon

Rooinek-valkie

Falco chicquera Daudin, 1800; *Bengal.*

PLATE 13 (OPP. P. 73) AD. AND IMM. PLATE 17.
Length 30—36 cm (♂ wing 203—227; ♀ 230—240; tail 134—165; tarsus 38—40; culmen 13,5—15,5). Iris dark brown; bill, base yellow; tip blue; cere and legs yellow.

Identification: Finely barred back, rufous nape and crown distinguish adult. Young bird is browner above, has broad black streaks on nape and broken bars on breast and flanks—see Plate 13, left = immature bird. Can breed in this dress. Sexes alike, female larger. In flight the broad black sub-terminal tail-band is conspicuous.

Distribution: From Transvaal, South West Africa, and the Kalahari to Gambia and the Sudan. Also occurs in India.

Habits: An African savanna veld falcon whose distribution seems to be largely governed by the existence of the Borassus Palm. In the extreme south the species is usually found along dry river beds with large trees from which it sallies forth after its prey with an extremely swift dashing flight.

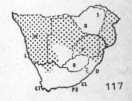

117

Food: Small birds up to the size of a dove, rats, lizards, grasshoppers, locusts and termites.

Voice: A shrill "kek-kek-kek" usually uttered towards dusk.

Breeding: The nest is built between the leaf bases of the Borassus Palm or else an old nest of some other species such as a crow or kite is used. Recorded as having young in October in Transvaal. Eggs, normally 4, described as pure white or yellowish heavily marked with reddish brown. Measurements (19) 41,8 × 31,9 (40,2—45,0 × 31,5—34,5). Incubation 32—34 days, fledgling 37.

LOCAL RACE:
(a) *F.c. horsbrughi* Gunning and Roberts, 1911: *Pretoria, Transvaal.* Measurements given above. Larger, and paler above than the race *b*. The dry west south to Kenhardt.
(b) *F.c. ruficollis* Swainson, 1837: *Senegal.* Central Africa south to Mozambique.

118 = 117 Imm.

119 Eastern Red-footed Kestrel

Oostelike Rooipoot-valkie

Falco amurensis Radde, 1863: *Amur River, Siberia.*

PLATE 13 (OPP. P. 73) ♀ AND ♂ AND IMM. PLATE 17 ♂ AND ♀.
Dimensions and soft parts as in No. 120.

Identification: White under wing-coverts distinguish male from the next species. Female more heavily streaked below than in No. 120. Young bird has blackish crown.

Distribution: Another migrant from Manchuria and Siberia, which comes as far south as the Transkei on the east and northern South West Africa on the west where it is rare. Once at Grahamstown.

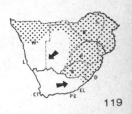

Habits: Also forms large flocks with other species and feeds very largely on the wing, looking very much like large swifts. Food is captured in the claws.

Food: Termites, insects and small mammals.

Voice: As for the next species.

119

120 Western Red-footed Kestrel
Westelike Rooipoot-valkie

Falco vespertinus Linnaeus, 1766: *Province of Petrograd.*

PLATE 13 (OPP. P. 73) ♂ AND ♀ AND IMM. PLATE 17 ♂ AND ♀
Length 28—30 cm (♂ wing 230—260; ♀ 230—253; tail 120—130; tarsus 28—30; culmen 12—13,5. 12 specimens. Ex Handbk. Brit. Birds). Iris dark brown; bill orange; tip bluish; legs orange.

Identification: Male very similar to the previous species but has dark under wing-coverts. Female quite different from that of preceding species. Young bird resembles female and has crown buff, not black as in young of No. 119, thus resembling young Hobby but paler and more closely barred below.

Distribution: A migrant from Europe where it breeds, occurring as far south as the Eastern Cape Province. Also common in northern South West Africa. Arrives in November and leaves the southern part of the area in late March. Not as common as No. 119 or 125.

Habits: Usually seen in flocks often consorting with Lesser Kestrels, No. 125, and other small hawks. Undoubtedly a very useful bird and therefore protected by sentiment and law in South Africa. Flight more falcon-like than most kestrels and does not hover so much.

Food: Insects, termites and small mammals.

Voice: "Ki-ki-ki-ki-ki", slower and more mournful than Rock Kestrel.

121 Dickinson's Kestrel
Dickinsonse Valk

Falco dickinsoni P. L. Sclater, 1864: *Chibasa, Shiré River, Nyasaland.*

PLATE 13 (OPP. P. 73). PLATE 17.
Length 28—30 cm (wing 210—236; tail 130—150; tarsus 35—38; culmen 16—17. 8 specimens, 4 ♀, 4 ♂). Iris brown; bill slate; cere and legs yellow.

Identification: The whitish head and generally greyish plumage are distinctive. Note pale grey rump and barred tail. Sexes alike. Young browner, particularly below.

Distribution: From the eastern Transvaal north to Tanzania and across to Angola and Etosha Pan, S.W.A. Quite common locally below 1 200 metres in Rhodesia.

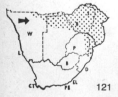

121

Habits: Nowhere common and mainly found where there are tall palms in which it roosts and nests. Usually seen perched on the twigs of dead trees, standing in open ground, whence it sallies forth after its prey. Sits very upright when at rest. Is strongly attracted by veld fires.

Food: Mainly large insects, locusts, lizards, frogs, crabs and small birds.

Voice: A curious call "Lill-loo" recorded.

Breeding: Nests in high palms or palm stumps. Also recorded on a bridge and in an old Hamerkop's nest. September to Decmber (3). Eggs, 3, white, heavily marked with reddish. Average (7) 38 × 30,8 (35,3—40,7 × 28,4—32).

121X   Grey Kestrel   Grysvalkie

Falco ardosiaceus   Bonnaterre and Vieillot, 1823: *Senegal.*

PLATE 13 (OPP. P. 73). PLATE 17.
Length 30—33 cm (wing 222—260). Eye brown; bill leaden grey; cere and bare skin round eye, legs and feet yellow.

Identification: Plumage uniform slate grey with dark shaft stripes. Broken light bars on underside of wing and tail feathers, primaries darker. Tail much longer than wings.
Distribution: West Africa to Ethiopia, south to Angola and Zambia. Recorded on the Okavango and Cunene rivers, Northern S.W.A.
Habits: An uncommon species which prefers forested glades or open savanna with patches of forest. Sits for long periods but feeds by hovering with a slow wing beat—often mobbed by small birds.
Breeding: Not recorded from southern part of its range. The species shows considerable individual variation from building an open nest, to hole-nesting or even usurping a Hamerkop's nest.

122   Greater Kestrel   Groot Rooivalk

Falco rupicoloides   A. Smith, 1830: *Groene River, Little Namaqua-*
                                                                        land.

PLATE 13 (OPP. P. 73). PLATE 17.
Length about 36 cm (♂ wing 260—274—283; ♀ wing 272—282—290; tail 148—177; tarsus 40—46; culmen 15—18. 30 specimens, 12 ♂, 18 ♀). Iris yellow to white; bill bluish base yellow; cere and legs yellow.

Identification: Sexes alike, rather similar to female of next species but much paler and more heavily barred above. Also slightly larger. Young birds have flight feathers tipped with buff and flanks streaked.
Distribution: General except the southern coastal strip from Van Rhynsdorp to Humansdorp.
Habits: Prefers rather drier country especially where there are acacia trees dotted about, otherwise open veld. Not an active bird, soaring seldom, usually seen singly or in pairs sitting on the top of trees, poles or other coigns of vantage. Sometimes occurs in fair numbers in the same field. Possibly migratory to some extent. Independent of cliffs.

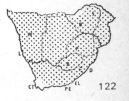

122

Food: Insects, mice, lower vertebrates and occasionally birds.
Breeding: Uses old crow or hawk nests (even those of the Secretary Bird); often on telephone poles, among the branches of trees, or on cliffs where trees are absent, lined with grass, lumps of hair and other rather coarser material. Breeds August to November, sometimes late to February. Eggs, 3 or 4. Dirty white, lightly marked all over with pale brownish and dried blood colour. Paler than Rock Kestrel's. Average (100) 43,3 × 34,5 (40—45,6 × 32—35,4). Incubation 30 and nestling period 30 days.

LOCAL RACE:
F.r. rupicoloides, A. Smith, 1830: *Groene River, Little Namaqualand.* Africa south of the Zambesi, other races in Kenya and Somaliland. Size as above.

123 Rock Kestrel   Rooivalkie

Falco tinnunculus Linnaeus, 1758: *Sweden.*

Native Names: Seotsanyana, se-Hotiana (S); Intambanane, Utebetebana (X); u-Mantebentebans, u-Tebetebana (P); u-Matebeni, u-Mate' beteni (Z); i-Godzi (D).

PLATE 13 (OPP. P. 73) ♂, ♀ AND IMM. PLATE 17.
Length 30—33 cm (♂ wing 217—236—248; ♀ wing 240—247—258; tail 147—164; tarsus 34—37; culmen 13,5—15. 38 specimens, 21 ♂ 17 ♀). Iris dark brown; bill bluish black; cere and legs yellow.

Identification: Males have bluer heads than females and tail is not barred. Very variable in markings, probably due to age; males not becoming fully adult for two or three years. Old females lose barring on tail and back and thus come to resemble males more closely. Young birds have crown rufous, backs strongly barred like females.

Distribution: General.

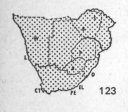

123

Habits: Found anywhere but more common in hilly and mountainous regions. Local in habitat, seldom straying far from its haunts. Also enters towns and nests on buildings. Usually seen in pairs, either sitting on telegraph-poles or other vantage points or hovering motionless looking for its prey. Hovers more than any other hawk, except possibly the Black-shouldered Kite No. 130. Without doubt an extremely valuable bird which should never be molested.

Food: Insects, mice and other small mammals, lizards and very occasionally birds.

Voice: Warning note "kir-r-r-re". Also a plaintive "klee-klee". A shrill "kekking".

Breeding: Usually nests on ledge in a cliff but occasionally in trees on old crow, hawk, or hamerkop nests. Eggs, August to October: the full clutch is 4, the ground colour heavily obscured by deep reddish brown markings all over. Average (100) 39,9 × 33,3 (35—43,3 × 30,3—35.) Incubation by female only, fed by male; period 31 days ±2. Both sexes feed young. Nestling period, 33 or 34 days.

LOCAL RACE:
F.t. rupicolus Daudin, 1800: *Cape of Good Hope:* South Africa north to Angola, Malawi and southern Tanzania. Birds from Rhodesia seem to be somewhat smaller, wings in males less than 225. Formerly considered two species 123 and 124.

125 Lesser Kestrel   Klein Rooivalkie

Falco naumanni Fleischer, 1818: *South Germany.*

PLATE 13 (OPP. P. 73) ♂ AND ♀. PLATE 17 ♂ AND ♀.
Length 28—30 cm (wing 224—246; tail 135—165; tarsus 30—34,5; culmen 12—14. Large series 40 from Africa ex Bannerman). Iris brown; bill blue-grey; cere and legs yellow; claws whitish.

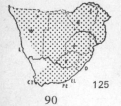

Identification: Male readily distinguished from other kestrels by unspotted back, pale underparts and grey-blue wing-coverts and secondaries. Female resembles female Rock Kestrel but is smaller and less red, tail barred rufous. Young birds resemble the female. White claws diagnostic at all stages.

Distribution: A migrant from Europe and Asia which does not breed here. Particularly common between Caledon and Mossel Bay, in the south-eastern Karoo, Free State and other parts of the Highveld.

125

Habits: Found in our summer months, arriving in late October and departing during the first week in March in the south-west Cape and mid- to late March further north. During the day disperses over the veld, commonly seen perched on any conspicuous post, fence or telegraph-wire. At night roosts in great hosts in large trees. Owing to its usefulness is protected by sentiment and law, consequently in the towns, where often the only large trees are to be found, it becomes quite a nuisance, soiling gardens and pavements with its droppings.
Food: Mainly insects such as locusts.
Voice: A high rattling "kik, kik, kik, kik."

LOCAL RACES:
(a) F.n. naumanni Fleischer, 1818: *South Germany.*
(b) F.n. pekinensis Swinhoe, 1870: *Shishshanling (Ming Tombs), near Peking.* In this race the grey of the wings spreads to the mantle. Size the same as the nominate race quoted above.

126   Pygmy Falcon   Dwergvalkie

Poliohierax semitorquatus (A. Smith), 1836: *Kuruman, Northern Cape.*

PLATE 13 (OPP. P. 73) ♂, ♀ AND IMM.
Length 19,5 cm (♂ wing 110—115—119 (11); ♀ wing 110—116—119 (13); tail 69—74; tarsus 24—28; culmen 10—10,5. 9 specimens, 4 ♂, 5 ♀). Iris light brown; bill yellow, base bluish; cere yellow; legs orange-yellow.

Identification: The female has the maroon mantle. Young birds have feathers of crown, neck and back edged with reddish.
Distribution: The dry west from Orange River northwards to Ovamboland, eastwards to western Transvaal. Sight records from Wankie and the Sabi Valley need confirmation. Also East Africa and Somaliland.
Habits: Usually seen perched on the topmost branches of dead trees, looking almost like a shrike. Flight very fast.
Food: Mainly lizards, snakes, insects and other small animals and birds.

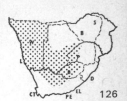

126

Voice: A short call note. Males sing prettily at pairing-time.
Breeding: Lays its eggs during August to October, in the chambers of Social Weavers' nests. Also recorded as using Buffalo Weaver and starling nests. The Weavers fear these little hawks but do not desert and perhaps derive some benefit from the association in defence against snakes, etc. Eggs, white, 2—4 usually to the clutch. Average (8) 28,8 × 22,8 (28—29,5 × 22—23,5). Male feeds the incubating female. Incubation 28—30 days. Nestling about 30 days.

LOCAL RACE:
P.s. semitorquatus (A. Smith), 1836: *Kuruman.* Southern Africa. Another race in Tanzania, Kenya, southern Ethiopia and Somaliland.

127   Cuckoo Falcon   Koekoekvalk

Aviceda cuculoides Swainson, 1837: *West Africa.*

PLATE 13 (OPP. P. 73) AD. AND IMM. PLATE 17.
Length 40 cm (♂ wing 293—305—328; tail 190—208; tarsus 31—38; culmen 18—22. 17 specimens). Iris brown, yellow in young; bill black; cere and legs yellow.

Identification: Gets its name from its similarity in colour to the European Cuckoo. Has double tooth on bill. Barred wings conspicuous in flight. Legs very weak. Young birds are brown above, feathers of wings and tail tipped

91

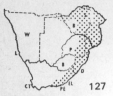

with buff. Tail barred light and dark brown. Below white, spotted with ovals of rufous, eyebrows broadly white.

Distribution: The forests of the south from George eastwards to East and West Africa. Also the denser growths of Acacia and Brachystegia elsewhere. Not recorded from South West Africa.

Habits: Although a forest bird, it ventures into open ground nearby, posting itself on a pole or other coign of vantage whence it can espy the animals below. At rest appears very squat, while in flight it is rather heavy, flapping slowly and then gliding for a space. Thus quite unlike a true falcon and not giving the impression of being fast on the wing. Sometimes soars and circles at considerable height over the forest.

Food: Lizards, particularly chameleons. Also insects.

Breeding: Nests in September and October, constructing a platform of sticks, in the branches of a large tree, with a little grass and hair for lining. Eggs, 2 or 3, white with spots and scrolls of brown to very dark brown, irregularly disposed over the surface. Average (11) 42,1 × 34,8 (41—43 × 33,3—37). Incubation 33 days.

LOCAL RACE:
4.c. verreauxi Lafresnaye, 1846: *Near Durban.* Also occurs in East Africa and Zaïre. The nominate race inhabits West Africa.

Family AQUILIDAE

The Eagles and Hawks comprise the greater number of the diurnal birds of prey. They vary considerably in size, form, colour and habits. An important aid to field-identification is the feathering of the lower half of the leg. In the true Eagles the leg is fully feathered, giving a trousered effect, while the Snake-Eagles as well as the other members of the family, all have the tarsus bare.

128   Black Kite   Swart Wou

Milvus migrans   (Boddaert), 1783: *France.*

PLATE 16 (OPP. P. 112) AD. AND IMM. PLATE 18 AD.
Length about 55 cm (wing ♂ 417—452, ♀ 430—465; tail longest feathers 230—260, middle feathers 20—30 shorter; tarsus 53—60; culmen 24—27. 12 specimens ex Hnbk. Brit. Bds.). Iris dark brown; bill black; cere and legs yellow.

Identification: Has a *black* bill at all stages. The young of the next species has a brown bill. General colour rather darker than the Yellow-billed Kite but whiter about the head. Young paler with brownish head. In flight like the next species, holds the wing bent back at the carpal joint; pattern as in Plate 18.

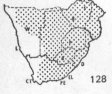

Distribution: Uncommon in our area but penetrates as far south as Natal and northern South West Africa, Transvaal and Orange Free State. Recorded, but rarely south of Orange River. A migrant from Europe where it breeds visiting us in the summer months October to February.

Habits: Similar to those of the next species but gathers in vast flocks which roost in large trees.

Food: Insects, small mammals, carrion, offal and palm-nut husks.

Voice: Alarm note "queeu-kiki-kiki-kik".

LOCAL RACE:
M.m. migrans (Boddaert), 1783: *France.*

129   Yellow-billed Kite   Geelbekwou

Milvus aegyptius   (Gmelin), 1788: *Egypt.*

Native Name: Untldyiyi Untdyila (X).

PLATE 16 (OPP. P. 112) AD. AND IMM. PLATE 18. AD.
Length about 55 cm (wing 408—420—438; tail, outer feathers 240—272, middle feathers 30—46 shorter; tarsus 41—49; culmen 23—27. 14 specimens, 7 ♂, 7 ♀). Iris brown; bill yellow, brown in young; cere and legs yellow.

Identification: Adults recognisable by yellow bill and darker head than Black Kite No. 128. Young have brown bills and are very similar to young Black Kites but are paler below. Young do not have forked tails. In flight adult's tail appears forked when closed but has almost straight trailing edge when open.
Distribution: Throughout our area but commoner in certain localities. Present during the summer months in numbers and a few probably present all the year.
Habits: Quite a common bird, usually seen sailing gracefully overhead or perched on the ground. In flight it appears very short-necked and has the distinctive habit of steering with its tail, twisting it from side to side as it changes direction. In Central Africa a daring thief, snatching food from baskets carried on the heads of natives, but in our area persecution has taught it wariness. Sometimes roosts on the ground.
Food: Rats, shrews, lizards, small birds, frogs, large snails and many insects, especially harvester termites. In the south-west Cape eats great numbers of the destructive mole-rats and should be rigorously protected. Takes chickens in the north but seldom appears to do so in the Cape. Carrion.
Voice: When disturbed near the nest a grating "chew, chi, chi, chi". Also a plaintive, querulous "kleeeuw" ending in a trill.
Breeding: Constructs a platform of sticks during September to December in the Cape, later in Natal, about 7 to 25 metres up in a tree; the nest usually well hidden among the leaves and branches. It is lined with dung, rags, wool, etc. Eggs, 2 or 3, white with light to dark brown markings, massed or circled mainly at the thick end. Average (100) 53,4 × 42,1 (49,5—58,7 × 38,6—46). Incubation by both sexes 38 days. Nestling period about 6 weeks.

LOCAL RACE:
M.a. parasitus (Daudin), 1800: *Middle Sundays River, Cape Province.* Southern Africa, Angola and East Africa. Considered by some as a race of No. 128.

130   Black-shouldered Kite   Blouvalkie

Elanus caeruleus   (Desfontaines), 1789: *near Algiers.*

Native Names: Umdlampuku (X); Matlakokoane, Phakoanetsoana (S); u-Xebel (Y).

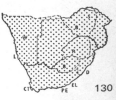

PLATE 16 (OPP. P. 112). AD. AND IMM. PLATE 18.
Length 30 cm (wing 260—267—280; tails 112—130; tarsus 28—34; culmen 15—18. 17 specimens). Iris red to orange; bill black; cere and legs yellow. Weight 235g.

Identification: Young birds have the breast and sides of neck brownish; also white tips to scapulars and flight feathers.
Distribution: Africa, except the north-western areas, India eastwards to the Philippine Islands, Australia and North and South America.

Habits: With the Rock Kestrel No. 123 probably the commonest hawk in our area. Found in more or less open country where there are scattered trees, usually near water. In flight, rather gull-like. Also hovers a great deal and if something is seen, drops down in a characteristic fashion, perhaps checking several times and finally descending with feet extended, onto its prey. It is considered quite harmless, as it never attacks poultry and is consequently protected by sentiment and law. Gathers in quite large numbers (50) to roost.
Food: Mice, insects, lizards, rats, moles, etc. An analysis showed 84% striped mouse, 12% lizards and 4% locusts.
Voice: A "fwee", slightly trilled, uttered by both sexes.
Breeding: Nests in trees 6—60 feet up, during spring in the Cape but at almost any time in Rhodesia. May use old nests of other birds. Eggs, 3 or 4, rarely 5, white, capped at the thick end or covered with broad *streaks* of brown and purplish brown. Average (100) 40,1 × 31,7 (36,8—44,3 × 28,6—32,8; one 46,1 × 34,8). Nestling period 35 days.

LOCAL RACE.
E.c. caeruleus (Desfontaines), 1789: *near Algiers*. Africa eastwards to India and Annam.

131 Bat Hawk   Vlermuisvalk

Macheiramphus alcinus Bonaparte, 1850: *Malacca*.

PLATE 16 (OPP. P. 112). PLATE 18.
Length 45 cm (wing ♂ 324—333—338, ♀ 336—347—360; tail 154—188; tarsus 57—64; culmen 16—17. 9 specimens, 4 ♂, 5 ♀, ex Chapin). Iris yellow; cere bluish grey; bill black; legs bluish white.

Identification: An extraordinary bird with owl-like eyes and the wings of a falcon, see Plate 18. Males are smaller and have a little more white on throat and abdomen than females which are fuscous in these areas, but very variable and not well understood. Young birds resemble adults. Note white eyelids.
Distribution: From Damaraland, Rhodesia, Transvaal, and Natal northwards throughout the tropics of Africa and eastwards to the Far East. Also Malagasy.
Habits: A rare bird but probably commoner than is generally believed. Crepuscular in habits, hiding most of the day in some dense-foliaged tree and emerging at dusk, with dodging, falcon-like flight, in pursuit of its prey which is seized with the feet in full flight and apparently swallowed whole. After an abortive attempt it is said to settle for a time before making another swoop. Also hunts by moonlight. Like owls, wing-beats are silent.

131

Food: Mainly bats but almost as many birds such as swifts, swallows and other birds which haunt rivers at dusk. Also beetles and small reptiles.
Voice: A shrill falcon-like "kwik-kwik-kwik-kwik-kwik."
Breeding: Nests in tall trees constructing a nest of large sticks, lined with smaller twigs and decorated with green leaves, during August to November and January in Rhodesia. Eggs, one, pale bluish-green, some marked with purple cloudings or brown specks mainly at the larger end. Average (6) 60,4 × 45,6 (57,6—64 × 43—48). Nests on *lateral* branches.

LOCAL RACE:
M.a. anderssoni (Gurney), 1865: *Otjimbinque, South West Africa*. Africa south of the Sahara and Malagasy.

132 Honey Buzzard Wespedief

Pernis apivorus (Linnaeus), 1758: *Sweden.*

PLATE 16 (OPP. P. 112). A, B AND C. PLATE 18. A, B AND C.
Length 54—60 cm (wing 375—425; tail 210—260; tarsus 53—60; culmen 21—23. 12 specimens ex Hnbk. Brit. Birds). Iris tawny yellow, brown in young; bill black; cere black above, yellow below; legs yellow.

Identification: The diagnostic feature is that the lores are covered with scale-like feathers, not bare with bristles. Otherwise very variable in colour, one phase quite commonly white below. Similar to Steppe Buzzard No. 154 but head smaller and more slender, making shoulders appear humped; tail longer and more rounded. Legs feathered half-way down the tarsus. In flight holds head high and shows two dark bands near *base* of tail and one at end, see Plate 18.

Distribution: A migrant from the northern hemisphere which occasionally reaches South Africa, as far south as Natal on the east.

Habits: Perches *within* canopy on thick branches near trunk—not in conspicuous position; also on the ground and ant heaps. A sluggish and rather tame bird. Often seen at the forest *edge*.

Food: Wasp-buzzard would be a more suitable name as it eats mainly wasp larvae, pupae and adults. The feathered lores doubtless assist in resisting stings. Also termites, bees, locusts and small reptiles.

132

Voice: A high squeaky "kee-er" and a rapid "kikiki".

133 Black Eagle Witkruis-arend

Aquila verreauxi: Lesson, 1830: *in the interior of the Cape of Good Hope.*

Native Names: le-Lyapela, Ntsu, Ntsu-kobokobo (S); u-Kosi (X and Z).

PLATE 14 (OPP. P. 96). AD. AND IMM. PLATE 12. AD. AND IMM.
Length about 84 cm (♂ wing 578, 583, 595; ♀ wing 590—624—640; tail 315—360; tarsus 105—110; culmen 42—47,5. 9 specimens, 3 ♂, 6 ♀). Iris light brown; bill leaden-horn; cere and legs yellow.

Identification: Adults unmistakable. Young bird is brown above, feathers edged with buff, cheeks and chest black, crown and mantle rich rufous. In flight adults and juveniles show whitish "windows" at base of primaries. Wings characteristically narrow at base, see Plate 12, broadest about two-thirds along length.

Distribution: Throughout our area, northwards through Rhodesia to Kenya and beyond to Israel.

Habits: Fortunately still fairly common in spite of ruthless and unwarranted persecution. A magnificent bird found only in mountainous or hilly country. Particularly graceful in flight, the normal method of hunting being to fly fast along cliffs and ridges, surprising prey by appearing suddenly round corners before it can dive for cover. In display execute tight "loops" after a dive and long vertical climb. Also lock claws and spiral earthwards as in other eagles.

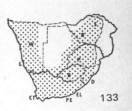

133

Food: Mainly dassies (hyraxes). Also ground birds such as guineafowl, small antelopes and young baboons. Credited with knocking even largish antelopes over precipices and reliably reported to molest leopards.

Breeding: The nest is placed on a ledge of a cliff, sometimes in a tree,

PLATE 14

133. *Aquila verreauxi.* Black Eagle. Witkruis-arend. Ad. and Imm.
134. *Aquila rapax rapax.* Tawny Eagle. Kouvoël. Colour stages A, B and C.
135. *Aquila nipalensis.* Steppe Eagle. Steppe-arend. Ad. and Imm.
136. *Aquila pomarina.* Lesser Spotted Eagle. Klein Gevlekte Arend.
Ad. and Imm.
142. *Polemaetus bellicosus.* Martial Eagle. Breëkop-arend. Adult and Imm.
143. *Stephanoaetus coronatus.* Crowned Eagle. Kroon-arend. Adult and Imm.
149. *Haliaeetus vocifer.* Fish Eagle. Visarend. Ad. and Imm.
151. *Terathopius ecaudatus.* Bateleur. Berghaan. ♂, ♀ and Imm.

133

Imm.

B

A

C

134

142

Imm.

Imm.

135

Imm.

136

149

Imm.

143
Imm

Imm.

151

♂

♀

143

K. B. NEWMAN '75

138

A

B

137

B

A

C

139

B

C

A

Imm

D

141

Imm.

Imm. B

Imm. A

146

140

Imm.

Imm. B

Imm. A

147

Imm.

145

148

Imm.

K. B. NEWMAN '75

PLATE 15

137. *Aquila wahlbergi.* Wahlberg's Eagle. Wahlbergse Arend. A, B and C.
138. *Lophaetus occipitalis.* Long-crested Eagle. Langkuif-arend. A and B.
139. *Hieraaetus pennatus.* Booted Eagle. Dwergarend. A, B, C and Imm.
140. *Hieraaetus dubius.* Ayres' Hawk Eagle. Klein Jagarend. Ad. and Imm.
141. *Hieraaetus spilogaster.* African Hawk Eagle. Afrikaanse Jagarend.
Ad. and Imm.
145. *Circaetus cinereus.* Brown Snake-eagle. Bruin Slangarend.
Ad. and Imm. A and B.
146. *Circaetus pectoralis.* Black-breasted Snake-eagle.
Swartbors-slangarend. Ad., Imm. A and B.
147. *Circaetus fasciolatus.* Southern Banded Snake-eagle.
Suidelike Gebande Slangarend. Ad. and Imm.
148. *Circaetus cinerascens.* Banded Snake-eagle. Gebande Slangarend.
Ad. and Imm.

usually inaccessible without ropes. It is a large structure, used, often with an alternative, year after year. Eggs, 1 or 2, are laid from March to July at intervals of 3 to 4 days; white, plain or blotched with red and purple. Average (30) 76,9 × 58,6 (71,7—83,4 × 56—62). Incubation by both sexes, 44 (3) and 46 (1) days. Usually only one chick survives if two eggs laid, one killing the other. Nestling 95—99 days.

134 Tawny Eagle   Kouvoël

Aquila rapax (Temminck), 1828: *South Africa.*

Native Names: Ntsu, Ntsukobokobo (S); u-Kozi (Z and G); i-Gamo (D).

PLATE 14 (OPP. P. 96). A, B AND C. PLATE 12. AD. AND IMM.
Length 65—72 cm (♂ wing 485—501—513; ♀ wing 525—545—560; tail 245—295; tarsus 73—92; culmen 36—44. 24 specimens, 14 ♂, 10 ♀). Iris yellowish freckled with brown; bill brown, black tip; cere and legs yellow.

Identification: Larger and paler than Wahlberg's Eagle No. 137, with an *oval* nostril and rather short, *rounded* tail (round and square respectively in Wahlberg's). See also under Lesser Spotted Eagle No. 136. The young bird (C) is paler than the adult, almost white below; above without dark centres to feathers. These birds fade to very pale blond, sometimes with darker head. Next stage is darker, mottled and streaked on sides of chest (B). This phase moults to adult (A). Gape ends at middle of eye.

134

Distribution: The Karoo regions northwards throughout our area and all Africa except the heavy forested regions. South-east Europe, Arabia and India. Now rather rare in Cape Province south of the Orange River.
Habits: A common species of the dry bushveld thorn country. Almost entirely absent from moister woodlands where it is replaced by No. 137. Rather a sluggish bird which kills its own prey but is not above resorting to carrion with vultures. Spends a great deal of time sitting on dead trees, often round hunting camps. At other times becomes quite bold and dashing even robbing other birds, or soars high overhead.
Food: Mainly game birds, hares, dassies, small antelope, ground squirrel, mongoose, snakes, chameleons, and small birds. Also carrion.
Voice: Usual note a high, rasping "kah" or "kow, kow".
Breeding: Nests at the very top of trees constructing a large platform of sticks with some straw and leaves for the centre when eggs are laid. The site is frequently changed. Lays in winter, March to July. Eggs, normally two (only one is usually reared) white either plain or with a few slight markings or dried blood-stains. Average (30) 71,5 × 56,3 (68—75,5 × 53—60). Incubation 42—44 days. Fledging 11—12 weeks.

LOCAL RACE:
A.r. rapax (Temminck), 1828: *South Africa.* Southern Africa, Angola and Malawi.

135 Steppe Eagle   Steppe-arend

Aquila nipalensis (Hodgson), 1833: *Valley of Nepal.*

PLATE 14 (OPP. P. 96). AD. AND IMM. PLATE 12. AD. AND IMM.
Length 75 cm (♂ wing 520—540, ♀ 560—600). Iris dark brown; bill black; cere and legs yellow.

Identification: Adults very similar to Tawny Eagle but darker and more uniform. Immature birds have two pale bars on closed wing and a broad white bar on rump (Imm. No. 134 does not). Adults have ginger on nape or crown and some white in upper tail coverts. Bill distinctly weaker than No. 134; gape prominent and extending to *back* of eye. In flight immature shows white trailing edge and band at rear of coverts.

Distribution: A migrant from south-eastern Europe and Asia. Recorded from Damaraland, Botswana, Transvaal, Tarkastad and Natal, particularly where harvester termites are active. Present here from November to February.

Habits: Congregates in flocks which spend a lot of time on the ground pursuing and eating termites. May also be seen in flocks sitting in trees or soaring often at a great height.

Food: Recorded as rats, quelea nestlings and mole-rats but largely termites. Reputed to be more of a scavenger than the last species.

LOCAL RACE:
The race recorded here is A.n. orientalis Cabanis, 1854: *near Sarepta, S.E. Russia.* In spite of its name it is the *western* race occurring in Russia and Turkestan.

136   Lesser Spotted Eagle   Klein Gevlekte Arend

Aquila pomarina   Brehm, 1831: *Pomerania*

PLATE 14 (OPP. P. 96). AD. AND IMM. PLATE 12. AD. AND IMM.
Length 65 cm (♂ wing 460—490; ♀ wing 480—500).

Identification: Another dark brown eagle, the adults difficult to tell in the field from the next and last two species. Has *narrow* ''stove-pipe'' feathering on legs (see Plate). Young birds have pale spots on wing-coverts and a rusty or buffish patch on the nape. Adults have white at base of tail and sometimes white in the upper tail-coverts. Has *round* nostril, *bill and legs weak.* In flight tips of primaries are bent *down.*

Distribution: A migrant from Europe recorded from South West Africa, Botswana, from Rhodesia, southern Mozambique and Zululand.

Habits: Little recorded of its behaviour in Africa, probably more common than previously believed because it is easily confused with other similar Eagles. Gathers in groups with the last species. In Europe frequents open wooded country.

Food: Small fry, frogs, small rodents, and birds; also takes termites.
Voice: Like the shrill yapping of a small dog.

LOCAL RACE:
The nominate form A.p. pomarina Brehm, 1831: *Pomerania, Prussia.* Visits Africa from eastern Europe and Russia.

137   Wahlberg's Eagle   Wahlbergse Arend

Aquila wahlbergi   Sundevall, 1851: *Mohapoani, Witfontein Mountains,*
W. Transvaal

PLATE 15 (OPP. P. 97), A, B, AND C. PLATE 12. TWO PHASES.
Length 55—60 cm (wing ♂ 400—435, ♀ 435—445; tail ♂ 215—230, ♀ 235—250; tarsus ♂ 71—76, ♀ 79—82; culmen ♂ 24—26,5, ♀ 27—29). Iris yellow; bill black; cere and legs yellowish.

Identification: Smaller than Tawny Eagle, with a *round* nostril and *square* tail. Three phases illustrated, of which B is least common. From adult Lesser Spotted Eagles distinguishable by size and more feathered legs. Young birds paler below. Crown of adult pale greyish, short crest present.

99

Distribution: Northern Cape Province, Orange Free State, Transvaal and Zululand, northwards to Angola on the west and Ethiopia on the east, and westwards north of the Congo forests to Ghana.

Habits: A common eagle in the moister thornveld savannas and *Brachystegia* where it is often observed sitting on top of trees. Also forages on the wing and is greatly attracted by veld fires. Soars frequently and to some height. Of rather mild disposition. Migratory in the south.

137

Food: Small rodents, birds, reptiles and large insects. Termites. Sometimes molests chickens.

Voice: A melodious whistle of two notes "pay, pay", also a harsh scream when driven from the nest. A rapidly repeated "kyip-kyip-kyip" used as a greeting call near the nest.

Breeding: Nest is placed in a tree, often in a valley. About 60 cm across when built but becomes larger as it is used over the years. Constructed of twisted sticks with finer twigs in the centre. Breeds September to February, mainly before November. Eggs, one or two, nearly always one in Central Africa. White, nearly plain or thickly clouded or spotted with reddish. Average (100) 61,1 × 48,6 (55—67 × 45,5—51). Incubation by female only, fed by male, 46—48 days (1). Nestling period, 72 days.

138 Long-crested Eagle   Langkuif-arend

Lophaetus occipitalis (Daudin), 1800: *Knysna District, Cape Province.*

Native Names: Isiphunguphungu (X); isi-Pumongati (Z); i-Finye (D).

PLATE 15 (OPP. P. 97), A AND B. PLATE 12. AD.
Length 53—58 cm (wing ♂ 350—376, ♀ 370—408; tail ♂ 192—200, ♀ 205—215; tarsus ♂ 92—97, ♀ 95—100; culmen ♂ 27—28, ♀ 29—30. Large series Bannerman + Roberts). Iris golden, brown in Imm.; bill black; cere greenish yellow; legs yellow.

Identification: Appears almost black and with long crest is unmistakable. Flight pattern distinctive, see Plate 12. Young birds not as dark, with some white feathers on nape, otherwise similar. Note legs dark, white in older birds.

Distribution: From Knysna (now absent) eastwards to Natal and thence to the tropics, Ethiopia and across to Senegal.

Habits: A bird of well-wooded and well-watered country, quite common in suitable areas. Usually observed perched on top of dead trees in forests and never displaying much activity, but sometimes soars, often in the morning, calling shrilly the while. Also found in thick bush away from forest.

138

Food: Largely mice and rats, also frogs, snakes, lizards, small birds, and very rarely, chickens. Wild figs also recorded.

Voice: A very noisy species in the air, uttering a variety of cat-call and shrieking sounds. The most characteristic call is a piercing "quee-er", "wee-ah" or "peerr-wee" (repeated).

Breeding: Nests in trees (possibly also using old nests of other species), 25—70 feet up. Nest small, about 60 cm in diameter. Eggs, 1 or 2, white blotched and streaked with rufous, chocolate or stone-colour and underlying faint lilac. Average (18) 58,6 × 47 (54,0—62,3 × 44,7—49,5).

139 Booted Eagle   Dwergarend

Hieraaetus pennatus (Gmelin), 1788: *Hungary.*

PLATE 15 (OPP. P. 97), A, B, C AND D IMM. PLATE 12. LIGHT AND DARK PHASES.
Length 48—52 cm (wing 350—405; tail 203—230; tarsus 56—61; culmen 21,5—23,5).
Iris yellow, brown in young; bill black; cere and legs yellow.

Identification: Occurs in two colour phases, either whitish or dark brown
below. These are shown on Plate 15. The Pale phase is much the commoner
here. Young birds are one or other phase from the start and stay the same
throughout life. Young pale-phase birds have the chest buff. Dark birds very
like Wahlberg's Eagle No. 137 but feet are heavier and bird smaller. In flight
from below, light birds show a line of black spots on rear edge of under
wing-coverts. Both phases show light "shoulder patches".
Distribution: A migrant from Europe and western Asia, where it breeds,
coming to Southern Africa during the summer months. Common in the drier
areas of the Karoo and Namaqualand, some birds staying over the winter.
November to March in Rhodesia.

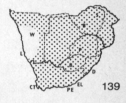

Habits: An extremely bold and rapacious little eagle which kills most of its
prey on the ground, usually swooping out of a tree at great speed.
Food: Small mammals and ground birds. Cannot be trusted with poultry.   139
Voice: A thin, high, descending "keee" and a sharp "bi-bi-bi-bi".
Breeding: Found nesting at Berg River and Swellendam last century.
Recently at Springbok, Nieuwoudtville, Ceres, Glenconnor, near Uitenhage,
Tarkastad and Burghersdorp. The nest is placed on a kranz.
Eggs: Two are normally laid, white, plain or lightly marked with rufous and
measuring about 60 × 47.

140 Ayres' Hawk Eagle   Klein Jagarend

Hieraaetus dubius (A. Smith), 1830: *Heeren Logement, Clanwilliam
District, Cape Province.*

PLATE 15 (OPP. P. 97), AD. AND IMM. PLATE 12 AD. AND IMM.
Length 46—55 cm (♂ wing 326—345, ♀ wing 360—420; tail 175—233; tarsus 56—65;
culmen 20,5—26). Iris yellow, bill black; cere greenish yellow; legs yellow.

Identification: Often confused with the African Hawk Eagle, No. 141, but
distinguishable as follows: The nape bears a distinct crest; the underparts are
heavily blotched, rather than streaked, with black; the forehead and eyebrow
are sometimes white, particularly in males, while in flight the inner primaries
are heavily barred and the tail bears three narrow bars of brown on grey; shafts
of primaries black. The African Hawk Eagle has no crest; underparts are
narrowly streaked thus appearing much whiter; the forehead and eyebrow are
never white; in flight the primaries are not barred and the tail shows a broad
sub-terminal bar (about 4 cm wide). Primary shafts are white. The young
Ayres' Hawk Eagle is cream or very pale buff below with a few streaks on
sides of chest. Crest present. The young African Hawk Eagle is chestnut below
with finer streaking on chest, breast and flanks. No crest. Ayres' Hawk Eagle
(adult) also has a white patch at the shoulder, absent in No. 141.

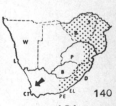

Distribution: Originally found in the Cape Province, even in the south-west
Cape but status to-day uncertain. From Natal northwards to Ethiopia and
Nigeria. Not recorded from South West Africa.   140

Habits: The smallest of the true eagles resident in Africa. A bird of wooded and forested hillsides and mountains, rare in collections. Very bold and dashing, catching its prey by flying switfly through the tree-tops. Has the habit of folding the wingtips to the tail and diving at great speed, appearing heart-shaped as it descends.

Food: Largely small birds, occasionally tree squirrels and ground gamebirds.

Voice: A high-pitched "keeeeeee-ee, -keee, -keee" also quite different from African Hawk Eagle.

Breeding: The nest is a large structure placed in a tree up to 14 metres. April—June, August, September. Eggs, 1, laid in late winter, dull white sparingly marked with brown or reddish and underlying lilac. Average (12) 55,7 × 43,9 (53,5—57,4 × 42,5—46). Incubation 45: Nestling 75 days.

141   African Hawk Eagle   Afrikaanse Jagarend

Hieraaetus spilogaster   (Bonaparte), 1850: *Ethiopia*

Native Name: le-Akavosane (Ch).

PLATE 15 (OPP. P. 97), AD. AND IMM. PLATE 12 AD. AND IMM.
Length 60—65 cm (♂ wing 412—446, ♀ wing 435—465; tail 255—290; tarsus 90—100; culmen ♂ 30—32, ♀ 32,5—34,5. 16 specimens, 14 ex Bannerman). Iris yellow, brown in young; bill black; cere and legs yellowish green.

Identification: Adult females *usually* more heavily spotted than males. For differences between this species and Ayres' Hawk Eagle, see No. 140. The young bird is browner above, rufous chestnut below with dark shaft streaks on chest and flanks and sometimes on breast and abdomen. Thus resembles Booted Eagle No. 139 but is larger, longer-legged with stronger feet and bill. Also more chestnut below than light phase of that bird.

Distribution: Senegal to Eritrea and southern Arabia, southwards to Cape Town on the east and northern South West Africa on the west. Now rare in Cape Province. Gemsbok National Park.

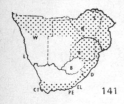

141

Habits: Found in mountainous or open country. Nearly always seen in pairs in close proximity. For its size an extremely bold and dashing bird, notorious for raids on poultry, consequently decimated in closely settled districts; not uncommon in the wilds. Hunts after the manner of a Sparrow-Hawk, dashing among trees and surprising its prey, often pursuing and killing it on the ground. Sometimes hovers and also soars to considerable heights. When disturbed at the nest, slips off and disappears quickly. Also returns to the nest very fast, either slipping through the trees or diving down from a height, straight onto it.

Food: Game birds, squirrels, small rodents, and reptiles.

Voice: A melodious and fluting "klu-klu-klukluee" or "Kluee, kluee".

Breeding: The nest, a large structure is placed high in a tree 9—15 m up, rarely on a cliff. Breeds in the winter months, June to October. Eggs 2, occasionally 1, dirty white speckled and blotched with reddish chestnut and underlying grey or purple. Average (50) 64,6 × 53,1 (59,4—69 × 47,6—54). Incubation by both sexes, mainly by female, 43 ± 1 days. Nestling 55—80 days. Only one young is reared.

142 Martial Eagle   Breëkop-arend

Polemaetus bellicosus   (Daudin), 1800: *Great Namaqualand.*

Native Name: Ukhozi (X).

PLATE 14 (OPP. P. 96), AD. AND IMM. PLATE 12 AD. AND IMM.
Length 78—83 cm (♂ wing 575—610, ♀ wing 620—675; tail 275—320; tarsus 97—120; culmen 40,5—49. 11 specimens, 5 ♂, 6 ♀). Iris yellow, brown in young; bill black; cere grey; legs bluish white.

Identification: Adult might be mistaken for the smaller Black-breasted Snake Eagle No. 146 but the white breast is spotted and tarsi feathered. Immature birds resemble young of Crowned Eagle but feathered legs are *not* spotted and flight pattern quite different, see Plate 12. Sexes alike. Female larger and more heavily spotted.
Distribution: Africa south of the Sahara, except West African and Congo forests.
Habits: This powerful and rapacious bird has been largely exterminated in the settled districts; still not uncommon in the wilder parts. Found in mountainous and open, but mainly drier, country. Now protected in many areas for its value in combating the dassie plague. Hunts by flying at some height and scanning the ground below or by watching from some vantage point. *Occasionally* hovers like a kestrel.

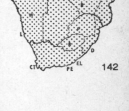
142

Food: Mainly dassies and ground-squirrels. Also game-birds, hares, monkeys, snakes, and rodents. Accused of killing lambs.
Voice: A loud ringing "kloo-ee, kloo-ee, kloo-ee, kloo-ee ku-lee". Also a low gulping "quolp".
Breeding: Constructs a nest of sticks either on the top of flat-crowned acacias or in the higher forks or branches of large trees, perhaps 60 metres up. Nest is used year after year and becomes huge, up to 2 metres across. Built by female, the male bringing sticks. Eggs, one, laid in winter, April to July; white thinly speckled with brown and slate-colour. Average (25) 80,7 × 64,1 (74—86,6 × 57—68,7). Incubation by female only, about 45 days. Nestling period 99 days.

143 Crowned Eagle   Kroon-arend

Stephanoaetus coronatus   (Linnaeus), 1766: *Coast of Guinea, West Africa.*

Native Names: u-Kozi (Z); Makhoana, mo-Kostatsi (S).

PLATE 14 (OPP. P. 96), AD. AND IMM. PLATE 12. AD. AND IMM.
Length 80—90 cm (wing ♂ 455—467—485, ♀ 500—520; tail ♂ 310—330, ♀ 345—370; tarsus 85—103; culmen 37—43,9 specimens, 6 ♂, 3 ♀). Iris yellow, grey-brown in young; bill black; cere and legs yellow.

Identification: Adults unmistakable. In flight, wings appear short and broad with conspicuous barring and dark rufous under wing-coverts. Young birds resemble young of the Martial Eagle No. 142 but have pinkish breasts and spotted legs. Young pass through a darker intermediate stage with dark marks on thighs. Sexes alike, female larger and darker below, markings on throat coalescing into black patches.
Distribution: From Knysna eastwards to Natal and Transvaal northwards to Central Africa as far as Guinea Bissau and Ethiopia.

143

Habits: This magnificent eagle occurs only where there are large forests, or patches of forest in open country. Probably the most powerful of the African eagles which hunts mainly by sitting on trees watching open glades in the forest below. It is able to fly almost vertically upwards, obviously useful among dense trees. Pairs display by mounting upwards with one, probably the male, repeatedly flying up and then swooping steeply in a dipping display.

Food: Small antelopes, dassies, monkeys; also recorded, mongoose and a mole.

Voice: Noisy for an eagle; male in display cries "keewik-keewik" and female a yelping "koi-koi-koi". Also "kui-kui-kui" repeated.

Breeding: The nest is built in large forest trees and used year after year until it is colossal. Eggs, 2, rarely only 1, are laid in late September or early October in the Cape; plain white or speckled and streaked with red-brown. Average (23) 68,2 × 53,6 (60,9—73,8 × 50,8—57,5). Incubation is by both sexes, 48 days. Nestling period 114 days, both parents feed the young.

144   Lizard Buzzard   Akkedisvalk

Kaupifalco monogrammicus   (Temminck), 1824: *Senegal.*
PLATE 16 (OPP. P. 112), PLATE 18.
Length 35—37 cm (wing ♂ 210—218—225, ♀ 222—233—248; tail 132—152; tarsus 48—54; culmen 16—18. 21 specimens, 9 ♂, 12 ♀). Iris red; bill black; cere and legs orange.

Identification: Might be mistaken for the Gabar Goshawk No. 162, but has very distinct white bar across tail when seen from behind. From the front, black line down throat is distinctive. Ovambo Sparrowhawk, No. 157, lacks both these features. Young birds very like adults, but breast washed with brown, back slightly darker, the feathers buff-edged and white bar on tail indistinct at the sides. Occasionally two white bars on tail.

Distribution: Senegal to Ethiopia southwards to Ngamiland, Transvaal, and Natal.

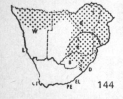

144

Habits: A common species in suitable localities, liking moister forested or well-wooded areas along rivers but found in fairly dry bush. Usually seen on forest edge. A bird of very direct flight, alternately flapping and gliding. Occasionally soars like a buzzard. Usually flies low and straight rising upwards into the branches of a tree.

Food: Rats, lizards, snakes, and insects. Very rarely birds, and small birds do not seem afraid of it.

Voice: A very musical descending series of half a dozen notes "klüh-klü-klü-klü", uttered while sitting very upright with the head slightly raised. Also a drawn-out whining note.

Breeding: Makes a nest of sticks in trees, lining it with green leaves and moss. Nest about 30 cms in diameter and placed from 6—12 metres up. Eggs 2, sometimes 3, are laid in August, October or November as a rule but also as late as May. They are white, more or less marked with slate-brown or red-brown. Average (80) 43,9 × 35,2 (40,2—47 × 33—37,5). One 49 × 35.

145 Brown Snake-eagle Bruin Slangarend

Circaetus cinereus Vieillot, 1818: *Senegal.*

PLATE 15 (OPP. P. 97), AD. AND IMM. A AND B. PLATE 11 AD. AND IMM.
Length 71—76 cm (♂ wing 508—550, ♀ 490—567; tail 245—295; tarsus 92—108; culmen 42—45. 19 specimens, 8 ♂, 11 ♀, Roberts + Bannerman). Iris yellow; bill black; legs whitish.

Identification: The Snake-Eagles or Harrier-Eagles all have the tarsus bare of feathers. Thus this species can be distinguished from other largish brown eagles by its unfeathered legs which are whitish in colour. Also has large yellow eyes and rather owlish expression due to feathers on back of head standing out almost like a ruff. Young bird is paler brown, the bases of the feathers white, giving a mottled effect. Then difficult to tell from young of next species, q.v. Wings *not* barred in flight.
Distribution: Senegal to Ethiopia then southwards, except the Congo forests, to northern South West Africa, Transvaal, Natal and the eastern Cape, where it is very rare. Common in the Zambezi valley east of Chirundu. Rare east of Bulawayo.

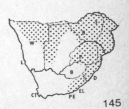

145

Habits: A fairly common bird of savanna and thorn-tree country. Usually seen perched on top of a tree from which most of its prey is taken. Also soars like most eagles. Normal flight rather clumsy.
Food: Mainly snakes and other small reptiles, also rodents and large insects. Occasionally ground birds.
Voice: A quiet bird. Normal call a loud, deep-toned "kok-kok-kok-kaaauw", from perched or soaring birds. At the nest various guttural or gull-like notes.
Breeding: A rather small, flimsy nest is placed in thorn trees or Euphorbias. The same nest is not always used year after year. Eggs, only one laid December to February, chalky white, sometimes marked with pale reddish-brown. Average (7) 74,3 × 60,9 (72—76 × 58—64). Incubation by female, only 49 days (Steyn). Nestling period about 109 days.

146 Black-breasted Snake-eagle Swartbors-slangarend

Circaetus pectoralis A. Smith, 1829: *South Africa.*

PLATE 15 (OPP. P. 97), AD. AND IMM. A AND B. PLATE 11 AD. AND IMM.
Length 63—68 cm (wing 490—530; tail 255—290; tarsus 85—90; culmen 32—37. 6 specimens). Iris yellow; bill black; cere olive-yellow; legs dirty white.

Identification: In general pattern rather like the much larger Martial Eagle No. 142, but legs unfeathered and breast not spotted. Sexes alike, female slightly larger. Young brown above, rufous below, the feathers with white bases; difficult to distinguish in the field from the young of the previous species, but paler above; more rufous, almost cinnamon below. Wings, even in young, barred in flight, cf. No. 145. Chin white in western birds.
Distribution: Southern Africa northwards to East Africa, Ethiopia and Somaliland. Rare in the south-west Cape.
Habits: Found in the drier areas of the Karoo and also savanna country but avoiding heavily wooded or forested areas. Not uncommon although badly decimated in farming areas, probably due to confusion with the Martial Eagle. Hunts mainly by soaring at some height, but also to be seen perched on a tree or telegraph-pole watching the ground beneath. At times unfortunately tame.

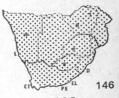

146

Sometimes hovers like a kestrel.

Food: Mainly snakes, also lizards, fish and small mammals, even bats. One record of a Leguaan 1 metre long. Often swallows snakes in flight.

Voice: An occasional loud shriek uttered while soaring.

Breeding: The nest, placed 4—7 metres up in a tree, is rather small, about 60 cm across. Eggs, on the other hand are large for the size of the bird. Average (10) 74,1 × 59,7 (71,7—77,9 × 56—66,6). They are white, sometimes spotted with reddish, usually only one being laid. Incubation, by both sexes, lasts 40—45 days (1). Breeds at various times of year. Nestling period about 90 days. Young fed by both sexes.

147　Southern Banded Snake-eagle
Suidelike Gebande Slangarend

Circaetus fasciolatus　Kaup, 1850: *Durban.*

PLATE 15 (OPP. P. 97). AD. AND IMM. PLATE 11. AD.
Length 55—60 cm (wing ♂ 363—370, ♀ 390; tail 245—265; tarsus 76—78; culmen 27—32,5. 3 specimens, 2 ♂, 1 ♀). Iris yellow; bill black; cere and legs yellow.

Identification: Very similar to the next species but shows *two* pale bars on tail, not one (a third may just be visible). Young bird paler, feathers above tipped with white; below white, spotted on head, throat, and breast with fulvous.

Distribution: Natal northwards on the eastern coastal belt to Kenya.

Habits: Rather a rare species. Usually seen in forest in the vicinity of rivers and vleis perched on a tree. Little else recorded.

Food: Snakes, small mammals and birds; beetles.

Voice: "Ko-ko-ho-ho-ho".

147　**Breeding:** Nests in trees. Accurate breeding data required.

148　Banded Snake-eagle　Gebande Slangarend

Circaetus cinerascens　Müller, 1851: *Sennar.*

PLATE 15 (OPP. P. 97), AD. AND IMM. PLATE 11. AD.
Length 55—60 cm (wing 267—408; tail 220—231; tarsus 80—84; culmen 31—33. 15 specimens, 3 ♂, 5 ♀, 7 unsexed; ex Bannerman). Iris yellow; bill black, yellow at base; cere and legs yellow.

Identification: Very like the preceding species but less clearly barred below and showing only *one* white bar in projecting portion of tail (another hidden by coverts except at sides). Sexes alike, female slightly, if at all, larger. Young dirty white below washed with brown; above brown.

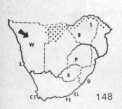

Distribution: Portuguese Guinea across to Ethiopia, south to the Okavango, Chobe and Zambezi and Angola except the Congo forests.

Habits: Little has been recorded except that it is usually found in the neighbourhood of rivers, perched conspicuously in large trees.

Food: Snakes, lizards, small mammals, fish and insects are recorded.

Voice: A rough grating "caw" and a series of loud monotonous notes rather like Fish Eagle but very mournful.

148　**Breeding:** The nest is large and placed 15—20 metres up in a tree. Eggs: data required.

149 Fish Eagle
Visarend

Haliaeetus vocifer (Daudin), 1800: *Keurboom River, Cape Province.*

Native Names: Unomakhwezana (X); i-Nkwazi (Z).

PLATE 14 (OPP. P. 96). AD. AND IMM. PLATE 12. AD. AND IMM.
Length 63—73 cm (wing ♂ 510—530—540, ♀ 565—605; tail 230—275; tarsus 80—90; culmen 38—44. 8 specimens, 5 ♂, 3 ♀). Iris brown; bill blackish; cere and legs yellow, grey in young.

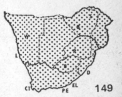

Identification: Adults unmistakable. Young bird is dark brown above, white below with dark centres to feathers giving a streaked effect. Immature birds have the abdomen blackish brown, not chestnut. Probably takes four to five years to reach maturity.
Distribution: From Cape Town northwards over all Africa south of the Sahara.
Habits: A beautiful bird which is happily still fairly common. Found on rivers, lakes, dams, estuaries, and even the open sea-shore, wherever fish can be caught. Exists largely on stranded and dead fish but also descends in a tremendous stoop at free-swimming fish in the water. Usually checks just before hitting the water but may go right under. Also harries other fish-eating birds and robs them. Has been observed to kill a heron and a coot.
Food: Fish, rats, the young of egrets, cormorants, and herons and occasionally even carrion. In Central Africa reported to kill flamingos.
Voice: One of the characteristic sounds of Africa, a loud challenging, yelping "kow, kow, kowkowkow" uttered with head thrown right back even while soaring.
Breeding: Nest a large structure of sticks placed high up in a large tree and difficult of access. In the Cape will nest on quite a low bush, 3 m high, on the edge of a cliff. Eggs are laid as early as May, more often in July and August in the south, January to July and October in Rhodesia, normally 2 to the clutch, white and rough. Average (32) 70,7 × 54,5 (67—77,5 × 50,8—57,3. Incubation apparently by female only; about 48 days. Nestling period about 60 days (2). Three chicks sometimes reared.

150 Bearded Vulture
Lammergeyer

Gypaetus barbatus (Linnaeus), 1758: *Africa=Oran, Algeria.*

Native Name: Seoli (S).

PLATE 10 (OPP. P. 72). PLATE 11. AD.
Length about 110 cm (wing 737—762; tarsus 101; tail 432—445; culmen 49). Iris red with yellow round pupil; bill black, cere bluish; feet ashy.

Identification: Black beard tufts diagnostic. In flight tail appears very long diamond-shaped when spread. When diving wings look pointed and whole bird looks like a huge falcon. Young have black throats and black on head and neck; below brown, iris brown.
Distribution: From Lesotho northwards through East Africa to North Africa, southern Europe east to the Himalayas and China. Originally occurred round Cape Town. Not yet recorded in Rhodesia.
Habits: A rare, vulture-like eagle that has almost disappeared with the advance of civilisation; now mainly confined to the Drakensberg but some-

times wandering further afield. A magnificent bird in the air, gliding at great speed along ridges in search of food.

Food: Carrion, particularly bones which it is said to drop from a height until they are broken when the marrow is eaten; if too hard they are swallowed whole and digested. Also mammals such as dassies.

Voice: A high ringing whistle.

Breeding: The nest is placed on a precipice and made of a few sticks, goats' hair, wool, etc. It is used year after year and for roosting when not nesting. Eggs, one or two; one from Basutoland is creamy white, thickly overlain with a suffusion of fine purplish grey and brownish yellow, with fine dark-brown dots here and there, capped at both ends with coalesced patches of sepia-yellow, and measures 83,5 × 68.

LOCAL RACE:
G.b. meridionalis Keyserling and Blasius, 1840: *Sunday's River, South Africa.* South and East Africa as far north as Ethiopia.

151 Bateleur   Berghaan

Terathopius ecaudatus (Daudin), 1800: *Pays d'Antiquois = Knysna.*

Native Names: Ingqanga (X); i-Ngqungulu (Z); Ntsu (S).

PLATE 14 (OPP. P. 96), ADS. AND IMM. PLATE 11. ADS. AND IMM.
Length 55—70 cm (wing ♂ 520—534—550, ♀ 500—528—550; tail 105—120; tarsus 65—75; culmen 35—37,5. 11 specimens, 7 ♂, 4 ♀). Iris hazel; bill black orange base; cere and legs coral-red.

Identification: Adults unmistakable. In flight, female shows a narrow, even band of black along trailing edge of secondaries; male shows an irregular, much broader band. At rest, therefore, female shows a grey patch on the side formed by the secondaries. Tail appears very short. Young birds are uniform brown as figured and have longer tails; in flight the feet do not project beyond the tail as they do in adults. In all stages of plumage the long upswept wings and mode of flight (see below) are characteristic. In East Africa a phase occurs with a cream back. Young birds take 7—8 years to reach mature plumage.

Distribution: From the eastern Cape Province (now very rare) and Orange River, northwards south of the Sahara.

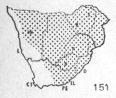

151

Habits: One of the best known and commonest of the large birds of prey in the savanna veld of Africa. Its striking appearance and colouring at once attract attention as it flies overhead, usually travelling fast across country rather than soaring in circles. Mode of flight very characteristic; the bird rocks from side to side as it steers, sometimes with the wings held up at quite an acute angle. The name Bateleur is said to have been given it by le Vaillant because of its habit of somersaulting, slow-rolling and performing other antics in the air.

Food: Reptiles, including snakes, small mammals, and carrion, especially *small* dead animals. Also termites. Birds may constitute half the prey.

Voice: A variety of short sharp barking calls.

Breeding: The nest, composed of sticks is fairly large and placed high up in trees. Also uses old nests of other species. Eggs, one, white sometimes stained or marked with rufous. Average (41) 77,4 × 61,4 (75—81,3 × 58,5—64,7). Incubation by both sexes, at least 55 days. Nestling period 110, 111 and 130 days.

152   Jackal Buzzard   Jakkalsvoël

Buteo rufofuscus   (Forster), 1798: *South Africa*.

Native Names: Indlandlokazi (X and Z); Khayoane. (S).

PLATE 16 (OPP. P. 112), A AND B AND IMMS. PLATE 18 ADS. AND IMM.

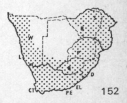

ADS. AND IMM.
Length 44—53 cm (wing ♂ 393—401—410, ♀ 423-432—444; tail 180—220; tarsus 76—85; culmen 24—30. 19 specimens, 8 ♂, 11 ♀). Iris brown; bill horn, tip black; legs and cere yellow.

Identification: In all adult plumages distinguished by almost black upper-parts and red tail. Northern birds *(augur)*, white below, southern chestnut with paler throat and upper chest. Young bird brown above with black on forehead, nape and mantle; below pale chestnut with a few dark shaft-streaks on chest. Pattern in flight distinctive, see Plate 18.

Distribution: Southern Africa north to Angola, Ethiopia and Somaliland.

Habits: A resident, fairly common species in the mountains but extending thence into the neighbouring plains. Usually seen soaring overhead or perched on some vantage point.

Food: Mammals, reptiles, and insects. Also dead animals killed on roads, etc. Occasionally chickens but on balance probably a useful bird.

152

Voice: A loud cry rather resembling that of the Black-backed Jackal. Also a sort of twittering cry.

Breeding: Nests on ledges of precipices or in trees and bushes growing on steep slopes or cliffs. Lays from June to October. Eggs, normally 2, white usually well-marked with reddish spots and speckles. Average (45) 59,7 × 47,4 (54,4—64,8 × 44—50,6). Nestling period between 46 and 51 days. Incubation 35—40 days. Larger young may kill the smaller chick.

LOCAL RACES:
(a) B.r. rufofuscus (Forster), 1798: *South Africa*. Confined to the Republic of South Africa including South West Africa. As illustrated.
(b) B.r. augur (Rüppell), 1836: *Abyssinia*. Rhodesia northwards to Ethiopia. Occurs in northern South West Africa. Also several sight records in South Africa, mainly in the drier areas. As illustrated.

153 See No. 152 *(b)*

154   Buzzard   Bruin Jakkalsvoël

Buteo buteo   (Linnaeus), 1758: *Europe, Savoy*.

Native Name: Isanxha (X)

PLATE 16 (OPP. P. 112), ADS. A, B, C; IMMS. A AND B. PLATE 18 ADS. A, B; IMM. C.
Length 45—50 cm (wing ♂ 350—385, ♀ 350—390; tail 175—195: tarsus 65—75; culmen 20—23. 15 specimens). Iris brown, bill black, cere and legs yellow.

Identification: Very variable in plumage. Three phases are illustrated of which (C) is mostly commonly seen. In flight all show whitish underwing with rufous coverts; note dark trailing edge.

Distribution: Occurs in summer over the whole of Southern Africa except the very dry parts of Little and Great Namaqualand.

Habits: The race which visits our area is known as the Steppe Buzzard and is the very common brown buzzard seen so commonly in summer (October to

154

SPARROWHAWKS

April) perched on a lamp-post, fence-pole or dead tree, patiently watching the ground below. Ringed birds recovered in Russia up to 12 000 kms away.
Food. Chameleons, lizards, frogs, insects, mice, rats and occasionally birds. On balance undoubtedly a most useful species to man.
Voice: A mewing "kee-you, kee-you". Very quiet while here.

LOCAL RACES:
B.b. vulpinus Gloger, 1833: *Sunday's River, Eastern Cape Province.* Size above. A very common migrant from Europe and Asia.

155 Mountain Buzzard   Berg-jakkalsvoël

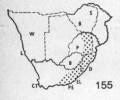

Buteo oreophilus   Hartert and Neumann, 1914: *Konitscha, S. Ethiopia*
PLATE 16 (OPP. P. 112), AD. AND IMM. PLATE 18. AD.
Length about 45 cm (wing ♂ 318—335—352, ♀ 330—349—362) tarsus 60; culmen 19,5—23. Iris yellow-brown with age; bill blackish; cere and legs yellow.

Identification: Shows a broad whitish, relatively (cf. No. 154C) unmarked band across lower chest. Thighs dark, appearing blackish in flight. Young have biscuit-coloured eyes which go brown in second year.
Distribution: From George and Knysna where it is common, eastwards to the eastern and northern Transvaal. Also East Africa to Ethiopia.
Habits: A resident species, associated with forest, including plantations of exotics, where it may often be seen perched quietly on a dead tree or fence pole. Frequently soars over the forest or nearby cliffs.
Food: Lizards, frogs taken on ground or in trees.
Voice: A shrill, ringing "Keeee-o" or "keeee". Calls a lot while No. 154 is mostly silent while here.
Breeding: The nest, a large structure of sticks is placed in a tree 9—15 metres up. September to October. Two eggs are laid. One, white and unmarked, measures 53,8 × 39,8 mm. Incubation about 30 days by female. Fledgling period 40± days.

LOCAL RACE:
B.o. trizonatus Rudebeck, 1957: *Knysna.* Confined to eastern South Africa.

156 Red-breasted Sparrowhawk   Rooibors-sperwer

Accipiter rufiventris   A. Smith, 1830: *South Africa*
Native Names: Ukhetshana (X); u-Mhloile (Z).
PLATE 19 (OPP. P. 113). ♀ PLATE 17.
Length 33—40 cm (wing ♂ 200—202—204, ♀ 230—235—245; tail ♂ 155—162, ♀ 180—195; tarsus 49—57; culmen 11—14. 14 specimens, 6 ♂, 8 ♀). Iris yellow; bill black; cere and legs yellow.

Identification: Almost uniform red chest of adult diagnostic. Young birds are streaked on chest and barred on breast, rather as in the picture of the young Gabar Goshawk No. 162 on Plate 19, but the markings are *pale rufous* on

110

white. Intermediate plumage resembles European species being entirely barred below with rufous on white.

Distribution: From the south-west Cape eastwards to Natal then north into the mountain forest of Transvaal and eastern Rhodesia above about 2 000 m. Also found in Malawi, Zaïre and Kenya to Ethiopia.

Habits: Not uncommon in thick woods and forests. Copses of large trees on the Karoo usually contain a pair. A typical sparrowhawk flying at speed through thick cover and beating along rows of trees relying on surprise to catch its victims. During courtship, pairs circle at some height over trees, calling loudly.

Food: Mainly birds, consequently taking young poultry. Also termites and insects.

Voice: Alarm call a harsh "chek-chek-chek-chek". Also a call of three drawn-out whistles.

Breeding: Nests in trees, making a small nest of sticks and laying from October to December. Eggs, 2 to 4, normally 3; white, heavily blotched at the larger end with light and dark brown. Average (38) 41,0 × 32,5 (36,7—44,5 × 30—36,1).

LOCAL RACE:
A.r. rufiventris, A. Smith, 1830: *South Africa*. From our area northwards to Kenya and Nigeria. Another race in Ethiopia.

157 Ovambo Sparrowhawk   Ovambo-sperwer

Accipiter ovampensis Gurney, 1875; *Okavango River*.

PLATE 19 (OPP. P. 113). ♀ PLATE 17.
Length 33—40 cm (wing ♂ 210—225, ♀ 245—253; tail ♂ 145—150, ♀ 160—190; tarsus 43—52; culmen 11—15. 16 specimens, Bannerman and Roberts). Iris orange-brown; bill black; cere and legs orange or yellow.

Identification: Very like the Little-banded Goshawk but darker grey on throat and cheeks and more clearly barred below. Some or no white on rump as opposed to Gabar Goshawk, No. 162, which has broad white rump at all stages, whereas young Ovambo has not and is less heavily streaked on chest. A rare melanistic form occurs.

Distribution: From the Komati River, Transvaal, west to Ovamboland, northwards to Ghana on the west and Ethiopia on the east.

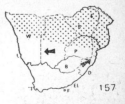

Habits: A tropical species occurring in the dry acacia veld along streams and rivers. Described as migratory, disappearing for some months in midsummer. Shy and elusive inhabiting the densest bush.

Food: Said to feed largely on insects but also recorded as killing a starling and a dove. Said not to attack poultry.

Voice: A five-syllabled "Coo-coo-coo-coo-cook" and a Kestrel-like scream.

Breeding: Nests in trees, usually in rather thick bush, from September to December. Eggs, 3, white clouded by slate and light to dark brown but variable. Average (23) 42,4 × 33,2 (37,8—45,4 × 36,5).

111

PLATE 16

128. *Milvus migrans migrans.* Black Kite. Swart Wou. Ad. and Imm.
129. *Milvus aegyptius parasitus.* Yellow-billed Kite. Geelbekwou.
Ad. and Imm.
130. *Elanus caeruleus.* Black-shouldered Kite. Blouvalkie. Ad. and Imm.
131. *Macheiramphus alcinus anderssoni.* Bat Hawk. Vlermuisvalk.
132. *Pernis apivorus.* Honey Buzzard. Wespedief. A, B and C.
144. *Kaupifalco monogrammicus.* Lizard Buzzard. Akkedisvalk.
152 *(a). Buteo rufofuscus rufofuscus.* Jackal Buzzard. Jakkalsvoël.
Ad. and Imm.
152 *(b). Buteo rufofuscus augur.* Augur Buzzard. Jakkalsvoël. Ad.
154. *Buteo buteo vulpinus.* Steppe Buzzard. Bruin Jakkalsvoël.
A, Ad. and Imm., B, Ad. and Imm. and C.
155. *Buteo oreophilus trizonatus.* Mountain Buzzard. Berg-jakkalsvoël.
Ad. and Imm.
163. *Melierax metabates mechowi.* Dark Chanting Goshawk.
Donker Witvalk. Adult and Imm.
165. *Melierax canorus.* Chanting Goshawk. Groot Witvalk.
167. *Circus ranivorus.* African Marsh Harrier. Paddavreter. Ad. and Imm.
168. *Circus macrourus.* Pallid Harrier. Vaal Paddavreter. ♂ and ♀.
169. *Circus maurus.* Black Harrier. Witkruis-valk. Ad. and Imm.
170. *Circus pygargus.* Montagu's Harrier. Blou Paddavreter. ♂ and ♀.
171. *Polyboroides typus typus.* Gymnogene. Ad. and Imm. A and B.
172. *Pandion haliaetus.* Osprey. Visvalk.

Imm A
154
154 A
154 B
C
155
132 A
132 B
Imm.
Imm.
132 C
Imm B
144
172
152 B
Imm
152 A
Imm
129
128
Imm.
130
Imm.
131
Imm
165
Imm A
171
Imm B
Imm
163
m
167
♂
168
♀
♂
170
♀
Imm
169

K B NEWMAN '76

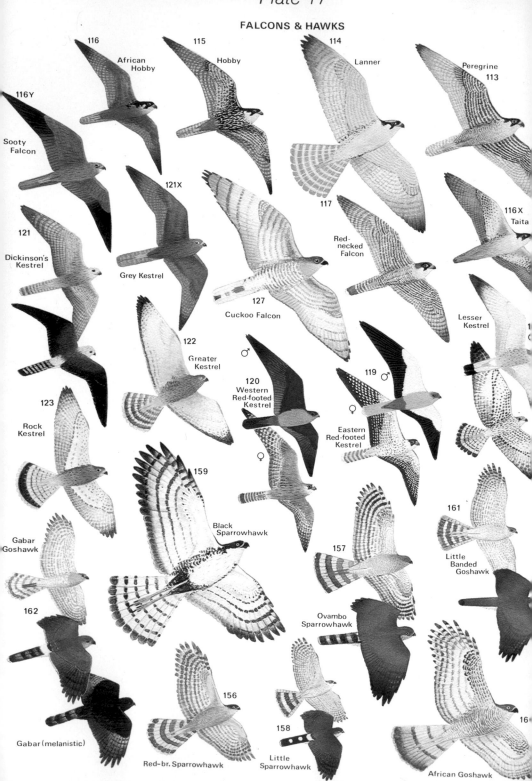

Plate 17

FALCONS & HAWKS

116

115

114

113

116Y

Sooty
Falcon

African
Hobby

Hobby

Lanner

Peregrine

121X

116X
Taita

121

Dickinson's
Kestrel

Grey Kestrel

Red-
necked
Falcon

Lesser
Kestrel

127

Cuckoo Falcon

122

Greater
Kestrel

♂

120
Western
Red-footed
Kestrel

119 ♂

♀

Eastern
Red-footed
Kestrel

123

Rock
Kestrel

♀

159

161

Gabar
Goshawk

Black
Sparrowhawk

157

Little
Banded
Goshawk

162

Ovambo
Sparrowhawk

156

158

16

Gabar (melanistic)

Red-br. Sparrowhawk

Little
Sparrowhawk

African Goshawk

Plate 18

BUZZARDS, KITES, HARRIERS, ETC.

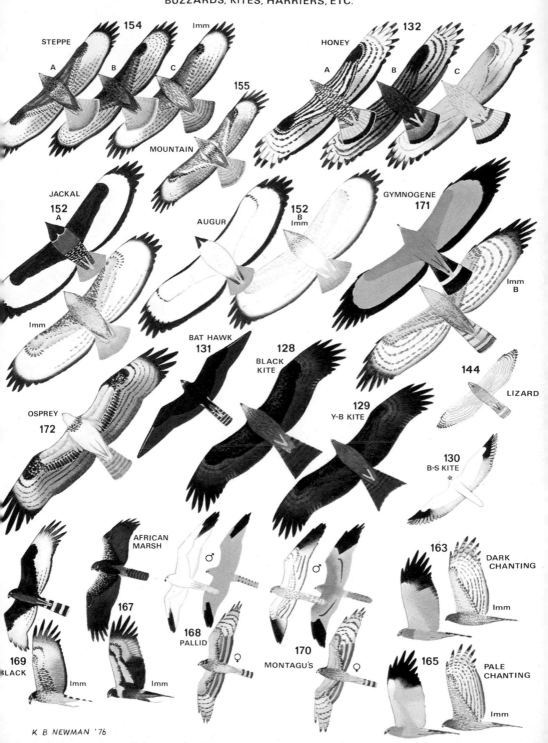

STEPPE 154 Imm
A B C

MOUNTAIN 155

HONEY 132
A B C

JACKAL 152 A

AUGUR 152 B Imm

GYMNOGENE 171

Imm B

Imm

BAT HAWK 131

BLACK KITE 128

LIZARD 144

OSPREY 172

Y-B KITE 129

130 B-S KITE

AFRICAN MARSH

♂

♂

163 DARK CHANTING

Imm

167

168 PALLID

♀

170 MONTAGU'S

♀

169 BLACK

Imm

Imm

165 PALE CHANTING

Imm

K B NEWMAN '76

157 ♀

162 ♀

162 Imm

Imm 161 ♀

162 ♀

♀ 160 ♂

160 Imm

156 ♀

♂ 159

Imm ♀ 159

♂ 158 Imm ♀

♂ 159

MIGHTON.
'37

PLATE 19

156. *Accipiter rufiventris rufiventris.* Red-breasted Sparrowhawk. ♀.
Rooibors-sperwer.
157. *Accipiter ovampensis.* Ovambo Sparrowhawk. Ovambo-sperwer. ♀.
158. *Accipiter minullus.* Little Sparrowhawk. Klein Sperwer.
Adult ♂ and Imm. ♀.
159. *Accipiter melanoleucus melanoleucus.* Black Sparrowhawk.
Swart Sperwer. Adult ♂, black- and white-breasted forms, and Imm. ♀.
160. *Accipiter tachiro tachiro.* African Goshawk. Afrikaanse Sperwer.
♂, ♀, and Imm.
161. *Accipiter badius polyzonoides.* Little Banded Goshawk.
Klein Gebande Sperwer. Adult and Imm.
162. *Micronisus gabar.* Gabar Goshawk. Klein Witvalkie.
Adult ♀ normal and black forms, and Imm.

158 Little Sparrowhawk   Klein Sperwer

Accipiter minullus (Daudin), 1800: *Gamtoos River, Cape Province*

Native Name: Ukhetshana (X).

PLATE 19 (OPP. P. 113), ♂ AND IMM. ♀ PLATE 17.
Length 23—25 cm (wing ♂ 136—141—145, ♀ 156—159—164; tail 105—130; tarsus 38—46; culmen 8—12. 22 specimens, 13 ♂, 8 ♀). Iris orange; bill black; cere yellow; legs orange.

158

Identification: Good field characters are the white upper tail coverts (tipped black in young) and two white "eye" spots on tail. Male slaty above, finer barred below with rufous flanks. Young birds as illustrated, note *white* throat *without* black line down centre, cf. African Goshawk No. 160.

Distribution: Sierra Leone to Ethiopia southwards over all Africa except the south-west Cape and drier parts of the Karoo and Namaqualand.

Habits: This diminutive Sparrowhawk is widely distributed over the savanna veld of Africa, usually near water. A bold little bird usually living in thick bush or isolated stands of large trees. Remarkably quick in flight, seizing its prey in its talons and disappearing in a flash through the trees. Inconspicuous at rest.

Food: Mainly small birds, Queleas and other seed-eaters being recorded in particular.

Voice: Male's call a high "kik-kik-kik-kik". Female's the same but deeper.

Breeding: Nest placed in a tree up to 25 m up; lined with green leaves. Eggs, laid from September to November, are greenish white, 2 or 3 to the clutch. Average (43) 34,8 × 28,1 (32,6—37,8 × 27—31,6). Incubation apparently by female only 32 days, fed by male. Nestling period, 22—26 days (2).

159 Black Sparrowhawk   Swart Sperwer

Accipiter melanoleucus A. Smith, 1830: *Baviaans River, Cape Province.*

PLATE 19 (OPP. P. 113) AD. BLACK-AND-WHITE FORMS AND IMM. ♀ PLATE 17.
Length 46—58 cm (wing ♂ 287—295, ♀ 333—342; tail 210—267; tarsus 73—90; culmen 18—24. 8 specimens, 5 ♂, 3 ♀). Iris orange; bill black; cere and legs yellow-green.

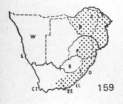

159

Identification: Very large size, white and black underparts combined with black back diagnostic. Brown, entirely *streaked* breast of young should avoid confusion with any other hawk. Might be mistaken for young African Hawk Eagle, No. 141, but of course legs are bare.

Distribution: Knysna eastwards to Natal then north to Ethiopia and across to the Congo and West Africa. Sparsely recorded in Rhodesia.

Habits: A forest species which also ventures into savanna country. Very bold and dashing.

Food: Little recorded but a menace to poultry. Birds and small mammals.

Voice: A ringing "Ku-Ku". Also "kek-kek-kek" and a low broken scream.

Breeding: A large nest about 60 cm across is placed in a tree, during July to November, about 12—20 metres up. It is lined with leaves. Eggs 2—4, greenish to greenish white, plain or speckled and dotted with light and dark blotches and smears of brown and yellowish brown with underlying ashy shading. Average (22) 54,8 × 42,1 (49,6—59,8 × 39,6—45,5).

LOCAL RACE:
A.m. melanoleucus A. Smith, 1830: *Baviaans River, Cape Province.* Occurs throughout the above range except West Africa where a smaller race occurs.

160 African Goshawk   Afrikaanse Sperwer

Accipiter tachiro   (Daudin), 1800: *Antiniquoi = Knysna.*

PLATE 19 (OPP. P. 113). ♂, ♀ AND IMM. ♀ PLATE 17.
Length 37—39 cm (wing ♂ 200—212—225, ♀ 240—247—257; tail 168—227; tarsus 57—69; culmen 15—20. 18 specimens, 8 ♂, 10 ♀). Iris yellow, brown in young; bill black; cere and legs yellow.

Identification: In spite of larger size rather similar to Little Sparrowhawk No. 158 but lacks white rump and spots on tail much fainter, if present at all. Young usually more clearly spotted below than shown in Plate 19, the spots on lower breast large, sometimes appearing as broad bars. Throat with a *black line* down the centre which is absent in young of Little Sparrowhawk.

Distribution: From the Cape Peninsula eastwards to Natal and Zoutpansberg, through eastern Rhodesia to Eritrea on the east, Angola and the Congo on the west.

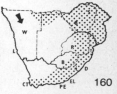

160

Habits: The common Goshawk of wooded parts and mountain forests. An extremely bold bird coming into heavily built-up suburbs of large towns. Very rapacious and a menace to poultry. Has the habit, in the early morning, of circling high up alternately flying and planing while making a clicking note every 3 to 6 seconds. May keep this up for half an hour. Sometimes soars over mountain ridges but usually seen flying at speed through trees or perched on them.

Food: Largely birds, but also crabs, lizards, mice, frogs, and grasshoppers.

Voice: A shrill repeated "wut-wut". A harsh "sckreeee" and a long plaintive, gradually ascending, crying note.

Breeding: Nests in early summer, constructing a hollow platform of sticks in a large tree, lining it with leaves. Eggs normally 2 but often 3, white and unmarked. Average (22) 45,7 × 36,4 (41,8—48,4 × 34,6—38,7). Incubation period at least 30 days. Nestling 32 days.

LOCAL RACE:
(a) A.t. tachiro (Daudin), 1800: *Knysna.* From Southern Africa to Angola and Malawi. Intergrades with the northern race. E. Rhodesia, Zambezi Valley, Southern Mozambique.
(b) A.t. sparsimfasciata (Reichenow), 1895: *Zanzibar.*

161 Little Banded Goshawk   Klein Gebande Sperwer

Accipiter badius   (Gmelin), 1788: *Ceylon.*

Native Name: Matzenella (S).

PLATE 19 (OPP. P. 113). ♀ AND IMM. ♀ PLATE 17.
Length 28—30 cm (wing ♂ 165—172—184, ♀ 185—191—200; tail 120—155; tarsus 40—48; culmen 10—12. 20 specimens, 9 ♂ 11 ♀). Iris yellow to red; bill blackish; cere and legs orange to yellow.

Identification: No white on rump whereas Little Sparrowhawk shows quite a lot, Gabar Goshawk a lot and the Ovambo Sparrowhawk some. White spots on

115

wing coverts and mantle not always present. Tail finely and evenly barred. Young resemble young of Gabar Goshwak to some extent but lack white rump and broad streaks on chest; belly with broader bands. Sexes alike.

Distribution: All Africa south of the Sahara except the Congo forests; eastwards to southern Asia. Absent from South-west and southern Cape, the drier Karoo and Namaqualand.

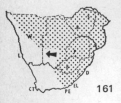

161

Habits: An active and bold little hawk, which inhabits savanna veld, particularly dry acacia country. Hunts by sitting in a leafy tree and swooping out at its prey.

Food: Insects but also small birds and small lower vertebrates especially lizards; small mammals.

Voice: A loud shrill ringing "kee, kee, kee".

Breeding: The nest is a small dovelike structure of twigs placed in a thorn tree. Laying occurs from August to December. Eggs, 3 occasionally 4, white very variably marked with blotches and cloudings or fine speckles of slate and light brown, some hardly marked at all. Average (59) 36,8 × 29,4 (33,4—40 × 28,1—31,3). Average (100) both African races 36,7 × 29,4. Incubation about one month. Nest lined with bark.

LOCAL RACE:
A.b. polyzonoides A. Smith, 1838: *N. of Lat. 26° S. Probably near Mafeking.* Southern Africa as far north as southern Zaïre and Tanzania above. Another race, *A.b. sphenurus*, occurs in north-east Africa.

162 Gabar Goshawk   Klein Witvalkie

Micronisus gabar (Daudin), 1800: *Zwart River, Graaff-Reinet District, Cape Province.*

Native Name: Mamphoko (S).

PLATE 19 (OPP. P. 113). NORMAL AND BLACK FORMS AND IMM.
PLATE 17. NORMAL AND BLACK FORMS.
Length 30-34 cm (wing ♂ 183—189—198 (15). ♀ 197—202—206 (10); tail 150—177; tarsus 42—48; culmen 11,5—14,5. 20 specimens, 13 ♂ 7 ♀), Iris crimson; bill black; base of bill, cere and legs reddish orange.

Identification: Resembles closely the Ovambo Sparrowhawk, No. 157 but has broad white rump at all stages and orange-red legs. Furthermore throat and upper chest are uniform grey, not streaked as in No. 157. A pure black form (with no white rump) occurs, about 7%. Young as figured in Plate 19.

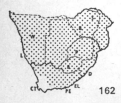

162

Distribution: Africa south of the Sahara except the Congo forests. Comes as far south as Springbok on the west and Montagu in the south but not the Cape Peninsula or Flats.

Habits: A common species of acacia thornveld. Generally keeps to thick cover and seen sitting inside trees. In habits bold and dashing quite unlike the Chanting Goshwaks.

Food: Lizards, large insects and small birds. Also mice and nestlings.

Voice: Alarm note like that of a Sparrowhawk. Also a repeated high-pitched chittering.

Breeding: Nest a smallish structure placed in a thorn-tree or quite high up. It incorporates various materials as lining; cotton waste, spider webs, rags, and mud. Eggs, usually 3, plain bluish white, are laid from August to December. Average (59) 39,5 × 31,5 (33,5—42,8 × 30—33). Incubation and fledging, 35 days.

163 Dark Chanting Goshawk   Donker Witvalk

Melierax metabates   Heuglin, 1861: *White Nile, between 6° and 7° N. lat.*

PLATE 16 (OPP. P. 112), AD. AND IMM. PLATE 18. AD AND IMM.
Length 50—56 cm (wing 295—323; tail 203—220; tarsus 76—83; culmen 20—21). Iris brown; bill horn-black, red at base; cere and legs vermilion.

Identification: Easily confused with the Chanting Goshawk No. 165 but rump finely barred with black, not pure white; the secondaries are grey, the same colour as the mantle and not almost white as in No. 165. Young as figured very similar to young of No. 165 but upper tail-coverts barred rather than spotted.
Distribution: Senegal to Ethiopia and Arabia, south to Angola, Okavango and Rhodesia. Transvaal as far south as Skukuza.
Habits: The southernmost race of a Central Africa species. Often to be seen perched on the top of trees or sailing about like the Pallid Harrier in search of its prey.
Food: Small animals such as lizards, small rodents or large insects. Said not to harm chickens.
Voice: A prolonged musical piping. Also a shrill whistle and a loud "kek".
Breeding: Nests in trees from August to October in Rhodesia. The nest is placed 10 to 30 feet up and is festooned with cobwebs. Eggs, usually 1, sometimes 2, are white, chalky and rough. Average (25) 53,1 × 41,6 (48,8—59,3 × 38—45,5). One 42 × 35,3.

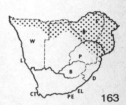

163

LOCAL RACE:
M.m. mechowi Cabanis, 1882: *Malanje, Angola.* From our area northwards to Kenya. Another race in north-east Africa and Arabia.

164 See No. 165

165 Chanting Goshawk   Groot Witvalk

Melierax canorus   (Thunberg), 1799: *South Africa = Great Karoo.*

PLATE 16 (OPP. P. 112). AD. AND IMM. PLATE 18. AD. AND IMM.
Length 53—63 cm (wing ♂ 328—346—362, ♀ 360—372—392; tail 228—268; tarsus 84—100; culmen 18,5—22. 23 specimens, 11 ♂, 12 ♀). Iris red-brown, yellow-green in young; bill blackish; cere and base of bill orange to brick-red; legs red, yellow in young.

Identification: Very like the last species but has pure white rump and almost pure white secondaries which contrast strongly, particularly in flight, with the back. Appears almost white and gull-like in flight. Larger than the Pallid Harrier No. 168 and showing darker tail, red legs and cere. Young, see No. 163. The red legs appear before the adult plumage.
Distribution: Cape Province, except the Cape Peninsula and southern coastal strip, north to the Cunene and western border of Rhodesia.
Habits: Often to be seen perched on the highest trees, or telegraph poles in dry country. Quite common in favoured localities such as parts of the Karroo. Inhabits mountainous or open country and desert. A sluggish bird, not at all

165

117

dashing, even catching much of its prey by walking about on the ground. Flight deliberate, almost gull-like.

Food: Mainly lizards, large insects and other small weak animals.

Voice: Mounts to a great height and performs a dipping display flight, uttering at the same time a loud, clear call.

Breeding: Nests in winter in the Cape Province, September to November in Rhodesia. The nest is placed on top of a bush, thorn-tree or telegraph pole and is lined with hair, wool and dung. Eggs, 1 or 2, bluish white. Average (20) 55,8 × 42,9 (50,5—60 × 40,6—45,7).

LOCAL RACE:
(a) *M.c. canorus* (Thunberg), 1799: *South Africa = Great Karoo.* As described above.
(b) *M.c. argentior* Clancey, 1960: *Sukses, S.W.A.* This is a lighter, more silvery form ranging from S.W.A. to the coast of Angola.

166   See page xxxi

167   African Marsh Harrier   Paddavreter

Circus ranivorus   (Daudin), 1800: *Cape Province.*

Native Name: Mankholi (S).

PLATE 16 (OPP. P. 112). AD. AND IMM. PLATE 18. AD. AND IMM.
Length 44—49 cm (wing ♂ 340—353—368, ♀ 365—375—395; tail 210—248; tarsus 72—82; culmen 19—22. 18 specimens 10 ♂, 8 ♀). Iris yellow, brown in young; bill black; cere and legs yellow.

Identification: The only harrier with deep chestnut chest and *pale patch* at the shoulder in flight. No white rump. Young birds have white across the chest as shown in Plate 16, and a variable amount of white on the nape.

Distribution: Throughout our region except South West Africa and the dry central Kalahari.

167

Habits: The common resident harrier of southern Africa occurring wherever there are large marshes. Is generally seen gliding over its home marsh; may also stray quite far over cultivated land or low scrub, but returns before long. Seldom alights on the ground, spending hours on the wing. Beats low over the ground with rather laboured flight and when prey is seen executes a curious half-roll and backward turn very suddenly falling as if shot.

Food: Frogs, water-rats, wounded birds and young chicks. Not normally considered harmful to poultry.

Voice: A mewing cry.

Breeding: Nests in the marshes constructing a mass of sticks and rushes in thick reeds or marshy growths. In the south-west Cape in August to December; slightly later further east and in the north. December to June and September in Rhodesia. Eggs, 3 to 5, are white slightly bluish, often stained by wet feet of the parents. Average South African (100) 46,8 × 37,1 (43—51,3 × 33,4—40). Incubation apparently mainly by female, the male catching food and dropping it on nest or passing it to female who flies up to meet him. Incubation 30, nestling 40 days.

168   Pallid Harrier   Vaal Paddavreter

Circus macrourus   (Gmelin), 1771: *Veronetz, South Russia.*

PLATE 16 (OPP. P. 112), ♂ AND ♀. PLATE 18 ♂ AND ♀.
Length 44—48 cm (wing ♂ 330—356, ♀ 345—391; tail 195—200; tarsus 63—70; culmen
15—17. 12 specimens ex *Handbk. Brit. Birds*). Iris yellow, brown in young; bill black;
cere and legs yellow.

Identification: Adult male as figured. Female very similar to female Montagu's Harrier No. 170 but ruff paler, more contrasting; breast less streaked. Young not distinguishable in the field from young Montagu's. In hand, at all stages the emargination of second primary is hidden by the primary coverts or just visible.

Distribution: A common migrant from south-eastern Europe and western Asia, which does not breed here. Comes as far south as the eastern Cape Province on the east and northern South West Africa on the west. Recorded once from Vergelegen, Western Cape. Arrives in late October and departs in April.

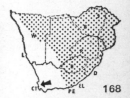

Habits: Usually seen flying across country, close to the ground and with characteristic mode of flight; the body does not rise and fall with each wing-beat as it does in Montagu's Harrier. Sometimes enters open woodland and is not exclusively a bird of open veld as Montagu's is. Practically never perches on trees, however.

Food: Mice, young birds, locusts and small lower vertebrates. Seen to take a Spike-heeled Lark.

Voice: The same as Montagu's Harrier.

169   Black Harrier   Witkruis-valk

Circus maurus   (Temminck), 1828: *Cape of Good Hope.*

PLATE 16 (OPP. P. 112). AD. AND IMM. PLATE 18. AD. AND IMM.
Length 48—53 cm (wing ♂ 331—347, ♀ 363—370; tail 230—265; tarsus 63—71;
culmen 18—20). Iris yellow; bill black; cere and legs yellow.

Identification: Adult unmistakable; white rump a good field character. Young bird confusing, being chocolate-brown with paler edges to feathers of back; eyebrow and sides of face whitish; below buff with white on belly and upper tail-coverts which distinguishes young from Marsh Harrier. In flight adults show beautifully banded wings and tail, see Plate 18.

Distribution: Normal range the Bredasdorp area, the Little and Great Karoo and Namaqualand; appears to wander extensively out of breeding season as far as Gibeon and Gamsberg in South West Africa, Lake Ngami in Botswana, southern Transvaal and southern Natal.

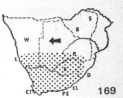

Habits: A resident species, though apparently given to local migration, usually found near rivers, dams, and vleis, in somewhat drier areas than the Marsh Harrier. Also quarters the veld miles from the nearest water. A species once thought to be becoming extinct but seen commonly recently. Soars high in the air over its breeding territory.

Food: Little recorded, doubtless frogs, lizards, rodents, and young birds.
Voice: "A shrill stridulous cry".
Breeding: The nest is placed in marshy vegetation and is composed of dry reeds and sticks lined with wool and hair. Eggs, 3 to 5, are white usually plain but sometimes marked with dark brown. Average (11) 47,2 × 38,3 (43,5—50,3 × 36,4—40,3).

170 Montagu's Harrier   Blou Paddavreter

Circus pygargus (Linnaeus), 1758: *England.*

PLATE 16 (OPP. P. 112) ♂ AND ♀. ♂. PLATE 18 ♂ AND ♀.
Length 40—47 cm (wing ♂ 340—380, ♀ 350—380; tail 200—220; tarsus 55—60; culmen 15,5—16. 12 specimens *ex Hnbk. Brit Bds.*). Iris yellow, brown in female and young; bill black; cere and legs yellow.

Identification: Male as figured; in flight shows narrow black wing-bar, absent in male Pallid Harrier No. 168. Female, more heavily streaked below than female Pallid, ruff less conspicuous. Young unstreaked below thus resembling young and female Pallid Harrier. In the hand, at all ages, the emargination of the second primary is about an inch beyond the primary coverts.
Distribution: A migrant from Europe and Asia which appears only in mid-summer and does not breed here. Recorded from November to March. Comes as far south as the eastern Cape Province. On the west to northern South West Africa.

Habits: Has the same sailing or gliding flight as the other harriers but is more buoyant than the Pallid Harrier, the body rising and falling with each
170 wing-beat. Occurs mainly on the open grass veld and is seldom seen in marshes.
Food: Rodents, young birds, and insects.
Voice: A shrill, querulous "kek-kek-kek".

171 Gymnogene

Polyboroides typus A. Smith, 1829: *Eastern Cape Province.*

PLATE 16 (OPP. P. 112) AD. AND IMM. A AND B. PLATE 18. AD. AND IMM. B.
Length 60—66 cm (wing ♂ 443—453—463, ♀ 457—483; tail 280—320; tarsus 83—100; culmen 22—26. 10 specimens, 7 ♂, 3 ♀). Iris dark brown; cere and bare cheeks yellow; bill black; legs yellow.

Identification: The bare face and white band across the middle of the tail distinguishes this bird from the Chanting Goshawks Nos. 163—5. The legs too are yellow not red. The young bird is confusing; "A" shows first plumage (note all yellow bill) "B" shows second plumage, rather paler below and with some white on the nape. All young show white at base of feathers when ruffled. Wings barred as in Plate 18. The rather vulturine head and ungainly appearance are distinctive at all ages. The feathers of the nape stand out almost like a ruff, giving a distinct owl-like expression. Soft parts of face flush red when breeding.

Distribution: From the south-west Cape (uncommon) eastwards to Natal and northwards to the Zambezi and beyond to Sennar on the west and Ethiopia on the east.

Habits: A curious bird which sometimes walks over the veld but is more often seen clinging to the trunks of trees, flapping wildly and falling about as it searches in cracks and holes for lizards, etc. On these occasions the legs appear almost double-jointed. Also to be seen perched quietly on some conspicuous post, especially along streams and the border of forests. Quite often soars, varying its flight with repeated upward flights followed by steep downward swoops, calling the while. A great robber of birds' nests, particularly those of weavers.

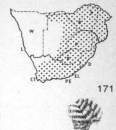

171

Food: Very varied, young birds, snakes, lizards, bats, insects, palm-nut husks, frogs, etc.

Voice: A thin screaming "peeeeeee" or "piiiii". Also described as curlew-like while soaring.

Breeding: Constructs the usual hawk-type of nest in the fork of a large tree or occasionally in a hole in a cliff. Eggs, two in number are laid in September—December, whitish, heavily covered with brownish and yellowish streaks. Average (39) 56,3 × 43,7 (51,4—61,4 × 40,7—46,4). Incubation by both sexes, mainly female, about 35 days. Fledgling 50—55 days.

LOCAL RACE:
P.t. typus A. Smith, 1829: *Eastern Cape Province.* Throughout Africa except West Africa where a shorter-winged race occurs.

172 Osprey   Visvalk

Pandion haliaetus (Linnaeus), 1758: *Sweden*

PLATE 16 (OPP. P. 112). PLATE 18. AD.

Length 55—63 cm (wing ♂ 420—463, ♀ 470—507; tail 170—240; tarsus 57—59; culmen 30—40. 5 specimens, 3 ♂, 2 ♀, sex rather doubtful). Iris yellow, bill black; cere blue-grey; legs greenish white.

Identification: White crown and dark line through eye render this species unmistakable. Young similar but crown streaked, feathers of back edged with buff.

Distribution: Cosmopolitan. Uncommon in Southern Africa. Recorded once from South West Africa (Marienhof), otherwise may appear anywhere.

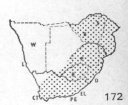

172

Habits: Essentially a bird of rivers, dams, and coastal lagoons. Probably migratory in our area though it does breed here. Likes to sit on a conspicuous bare branch over the water. When fishing flies with alternate flapping and gliding flight searching for its prey. On sighting it, hovers for a few seconds with legs dangling and then drops to the water disappearing in a cloud of spray. May submerge completely. On rising with a fish, which is carried head foremost, shakes the water off its plumage with a convulsive shake. Often harassed by the Fish Eagle which steals its prey.

Food: Fish, captured alive and very rarely other small animals.

Voice: A descending whistling "tchip, tchip, tchip".

Breeding: Recorded once nesting in trees in South Africa during November. Eggs, 2 or 3, white marked with red and yellowish brown to a variable extent.

121

FRANCOLINS

Average (8) 59,5 × 44,7 (53,8—62,7 × 41,2—46). Incubation period 35 days (Europe). Nestling period 52—70 days (Europe).

LOCAL RACE:
P.h. haliaetus (Linnaeus), 1758: *Sweden*. The race occurring in Europe and Asia.

Family PHASIANIDAE

Members of this family comprise the well-known Pheasants, Partridges and Quails, and to it our domestic fowls are also referred. They are terrestrial birds only taking to trees when disturbed by enemies or to roost. They nest in hollows in the ground under bushes or tufts of grass, and most species lay fairly large clutches of eggs. The chicks can run soon after being hatched and develop flight feathers soon afterwards, this enabling them to escape their enemies by running away and hiding at first and later by flight for short distances. The larger species are all very local in their habitat, and consequently develop into different species and genera in great variety according to the conditions of their environment: but the smaller quails are more restless and migratory in habits. Their diet consists of bulbs, seeds and vegetable matter, varied very often with insects and their larvae. They have tasty flesh and are much sought after by sportsmen, besides carnivorous birds, mammals and reptiles. Most of the species are gregarious and have very distinctive call-notes, by means of which they are able to foregather when dispersed by enemies, and also challenging crowing notes in males of pugnacious species.

173 Coqui Francolin   Swempie

Francolinus coqui (A. Smith), 1836: *near Kurrichane, Western Transvaal.*

Native Name: i-Swempie (Z).

PLATE 20 (OPP. P. 128) ♂ AND ♀
Length about 28 cm (wing ♂ 130—137—144, ♀ 128—132—139; tail 60—73; tarsus 28—35; culmen 19—23. 22 specimens, 12 ♂, 10 ♀). Iris hazel; bill ashy horn; legs yellow.

173

Identification: Adults unmistakable, see Plate 20. Young resemble adults but are browner (less chestnut) above and more buffy below.
Distribution: From Natal, Transvaal and northern South West Africa, Waterberg plateau, northwards to East Africa as far north as Somaliland.
Habits: An inhabitant of grass country where there are trees or shrubs. In drier country may frequent bush-covered sand-dunes. Sits very tight and flushes reluctantly, but once airborne flies quite far before settling again. Typically a ground bird, only taking to trees when chased by dogs and roosting on the ground.
Food: Seeds and insects.
Voice: A loud penetrating "kwee-kit, kwee-kit", heard mostly in the morning, at mid-day and evening. The name "Swempie" is onomatopoeic. Alarm note "chirr-r-r-r".
Breeding: Nests from October to March under a tuft of grass. Nest a slight hollow lined with grass and leaves. Eggs 4 to 6, varying in different clutches from white to pale pink. Average (40) 32,8 × 27,0 (31—35,7 21,6—29,3).

122

LOCAL RACES:
(a) *F.c. coqui* (A. Smith), 1836: *near Kurrichane, Western Transvaal.* As figured, size given above. Transvaal, Botswana and Matabeleland.
(b) *F.c. hoeschianus* Streseman, 1937: *Waterberg, S.W.A.* Female paler red, more barred, on chest. Confined to the Waterberg plateau.
(c) *F.c. vernayi* (Roberts), 1932: *Tsotsoroga Pan, Ngamiland.* Characterised by fewer bars below. Northern Botswana.
(d) *F.c. campbelli* (Roberts), 1928: *Mount Edgecombe, Natal.* Natal Zululand and southern Mozambique.

174 Crested Francolin — Bospatrys

Francolinus sephaena (A. Smith), 1836: *Marico River, Western Transvaal.*

Native Name: isi-Kehle (Z).

PLATE 20 (OPP. P. 128).
Length 33—35cm (wing ♂ 162—167—170, ♀ 155—160; tail 82—100; tarsus 38—45; culmen 23—26,5. 10 specimens, 7 ♂, 3 ♀). Iris hazel; bill brown; legs red.

Identification: Very similar to the next species but is not streaked on the belly. Male slightly larger, and has spurs. Female finely barred on back with brown and black. Young have eyebrow buff and only fine streaking on chest.
Distribution: From Zululand (Umfolozi) to Ethiopia across to Transvaal, Botswana and northern South West Africa.
Habits: Found only in the matted bush, usually in moister parts of the acacia veld, also likes the neighbourhood of koppies. Ventures out into old lands to feed. Commonly found in pairs, often accompanied by young birds from the previous nesting season. Has the interesting habit of cocking its tail vertically so that it looks like a bantam. Roosts in trees. Not easily flushed as it prefers to slink off into thick cover.
Food: Bulbs, seeds, berries and insects.
Voice: Call sounds like "Beer and Cognac", "kwerri kwetchi" or "tcheker-itch" often repeated. After going to roost the cock crows loudly and is answered by the female, unless she is brooding, when she keeps quiet.
Breeding: Eggs are laid from October to March and May in a shallow depression lined with a few strands of grass. They number 4 to 9 and are white to cream or pinkish, very hard and thick-shelled. Average (43) 39,3 × 30,4 (37,1—43,2 × 28,8—32,4). Incubation 19 days (c).

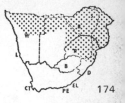

174

LOCAL RACES:
(a) *F.s. sephaena* (A. Smith), 1836: *Marico River, W. Transvaal.* Western Transvaal and southern Botswana. As figured. The largest form, much vermiculated below. Size above.
(b) *F.s. zuluensis* (Roberts), 1924: *Umfolosi Game Reserve.* Zululand and southern Mozambique. Somewhat smaller (wing ♂ 156—162 (3), ♀ 144—150 (5) and darker in general, much vermiculated below.
(c) *F.s. zambesiae* Mackworth-Praed, 1920: *Mesanague, Mozambique.* Eastern Transvaal to the Zambesi Valley from about Chirundu eastwards. Wing ♂ 153—157—165 (9), ♀ 147—151—157 (7). Paler than (b).
(d) *F.s. thompsoni* (Roberts), 1924: *Grootfontein, South West Africa.* South West Africa and southern Angola across to Matabeleland. Paler than (a), very little vermiculated below. Wing ♂ 157—163—170 (17), ♀ 148—153—157 (9).

123

175 Kirk's Francolin — Mosambiek-bospatrys

Francolinus rovuma Gray, 1867: *Rovuma River, Tanganyika*.
PLATE 20 (OPP. P. 128).
Length 32—34 cm (wing ♂ 152, ♀ 146; tail 85—90; tarsus 36—42; culmen 22—24). Iris brown; bill blackish; legs red.

Identification: Rather similar to the last species but streaked on lower abdomen. Sexes alike but only male has spurs.

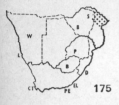

Distribution: Mozambique northwards along the coast to Somaliland.

Habits: Inhabits the country along rivers and near marshes where it is usually seen in small coveys keeping close to thick cover. General habits like those of the last species.

Food: Seeds, roots and vegetable matter such as bulbs, shoots, etc. Also insects and snails.

175

Voice: Very noisy, normal cry a harsh, squeaky "cheek-chick-a-chika; cheek-chick-a-chika".

Breeding: The nest is a scrape on the ground, among grass or under bushes. Eggs are cream-coloured with darker specks. They are laid during June and July.

LOCAL RACE:
F.r. rovuma Gray 1867: *Rovuma River, Tanganyika*. From our area as far north as Somaliland, north of which another race occurs.

176 Grey-wing Francolin — Bergpatrys

Francolinus africanus Stephens, 1819: *Hottentot country* = *King William's Town, Cape*.

Native Name: Isakhwatsha (X).

PLATE 20 (OPP. P. 128).
Length 33 cm (wing ♂ 158—162—165, ♀ 150—159—166; tail 62—80; tarsus 32—41; culmen 25—30. 19 specimens, 10 ♂, 9 ♀). Iris brown; bill brown; legs yellowish brown.

Identification: Very similar to other "partridges" but with lower abdomen barred with black combined with circlet of black and white barring round neck. Throat grey. Males only have spurs, sexes otherwise alike. Young have black cross-barring on lower throat and are generally duller.

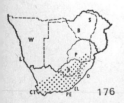

Distribution: Flats and mountainous areas of Cape Province, Natal, Orange Free State and Swaziland. Occurs again in the high mountains of East Africa as far north as Ethiopia.

Habits: A fairly common bird in the Cape while in the Drakensberg it formerly occurred in very large coveys but latterly appears to have decreased in numbers. It occurs in grassy patches on the hillsides in coveys. When

176

flushed the coveys have the distinctive habit of rising with loud squealing notes and disappearing round a shoulder of the mountain or over a precipice.

Food: Bulbs, seeds and insects.

Voice: Apart from the squealing mentioned above utters call, mainly in the mornings and at sunset of "squea-*kee*oo, squea-*kee*oo".

Breeding: Nests under a tuft of grass, laying about six eggs, August—October in the Cape; later, November in Natal; in colour yellowish brown, sometimes speckled with brown and slate. Average (33) 38,8 × 30,4 (36—41,8 × 28,7—32,5).

LOCAL RACE:
F.a. africanus Stephens, 1819: *Hottentot country* = *King William's Town, Cape.*

177   Shelley's Francolin   Laeveldpatrys

Francolinus shelleyi Grant, 1890: *Hartley Hills, Umfuli River, Rhodesia.*

Native Names: i-Dambira (D); i-Tendele (G).

PLATE 20 (OPP. P. 128).
Length about 33 cm (wing ♂ 168—170—175; ♀ 160—165—172; tail 65—87; tarsus 34—44; culmen 27—34. 17 specimens, 7 ♂, 10 ♀). Iris brown; bill grey, mandible yellow at base; legs yellow.

Identification: Distinguishable from other "partridges" by the very chestnut chest and flanks enclosing an area of bold black and white barring. Sexes alike, male only spurred. Young bird paler with streaks on throat.
Distribution: From the foothills of Natal northwards to Malawi and beyond Uganda. Common in Mashonaland, rare westwards.
Habits: Found in stony ground, as a rule, where the grass is fairly short. Also found in lightly wooded country. Lies very close when disturbed.
Food: Roots, bulbs and insects.
Voice: A musical whistle, unlike other Francolins, sounding like "Tel-él-kebir" or "I'll-drink-yer-beer" repeated three or four times.
Breeding: Nests under a tuft of grass, the shallow depression being lined with grass, during August to September. Eggs 4 to 7, vary from white to pinkish, in some cases finely spotted with brown. Average (30) 38,0 × 31,1 (35,2—40,4 × 28,7—32,3).

177

LOCAL RACE:
F.s. shelleyi Grant, 1890: *Umfuli River, Rhodesia.* This race occurs in our area northwards to Tanzania and Uganda.

178   Redwing Francolin   Rooivlerk-patrys

Francolinus levaillantii (Valenciennes), 1825: *Cape* = *Swellendam*

Native Names: in-Tendele (Z); Intendele (X); Khoale (S).

PLATE 20 (OPP. P. 128).
Length about 38 cm (wing 160—167—176; tail 60—74; tarsus 40—45; culmen 31—37. 11 specimens). Iris hazel; bill dusky, yellow base; legs yellow.

Identification: Similar to the next species, from which it may be distinguished by the broader band of black and white feathers below the throat, Sexes alike, female usually spurless. Young paler, "necklace" less distinct, buffy-white and black.
Distribution: Southern Cape Province, Natal, northwards to Zoutpansberg. Also occurs in Tanzania and Kenya.
Habits: A fairly common inhabitant of moister grasslands, particularly in the mountains where it favours sheltered valleys and reedy situations. Commonly found in coveys comprising the family party of the last brood. Flies strongly

178

and usually quite far when flushed, but does not readily flush a second time. Sleeps in parties.

Food: Insects, seeds and bulbs.

Voice: "Chirrya-cheep, chirrya-cheep, chirrya-cheep", mainly morning and evening.

Breeding: Nests are situated in tufts of grass from March to July in the Eastern Cape. During summer, October to February, in Natal. Eggs are variable, 3 to 5 in the normal clutch, brownish yellow, usually spotted. Average (25) 40,3 × 32,6 (38,5—43,2 × 31—34).

LOCAL RACE:
F.l. levaillantii (Valenciennes), 1825: *Cape = Swellendam.* Throughout our area. Size above.

179 Orange River Francolin   Kalahari-patrys

Francolinus levaillantoides   A. Smith, 1836: *Upper Orange River.*

Native Names: Khoale (S); Mashokh (Ch.).

PLATE 20 (OPP. P. 128), NOS: 179 *(a), (b), (d), (e), (f)* AND 180.
Length 33—35cm (wing 156—165—173; tail 71—82; tarsus 34—41; culmen 25—31. 21 specimens). Iris hazel; bill horn; legs yellowish brown.

Identification: Similar to the last species, but the bands of black and white feathers which start above the eyes do not meet at the back of the neck as they do in the Redwing Francolin. The patch of similar feathers at the base of the throat is also much smaller. Sexes alike but no spurs in female.

Distribution: From the Orange Free State and southern Transvaal across the Kalahari to northern South West Africa. Also southern Mozambique.

Habits: Much the same as its congeners but essentially a bird of drier veld. Usually found in coveys of up to a dozen individuals on open plains, or in the Kalahari, around pans. In South West Africa also found in mountainous country.

 179

Food: Bulbs and corms of Moraea, seeds and insects.

Voice: Normal call uttered at sunrise and sunset—"kibitele, kibitele, kibitele" (*I am choking* in Bechuana), or "pirrie-perrie, pirrie-perrie, pirrie-perrie".

Breeding: The nest is a scrape under a tuft of grass. Eggs normaly 5—8, are yellowish brown sometimes with brown speckles. Average (17) 36,9 × 28,9 (34,4—40,7 × 28—32). Laid February to May in Transvaal, also September.

LOCAL RACES:
(a) F.l. levaillantoides A. Smith, 1836: *Upper Orange River.* As figured on Plate 20, *(a)* and *(b).* Orange Free State, southern Mozambique, southern and western Transvaal and southern Botswana.
(d) F.l. pallidior Neumann, 1908: *South of the Cunene River = Tsumeb.* As figured. Wing 160—172 (6). Tsumeb area of South West Africa.
(e) F.l. langi (Roberts), 1932: *Nkate, N. Botswana.* A very pale form, particularly above. Northern Botswana.
(f) F.l. kalaharica (Roberts), 1932: *Damara Pan, Central Kalahari.* As figured. As pale as *(e)* but rufous spots on flanks and breast almost absent. Central Kalahari.
(g) F.l. watti Macdonald, 1953: *Windhoek.* Reddest of the western races but generally paler than the eastern forms. Necklace narrow.
(h) F.l. jugularis Büttikofer, 1889: *Gambos, Angola.* Slightly paler than *(d).* Necklace of black and white feathers much broader.

181 Cape Francolin   Kaapse Fisant

Francolinus capensis   (Gmelin), 1789: *Cape of Good Hope.*

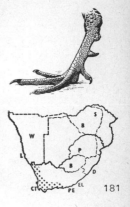

PLATE 21 (OPP. P. 129).
Length 40—42 cm (wing ♂ 218—227, ♀ 205; tail 93—115; tarsus 53—63; culmen
19—24). Iris reddish brown; bill dark horn, base orange; legs dark yellow.

Identification: One of the larger, darker Francolins with no red on throat and
with broad white streaks on feathers of belly. Sexes alike, females without
spurs unless very old.

Distribution: Confined to the south-west Cape north to the Orange River and
eastwards to Uitenhage.

Habits: Frequents the sheltering scrub along streams and rivers, but not the
heavy forests. Crows loudly at sunrise and sunset. Usually in coveys consisting of family parties but often seen alone. Quite a common bird in favoured
localities, many gathering to drink in the late afternoon. Becomes very tame
around farm houses.

181

Food: Bulbs, seeds, berries and insects.

Voice: A loud crowing cackle.

Breeding: The nest is placed under a bush during September to December.
Eggs, normally 6—8 but up to 14 recorded (? two females), are pale pink or
purplish pink. Average (19) 48,6 × 37,5 (42—55,7 × 35,6—38,8).

182 Red-billed Francolin   Rooibek-fisant

Francolinus adspersus   Waterhouse, 1838: *Kuisib River, Damaraland.*

PLATE 21 (OPP. P. 129).
Length 30—38cm (wing ♂ 171—183—201, ♀ 156—167—175; tail 80—105; tarsus
40—50; culmen 17—22. 61 specimens, 31 ♂, 30 ♀). Iris brown; bill red, bare face
yellow; legs red.

Identification: The red bill and bare yellow skin round eye are distinctive in
combination with the finely *barred* feathers of the belly. Sexes alike, but males
only spurred. Young have mantle similar to rest of back; some scapulars
tipped black.

Distribution: A bird of the dry areas of South West Africa, the Kalahari,
southern Angola, north-western Rhodesia and western Transvaal.

Habits: A common bird found in large coveys of up to twenty. Feeds in the
open and when disturbed either runs fast for cover or flies into trees. Usually
found near water or in dry watercourses where water is found for part of the
year.

182

Food: Seeds, plant shoots and insects.

Voice: Extremely noisy, the crowing notes harsher and more irritating even
than the Cape Francolin.

Breeding: Nests in Damaraland in late summer (March) and in Ngamiland,
where it is very common, in winter—May and June. Eggs, 6 to 8, vary from
creamy to brownish yellow. Average (65) 42,2 × 33,4 (38,9—46,5 ×
.31,9—35,2).

PLATE 20

173. *Francolinus coqui coqui.* Coqui Francolin. Swempie. ♂ and ♀.
174. *Francolinus sephaena sephaena.* Crested Francolin. Bospatrys.
175. *Francolinus rovuma.* Kirk's Francolin. Mosambiek-bospatrys.
176. *Francolinus africanus.* Grey-wing Francolin. Bergpatrys.
177. *Francolinus shelleyi shelleyi.* Shelley's Francolin. Laeveldpatrys.
178. *Francolinus levaillantii levaillantii.* Redwing Francolin.
Rooivlerk-patrys.
179 *(a).* *Francolinus levaillantoides levaillantoides.* Orange River Francolin.
Kalahari-Patrys.
179 *(b).* *Francolinus levaillantoides levaillantoides.* Orange River Francolin.
Kalahari-Patrys.
179 *(d).* *Francolinus levaillantoides pallidior.* Orange River Francolin.
Kalahari-Patrys.
179 *(f).* *Francolinus levaillantoides kalaharica.* Orange River Francolin.
Kalahari-Patrys.
189. *Coturnix coturnix africana.* African Quail. Afrikaanse Kwartel.
♂ and ♀.
190. *Coturnix delegorguei delegorguei.* Harlequin Quail. Bont Kwartel.
♂ and ♀.
191. *Coturnix adansoni.* Blue Quail. Blou Kwartel. ♂ and ♀.
Not to scale. Should be smaller.

181

182

184 ♂

♀ 184

183

188 A

188 C

188 E

185

188 B

188 D

192 A

192 B

193

K. NEWMAN '76

PLATE 21

181. *Francolinus capensis.* Cape Francolin. Kaapse Fisant.
182. *Francolinus adspersus.* Red-billed Francolin. Rooibek-fisant.
183. *Francolinus natalensis.* Natal Francolin. Natalse Fisant.
184. *Francolinus hartlaubi bradfieldi.* Hartlaub's Francolin.
Hartlaubse Fisant. ♂ and ♀.
185. *Pternistis swainsoni swainsoni.* Swainson's Francolin. Bosveldfisant.
188 *(a). Pternistis afer castaneiventer.* Red-necked Francolin.
Rooikeel-fisant.
188 *(b). Pternistis afer notatus.* Red-necked Francolin. Rooikeel-fisant.
188 *(c). Pternistis afer lehmanni.* Red-necked Francolin. Rooikeel-fisant.
188 *(d). Pternistis afer swynnertoni.* Red-necked Francolin. Rooikeel-fisant.
188 *(e). Pternistis afer cunenensis.* Red-necked Francolin. Rooikeel-fisant.
192 *(a). Numida meleagris coronata.* Crowned Guinea-fowl. Tarentaal.
192 *(b). Numida meleagris mitrata.* Crowned Guinea-fowl. Tarentaal.
193. *Guttera edouardi edouardi.* Crested Guinea-fowl. Kuifkop-tarentaal.

129

183 Natal Francolin — Natalse Fisant

Francolinus natalensis   A. Smith, 1834: *Durban, Natal.*

Native Name: isi-Kwehle (Z).

PLATE 21 (OPP. P. 129).
Length 30—38 cm (wing ♂ 169—177—188, ♀ 155—162—170; tail 76—100; tarsus 35—51; culmen 15—21. 39 specimens, 30 ♂, 9 ♀). Iris hazel; bill pink; legs red.

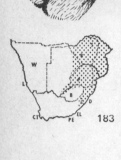

Identification: Resembles the last two species but has neither the fine barring below and bare skin round eye of the Red-billed Francolin, nor the white streaking on the flanks of the Cape Francolin. Sexes alike, female usually lacks spurs. Young tinged with chocolate on chest and upper parts.
Distribution: Orange Free State, Natal, Transvaal and Rhodesia below 900 metres in Mashonaland but up to 1 500 metres in the Midlands.
Habits: Occurs in the acacia scrub, especially where there are rocks as well, though often away from them, along the banks of streams and rivers. A fairly common species. Roosts at night in trees, to which it also retires when disturbed during the day. Coveys usually number less than ten birds.

183

Food: Seeds and insects.
Voice: Most often to be heard at sunrise and sunset, sounding like "kwaali, Kwaali, kwaali", whence the native name.
Breeding: Breeds in the latter part of summer, January and February, and also in winter, April to July; eggs, creamy yellow. December to September in Rhodesia. Average (22) 42 × 34,6 (39,1—46,8 × 31,7—36,6).

LOCAL RACE:
Francolinus natalensis natalensis A. Smith, 1834: *Durban, Natal.* As above. Other races extralimital.

184 Hartlaub's Francolin — Hartlaubse Fisant

Francolinus hartlaubi   Bocage 1869: *Huilla, Angola*

PLATE 21 (OPP. P. 129), ♂ AND ♀.
Length 25—28 cm (wing ♂ 142—147—155. ♀ 137—139—141; tail 70—90; tarsus 29—34; culmen 20—25. 12 specimens, 6 ♂, 6 ♀). Iris hazel; bill yellowish brown; legs ochre yellow.

Identification: Quite distinctive, sexes not alike, see Plate 21. Spurs are flattened excrescences in male, small knobs in female.
Distribution: Southern Angola southwards to northern South West Africa.
Habits: Occurs only in rocky places; when flushed flies just far enough to disappear round a corner or take refuge on top of high rocks. Roosts at night among rocks or on a precipice.
Food: Berries, insects, bulbs and seeds.
Voice: Calls at sunrise and after sunset, though it may be heard during the day when cloudy. Call somewhat resembling that of the Redwing Francolin. Also a squeaky alarm note when flushed.

184

Breeding: A nest containing one broken and two whole eggs was found by Mr. H. Hare in a nook on the ledge of a precipice at Waterberg on 15th May, 1937, from which the sitting hen had evidently been carried off by some carnivorous animal, as there were feathers from its breast lying about the nest. The eggs are uniformly creamy coloured, oblong in shape and measure 43,5 × 29,8 and 42 × 29. Nest found near Windhoek in June.

LOCAL RACES:
(a) F.h. bradfieldi (Roberts), 1928: *Waterberg Police Post*. As figured in Plate 21, size above, Waterberg, Otavifontein and Tsumeb.
(b) F.h. crypticus Streseman, 1939: *Onguati, Kaokoveld*. Brighter coloured above and below. Wing ♂ 146—148 (2), ♀ 134—138 (4), Kaokoveld from Erongo to Huab River.

185 Swainson's Francolin   Bosveldfisant

Pternistis swainsoni (A. Smith), 1836: *North of Kurrichane*.

Native Names: le-Khuku, le-Khokhoa (Ch.).

PLATE 21 (OPP. P. 129).
Length 34—39 cm (wing ♂ 187—192—202, ♀ 170—180—187; tail 71—90; tarsus 46—60; culmen 20—25; 23 specimens, 13 ♂, 10 ♀). Iris brown; bill black above, mandible red; legs black.

Identification: The lack of white striping on the feathers of the belly prevents confusion with the next species. Young bird is feathered on throat which is whitish; cheeks and above eye also creamy; more rusty above and below, bill black. Note that legs are black, not red in adults.

Distribution: The dry bushveld savanna in and around the Kalahari Desert, extending into similar dry thornveld in the eastern Transvaal, the Vaal River, Damaraland, Ovamboland and north-western Rhodesia. Also Mozambique.

185

Habits: Its favourite haunts are near streams and waterholes, though it sometimes occurs far from water in the dry season, being able apparently to find sufficient moisture for its needs in bulbs, wild melons, etc. May be seen singly but is usually in family parties of about six. Males have the habit, at sunrise, of standing on a bare branch or antheap and crowing loudly. They also crow in the evening after retiring to roost in trees. Come to drink in the morning and evening. When alarmed run with crouching, drawn-out bodies through the grass with almost snake-like movements.

Food: Seeds, bulbs and insects.

Voice: A loud harsh crowing, sounding like "kwahli" repeated about six times, the first loudest and the last few dying down and rapid.

Breeding: Nests mainly from December to May, but also recorded in every month except July. The nest, lined with grass, is well hidden and normally contains 4—5 eggs. Average (42) 44,1 × 35,9 (42,5 × 47,6 × 34,5—38,2).

LOCAL RACES:
(a) P.s. swainsoni (A. Smith), 1836: *North of Kurrichane, W. Transvaal*. As figured on Plate 21. Size given above. East of the Kalahari.
(b) P.s. damarensis Roberts, 1931: *Otjiwarongo, South West Africa*. Damaraland Plateau. A large form with a rather heavier bill (culmen up to 27); paler below with thinner shaft stripes. Wing ♂ 203—207 (4), ♀ 182—192 (4).
(c) P.s. gilli Roberts, 1932: *Ondongua*. Ngamiland, eastwards to north-west Matabeleland and northern Mashonaland. A small form paler and thinly striped below. Wing ♂ 187—197 (8), ♀ 164—175 (11).
(d) P.s. lundazi (White), 1947: *Lumpamadzi R. Lundazi, Zambia*. Botswana north of Lake Ngami and Lake Dow.

186 See under **188** *(g)*

187 See under **188** *(e)* and *(f)*

188   Red-necked Francolin   Rooikeel-fisant

Pternistis afer   (Müller), 1776: *Africa* = Benguella.
Native Name: Inkwali (X and Z).

PLATE 21 (OPP. P. 129), *(a)*, *(b)*, *(c)*, *(d)* and *(e)*.
Length variable with race 25—38 cm (wing ♂ 206—209—215, ♀ 183; tail 81—100; tarsus 48—60; culmen 21—25. 6 specimens, 5 ♂, 1 ♀). Iris brown; bill and legs red.

Identification: The bare red throat, combined with flanks streaked with white, is distinctive. Young birds lack the red throat, and the feathers below are edged with chestnut. Sexes alike, female smaller and without spurs.
Distribution: From George eastwards to Mozambique and across Transvaal and Rhodesia to the Cunene River. Also through Zambia to Tanzania.
Habits: Usually found in small parties in thick bush at the edge of forest or round cultivated lands. When dogs are set at it, invariably takes refuge in thickly-foliaged trees.
188 Food: Roots, bulbs, insects and seeds.
Voice: Very noisy, like other Francolins uttering a harsh crowing note at sunrise and sunset, "choorr, choorr, choorr, chwirr," fading away at the end. In flight makes a loud unmusical "kek, kek, kek". Also a clucking alarm note in trees.
Breeding: In the Eastern Cape breeds from April to August, but in midsummer further north (See under *(e)*). Eggs are yellowish. Average (29) 45,3 × 35,9 (41,8—49 × 35—38).

LOCAL RACES:
(a) P.a. castaneiventer Gunning and Roberts, 1911: *Fort Beaufort.* As figured in Plate 21 *(a)*. Size given above. Port Elizabeth eastwards to Natal. Mainly black below but with some chestnut.
(b) P.a. notatus Roberts, 1924: *Knysna.* As shown on Plate 21 *(b)*, entirely black below, apart from the white striping.
(c) P.a. lehmanni Roberts, 1931: *Eastern Transvaal.* As shown on Plate 21 *(c)*. White stripes below much broader, Eastern Transvaal.
(d) P.a. swynnertoni Sclater, 1921: *Chirinda Forest, Rhodesia.* As figured in Plate 21. Beira and eastern Rhodesia. Breeds November to May.
(e) P.a. cunenensis Roberts, 1932: *Cunene River.* As figured. Has under parts of the body white with double black stripes. Also rather smaller. Wing ♂ 175—190; ♀ 160—170. Comes within our limits on the Cunene River.
(f) P.a. humboldti (Peters), 1854: *Tete.* Similar to *(d)* above but less white about the face. Wing ♂ 195—198 (4), ♀ 175—190 (2). Mid-Zambesi Valley, east of Quebrabrassa rapids.

188X   Chukar Partridge

Alectoris chukar.   Introduced, occurs on Table Mountain, near Villiersdorp, on Robben Island and in Natal.

189   African Quail   Afrikaanse Kwartel

Coturnix coturnix   (Linneaus), 1758: *Sweden.*

Native Names: Isagwityi (X); isi-Queque (Z).

PLATE 20 (OPP. P. 128), ♂ AND ♀.
Length about 18 cm (wing 97—101—107; tail 32—40; tarsus 23—25; culmen 12—15.
16 specimens). Iris light brown; bill almost black; legs flesh.

Identification: Males easily recognisable; female very like female of next
species but lacks a collar round the neck. Young males and non-breeding
males lack black throats.

Distribution: Migratory; may appear anywhere in the south east, arriving in
September and departing again about April. Winter records of the southern
race from South West Africa indicate a migration to this area from the south
east of the Republic. Also found all over Africa, Europe and Asia.

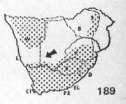

189

Habits: A restless bird which appears in grassy districts or lucerne fields in
many districts of South Africa. A few remain throughout the year. May be
very common in favoured localities and is shot a great deal even when
breeding. Usually heard calling from thickish cover or seen as they suddenly
flush at one's feet and dart swiftly away, with a startling whirr and squeaky
note, only to settle again farther on. Often they spring up in two's, fly parallel
for a time and then cross over, sportsmen who are aware of this waiting until
they do so and bagging both in one shot.

Food: Small seeds, insects and vegetable matter.

Voice: Normal call a penetrating "whit-*whit*tit, whit-*whit*tit", uttered by day
and night. When flushed goes "pree, pree, pree".

Breeding: The nest, a shallow cup of grass, is placed under a tuft, often in
standing grain, and is thus often destroyed during reaping or discovered and
taken by the harvesters. Breeding occurs during September and October in the
Cape, but from November to March as one goes further north. Clutches are
large, usually 6; but up to 10 to 12 eggs are sometimes found (? 2 females).
Eggs, yellowish, mottled with large blotches of brownish, but very often one
or two eggs in the clutch finely spotted. Average (100) 28,9 × 22,3
(25,9—31,2 × 20,8—24). Incubation by female only, 18—20 days (Europe).

LOCAL RACES:
(a) C.c. africana Temminck and Schlegel, 1849: *Cape Province.* Africa. Occurs in the
southern part of the continent. Summers in the Republic and winters in S.W.A. Darker
than the nominate but paler than the next race.
(b) C.c. erlangeri Zedlitz, 1912: *Cunni near Haror, E. Ethiopia.* A highlands form
resident in Rhodesia darker than *(a)*.

190   Harlequin Quail   Bont Kwartel

Coturnix delegorguei   Delegorgue, 1847: *Upper Limpopo River.*

Native Name: si-Kwaqa (G).

PLATE 20 (OPP. P. 128),♂ AND♀.
Length about 18 cm (wing 89—95—100 (37); tail 29—37; tarsus 19—25; culmen
11—13. 25 specimens). Iris brown; bill black; legs salmon.

Identification: Males unmistakable; females resemble female African Quails
but have "necklace" of black, and darker streaking on chest. Young birds are
dull equivalents of their respective sexes.

133

190

Distribution: In our area, a migrant as far south as the Eastern Province (rare) and the drier west north of the Orange River where it is more commonly met with. Otherwise all Africa south of the Sahara except the Congo forests.
Habits: Very similar to the African Quail, but usually found in drier treeless grassveld particularly round vleis. Usually arrives in September and departs in May but movements tend to be irregular, appearing sporadically in fair numbers and as mysteriously disappearing.
Food: Seeds mainly, also insects and green shoots.
Voice: Male utters a loud ringing "wit wit-wit wit wit-wit it".
Breeding: Recorded as nesting in the period August to October but also as late as March. Nest and eggs similar to those of African Quail but spots usually much finer. Average (50) 28,4 × 22,2 (26,9—30 × 21—23,6). Incubation by female only, 18 days.

LOCAL RACE:
C.d. delegorguei Delegorgue, 1847: *Upper Limpopo River*. The African race, others in Arabia and St. Thomé.

191 Blue Quail   Blou Kwartel

Coturnix adansoni   Verreaux 1851: *Gabon.*
PLATE 20 (OPP. P. 128).♂ AND♀.
Length about 15 cm (wing 76—81—85; tail 25—33; tarsus 18—20; culmen 10.5 specimens). Iris red, bill black, legs yellow.

Identification: Both sexes quite distinctive. Young birds resemble their respective parents.
Distribution: The low country of eastern Cape Province to Natal, Transvaal, Rhodesia and Central Africa except the forests.

191

Habits: A very uncommon bird in our region. Little has been recorded, but it is reported to favour the borders of swampy ground in grassy districts. It is migratory in some areas but its exact status is unknown. Usually found in pairs or small numbers. Fast on the wing.
Food: Mainly small seeds, less insectivorous than the other quails.
Voice: A piping whistle of three notes going down the scale in semi-tones, the first loud and shrill, the others softer. Rather like the Little Bee-Eater.
Breeding: Recorded nesting from December to April, on the ground with a slight nest of a few wisps of dry grass. Eggs 6 to 8, cream or pale olive, plain but very rough and hard. Average (16) 25,5 × 19,8 (23,6—28,4 × 19—21).

Family NUMIDIDAE

Guinea-fowls are related to the Pheasants and Partridges, but are sufficiently distinct to be grouped in a separate family. They do not develop spurs but use their beaks as a means of defence and in fighting amongst themselves. The head is naked, except, in some cases, for a topknot of feathers; in the genus *Numida* there is a horny casque on the head. In colour they are spotted with white or pale blue on a dark background, and to varying degrees develop blue patches or stripes. In shape all have drooping hindquarters, like our Partridges and Francolins. They are highly gregarious in habits, flocks containing hundreds of individuals being not uncommon: but during the breeding season

134

they pair off and remain in family parties until the chicks are large, when the parties often join up into the huge flocks mentioned. Nests are hollows in the ground, lined with grass, hidden in a thick patch of grass or small bushes. The eggs are uncommonly hard. Their diet consists of insects, vegetable matter, seeds and grain.

192   Crowned Guinea-fowl Tarentaal

Numida meleagris   (Linnaeus), 1758: *Nubia*.

Native Names: Impangele (X, Z and G); Khaka (S and Ch); i-Hanka (D).

PLATE 21 (OPP. P. 129), RACES *(a)* and *(b)*.
Length 53—58 cm (wing ♂ 270—282—294, ♀ 260—275—286; tail 140—177; tarsus 63—73; culmen 21—26. *25 specimens, 15♂, 10♀*). Iris brown; bill light horn; legs horn to blackish.

Identification: The only Guinea-fowl in our area with a casque on the head. Sexes alike. Young much browner with white streaks on feathers of neck.
Distribution: Formerly found from Uitenhage eastwards to Natal and Mozambique across through Transvaal to South West Africa. Now introduced to the south-west Cape and other areas. Beyond Southern Africa extends to Senegal and south-west Arabia.
Habits: A common species, found chiefly in the thorny scrub and savanna veld, particularly along rivers and around vleis. Wanders a great deal during the non-breeding season. They are great runners, but when dogs are set at the flocks they scatter and take to the foliage of big trees, where they are difficult to see; they roost in flocks in large trees. When fired at with guns or otherwise attacked, they scatter and hide, if not in trees, then in grass or matted bushes. May form flocks numbering several hundred.
Food: Very varied; seeds, bulbs, insects of all sorts, snails, ticks, wireworms, flowers, etc.
Voice: Alarm note a stuttering, rattling kek, kek. Normal call a monotonous "come back, come back". Also translated as "Andikatale" ("I don't care"). Prior to roost usually call a grating, rapidly stuttered "kekekekekek . . .", or "chercheng-chercheng", etc.
Breeding: Eggs are laid during the rains, usually in October to March. The nest is a scrape under a bush or hedge and the clutch is normally 6—8 but as many as 38 eggs have been found in a nest, several females presumably contributing. Eggs are yellowish, with deep pore marks, smooth but very hard, usually rather flattened at the thick end and pointed at the thin. Average (100) 52,5 × 40,0 (48,8—56 × 35,5—42,5).

LOCAL RACES:
(a) N.m. coronata Gurney, 1868: *Uitenhage*. Casque high and broad; lower throat feathers not barred, usually striped. Eastern Cape, Natal, Zululand and Transvaal. Plate 21 *(a)*.
(b) N.m. mitrata Pallas, 1767: *Madagascar*. With a low horny casque; small feathers round lower neck barred. Malagasy and the coast of Mozambique, coming within our limits in the lower Zambesi Valley, Western Transvaal, eastern Kalahari and Matabeleland.
(c) N.m. papillosa Reichenow, 1894: *Mabeleapudi*. Casque fairly broad, long and arching backwards over the nape; papillae on cere well developed in males. Western Kalahari and Ngamiland. Size given above. Small feathers round neck spotted.

(d) N.m. damarensis Roberts, 1917: *Windhoek, S.W.A.* Casque high, narrow and long; papillae on cere always well developed, in both sexes.

193   Crested Guinea-fowl   Kuifkop-tarentaal

Guttera edouardi   (Hartlaub), 1867: *Coast of Natal.*

Native Names: i-Kangele (Tonga); i-Hangatori, Ndhori (D).

PLATE 21 (OPP. P. 129),
Length about 50 cm (wing ♂ 253—269—280, ♀ 258—268—279; tail 114—135; tarsus 63—80; culmen 23—30. 25 specimens, 13, ♂ 12♀). Iris red; bill yellowish horn; legs black.

Identification: The tuft of feathers on the crown prevents confusion with No. 192. Sexes alike. Young barred above with chestnut, black and buff; below blackish with buff edgings to the feathers.

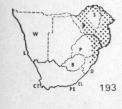

Distribution: Natal, through Zululand, Mozambique and Rhodesia to Central Africa and Ghana.

Habits: A very local species, haunting only certain choice patches of forest and perhaps not occurring in other forests not far off. Seldom leaves the shelter of thick bush or forest for any distance, though coming out into the open on the borders, and when alarmed at once taking to flight and hiding effectively in the foliage of big trees. Flocks of a score or more are not infrequently seen. They follow Vervet monkey troops to feed on falling fruit etc.

Food: Roots, fruit, insects, snails, millipedes and seed.

Voice: A rattling alarm note. During the breeding season utters a challenging note like "tick-tack ticktack tirr tirr tirr".

Breeding: Eggs are laid from October to January; in shape they resemble those of the last species while the clutch is normally 5 or 6, though 14 (? 2 females) have been reported. Average (35) 52,4 × 40,9 (49—55,5 × 37,8—43,4).

LOCAL RACES:
(a) G.e. edouardi (Hartlaub), 1867: *Coast of Natal.* As shown on Plate 21. Southern Malawi, Zambesi Valley and Mozambique southwards to Natal. Size above.
(b) G.e. symonsi Roberts, 1917: *Karkloof, Natal.* Restricted to the forests of Karkloof, Natal. Bluer-spotted and less chestnut-marked. Size similar to *(a)*.

Family TURNICIDAE

Diminutive Quail-like birds that differ from the Phasianidae in lacking the hind toe: the hens are larger and more handsomely coloured than the cocks, the latter incubating the eggs and providing for the young, the former amusing themselves by fighting with other hens. They feed on insects and small grain and nest under a tuft of grass, laying up to five eggs, as a rule, and not large clutches like the true Quails. Their habitat is grass, especially where it is short and scattered, where they can run. They have a habit of getting up at one's feet, flying off for a little way and settling again, then running very fast to one side, so that when followed up they are not found where they settled, but some distance away.

194   Hottentot Button-quail   Kaapse Kwarteltjie

Turnix hottentotta   (Temminck), 1815: *Cape of Good Hope*.

Native Names: Mabuaneng, Sekwirie (S).

PLATE 22 (OPP. P. 144).
Length ♂ 14 cm, ♀ 15 cm (wing ♂ 73, 79, ♀ 78—80—82; tail 32—36; tarsus 22—25; culmen 9—10. 7 specimens, 2 ♂, 5 ♀). Iris brown; bill horn; legs flesh.

Identification: Rather similar to the next species but distinguishable by the rufous cheeks and dark, blackish rump. Female larger and brighter than male. Young birds are spotted right across the chest.

Distribution: From Cape Town eastwards round the coast to Natal, thence to eastern Transvaal, Rhodesia, Central and West Africa.

Habits: Not a common bird. Found in the moister grasslands and mountainous regions but not often seen as they skulk among the grass. In favoured localities, however, quite a few are shot by quail hunters. Flight straight and fast and after alighting run away into the undergrowth.

Food: Seeds and insects.

Voice: Similar to that of the next species but lower pitched.

Breeding: Eggs are laid on the bare ground during December to January in the Cape, December to February in Rhodesia. They number 2—5 (full clutches) and are yellowish grey very thickly speckled with spots and blotches yellowish and darker brown. Measurements 21,5—24,5 × 17,3—20 (4). Incubation by male only 12—14 days (Priest).

LOCAL RACES:
(a) T.h. hottentotta (Temminck), 1815: *Cape of Good Hope*. As figured on Plate 22. Cape Province as far east as Port Elizabeth. Size above.
(b) T.h. nana (Sundevall), 1851: *Lower Caffraria = Natal*. Rufous of chest and throat much brighter than in *(a)*, rump more blackish. Eastern Province, Natal and Mozambique. Size similar, wing 75—82; tarsus shorter, 21 (3).
(c) T.h. luciana (Stoneham), 1931: *Trans-Nzoia, Kenya*. Rhodesia.

195 = 194 *(b)*

196   Kurrichane Button-quail   Bosveld-kwarteltjie

Turnix sylvatica   (Desfontaine), 1787: *Near Algiers*.

Native Names: 'Mperinyane (Ch); i-Ngolwane (X).

PLATE 22 (OPP. P. 144).
Length 14—15 cm (wing ♂ 76—81, ♀ 81—85; tail 28—39; tarsus 18—22; culmen 10—12). Iris cream; bill bluish; legs flesh.

Identification: The absence of chestnut on the sides of the head and the heart-shaped black marks on the side of the chest distinguish this species from the last. Females larger and brighter than males. Young have spots all over chest, spots on wing smaller.

Distribution: Throughout our area north of Port Alfred and the Orange River; Africa, southern Europe and Arabia.

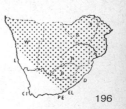

Habits: The commoner Button-Quail in South Africa, found in dry parts of the country, including the Kalahari. Favours dry open grass country or old cultivated fields now lying fallow. Probably more common than is generally thought, as it runs away into the grass when disturbed. After landing adopts a curious attitude, standing bolt-upright and walking on tip-toe. Does not fly far when flushed and flies lower and less strongly than ordinary quail.

Food: Seeds and insects in about equal proportions.

Voice: Females make a curious, ventriloquial whirring sound consisting of two notes repeated quickly. Uttered with the bill closed and neck distended.

Breeding: The nest is placed under an overhanging tuft of grass and is a hollow lined with grass. Breeding may occur throughout the year but is usually heaviest in February and March. Eggs 2—4, cream-coloured ground, thickly speckled and spotted with brown, red-brown and slate. Average (60) 23,4 × 18,6 (20,3—26,2 × 16,9—20). Incubation by male, assisted in the earlier stages by the female; 13—15 days (in captivity). Care of the young is entirely undertaken by male.

LOCAL RACE:
T.s. lepurana (A. Smith), 1836: *Kurrichane*. Africa south of the Sahara.

Family RALLIDAE

Members of this family are all skulkers, either in weed-covered moist ground or in marshes, and are adapted to the latter in their long toes, which support them in water thinly covered with vegetation. Some are fairly large (e.g. Purple Gallinule), while other are quite small (e.g. Fluffy-tailed Crakes). They feed on water-insects and in some cases on soft water-plants and bulbs. Their nests are usually accumulations of water-weeds hidden amongst the growing plants, and eggs are light pinky whitish or buffish and spotted in most cases, the exceptions being members of the genus *Sarothrura*, which lay immaculate white eggs. Although normally of such lethargic habits, some of the smaller species undertake long migrations, the Corn and Spotted Crakes, which breed in Europe migrating as far south as South Africa.

197 Water Rail   Riethaantjie

Rallus caerulescens   Gmelin, 1789: *Cape of Good Hope*.

Native Name: Mapakapaka (S).

PLATE 22 (OPP. P. 144).
Length 37—38 cm (wing 109—116—122; tail 40—49; tarsus 38—43; culmen 39—51. 12 specimens). Iris red to red-brown; bill and legs red. Weight 154—205 g.

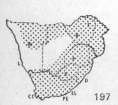

197

Identification: The long red bill and red legs are distinctive. Young, sooty brown with whitish throat and centre of breast; lower flanks barred with rufous, under tail-coverts barred with white.

Distribution: Cape Province north to Angola and Ethiopia. In South Africa only absent from the dry western districts.

Habits: Not uncommon in large marshy areas, especially where there are reeds. It keeps much to the shelter of the vegetation, but when all is quiet ventures into the muddy water outside, displaying jerky movements, flirting its tail and poking its bill here and there into the ooze. In flight the long legs dangle. Swims quite well.

Food: Small water animals, crabs, insects and worms. Also dead crabs.

Voice: Warning note a low, growling purr. Normal call a loud high-pitched "Creeeea" followed at once by a harsh, rapid "crak, crak, crak . . . .".

Breeding: The nest, placed inside the border of the vegetation, is about 15 cm across with a fair depression. It is constructed, just above the water, of reed and rush blades. Eggs 3 to 6, creamy white with scattered red-brown and underlying slate coloured spots and speckles, more concentrated at the thick end. Laying occurs during October to January in Natal and the eastern Cape; January to March in Rhodesia. Average (29) 38,5 × 27,5 (36,5—40 × 25,8—28,7). Incubation 20 days, by both parents.

198 Corncrake   Kwartelkoning

Crex crex   (Linnaeus), 1758: *Sweden.*
PLATE 22 (OPP. P. 144).
Length 37 cm (wing 130—150; tail 40—50; tarsus 34—43; culmen 20—23. 15 specimens ex *Hnbk. Brit. Bds.*). Iris and bill brown; legs flesh.

Identification: Chestnut wing-coverts distinguish it from all other crakes in our area; they are conspicuous in flight. Young darker on head and chest.
Distribution: A migrant from Europe during the summer months, coming as far south as the eastern Cape Province. Common in Rhodesia. Reported to breed in South Africa, though probably confused with the next species.
Habits: Found in the grass and weeds fringing streams but mainly in drier localities such as rank grass in old cultivation and on aerodromes. Flight sluggish, with legs dangling.
Food: Mainly insects and some aquatic vegetation (Europe).
Voice: Silent here, but when breeding a loud rasping, continued night and day; reproducible by running a piece of wood across the teeth of a comb.

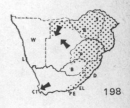

199 African Crake   Afrikaanse Riethaan

Crex egregia   (Peters), 1854: *Tete, Portuguese East Africa.*
PLATE 22 (OPP. P. 144).
Length 20—23 cm (wing 123—126—129; tail 37—47; tarsus 39—43; culmen 22—25. 8 specimens). Iris red; bill grey with dusky culmen, base purplish; legs brown.

Identification: Short bill prevents confusion with Water Rail, No. 197. More boldly barred below than Spotted Crake No. 201. Young bird is brownish on breast, barring indistinct, almost spotted; face whitish, edgings to feathers of back paler, more rufous than olive. Nestling black.
Distribution: From Natal, Transvaal and Mozambique, northwards to Ethiopia and across to Gambia.
Habits: Found along grass- and weed-fringed streams, where it may be flushed but flies only a little way and dives into the vegetation again. Also found far from water in grassy country and not normally in reedy situations. Moves about and has been described as migrating but whether this is on a large scale or merely movement to favourable localities with the rains, is not certain.
Food: Aquatic insects, snails, grasshoppers, ants and worms.
Voice: A high-pitched, rapid series of 8 or 9 whistling notes.
Breeding: The nest is placed in tall grass, sometimes near a marsh and is constructed of grass; a shallow cup just large enough to contain its eggs. Eggs

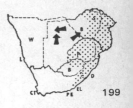

139

4 to 7, white or pinkish marked with brown blotches and underlying pinky slate-grey or purplish; laid December to March. Average (68) 34,3 × 25,2 (32,8—36 × 24,2—27). Incubation probably by both sexes, as males have been shot off eggs; about 14 days (Priest).

200 Striped Crake   Gestreepte Riethaantjie

Porzana marginalis   Hartlaub, 1857: *Gabon.*
PLATE 22 (OPP. P. 144) ♂ AND ♀.
Length about 20 cm (wing 103—112; tail 47—49; tarsus 32—36; culmen 16—18. 6 specimens ex Chapin). Iris hazel-brown; bill greenish, culmen dark; legs olive.

Identification: Above olive-brown with white streaks on the margins of the feathers of the upper back and wings; head and neck grey with the crown, nape, breast and flanks washed rufous; rump and tail black with some rufous edging; primaries dark brown with a greyish suffusion, outer web of outermost feather white; below blue-grey with pale margins, throat white and under tail-coverts rufous. Female duller, with breast, flanks, cheeks and crown washed with grey; young browner above, rufous on face and flanks. Note the remarkably thick bill, dark above and at base. See next species.
Distribution: Recorded from odd, widely scattered localities all over Africa. In Southern Africa from East London, Durban, Ovamboland and several localities in Rhodesia; also southern South West Africa. Migratory?
Habits: Little recorded. Inhabits short, damp grasslands.
Breeding: A nest described from Nigeria is a small, shallow depression in the ground, lined with grasses and well concealed. Eggs 5, heavily marked with reddish brown, almost like a small kestrel's egg; measuring (5) 28,7—29,9 × 21,3—21,9. Andersson also described this bird as breeding in Ovamboland. Breeds December to February in Rhodesia.

201 Spotted Crake   Gevlekte Riethaan

Porzana porzana   (Linnaeus), 1766: *France.*
PLATE 22 (OPP. P. 144).
Length about 20 cm (wing ♂ 113—125, ♀ 109—120; tail 43—49; tarsus 30—37; culmen 18—21. 16 specimens ex *Handbk. Brit. Birds*). Iris brown; bill base yellow with orange at base of culmen, rest green; legs pale olive-green.

Identification: Resembles most the African Crake No. 199 but not as clearly barred on belly and has yellow and green bill. Female duller than male; young similar to female but breast buffish with few spots. Note slender bill.
Distribution: A non-breeding visitor to our area from Europe and Asia recorded as far south as Lesotho, Natal, Potchefstroom and northern South West Africa, from December to May.
Habits: A skulking species about which little has been recorded in Africa except that it occurs in swamps and marshes. In Europe rather crepuscular. Jerks its tail up and down at each step when excited; normally carries body rather low with legs well bent (Europe).
Food: Aquatic insects and plants.

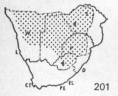

201

Voice: Male in Europe makes a sharp "trick-track" repeated with clocklike regularity. Probably silent in Africa.

202 Baillon's Crake   Kleinste Riethaantjie

Porzana pusilla   (Pallas), 1776: *Dauria, Manchuria.*

Native Names: Isizinzi (X); isi-Zinze (Z).

PLATE 22 (OPP. P. 144).
Length about 18 cm (wing 80—84—88; tail 37—46; tarsus 24—28; culmen 16—19. 22 specimens). Iris red; bill green, culmen black; legs greyish flesh.

Identification: Rather similar in colour to the African Crake but much smaller and flecked with white on the mantle. Female has throat and centre of chest whitish. Young barred with brown on chest.

Distribution: Cape Town eastwards and from northern South West Africa northwards through Africa to Europe, Asia, the Philippines, Australia and New Zealand.

Habits: Frequents marshy ground, especially where the vegetation is short, making rat-like runs or burrows through the grass. When disturbed and anxious, jerks its tail up and down and its head back and forth with each step. If flushed flies a short distance and dives into the vegetation again.

Food: Insects, green plants and seeds.

Voice: A husky "churr, churr". Also a quiet husky "chrrrr" (slow and drawn-out) "wirr, wirr, wirr" (rapid). Also a frog-like bubbling.

Breeding: The nest, a cup of grasses or leaves, is placed in short grass or rushes which are curled over to hide the eggs. Eggs 4 to 6, are olive, the ground colour buffy, hidden by elongate marks of olive. Average (21) 28,3 × 20,2 (26—31 × 19,4—21,3).

LOCAL RACE:
P.p. obscura Neumann, 1897: *Kibaya, Pangani Dist.,* Southern Africa as far north as Ethiopia; also Malagasy. Size above.

203 Black Crake   Swart Riethaan

Limnocorax flavirostris   (Swainson), 1837: *Senegal.*

PLATE 22 (OPP. P. 144).
Length 20—23 cm (wing ♂ 98—106—110, ♀ 96—101—110; tail 36—49; tarsus 37—44; culmen 23—28. 23 specimens, 10 ♂, 13 ♀). Iris red, greenish grey in young; bill light yellowish green; legs dull red, bright red when breeding, brownish in young.

Identification: Unmistakable. Chicks black at first and downy, becoming grey with white on throat; bill black, with white tip and pink behind each nostril.

Distribution: Africa south of the Sahara.

Habits: Occurs, quite commonly, in marshes and on the borders of streams and rivers where there are reeds and water plants to give it shelter, Not as shy as other crakes, often coming right out into the open when things are quiet. Usually seen in pairs or small parties and where there are water plants they walk on them almost like jacanas. Flies low across the water but fairly strongly.

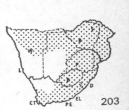

202

203

FLUFFTAILS

Food: Insects, seeds, aquatic plants, snails and small fish. Also heron eggs.
Voice: A deep growling "churr", preceded by higher-pitched clucking sounds. Also makes individual chucks while walking about. Performs duets.
Breeding: Constructs a fairly deep cup of rushes, grass and water plants on the water or just above it during September to February (August to February, April and June in Rhodesia). Immature birds sometimes assist with nest-building and caring for young. Eggs normally 3 but may be up to 5 or 6, cream, finely spotted, but fairly massed at the obtuse end with light brown and underlying purplish slate very small markings. Average (21) 33,8 × 24,2 (31—35,7 × 23—26). Incubation period 14 *(c)* to 19 days.

204 White-winged Flufftail   Witvlerk-vleikuiken

Sarothrura ayresi (Gurney), 1877: *Potchefstroom.*
PLATE 22 (OPP. P. 144) ♂ AND ♀.
Length about 14 cm (wing 75—78; tail 44; tarsus 18—19; culmen 12,5). Iris hazel; bill and legs dusky pink.

Identification: As illustrated. White secondaries show up in flight. Note also white line on leading edge of wing.
Young similar to female but with few white markings; throat, centre of chest and belly whitish; chest mottled black and white.
Distribution: Recorded first from Potchefstroom (2) then Bloemfontein, King William's Town and Suikerbosrand recently; also in Ethiopia but so far not in the intervening territory.
Habits: Very little recorded except that it inhabits marshes and flooded areas and is flushed with difficulty.
Food: Water insects.

205 Red-chested Flufftail   Rooibors-vleikuiken

Sarothrura rufa (Vieillot), 1819: *Africa = Cape Province.*
PLATE 22 (OPP. P. 144) ♂ AND ♀.
Length 15—17 cm (wing 76—80; tail 40—55; tarsus 23—24; culmen 13—14. 4 specimens). Iris dark brown; bill bluish, upper mandible dusky; legs grey-brown.

Identification: Rather similar to the Buff-spotted Flufftail, No. 206, but red extends lower, on to chest, upper breast and mantle. Female paler on chest than female of No. 206. Young black with white flecks on wing coverts, mantle and rump.
Distribution: From Cape Town eastwards along the coast to Ethiopia; on the west from Ovamboland and Angola northwards and westwards to West Africa.
Habits: Not uncommon where there are suitable situations, rank growth in the middle of marshes, in which it skulks and is seldom seen except when flushed into flight for a few yards.
Food: Seeds, insects (ants) and snails.

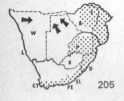
205

Voice: A strong "duehh, dueh, dueh" continued for ten to fifteen seconds; "haw-boo" which at a distance sounds like "boo-boo-boo-boo-boo-boo", and various humming and cheeping sounds. Also a thin, rather squeaky, rapid "dui" repeated about eight times, not nearly so strong as the "dueh" call. Calls at night and on dull days.

Breeding: Nest situated among reeds at ground level, cup shaped, constructed of grass fronds lined with rootlets or made of dead leaves. Eggs 3—5 white (6) 28,0 × 20,8 (27,4—28,6 × 19,2—21,7). In Rhodesia breeds during January and February, i.e. during the rains. November—January in the Cape. Both sexes incubate, about 14 days.

LOCAL RACE:
S.r. rufa (Vieillot), 1819: *Africa = Cape Province.*

206   Buff-spotted Flufftail   Gevlekte Vleikuiken

Sarothrura elegans   (A. Smith), 1839: *Durban.*
PLATE 22 (OPP. P. 144) ♂ AND ♀.
Length 17 cm (wing 86—91; tail 33—44; tarsus 24—27; culmen 14—16. 7 specimens). Iris brown; bill grey; legs brownish grey.

Identification: Body more spotted and red on chest not extending as far down as in the last species; tail not as large. Female has no red on head.

Distribution: From Elgin eastwards and northwards to Somaliland and thence across to Cameroon. Once at Orange River mouth.

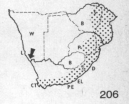

206

Habits: Found in forest and moist situations and old lands adjoining forest. Not often observed on account of its skulking habits, but those who have heard its mournful call assert that it is probably more plentiful than appears from definite records.

Food: Mainly insects; also snails and seeds.

Voice: Heard most at night, a mournful wailing whistle, almost like a tuning fork, produced as a crescendo for a few (2—3) seconds and then dying away abruptly. Produced apparently by the male only and attributed by natives to snakes, chameleons and skinks. At sunset may climb into a bush about five feet up and call. Hisses like a snake. Also goes "peep, peep".

Breeding: The nest, constructed of grass and lined with rootlets, is a cup with grass pulled over to form a roof. It is placed on the ground. Eggs 3 or 4, white and glossy, 30 × 22 and 25 × 19,8. November to February.

LOCAL RACE:
S.e. elegans (A. Smith), 1839: *Durban.*

206X   Chestnut-headed Flufftail

Sarothrura lugens   Böhm, 1884: *Ugalla, Tanganyika.*
PLATE 22 (OPP. P. 144). ♂ AND ♀.
Length about 15 cm (wing 70—74; tail 40—55; tarsus 17—20,5; culmen 13—14, 6 ♀ specimens). Iris brown; bill dark slate with pinkish base of lower mandible, feet and toes dark slate.

Identification: Male with head and neck dark chestnut, chin whitish and rest of body black streaked with white. Differs from 205 and 206 in having head and neck only rufous and from 207 by black tail. The female differs from

143

PLATE 22

194. *Turnix hottentotta hottentotta.* Hottentot Button-Quail.
Kaapse Kwarteltjie.
196. *Turnix sylvatica lepurana.* Kurrichane Button-quail.
Bosveld-kwarteltjie.
197. *Rallus caerulescens.* Water Rail. Riethaantjie.
198. *Crex crex.* Corncrake. Kwartelkoning.
199. *Crex egregia.* African Crake. Afrikaanse Riethaan.
200. *Porzana marginalis.* Striped Crake. Gestreepte Riethaantjie. ♂ and ♀.
201. *Porzana porzana.* Spotted Crake. Gevlekte Riethaan.
202. *Porzana pusilla obscura.* Baillon's Crake. Kleinste Riethaantjie.
203. *Limnocorax flavirostris.* Black Crake. Swart Riethaan.
204. *Sarothrura ayresi.* White-winged Flufftail. Witvlerk-vleikuiken. ♂ and ♀.
205. *Sarothrura rufa.* Red-chested Flufftail. Rooibors-vleikuiken. ♂ and ♀.
206. *Sarothrura elegans.* Buff-spotted Flufftail. Gcvlekte Vleikuiken. ·
♂ and ♀.
206X. *Sarothrura lugens.* Chestnut-headed Flufftail. ♂ and ♀.
207. *Sarothrura affinis.* Striped Flufftail. Gestreepte Vleikuiken. ♂ and ♀.
207X. *Sarothrura boehmi.* Streaky-breasted Flufftail. Boehmse Vleikuiken.
♂ and ♀.

228

209

208

208X

229

K N

211

210

212

♀ 213 ♂

PLATE 23

208. *Porphyrio porphyrio madagascariensis.* Purple Gallinule.

Koningriethaan.

208X. *Porphyrula martinica.* American Purple Gallinule.

209. *Porphyrio alleni.* Lesser Gallinule. Klein Koningriethaan.

210. *Gallinula chloropus meridionalis.* Moorhen. Waterhoender.

211. *Gallinula angulata.* Lesser Moorhen. Klein Waterhoender.

212. *Fulica cristata.* Red-knobbed Coot. Bleshoender.

213. *Podica senegalensis petersi.* Finfoot. Watertrapper. ♂ and ♀.

228. *Actophilornis africanus.* African Jacana. Langtoon.

229. *Microparra capensis.* Lesser Jacana. Dwerg Langtoon.

similar species in having white markings and more spotted sides of neck and flanks than the others which are barred.

Distribution: Angola, south-west Zaïre and Zambia. Recorded near Inyanga, eastern Rhodesia.

Habits: A rare, little known species which has similar habitat preference to No. 205.

Food: Insects, and seeds.

Voice: A crescendo of rapid notes "koh-koh-koh", about 3 per second and lasting for half a minute.

Breeding: Nest unknown.

LOCAL RACE:
S.l. lynesi (Grant and Praed), 1934: *Nsombo, Lake Bangweulu.*

207   Striped Flufftail   Gestreepte Vleikuiken

Sarothrura affinis   (A. Smith), 1828: *Cape Colony.*

PLATE 22 (OPP. P. 144) ♂ AND ♀.
Length 15 cm (wing 70—73; tail 35—40; tarsus 17—18; culmen 11—13). Iris dark brown; bill black, mandible whitish; legs grey.

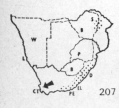

207

Identification: Red tail in male distinctive; dusky in female.

Distribution: Cape Flats eastwards to northern Natal. Again in the highlands of eastern Rhodesia. North to Sudan and Kenya.

Habits: Occurs in rank vegetation and grass on the borders of forests. When flushed flies a short distance but does not easily flush again.

Food: Insects, seeds and vegetable matter.

Voice: A note sounding like "huuuuu", increasing in intensity for a second or so and repeated every 1½ seconds.

Breeding: The nest is shallow, sometimes with a roof of grass. Eggs 4—5, dull white, measuring (11) 23,8—28,3 × 19,5—21,6, laid December to February. Both sexes incubate.

LOCAL RACE:
(a) S.a. affinis (A. Smith), 1828: *Cape Colony.* South Africa. Formerly known as *S. lineata.*
(b) S.a. antonii (Madarasz and Neumann) 1911: *Ndassekera, Kenya.* Eastern Rhodesia northwards.

207X   Streaky-breasted Flufftail   Boehmse Vleikuiken

Sarothrura boehmi   Reichenow, 1900: *Likulwe, Congo.*

PLATE 22 (OPP. P. 144) ♂ AND ♀.
Length about 15 cm (wing 80—88; tail 32—35; tarsus 18—19,5; culmen 13,5—14,5). Iris brown; bill, maxilla black, mandible white; legs slate.

Identification: In general appearance rather like the Red-chested Flufftail, No. 205, but in the male only the head and neck are rufous; underparts are whiter. The tail is black, thus preventing confusion with the Striped Flufftail, No. 207.

Distribution: West Africa to Kenya southwards to Malawi and eastern Rhodesia.

Habits: Found in swampy, flooded areas, mainly on the margins where the grass is short and sparse.

Food: Small seeds and insects.

Voice: A note sounding like "were", preceded by a grunt (only audible at

close quarters) giving a note like "g'were". Repeated once per second for half a minute or so.
Breeding: The nest is saucer-shaped, made of dry grass and about an inch thick, placed in a tuft from one to three inches above the wet ground with the tops of the grass pulled over and interwoven to hide the nest. Eggs 3 or 4, creamy white to white occasionally with pinpoints of brown; laid in January—March in Rhodesia. Average (13) 26,9 × ·19, the largest 28 × 20,5, the smallest 25 × 19. Male is recorded as incubating.

208 Purple Gallinule   Koningriethaan

Porphyrio porphyrio (Linnaeus), 1766: *West Medditerranean.*
PLATE 23 (OPP. P. 145).
Length 46 cm (wing 225—237—248; tail 82—101; tarsus 70—92; culmen 56—71; width of shield 18—24. 15 specimens). Iris red; bill crimson, shield red; legs red.

Identification: Unmistakable except for the Lesser Gallinule which is much smaller and has frontal shield green and more pointed behind. Sexes alike. Young dull, almost brownish; legs reddish brown.
Distribution: Africa, southern Europe eastwards to India and Lord Howe Island.
Habits: Quite a common resident, occurring in situations where there are thick reed beds standing in water; sewerage farms are particularly favoured, especially where there are open shallows and sheets of water. Usually seen tramping about in the shallows amongst the weeds and upon alarm takes to the shelter of the reed beds, either by hastening with a curious high-stepping gait or, more reluctantly, by flying rather heavily with legs trailing. In some areas and at some times of the year not at all shy. Often climb quite high into the aquatic vegetation. Flirts the tail while walking, revealing white under tail-coverts.

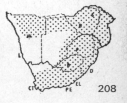

208

Food: Roots of reeds, flowers, insects and even the eggs and young of other nesting birds.
Voice: Various weird and uncanny shrieks and groaning noises. Also a deep bubbling explosive note.
Breeding: The nest is a fairly massive structure of broad reeds placed well above water level. Breeds September to January in the Cape, throughout the year in Transvaal and further north. Eggs 4 or 5, pinky buff with large scattered spots and small underlying speckles of brown, slate and slate-brown. Average (20) 55,6 × 37,6 (53—59,9 × 35,2—40).

LOCAL RACE:
P.p. madagascariensis (Latham), 1801: *Madagascar.* Africa and Malagasy.

208X American Purple Gallinule

Porphyrula martinica (Linnaeus), 1766: *West Indies.*
PLATE 23 (OPP. P. 145).
Length about 33 cm (wing 162—181; tail 64; tarsus 58—62; culmen 38—48. 5 specimens). Iris red; bill line yellow at tip and deep red at base; legs yellow.

Identification: Adult much the same as 208 in general plumage colour but has yellow tip to bill, white shield and yellow legs. Young brownish and similar to 208 but has brownish shield and yellowish legs.

147

Distribution: From the Southern United States south to Buenos Aires, Tristan da Cunha and South Georgia. There are over twelve records for South Africa (Western Cape).

Habits: Several of the birds recorded were immature and brought to authorities in an exhausted state, usually dying shortly afterwards despite all attempts to revive them.

209 Lesser Gallinule   Klein Koningriethaan

Porphyrio alleni Thompson, 1842: *Idda, Nigeria*

PLATE 23 (OPP. P. 145).

Length about 25 cm (wing 144-160; tail 66—73; tarsus 45—56; culmen 35—40). Iris red; bill red; frontal shield brown or green; legs brownish red, scarlet on front edge.

Identification: See under No. 208. Young, buff below, flight feathers greenish and back pale brown.

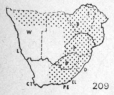

Distribution: Africa south of the Sahara but not the south-west Cape. Also in Malagasy. Commoner in the northern parts of our area.

Habits: Rather similar to the No. 208 but shyer. Very fond of the flowers of reeds and spends much of its time clambering about to reach them. Also comes into the open and walks on waterlilies like a jacana. Can swim well.

Food: Grass-seeds, spiders, insects and reeds.

Voice: A clucking alarm note and other frog-like noises.

Breeding: The nest is a loosely constructed cup of dry reeds a few inches above the water, either in the reeds or on floating water plants. Breeds February to May and September. Eggs 4 or 5, dirty-white, with small underlying purple shell markings and superficial markings of reddish brown, the latter very sharp and not large. Average (41) from Nigeria 36,2 × 26,1 (31,8—39,2 × 23,6—27,5).

210 Moorhen   Waterhoender

Gallinula chloropus (Linnaeus), 1758: *Middlesex, England.*

Native Name: Khokhonoka (S).

PLATE 23 (OPP. P. 145).

Length 30—36 cm (wing 143—162—177; tail 65—77; tarsus 38—48; culmen 38—44. 26 specimens). Iris red; bill red, tip greenish yellow; legs olive-green, garter just above tarsal joint dark red.

Identification: The dull black plumage combined with red bill and shield are distinctive except for the Lesser Moorhen, No. 211, which is much smaller and has the shield more pointed at the back (see Plate 22) and beak yellow. Sexes alike. Young browner, flanks buff.

Distribution: Africa south of the Sahara; Europe and western Asia.

Habits: Widely distributed and common where there are sheets of water and rivers bordered by rushes and reeds; usually seen either swimming in the water, wading in shallows, or even venturing into the veld adjoining. When alarmed, flirts the tail revealing the white of the under tail-coverts. Rather shy and usually heard more often than seen, but if unmolested venturing into the open.

Food: Insects, seeds and soft vegetable matter.

Voice: Normal call a cheerful "kr-rrrrk", fairly high pitched and descending about a semitone.

Breeding: Constructs a rather neat nest of blades of rushes and reeds in the shelter of matted vegetation above water level; sometimes in the lower branches of a tree standing in water. Usually well hidden from above. The incubating bird may sit very close. Breeds winter to early summer in the Cape, mainly in September and October; in Transvaal September to April and in Rhodesia February to March and July to September. Eggs 4 to 6 but 11 recorded (? two females), dark buff with scattered red-brown and slate-coloured spots, freckles and blotches, somewhat concentrated at the thick end. Average (100) 42,3 × 30,6 (38—46,3 × 28,3—35). Incubation period in captivity about 3 weeks. Both sexes incubate. Chicks leave the nest within 2 or 3 days of hatching and can fly at 6 or 7 weeks.

LOCAL RACE:
G.c. meridionalis (Brehm), 1855: *South Africa.* Africa south of the Sahara. Size as given above. The nominate race occurs in Europe.

211 Lesser Moorhen   Klein Waterhoender

Gallinula angulata   Sundevall, 1850: *Lower Caffraria = Natal.*
PLATE 23 (OPP. P. 145).
Length about 23 cm (wing 132—146; tail 56—60; tarsus 38—40; culmen 18—21. 15 specimens ex Bannerman). Iris red; bill yellow, culmen and frontal shield red; legs greenish.

Identification: Rather similar to the last species, see under No. 210. Females duller and browner than males, chin almost white. Young have top of head and neck brown.
Distribution: Absent from south-west Cape, only becoming common north of Natal and Damaraland on the west. Extends over Africa south of the Sahara. In Rhodesia probably commoner than the last species.
Habits: Similar to those of the Moorhen, No. 210, but is more secretive, rarely venturing on to open sheets of water. Said to be a migrant but little recorded in this respect.
Food: Seeds, flowers of reeds and insects.
Voice: Very similar to the Moorhen.
Breeding: Nest smaller but otherwise similar to that of the last species; usually partly concealed from above. Eggs 4 to 9, buff with sparing speckles and large angular blotches of red-brown. Laying occurs in December to March but mainly in February in Rhodesia. Average (82 from West Africa) 34,1 × 24,8 (31—37,2 × 23—27).

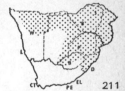

211

212 Red-knobbed Coot   Bleshoender

Fulica cristata   Gmelin, 1789: *Malagasy*
Native Names: Mokhetle (S); Unonkqayi, Unompemvana (X).

PLATE 23 (OPP. P. 145).
Length about 43 cm (wing 201—215—225; tail 50—60; tarsus 55—63; culmen 55—64. 71 specimens). Iris red, brown in young; bill and shield light blue; legs dark green.

Identification: Sexes alike. Red knobs on shield swell when breeding. Young dark ashy brown, a few white edges to neck feathers; cheeks and throat whitish.

149

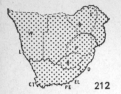

212

Distribution: Southern Africa north to Ethiopia. Also southern Spain, Morocco and Malagasi. Not in West Africa.

Habits: Common wherever there are largish sheets of water, even those devoid of reeds. Usually seen swimming about singly or in large parties. Often localised in one part of a lake or dam. Occasionally comes out on to the edge. Very pugnacious, spending a great deal of time chasing each other spattering across the water, almost taking off and running on the surface with their feet, ending up in a swooshing belly-skate across the water. Fly strongly when sufficiently disturbed, with the feet sticking out beyond the tail.

Food: Insects and water plants, including *Marsilia*.

Voice: Normal note "clukuk" and a strange humming, breathy "Vvvvv". Alarm note a snorting "tcholf".

Breeding: Constructs a large cup-shaped nest of reeds or trailing water plants in shallow water, often with no attempt at concealment. Also makes many "false nests", resting platforms on which no eggs are laid. Laying occurs in the winter but also throughout the year, mainly October to November in the Cape; March to August in Rhodesia. Eggs 3 to 11 (? two females), stone colour, small with round dots of purplish brown; a few dots reach 2 mm or so. Average (200) 52,9 × 37,4 (49—61,1 × 32,8—40,3). Two females are known to have laid in one nest. Incubation 18—25 days.

Family HELIORNITHIDAE

Aquatic fresh-water birds having some resemblance to the Anhingas, but with shorter and stouter neck and beak, and lobed instead of webbed toes. They occur on small streams overshadowed by trees, and are of shy disposition. Their diet consists of small water-animals captured in the water by swimming or diving. Three genera and three species are known, one from South America, another from south-eastern Asia and the third from the tropics of Africa.

213   Finfoot   Watertrapper

Podica senegalensis   (Vieillot), 1817: *Senegal.*

PLATE 23 (OPP. P. 145) ♂ AND ♀.

Length ♂ 63 cm (wing ♂ 250, ♀ 203; tail ♂ 187, ♀ 157; tarsus ♂ 44,5, ♀ 35; culmen ♂ 55,5, ♀ 48). Iris hazel; bill orange-red, culmen darker; legs orange-red.

Identification: Sexes as illustrated. Young birds resemble females but have fewer white spots above.

213

Distribution: From Groot River (Nature's Valley) eastwards to Ethiopia and across to Senegal. Widespread and quite common in Rhodesia.

Habits: Found on quiet streams overgrown with trees and thick bush. Also on dams and other peaceful waters. Probably far commoner than is generally believed since it is not often seen; usually a splash among the trees lining the bank of a river is all that betrays its existence. When startled, has the peculiar habit of running along the surface of the water with flapping wings, until out of sight round a bend; if checked in its flight in that way it will dive and attempt to hide under weeds or branches overhanging the water. When once flushed, flies strongly.

Food: Apparently mainly insects; also crabs, snails, frogs, fish and insect larvae.

Voice: A subdued "sqork" like a frightened domestic hen. Also said to make a low reiterated booming sound.

Breeding: The nest is placed on a branch overhanging water and is made of sticks lined with reeds, coarse grass and leaves. Eggs 2, are laid from September to November and occasionally in April. They are pale buffy green in ground colour, streaked and blotched with umber, red-brown and purplish brown. Measurements: 52 × 41; 57,1 × 42,1, 58,0 × 41,6.

LOCAL RACE:
P.s. petersi Hartlaub, 1852: *Mozambique Province, P.E.A.* Southern Africa, the nominate race in Senegal and others in Central Africa.

Family GRUIDAE

Members of the Crane family are large birds of terrestrial habits, having some resemblance to Storks, from which they differ in their shorter bill with the nostrils open and situated near the middle of the bill, besides other osteological characters. Unlike the Storks they have voices, uttering loud cries when in flight, and nest on the ground and not in trees or high positions; eggs are also greenish to olive instead of white, showing more resemblance to those of the Bustards. They feed on insects, small animals, seeds and vegetable matter. They are fond of display by dancing and have usually some ornamental character about the face.

214 Crowned Crane   Mahem

Balearica regulorum   (Bennett), 1833: *Eastern Cape Province.*

Native Names: Ihem (X); u-Nohemu (Z); le-Hemu (S).

PLATE 24 (OPP. P. 160).
Length about 105 cm (wing 606; tail 265; tarsus 190; culmen 66). Iris ashy; bill black; legs black.

Identification: Unmistakable. Sexes alike. Young birds are much browner, the cheeks are feathered, not bare, and the crest is small and ragged.

Distribution: From around King William's Town eastwards to Kenya and on the west from Ngamiland to the Congo.

Habits: This species frequents the borders of swamps, usually in family parties or pairs, and was at one time not uncommon, but has latterly become scarce owing partly to the drainage of swamps and partly to being harassed by thoughtless people taking the young for pets. Roosts in numbers in river beds. Tame birds, which enjoy protection from the natives in the belief that they bring rain.

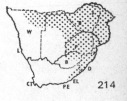

Food: Small animals such as frogs and reptiles, insects and grain.

Voice: A two-syllabled trumpet hence the name Mahem. Also a deep booming breeding call.

Breeding: The nest is constructed by stamping down and drawing together matted marsh vegetation into a heap. Two eggs form the normal clutch and are laid from December to February. They are pale bluish with overlying white. Average (24) 83,9 × 56,7 (76,7—92,2 × 52—59,8).

LOCAL RACE:
B.r. regulorum (Bennett), 1833; *Eastern Cape Province.*

215   Wattled Crane   Lelkraan

Grus carunculatus   (Gmelin), 1789: *Cape of Good Hope.*

Native Names: Iqaqolo (X); Mothlathomo (S).

PLATE 24 (OPP. P. 160).

Length about 120 cm (wing 627—653; tail 253—279; tarsus 304; culmen 135). Iris orange-yellow; bill light reddish-brown, warts at base red; legs black.

Identification: The large size and two wattles hanging from the face make this species unmistakable. In colour they appear like white birds with dark waistcoats. Female has the crown whiter and wattles small. Young has white crown and little trace of warts or wattles. Chick buff with brown back, wings and thighs.

Distribution: Southern Africa, except the western Cape Province and dry areas, northwards to Zaïre and Somaliland.

Habits: Uncommon. Frequents the borders of swamps and the grassy veld adjoining, usually in small parties often wading in shallow water. A very wary species which does not allow a close approach.

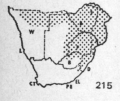

Food: Small reptiles, frogs, insects, etc., and sometimes grain.

215   **Voice:** A loud drawn-out guttural but bell-like "hornk". Also various jabbering sounds.

Breeding: Nests are made in swamps, preferably on islets covered with vegetation, which is drawn into a heap; but sometimes has been known to gather weeds and rushes into a mass upon bare rocks on islets. Two eggs appear to be the normal clutch, ground colour pale pinkish or biscuit, dappled and blotched with elongate marks of light red-brown to dark brown, intermingled with slate, olive and purple. They are laid from August to June in Natal, April to December and February in Rhodesia. Average (52) 101,9 × 65,3 (93,5—116,5 × 55,9—71,5). Incubation 32—40 days.

216   Blue Crane   Bloukraan

Anthropoides paradisea   (Lichtenstein), 1793: *Inner South Africa.*

Native Names: Indwa (X); i-Ndwa (Z); Mokhokoli (S).

PLATE 24 (OPP. P. 160).

Length about 105 cm (wing 560, the long secondaries projecting about 445 beyond the primaries; tail 228; tarsus 235; culmen 76). Iris dark brown; bill pinkish; legs black.

Identification: The swollen head and long trailing secondaries render this bird unmistakable. Sexes alike, female slightly smaller. Young birds lack the long plumes, are lighter grey and the top of the head is light chestnut.

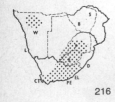

Distribution: Confined to the Karoo and grassveld areas of South Africa. Recorded visually from Mashonaland. Now also Western Cape and Etosha.

Habits: A common species, usually found near water but also in quite dry country at times. Moves about in pairs but may be seen in large flocks, perhaps on migration. Frequently soars in pairs to a great height and utters

216   loud cries. In great demand as a garden pet but may be dangerous to children from its habit of pecking at the ankles and eyes. Sometimes roosts standing in water.

Food: Very catholic in its taste, eating small reptiles, grain, fish, locusts and in captivity almost everything.

Voice: A very distinctive, guttural, rattling croak, very loud; like "krraaaarrrk" repeated several times.

Breeding: A slight nest of small stones may be made or there may be no nest; the eggs being laid on the bare ground during November to February. They are elongate, brownish yellow, obscured by elongate dappling, blotching or clouding of various shades of brown and olive. Fine pitting is also visible. Average eggs (60) 93,0 × 59,9 (83,8—100 × 52—64,6). Incubation by both sexes, mainly by female—30 days (5). Newly hatched chicks can swim strongly.

Family OTIDAE

The Bustards are better represented in Africa than in other continents, especially in South Africa. They are fairly large to large terrestrial birds of the plains or savannas, having only the three front toes present, fairly long legs, and the upper parts of the plumage plainly coloured as in terrestrial birds which crouch to avoid being seen by large birds of prey. They have distinctive cries and peculiarities of display, either on the ground or in the air, which are very attractive.

217   Kori Bustard   Gompou

Otis kori   Burchell, 1822: *Confluence of Vaal and Orange Rivers.*

Native Names: Khori (Ch); Iseme (X).

PLATE 24 (OPP. P. 160).
Length ♂ about 135 cm, ♀ about 112 cm (wing ♂ 717—747—798; ♀ 575—608—685; tail 310—430; tarsus 177—235; culmen 72—124. 21 specimens, 9 ♂, 12 ♀). Iris yellow; bill light horn; legs yellowish.

Identification: Huge size and lack of reddish on hind-neck render this species unmistakable. Female much smaller than male. Young paler on crown, mantle more freckled; no long plumes on neck.

Distribution: Southern Africa north to Ethiopia. Throughout our area except forested and montane areas.

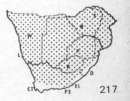

217

Habits: Frequents the dry savannas where there is fairly long grass, over which it can see the approach of enemies more easily than the smaller species. Also found on the open Karoo. Takes to flight reluctantly and walks rapidly with long strides, but when followed too closely springs in the air and flies with great power. It is migratory like the other large species but its exact movements are unknown. Has been badly shot out in the settled areas but is happily still common in the Kalahari National Park and is found in the Kruger Park. Males inflate their throats during courtship.

Food: Carrion, seeds, insects and small reptiles or mammals. Also reputed to be particularly fond of the gum of acacia trees.

Voice: Mating call a deep "wum, wum, wum, wum, wumwum".

Breeding: Recorded as breeding from October to February. The eggs number 1 or 2 and are oval, almost equally rounded at both ends; the ground-colour a pale olive-brown, sparingly mottled with a darker shade of the same colour and brown, the colour tending to be in streaks. Average (17) 80,9 × 58,9 (71,9—86,9 × 54,2—63).

LOCAL RACE:
O.k. kori Burchell, 1822: *Confluence of the Vaal and Orange Rivers.* Throughout our area; another race in East Africa. Size above.

218 Ludwig's Bustard   Ludwigse Pou

Otis ludwigii Rüppell, 1837: *Graaff-Reinet.*

Native Names: Iseme (X and Z).

PLATE 24 (OPP. P. 160).
Length 75—90 cm (wing ♂ 500—555, ♀ 433—452—470; tail 210 —260; tarsus 110—140; culmen 46—60. 7 specimens, 2 ♂, 5 ♀). Iris greyish brown; bill dark horn; legs greenish white.

Identification: Often confused with the next species but lacks the black on the crown and the black and white on wings and tail found in that species. Also, the front of the neck is brown not grey. Females are smaller.

Distribution: The drier western districts of South Africa as far north as Damaraland and southern Transvaal. Migratory to some extent, possibly moving coastwards in winter but little known.

Habits: Occurs in the open plains, usually in parties of three or four or in pairs while breeding; conspicuous when stalking along sedately, but easily overlooked if squatting.

218

Food: Vegetable matter, grasshoppers, beetles, mice, lizards and seeds.

Voice: Not recorded.

Breeding: Two eggs are laid on the bare ground during December to March. They are light olive, obscurely clouded with mixed light brown and slate. Average (7) 72,8 × 52 (68,4—74,7 × 44,6—58,7).

219 Stanley Bustard   Veldpou

Otis denhami Children, 1826: *Lake Chad.*

Native Name: Iseme (X and Z).

PLATE 24 (OPP. P. 160).
Length ♂ 100—107 cm, ♀ 80—87 cm (wing ♂ 557—583, ♀ 460—482; tail 250—305; tarsus 130—170; culmen 65—80). Iris light hazel; bill horn, tip dark; legs yellowish white.

Identification: See under previous species. Female is smaller and has centre of crown whitish while the grey of neck is replaced by vermiculated white and brown; less black and white on wing. Young resemble female.

Distribution: Replaces the previous species in the moister east of our area but also occurs in dry areas. Northern South West Africa but not Rhodesia. Also occurs throughout Africa south of the Sahara.

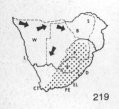

Habits: Usually to be found in grass-covered country with or without trees. Moves about restlessly but its movements are not known accurately. Occurs in small parties and is extremely wary and difficult to approach. When disturbed,

219

walks away strongly, finally taking to flight and soon disappearing. Males have an elaborate courtship, inflating their neck pouches and dancing before the females.

Food: Large insects, vegetable matter and small animals; in fact almost anything.
Voice: A deep barking sound and a booming noise when displaying to the female.
Breeding: Two eggs are normally laid in a slight scrape during October to December. They are pale olive-brown with obscure elongated smudges of brown, darker olive-brown and slate. Average (18) 76,1 × 55,6 (69,8—82,3 × 53—58). Incubation by both sexes.

LOCAL RACE:
O.d. stanleyi Gray, 1831: *Cape of Good Hope.* Throughout our area; size above.

220 Karoo Korhaan   Vaal Korhaan

Eupodotis vigorsii   (A. Smith), 1831: *South Africa* = *Beaufort West.*
PLATE 24 (OPP. P. 160).
Length 56—60 cm (wing ♂ 334—354—360; ♀ 317—326—330; tail 155—180; tarsus 80—90; culmen 34—41. 13 specimens all races, 9 ♂, 4 ♀). Iris brown; bill slate; legs yellow.

Distribution: Essentially a bird of the Karoo and South West Africa. Moves about restlessly, often migrating over into the Bredasdorp area.
Habits: Favours dry, stony ground where there are scattered, stunted bushes. Usually seen in pairs but very often in threes, perhaps the young of the previous year forming the trio. Among farmers it is believed to presage wind by calling early in the morning. If it believes it is not seen will often squat and by approaching tangentially an observer may get very close to it. In flight usually silent.

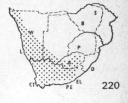

220

Food: Seeds, vegetable matter and insects; stones usually present.
Voice: A frog-like duet uttered morning and evening, sounding like "squark (♂) . . . kok (♀), squark . . . kok", hence the description "hotnot, plat-voet".
Breeding: Two eggs are normally laid, sometimes only one, during December to March, in a shallow scrape in the ground; in colour yellowish olive, dappled and smudged with red-brown and slate. Average (14) 53,5 × 41,8 (48,4—61 × 40—43).

LOCAL RACES:
(a) E.v. vigorsii (A. Smith), 1831: *Beaufort West.* As figured. Size above. The Karoo and Bushmanland.
(b) E.v. namaqua (Roberts) 1932: *Gibeon, S.W.A.* Paler than *(a)* and less barred. Upington and lower Orange River Valley to Konkiep and Gibeon in Great Namaqualand.
(c) E.v. barlowi (Roberts), 1937: *Aus.* The least barred and palest pinky form. Size the same. Great Namaqualand in the region of Aus and borders of the Namib.
(d) E.v. fitzsimonsi (Roberts), 1937: *between Kobos and Maltathöhe.* Less bleached above, more pinky and darker coloured on the crown and back; less white below. Sizes as above. Northern Great Namaqualand.
(e) E.v. ruepellii (Wahlberg), 1856: *Onasis, Damaraland.* Illustrated. ♂ 320—330—340; ♀ 293—308—323; tail 145—165; tarsus 78—86; culmen 37—45. 8 ♂, 7 ♀ Damaraland northwards.

221   See **220** *(e)*

222 White-bellied Korhaan   Natalse Korhaan

Eupodotis cafra (Lichtenstein), 1793: *King William's Town district, Cape Province*

Native Name: i-Nkakalo (Z).

PLATE 24 (OPP. P. 160).

Length ♂ about 53 cm, ♀ about 48 cm (wing ♂ 290—294—302, ♀ 270—278; tail 130—145; tarsus 85—93; culmen 28—35. 12 specimens, 9 ♂, 3 ♀). Iris light brown; bill yellowish; legs yellowish white.

Identification: The only small Korhaan with a white belly in both sexes. The blue-grey throat and upper chest of the male also distinctive; it is lacking in the female which is otherwise similar but without black throat band. Young birds have the crown speckled, otherwise like adults.

Distribution: Eastern Cape Province, Natal, northern Transvaal and Botswana. Beyond our limits to Somaliland and across to Senegal.

Habits: A bird of open grassveld, usually seen in small parties walking slowly over the veld. Apparently subject to local movements.

Food: Insects.

Voice: A wild, rattling, crowing note that can be heard at a great distance, others joining in when in parties. When flying utters a note like "kuk-pa-wow".

Breeding: Two eggs form the normal clutch and are laid in December and January. In colour they are pale olive, clouded with darker olive and brown. Average (14) 50,2 × 39,7 (46,4—56,8 × 38,3—42).

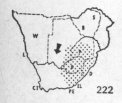

222

LOCAL RACE:
E.c. cafra (Lichtenstein), 1793: *King William's Town district.* Southern Africa and Angola. Other races to the north. Size above.

223 Blue Korhaan   Blou Korhaan

Eupodotis caerulescens (Vieillot), 1820: *Eastern Cape Province.*

PLATE 24 (OPP. P. 160).

Length 50—58 cm (wing 327—337; tail 160—173; tarsus 86—95; culmen 30—32. 3 ♂ specimens). Iris tawny; bill dusky, yellow at base; legs yellow.

Identification: The only Korhaan which is entirely blue below; sexes similar, but cheek of female brownish. Young resemble adult female but blue paler; face and eyebrow browner in young female than young male.

Distribution: Confined to the eastern Karoo (from Beaufort West eastwards), Griqualand West and the grassveld of upper Natal, Orange Free State and the southern Transvaal.

Habits: This striking, distinctively coloured species is usually seen in parties of four or five individuals, walking through the grass of the Karoo or Highveld.

Food: Probably mainly insects but also seeds and vegetable matter.

Voice: A loud call described as "knock-me-down, knock-me-down, me-down-medown".

Breeding: The eggs, nearly always 2, are laid in a depression in the ground, during November to February but also recorded in August. They are oval, pale brown with a greenish tinge, with overlying darker streaks. Average (24) 57,8 × 42,8 (49,5—60,8 × 40,3—46).

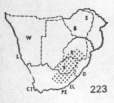

223

224 Red-crested Korhaan Boskorhaan

Eupodotis ruficrista (A. Smith), 1836: *Latakoo* = *Kuruman*

Native Name: Khoara-khoara (Ch).

PLATE 24 (OPP. P. 160).
Length about 50 cm (wing ♂ 255—269—290, ♀ 238—252—262; tail 126—152; tarsus 76—84; culmen 34—38. 37 specimens, 21 ♂, 16 ♀). Iris pale yellow; bill ashy, base yellow; legs whitish.

Identification: In courtship red crest of the male is distinctive. The female resembles the male but lacks the crest while the chest is mottled not grey, nor is there grey on the head; the black chin of the male is absent and there is a zone of white between the black belly and the mottling of the chest. Young birds resemble the female but have buffy tips to the primaries.

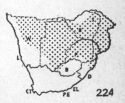

224

Distribution: Zululand and Griqualand West northwards to Ethiopia and Senegal.

Habits: A common species of the dry acacia savannas, often found in quite thick bush where there are open patches and often near koppies. A very fast flier. When flushed dashes away, usually getting behind trees, at great speed in a curving flight. In the breeding season conspicuous on account of the spectacular display of the male. Rising to some height from the ground, sometimes clattering its bill, it suddenly tumbles over and drops straight down; when close to earth, just as one expects to see it crash, suddenly spreads its wings and glides away for some distance and settles. Normally silent in flight, hence the sportsman's name of "Silent Member".

Food: Vegetable matter, acacia and Brachystegia seeds; gum and fruits; beetles, ants, centipedes and grasshoppers.

Voice: Utters about 12 tongue-clicks which develops into a high pitched "kyip" (about 6) gathering volume to a loud "keeweep" (about 4 times). The call may be repeated several times before being followed by the spectacular "rocket" flight described above. When breeding goes "wak, wak, wak, rising in volume and speeding up to a double "wuka wuka, wuka" with finally a thin piping note between each phrase. Alarm note "krock".

Breeding: Eggs are laid from October to February, the normal clutch 2 but sometimes only 1 is laid; greenish yellow to pinky and dark olive-yellow, dappled or smudged with darker shades of red-brown, brown and slate in varying degree. Average (15) 49,5 × 42,7 (46,2—54 × 37—45,2).

LOCAL RACE:
E.r. ruficrista (A. Smith), 1838: *Latakoo* = *Kuruman.* Throughout our area, Angola and Zambia.

225 Black Korhaan Swart Korhaan

Eupodotis afra (Linnaeus), 1758: *Cape of Good Hope.*

PLATE 24 (OPP. P. 160), ♂ and ♀.
Length about 53 cm. (wing ♂ 263—276—299, ♀ 260—270—282; tail 115—150; tarsus 74—92; culmen 30—37. 14 specimens, 10 ♂, 4 ♀). Iris light brown; bill greyish brown, base pinky red; legs yellow.

Identification: Very distinctive, see Plate 24. Sexes different, female has only the belly black; head and neck barred with black and pale rufous; lower chest

157

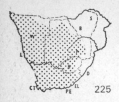

and behind ear-coverts white. Female often confused with No. 227. Young bird with longitudinal striped head and neck.

Distribution: Cape Town to Ovamboland on the west coast across to Rhodesia, Transvaal, Orange Free State and the eastern Cape Province. Does not occur east of the Drakensberg.

Habits: A common species, found in a variety of habitats from coastal sand-dunes to the grassy wastes of the highveld. Males are extremely noisy and conspicuous, but females are correspondingly shy, unobtrusive and difficult to flush. In the breeding season, males fly around at a height of about fifteen metres uttering their characteristic cry; when alighting the feet dangle and once on the ground they make off at some speed on foot.

Food: Vegetable matter, including seeds and insects.

Voice: Extremely noisy, the cocks uttering a loud, raucous "krracker, krracker" throughout the day, mainly in the breeding season.

Breeding: The nest is merely a scrape in the ground, sometimes lined with a little grass and extremely difficult to find due to the watchfulness of the male and the secretiveness of the female. One or 2 eggs are laid, August to October in the Cape, October to February further north; olive-green or brown, spotted and blotched with brown and purple. Average (30) 54,0 × 43,8 (46,3—58,9 × 40,3—46,5).

LOCAL RACES:
(a) *E.a. afra* Linnaeus, 1766: *Cape of Good Hope*: South-west Cape, Southern Karoo and Little Namaqualand. As shown in Plate 24. Wing ♂ 295, ♀ 277—282 (2).
(b) *E.a. afroides* (A. Smith), 1831: *Flats near Orange River*. Bushman Flats, Orange River, eastwards to Orange Free State and western Transvaal. Flight feathers have white elongate markings which form a white "window" in flight.
(c) *E.a. kalaharica* Roberts, 1932: *Gomodimo Pan, Central Kalahari*. Paler than (b); size given above. Botswana north to Mababe Flats, east to Nkate and Mahalapye.
(d) *E.a. damarensis* Roberts, 1926: *Omutako Flats, near Okahandja*. Rather like (b) but light bars above, lighter and redder; upper tail-coverts and tail whiter. South West Africa east to Molopo River and north to Kobos and Windhoek.
(e) *E.a. etoschae* (Grote), 1922: *Okaukweyo, Ovamboland*. Much paler than (d) with light bars almost whitish and very narrow.

226 = 225 (e)

227 Black-bellied Korhaan   Langbeen-korhaan

Eupodotis melanogaster   (Rüppell), 1835; *Lake Tana, Ethiopia.*

Native Name: u-Nofunjwa (Z)

PLATE 24 (OPP. P. 160).
Length 58—65 cm (wing ♂ 360—364—375, ♀ 335—350; tail 170—203; tarsus 123—140; culmen 40—48. 10 specimens. 8 ♂, 2 ♀). Iris brown; bill yellow; legs yellowish brown.

Identification: A thin-necked, long-legged species which might be confused with the Red-crested Korhaan, No. 224, except that in the male the red crest of that species is missing and the black of the belly extends in a thin line up the throat. Note *brown* iris—cf. No. 224. Sexes are quite different, the female having a white belly, thus avoiding confusion with the female Red-crested which has the belly black. The young bird resembles the female, but has wing feathers edged with buff.

Distribution: Africa south of the Sahara (except the Congo forests), as far south as Pondoland on the east and Ngamiland on the west.

Habits: Frequents the savannas and even rather marshy ground bordering them, where the grass is not loo long to prevent its seeing the approach of its enemies. Usually seen in pairs, the birds in general being rather tame and difficult to flush. After repeated calling the male indulges in spectacular flights displaying the white primaries, dropping with its wings held over its back.

Food: Insects, particularly dung-beetles, also grasshoppers, caterpillars, crickets and mantises; seeds rarely.

Voice: Standing on an antheap or slight prominence utters a whistled "quick" followed about 5 seconds later by an explosive "pop" like a cork being withdrawn from a bottle. May then fly as described above.

Breeding: Eggs are laid on the bare ground among grass, often near the base of a tree. They may number 1 or 2, almost round, mottled, dappled or clouded brownish olive over a lighter olive ground. They are laid from October to February. Southern eggs are large. Average (54) 57,8 × 51,8 (50,1—62 × 48,4—55).

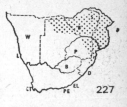

LOCAL RACE:
E.m. notophila (Oberholser), 1905: *Durban, Natal.*

Family JACANIDAE

Peculiar for their very long toes and claws, which make them look ungainly, but are very serviceable in running over the floating lilies and other vegetation in quiet stretches of water. Feed on water-insects and small animals and nest on a floating platform made of water-weeds drawn together, the eggs remarkable for their glossiness, looking as though french-polished, with black scroll marks on a yellowish ground. Mainly tropical in distribution; only two species occur in Africa.

228   African Jacana   Langtoon

Actophilornis africanus   (Gmelin), 1789: *Ethiopia.*

Native Names: i-Nkukumezara (G); Matenda-lezebu (Z).

PLATE 23 (OPP. P. 145).
Length 25—30 cm (wing 143—156—180; tail 38—56; tarsus 56—68; culmen 47—58. 19 specimens). Iris blackish brown; bill bluish grey, shield light blue; legs slate.

Identification: Unmistakable; sexes alike, female slightly larger but size very variable. Young birds have white underparts, the back oily brown.

Distribution: Africa south of the Sahara. Rare in southern and western Cape Province. Absent from the drier areas.

Habits: Not uncommon on lagoons and weed-fringed lakes or quiet rivers in the tropics but rarer to the south. To some extent probably migratory as individuals appear suddenly where they had not been seen before, but such movements need mapping out. This species is active in running over the water-lilies and other aquatic vegetation hence the popular name of "Lily-

PLATE 24

214. *Balearica regulorum regulorum.* Crowned Crane. Mahem.
215. *Grus carunculatus.* Wattled Crane. Lelkraan.
216. *Anthropoides paradisea.* Blue Crane. Bloukraan.
217. *Otis kori kori.* Kori Bustard. Gompou.
218. *Otis ludwigii.* Ludwig's Bustard. Ludwigse Pou.
219. *Otis denhami stanleyi.* Stanley Bustard. Veldpou.
220 *(a). Eupodotis vigorsii vigorsii.* Karoo Korhaan. Vaal Korhaan.
220 *(e). Eupodotis vigorsii rüppellii.* Rüppell's Korhaan.

Damara Vaal Korhaan.
222. *Eupodotis cafra cafra.* White-bellied Korhaan. Natalse Korhaan.
223. *Eupodotis caerulescens.* Blue Korhaan. Blou Korhaan.
224. *Eupodotis ruficrista ruficrista.* Red-crested Korhaan. Boskorhaan.
225. *Eupodotis afra afra.* Black Korhaan. Swart Korhaan. ♂ and ♀.
227. *Eupodotis melanogaster.* Black-bellied Korhaan. Langbeen-korhaan.

225 ♂ ♀ KN 224 223 27 220 E A 218 222 217 219 215 216 214 NLIGHTON '37

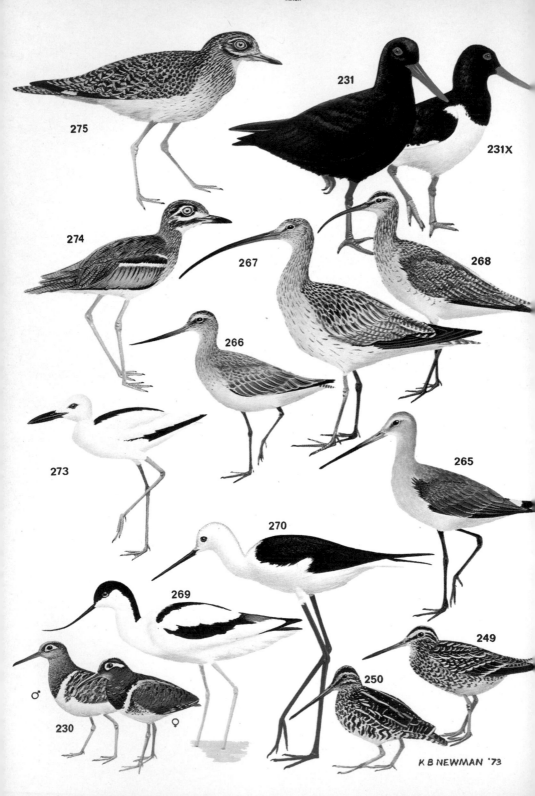

275

231

231X

274

267

268

266

273

265

270

269

249

230

250

K B NEWMAN '73

PLATE 25

230. *Rostratula benghalensis.* Painted Snipe. Goudsnip. ♂ and ♀.
231. *Haematopus moquini.* Black Oystercatcher. Tobie.
231X. *Haematopus ostralegus.* European Oystercatcher. Bont Oestervanger.
249. *Gallinago media.* Great Snipe. Dubbelsnip.
250. *Gallinago nigripennis.* Ethiopian Snipe. Afrikaanse Snip.
265. *Limosa limosa.* Black-tailed Godwit. Grutto.
266. *Limosa lapponica.* Bar-tailed Godwit. Rosse Grutto.
267. *Numenius arquata arquata.* Curlew. Wulp.
268. *Numenius phaeopus phaeopus.* Whimbrel. Klein Wulp.
269. *Recurvirostra avosetta.* Avocet. Bont Elsie.
270. *Himantopus himantopus meridionalis.* Stilt. Rooipoot-elsie.
273. *Dromas ardeola.* Crab Plover. Krapstrandloper.
274. *Burhinus vermiculatus vermiculatus.* Water Dikkop. Waterdikkop.
275. *Burhinus capensis.* Dikkop. Dikkop.

trotter''. Dives and swims when necessary and a strong flier, carrying its long toes trailing out behind. When not breeding may form large flocks of many hundreds—a wonderful sight. After landing, raises its wings above its head.
Food: Insects, aquatic larvae, snails and seeds.
Voice: A husky, whirling, rattling screech while flying. Also a mournful whining grating "kyowrrr, kyowrrr" and a short coot-like cry.
Breeding: Breeds in the months November to March but also recorded in June and July. Nest, a floating structure of water plants often half-submerged, usually placed in a quiet bay. It may be moved if flooding threatens. Polyandrous. The male incubates. Eggs 3—5, normally 4, are extremely beautiful pyriform objects, tan-yellow in ground colour almost hidden by long lines, dots and scrolls of black, the whole egg having a very high gloss as if varnished. Average (100) 33,0 × 23,2 (30,5—37,4 × 21,5—24,8). Incubation 21—24 days. The chicks are very precocious and soon leave the nest to run about on the water plants. All four young are often carried under the adult's wings, legs dangling out.

229 Lesser Jacana   Dwerg Langtoon

Microparra capensis   (A. Smith), 1839: *Algoa Bay*.
PLATE 23 (OPP. P. 145).
Length about 15 cm (wing 85—90—96; tail 29—36; tarsus 32—36; culmen 16—19. 16 specimens). Iris hazel; bill brown; legs greenish brown.

Identification: Similar in general pattern to the young of the previous species, but distinguishable by lacking a shield and black on the crown. In flight shows a white band at the end of the secondaries. Sexes alike. Young birds have crown blackish and nape golden chestnut.
Distribution: From the eastern Cape Province and Ngamiland northwards to the Sudan.

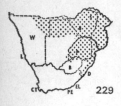

229

Habits: Frequents only quiet lagoons, lakes and streams where there are plenty of water-lilies and other water-plants to give it support and shelter. Frequently bobs its head; flies strongly and also raises its wings after alighting. On account of its small size and retiring habits, frequently overlooked. Requires less substantial vegetation than No. 228, thus often found where the larger species is absent.
Food: Insects and water plants.
Voice: A sharp "kruk".
Breeding: The nest is a small accumulation of water-weeds floating on the water and its eggs, 3—4, are rather similar to those of the larger species, No. 228, but are darker and more blotched with fewer lines. Average (9) 25,1 × 18,5 (24,3—26,6 × 18—18,9). Recorded breeding in March and April; February to April, July to August in Rhodesia.

FIELD IDENTIFICATION OF WADERS

Waders are reputedly difficult to identify in the field largely because the average observer is unaware of the characters which distinguish the species. Some waders are easy to identify, but others, even to the most experienced, are difficult; however, by a process of elimination, aided by the following remarks, it should be easy to identify the commoner species.

Comparative size is of course the first aid to tracking down a species. Compare the bird with some other familiar bird near it and then compare the measurements given for the two species in the book. One cannot judge the actual size of a bird at a hundred yards distance with any degree of accuracy.

The most important clue is the bill; its comparative length, whether it tapers to a point or whether the tip is slightly thicker than the centre and whether it is straight or slightly curved, up or down. At the same time the length of the legs and sometimes their colour will help.

Of the plumage the most important characters to determine are: *(a)* The presence or absence of a white wing bar, and if present, whether it is in the middle or along the trailing edge of the wing. *(b)* The pattern of the rump, whether white with or without a dark central line or whether uniform with the colour of the back. *(c)* The presence or absence of any well-defined stripe above the eye.

Naturally any obvious markings such as dark brown or black bars on tail or chest bands should be recorded. Observations should be made of the bird in flight as well as on the ground.

Family ROSTRATULIDAE

The Painted Snipes have the appearance of true Snipes in respect of their shape and long bill: but morphologically have proved to be so different that they are placed some distance apart. There are only three species in the family, distributed mainly in the southern hemisphere; in South America and Australia, in each of which there is a species; in Africa and India, where the same species occurs. The bill is not pitted like that of the true Snipe, the eyes are differently placed and the females are more handsomely coloured than the males and do not incubate the eggs, that duty being left to the plainer-coloured male! Like true Snipes they frequent marshes and feed on worms and insects of the mud, but lay their eggs, which are more Plover-like in markings, on the ground and not in the marsh vegetation: nor do they "drum" with their tail-feathers when in flight during the breeding season.

230 Painted Snipe   Goudsnip

Rostratula benghalensis   (Linnaeus), 1758: *Asia.*

PLATE 25 (OPP. P. 161). ♂ AND ♀.
Length ♂ 24 cm, ♀ 27 cm (wing ♂ 121—128—132, ♀ 136—139—145; tail ♂ 36—41—46, ♀ 41—43,9—47; tarsus ♂ 35—39,6—42, ♀ 39—41,9—44; culmen ♂ 41—44,4—47; ♀ 43—46,8—50,5. 31 specimens, 15 ♂, 16 ♀). Iris dark brown; bill purplish brown; legs and feet dull slaty blue to greenish ochre.

Identification: Male darker purplish brown on hind neck and back than illustrated. Immatures resemble the male. In flight (see below) the four golden bars down length of back are conspicuous and the flight feathers are dark, marked with large golden markings.

Distribution: Occurs south of the Sahara, in southern Asia to China and Sunda Islands. In Southern Africa it is widely distributed but local; considered rare in the eastern Cape.

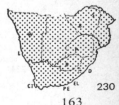

230

163

Habits: Resident but subject to local movements and thus in some areas occurring sporadically. Nowhere common, usually overlooked because of its skulking habits. It occurs on the border of swamps rather than in their depths, usually along the edge of the water-line and nearly always near reeds where it can gain hiding. Tend to remain stationary when alarmed or even after they have just landed, and in this way their camouflage merges remarkably into the background. When flushed they fly up awkwardly, often with feet dangling and the straight, slow flight is usually for a short distance only. The wings are rounded. More rail-like in habits than other snipe and when alarmed bob their hindquarters up and down.

Food: Insect larvae, worms, small molluscs and some grass-seeds.

Voice: The female has a croaking guttural note, whilst that of the male is shriller—like the sound made by blowing across the mouth of a bottle.

Breeding: The nest is a slight depression with practically no lining, although occasionally there are many small pieces of thin broken reeds. Placed near water, occasionally fairly exposed, although sometimes hidden by reeds. August to November in the Cape, extending to April in the Transvaal. Eggs 3—5, pyriform, yellow in ground colour, almost hidden by numerous blots, dots and irregular-shaped markings of black. Average (21) 34,6 × 25,2 (33—36,9 × 23,6—26,5). Incubation 19 days (2).

LOCAL RACE:
R.b. benghalensis (Linnaeus), 1758: *Asia.*

Family HAEMATOPODIDAE

Plover-like birds of the seashore, characterized by a wedge-like bill, which is slightly longer than the head, the mandibles not meeting at the tip and flattened, the sides compressed to form thin blades at the tip; the legs short, only three toes, and the plumage coloration more or less black. They subsist largely upon mussels, to which the bill seems adapted. They are cosmopolitan in distribution. Four species are recognized.

231   Black Oystercatcher   Tobie

Haematopus moquini   Bonaparte, 1856: *Africa = Cape of Good Hope*
PLATE 25 (OPP. P. 161).
Length about 51 cm (wing 260—266—270; tail 102—104—110; tarsus 47—51,8—55; culmen 62—68,5—72,5. 7 specimens). Iris red with eyelids orange; bill red; legs red.

Identification: Jet-black colour with orange legs and bill make this bird very easy to recognize. Sexes alike. Juveniles brown-black with orange legs and bill.

Distribution: A west coast species from Angola south to the Cape Province. Rare in Natal.

Habits: A resident limited to the seashore, coastal islands, lagoons and estuaries. Usually occurring in pairs, but small flocks (up to 40) may be found in winter and spring—apparently formed by first and second-year birds. Frequents all shore habitats from sandy beaches to rocky coasts. Feeds along the water level, prising mussels from the rocks, breaking them in crevices, or taking fauna from sandbanks and beaches. Also feeds actively at night. An

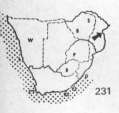

231

active and agile bird, working quickly on exposed rocks or probing to the full length of its bill in soft sand.

Food: Molluscs, *Mytilus, Donax* and whelks, crustacea and annelids.

Voice: The alarm note is a series of sharp "kik-kik-kiks". Frequently calls a clear and shrill "klee-weep, klee-weep", or "tsa-peee, tsa-peee".

Breeding: Makes a nest scrape in the form of a slight hollow on sand, pebbles or debris, sometimes lined with a few shell fragments. Eggs 1—4, usually two, from October to March; slightly pointed at the acute end, stone-coloured with irregular spots and scrolls of pale purplish and very dark brown. Single brooded, though may replace damaged clutches. Incubation 28—30 days. The chicks are unable to fly until about 45 days old. Average (80) 60,7 × 41,9 (55,4—66 × 40—44,5).

LOCAL RACE:
H.m. moquini Bonaparte, 1856: Cape of Good Hope.

231X   European Oystercatcher   Bont Oestervanger

Haematopus ostralegus   Linnaeus, 1758: *Europe = Oeland, Baltic.*

PLATE 25 (OPP. P. 161).
Length about 43 cm. (wing 262; tail 107; tarsus 56; bill 86—87.)

Identification: A large bird, with bold pied pattern. The belly and rump are white. Non-breeding plumage has a white chin. In flight the broad white wing bar and broad black terminal bar of tail are conspicuous features.

Distribution: Europe east to Central Asia, south in winter as far as Central Africa. Recorded from Langebaan, Cape Peninsula, Plettenberg Bay, Gamtoos River mouth and East London. Also South West African coast.

Habits: A rare Palaearctic migrant recorded only from the coast. Single birds only recorded, usually in loose association with the Black Oystercatcher, No. 231, but staying slightly apart from them. Rather nervous and quick to take alarm and fly. Similar in general habits to the Black Oystercatcher. One record of a bird overstaying during our winter and moulting into breeding plumage; black chin (Shewell).

Voice: With practice the second note of the double call is said to sound a trifle higher than that of the Black Oystercatcher.

LOCAL RACE:
H.o. longipes Buturlin, 1910: *Tomsk.*

Family ARENARIIDAE

Plover-like birds with short legs, with reticulate scales behind, hind to, present, and bill about the same length as the head, level on the culmen the tip thin and rather flattened and with a groove for the basal half from the nostrils, but no dertrum (or hardened, rather swollen tip) like that of Plovers. There are only two species, one with a restricted distribution in western North America and the other practically cosmopolitan. The present species breeds in the Arctic regions only, coming south of the Equator in all continents during the northern winter.

232 Turnstone   Steenloper

Arenaria interpres (Linnaeus), 1758: *Europe and North America*
= *Gothland, Sweden*
PLATE 26 (OPP. P. 184). PLATE 28.
Length 23 cm (wing 141—149—155; tail 57—61—64; tarsus 23—24,1—26; culmen
20—21,9—23,5. 7 specimens). Iris dark brown; bill black; legs orange.

Identification: Mottled winter plumage illustrated. The unmistakable flight
pattern is figured. In summer plumage the head and neck attain a black-
and-white pattern, the scapulars and wing-coverts a bright chestnut, giving
generally a more pied effect.

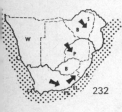

Distribution: Almost cosmopolitan. Found around the entire seaboard. Rare
inland; recorded from the Central African lakes, the Zambesi River in
Rhodesia and at Pretoria.

Habits: A common migrant along rocky or muddy shore lines, commonest
along the west coast as far south as Langebaan. Wintering birds recorded from
the east and west coast, these birds sometimes moulting into partial breeding
plumage. Never recorded in large flocks; in numbers up to 20, but may
congregate in much larger numbers on suitable feeding haunts. Feed at
low-tide, working exposed rocks, pebbles and tidal flats; if small rocks are
present may be observed to turn these over in search of food. Active with
quick action when feeding, busily turning from side to side as they probe the
surface. When flushed they fly off low over the water, flying strongly and
calling. Courtship observed before departure to the breeding grounds.

Food: Small crustacea and molluscs.

Voice: When put to flight "kit it it it" or "chidda-chidda-chidda". In display
a sound like pulling one's thumb across wet glass.

LOCAL RACE:
A.i. interpres (Linnaeus), 1758: *Europe and North America* = *Gothland, Sweden.*
Another race in North America.

Family CHARADRIIDAE

Plovers are terrestrial birds of small to medium size; bill not longer than the
head and with a dertrum or *hardened swelling at the apical part*, but variable
in length and shape; the legs fairly long and the hind toe small or absent, other
toes usually not long. They occur in open dry ground or on the margin or
marshes. Generally 60 species recognized.

233 Ringed Plover   Ringnek-strandlopertjie

Charadrius hiaticula Linnaeus, 1758: *Europe and North America* =
Sweden.
Native Name: Unokrekre (X).
PLATE 26 (OPP. P. 184). PLATE 28.
Length about 16 cm (wing 118—124,7—132; tail 48—55,6—60; tarsus 22,5—
24,4—26,5; culmen 13,5—14,5—16. 22 specimens). Iris brown; bill yellow-orange;
legs and feet orange-yellow.

Identification: The orange-yellow legs distinguish this species at all stages of
its plumage changes. The adult is illustrated. Differs from other small plovers

by its single broad band across chest. Immature birds are dark brown instead of black around eye, ear coverts and sides of chest. The bar is not always complete but is always *dark brown* and reaches nearly across the front. In flight the white wing-bar is conspicuous, and the sides and tip of tail are white.

Distribution: Europe, Asia and Greenland, south in winter. Throughout the area but mainly a coastal bird. Birds ringed at Rondevlei recovered 9 600 kms N in France and 16 500 kms NNE in U.S.S.R.

Habits: A summer migrant, rarely remaining through the winter; apparently migrating down the Rift Valley as well as the east and west coasts. Found along the edge of water, along the shore, in lagoons, estuaries and vleis; also occurs on dried-up pans. Usually in small parties, never large flocks of its own species; but it may occur loosely in large flocks of mixed species. Feeds on exposed mud and sandbanks, rarely wading in the water. Runs rapidly, stopping suddenly to pick up food and then runs on, keeping its head up except when actually pecking. Feeds actively day and night depending on the tides.

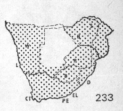

Food: Molluscs, crustacea and insects.

Voice: A pretty whistle rendered as "too-ti" or "tiuu-it".

LOCAL RACE:
C.h. tundrae (Lowe), 1915 *Yenesei Valley*. Size as above. Smaller and darker than the nominate race which has not been recorded in our area.

234 Mongolian Sandplover   Mongoolse Strandlopertjie

Charadrius mongolus   Pallas, 1776: *Mongolia*.

PLATE 26 (OPP. P. 184). PLATE 28.
Length 19 cm (wing 124, 125; tail 46,7, 48; tarsus 32,2, 33,7; culmen 16,5—18,0. 2 specimens). Iris brown; bill black; legs olive-grey-brown.

Identification: Probably mistaken for young White-fronted Sandplover. This bird has *no white bar on hind neck* which the White-fronted Sandplover has at all stages; otherwise similar in size and general appearance but has a much *heavier bill*. This bird is not suffused with buff below, like No. 235, and the marks at the side of chest are also fairly large not neat and small. There is a line of greyish brown *from the bill*, below eye, broadening to a wide ear patch. In breeding plumage, has black on the forehead as No. 235; behind eye is a pale chestnut band encircling crown and a dark chestnut band across breast. See No. 239 from which it differs only by size (in the non-breeding plumage) and comparatively slighter bill.

Distribution: Central and eastern Asia. Migrating south. Recorded from Kenya, one from Zaïre. Specimens from Swakopmund, South West Africa, Swartkops, eastern Cape, Durban and Mozambique.

Habits: Probably overlooked and not as rare as records reflect, though undoubtedly uncommon. One flock of 15 seen Durban where it has been recorded more frequently in recent years.

LOCAL RACE:
C.m. atrifrons Wagler, 1829: *Bengal, India*, Size as above.

167

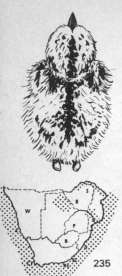

235   White-fronted Sandplover   Vaal Strandlopertjie

Charadrius marginatus   Vieillot, 1818: *No locality = Cape Peninsula.*

PLATE 26 (OPP. P. 184). PLATE 28.

Length about 18 cm (wing 103—109,5—115; tail 45—50,3—54; tarsus 23—25,3—29; culmen 15,5—16,9—18. 24 specimens). Iris dark brown; bill and legs black.

Identification: The male has a more conspicuous black line behind eye and usually small dark patches on sides of breast. Flight pattern figured; note feet do not extend beyond tail. See Kittlitz's Sandplover, No. 237, for comparison. Immature lacks any black on head but white band across nape is present. Nestling grey above, mottled with black forming lines down centre of crown and back, ear coverts and sides of back; white below.

Distribution: A species mainly coastal but also recorded from the larger rivers and inland lakes.

235

Habits: Frequents sandy shores, dunes and sandy rivers where it occurs singly or in small parties. Resident but occasionally non-breeding birds flock with possibly some sort of local movement. Runs along the sand so rapidly it appears almost to glide, sometimes with a peculiar sideways action. Feeding method is to run rapidly, then stop suddenly, peck the object off the surface and then run on a few steps, always with head up. When put to flight it calls (see below) and flies off rapidly and low to settle a little further on.

Food: Insect larvae, small crustacea and worms.

Voice: In flight a soft "wit" or "twirit". Alarm note is a loud "kittup" or a long drawn out "churrr".

Breeding: Constructs a number of nest scrapes before laying. The nest is a slight depression in the sand, rarely on shingle, usually on some slight mound commanding a good view, or in debris at the highwater mark. The eggs are usually partially covered with sand. Breeds throughout the year, mainly August—September. Eggs usually 2, 1—4 recorded, pointed ovals, creamy buff, marked with fine lines of dark brown scattered over the surface. Average (150) 32,8 × 23,3 (29,5—37 × 21—25). Incubation 27—33 days. Nestling period 35—38 days.

LOCAL RACES:
The birds from the western Cape are white below and grey-brown above. There is a gradual cline to the north along the west coast, and to the east and north along the Indian Ocean. Further north they become more suffused with buff below and more tawny brown upper parts. Two races are recognized:
(a) *C.m. marginatus* Vieillot, 1818: no locality = *Cape Province.* Cape Triangle. With very little if any pink suffusing below, size as above.
(b) *C.m. tenellus* Hartlaub, 1861: *Madagascar.* Transkei coast, Natal and Limpopo River northwards. Generally darker above and more pinky below. Size overlap in Natal but Limpopo River birds smaller: wing 100—102—103; tail 45—47,2—49; tarsus 23—23,2—24; culmen 14—15,2—16,5. 5 specimens.

236   Chestnut-banded Sandplover
Rooiband-strandlopertjie

Charadrius pallidus   Strickland, 1852: *Damaraland.*

PLATE 26 (OPP. P. 184). AD AND IMM. PLATE 28.

Length 15 cm (wing 100—102,3—105; tail 39—41,4—44; tarsus 26—27,6—29; culmen 12,5—13,3—14. 13 specimens, 7 ♂, 6 ♀). Iris dark brown; bill black; legs olive.

Identification: Male illustrated. Female lacks the black on the forehead and lores. From a distance may be overlooked for the White-fronted Sandplover,

No. 235, but this species appears shorter and therefore more chubby; the chest band always present except in first plumage. Juvenile has no black on head and the band is incomplete, being merely two grey patches at sides of breast, thus easily confused with the last two species. Nestling grey intermingled with black markings above, forming lines down centre of crown and back, ear coverts and sides of back. White below.

Distribution: Coastal from Angola in the west, around the south as far as Beira. Occurs on large inland temporary vleis and especially saltpans.

Habits: Very local in habit, being especially partial to saltpans and coastal lagoons. Resident, but subject to local movements; on occasions in flocks of over 50 birds, although usually found singly or in pairs. Feeds in a similar manner to the White-fronted Sandplover, No. 235. A much shyer bird than the preceding species, particularly wary when nesting, flying off very low over the ground at the slightest danger.

Food: Unrecorded.

Voice: Practically indistinguishable from the White-fronted Sandplover.

Breeding: Recorded from Swartkops (Eastern Province), coastal saltpans of the south-west, Van Wyks Vlei and Barberspan; around the edges of saltpans and vleis on very flat terrain. The nest is a shallow scrape, sometimes lined with mollusc shells or quartz chips, situated on stony ground, dried bleached aquatic weeds or open sandy areas. Recorded all months except February, March, June and July. Eggs 2, putty-coloured with fine spots and scrawls of sepia with underlying ones of grey—evenly spread. Average (29) 30,6 × 22,6 (28,6—32,9 × 21,7—24,4).

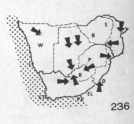

236

LOCAL RACE:
C.p. pallidus Strickland, 1852: *Damaraland.* Another race in Central Africa.

237 Kittlitz's Sandplover Geelbors-strandlopertjie

Charadrius pecuarius Temminck, 1823: *Cape of Good Hope.*

PLATE 26 (OPP. P. 184). PLATE 28.
Length 16 cm (wing 98—110—113; tail 42—44,6—49; tarsus 27—29,5—31; culmen 15—16,4—18. 19 specimens). Iris dark brown; bill and legs black.

Identification: Darker generally than the White-fronted Sandplover. Note the black line behind eye twists down and around nape below the white band. Female has the narrow line across the forehead dark brown instead of black. In flight the feet extend beyond tail. Immature birds have the pattern of adult but no black or white on head, being suffused with buff and the darker lines light brown. Nestling greyish above, speckled black with dark centre line on back, white below.

Distribution: Throughout Africa south of the Sahara.

Habits: A common resident usually occurring in small parties, less frequently singly or in pairs. Large flocks (over 100) are often observed for short periods, indicating some sort of local movement. Found on open dry flats near water, dried-up pans, aerodromes and similar flat exposed habitats. Not a very shy bird; when disturbed flies several feet above the ground and settles some way off. Feeding habits as No. 235. When young are present it resorts readily to the "broken wing" act.

237

169

Food: Crustacea, small molluscs, insects and their larvae.
Voice: In flight a "tip-peep", a trill similar to No. 235, "trit-tritritritrit", also an alarm "chirrt" or "prrrt".
Breeding: Digs a number of scrapes, finally occupying one which it fills with material from the vicinity of the nest, pebbles, twigs, dung, or dried flower heads. This material is always kicked over the eggs by a rapid sideways action of the feet before the nest is left, and kicked off when the parent returns to incubate. The nest is situated on rough flat terrain. Breeds throughout the year, mainly from July to November. Eggs 2, creamy yellow, fairly thickly covered all over with overlapping black, thin, wavy lines. Average (100) 31,9 × 22,2 (28,6—34,4 × 19,0—23,2). Incubation (4) 23—26 days.

238 Three-banded Sandplover Drieband-strandlopertjie

Charadrius tricollaris Vieillot, 1818: *Africa = Cape Town.*

Native Name: Unokrekre (X).

PLATE 26 (OPP. P. 184). PLATE 28.

Length 18 cm (wing 104—110—119; tail 56—62,3—67; tarsus 21—22,8—24; culmen 14—15,7—17,5; 48 specimens). Iris hazel, with red wattle around eye; bill black with reddish base; legs flesh-coloured. Weight 30,5 g.

Identification: Two narrow black bands across chest separates this species from the Ringed Plover, No. 233, and the legs are *not* orange. In flight this species has a conspicuous white wing bar and the tail has a *white terminal bar* and white outer feathers. The young have an incomplete, brown upper chest band, the lower band has the black feathers with narrow white tips; more uniform coloured on the head with dull white and dark brown; upper parts brown with feathers edged buff. Nestling boldly patterned, otherwise similar to previous species.
Distribution: The whole of Africa south of the Sahara and in Malagasy.
Habits: A resident species, widely dispersed on the edge of inland lakes, pans and rivers where there is mud, clear sandy, or hard soil, shoreline, but also sometimes on the seashore. Occasionally on rubbish dumps. Occurs singly or in family parties, though occasionally gathering in loose flocks of up to forty. Often heard first, then seen, standing still with body sloping forward, bobbing head and body with each call. When put up, it calls and flies off with characteristic jerky flight to settle a little further on. When feeding pecks continually while walking but not infrequently runs in starts as other Sandplovers.
Food: Terrestrial and acquatic insects and their larvae; worms, crustacea and small molluscs.
Voice: A high-pitched whistle "wick-wick" or "tiuu-it, tiuu-it".
Breeding: A shallow depression is made, often with little pebbles or shells around the edge. Situated amongst stoney patches or on gravel. May to January, only starting in August in the Cape. Eggs 2, ground colour, creamy, covered by masses of fine hair-lines forming one or two broad darker rings around the broad end. Average (67) 29,9 × 22,1 (27—32,5 × 20,5—24,1).

LOCAL RACE:
C.t. tricollaris Vieillot, 1818: *Africa = Cape Town.* Another race occurs in Malagasy.

239 Great Sandplover — Groot Strandloper

Charadrius leschenaultii Lesson, 1826: *Pondicherry.*

PLATE 26 (OPP. P. 184). PLATE 28.
Length 22 cm (wing 135—145; tail 55—65; tarsus 35—38; culmen 21—25). Iris dark brown; bill black; legs greenish yellow.

Identification: Somewhat similar to a White-fronted Sandplover, but larger with a *noticeably heavier bill.* No white line on nape as in that species. The *patch on sides of chest* is variable in colour from dull light brown to chestnut, and in extent from side patches to a complete broad band across chest. There is also a *brown patch about the eye and eary coverts* with a thin extension from eye to bill. It stands a head higher than Curlew Sandpiper, No. 251, and Ringed Plover, No. 233. Differs from Mongolian Sandplover, No. 234, by being slightly larger and by its proportionally larger bill.

Distribution: Eastern Asia and the Red Sea. South to the islands of western Indian Ocean; East African coast and lakes. Recorded regularly down the coast as far as Port Elizabeth. Also from Rondevlei, Cape, Langebaan and up the coast of South West Africa.

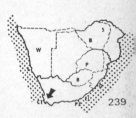

Habits: An uncommon migrant from October to May along the eastern shores. Rare and irregular on the west. Usually seen in small parties, very often in company with other waders which frequent tidal mud- and sandbanks. Not as shy as other waders and when put to flight do not go far. When the tide is in they rest amongst vegetation or on sand patches above the water-line.

240 Caspian Plover — Asiatiese Strandloper

Charadrius asiaticus Pallas, 1773: *South Tartary.*

PLATE 26 (OPP. P. 184). PLATE 28.
Length 22 cm (wing 142—148; tail 50—60; tarsus 37—41; culmen 19—21). Iris dark brown; bill black; legs greenish yellow.

Identification: Male illustrated; a much thinner bill than Great Sandplover. A small *terrestrial* plover (see under Habits) which may be confused with the previous species in certain stages of its plumage. Immature and female birds have a broad chest-band which may taper a bit towards the centre, to the extent that it appears to be an incomplete band. The dark patch behind and below the eye is much bigger than in the Great and Mongolian Sandplovers; also, the superciliary eye-stripe is broader in this species. In flight the white primary shafts are conspicuous.

Distribution: South Russia, wintering in western India, Arabia and Africa. Sparsely distributed in suitable country throughout Southern Africa, rare in the south-west Cape.

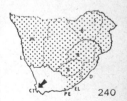

Habits: A migrant recorded from September to February, present in small flocks. Birds of open grassland, independent of water, though quite often recorded on flats near water. May be mistaken for coursers, having the same habit of running away when disturbed rather than flying off. When flushed, all take to the wing together, circling about and settling again; individuals often coming to a halt near some vegetation or mound which aids their camouflage.

Generally a restless bird, moving from place to place after short stays. Active flyers at night.

Food: Almost entirely insects but grass seeds also taken. Fond of harvester ants.

Voice: A whistling "ku-wit".

240X   Eastern Golden Plover   Goue Strandloper

Pluvialis dominica   (P. L. S. Müller), 1776: *San Domingo.*

PLATE 26 (OPP. P. 184). PLATE 28.
Length 24 cm (wing ♂ 165—174, ♀ 158—175; tail 59—65; tarsus 39—46; culmen 21—27; 12 specimens ex *Handbk. Brit. Birds*). Iris dark brown; bill black; legs slate-grey.

Identification: Distinguished from the next species in non-breeding plumage by *light grey axillaries* uniform with under-wing. In the field very similar to immature Grey Plover but this is a slightly smaller bird and the spotting tends to be golden and not white or buffish as in the next species. Distinguished from the Knot, No. 254, by its shorter bill, longer legs and speckled upper parts.

Distribution: Eastern Asia to America. Wintering in America, Pacific Islands, Australia and less frequently in Africa. Few records for Southern Africa; specimen from Cape Peninsula (March 1953), Zoetendalsvlei, Cape Agulhas, and sight records at Keiskama River, Eastern Cape and Walvis Bay.

Habits: A very rare straggler. Similar in habits to the Grey Plover. Both the specimens in 1953 were confiding birds and allowed a close approach, certainly tamer than the Grey Plover.

LOCAL RACE:
P.d. fulva Gmelin, 1789: *Tahiti.* The asiatic form distributed from Asia to Alaska. Generally more yellow about head and neck. Distinguished from other Golden Plover by its grey underwing.

241   Grey Plover   Grys Strandloper

Pluvialis squatarola   (Linnaeus), 1758: *Europe = Sweden.*

PLATE 26 (OPP. P. 184). PLATE 28.
Length 30 cm (wing 195—198—206; tail 67—74—82; tarsus 42—45—47; culmen 29—29,8—31; 6 specimens, 1 ♂, 5 ♀). Iris dark brown; bill black; legs ash-grey.

Identification: Winter plumage illustrated. In flight the *black axillaries* ("dirty armpits") form a most conspicuous identification aid. The size, high forehead, short bill and long legs, distinguishes this plover from other waders along the shore, c.f. No. 254. In summer plumage the underparts from the chin to lower belly are totally black, bordered by a broad white margin; the back is darker so that the white markings show up more. Black spots appear first on the chest and belly.

Distribution: Northern Europe, Asia and America. Wintering south almost everywhere. Around our entire coastline, occasional inland records from

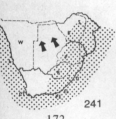

241

Botswana, Rhodesia, Transvaal, Lesotho and central and eastern Cape Province.

Habits: A migrant from late August to early May, wintering birds common on the west coast. Occurs singly or in small flocks when feeding but may gather in large numbers at high-tide; records of 500 not uncommon on the west; one record of over 2 000. An estuarine bird for the main part, found especially where there are large sand or mudbanks exposed by tides. Typical plover habits of running in starts, pausing and perhaps picking some item of food, bending its body down then coming upright with head up before running on again. Rather shy. Sometimes arrive in partial breeding plumage. Prior to their departure, March, occasionally earlier, they begin to assume breeding plumage, sometimes completing the change before departure. At this period these birds become more plump in appearance due to an accumulation of fat deposits under the skin. Quite often feed at night as well as during the day.

Food: Crustacea: (Hymenosoma, Callianassa), small molluscs.

Voice: An attractive whistle "tlui-tlui" which carries far.

242   Crowned Plover   Kiewietjie

Stephanibyx coronatus   (Boddaert), 1783: *Cape of Good Hope.*

Native Names: Igxiya (X); 'Mbagaqwa (Z); le-Tetshane, le-Tletleroane, Mororoane (S).

PLATE 26 (OPP. P. 184).
Length 30 cm (male: wing 192—204—216; tail 85—93—101; tarsus 61—69,5—73; culmen 28—30,6—33; female averages: wing 200,5; tail 90,4; tarsus 66,8; culmen 31,0. 33 specimens, 23 ♂, 10 ♀). Iris orange, biscuit-yellow when young rarely brown; bill and legs red-orange, greenish yellow when young.

Identification: The black crown with white rim and the red legs distinguish this plover from other species. The immature attains the crown markings whilst still in its speckled plumage; also, the lower edge of the breast has a black bar, see No. 243. Nestling differs from other plovers by having the coronal circlet indicated by paler tipped down and breast sandy coloured merging to an ashy breast band.

Distribution: Widespread but local all over South Africa to north-eastern Africa.

Habits: A common resident species. Usually found in pairs or small parties; to some extent gregarious (up to 40), particularly after the breeding season (i.e. March—July) when it becomes restless—moving from one district to another. Shows a preference for open veld in dry localities, especially where the grass is short; also in patches of open ground among bush and on cultivated lands. Runs with body held horizontal then suddenly stops, standing upright and stationary or, if feeding, bends body downwards and pecks food with a forward thrust of the head. It becomes very noisy and attentive to intruders, swooping at them with wild cries particularly when eggs or young are threatened.

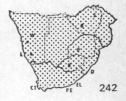

242

Food: Beetles, grasshoppers, insect larvae, caterpillars and ladybirds.

Voice: "Kie-wieet", also in flight "kree-kree-kreekreeip-kreeeip".

Breeding: The nest is a scrape, usually on broken gravelly or cultivated land and sometimes lined with pebbles or twigs, occasionally well lined. Occasionally nest in loose colonies. From June to March, September (Cape) and October (Transvaal) to November, March to December in Rhodesia. Eggs 2—4, usually 3, rarely 5 (two females recorded); dull olivaceous-brown covered with small scattered dots and lines of slate or black. Average (150) 40,1 × 29,0 (36,2—44 × 26—31,4). Incubation 28—32 days.

LOCAL RACE:
S.c. coronatus (Boddaert), 1783: *Cape of Good Hope.* Generally distributed except to the north-east of its range where a paler race exists.

243   Black-winged Plover   Swartvlerk-kiewietjie

Stephanibyx melanopterus   (Cretzschmar), 1826: *Djedda, Arabia.*

Native Names: i-Titihoya (Z); Kweriekwerie (Sh).

PLATE 26 (OPP. P. 184).
Length about 27 cm (wing 198—216; tail 68—76; tarsus 53—59; culmen 25—28). Iris pale yellow, narrow scarlet eyelids; bill black; legs dark scarlet.

Identification: May be confused with the next species but differs as follows: black chest band much broader; the upper parts with a purplish sheen; the secondaries black-tipped giving the impression of a *white bar on the wing*; the under-wing is white and this species has scarlet eyelids; compare No. 244. White of forehead extends above the eye. Immature differs from the immature of the Crowned Plover by lacking dark markings on the crown and having no dark line across the lower part of the greyish chest. Nestling distinguished from next species by presence of dark line on the dorsum and a dark patch on either side of the pelvic region.

Distribution: In summer, August to April, from the eastern Cape (from Mossel Bay) northwards along the Drakensberg and adjoining foothills and plateau in a narrow belt to Zoutpansberg; northwards to Ethiopia. Winters at lower levels especially along the neighbouring coastal flats from April to July.

Habits: Not uncommon migrant, although some birds remain in their 243 wintering quarters all the year. Generally similar to the previous species except in its preference for moister localities. Social in winter quarters sometimes in flocks of up to 50 birds, though more often in smaller parties.

Food: Beetles and their larvae, flies, worms and grubs.

Voice: Has a fine vocabulary of curses of varied pitch and intensity rising to high screams, "che-che-che-chereck" and "titihoya".

Breeding: The nest is a hollow, scraped in peaty soil or on a slight rise; the eggs sometimes placed thin end downwards so that only the tops show. August to October. Eggs 3—4, darker than Crowned Plover with large, confluent smudges of blackish, quite numerous. Average (44) 41,5 × 29,4 (36,5—46,5 × 26,7—31,3).

LOCAL RACE:
S.m. minor Zedlitz, 1908: *St. John's River, Pondoland.* The southern race extending from the Cape to the equator. Smaller than nominate race.

244 Lesser Black-winged Plover
Klein Swartvlerk-kiewietjie

Stephanibyx lugubris   (Lesson), 1826: *Senegal.*

Native Name: Titihoya (Z).
PLATE 26 (OPP. P. 184).
Length about 22 cm (wing 158—186; tail 66—77; tarsus 54—60; culmen 20—23). Iris orange-yellow; bill black; legs dark brown.

Identification: Easily confused with the previous species, see No. 243. The black band at base of chest is narrow; upper parts tinged olive-brown; *secondaries wholly white*; underwing ash-brown and white. The eyelids are brown and the white forehead patch does not extend back as far as the eye. The legs are dark brown in this species. For immature and nestling, see previous species.
Distribution: Coastal from about Durban, Natal, northwards to the Zambesi. Beyond this extending to Zambia, East Africa and westwards to Gambia.
Habits: Similar in habits to Crowned Plover, No. 242, also in showing preference for drier habitats. Usually occurring in small parties; as common as the previous species. Avoids detection by standing still, when disturbed runs, if pursued takes to flight.
Food: Insects and their larvae, a few grass seeds.
Voice: A clear piping "thi-wit".
Breeding: Recorded from northern Zululand September and October. No nest is made, the eggs being laid on ground among open patchy soil and grass (Bell Marley). Eggs 2—4, similar to those of the Crowned Plover but smaller. Average (5) 34,6 × 26,3 (33—35,6 × 25,3—27). Incubation 18—20 days. Nestlings remain with parents about two months.

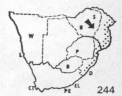

244

245 Blacksmith Plover
Bontkiewietjie

Hoplopterus armatus   (Burchell), 1822: *Klaarwater, Hay Dist., C.P.*

PLATE 26 (OPP. P. 184).
Length 30 cm (wing 202—219; tail 84—92; tarsus 70—76; culmen 25—31). Iris bright carmine; bill and legs black. Weight 110—195 g. Age 72 months.

Identification: An unmistakable black, grey and white plover. Under wing-coverts white. The flight pattern is bold black and white, and this, coupled with slow regular beats of rounded wings, makes identification easy. Immature brownish with little white on forehead; off-white chin and throat merging to buff speckled brown chest, darker on back and speckled with off-white nape patch; tail as adult. Nestling mottled sandy and sepia above, crown line and back darker; neck-band and underparts white, except breast bar which is speckled.
Distribution: South Africa north to Angola and Kenya. Commonest in the northern Cape, Orange Free State and Transvaal; somewhat local elsewhere. Established in the south-west Cape recently.

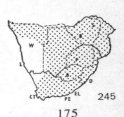

245

Habits: Resident, occurring in pairs or small parties though congregating in larger groups during the non-breeding period. Restless, appearing temporarily when conditions are suitable; partial to damp situations on the borders of pans, near streams and rivers where the grass is short, especially where flood waters are apt to soak the flats. Silent and when not feeding very still unless disturbed, when they will fly out at an intruder and utter harsh clinking notes, sounding like a hammer on an anvil.

Food: Insects, worms and small molluscs.

Voice: See above; "klink, klink, klink, klink".

Breeding: The nest is a depression or shallow scrape often situated near water; lined with a few twigs, grass and little stones. July to November in the Cape, starting earlier further north; March, April and June in Transvaal; throughout the year in Rhodesia. Eggs 2—5, usually 4, once 6 (? two females); similar to the Black-winged Plover. No. 243. Average (100) 39,6 × 29,0 (37—42,5 × 27—30,7). Incubation period 26 days.

246   White-crowned Plover   Witkop-kiewietjie

Xiphidiopterus albiceps   (Gould), 1834: *Niger River*.

PLATE 26 (OPP. P. 184).
Length about 30 cm. (wing 200—209—218; tail 90—100—105; tarsus 71—74,4—77; culmen 30—32,1—33; 7 specimens). Iris yellow; bill black at tip, base yellow merging on to yellow lappets (about 2,5 cm long) with black centre marks; legs grass-green. Black spur on wing about 17 mm.

Identification: The only other plover with wattles, No. 247, has black on the crown, throat and belly. In flight the outer primaries appear black whilst the inner ones and the secondaries are white; flight slow, buoyant and deliberate. Male has thin black line between white and brown on crown. Immature has similar pattern to adult. Feet larger than illustrated.

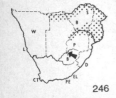

246

Distribution: A tropical species extending from the Limpopo River, Zambesi River and beyond, south of the Sahara desert. Recorded in Rhodesia below 1 000 metres on the Zambesi, Sabi and Limpopo Rivers. Old records from Potchefstroom and Pafuri.

Habits: Resident, usually found in small parties, sometimes singly. Confined to mud or sandbanks along rivers, sometimes to sandy beds of dried-up rivers but usually near water. Slightly jumpy when alarmed, and takes to flight readily, flying off calling. This is the Plover which is said to peck at gaping crocodiles' mouths—cleaning the food from between the teeth. Recorded to wet belly feathers to cool eggs.

Food: Insects, including mantises and a bone from frog or fish recorded.

Voice: Likened to the Oystercatcher, No. 231, and also the Skimmer, No. 306. A sharp "keep" or "peep" which may be repeated many times.

Breeding: Lay eggs during periods of low water on the rivers. July to October on the Zambesi River. The nest is a shallow pit scooped out of hard sand. Eggs 3 or 4, creamy buff, marked with spots and underlying lines of brown and mauve chiefly around the broad end. Average (9) 43,2 × 29,9 (41,2—44,5 × 28—31).

247   Wattled Plover   Lelkiewiet

Xiphidiopterus senegallus   (Linnaeus), 1766: *Senegal.*

PLATE 26 (OPP. P. 184).
Length 35 cm (wing 221—232—247; tail 96—99—107; tarsus 80—85,3—91; culmen
31—34,1—37,5. 15 specimens, 9 ♂, 6 ♀). Iris lemon-yellow; bill black-tipped with
yellow base merging on to red to orange wattle and yellow eyelids; legs greenish yellow.

Identification: The presence of a wattle distinguishes this and the previous
species from other plovers, even in the young stage. The black border to its
white crown, black throat and black breast-bar separates this species from No.
246. Chin white. In flight the secondaries show white except the outer ones,
which, with the primaries, are black. Immature has a smaller white crown; the
chin and throat streaked black and white. Nestling with black patches on
crown and back.

Distribution: Widely distributed south of the Sahara. Occurs in Ovamboland,
northern Botswana, Rhodesia, central and southern Transvaal, east to Zululand
and in Natal as far as lower Tugela River. An old record from Port Elizabeth
(Rickard).

Habits: A not uncommon resident, though said to move south during the
rains to breed along its southern limits. Frequently met with singly or in pairs
but more generally in small parties, seasonally in larger flocks. Found only   247
near water, rivers, vleis or marshes. Quite a tame species, and when breeding
calls loud and persistently, quite often at night.

Food: Insects, large coleoptera, aquatic insects and a little grass seed.

Voice: A shrill "peep-peep".

Breeding: The nest is a depression in the mud or earth with a few bits of
grass or pebbles, near water, often on a slight mound. July to December. Eggs
3—4, rarely 2; dull buff, blotched and marked with black and brown. Average
(42) 49,3 × 35,2 (44,9—53,8 × 32,9—36). Incubation 30—32 days.

LOCAL RACE:
X.s. lateralis (A. Smith), 1839: *Tugela River, Natal.* Differs from the other races by
presence of black bar demarcating the light-brown breast from the white belly. Size as
given above, the southern race extending as far north as Angola and central Uganda.

248   Long-toed Plover   Witvlerk-kiewietjie

Hemiparra crassirostris   (Hartlaub), 1855: *Nubia = White Nile*
                                            .between lat. 3° and 4° N.

PLATE 26 (OPP. P. 184).
Length about 30 cm (wing 187—201—210; tail 90—95—100; tarsus 71—74—77;
culmen 32—32,6—34,5. 8 specimens). Iris red and red eyelids; bill-tip black, red-mauve
at the base; legs carmine to mauve with dark scutes on tarsi and toes.

Identification: This long-toed plover is only found on floating aquatic vege-
tation. Distinguished by its white wing except for the three outer primaries
which are black (see below). Except for black hind neck and nape it has a
white head.

Distribution: From Lake Chad and southern Sudan southwards and eastwards to the Zambesi River and further down the coastal belt as far as St.
Lucia, Zululand.   248

177

Habits: Rare in the south, usually resident. Occurs singly, in pairs, or in small family parties always near water and for the most part on aquatic vegetation in marshes, rivers and lakes. As at home on lilies as the Jacana, No. 228. Normally a very shy bird but it becomes bold during the breeding season. In flight it has been compared to a small white heron on account of the almost completely white wings.

Food: Aquatic insects, maggot-like larvae, dragon-fly nymphs and small snails.

Voice: A loud plaintive "wheet". In flight a loud clicking "kick-k-k-k, kick-k-k-k".

Breeding: Records from St. Lucia, October 1934. The nest is a shallow depression lined with grass, on floating vegetation or grass, within 100 metres of water. The birds are particularly cunning when nesting and nests are difficult to find. Eggs 2, greyish green with usual intermingled brown markings. Average (5) 44,9 × 31,0 (40—47,8 × 27,3—33,5).

LOCAL RACE:
H.c. leucoptera (Reichenow), 1889: *Quelimane.* The southern race with white inner primaries and secondaries. Size as above. From southern Tanzania to the south.

Family SCOLOPACIDAE

The Snipes are Plover-like birds in general appearance, but may be recognized at once by their *longer bill, which is longer than the head*, and certain morphological characters. Practically all our species are migratory and breed only in the northern hemisphere, and though one Snipe breeds here it is also migratory within the continent. Birds of the marshes, streams, rivers, lakes and seashores, where they procure their food—consisting of worms, water-insects and other small water-animals—by probing in the mud or ooze. Eggs are laid in nests formed by gathering grass or other vegetable matter into a saucer-shape in a depression or inside a tussock of grass. Some 75 living species are recognized.

249 Great Snipe   Dubbelsnip

Gallinago media (Latham), 1787: *England.*

PLATE 25 (OPP. P. 161).
Length about 28 cm (wing 142—150; tail 50,5—58; tarsus 34—36; culmen 60—68). Iris brown; bill yellowish brown; legs black.

Identification: Similar to the next species but the wing is longer and more pointed. The white spots on the wing are conspicuous. The outer tail feathers are pure white. The *belly is buffish with black markings*. See Habits and compare No. 250.

Distribution: Europe to Siberia, south in winter. Recorded from East London district, and from Potchefstroom northwards. An old record for the Cape Division.

Habits: A migrant recorded from October to March, although Horsbrugh states he has observed it throughout the year in the Transvaal. Present status indicates that the bird is not as common as it used to be, but subject to occasional influxes. Usually found singly or in pairs. When flushed rises without a sound, giving a quick twist and attaining great speed almost immediately; flies off straight.

249

250 Ethiopian Snipe   Afrikaanse Snip

Gallinago nigripennis Bonaparte, 1839: *Cape of Good Hope.*

Native Names: Umnqunduluti (X); u-Nununde (Z); Koekoelemao (S).
PLATE 25 (OPP. P. 161).
Length about 28 cm (wing 125—139; tail 51—59; tarsus 32—35; culmen 73—88). Iris brown; bill black; legs greenish brown or yellow-green.

Identification: Distinguished from the previous species by its longer bill, *white belly* and barred outer tail feathers. This species has longitudinal buff bars along the scapulars, and lacks the conspicuous white spotting on coverts. Very difficult to distinguish in the field from the Great Snipe. In flight the wings are more rounded.

Distribution: Found throughout South Africa, extending northwards to Angola and East Africa to Ethiopia.

Habits: A resident, subject to local movements probably due to drying-up of their habitats. Common where there are vleis or marshes with flooded short grass. Flight somewhat heavy, slow and very erratic in direction. When breeding easily detected by active aerial displays; these are accompanied by drumming, caused by the vibration of the outer two tail feathers against each other in rapid flight. Drumming continued until the eggs are hatched. During this period the birds, when flushed, utter a sucking sound like a foot being drawn out of mud.

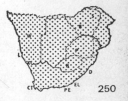

250

Food: Larvae of flies, beetles, dragonflies, worms, small crustacea and molluscs.

Voice: See above. Alarm note a quiet "tchek".

Breeding: The nest is built of grass woven into a platform hidden beneath a tuft of grass, the blades of which are pulled over to give shade and protection. April, June to October. Eggs 2, glossy and sharper pointed than Plovers; olive-buff with scattered spots of slate and large slate-brown, olive-brown or black blotches. Average (53) 41,4 × 29,7 (36,9—44,8 × 27—32).

LOCAL RACES:
(a) G.n. nigripennis Bonaparte, 1839: *Cape of Good Hope.* Shorter bill than race *(b)*; size as above. Southern and eastern race.
(b) G.n. angolensis Bocage, 1868: *Huilla, Angola.* Longer billed than *(a)*; bill 85—93,5—103 (14). Ngamiland, Angola, overlapping *(a)* in Zambia and Rhodesia.

251 Curlew Sandpiper   Krombek-strandloper

Calidris ferruginea (Pontoppidan), 1763: *Denmark.*

PLATE 29 BR. AND N. BR. (OPP. P. 185). PLATE 27.
Length 20 cm (wing 122—127—133; tail 44—48,5—51; tarsus 28—30,1—31; culmen 35—37,7—41. 8 specimens). Iris dark brown; bill olivaceous black; legs olivaceous brown. Age 132 months. Weight summer mean 57,1 g. Premigration 79,4 g.

Identification: A medium-small wader with fairly long decurved bill and white upper tail-coverts. Shows characteristic hunched silhouette with high shoulders curving down to rump and slightly up again at tail. Has a slight white eye-stripe and in flight shows a fairly noticeable white wing bar. Partial

179

breeding plumage recorded from March to September. Full breeding plumage of males is bright orange-cinnamon and may be seen in April.

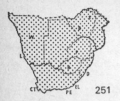

Distribution: Arctic Asia, coming south in winter. Throughout Southern Africa in suitable habitats.

Habits: A very common migrant, arriving at the end of August and departing late April. More common on pans and vleis of the southern Transvaal, Orange Free State, south-west Cape and west coast than elsewhere. Wintering birds quite common, sometimes in flocks of up to 50; summer flocks may have over 2 000 birds, though usually in groups of from 10 to 200. Usually feed on wet mud or sand around any open water, not often in wet grassy localities. They feed walking forward with body horizontal, probing the whole bill in and out as they walk, lifting the head between probes. Rest in close-packed flocks and when disturbed stretch their wings up above their backs—all following the leader—before they start to shuffle about. In flight they all stay close together and call repeatedly in an excited twitter, as they flash about in beautiful aerobatics. Migration records Paarden Island to U.S.S.R. 14 241 km, Ronde-vlei to U.S.S.R. 10 600 km; recoveries in Angola, Zaïre and Iran.

Food: Crustacea and worms.

Voice: A whistled "chirrip". When chasing each other, pairs utter a "chit-chit".

251X   Pectoral Sandpiper

Calidris melanotos   (Vieillot), 1819: *Paraguay, South America.*

PLATE 29 (OPP. P. 185). PLATE 27.
Length about 19 cm (wing 135; tail 58; tarsus 28; culmen 27,5. 1 specimen). Legs yellowish.

Identification: Likely to be confused with the Curlew Sandpiper No. 251 but differs from that species by having a shorter straighter bill. Rump with dark central line chest markings more definite and forming an abrupt edge or line with edge of white belly. The general coloration of upper parts is buffish-brown and not grey brown of 251. No white wing bar in flight. Leg yellowish. Call distinctive.

Distribution: An American species which occurs as a vagrant in Europe, Asia and Japan. Recorded in Kenya; from Rhodesia also, Botswana, Howick, Port Alfred, Rondevlei (Cape) and Pretoria.

Habits: This rare vagrant occurs in company with Curlew Sandpiper and Little Stint usually in muddy grassy shallow pans.

Voice: A characteristic note uttered when flushed—"Kriek-kriek" or "Trrreeek".

251Y   Dunlin

Calidris alpina   (Linnaeus), 1758: *Lapland.*

PLATE 29 (OPP. P. 185). PLATE 27.
Length 18 cm (wing 109; tail 36; tarsus 23; culmen 29). Eyes, bill and legs blackish.

Identification: Very similar to the Curlew Sandpiper but distinguished in flight by dark central line down rump with side of rump white. Bill slightly shorter and straighter than 251.

Distribution: Holarctic region wintering south to North and East Africa, India. First recorded at Rondevlei, Cape, 12 Nov. 1959. Sight recorded from the Cape, Swakopmund and Rosherville Dam, Transvaal.

Habits: Similar to 251 but in the north tends to be found more along coastal areas than inland. Most sight and trapping records are of single specimens in company with Curlew Sandpiper. Those records from the Transvaal are of flocks up to 29 together.

LOCAL RACE:
Several races recognized but until a specimen is available race cannot be determined satisfactorily.

251Z   Broad-billed Sandpiper

Limicola falcinellus (Pontoppidan), 1763: *Denmark.*

PLATE 29 (OPP. P. 185). PLATE 27.
Length about 17 cm (wing 101—113; tail 35—42; tarsus 20—23; culmen 30—36). Iris dark brown; bill horny black, strongly tinged with olive green; legs dark lead, juvenile yellowish olive. Weight 26—37,5 g.

Identification: Rather like No. 251 but stripes above eye fork and usually with a black patch at angle of wing, like No. 255, which distinguish it readily. Greyer and whiter than 251 and 253. In flight the black centre of rump and tail with white sides (slightly barred) are conspicuous—more so than No. 251Y. A close view will show shorter legs, more spotting on cheeks and breast and the decurved flattened tip of bill.

Distribution: Northern Europe and Asia south in winter. First specimens recorded in 1965 Swakopmund subsequently recorded in Rhodesia and Durban.

Habits: A summer visitor recorded from September through to January. Reputedly solitary and secretive, sometimes in small flocks but seldom mixes with other Sandpipers. In South West Africa in association with 251 and 253. Said to pick its food from the surface rather than probe.

252   See page xxxi

253   Little Stint   Klein Strandloper

Calidris minuta (Leisler), 1812: *Near Hanay, Germany.*

PLATE 29 (OPP. P. 185). PLATE 27.
Length about 14 cm (wing 95—98—104; tail 39—41,6—44; tarsus 19—20,6—22; culmen 17—18,3—20. 12 specimens). Iris black; bill and legs black. Age 86 months, weight (18) 22—24—29 g.

Identification: Our smallest wader, clearly mottled on back, bill shorter than head. See figure for flight pattern. Breeding plumage begins to appear in April.

Distribution: Northern Europe and west Siberia, south in winter. Occurs throughout southern Africa wherever suitable habitats exist.

Habits: A very common migrant, arriving September and departing late April or early May. Winter records not uncommon, but not as numerous as No. 251.

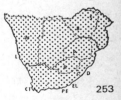

253

Flocks of from a few birds up to 200 or 300, occasionally up to 900. Frequently associated with the Curlew Sandpiper, No. 251, from which it can be distinguished by its smaller size and shorter bill. The feeding habits of this bird are also diagnostic; the busy feeding is carried out with head down all the time; the whole flock often presenting a mass of backs as the birds walk about and peck from side to side without wasting the time and energy to lift up their heads and look about. In flight they tend to bunch, showing as they wheel about grey-brown upper parts and then flashing white underparts, twittering excitedly as they fly here and there. Several ringing records from Cape to U.S.S.R.—one found 11 000 km NNE.

Food: Crustacea, daphnia and copepods; mosquito and chironomid larvae.

Voice: A "chit" or "tit" repeated and usually uttered in a twittering chorus.

253X   Red-necked Stint

Calidris ruficollis   (Pallas), 1776: *Eastern Siberia.*

PLATE 29 (OPP. P. 185). PLATE 27.
Length about 15 cm (wing 100—108; tail 44—47). Iris, bill and legs black.

Identification: Almost identical to the Little Stint in winter plumage, perhaps a little larger and shorter legged and bill shorter and thicker. The upper parts much paler and purer grey, the mantle without a brown wash. The back appears paler because back feathers have a thin dark central line rather than the fuscous blobs of No. 253. Partial breeding plumage recorded in October in the form of rufous buff on side of upper neck.

Distribution: Siberia to Alaska extending south in northern winter to New Zealand and Australia. Two specimens collected in Durban Bay November and December (1963). Other records include Swartkops. South African records are so far limited to the period October to December. Small numbers seen, up to nine only.

Habits: The same in habits as Little Stint.

254   Knot   Knoet

Calidris canutus   (Linnaeus), 1758: *Sweden.*

PLATE 29 (OPP. P. 185). PLATE 27.
Length about 25 cm (wing ♂ 162—171, ♀ 164—174; tail 50,5—66,5; tarsus 27,5—31; bill ♂ 30—34, ♀ 31,5—38,5. 12 specimens ex *Handbk. Brit. Birds*). Iris brown; bill black; legs olive-green.

Identification: May be confused with the Ruff, No. 256, but distinguished by its more uniform back, uniform upper tailcoverts and dark legs. Somewhat similar to the Grey Plover, No. 241, but smaller. Distinguished by its longer tapering bill, shorter legs and by lack of black axillaries. Habitat preference also separates these species in Southern Africa. Compare Nos. 240X, 241 and 256. The rich chestnut breast is attained in April prior to departure.

Distribution: Arctic regions; south in winter. Recorded along the South West African coast as far south as Langebaan and in the south-west Cape. Also reliably from Gamtoos and Kowie River mouths and Pondoland coast, and one inland record from Graaff-Reinet. Also Durban and Richards Bay.

254

Habits: A rare migrant recorded from October to April. Except for one record, coastal in habits. Occurs singly, but at Langebaan and Walvis Bay flocks of up to 150 are recorded. Its plump appearance and habit of feeding and flying in dense flocks is characteristic. Probes bill into sand several times between steps as it moves forward. The flight is swift and strong and flocks perform aerial evolutions similar to those of smaller waders. Single birds may join flocks of other species.

Voice: A single note "knut", though usually silent.

LOCAL RACE:
C.c. canutus (Linnaeus), 1758: *Sweden.* As above, another race occurs in America.

255 Sanderling   Drietoon-strandloper

Calidris alba (Pallas), 1764: *Coast of the North Sea.*

PLATE 29 (OPP. P. 185). PLATE 27.
Length about 19 cm (wing ♂ 117—130, ♀ 120—130; tail 46—55; tarsus 22—26; bill ♂ 23,5—26,5, ♀ 23—28,5. 12 specimens ex *Handbk. Brit. Birds*). Iris brown; bill and legs black.

Identification: *Its white appearance, short heavy bill and dark shoulder patch are diagnostic.* Has only three toes. The white wing bar is conspicuous in flight as figured. In breeding plumage, which is rarely recorded, the head, back and breast are chestnut; traces of this occur as late as October and begin to appear again before departure in April.

Distribution: Arctic regions, wintering in the south. In our area along the entire coastline with inland records for Rhodesia, Botswana, Transvaal and eastern Cape.

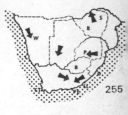
255

Habits: A common migrant along the coast but most inland records are of single vagrants; September to May. Wintering birds in flocks of up to 50 are not uncommon (Gamtoos River). Usually occurs in flocks of 20 to 200. This small, plump species is common along the open shore, where it runs up and down in compact flocks with the breaking and receding waves. When feeding keeps head permanently down, ploughing along the sand with its bill (leaving a distinct furrow) and moving about rapidly. A bird ringed at Langebaan was recovered 12 714 km NNE in the U.S.S.R.

Food: Small crustacea, molluscs, larvae of various kinds and remnants of small fish and shrimps.

Voice: A whistled "twick twick".

256 Ruff   Kemphaan

Philomachus pugnax (Linnaeus), 1758: *Sweden.*

PLATE 29 (OPP. P. 185). PLATE 27.
Length ♂ 30 cm, ♀ 24 cm (wing ♂ 170—183—190, ♀ 152—156—162; tail ♂ 66—67,1—68, ♀ 51—57,2—61; tarsus ♂ 45—49,2—52, ♀ 38—40,2—42; culmen ♂ 33—34,3—35, ♀ 30—30,9—32. 18 specimens, 6 ♂, 12 ♀). Iris dark brown; bill dark brown; legs variable from dull greenish grey to bright orange. Weight 95—151 gms.

Identification: A medium-sized wader having a boldly mottled back and a lightish patch at the base of bill. Often confused with the Redshank, No. 261, because of the orange legs; but shorter bill, flight pattern (see below), and

183

PLATE 26

232. *Arenaria interpres interpres.* Turnstone. Steenloper.
233. *Charadrius hiaticula.* Ringed Plover. Ringnek-strandlopertjie.
234. *Charadrius mongolus.* Mongolian Sandplover. Mongoolse Strandlopertjie.
235. *Charadrius marginatus marginatus.* White-fronted Sandplover.
Vaal Strandlopertjie.
236. *Charadrius pallidus pallidus.* Chestnut-banded Sandplover.
Rooiband-strandlopertjie.
237. *Charadrius pecuarius.* Kittlitz's Sandplover. Geelbors-strandlopertjie.
238. *Charadrius tricollaris tricollaris.* Three-banded Sandplover.
Drieband-strandlopertjie.
239. *Charadrius leschenaultii.* Great Sandplover. Groot Strandloper.
240. *Charadrius asiaticus.* Caspian Plover. Asiatiese Strandloper.
240X. *Pluvialis dominica.* Eastern Golden Plover. Goue Strandloper.
241. *Pluvialis squatarola.* Grey Plover. Grys Strandloper.
242. *Stephanibyx coronatus coronatus.* Crowned Plover. Kiewietjie.
243. *Stephanibyx melanopterus minor.* Black-winged Plover.
Swartvlerk-kiewietjie.
244. *Stephanibyx lugubris.* Lesser Black-winged Plover.
Klein Swartvlerk-kiewietjie.
245. *Hoplopterus armatus.* Blacksmith Plover. Bontkiewietjie.
246. *Xiphidiopterus albiceps.* White-crowned Plover. Witkop-kiewietjie.
247. *Xiphidiopterus senegallus lateralis.* Wattled Plover. Lelkiewiet.
248. *Hemiparra crassirostris leucoptera.* Long-toed Plover.
Witvlerk-kiewietjie.

238

235

Imm

236

237

240

232

233

234

240 X

239

241

242

243

244

245

247

246

248

K B NEWMAN '73

Plate 27

WADERS

DUNLIN
251Y

LITTLE STINT
253

PECTORAL S P
251X

251Z

BROAD-
BILLED S P

RED NECKED
STINT
253X

GREY PHALAROPE
271

251
CURLEW S P

WOOD S P
264

259

272
RED NECKED
PHALAROPE

255

GREEN S P

COMMON S P
258

SANDERLI

254
KNOT

256
RUFF

TEREK S P
257

REDSHANK
261

MARSH S P
262

GREENSHANK
263

K B NEWMAN '73

Plate 28

SMALL PLOVERS

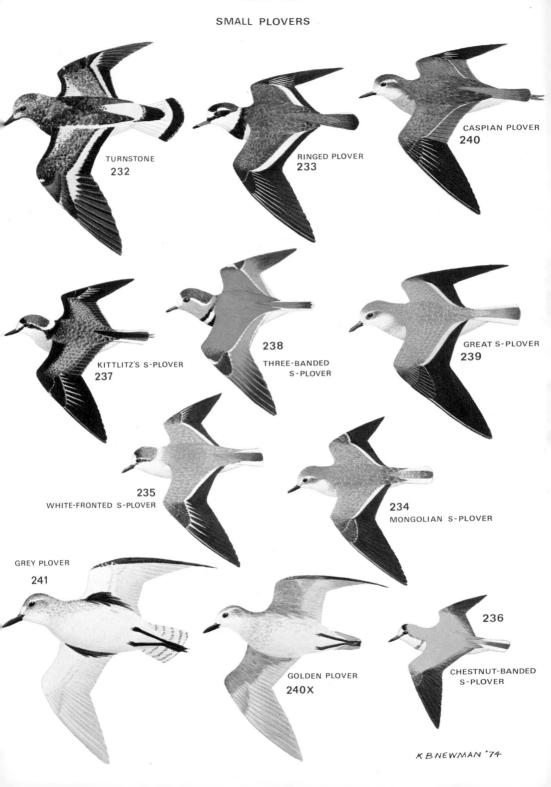

TURNSTONE
232

RINGED PLOVER
233

CASPIAN PLOVER
240

KITTLITZ'S S-PLOVER
237

THREE-BANDED
S-PLOVER
238

GREAT S-PLOVER
239

WHITE-FRONTED S-PLOVER
235

MONGOLIAN S-PLOVER
234

GREY PLOVER
241

GOLDEN PLOVER
240X

CHESTNUT-BANDED
S-PLOVER
236

KBNEWMAN '74

251
Br.
Br.

253
Br.

253X

251Y

251X

251Z

257

259

Br.
254

264

Br.
255

258

272

262

261

271

263

256
♂
♂
♀

KB NEWMAN '73

PLATE 29

251. *Calidris ferruginea.* Curlew Sandpiper. Krombek-strandloper.

Br. and N-Br.

251X. *Calidris melanotos.* Pectoral Sandpiper.

251Y. *Calidris alpina.* Dunlin.

251Z. *Limicola falcinellus.* Broad-billed Sandpiper.

253. *Calidris minuta.* Little Stint. Klein Strandloper. Br. and N-Br.

253X. *Calidris ruficollis.* Red-necked Stint.

254. *Calidris canutus.* Knot. Knoet. Br. and N-Br.

255. *Calidris alba.* Sanderling. Drietoon-strandloper. Br. and N-Br.

256. *Philomachus pugnax.* ♂ Ruff, ♀ Reeve. Kemphaan.

257. *Xenus cinereus.* Terek Sandpiper. Terekruiter.

258. *Tringa hypoleucos.* Common Sandpiper. Gewone Ruiter.

259. *Tringa ochropus.* Green Sandpiper. Witgatje.

261. *Tringa totanus.* Redshank. Tureluur.

262. *Tringa stagnatilis.* Marsh Sandpiper. Moerasruiter.

263. *Tringa nebularia.* Greenshank. Groenpoot-ruiter.

264. *Tringa glareola.* Wood Sandpiper. Bosruiter.

271. *Phalaropus fulicarius.* Grey Phalarope. Franjepoot.

272. *Phalaropus lobatus.* Red-necked Phalarope. Rooihals-franjepoot.

shorter legs distinguish this species. Male much larger than female although not all flocks are of mixed sexes. In flight the white wing-bar and white patches on either side of the dark central line on the rump are easily seen. Breeding plumage in the male is recorded in the form of white or black markings on neck and head; traces recorded throughout their stay here. See also No. 254.

Distribution: Europe and Asia, wintering to the south. Throughout our area.

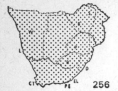

256

Habits: A very common migrant, arriving late August and departing in April. Wintering birds not common. Gregarious in flocks of half-a-dozen to 200, but recorded up to 1 000. Large flocks are usually of mixed sexes. Occurs near water in short, marshy vegetation or on inland mudbanks of vleis and dams; never on open sand at the coast and seldom in saline marshes. Also recorded on grass or wheat lands away from water. The flight is strong with regular wing-beats. When alarmed the body is held upright and all heads are stretched upwards in unison; when feeding the body is horizontal and in silhouette the shoulders are high, back curved down and then up at tail; the long tertiaries curl up and blow about if there is a strong wind. A bird ringed in Salisbury was recovered 7 152 kms NNE in U.S.S.R.

Food: Insects, crustacea, worms, molluscs and seeds.

Voice: Appear to utter no sound at all.

257 Terek Sandpiper   Terekruiter

Xenus cinereus Güldenstädt, 1775: *Terek River, S.E. Russia.*

PLATE 29 (OPP. P. 185). PLATE 27.
Length about 23 cm (wing ♂ 126—141, ♀ 127—140; tail 47—56; tarsus 25—28; bill ♂ 43—49, ♀ 44—52. 12 specimens ex *Handbk. Brit. Birds.*) Iris dark brown; bill orange at base merging to black tip; legs orange-yellow.

Identification: A stumpy-legged wader with a long upcurved bill. The uniform light greyish upper-parts, light eye-stripe and orange-yellow legs distinguish this species. Bill long, slender as illustrated. Dark patch on shoulder of wing and grey streaks on side of breast may be noted in the field. In flight the white ends of the secondaries and uniform pale rump are noticeable. Traces of breeding plumage may occur before departure; head and upper-parts become darker and a dark V begins to show on their backs.

Distribution: Siberia and Eastern Europe; south in winter. Around our coast. A rare vagrant inland, recorded from Rhenosterspruit, O.F.S., on the Rand near Pretoria, Lake Ngami and Fort Victoria

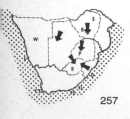

257

Habits: A regular migrant, not common; recorded from October to May with a few wintering records. Commonest on the east and west coasts. Found along estuaries, lagoons and near mangrove swamps. Usually in small flocks but single birds not infrequent. A lively little bird which has a characteristic bobbing of its hindquarters as it moves actively about, jabbing its bill down full length here and there. Can run at great speed with body held low and feet moving rapidly. Commonly perches on the dead twigs of partly submerged trees and apparently roosts there at night. A bird ringed at Langebaan recovered U.S.S.R. 12 640 km NNE.

Food: Small crustacea, molluscs and aquatic insects.

Voice: A clear whistle "tu-tu-tu", in flight or at rest.

258   Common Sandpiper   Gewone Ruiter

Tringa hypoleucos   (Linnaeus), 1758: *Europe = Sweden.*

PLATE 29 (OPP. P. 185). PLATE 27.
Length about 19 cm (wing 109—111—115; tail 51—53,3—56; tarsus 22—23,2—24; culmen 24—25—26. 9 specimens). Iris brown; bill dark brown; legs greenish grey.

Identification: See No. 259. At rest the wing appears dark against the white breast; a white patch extends up above the shoulder. The longish bill, definite eye-stripe and buffish area on the sides of upper-chest aid identification. In flight the wing bar is conspicuous and well displayed by characteristic flight, low over the water with spasmodic wing action, the wings moving only a small angle from the horizontal. Under wing-coverts lightish.
Distribution: Europe and Asia wintering in the south. Throughout southern Africa in suitable localities.
Habits: A common migrant arriving mid-August and departing by the first week of May. Generally distributed near water, especially quiet streams, rivers and estuaries; commonest along the Natal coast where communal roosts of up to 30 birds may occur. Normally occurs singly or in pairs, gathering to roost together often on small boats. Frequent the same locality for most of their sojourn in the south. Have the characteristic habit of bobbing the hinder part of body up and down while feeding and walking. When feeding probes the bill half its length into the mud.
Food: Insects and their larvae, molluscs and crustacea.
Voice: A high-pitched "tsee-see-see" or "tiuu-tiuu-tiuu-tiuu-tiuu".
Breeding: Recorded from Kenya, Uganda and Tanzania. Courtship observed from January in Natal.

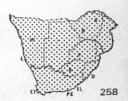

259   Green Sandpiper   Witgatjie

Tringa ochropus   (Linnaeus), 1758: *Europe =Sweden.*

PLATE 29 (OPP. P. 185). PLATE 27.
Length about 23 cm (wing 141—148; tail 54—59; tarsus 32—34; culmen 33,5—38. 3 specimens). Iris dull brown; bill black-brown, darkish green at base; legs olive-green.

Identification: Confused with the Wood Sandpiper, No. 264. The upper parts are darker and contrast with the brilliant white rump, upper tail and belly. Speckled back and no wing-bar separates this and the Wood Sandpiper from the Common Sandpiper, No. 258. In flight the *under wing-coverts are blackish.* Tail is white at base and barred with a few bars at the end only (see No. 264).
Distribution: Northern and central Europe across to Asia, wintering in the south. Irregular south of the Zambesi, vagrants as far south as Fort Beaufort and Knysna, eastern Cape, Botswana, not in the west.
Habits: A very rare migrant recorded from October to March. Prefers quieter streams and rivers like the previous species and also becomes attached to certain feeding grounds. When flushed is said occasionally to fly off high with jerky flight. Does not occur in flocks.
Voice: High-pitched treble note "tui-tui-tui".

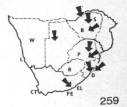

260   See page xxxi

261   Redshank   Tureluur

Tringa totanus   (Linnaeus), 1758: *Europe = Sweden.*

PLATE 29 (OPP. P. 185). PLATE 27.
Length about 25 cm (wing 147—157; tail 57—65; tarsus 43—48; culmen 39—42. 11 ♂
specimens. Race *T.t. totanus* ex *Handbk. Brit. Birds*). Iris brown; bill pink-horn, orange
towards base; legs orange-red.

Identification: Because Nos. 256, 257, 262 and 264 may have orange-yellow
legs there is some confusion. This species is longer legged and more slender in
appearance than Ruff and Terek Sandpiper and with a heavier bill than the
Marsh Sandpiper. Has a brownish uniform coloured back (not spotted). In
flight the white rump and *white edge to the secondaries* forming a white
margin to the wing are conspicuous. Distinguished from Terek Sandpiper by its
white rump and the fact that feet extend beyond tail in flight. See also No.
262. Note that the straight bill is pink at the base and the light eye-stripe aids
identification.
Distribution: Europe and Asia, wintering to the south. South West Africa
coast, western Cape, Port Elizabeth, Durban, also inland from southern
Transvaal, Bloemfontein, Welkom and Graaff-Reinet.
Habits: A very rare migrant except at Walvis Bay where it is not uncommon.
Single records for other localities. Two records of wintering birds. Generally a
shy restless bird which when alarmed stretches its neck up and bobs its body

261

up and down. The gait is brisk and it is generally more graceful than the
Greenshank, No. 263. The flight is swift and rather erratic, flying up and
away; holds its wings momentarily raised above the back after alighting. The
call is diagnostic.
Voice: A musical whistled "tleu-hu-hu".

LOCAL RACE:
Racial status unknown. Several races are recognized and two are recorded from East
Africa: *T.t. totanus* and *T.t. eurhinus.*

262   Marsh Sandpiper   Moerasruiter

Tringa stagnatilis   (Bechstein), 1803: *Germany.*

PLATE 29 (OPP. P. 185). PLATE 27
Length about 23 cm (wing 134—139—145; tail 55—57,6—62; tarsus 47,5—52,3—56;
culmen 39—41,1—43. 17 specimens). Iris dark brown; bill black; legs dusky olive to
light orange-yellow.

Identification: A smaller version of the Greenshank, No. 263; differing from
that species by its slightly smaller size, *thin bill*, which tapers to the tip and
different call note. The feet project far beyond the tail in flight. Has been
confused with the Wood Sandpiper, No. 264, from which it differs by
presence of white back and rump in flight; also confused with the Redshank,
No. 261, when the legs are orange-yellow, but thin tapering bill and lack of
any wing-bar distinguishes this species.
Distribution: Eastern Europe and Asia, wintering to the south. Generally

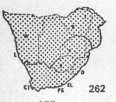

262   distributed throughout Southern Africa at suitable localities.

Habits: A common migrant occurring from September to April, though many birds remain in the south throughout the year. Usually singly or in small parties, but flocks of up to 100 not at all uncommon; very often in company with Greenshank and less often with other waders. A small and graceful edition of the Greenshank but tamer and with quick and active habits. When put to flight it calls in alarm, a loud whistled "tchick" repeated frequently, not in the triple phrase of the Greenshank.

Food: Insect larvae, small molluscs and crustacea.

Voice: See above. A single "tchick". The alarm when uttered by a flock becomes almost a twitter and is similar to that of a party of Wood Sandpiper.

263 Greenshank   Groenpoot-ruiter

Tringa nebularia   (Gunnerus), 1767: *Norway.*

PLATE 29 (OPP. P. 185). PLATE 27.
Length about 32 cm (male: wing 174—186—204; tail 68—74,4—82; tarsus 57—60—66; culmen 50—54,3—60. Female averages: wing 192; tail 76,0; tarsus 61,0; culmen 55,3. 40 specimens, 13 ♂, 27 ♀). Iris brown; bill bluish slate to horn coloured; legs pale olive-green.

Identification: Full winter dress lacks definite markings on head which thus appears much lighter. Largish size, colour and call note are diagnostic. Generally a greyish rather than brownish wader. Has long legs and a long heavy bill that is thick right to the tip and slightly curved upwards. In flight, which is usually accompanied by very typical call note (see below), the wing is dark with no wing-bar and the white rump and lower back are conspicuous.

Distribution: North Europe and Asia, wintering to the south. Throughout Southern Africa.

Habits: A common migrant, arriving first in July but mainly in August and departing late April; wintering birds not uncommon. Usually met with singly or in small groups but flocks of up to 150 may be found in estuaries. A conspicuous species which flies off violently when disturbed, uttering its loud, resonant, triple note. Found always near water from the smallest roadside pool to the open sea coast where it may feed in rock pools at low water. Feeds with a rapid action, wading about often in deepish water to the full length of its legs; walks for the most part with its head up, bending down to pick off the surface of the water or probe its bill into the sand. Sometimes bobs its hindquarters when alarmed.

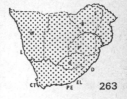

263

Food: Insects, small molluscs and crustacea.

Voice: A clear and fluting "tew-tew-tew" which can be heard from a considerable distance.

264 Wood Sandpiper   Bosruiter

Tringa glareola   (Linnaeus), 1758: *Europe = Sweden.*

PLATE 29 (OPP. P. 185). PLATE 27
Length about 20 cm (wing 119—127—133; tail 46—50,3—56; tarsus 33—36,4—38; culmen 27—28,5—31. 21 specimens). Iris dark brown; bill black-brown with greenish olive base; legs greenish olive to orange-yellow.

Identification: Medium size, longish bill, light eye-stripe, medium legs and *spotted back* distinguish this species. In flight the white rump, light underwing,

189

lack of wing-bar and the barred tail separate this species from other similar birds. May be confused with Common Sandpiper, No. 258, and Green Sandpiper, No. 259, which are similarly proportioned; No. 258 has uniform coloured back and conspicuous wing-bar; No. 259 has dark underwing and a few bars on an otherwise white tail. Has been confused with Nos. 261, 262 and 263, but all these have longer bills and longer legs.

Distribution: Europe and Northern Asia, south in winter. Generally distributed throughout southern Africa.

Habits: A common migrant, arriving at the end of August and departing early May, occasionally wintering here. Frequents pools, streams, estuaries and in particular flooded grassy marshes where it usually occurs in small parties. Single birds are commonest but flocks of up to 50 birds are recorded. When disturbed may seek refuge under overhanging vegetation (a rare habit for waders), otherwise stretches its neck up and may bob before flying off. Feeds along the shore, usually out of water or in flooded grass, pecking off the surface rather than probing for its food.

Food: Insects, small crustacea, molluscs, spiders, frogs and fish.

Voice: When put up calls a shrill ''chiff-iff-iff'', also a high-pitched ''tchi-tchi-tchi-tchi-tchi''.

265 Black-tailed Godwit   Grutto

Limosa limosa (Linnaeus), 1758: *Europe = Sweden.*

PLATE 25 (OPP. P. 161).
Length about 40 cm (wing ♂ 205—226, ♀ 215—240; tail 74—89; tarsus 75—82; culmen ♂ 82—107, ♀ 104—126. 12 specimens ex *Handbk. Brit. Birds*). Iris brown; bill brown with flesh-pink base; legs lead to black.

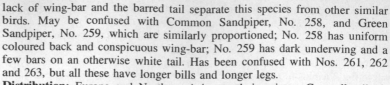

Identification: Large size, long legs and heavy straight, very long bill distinguish this and the next species from other waders. In resting birds, winter plumage practically indistinguishable from No. 266; longer straighter bill and longer legs can only be observed when both are together. Flight pattern is unmistakable, and feet extend 9-10 cm beyond the tail. In summer plumage distinguished from No. 266 by white belly. See No. 266 for comparison with other species.

Distribution: Europe and Asia, south in winter. A single specimen collected south of Durban (1911). Sight records from the south-west Cape, one at Graaff-Reinet. Also Welkom, O.F.S., St. Lucia, Durban and Port Elizabeth.

Habits: A very rare vagrant. Said to have a preference for fresh water otherwise similar to the next species.

LOCAL RACE:
L.l. limosa (Linnaeus), 1758: *Europe = Sweden.* Another race occurs from eastern Siberia which differs by having a shorter bill and wing.

266 Bar-tailed Godwit   Rosse Grutto

Limosa lapponica (Linnaeus), 1758: *Lapland.*

PLATE 25 (OPP. P. 161).
Length about 38 cm (wing ♂ 202—216, ♀ 211—227; tail 67—77; tarsus 46—51; culmen ♂ 72—83, ♀ 95—106. 12 specimens ex *Handbk. Brit. Birds*). Iris brown; bill brown with *flesh-pink or orange base:* legs dark greyish green.

Identification: See also under No. 265. Distinguished from the Greenshank, No. 263, by size, orange base of bill, comparatively longer legs and bill, and

190

feeding habits. The summer plumage is a rich chestnut on head, neck and underparts. In flight the light barring on tail shows only at close range. Not dissimilar to the Whimbrel, No. 268, in flight pattern, but of course the straight bill is diagnostic.

Distribution: Europe, Asia to Alaska, wintering in the south. Fairly common along the west coast as far as Langebaan, elsewhere irregularly recorded around the coast. Two records from southern Transvaal.

Habits: A migrant arriving in August leaving early May; very few wintering records. Along the west coast it occurs in flocks of from 20 to 100, occasionally more; elsewhere only single birds recorded. Usually feeds in very shallow water or on exposed sand or mudbanks. When feeding, unlike Greenshank, this bird keeps its head down most of the time, energetically probing its bill full length into the mud; sometimes even part of their heads is immersed under water. A bird ringed at Swartkops E.P. recovered in Iran 8 293 km North.

266

LOCAL RACE:
L.l. lapponica (Linnaeus), 1758: *Lapland.* Another race occurs in eastern Siberia.

267 Curlew   Wulp

Numenius arquata   (Linnaeus), 1758: *Europe = Sweden.*

PLATE 25 (OPP. P. 161).
Length about 59 cm (wing ♂ 269—281—302, ♀ 286—299—312; tail ♂ 100—109—115, ♀ 108—116—125; tarsus ♂ 73—80,8—85, ♀ 78—84,4—90; culmen ♂ 118—130—155, ♀ 156—161—172. 20 specimens, 8 ♂, 12 ♀). Iris brown; bill dark horn; legs greenish grey.

Identification: Very large size and curved bill distinguish this species from all waders except the Whimbrel, No. 268. There is considerable difference in size between the sexes and the smaller male is easily mistaken for the next species; for comparison see No. 268. The rump appears white. The bill is usually straight for half its length before decurving and for field identification is said to be approximately half the length of the body, or greater than two-and-a-half times the length of the head. See under races.

Distribution: Europe and Asia, wintering in the south. Throughout south eastern Africa, but not common inland; commonest along the eastern coast.

Habits: A common coastal migrant arriving in August and departing in March, though many winter in the south. Most inland records from October to December, less often January to July. Usually in small parties, flocks of 50 to 60 not uncommon; inland records of single birds except for two records of small flocks. Rather shy. Found along the shore, estuaries and tidal parts of rivers and along inland waters; usually walks about out of the water. Probes its bill right into the soft mud, bringing its head up between feeding.

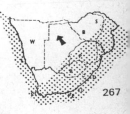

267

Food: Crabs, mud prawns.

Voice: Onomatopoeic "cur-lew" also written "crooee-crooee". A harsher "currree".

LOCAL RACES:
(a) *N.a. arquata* (Linnaeus), 1758: *Europe = Sweden.* This race is more buff and more heavily streaked, especially on underparts and rump. A single specimen from "Transvaal". Size slightly larger than above, except for bill which is smaller (culmen ♂ 100—124, ♀ 130—152. 12 specimens ex *Handbk. Brit. Birds*).

(b) N.a. orientalis Brehm, 1831: *East Indies*. A much lighter bird than *(a)*; the axillaries may be marked, as in *(a)*, but birds with pure white axillaries definitely belong to this race. Size as above. Practically all specimens in our museums belong to this race.

268   Whimbrel   Klein Wulp

Numenius phaeopus (Linnaeus), 1758: *Europe =Sweden*.

PLATE 25 (OPP. P. 161).
Length about 43 cm (wing 222—232—245; tail 90—94—104; tarsus 54—57,3—63; culmen 72—79,9—85. 8 specimens, 5 ♂, 3 ♀). Iris dark horn; legs greenish black.

Identification: Female larger than male. Similar to the Curlew, No. 267, but distinguished by two dark lines on crown and shorter bill. The effect of the lines on crown is to show a definite eye-stripe. The bill is curved throughout and for field identification is said to be from two to two-and-a-half times the length of head, or definitely less than half the length of its body. In flight, if the decurved bill is not visible, can be confused with the Bartailed Godwit, No. 266; but the underparts in this species are darker (see also under Habits).
Distribution: Europe to western Siberia, wintering in the south. Recorded around our coast and once at Welkom, O.F.S. and Nossop River.
Habits: A common migrant, recorded from September to April with many wintering birds. More common than the previous species on the south-west coast, and to a lesser extent on the Natal coast. Usually seen singly or in small parties, occasionally in flocks of up to 50. A shy bird like No. 267, not allowing a close approach and similar in general habits. The bringing up of the head between feeding probes helps to distinguish this species from the Bartailed Godwit, No. 266. May mix freely with the Curlew, though usually remaining separate if flocks are present.
Voice: A six- or seven-syllabled rippling call rendered "tetti-tetti-tetti-tetti-tetti-tet" or "peep-eep-eep-eep-ee".

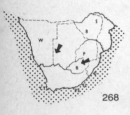
268

LOCAL RACE:
N.p. phaeopus (Linnaeus), 1758; *Europe =Sweden*.

Family RECURVIROSTRIDAE

Distinguishable from the Snipe family by the extremely long legs and slender bill, the latter either straight or upcurved. Seven known species.

269   Avocet   Bont Elsie

Recurvirostra avosetta   Linnaeus, 1758: *Europe =Italy*.

PLATE 25 (OPP. P. 161).
Length about 43 cm (wing 213—215—222; tail 80—81,3—84; tarsus 82—85,1—90; culmen 76—81,1—86. 7 specimens). Iris crimson; bill and legs black.

Identification: Predominantly white with bold black markings. The bill is up-curved and very thin. Immature is dark brown instead of black. In flight the wing pattern is conspicuous with three black patches on either side separated by white.

Distribution: Europe, Asia, Africa and Malagasy. Generally distributed, perhaps commonest in the south-western Cape.

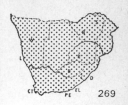

269

Habits: A not uncommon resident in most parts but subject to local movements due to drying-up of temporary vleis. Migrants apparently make the large flocks of several hundred, which may be recorded in summer. Usually occurs singly or in small parties which never remain in the same place for long. Fly in close formation and will often alight on the water. In shallow water feed with a characteristic motion, sweeping the upcurved bill from side to side. In deep water it swims and "up-ends" like a duck. Gait is usually a brisk walk.

Food: Aquatic insects, crustacea, molluscs and annelids.

Voice: A clear liquid "kluut", flocks calling together in a continuous twitter. Alarm note is "cwit-cwit-cwit . . .".

Breeding: Recorded throughout the western Cape, Karoo, southern Transvaal and Zululand. The eggs are laid in a shallow scrape, with twigs and grass, placed on a bank near water; usually on an island in a temporary vlei. August to October. Eggs 3—5, ovate, greenish grey and spotted lined with blackish and underlying slate. Appear large for size of the bird. Average (18) 51,5 × 35,2 (48—53,9 × 34,2—37). Incubation 22—24 days (Priest) by both sexes. Nestling takes about 6 weeks before it can fly.

270 Stilt   Rooipoot-elsie

Himantopus himantopus   (Linnaeus), 1758: *Southern Europe.*

PLATE 25 (OPP. P. 161).
Length about 38 cm (wing 215—226—235; tail 74—80,9—91; tarsus 106—115—130; culmen 58—63,5—68. 14 specimens). Iris brown-red when breeding; bill black; legs red, pale pink when young.

Identification: Male illustrated. The mantle and scapulars are brown in female and immature; the latter may also have sooty brown on crown, nape and hind neck. The first plumage is light brown speckled with buff on upper parts, hind neck and crown, white below. In flight the long red legs extend well beyond tail, the black wings are quite pointed and the immature birds have trailing edges of the wing white.

Distribution: Southern Europe and Asia, Africa and Malagasy. Found throughout southern Africa.

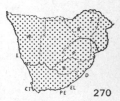

270

Habits: A common resident with local movements, found wherever there is water, preferring marshy areas. Usually occur singly or in small parties, but flocks of up to 500 in the south-west Cape. Feed wading in the water usually up to their "knees", rarely swimming. When alarmed readily take to flight, persistently flying over one's head shrieking their alarm note. Feed largely by picking the food from the surface of the water or mud.

Food: Larvae of insects, small crustacea and molluscs.

Voice: A sharp "kik-kik-kik-kik" or a "kyik" loud and penetrating.

Breeding: Breeding recorded from South West Africa, south-western Cape, southern Transvaal and Zululand. The nest is a shallow depression of grass and/or twigs placed on marshy ground or floating on aquatic vegetation. May to December. Eggs 2-7, usually 4, stone-coloured with dark brown blotches and spots. Average (100) 42,8 × 30,8 (36,8—47,1 × 26,4—33,8). Incubation 24—27 days by both sexes.

PHALAROPES

LOCAL RACE:
H.h. meridionalis (Brehm), 1843: *South Africa*. Separated on the basis of shorter wings and longer tail. Size as above. The breeding male birds lack black on nape and hind neck.

Family PHALAROPIDAE

Plover- or Snipe-like birds characterized by lobed webbing on the toes, serrated edge of the tarsi in front, and flattened, rather hollowed bill, with a groove on the side running for most of the length. There are but three species, placed in as many genera, one in temperate America and the other two circumpolar, breeding in the north and coming south on migration. Like the Painted Snipe, the males incubate the eggs and are the plainer-coloured of the pair in the summer plumage, which is much handsomer than in the winter. They swim more than other waders and often seek their food far from land on the surface of the water, hence, no doubt the webbed toes and flattened bill.

271 Grey Phalarope   Franjepoot

Phalaropus fulicarius   (Linnaeus), 1758: *America = Hudson Bay*.

PLATE 29 (OPP. P. 185). PLATE 27.
Length 18 cm (wing ♂ 121—131, ♀ 137; tail 62—64; tarsus 21—22; culmen ♂ 21,5, ♀ 25. 3 specimens, 2 ♂, 1 ♀). Iris brown; bill yellow base with black tip; legs yellow to horn coloured.

Identification: Illustration shows winter plumage. Generally grey and white. Note dark patch about eye and ear-coverts, which distinguishes this bird from the Sanderling, No. 255. The habits differ. In flight there is a white wing-bar and white on either side of a dark line down rump. See No. 272.
Distribution: Arctic regions of Europe and America, south in winter. Recorded from the west coast seas. Inland records rare, from Okahandja, South West Africa; Cape Town, Orange Free State, Botswana and Rhodesia. Several eastern Cape records.
Habits: Apparently common on the cold seas of the Benguela current south of Orange River, otherwise a rare straggler. Recorded in all months except March to July, October and December. Mainly a marine bird, commonly observed swimming, though may feed along the shore. Feeds typically by swimming in circles on the surface of the water. Floats buoyantly on the water with neck held straight up. Has a characteristic erratic flight, flitting over water, but flies swiftly when not feeding.

271

272 Red-necked Phalarope   Rooihals-franjepoot

Phalaropus lobatus   (Linnaeus), 1758: *Hudson Bay, North America*.

PLATE 29 (OPP. P. 185). PLATE 27.
Length about 16 cm (wing ♂ 106, ♀ 110; tail ♂ 46.5, ♀ 43; tarsus 19; culmen 23). Iris brown; bill black; legs blackish.

Identification: Can only be distinguished from the previous species at close range. Feet are black. The bill is longer and noticeably slender; darker back with white streaks. Wing-bar in flight appears more conspicuous owing to darker wings and darker rump (see Plate 27).

Distribution: America, Asia and Europe, south in winter. A record from Cape St. Francis (November 1935) in the eastern Cape.Five birds recorded at Strandfontein January 1971 and a sight record at Van der Bijlpark.

Habits: As for the previous species.

Family DROMADIDAE

A peculiar bird; with white plumage, strong, pointed bill, and perforated nostrils. Terrestrial in habits and having consequently long legs. It contains only one genus and species, occurring on tropical shores bordering the Indian Ocean. It feeds mostly on crabs, is gregarious in small or large parties and has the unusual habit, for a Limicoline bird, of nesting in burrows in the sand, the eggs pure white which is also unusual.

273 Crab Plover   Krapstrandloper

Dromas ardeola   Paykull, 1806: *India.*

PLATE 25 (OPP. P. 161).

Length about 38 cm (wing ♂ 208, ♀ 200; tail 122; tarsus 86; culmen 56). Iris dark brown; bill black; legs light slate-grey. Iris red when breeding.

Identification: First field impressions are long, light-coloured legs and white head. The bill is heavy and long in proportion to the head. The male has wing-coverts whitish grey. Flight is similar in action to the Dikkop, No. 275, with stiff unbending pointed wings and legs protruding well beyond tail; the black remiges and lesser primary coverts against white of rest of wing are conspicuous. Female lacks black mantle and has greyer wing covers.

Distribution: Islands and coastal areas of the north-eastern Indian Ocean from Malagasy north. Recorded from Mozambique and Natal, irregularly as far south as Durban. Also Port Elizabeth.

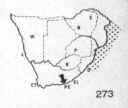

273

Habits: A rare vagrant to our area, recorded during the summer months only. Coastal on sand banks and mangrove swamps where it wades along the water-line seeking its food. Not at all shy and when flushed circles around to settle a short distance away. Runs with its long neck withdrawn, having a springy easy action reminding one of an ostrich. When feeding maintains an upright posture, only jabbing at a crab or some crustacean when it is seen.

Food: Crabs.

Voice: A harsh tern-like "croook". When put to flight a sharp "cheeruck".

Family BURHINIDAE

Large Plover-like birds, characterized by the absence of the hind toe, long legs with thickened tibiotarsal joint, big head and eyes, rather short, stout bill, with the nostrils as long slits and perforated from side to side. Found in all the tropical and temperate countries and represented by five genera, of which two occur in Africa. Crepuscular and nocturnal in habits, when they utter a rather melancholy whistling note; during daylight squatting on the ground amongst

195

rocks or herbage. Lay only two eggs normally, resembling those of Plovers, but less pear-shaped and with large blotches of brown. Feed largely upon insects, but also other small animals.

274 Water Dikkop   Waterdikkop

Burhinus vermiculatus   (Cabanis), 1868: *Lake Jipe,*
Kenya-Tanganyika Boundary.

Native Name: Ingqangqolo (X).

PLATE 25 (OPP. P. 161).

Length about 40 cm (wing 191—205—211; tail 98—109—118; tarsus 72—74,8—77; culmen ♂ 41—44—46, ♀ 40—41,3—44. 16 specimens, 12 ♂, 4 ♀). Iris pale green; bill black, yellowish base; legs pale greenish slate.

Identification: The large squarish head and large light eye distinguish this and the next species from the plovers. This species is distinguished from No. 275 by the distinct pale bar covering most of the wing; with wing folded there is a narrow white line above the grey coverts. In flight there is a small black-and-white patch at tip of the wing and a broad grey proximal patch.

Distribution: Tropical and southern Africa. Widespread throughout southern Africa.

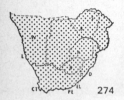

274

Habits: Not uncommon and resident where there are large perennial rivers or lakes with a certain amount of bush or forest cover and no frost. Never found far from water. During the daylight hours, squats on the ground under bushes. When disturbed is reluctant to fly and consequently runs away with head down, or makes a rapid run before taking to flight. Flies with rapid wing-beats alternated with slower flapping. Flies and calls at night as the next species does.

Food: Insects, crustacea and molluscs.

Voice: A loud harsh "whee" or "whee-yu-e", repeated frequently.

Breeding: The eggs are laid on bare ground or sand amongst scattered driftwood or under low bushes. September to December. Eggs 2, similar to those of the next species. Average (29) 49,5 × 35,6 (44—54 × 32,7-—38,7). Incubation about 24 days.

LOCAL RACE:
B.v. vermiculatus (Cabanis), 1868: *Lake Jipe, Kenya-Tanganyika boundary.* Another race which occurs from Liberia to Uganda is darker above.

275 Dikkop   Dikkop

Burhinus capensis   (Lichtenstein), 1823: *Cape of Good Hope.*

Native Names: Tapiane, Khoklho-er-lira (S); Ingqangqolo (X); um-Begagwa (Z); Kanyurwa-howe (Zw).

PLATE 25 (OPP. P. 161).

Length about 44 cm (wing 223—231—242; tail 112—123—138; tarsus 87—95—105; culmen 34—36,8—40,5. 36 specimens, 19 ♂, 17 ♀). Iris yellow; bill yellow with black tip; legs bright yellow.

Identification: Distinguished from the previous species by lack of wing-bar. This bird is mottled on the wing as on back. In flight no wing-bar, a small white square near the tip of wing and another white spot on primary coverts.

Distribution: From Senegal and the Sudan south to the Cape. Widely distributed throughout southern Africa.

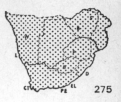

275

Habits: A common resident, occurring in dry situations, open fields, scrub country and peri-urban areas. Hides during daylight hours among stones in the open or among bushes. When disturbed rises suddenly from its squatting position, in which it is almost invisible, runs off with its head down; flies with rapid wing-beats, settling again, spreading its wings before rapidly folding them. At night often comes about homesteads, where its melancholy whistling notes cause misgivings in the minds of the superstitious.

Food: Insects, small crustacea, molluscs and certain grass seeds.

Voice: A loud but plaintive "tche-u" the end of the note drawn out and gradually tailing off. Also an excited "pi-pi-pi-pi-pi". Very often heard on moonlight nights.

Breeding: The eggs are laid on bare ground, usually in open country though sometimes in a clearing; often close to dung or some plant. September to April, though mainly about October and November. Eggs 2, rarely 1, ground colour varies from cream to buff, blotched and spotted with chocolate brown to a varying degree. Average (100) 52,0 × 37,8 (46,9—58 × 34,6—40,8). Incubation 24 days by both sexes.

LOCAL RACES:
B.c. capensis (Lichtenstein), 1823: *Cape of Good Hope.* As above. Throughout except Damaraland.
B.c. damarensis (Reichenow), 1905: *Damaraland.* Size as above but paler. Confined to South West Africa.

Family GLAREOLIDAE

Ploverlike birds characterized by morphological differences in the skull, bill rather short, with the nostrils situated at the base and not in a groove. The family is subdivided into two subfamilies, the Pratincoles, which have long wings and short legs with the hind toe present, and the Coursers *(Cursoriinae),* which have shorter wings, long, slender legs and no hind toe. The former are migratory birds which habitually follow migratory swarms of locusts and catch them in the air as well as on the ground, while the latter are not migratory, or migratory only for short distances, and do not take their prey in flight—that is, of terrestrial rather than aerial habits. They nest on the bare ground, the normal clutch being two, but in some cases only one egg. Some species of Coursers are crepuscular and nocturnal in habits, hiding, like the Dikkops, by squatting flat during daylight and only venturing to hunt for their insect food at dusk.

276 Burchell's Courser   Bloukop-drawertjie

Cursorius rufus Gould, 1837: *"in insulis Oceani Indici"* =
Potchefstroom.

Native Name: Mokopjane (Ch).

PLATE 30 (OPP. P. 208).
Length about 23 cm (wing 132—135—138; tail 48—51,2—53; tarsus 46,5—48—51; culmen 21—22,9—25,5. 13 specimens, 9 ♂, 4 ♀). Iris brown; bill dusky; legs grey-white.

Identification: Differs from the next species by the presence of blue-grey at the back of the crown rufous back, and by its uniform pale brown breast

197

terminated by black bar across lower chest. Outer tail feathers are white-tipped. In flight, primaries and primary coverts black; secondaries ash-brown with broad white terminal bar; the secondaries appear white from below. Immature mottled above, no white or black bands on neck.

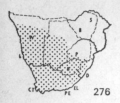

Distribution: Occurs only in southern Africa; from Damaraland south and as far east as Carolina, Mooi River and Matatiele. Not along the eastern coastal belt to George.

Habits: Subject to local movements, although said to be resident in some areas. Found on inland grassy or barren flats usually in small groups of five or six rarely up to 15. Frequents veld where the grass is short or recently burnt off. Has an upright stance and bobs its hindquarters like a sandpiper. Runs with very great rapidity; after an interval it stops and bobs, moving backwards and forwards and swaying from side to side.

276

Food: Seeds and insects, especially harvester termites.

Voice: A grunting "whowk". In flock a 3 syllable "kok-kok-kwich".

Breeding: Lays its eggs on bare ground, often where there are small round droppings of animals, which the eggs resemble. August to November. Eggs 2, rounded ovals without gloss, pale fawn, nearly covered by thin hair-like black lines. Average (16) 31,1 × 24,2 (28,6—32,9 × 23,3—26,2).

277 Temminck's Courser   Trekdrawertjie

Cursorius temminckii Swainson, 1822: *Senegal.*

Native Name: Ucelithafa (X).

PLATE 30 (OPP. P. 208).
Length about 20 cm (wing 118—124—132; tail 41—45,9—50; tarsus 37—39,9—43; culmen 19—20,2—22. 27 specimens, 14 ♂, 13 ♀). Iris reddish brown; bill blackish brown; legs grey-white.

Identification: Distinguished from No. 276 by rufous on back of crown, greyer back, by rufous colouring on lower chest and a large black patch which extends down between the legs. The outer tail-feathers wholly white. In flight the under-wing appears black with narrow white terminal bar on the secondaries. The immature has crown and upper parts speckled light buff on brown, but the white neck-band and head pattern of adult is present; also the patch between the legs is darkish brown.

Distribution: Senegal to East Africa and southern Africa. As far south as Okahandja and Port Elizabeth in eastern Cape.

Habits: Subject to considerable local movements and known only as a migrant at the southern limits of its distribution from February to August. A restless bird, appearing wherever the veld is burnt off or at other times in shorter grassveld. Similar in habits to previous species.

277 **Food:** Almost entirely insects, molluscs, seeds, bugs and grasshoppers.

Voice: A metallic sharp "err-err-err" usually uttered while in flight.

Breeding: Rhodesia, Transvaal, Natal and at Tarkastad in the Cape from July to January. The eggs are usually laid on flat ground with no nest structure, but one nest is recorded with bits of dung forming a ring about the eggs. Eggs 2, round, occasionally slightly pointed and similar to those of No. 276. Average (27) 27,5 × 22,6 (25—32,3 × 21,5—24,8).

278 Double-banded Courser   Dubbelband-drawertjie

Rhinoptilus africanus (Temminck), 1807: *Namaqualand*.

Native Name: Sekholokhol (G).

PLATE 30 (OPP. P. 208).
Length about 22 cm (wing 145—151—159; tail 61—65,4—73; tarsus 49—53,7—59; culmen 13—14,1—15. 28 specimens, 18 ♂, 10 ♀). Iris dark brown; bill black; legs white. Weight 97,4 g.

Identification: Its small size and lack of contrasting head patterns separate this from the next two species. Bold pattern on back and two breast bands conspicuous. In flight the first 4 primaries are black, the rest of wing is rufous above and below; upper tail-coverts white. Sexes alike.

Distribution: Western areas of southern Africa. Absent from Rhodesia and Natal. In red soil veld along Olifants River, Mozambique.

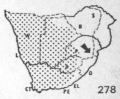

278

Habits: For the most part resident but subject to local movements in some areas; locally common wherever it is met with. Usually in pairs or small flocks amongst scattered bushes or on dry pans in the sandy veld, essentially an open grassland dweller. Owing to its drab mottled plumage easily overlooked, usually noticed first when running. Reluctant to fly, usually running away. Active during the day as well as at night.

Food: Ants and harvester termites.

Voice: Usually silent. Call rendered "woo-woo-woo-wook" or at night flying "chikee-chikee-chikee-kee-kee-kee" or a thin whistled "pee-wee" when put to flight.

Breeding: A single egg is laid on bare ground, often amongst game droppings. Egg has creamy buff ground colour with thin hairlike lines of brown, sometimes concentrated to form a sort of band. Average (8) 30,8 × 25,4 (27,9—33,8 × 23,5—26,1). Both sexes incubate.

LOCAL RACES:
(a) R.a. africanus (Temminck), 1807: *Namaqualand*. Found throughout Namaqualand and the western Kalahari except N.E. Botswana. Lighter in colour than *(b)* and with thinner stripes below. Size as above.
(b) R.a. granti W. Sclater, 1921: *Deelfontein*. Cape Province south of Orange River, O.F.S. to Transvaal. Darker with heavier streaks below.
(c) R.a. erlangeri Niethammer and Wolters, 1966: *40 km east of Cape Cross*. A much paler form than the nominate and more buffy-stone coloured. From Windhoek north to Ovamboland on the west and the Kaokoveld.
(d) R.a. traylori Irwin, 1963: *Kedia, Lake Dow, Botswana*. Paler than nominate and also distinguished by the greyness of the mantle. The north east of the distribution of the species in Botswana, to Etosha and Ovamboland.

279 Three-banded Courser   Drieband-drawertjie

Rhinoptilus cinctus (Heuglin), 1863: *Gondokoro, Southern Sudan*.

PLATE 30 (OPP. P. 208).
Length about 28 cm (wing 162—165; tail 81—85; tarsus 69—76; culmen 19,5—20. 4 specimens, 2 ♂, 2 ♀). Iris light brown; bill black, yellow at base; legs ochreous to yellow.

Identification: The bar across throat should be brown, not black as illustrated. Distinguished from previous species by larger size and the chestnut bar across breast. The upper tail-coverts white, and sexes alike. No white band runs across hind nape. Immature similar in general pattern but lower chestnut band hardly present. Nestling covered with dirty white down, somewhat darker on the head.

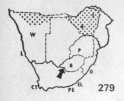

Distribution: Drier country of eastern and southern Africa. Recorded within our area from Ovamboland and Rhodesia, with an old record for Griqualand West.

Habits: Widely but sparsely distributed in Rhodesia, where it is reputed to be migratory from April to November. Inhabits drier bush, mopane and thorn country; not found in Brachystegia forest, essentially an open woodland species. These birds are remarkably agile. At the slightest alarm they "freeze" and may be closely approached.

Food: Insects.

Voice: "Chuck-a-chuck or chuck-a-chuck-a-chuck-a-chuck" of even speed also "Wick-er-wick-er-wick-er-wick-wick-wick" accelerating and fading; calls at night.

Breeding: Recorded from Rhodesia, June to November, April. The eggs are laid in a scrape in the ground sometimes lined with bits of twigs. Eggs 2, light brown heavily overlaid with marks and scrawls of darker brown over the entire surface; two measure 37 × 26 and 39 × 27.

LOCAL RACE:
R.c. seehbohmi Sharpe, 1893: *Ondongua, Ovamboland*. The local race more pinkish below and first V on throat buff.

280 Bronze-wing Courser   Bronsvlerk-drawertjie

Rhinoptilus chalcopterus (Temminck), 1824: *Senegal*.

PLATE 30 (OPP. P. 208).
Length about 25 cm (wing 176—180—186; tail 77—80,4—84; tarsus 71—75,8—80; culmen 20—22,5—24. 8 specimens). Iris dark brown; eyelid red; bill black; base of lower mandible and gape red; legs purplish red.

Identification: Sexes alike but some females may be rufous instead of brown behind eye and on the ear-coverts. In flight a white wing-bar and white tail-coverts are conspicuous: under-wing white with black tips to remiges.

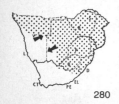

Distribution: Senegal and East Africa southwards to Damaraland, western Orange Free State, Natal and north-east Cape. Furthest south is East London. Also Kalahari National Park.

Habits: The northern and western populations are apparently resident but subject to local movements. However, birds from the south-east are migratory and are recorded from September to May; resident in Rhodesia. Generally occurs in pairs or small groups. Mainly nocturnal, sleeping during the day on the ground amongst small bushes and in sheltered timbered areas, moving to more open ground and roads at night. More plover-like in habits than other coursers and more timid.

Food: Insects, especially grasshoppers.

Voice: Similar to Dikkop, No. 275, "ji-ku-it". Also a harsh plaintive "grorr-raang". Usually heard only at night.

Breeding: Recorded September and October in Rhodesia; earlier to the north. The eggs are laid on the bare ground. Eggs 3, sometimes 2, handsomely marked, rich buff with bold spots of mauve or lavender and super-imposed blotches of dark brown, sepia and black. Average (31) 37,2 × 27,0 (32,6—40,0 × 25,2—28,3).

281 Red-winged Pratincole   Gewone Kleinsprinkaanvöel

Glareola pratincola (Linnaeus), 1766: *Austria.*

Native Name: u-Whamba (Z).

PLATE 30 (OPP. P. 208).

Length 27 cm (wing 176—189—194; tail 107—113—118; tarsus 28—29,3—31; culmen 17—17,8—18,5. 4 specimens). Iris brown; bill black with red base; legs greyish.

Identification: Distinguished from the next species by its *rufous axillaries* and generally lighter upper parts. Sexes alike. Immature similar to adult but lacks black markings on head and around throat-patch; tail not so deeply forked. Young has buffy throat, heavily speckled breast, upper parts sepia and spotted except for white upper tail-coverts.

Distribution: Southern Europe east to north-west India and south to Ngamiland, Rhodesia, Natal and Matatiele. A single specimen probably from Otjimbingwe, South West Africa, by Andersson, and one from George, Cape, last century.

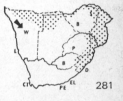

281

Habits: Generally rare, but not uncommon in Zululand and widely distributed below 900 metres in Rhodesia. Subject to considerable fluctuations in numbers but usually recorded in small flocks near water on river sandbanks, along flats on the edge of lakes or along the coast. Very swallow-like in flight and feeds mainly on the wing, catching insects over pools or water. When flushed they usually fly some distance.

Food: Insects, including locusts, and molluscs.

Breeding: An exceptional record by A. Millar of hundreds breeding in ploughed fields in Natal, 1907 and 1908. More recently at Umvoti River and Durban. Several Zululand records. Also recorded from Caprivi Strip. Usually breed in small colonies on sandbanks near water. The nest is a shallow scrape in the sand. November in Natal and Zululand, August to November in Rhodesia. Eggs 2—3, pale cream to rich buff, marked heavily with blotches and scrawls of black or brown with under-laying pale purplish marks. Average (31) 32,2 × 23,9 (29,5 × 22,9—25,6).

LOCAL RACE:
G.p. fuelleborni Neumann, 1910: *Lake Rukwa.* Much darker than other races from the north.

282 Black-winged Pratincole
Swartvlerk-kleinsprinkaanvöel

Glareola nordmanni Fischer, 1842: *South Russia.*

Native Name: Lehlakangoato (S).

PLATE 30 (OPP. P. 208).

Length about 27 cm (wing ♂ 190—196—198, ♀ 177—185—188; tail ♂ 95—102—115, ♀ 84—92—100; tarsus ♂ 35—38—40, ♀ 35—37,2—39; culmen ♂ 15,5—16,5—17, ♀ 16—17,5—19,5. 9 specimens, 4 ♂, 5 ♀). Iris dark brown; bill and legs black.

Identification: Distinguished from No. 281 by its black axillaries and underwing and general darker appearance above.

201

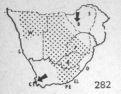

Distribution: South-east Europe and West Asia, wintering in Africa. Occurs in Damaraland, Lake Ngami area, south to Upington, Port Elizabeth; throughout the Orange Free State, southern Transvaal and western Natal. A single record for Cape Division (last century) and one near Bulawayo, Rhodesia.

Habits: A migrant from October to March. Ranges in huge flocks, sometimes appropriately referred to as swarms. These flocks follow locusts which form the main diet of this species. Also feeds on the ground, especially on small locust "voetgangers".

Food: Insects, mainly locusts; also winged termites.

282X Madagascar Pratincole

Glareola ocularis Verreaux, 1833: *Madagascar.*

PLATE 30 (OPP. P. 208).
Length about 20 cm (wing ♂ 197—201, ♀ 190—195, ex Jackson). Iris brown; bill black, orange at base; legs black.

Identification: Differs from the two previous species by having throat, sides of face and chest earth-brown. Differs from these two and the next species by its *pale chestnut breast,* axillaries and under-wing. Distinguished from No. 283 by black legs, also by lacking the white on nape, although this species has a small white patch behind and below eye.

Distribution: Malagasy, migrating to East Africa. Recorded from the Zambesi River by Kirk. Benson suggests the specimen came from Anjouan Island.

Habits: Little recorded. Apparently similar to the next species and shows a preference for water and settling on rocks or reed-covered islands.

283 White-collared Pratincole
Withals-kleinsprinkaanvoël

Galachrysia nuchalis (Gray), 1850: *Fifth cataract of the Nile, near Berber.*

PLATE 30 (OPP. P. 208).
Length about 18 cm (wing 140—145; tail 55—60; tarsus 9—21; culmen 12—14). Iris brown; bill black, coral-red at base; legs coral-red.

Identification: The diagnostic white collar which starts behind and below eye and forms a ring around the nape; sometimes the ring is incomplete on the hind neck. Coral-red legs distinguish this from other pratincoles.

Distribution: Tropical Africa as far south as the Zambesi River and lower Sabi River in Rhodesia.

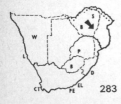

Habits: A resident species which may move locally during floods. Confined to rivers and lakes, especially rocky or boulder-strewn stretches where, when disturbed, it can flit from rock to rock. It occurs in small flocks. Flies over the water like a swallow, catching insects on the wing.

Voice: A repeated "kek-kek-kek-kek".

Breeding: Recorded on the Zambesi, September to October. The eggs are laid on bare rock in rough cracks or depressions. Eggs 2—3, and quite variable in colouring and marking, creamy-coloured. Average (5) 30,7 × 21,9 (30—32 × 21,5—22,1).

LOCAL RACE:
G.n. nuchalis (Gray), 1850: *Fifth cataract of the Nile, near Berber.* The southern race; size above.

Family STERCORARIIDAE

Oceanic Gull-like birds characterized by having the bill stout and hooked at the tip, most of the base above and nostrils covered by a flat, horny plate, the tarsus rough at the back, the claws curved and sharp and the tail with long middle feathers. As with other sea-birds, the wings are long and pointed. They are largely parasitic upon other birds, which they rob of their prey. Eggs are laid on the ground or moss in a depression and two form the clutch.

284 Arctic Skua   Withals-roofmeeu

Stercorarius parasiticus (Linnaeus), 1758: *"Intra tropicum"* = *coasts of Sweden.*

PLATE 31 (OPP. P. 209). A AND B.
Length about 46 cm (wing ♂ 305—328, ♀ 305—322; tail 175—215, juv. 118—140; tarsus 42—45; bill 27—30. 12 specimens ex *Handbk. Brit. Birds).* Iris dark brown; bill blackish brown, dark tip; legs black.

Identification: Easily confused with No. 285, which also has a marked cap on head. All skuas show light white patches at base of primaries in flight. This species has *centre tail-feathers straight, pointed and longer than rest of tail.* There are three phases. *Dark phase,* illustrated A. *Intermediate phase,* with light chin, throat and cheek (showing up dark cap), merging to dark chest. *Light phase,* illustrated B; often has a dark breast band. Winter plumage of this phase is closely barred and mottled. Juveniles are dark brown, streaked and barred and lack the dark cap; central tail-feathers hardly longer than rest of tail.
Distribution: Arctic and sub-arctic regions, south in winter to the African coast. Around our coastal regions, not extending beyond Zululand.
Habits: A migrant, not uncommon along southern and western Cape, September to March, April. A marine bird, usually ranging inshore and sometimes within harbours. Occurs in pairs or small loose parties; flies like a gull well above the sea and tends to flap its wings even more than a gull. Depends to a large extent upon food stolen from Gulls and Terns which pairs attack and pursue vigorously. Gathers about line-fishing boats and takes offal, on such occasions quite often calls a wailing "ka-aahr".

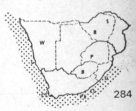

284

285 Pomatorhine Skua   Groot Withals-roofmeeu

Stercorarius pomarinus (Temminck), 1815: *Arctic regions.*

PLATE 31 (OPP. P. 209). AD. AND IMM.
Length about 50 cm (wing ♂ 348—375, ♀ 340—373; tail 190—225, juv. 130—152; tarsus 48—56; culmen 35—40. 12 specimens ex *Handbk. Brit. Birds*) Iris dark brown; whitish in juvenile; bill yellowish brown, dark tip; legs black.

Identification: A heavier bird than No. 284 with a heavier bill. Differs from the last species by having the *long central tail-feathers rounded at their ends and twisted* so that the tip is *perpendicular* to the rest of tail; sometimes these feathers may be broken off. There are two phases: *Light phase* illustrated; differs slightly by having more barring on the flanks, under tail-coverts are

203

brownish. *Dark phase* is similar to previous species. Juvenile is slightly more barred on rump than last species, but very difficult to distinguish in the field.
Distribution. Arctic regions, wintering to the south. Recorded around the coast as far as Mossel Bay.
Habits: Not as common as the previous species. Does not usually come close inshore. Recorded as late as April.

285

286 Antarctic Skua   Bruin Roofmeeu

Catharacta skua Brunnich, 1764: *Iceland.*

PLATE 31 (OPP. P. 209).
Length 61 cm (wing 366—380—398; tail 140—147—157; tarsus 64,3—67,4—70; culmen 46,5—48,7—50,8. 16 specimens, Falkland Islands ex Murphy). Iris light brown; bill and legs black.

Identification: Rather larger and heavier in build than the other Skuas and more like immature of the next species in general appearance. The typical white "window" at base of primaries is conspicuous in this species. Some birds are uniform brown as illustrated; others are much redder in appearance, especially on collar.
Distribution: Southern and sub-antarctic regions. Recorded around our coast as far north as Maputo.

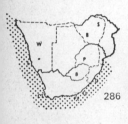

Habits: Present all the year round, common from April to September. Occurs both out to sea and off-shore, even coming into harbours. Generally a scavenger and therefore follows trawlers or fishing boats to pick up offal. However, it also attacks Gulls and Terns for any food they may have. Quite a confiding bird and will come in close to boats.
Voice: Plaintive "queee-kek-kek".
Food: Preys on eggs and young birds; pirates other birds; refuse from ships.

LOCAL RACES:
Two races occur in approximately equal numbers. There is considerable variation in colour in all populations.
(a) C.s. antarctica (Lesson), 1831: *Falkland Islands.* Smaller in size than *(b).* The birds from Tristan da Cunha are of this race. Size as above.
(b) C.s. lönnbergi (Matthews), 1912: *New Zealand Seas.* Larger than other races. This race occurs on Marion Island (wing 397—400—416; tail 143—153—162; tarsus 70,8—75—79,3; culmen 53,5—55,6—58,2. 14 specimens from South Georgia ex Murphy).

Family LARIDAE

Gulls are well known at all the ports from their habit of flying around ships and alighting on the water to pick up scraps thrown overboard. They are fairly large birds; adults of white plumage, with long wings, short tails and legs; webbed feet with weak claws; strong bill with the nostrils open from side to side and situated in the middle of the maxilla at the front of a long groove. They are largely scavengers, subsisting upon dead fish and other fleshy food found floating on the water or lying on the beaches, and also robbing other birds of their eggs, and even killing the young when the opportunity offers. Two or three eggs form the clutch, laid in a depression, and resemble those of Plovers, to which, indeed, the Gulls are distantly related. Seventy-eight species are recognized, world wide in distribution.

287 Southern Black-backed Gull   Swartrug-meeu

Larus dominicanus Lichtenstein, 1823: *Coast of Brazil.*

Native Name: Ingabangaba (X).

PLATE 31 (OPP. P. 209), AD. AND IMM. A AND B.
Length about 60 cm (wing 400—413—425; tail 152—162—170; tarsus 59—63,8—66; culmen 50—53,7—58,5. 9 specimens). Iris greyish with red eyelids; bill yellow with orange-red patch on tip of lower mandible; legs bluish yellow, black in immature birds.

Identification: Immature is mottled brown all over; as they mature, the change to adult plumage occurs gradually; the rump becomes barred, then white illustrated as Imm. A; later the head becomes white, illustrated as Imm. B. Lastly the tail and flight feathers change from brown to white and black. Nestling mottled dark brown on grey, soft parts dark.

Distribution: Coastal from Angola around to Maputo. Rarely inland; Lake Chrissie, Barberspan, Springs and Bon Accord in Transvaal and Lake Mentz in eastern Cape (see 287X).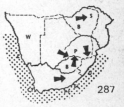

Habits: A common resident on the west and southern coast but a migrant to Natal and north. Found along the shore, coastal islands, in estuaries and up larger rivers, and now attracted to rubbish dumps of towns several miles from the sea. May follow ships out to sea, as much as 96 km from land, between June and February; at other times remains inshore.

Food: Offal. Shell fish, especially the sand mussel *Donax*, which the birds obtain by trampling in shallow water. They then fly up 15 metres or so and drop the shell to break it.

Voice: "Meeu", a plaintive cry. When disturbed utters a "kok-kok-kok".

Breeding: Nests colonially on coastal islands, occasionally on uninhabited parts of mainland such as cliffs or extensive flats. The nest is a scrape in the soil, often near some protective rock or bush; built up of grass, twigs and large feathers to a varying degree. Breeds September to March but mainly in November. Eggs 2—3, ground colour light green, turquoise or brown ochre, markings variable in size and colour from dark brown to black. Average (100) 68,6 × 47,6 (62,5—76,9 × 44,5—51,8).

287X Lesser Black-backed Gull

Larus fuscus Linnaeus, 1758: *Sweden.*

PLATE 31 (OPP. P. 209).
Length about 53 cm (wing 372—439). Eyes cream; bill yellow; legs of adults bright yellow; immature have feet and toes flesh coloured.

Identification: Distinguished from 287 by yellow feet, pale cream iris, more slender bill. In flight the white trailing edge of wing is narrower. Female noticeably smaller than male. Immature has yellow flesh-coloured legs.

Distribution: Northern Europe extending south to central Africa. Recorded from the Zambesi River and the Caprivi, Lake Ngami, Durban.

Habits: A rare vagrant but all inland records should be carefully checked for this species. Reputedly recorded in Durban all months but confirmed for October, November and May.

LOCAL RACE:
L.f. fuscus Linnaeus, 1758: *Sweden.* As above.

288 Grey-headed Gull   Gryskop-meeu

Larus cirrocephalus   Vieillot, 1818: *Brazil.*

PLATE 31 (OPP. P. 209). BR. AND N-BR.

Length about 43 cm (wing 285—311—329; tail 110—118—127; tarsus 44—48,3—51; culmen 35—38,4—41. 24 specimens). *Iris yellow-white;* bill and legs crimson in breeding condition, otherwise reddish black. Age 70 months.

Identification: Adult breeding dress unmistakable but non-breeding dress could be confused with 289 except that this species is larger and always has some marks on head. Note whitish eye. Immature birds have irregular brownish markings on ear-coverts and sometimes on the crown; the mantle and wing-coverts are mottled with ashy brown; there is no white subterminal patch on primaries; initially there is a black subterminal bar on tail; legs brown, bill yellowish. Nestling mottled brown, soft parts lead.

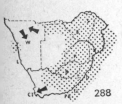

288

Distribution: Africa from Gambia south. Absent from coastal areas between Walvis Bay and Port Elizabeth except for vagrants and breeding colonies irregularly at the Cape.

Habits: Predominantly a fresh-water gull and found on practically all large inland waters and lakes. Coastal resident from Natal, regularly wandering as far as Port Elizabeth. A graceful bird and quite tame. Readily takes offal.

Food: Fish, scraps of bait, etc, offal, insects and the nestlings of other species.

Breeding: Colonial. A single bird recorded apparently breeding in a colony of Silver Gulls on Robben Island. July to November. Nests are built of dried grass on flat ground, usually near water; also uses old coots' nests. Eggs 2—3, ground colour blue-green to rich brown with variable dark brown blotches. Average (50) 53,9 × 37,9 (48,6—58,6 × 36,0—40).

288X White-eyed Gull

Larus leucophthalmus   Temminck, 1825: *Shore of the Red Sea.*

PLATE 31 (OPP. P. 209). BR. AND N-BR.

Length 42 cm (wing 291—341). Iris adult white, brown in immature; bill red with black tip in adult, reddish black with black tip in immature; legs dirty yellow.

Identification: Very slightly larger than 288 but more grey-brown and darker with head markings black; head and neck black in breeding plumage but only top of head and nape blackish in non-breeding condition. Colour of bill important at all ages. Could be confused with the Sooty Gull (see p. xxxii) which has sooty brown on head and different coloured bill in all stages.

Distribution: Red Sea and Gulf of Aden, south. Sight records from Beira, Durban and Port Elizabeth.

Habits: Associates with other Gulls along the coast. On the surface seems to sit deeper than No. 288 and is more nimble in feeding from the water's surface, with rapid jabs, twisting and turning rapidly and frequently.

Voice: Usually silent.

289 Silver Gull   Sterretjie

Larus novaehollandiae Stephens, 1826: *New South Wales.*
PLATE 31 (OPP. P. 209). A AND B.
Length about 38 cm (wing 267—277—295; tail 102—106—112; tarsus 42—44,7—47;
culmen 32—35—38,5. 7 specimens). Iris white or brown with red eyelid; bill and legs red,
black in non-breeding condition. Age 121 and 127 months.
Identification: Some birds in breeding condition have a faint ring of lavender
round the neck and throat but this is not a constant characteristic. (B). The
immature is practically the same as in No. 288; there are usually fewer
markings on head, while the bill and legs are dark brown. Subterminal black
tail band present. The eye is brown and remains brown for first white moult.
Distribution: Confined to the coastal cold-water area from Walvis Bay to
Cape Infanta. One in Durban 1900. A straggler collected at Makarikari pan.
Habits: A resident species from coast and islands that does not wander much
out to sea. Has recently adapted itself to man, settling on market-places,
rubbish dumps and even following cultivators in the western Cape. A noisy
gregarious species that is not very shy and allows a close approach.

289

Food: "Paddles" for marine creatures in shallow water over mud or sand; fish,
offal and at night insects, caught at street lights. Earthworms.
Voice: "Kwarrk" or "kwarrr". At breeding colony "kek-kek-kek-kek".
Breeding: Colonial nesters on the coastal islands off the south-west Cape.
The nest is constructed on the ground, frequently between or beneath covering
vegetation; constructed of roots, twigs or grass and not infrequently containing
bleached snail shells. April and July to September. Eggs 2, sometimes 3,
though 1 egg with a snail shell or stone often completes the "Clutch";
greenish ochre to light brown with light brown markings all over, sometimes
more at large end. Average (100) 52,2 × 37,1 (47,4—56,9 × 34,1—40,3).
Recently bred on mainland and factory roofs.

LOCAL RACE:
L.n. hartlaubii (Bruch) 1853: *Cape of Good Hope.*

289X Sabine's Gull

Larus sabini Sabine, 1818: *W. Greenland.*
PLATE 31 (OPP. P. 209). BR. AND N-BR.
Length 33 cm (wing 245—268; tail 78—98 inner and 102—117 outer; tarsus 31,4—34,5;
bill 26,1—28,1. 9 specimens). Iris dark brown; bill black with a yellow tip; legs and feet
dusky grey to flesh with lighter yellow webs.

Identification: Easily distinguished in flight by the black tip to wing, the
remainder of flight feathers white; the black bill with a yellow tip and by the
forked tail. Adults in winter plumage have black-brown nape markings. The
immature has a distinct broad black terminal bar on tail.
Distribution: An Arctic Circle breeding species which migrates south in the
northern winter. Recently it has been found to winter in numbers off the coast
of South West Africa, the Cape and east as far as Bird Island, Algoa Bay.
Habits: Appears to remain at sea, rarely coming close to land. Associates
with terns or Silver Gull. Has a graceful tern-like flight. Often settles on
the water. Flocks of up to 20 recorded; November to March with odd records
the rest of the year.
LOCAL RACE:
L.s. sabini Sabine, 1818: *W. Greenland.* The race occurring in the Atlantic.

PLATE 30

276. *Cursorius rufus.* Burchell's Courser. Bloukop-drawertjie.
277. *Cursorius temminckii.* Temminck's Courser. Trekdrawertjie.
278. *Rhinoptilus africanus africanus.* Double-banded Courser.
Dubbelband-drawertjie.
279. *Rhinoptilus cinctus seebohmi.* Three-banded Courser.
Drieband-drawertjie.
280. *Rhinoptilus chalcopterus.* Bronze-wing Courser. Bronsvlerk-drawertjie.
281. *Glareola pratincola fulleborni.* Red-winged Pratincole.
Gewone Kleinsprinkaanvoël.
282. *Glareola nordmanni.* Black-winged Pratincole.
Swartvlerk-kleinsprinkaanvoël.
282X. *Glareola ocularis.* Madagascar Pratincole.
283. *Galachrysia nuchalis.* White-collared Pratincole.
Withals-kleinsprinkaanvoël.
307. *Pterocles namaqua.* Namaqua Sandgrouse. Kelkiewyn. ♂ and ♀.
308. *Pterocles burchelli.* Spotted Sandgrouse. Gevlekte Sandpatrys. ♂ and ♀.
309. *Pterocles gutturalis gutturalis.* Yellow-throated Sandgrouse.
Geelkeel-sandpatrys. ♂ and ♀.
310. *Pterocles bicinctus bicinctus.* Double-banded Sandgrouse.
Dubbelband-sandpatrys. ♂ and ♀.

SKUAS, GULLS & THE SKIMMER

POMATORHINE SKUA

285

Imm

284
ARCTIC SKUA

A

B

287
Imm A

287
Imm B

287
SOUTHERN
BLACK-BACKED
GULL

287

286
ANTARCTIC SKUA

287X
LESSER BLACK-BACKED GULL

N-Br

288X

WHITE-EYED GULL
Br

288X N-Br

288
GREY-HEADED GULL

288 N-Br

289
SILVER GULL

A

289 B

N-Br

N-Br

289X
SABINE'S
GULL

306
SKIMMER

306

K B NEWMAN '76

PLATE 31

284. *Stercorarius parasiticus.* Arctic Skua. Withals-roofmeeu. A and B.

285. *Stercorarius pomarinus.* Pomatorhine Skua. Groot Withals-roofmeeu.
Ad. and Imm.

286. *Catharacta skua.* Antarctic Skua. Bruin Roofmeeu.

287. *Larus dominicanus.* Southern Black-backed Gull. Swartrug-meeu.
Ad. and Imm. A and B.

287X. *Larus fuscus.* Lesser Black-backed Gull.

288. *Larus cirrocephalus.* Grey-headed Gull. Gryskop-meeu. Br. and N-Br.

288X. *Larus leucophthalmus.* White-eyed Gull. Br. and N-Br.

289. *Larus novaehollandiae hartlaubii.* Silver Gull. Sterretjie. A and B.

289X. *Larus sabini.* Sabine's Gull. Br. and N-Br.

306. *Rynchops flavirostris.* Skimmer. Waterploeër.

TERNS

Family STERNIDAE

The Terns differ from the Gulls in having straighter, more slender and pointed bills, longer tails, in most species forked; long, pointed wings, smaller legs and feet. They subsist largely upon small fish, which are captured by diving from a height above the water, like Kingfishers. Nests are placed on the ground, preferably on short grass, the eggs Plover-like. Most species frequent the sea-coasts, but some frequent only the inland waters.

290 Caspian Tern   Reuse Seeswael

Hydroprogne caspia (Pallas), 1770: *Caspian Sea.*

PLATE 32 (OPP. P. 224). BR. AND N-BR.
Length about 56 cm (wing 398—408; tail 140—145; tarsus 40—46; culmen 70—72. 2 specimens). Iris reddish brown; bill vermilion; feet black.

Identification: Large size and large red bill distinguish this species. Non-breeding plumage shows white streaks on forehead and crown. Immature birds distinguishable from non-breeding condition by brownish mottling on back. Nestling dirty grey, eye brown, nape and bill orange-red.
Distribution: Europe, Asia, Australia and Africa. Around the coast, in estuaries and large lakes near the sea. Found up the Zambesi River and occasionally recorded from large inland lakes.

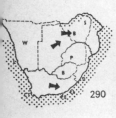

290

Habits: Resident and except in Zululand, sparsely distributed. At St. Lucia, Zululand, a large colony breeds and the birds are very common, elsewhere only one or two may be seen. More gull-like in size and flight than other terns. Quite often seen resting in company with other terns, but they usually hunt on their own.
Food: Small fish including *Tilapia, Hemiramphis* and *Mugil.*
Voice: A loud and raucous "krake-kraaah" or "kraark".
Breeding: The Cape and Zambesi in December and January, and in July at St. Lucia. Nests in association with gulls, forming colonies if in sufficient numbers. The nest is a scrape on the sand or ground, lined with incidental scraps; one record of a nest decorated with red locust legs and another with white and blue shells. Eggs 2, surface rough, ground colour greenish, with small sparse markings of dark purple. Average (40) 63,1 × 43,9 (56,8—96,2 × 40,9—47,4).

290X Gull-billed Tern

Gelochelidon nilotica (Gmelin), 1789: *Egypt.*

PLATE 32 (OPP. P. 224). BR. AND N-BR.
Length 38 cm (wing 290—333). Iris dark-brown; bill and feet black.

Identification: This tern is gull-like, not only in having a thick short bill but also in feeding on the water though not in flight. Nevertheless it has the slender body and wings, as well as forked tail of the tern. In non-breeding dress has black patch about the eye and is streaked on the nape.
Distribution: Europe and Asia moving south in the non-breeding season as far as the Tanzanian coast. Predominantly on inland waters in East Africa. Collected from Lake Dow, Lake Ngami, Botswana. Recorded from Gorongoza Reserve and Durban.

210

Habits: Usually occurs in flocks in the south. As noted above feeds on the water rather than in flight. Frequently recorded attending grassfires to hawk insects. Recorded December, January, June and July.
Voice: A harsh "Koowaak".

LOCAL RACE:
G. n. nilotica (Gmelin), 1789: *Egypt.*

291 Common Tern   Gewone Seeswael

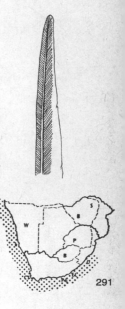

Sterna hirundo   Linnaeus, 1758: *Europe = Sweden.*

Native Name: Unotenteza (X).

PLATE 32 (OPP. P. 224). BR. AND N-BR.
Length about 33 cm (wing 233—280; tail 85—150; tarsus 18—20; culmen 33—39,5. 10 specimens). Iris dark brown; bill red at base otherwise black (winter); legs red.

Identification: Easily confused with Nos. 293 and 294. Compared with the Arctic Tern, No. 294, the bill is proportionately longer (1½ times the distance between back of eye and front of forehead); the tarsus is longer; the bill is red with black tip, but shows more black in non-breeding condition; the legs are red or reddish. In flight against the light, only the inner primaries appear semi-transparent. Except for this feature, the immatures are indistinguishable from those of No. 294. See No. 292.
Distribution: Europe, Asia and eastern North America, south in winter. Found around the coast, recorded further north than Natal on the east coast to Bazaruto. Very rare inland.
Habits: A migrant; ringed birds have been recovered along our shores from England, Norway, Finland, Denmark and Germany. Present from August to April in bulk but there are records throughout the year. Since there is much confusion in the field between this and the Arctic Tern, details of habits are wanting. The buoyant swallow-like flight of these terns is a familiar sight off-shore. They occur especially around estuaries where they roost on sand-banks or in harbours on boats.

291

LOCAL RACE:
S.h. hirundo Linnaeus, 1758: *Europe=Sweden.* Another race in eastern India reputed to occur but more evidence is required.

292 Antarctic Tern   Grysbors-seeswael

Sterna vittata   Gmelin, 1789: *Kerguelen.*

PLATE 32 (OPP. P. 224). BR. N-BR. AND IMM.
Length about 40 cm (wing 252—267; tail 161—183; tarsus 18,4—20; culmen 34,6—37,7. 9 specimens, 6 ♂, 3 ♀, ex Murphy 1938). Iris dark brown; bill blood-red; legs coral-red. Age 20 years.

Identification: May be distinguished in breeding condition by dove-grey underparts, nearly as dark as back; bright bill, white line between black cap and grey under-parts that extends from bill, below eye to back of ear-coverts.

211

Non-breeding birds have white chin and throat and lose most of the grey on under-parts. The *tail is wholly white* and the outer tail-feathers are very long. Under wing-coverts white. Immature birds have black bills and shorter tails but the markings on upper-parts and tail are dark brown, giving a barred effect—dark shoulder-bar as in immatures, Nos. 291 and 294.

Distribution: Southern Antarctic seas. Locally recorded from Bird Island, Algoa Bay, west to Cape Town. One record of a bird from Pirie, near King William's Town.

292

Habits: Rarely recorded from July to September. Occurs mainly near islands. Apparently not regular. Immature birds recorded from Dyers Island and Bird Island and there is evidence that after breeding (irregular) they move west to the open sea. This bird has a graceful undulating flight frequently hovering over water. Usually gregarious.

Food: Small fish and crustaceans and scraps from ships.

Voice: A shrill "trr-trr-kriah".

Breeding: Miss M. Courtenay-Latimer recorded this species breeding on Stag Island (Bird Island Group) in August, 1937. Eggs 3, lightly marked all over and having heavy purplish undermarkings. 43,0 × 28,8; 44,6 × 30,4; 45,8 × 30,2.

LOCAL RACE:
S.v. tristanensis Murphy, 1938: *Tristan da Cunha.* All specimens are of this northern race. Size as above. Distinguished from other races by its longer tail.

293   Roseate Tern   Rooibors-seeswael

Sterna dougallii   Montagu, 1813: *Cumbrae Is., Firth of Clyde.*

PLATE 32 (OPP. P. 224). BR. AND N-BR.
Length about 36 cm (wing ♂ 223—236, ♀ 218—233; tail 140—205; tarsus 19—21; culmen 37—40. 12 specimens ex *Handbk. Brit. Birds).* Iris dull brown; bill black with red base in breeding condition; legs red.

293

Identification: Distinguished from Nos. 291, 292 and 294 by its *long slender bill*; from Nos. 291 and 294 by its long outer tail-feathers which are white. White under-parts in breeding plumage show a distinct pink tinge. The forehead and crown, white in non-breeding plumage, are black when breeding. Immature birds indistinguishable from other young terns except by long slender bill.

Distribution: Atlantic, Mediterranean, Indian and eastern Pacific Oceans. From Algoa Bay to the Cape. Rare Natal and Mozambique observations.

Habits: Poorly documented because of confusion with Nos. 291 and 294. During breeding season is not recorded far from nesting sites.

Voice: A harsh "chipik chipik".

Breeding: Recorded from Dyers Island and Bird Island; July on Dyers Island, August to October on Bird Island and recently on the mainland at Cape Recife. Eggs 2, cream or light ochre with variable black markings and large purplish underlying blotches. Average (50) 42,8 × 30,0 (37,1—47,7 × 27,2—32,1).

LOCAL RACE:
S.d. dougallii Montagu, 1813: *Cumbrae Is., Firth of Clyde.* Another race based on one specimen needs confirmation.

294 Arctic Tern   Europese Grysbors-seeswael

Sterna paradisaea Pontoppidan, 1763: *Christiansöe, Denmark.*

Native Name: Unotenteza (X).

PLATE 32 (OPP. P. 224). BR. AND N-BR.
Length about 33 cm (wing 260—282; tail 158—200; tarsus 15—17; culmen 30—33. 12 specimens ex *Handbk. Brit. Birds*). Iris light brown; bill wholly black, in breeding condition wholly red; legs black, coral-red in breeding condition.

Identification: Easily confused with Nos. 291 and 293. In semi-breeding plumage, which may be seen during October, the under-parts are very light sooty grey, but the short dark-edged tail distinguishes it from the Antarctic. Compared to the Common Tern the bill is proportionately shorter (approximately equal to the distance between back eye and front of forehead); bill wholly black or wholly red; tarsus shorter. In flight against the light *all* the primaries appear semi-transparent.

Distribution: Europe and Northern America, south in winter. Recorded from around our coast, not beyond Natal. Very rare inland.

Habits: A migrant from Europe and America; one bird, a fledgling ringed in Labrador on 28th July, was recovered on 14th November, 1928, at Margate, Natal, a Greenland bird recovered at Doringbaai 12 500 km south. The large flocks of terns recorded early in October are probably mainly of this species. Specimens recorded from July to November and again in May. They are presumed to migrate further south. See also No. 291. The flight is more direct than 292. Often rests on flotsam.

Food: Euphausids and krill.

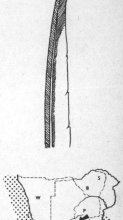

294

295 Sooty Tern   Swart Seeswael

Sterna fuscata Linnaeus, 1766: *S. Domingo.*

PLATE 32 (OPP. P. 224). BR. AND IMM.
Length about 43 cm (wing ♂ 275—310, ♀ 272—290; tail 157—173; tarsus 22—25; culmen 39—48. 14 Atlantic specimens ex *Handbk. Brit. Birds*). Iris dark brown; bill and legs black.

Identification: Note the black, deeply-forked tail with white outer feathers. The immature is more brown-black on upper-parts than adult, and dark brown below, not white. Slightly larger than 295X see under that species for differences.

Distribution: Tropical and subtropical seas, occurring down our east coast. Specimens from Port Alfred and Bird Island, Algoa Bay. Occurs occasionally along Natal coast. Kruger National Park.

Habits: This species occurs normally only after cyclones blow from the east; on such occasions they are also blown inland. Numbers up to 60 at a time have been recorded, usually social. The flight is slower with more flexible wing strokes than 295X.

Voice: Nasal three syllabled "waanyiwaa".

LOCAL RACE:
S.f. nubilosa Sparrman, 1788: *Finland = E. India.*

295X   Bridled Tern

Sterna anaethetus   Scopoli, 1786: *Panay, Philippines.*

PLATE 32 (OPP. P. 224).
Length 42 cm (wing 268; tail 170—182—201; culmen 38—41—43; tarsus 20—22—23. 10 specimens). Iris dark brown; bill and legs black.

Identification: Distinguished from 295 by white line over eye extending well beyond eye. The upper parts are brownish black in this species but black in 295.
Distribution: Recorded only from Natal, Durban. December and March.
Habits: Like 295 normally seen after cyclonic conditions. The wings appear slightly broader and thus give a more stiff winged more rapid stroke when flying. Up to five seen together.
Voice: Described as a repeated syncopated yap.

296   Sandwich Tern   Groot Seeswael

Sterna sandvicensis   Latham, 1787: *England = Sandwich, Kent.*

PLATE 32 (OPP. P. 224). BR. AND N-BR.
Length about 40 cm (wing 267—288—302; tail 105—121—152; tarsus 24—26,1—29; culmen 46—52,2—57,5. 12 specimens). Iris dark brown; bill black with yellow tip; legs black. Age 113 months plus.

Identification: The diagnostic feature is the *yellow tip to bill*, visible from a considerable distance; if too far to be seen the black portion gives the impression of a short heavy bill. Similar to the common Tern but larger with the general appearance of a shorter, fatter body than other terns. In breeding plumage, attained late April, the forehead and crown are completely black and there is a pinkish tinge on under-parts.
Distribution: Western and eastern Atlantic migrating south. Found around our coasts, as far north as Inhambane, Mozambique.

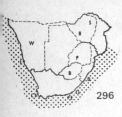

296

Habits: A common migrant, from August to April in the Cape in large numbers; regular in Natal October to January. Occasional wintering birds. Usually occurs in flocks, some numbering many hundreds. Generally a noisy tern especially when roosting at night, when the clamour of hundreds of shrieking birds seems to go on right through the night.
Voice: A strident rasping "kirrik-kirrik".

LOCAL RACE:
S.s. sandvicensis Latham, 1787: *England = Sandwich, Kent.* Other races to the west.

297   Lesser Crested Tern   Kuifkop-seeswael

Sterna bengalensis   Lesson, 1831: *Indian coasts.*

PLATE 32 (OPP. P. 224). BR. AND N-BR.
Length about 43 cm (wing 260—275; tail 103—123; tarsus 23—24; culmen 50-53. 2 specimens). Iris black; bill orange-yellow to orange; legs black.

Identification: A large-billed tern similar to the next species but distinguished by orange-yellow bill and appreciably smaller size. Forehead and crown black in breeding plumage. Immature is mottled with light brown on upper wing-coverts, back and mantle.

Distribution: Indian Ocean from the Red Sea eastwards. Regularly down the east coast as far as Zululand. A single specimen from Knysna.
Habits: Recorded both in summer and winter in the estuaries of Zululand, in flocks of up to 20 in summer. The small flocks are often in association with other terns, especially Sandwich Terns in Natal.

LOCAL RACE:
S.b. par (Mathews and Iredale), 1921: *Red Sea.* The western race.

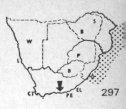

298 Swift Tern   Geelbek-seeswael

Sterna bergii Lichtenstein, 1823: *Cape of Good Hope.*

PLATE 32 (OPP. P. 224). BR., N-BR AND IMM.
Length about 50 cm (wing 322—342—350; tail 132—140—155; tarsus 28—30,1—32; culmen 54,5—57,7—60,5. 7 specimens). Iris dark brown, bill chrome-yellow, often tinged greenish at base; legs black normally.

Identification: A large tern, with large yellow bill. In breeding plumage has forehead and crown black. Immature has yellow bill, black-and-white barred upper-parts with buff-edged feathers—quite a mottled plumage.
Distribution: Indian Ocean and western Pacific coastal areas. Recorded around our coastal waters, up into the Atlantic as far as Swakopmund, South West Africa. Also Zambia.
Habits: Usually occurring in small parties along the coast or in estuaries. One bird ringed on Robben Island was recovered in Zululand. A social bird, forming flocks of up to 50, but if only a few they associate with gulls and other terns. A more graceful tern than others in flight, an impression gained because of its very long and narrow wings which work with a quick high action. Often calls on the wing.

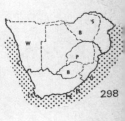

Food: Fish, such as mullet, sardines and *Rhabdosargus.*
Voice: A loud, screaming "kreee-kreee".
Breeding: Colonial, nesting in close proximity to each other and often in association with Silver Gulls. Nest usually on some open, flat area, March to October. A shallow scrape is made, sometimes lined with a little grass. Eggs 1—2, ground colour light turquoise, pale pink or whitish; either heavily marked with brown, especially at the large end, or evenly marked with light brown. Average (88) 62,1 × 43,0 (55,4—66,8 × 39,3—45,3).

LOCAL RACES:
(a) S.b. bergii Lichtenstein, 1823: *Cape of Good Hope.* Lighter above; smaller, size as above. Walvis Bay around to Maputo. Also Zambia.
(b) S.b. velox Cretzschmar, 1827: *Coast of the Red Sea.* Darker grey above, larger; wing 337—377; tail 191; culmen 64. Imhambane, Mozambique, northwards.

299 Little Tern   Klein Seeswael

Sterna albifrons Pallas, 1764: *Holland.*

PLATE 32 (OPP. P. 224). BR. AND N-BR.
Length about 23 cm (wing 164—180; tail 75—95; tarsus 15—18; culmen 27—32. 12 specimens ex *Handbk. Brit. Birds).* Iris dark brown; bill yellow with black tip; legs orange to brownish, yellow in juvenile.

Identification: The small size distinguishes this and the next species from all other terns. Separable from the Damara Tern by its yellow bill.

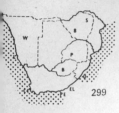

299

Distribution: Atlantic and Indian Ocean coasts. On the east, extends down as far as Durban, Natal. From the west extends around the coast as far as Port Elizabeth.
Habits: A rare migrant on the west but not uncommon on Zululand coast. Generally not as social as other terns and thus usually seen on their own. It has a quicker wing beat than other terns and appears to flit here and there.

LOCAL RACES:
(a) S.a. albifrons Pallas, 1764: *Holland.* Size as above. Rare, from Port Elizabeth, westwards.

300 Damara Tern   Damara-seeswael

Sterna balaenarum   (Strickland), 1852: *Damaraland, probably Walvis Bay.*

PLATE 32 (OPP. P. 224). BR., N-BR. AND IMM.
Length about 23 cm (wing 160—167—171; tail 62—63,8—65; tarsus 12—12,9—13,5; culmen 27,8—29,9—32. 4 specimens). Iris dark brown; bill black; legs yellowish.

Identification: Compare No. 299. Small size and black bill distinguish this species. Non-breeding birds have white forehead and crown. Immature has brownish markings on wing-coverts. Shorter legs.

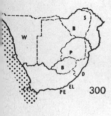

300

Distribution: Confined to the coasts of Angola, South West Africa, and Cape. From Luanda south to Cape Agulhas.
Habits: A tern found along the cold-water open coast and in sandy bays. Usually in small parties, occasionally singly; they hunt separately from other terns but roost communally with other species. Much quicker in flight and much more swallow-like than larger species. Calls a lot when fishing, and has a characteristic call when flushed from roost.
Voice: A high pitched "tsit-tit" repeated several times. Also "tit-tit".
Breeding: Recently recorded regularly in gravel plains about 1 km from the sea breeding in loose aggregations. Clutch recorded as one egg only in Walvis Bay. Recorded from near Table Bay and in January at Walvis Bay. The nest is a scrape in the sand on pebbly flats. Eggs 1, tern-like. Average (11) 32,9 × 23,9 (30,9—35,2 × 23,1—25). Incubation 18—21 days.

301-302 See page xxxii

303 Noddy   Bruin Sterretjie

Anous stolidus   (Linnaeus), 1758: *American seas = West Indies*

PLATE 32 (OPP. P. 224). BR. AND N-BR.
Length about 40 cm (wing 253—290; tail 138—175; tarsus 22—25; culmen 38—53). Iris brown; bill black; legs reddish brown.

Identification: Sooty brown all over, except for some white on the forehead, which merges into lavender-grey on the crown and with a semicircle of white below the eye. Throat and sides of head lead in breeding condition, sooty brown in non-breeding plumage. Flight feathers slightly darker. Juvenile has white tips to feathers of upper parts.

Distribution: Oceanic both in Atlantic and Indian Oceans. A single live bird came ashore in Durban, January 1969.
Habits: Unternlike, lethargic with a slowish flight. Settles on the water to feed and does not dive as typical terns. True vagrant.
Food: Fish.
Voice: Shrill "pee" "pay-eee" and a deep croacking "karr-karr".

304   White-winged Black Tern   Witvlerk-swartswael

Chlidonias leucoptera (Temminck), 1815: *Shores of the Mediterranean.*

PLATE 32 (OPP. P. 224).
Length about 23 cm (wing ♂ 200—218, ♀ 192—210; tail 67—75; tarsus 19—22; culmen 23—24. 12 specimens ex *Handbk. Brit. Birds*). Iris dark brown; bill black, crimson when breeding; legs orange-red.

Identification: This and the next species distinguished from Sea Terns by having square tails. In breeding or partial breeding plumage the black body and under wing coverts with white rump are distinctive. Winter plumaged birds 304, 305 and 305X are easily confused. This species has black ear coverts the adult with speckled crown, juvenile darker. Always with white collar at back of crown.
Distribution: Europe and Asia wintering to the south. General throughout Southern Africa.
Habits: A common migrant to fresh-water areas of the western Cape and southern Transvaal, elsewhere somewhat irregular. Arrives in late July and departs in April; traces of breeding plumage recorded up to October and from February. Several winter records. Usually in small flocks, but in favoured haunts flocks of up to 2 000 birds occur. Unlike sea terns these birds generally hawk insects over water, usually skimming just over the surface as it flies slowly into the wind. Hawk insects over grasslands away from water.

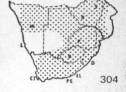

304

Food: Includes American Bolworm, Lucerne Butterfly and small butterflies taken over open grassveld. Over water *Limnothrissa* most important fish, also *Haplochromis* and *Synodontis* and aquatic insects.

305   Whiskered Tern   Witbaard-meerswael

Chlidonias hybrida (Pallas), 1811: *South Russia.*

PLATE 32 (OPP. P. 224). BR., N-BR. AND IMM.
Length about 24 cm (wing ♂ 232—250, ♀ 230—242; tail 83—90; tarsus 22—25; culmen 30—34. 12 specimens ex *Handbk. Brit. Birds*). Iris red-brown; bill black, red when breeding; legs crimson.

Identification: The bill is longer and heavier and there is no collar behind black of crown. See No. 304. In winter plumage there is a dark line through eye to crown, no separate ear covert patch. Back and rump paler than 304. In breeding plumage distinguished by dark upper wing-coverts and light under wing-coverts; rump grey.
Distribution: Southern Europe, south in winter. General throughout Southern Africa.

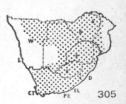

305

217

Habits: Common, much as for the last species with which it is so easily confused that field records become unreliable. This species may hawk insects as No. 304, but usually tends to feed by diving into the water from a height of a metre or two.

Food: Aquatic insects. The frog *Hyperolius* often taken.

Breeding: Recorded almost throughout the year in odd localities. Rhodesia; Verloren vallei, Faure and Kouebokkeveld, Cape; Mkarikari pans, Botswana, Witbank and near Belfast, Transvaal. The nest is built of dry grass placed on floating scum, reeds or old nests. Eggs 2—3, cream-coloured, sometimes tinged green, blotched with reddish brown. Incubation 25, 26 and 29 days.

LOCAL RACE:
C.h. sclateri (Mathews and Iredale), 1921: *Cape Peninsula, South Africa*. Much darker than northern race in breeding and non-breeding conditions. Size as above.

305X   Black Tern   Swart Meerswael

Chlidonias nigra   (Linnaeus), 1758: *Sweden*.

PLATE 32 (OPP. P. 224). BR., N-BR. AND IMM.
Length about 22 cm (wing 195—215; tail 75—90; tarsus 14—17; bill 25—30 mm). Iris brown; bill black, dark crimson in breeding dress; legs red-brown.

Identification: Almost indistinguishable from No. 304 and 305 in winter plumage. Crown almost entirely black merged with black ear coverts. The black patch in front of eye larger than in 304 and 305. Fore-edge of wing darker, the dark line ending as a distinct blackish patch on sides of breast; fairly broad white collar. Tail squarish. Slim build with full wing beat gives a characteristic dynamic action to this species. The rump is brownish grey in juvenile and winter birds. Note slightly smaller size and distinctively shorter tarsus.

Distribution: Europe and Asia south to Africa north of the equator in winter. Recorded as far south as Walvis Bay in South West Africa and Natal.

Habits: Although recorded out to sea it usually occurs along quieter coastal waters and in the immediate interior. In recent years a number of sightings indicate that this species is more common than previously recorded. Observations from SWA. Lake Ngami, many from Natal coastal regions, one from Pietermaritzburg. Usually in association with other lake terns.

Food: Takes insects, even flying ants over land.

Voice: Screeching "ski-aah".

Family RYNCHOPIDAE

Lake-frequenting birds having much the appearance of Terns except for the peculiar prolongation of the lower mandible beyond the upper. The whole of the lower and most of the upper mandibles compressed, thin and blade-like; the nostrils are oval and open from side to side near the base of the maxilla. The wings are longer than in the marine Terns and project as far beyond the tail as in the shorter-tailed lacustrine Terns of the genus *Chlidonias*; the tail is forked. Five forms in one genus only make up this family, one being found in southern India and Burma, one in Africa and the other three in the New World.

306   Skimmer   Waterploeër

Rynchops flavirostris   Vieillot, 1816: *Australia (error) = Senegal.*

PLATE 31 (OPP. P. 209).
Length about 38 cm (wing 325—349—374; tail 113—119—127; tarsus 23—24,9—26; culmen 48—56,6—60; lower mandible 56—75,6—85. 7 specimens). Iris brown; bill vermilion to deep orange, paler below; legs vermilion.

Identification: A long-winged tern-like bird, with conspicuous red flattened bill. Under-wing secondaries appear whitish. Immature has streaked forehead, buff-edged feathers above and the bill is blackish with yellowish base. Nestling tern-like with normal bill.

Distribution: Coasts and rivers of Africa. Occurs on the Zambesi and its tributaries, on the Okavango and its swamps, Lake Ngami and Lake Dow. Recorded at St. Lucia fairly recently and there are old records for the Vaal River and Potchefstroom. Also Sabi river, Karkloof in Natal and Durban.

Habits: Not uncommon on the Zambesi; present status in Zululand vague but not as common as it was. A long-winged fast-flying bird which skims low over the water, especially at dawn and dusk, flying so low that it can dip its bill into the water when it sees fish. Also flies on moonlit nights. Rests on sandbanks when not feeding but very wary and not allowing one to approach very close.

Food: Fish.

Voice: A loud sharp "kik-kik-kik".

Breeding: Recorded from the Caprivi Strip, Lake Ngami, Zambesi and St. Lucia, September to October. The eggs are laid in a deep, hollow scrape in the sand of a sandy spit. Eggs 3, occasionally 4, buffy stone-coloured, boldly blotched with slate, purplish and blackish. Average (9) 40,5 × 28,7 (38,5—41,9 × 28,1—29,6).

Family PTEROCLIDAE

Sandgrouse have very short bills and short legs; the tarsus feathered in front to the base of the toes; strong and rather pointed wings; close-set plumage with the upper and under tail-coverts nearly as long as the tail and upper-parts, cryptically coloured, usually spotted, the under-parts with definite colour-patterns, often barred, the males more handsomely coloured than females. They feed mainly on hard seeds. The eggs are not pointed at one end as plovers' eggs but are oval, equally rounded at both ends. They are laid in a hollow scraped in the ground and thinly lined with grass or dry fibrous leaves, as a rule in South Africa in the cold months, three eggs forming the normal clutch. When breeding, males wet their breast feathers and carry water to the young to drink. They are considered "game birds" as they afford good shooting and eating, though inclined to be tough.

307   Namaqua Sandgrouse   Kelkiewyn

Pterocles namaqua   (Gmelin), 1789: *Namaqua country.*

PLATE 30 (OPP. P. 208) ♂ AND ♀.
Length about 28 cm (wing ♂ 167—172—180, ♀ 160—165—170; tail 79—101—135; tarsus 21—24—26; tarsus 21—24—26; culmen 12—12,8—15. 20 specimens, 10 ♂, 10 ♀). Iris dark brown; bill bluish slate; legs lavender.

Identification: Distinguished from other sandgrouse by the *long pointed tail.* The male identified by its breast bar with dark rufous lower breast and belly. The female differs from the female of No. 310, which is also barred below, by yellow colouring of throat and V-markings on the chest. Dove-like flight of sandgrouse is rapid; usually they fly high.

Distribution: From Angola south through Botswana, southern and western Transvaal, Orange Free State and Cape Province to Matatiele and Kei Road. Not on the Cape Peninsula. Absent from Rhodesia and Natal. Headquarters Namaqualand and the Karoo.

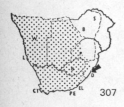 307

Habits: A migrant at the extremities of its range but resident in the dry western country. Subject to considerable local fluctuations. Usually occurs in flocks of a dozen to twenty but near waterholes in the morning and at dusk they gather in hundreds, sometimes even thousands, and are then trapped or shot by Natives and Europeans for food. They are found as a rule where grass is short. The flight is rapid and as they glide down to water twisting and turning they give their onomatopoeic "kelkiewyn".

Breeding: Nest on open grasslands or bare Karoo veld or on rocky sandstone koppies, sometimes colonially with nests placed about a metre from each other. The eggs are laid in a scrape which may be lined with some grass. Eggs 2, usually 3, buffy with slate-grey undermarkings and red-brown to slate-brown speckles and smudges, altogether rather darker than other sandgrouse. Average (16) 35,8 × 24,8 (34,9—39,3 × 23,9—25,9). Incubation 21 days; first chick remains in the nest until second hatches. Chicks fly at 3 weeks.

308   Spotted Sandgrouse   Gevlekte Sandpatrys

Pterocles burchelli   W. Sclater, 1922: *near Griquatown.*

PLATE 30 (OPP. P. 208) ♂ AND ♀.
Length about 25 cm (wing 159—167—176; tail 55—67,5—77; tarsus 24—25,9—29; culmen 11—12,1—14. 15 specimens). Iris light brown with gamboge eyelids; bill black; legs dusky yellow.

Identification: Distinguished by their spotted under-parts. Sexes differ; male has throat and belly unmarked, whilst female has light ochre chin and throat, and cross bars on belly.

Distribution: Northern Damaraland (Quickborn, Gobabis), thence south to the Orange River. On the east from the Caprivi Strip, Nkate in Botswana, Wankie in Rhodesia, Rustenburg (and Zoutpansberg) south to the Vaal River.

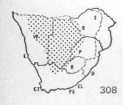 308

Habits: Not a very common species but like the last gathers in numbers near water holes about 10 a.m. Usually occurs in pairs and when disturbed from the ground utters a rapid clucking alarm note. Not easily distinguished in flight from No. 310, but buff under-parts, if visible, should distinguish it.

Voice: Onomatopoeic in Sechuana "Mokhwarakhwara".

Breeding: Eggs laid, July to September, on the bare ground; 3 in number, with greenish sheen when fresh; creamy white with small dots and smudges of greyish slate, overlaid by small—rarely large—smudges of red-brown. Average (6) 37,5 × 26,0 (36,3—38 × 25,5—26,5).

LOCAL RACES:
(a) *P.b. burchelli* W. Sclater, 1922: *Near Griquatown.* Throughout its range excepting Botswana. Size above.
(b) *P.b. makarikari* (Roberts), 1932: *Nkate, N. Bechuanaland.* A paler race from northern S.W.A. and northern Botswana (wing 160—172; tail 61—72; tarsus 27—31; culmen 11—13,5).

309   Yellow-throated Sandgrouse   Geelkeel-sandpatrys

Pterocles gutturalis   A. Smith, 1836: *Near Kurrichane, W. Transvaal.*

PLATE 30 ♂ AND ♀ (OPP. P. 208).
Length about 30 cm (wing ♂ 205—214—222, ♀ 198—210—221; tail 69—80—89; tarsus 25—28—32; culmen 13—14,3—16. 16 specimens, 9 ♂, 7 ♀). Iris dusky brown; bill light bluish horn; legs dark brown.

Identification: Dark rich chestnut of belly is distinctive and both sexes have a black line from base of bill to eye. The male has a conspicuous black line across throat; the wing-coverts are variable and may be a much richer buff than illustrated. The under-wing in both sexes is dark, practically black, distinguishing this species from other sandgrouse.
Distribution: From East Africa south to the Kalahari, Damaraland, western Matabeleland and western Transvaal.
Habits: Not uncommon on bare ground and sandveld. The largest of the sandgrouse, occurring singly, in pairs or in family parties; like the other species gathers in large numbers at waterholes but not with the same regularity. When flushed they rise with a sudden burst of whirring wings—a feature common to all the sandgrouse.
Food: Seeds and bulbous roots.
Voice: Uttered only on the wing, "tweet-weet-tweet-weet".
Breeding: Said to lay 2 or 3 eggs on open ground. Eggs dusky brown marked with lines and blotches of umber forming a zone towards the base. One egg given as 43 × 27,5.

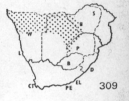
309

LOCAL RACE:
P.g. gutturalis A. Smith, 1836: *Near Kurrichane, W. Transvaal.* Another race occurs from Tanzania northwards.

310   Double-banded Sandgrouse   Dubbelband-sandpatrys

Pterocles bicinctus   Temminck, 1815: *Great Fish River, South West Africa.*

PLATE 30 (OPP. P. 208) ♂ AND ♀.
Length about 25 cm (wing ♂ 171—179—188, ♀ 169—175—183; tail 74—79,6—88; tarsus 24—26,3—29; culmen 15—16,1—17. 26 specimens, 15 ♂ and 11 ♀). Iris hazel with yellow skin around eye; bill and legs yellowish brown. Weight ♂ 234, ♀ 239 g (19 each).

Identification: Distinguished from No. 307 by rounded tail and yellow legs; male by white and black bars on forehead and crown and by barred black-and-white under-parts; female has very fine bars on belly and the throat is not tinted yellow.
Distribution: From Angola and Rhodesia south to the Republic; from Kamaggas on the west across to Kuruman, northern Cape; Rustenburg; southern Transvaal; and Olifants River in Mozambique.

310

221

PIGEONS

Habits: A fairly common species of dry savannas and bushveld rather than the open spaces of the previous species. Generally occurs in flocks which congregate at dawn and dusk at waterholes to drink. In the breeding season they split up and form pairs.

Voice: When flushed utters a loud "chuck-chuck".

Breeding: The eggs are laid on the bare ground amongst short grass, apparently frequently under baobab trees. Occasionally a thin lining of grass is given to the nest. May to August. Eggs 3 or 4, pinkish brown to salmon-pink in ground colour with purplish slate to red-brown markings. Average (5) 37,9 × 27,3 (35,6—39,2 × 26,8—27,8).

LOCAL RACES:
This species shows a size cline from large in the west to small in the east and a colour cline from light in south-west to darker in the east and north.
(a) P.b. bicinctus Temminck, 1815: *Great Fish River, South West Africa.* From Kamaggas in south to Onguma in north. Size as above. Intermediate colour, large size.
(b) P.b. multicolor Hartert, 1908: *Rustenburg, Transvaal.* Transvaal, southern Rhodesia, Mozambique (wing ♂ 168—178—188, ♀ 167—173—187; tail 71—78—88; tarsus 24—26—28; culmen 15—16—18. 24 specimens, 13 ♂, 11 ♀. Darker and large race.
(c) P.b. usheri (Benson), 1947: *Tambara, Portuguese East Africa.* The lower Zambesi Valley and northern Rhodesia. Wing 161—171 (13). Dark and small.

Family COLUMBIDAE

The Doves and Pigeons are too well known to need description. The Green Pigeons *(Treronidae)* form an easily recognized group and are here kept as a distinct family, though some systematists also place them in the *Columbidae*. The larger Pigeons and some of the Doves lay glossy white eggs, but the Namaqua, Cinnamon and Metallic-spotted Doves lay creamy-coloured eggs. Two eggs form the normal clutch, but in some cases only one egg is laid. The nest is invariably a mere platform of sticks, placed in various situations according to the habitat of the species. They feed on seeds and berries, often very hard-shelled nuts, and their mouths, though small, are adapted in that event to expand at the gape so that these hard nuts can be swallowed: the food then lies in the crop and is softened before passing to the stomach for digestion. These species drink water regularly for the purpose of aiding the softening and digestive processes. The young are fed upon softened food disgorged for the purpose and mixed with a milky substance which gives rise to the expression "pigeons' milk".

311 Rock Pigeon   Bosduif

Columba guinea Linnaeus, 1758: *Guinea.*

Native Names: le-Eba, le-Evakhotho, le-Evarope (S); Matseba (Ch); i-Juba (Z); Ivukutu (X).

PLATE 33 (OPP. P. 225).
Length about 33 cm (wing 219—226—233; tail 105—125; tarsus 24—28; culmen 20—24. 11 specimens). Iris yellowish white; bill blackish; cere whitish, bare skin round eye red; legs red. Weight 315—355—390 g.

Identification: The bare red face and spotted wings render this bird quite distinctive. Sexes alike but males more powerfully built and brighter, particularly around the neck. Young birds generally similar but lack red faces.

222

Distribution: From Guinea to Ethiopia, south to Cape Town.

Habits: A common species wherever there are rocks or artificial structures such as mine-shafts and buildings. Also frequents caves along the seashore. Recently it has taken to more open country where grain is grown, roosting in the newly ploughed fields or in trees. It is wary when fired at. Farmers resort to the practice of making a "hide" on the border of the lands and when the first birds are shot they are left lying there, the others circling round and coming back again and again, more being shot each time. Usually seen in pairs but when not breeding may form large flocks of several hundred. Claps its wings while flying usually when displaying.

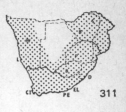

311

Food: Largely grain. Also seeds of the duiweltjie-doring (*Tribulus*).

Voice: A loud ringing, cooing sounding like "doo, doo, doo, doo, doo, doo, doo, doo, doo", rising gently to a crescendo and then descending.

Breeding: The nest is a platform of sticks and roots, placed by the female on a ledge or rock, on a precipice, in a cave or mine-shaft, on a building or on the side of a donga. Occasionally in trees. Breeds all the year round in most areas. Eggs, usually 2, sometimes only 1, glossy white. Average (62) 36,4 × 27,6 (33,8—41,1 × 25—31,2). Incubation 15—17 days by both sexes. Nestling period 25—26 days, both parents feed.

LOCAL RACES:
(a) *C.g. phaeonota* Gray, 1856: *South Africa = Hout Bay, Cape Province*. General except South West Africa. As figured, size above.
(b) *C.g. bradfieldi* (Roberts), 1931: *Waterberg*. Paler than *(a)*. Wing 212—224—241. South West Africa east to Botswana south to Brandvlei.

312 Rameron Pigeon   Geelbek-bosduif

Columba arquatrix Temminck and Knip, 1809: *Anteniquoi = Knysna*

Native Names: Izuba (X); i-Vugute (Z); le-Phepane, le-Evamphapane (S).

PLATE 33 (OPP. P. 225).
Length about 40 cm. (wing 214—226—245; tail 125—147; tarsus 21—27; culmen 18—22, 16 specimens). Iris pale yellow to light brown; bare skin round eye, bill and legs yellow.

Identification: Even in flight the yellow bill and legs are conspicuous and diagnostic. Sexes alike, females slightly smaller and duller. Young birds have heads mixed grey and purple, the back brownish.

Distribution: From Cape Town eastwards to Transvaal, eastern Rhodesia, Angola and the mountains of East Africa and Cameroons.

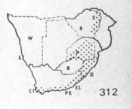

312

Habits: A fairly common species of the forests, a few remaining throughout the year, their numbers becoming augmented at times due to local movements which are regulated by food available. They often fly long distances from the mountains to feed on olive groves, etc. Fond of sunning themselves in small numbers scattered about on dead twigs of very high trees. Seldom come to the ground except to drink at certain places. Form fairly large flocks when not breeding. Very strong on the wing. Make quite a noise feeding, flapping their wings to balance on slender twigs while gathering fruits.

Food: Seeds, wild fruits and berries, particularly of wild chestnut, yellowwood and stinkwood trees. Also very partial to olives, hence the popular name "Olive Pigeon".

Voice: A low, hoarse "coo" which sometimes breaks into two or three syllables.

PLATE 32

290. *Hydroprogne caspia.* Caspian Tern. Reuse Seeswael. Br. and N-Br.
290X. *Gelochelidon nilotica.* Gull-billed Tern. Br. and N-Br.
291. *Sterna hirundo.* Common Tern. Gewone Seeswael. Br. and N-Br.
292. *Sterna vittata.* Antarctic Tern. Grysbors-seeswael. Br. and N-Br.
293. *Sterna dougallii.* Roseate Tern. Rooibors-seeswael. Br. and N-Br.
294. *Sterna paradisaea.* Arctic Tern. Europese Grysbors-seeswael.

Br. and N-Br.

295. *Sterna fuscata.* Sooty Tern. Swart Seeswael. Br. and Imm.
295X. *Sterna anaethetus.* Bridled Tern.
296. *Sterna sandvicensis.* Sandwich Tern. Groot Seeswael. Br. and N-Br.
297. *Sterna bengalensis.* Lesser Crested Tern. Kuifkop-seeswael.

Br. and N-Br.

298. *Sterna bergii.* Swift Tern. Geelbek-seeswael. Br., N-Br. and Imm.
299. *Sterna albifrons.* Little Tern. Klein Seeswael. Br. and N-Br.
300. *Sterna balaenarum.* Damara Tern. Damara-seeswael. Br. and N-Br.
303. *Anous stolidus.* Noddy. Bruin Sterretjie.
304. *Chlidonias leucoptera.* White-winged Black Tern. Witvlerk-swartswael.

Br., N-Br. and Imm.

305. *Chlidonias hybrida.* Whiskered Tern. Witbaard-meerswael.

Br., N-Br. and Imm.

305X. *Chlidonias nigra.* Black Tern. Swart Meerswael. Br., N-Br. and Imm.

TERNS

296 SANDWICH
N Br
Imm
295 SOOTY
295 X BRIDLED
294 N Br ARCTIC N Br
293 N Br ROSEATE N Br
292 N Br Imm N Br
ANTARCTIC Imm
291 N Br COMMON N Br
290 X N Br N Br
GULL-BILLED
290 N Br
CASPIAN

LESSER CRESTED
297
N Br
SWIFT
298
N Br
Imm
N Br N Br
LITTLE 299
N Br
N Br DAMARA 300
NODDY 303
N Br
N Br
N Br
W-W BLACK 304
Imm
N Br
N Br 305
N Br
WHISKERED Imm
BLACK 305 X
N Br
N Br Imm

K. NEWMAN '76

311A

312

31 ♂

314

316

315

317

318 ♂ ♀

322

319 ♀ ♂

321

320

323A

323B

323D

NIGHTON '36

PLATE 33

311 *(a). Columba guinea phaeonota.* Rock Pigeon. Bosduif.
312. *Columba arquatrix arquatrix.* Rameron Pigeon. Geelbek-bosduif.
313. *Turturoena delegorguei delegorguei.* Bronze-naped Pigeon.
Withals-bosduif. ♂.
314. *Streptopelia semitorquata.* Red-eyed Turtle Dove. Groot Ringduif.
315. *Streptopelia decipiens ambigua.* Mourning Dove.
Klein Rooioog-tortelduif.
316. *Streptopelia capicola capicola.* Cape Turtle Dove. Tortelduif.
317. *Stigmatopelia senegalensis senegalensis.* Laughing Dove.
Rooibors-duifie.
318. *Oena capensis capensis.* Namaqua Dove. Namakwa-duifie. ♂ and ♀.
319. *Turtur tympanistria.* Tambourine Dove. Witbors-duifie. ♂ and ♀.
320. *Turtur afer.* Blue-spotted Wood Dove. Blouvlek-duifie.
321. *Turtur chalcospilos chalcospilos.* Emerald-spotted Wood Dove.
Groenvlek-duifie.
322. *Aplopelia larvata larvata.* Cinnamon Dove. Kaneel-duifie.
323 *(a). Treron australis delalandii.* Green Pigeon. Papegaai-duif.
323 *(b). Treron australis vylderi.* Green Pigeon. Papegaai-duif.
323 *(d). Treron australis damarensis.* Green Pigeon. Papegaai-duif.

Breeding: Nests are built low or fairly high up in trees outside the forest, or on its border. Only one egg is laid, glossy white, during November to February in the Cape and January to April in Transvaal. Average (9) 39,4 × 29,7 (37,5—41,5 × 27,4—31,5). Incubation by both sexes, 16 days (Kenya). Nestling period 20 days.

LOCAL RACE:
C.a. arquatrix Temminck and Knip, 1809: *Anteniquoi* = *Knysna*. Size above. Africa, another race in Fernado Po.

313 Bronze-naped Pigeon   Withals-bosduif

Turturoena delegorguei (Delegorgue), 1847: *Port Natal* = *Durban*.

PLATE 33 (OPP. P. 225). ♂.
Length 28—30 cm (wing ♂ 180, ♀ 165; tail 100—110; tarsus 19—21; culmen 18). Iris dark brown; bill ashy; ring round eye and legs pink.

Identification: White collar distinctive in male. Female has no white collar and head is brown. Young resembles female but the head and nape are grey.

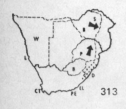

313

Distribution: From Pondoland northwards to Tanzania and the Sudan. Not uncommon in the Ngoye forest, Zululand.
Habits: A rare species which inhabits thick bush and forests. Little is known about it except that it is usually seen in pairs sitting quietly in the tops of tall trees. Feeds in the early morning and again in the evening, scrambling and fighting for fruit in the upper branches.
Food: Berries, wild figs and other fruit.
Voice: A descending series of 7 to 10 "du, du, du's . . ." the first 3 soft and higher pitched than the others.
Breeding: Recorded nesting November to April. The nest typical of a pigeon and placed high (5 to 7 metre) in a tree. Eggs 2, glossy white, measuring about 30 × 22 (Kenya). Both sexes incubate and feed the young.

LOCAL RACE:
T.d. delegorguei (Delegorgue), 1847: *Port Natal* = *Durban*. As illustrated. Southern Africa north to Tanzania.

314 Red-eyed Turtle Dove   Groot Ringduif

Streptopelia semitorquata (Rüppell), 1837: *Taranta Mountains, Abyssinia.*

Native Names: Indlasidudu, Umakhulu (X); le-Evamosu (S); i-Hope (Z); i-Gowara (D); i-Kopoya (G).

PLATE 33 (OPP. P. 225).
Length 33-36 cm (wing 180—192—204; tail 120—142; tarsus 18—23; culmen 15—19. 32 specimens). Iris orange-red, bare skin round eye dark red; bill blackish; legs purplish red. Weight 240—250—261 g. Juv. 177—218 g.

Identification: Large size, darker colour, often with lighter head, and red eye distinguish this species from the Cape Turtle Dove, No. 316. In flight shows grey-brown terminal band on the tail whereas the Cape Turtle Dove shows white. Sexes alike. Young birds lack the black collar, and the skin round the eye is dull grey.

Distribution: From Clanwilliam (recently arrived) eastwards to Transvaal (except the dry west), the northern Kalahari, Angola and northwards on the east to the Sudan and Arabia.

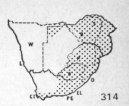

314

Habits: A common but localised species, found in heavy thorn-tree country and riverine lowland forests. A rather sluggish bird spending much of its time in trees but also seeking food on the ground. Like the Turtle Dove, displays by flying steeply upwards, checking and then descending in a planing flight with wings held rigidly out.

Food: Largely berries taken in the trees but also seeds, fruits, tubers and termites.

Voice: Normal call is one of the most characteristic sounds of Africa: "Coo, coo, cook-KOO-kuk coo", the fourth syllable slightly stressed, the last two lower in pitch. This call sometimes starts at different points. Also makes a hoarse "kraa".

Breeding: The nest is placed in a tree, low bush or creeper, even on top of a tree-fern, usually about 2—3 metres up. Breeds from September to April. Eggs 2, occasionally only 1, white. Average (55) 30,8 × 23,8 (27,2—34 × 22,3—25,5).

LOCAL RACE:
S.s. semitorquata (Rüppell), 1837: *Taranta Mountains, Abyssinia.* As above.

315 Mourning Dove   Klein Rooioog-tortelduif

Streptopelia decipiens (Finsch and Hartlaub), 1870: *East Africa = Dongola.*

PLATE 33 (OPP. P. 225).
Length 30 cm (wing 160—167—180; tail 107—118; tarsus 22—24; culmen 18—19. 13 specimens). Iris yellow, skin round eye red; bill brown; legs purplish pink.

Identification: The red skin round the eye prevents confusion with the Cape Turtle Dove, No. 316. Smaller and lighter (almost white) on the belly than the Red-eyed Turtle Dove, No. 314, and with a darker crown. Sexes alike. Young birds are browner than adults. Note pale eye.

Distribution: Eastern Transvaal, the Limpopo and Zambesi valleys, northern Botswana, Kaokoveld to Angola and northwards to the Sudan. Common at Satara camp in the Kruger Park; also Letaba.

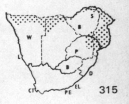

315

Habits: A very tame species, in some localities, frequenting native kraals, Acacia trees along rivers and cultivated areas, searching for food among animals and houses and consequently localised.

Food: Weed seeds and grain.

Voice: Rather quiet, "ku k kurr" sounds, repeated two or three times with some variation. Also a harsh explosive, guttural sound between a growl and a coo made just after landing with raising of the tail.

Breeding: Nests in small trees; 2 eggs, white, are recorded in June and July. Measurements 30,2 × 22,5; 29,5 × 22,6 and 30,3 × 22.

LOCAL RACE:
S.d. ambigua (Bocage), 1881: *Dombé, Southern Angola,* Southern Africa, Angola, Malawi and southern Tanzania.

316 Cape Turtle Dove — Tortelduif

Streptopelia capicola (Sundevall), 1857: *Rondebosch, Cape Province.*

Native Names: i-Hope (Z); Ihobe (X); i-Gugularana (G); i-Dekururu (D); le-Ebana-khoroana (S).

PLATE 33 (OPP. P. 225).
Length 28 cm (wing 148—157—166; tail 90—112; tarsus 18—22; culmen 12—15. 32 specimens). Iris black; bill black; legs purplish red. Weight, Ad. 141—161 g. Juv. 112—147 g.

Identification: Very variable, some light, others almost sooty. Cannot be confused with the other very common dove, the next species, due to its black collar. Sexes alike. Shows *white* tips to tail in flight. Young birds duller with pale edges to feathers.

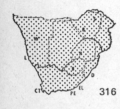

316

Distribution: Throughout Southern Africa northwards to the Sudan and Ethiopia.

Habits: Probably the commonest dove in South Africa and found almost anywhere. Spends much of its time on the ground wandering about in search of food, walking with characteristic bobbing of its head back and forth with each step. Like the Red-eyed Turtle Dove, No. 314, also displays by climbing steeply and soaring down in a spiral, sometimes calling the while. Known to live 35 years in captivity.

Food: Grain and seeds, particularly those of the milkweed *(Euphorbia).*

Voice: Normal call a loud, rather harsh, carrying, coo, "How's father, how's father" or better, "Werk stadig, werk stadig", the accent in both languages being on the *a*. Also a snarling "kooorrr" uttered on alighting.

Breeding: Nests in any convenient tree at any height from 1 to 12 metres and at any time of year but mainly in September to October and April to May. The female builds the nest with sticks brought by the male, who is very particular in his choice of suitable material. The same nest may be used several times. Use of an old Thrush nest also recorded. Eggs number 2, pure white. Average (100) 28,1 × 21,7 (25,4—30,5 × 19,3—23,4). Incubation by both sexes, 12 days (2). Nestling period 16—17 days (3). Both sexes feed the young.

LOCAL RACES:
(a) S.c. capicola (Sundevall), 1857: *Rondebosch, Cape Province.* The darkest race. Cape Province.
(b) S.c. tropica (Reichenow), 1902: *Songea, Tanzania.* Intermediate in colour. Size given above. Transvaal and Natal. North of the Kalahari Desert and Zululand. Outside our limits to Tanzania and Uganda.
(c) S.c. damarensis (Finsch and Hartlaub), 1870: *Damaraland.* Very pale all over. South West Africa, Botswana and Orange Free State.

317 Laughing Dove — Rooibors-duifie

Stigmatopelia senegalensis (Linnaeus), 1766: *Senegal.*

Native Names: Mokuroana, le-Ebana-khoroana, le-Evakoko (S); Ihotyazana (X).

PLATE 33 (OPP. P. 225).
Length about 25 cm (wing ♂ 134—139—147, ♀ 132—137—144; tail 100—115; tarsus 18—21; culmen 13—16,5. 28 specimens, 18 ♂, 10 ♀). Iris black to hazel; bill black; legs purplish red. Weight 76—103—135 g.

Identification: This very common dove has a speckled reddish chest but no black collar. Male brighter and redder on chest. Young birds lack the chest markings, are duller and have brownish heads.

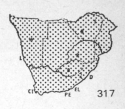

Distribution: Africa south of the Sahara, Arabia and Asia Minor to India.
Habits: One of the commonest and best-known birds in South Africa, often frequenting gardens and a general favourite from its quiet ways and gentle notes. Spends much of its time walking about on the ground in a characteristically hunched-up attitude and taking rather short steps, with the head bent downwards. May form flocks when not breeding. Like the Turtle Doves, flies upwards steeply and planes down again.

317

Food: Seeds and grain crops, occasionally insects such as termites.
Voice: A quiet, gentle, descending, bubbling "cooroocoo-co-coo-coo".
Breeding: The nest is generally placed in low trees about 3 metres from the ground, sometimes higher—up to 6 metres or so—but quite often almost at ground level. It is a flimsy platform of sticks and may be used several times., Eggs are laid throughout the year but mainly in the periods September to October and March to April. Two is the normal clutch, white and glossy. Average (71) 26,1 × 20,1 (24,1—29,5 × 19,1—22,8). Incubation is by both sexes. Nestling period 14½—17½ days. The young leave the nest rather prematurely and are often picked up by well meaning people who think they have fallen out too soon. They should be left where found.

LOCAL RACE:
S.s. senegalensis (Linnaeus), 1766: *Senegal*. Africa south of the Sahara.

318 Namaqua Dove   Namakwa-duifie

Oena capensis (Linnaeus), 1766: *Cape of Good Hope*.

Native Names: Isavukazana (X); le-evanakhoroana (S); Letsebaru (Ch); i-Gomboza (Z).

PLATE 33 (OPP. P. 225) ♂ AND ♀.
Length 27 cm (wing ♂ 102—107—112, ♀ 102—103—106; tail 125—150; tarsus 13—15. 23 specimens, 17 ♂, 6 ♀). Iris brown; bill, base purple, apex orange; ♀ bill blackish; legs purple. Weight 39—45 g.

Identification: The long tail prevents confusion with any other dove. Sexes different as illustrated. Young birds resemble the female but are barred below, the feathers of the back tipped with black, white and buff.
Distribution: Senegal and the Sudan to Cape Town. Also Malagasy and Arabia.

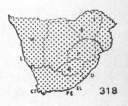

Habits: Quite a common species in the drier areas of South Africa. Usually seen searching for food on the ground in old cultivated lands or gardens, where it walks rather hunched up. Seldom perches at any height, usually on fences or low bushes. Flies very fast, showing cinnamon wings. After alighting raises the tail and lowers it slowly. Seems to be some extent migratory, appearing in larger numbers at different times of the year. Drinks at midday.

318

Food: Small seeds, teff particularly favoured.
Voice: A low note, sounding like "twooh, hoooo", the first syllable explosive.
Breeding: Nests low down on dry bushes, aloes, or even on dry twigs of small trees that have fallen to the ground. The nest is rather more solid than most doves' nests and is lined with fine rootlets. Eggs 2, cream or pale yellow, rather pointed; may be laid at any time of year, with peaks in May and

September to November. Average (69) 21,5 × 15,8 (19,5—24,5 × 14,7—17,7). Incubation by both sexes, 13—16 days. Nestling period 16 days.

LOCAL RACE:
O.c. capensis (Linnaeus), 1766: *Cape of Good Hope.* Throughout Africa and Arabia. Another race in Malagasy, size above.

319 Tambourine Dove   Witbors-duifie

Turtur tympanistria (Temminck and Knip), 1810: *S. Africa = Gamtoos River, Cape.*

Native Names: Isavu (X); isi-Belu (Z); isi-Bambalam (G); Chipuri (D).

PLATE 33 (OPP. P. 225) ♂ AND ♀.
Length about 23 cm (wing ♂ 113—117—120, ♀ 111—115—119; tail 80—95; tarsus 18—21; culmen 15—17. 18 specimens, 12 ♂, 6 ♀). Iris brown; bill and legs purplish.

Identification: The only dove with white face and under-parts. Bars on rump faint. Female not as white below as illustrated. Young birds have eyebrow, sides of chest and flanks barred and tinged rufous while the tail is rufous and lacks the bar found in the adult; feathers of upper-parts edged with buff.

319

Distribution: From Swellendam district eastwards to eastern border of Rhodesia and northwards to West and East Africa.

Habits: Inhabits rather dense bush through which it is able to fly swiftly, dodging with facility. Feeds entirely on the ground and can often be found where there are Castor Oil plants. Usually found singly or in pairs. Riparian habitat favoured further north.

Food: Weed seeds, grain and particularly Castor Oil plant seeds. Termites.

Voice: A mournful series of "dus" similar to the next species but ending more rapidly, almost in a rattle; does not descend the scale.

Breeding: The nest is the usual platform of twigs and roots, placed in a small tree. Eggs 2, creamy white, laid from October to December, between September and May in Rhodesia. Average (24) 24,1 × 18,2 (22,8—25,3 × 17,3—19). Incubation by both sexes.

LOCAL RACE:
T.t tymparistria (Temminck and Knip), 1810: *S. Africa = Gamtoos River, Cape.* As above.

320 Blue-spotted Wood Dove   Blouvlek-duifie

Turtur afer (Linnaeus), 1766: *Senegal.*

PLATE 33 (OPP. P. 225).
Length 22 cm. (wing 111—113—117; tail 79—84; tarsus 17—19; culmen 13—15. 6 specimens). Iris brown; bill red, tip yellow; legs purplish red.

Identification: Very similar to the next species but has a *red* beak with a yellow tip; the wing spots are blue, not green. With *practice* may be differentiated from the next species in flight by showing no grey in the colour of the upper-parts which the Emerald-spotted Wood Dove shows. Sexes alike. The young bird resembles the young of the Tambourine Dove, No. 319, but has the belly buff, not white.

Distribution: West and Central Africa coming within our limits as far as Beira and Louis Trichardt, northern Transvaal. Confined to the eastern border of Rhodesia.

Habits: Frequents rather heavier woods than the next species and in many parts is thus more or less confined to stream and river banks. Also found in clearings in evergreen forest. Like the next species is often flushed along roads.

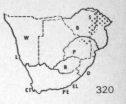

320

Food: Seeds.

Voice: Similar to that of the next species but more muffled; the call slower and cut off in the middle of the final descending run.

Breeding: The nest is the usual flimsy structure of rootlets and thin plant stems, placed in a tree usually about 3 metres up. Recorded nesting in December; August in Rhodesia. Eggs 2, slightly glossy and cream or distinctly buffy in colour. Measurements: 23,4 × 17,5, 22,7 × 17,2 and 22,5 × 16,9.

321 Emerald-spotted Wood Dove   Groenvlek-duifie

Turtur chalcospilos (Waglet), 1827: *Terra caffrorum = Eastern Cape Province.*

Native Names: isi-Kombazana (Z); isi-Vukazana (X).

PLATE 33 (OPP. P. 225).
Length 20 cm (wing 112—115—123; tail 70—80; tarsus 16—18; culmen 13—15. 13 specimens). Iris brown; bill blackish; legs purple.

Identification: The green wing-spots, black bill and in flight greyer appearance differentiate this species from the last. Sexes alike. Young birds similar to those of the last species but secondaries blacker; no bars on rump.

Distribution: From about Worcester north-eastwards to Ethiopia and across the northern Kalahari to Angola.

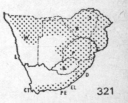

Habits: A common bird of wooded country and dry thornveld savannas where water is available. Frequently to be seen in clearings and is common on dirt roads in the late afternoon. Rises with remarkable suddenness, giving a clap with its wings as it does so. Also lands abruptly and immediately raises its tail once or twice.

321

Food: Small grain and weed seeds. Also termites.

Voice: One of the most characteristic and monotonous sounds of the bush. Consists of a series of coos, "du, du . . . du; du . . du . . du, du . . dudu, du, du, du, du, du, du, du, du, du", the final run descending quickly. Likened by various native tribes to "My mother is dead! My father is dead! All my relations are dead! Oh, oh, oh, oh, oh . . ."

Breeding: The nest is a platform of sticks and rootlets, usually about 2—3 metres from the ground in a small tree, bush or bamboo. Two cream-coloured eggs are laid from August to June. Average (28) 23,1 × 17,4 (20,6—24,5 × 15,8—18,2). Incubation by both sexes. Nestling period 16 days.

LOCAL RACES:
(a) *T.c. chalcospilos* (Wagler), 1827: *Terra caffrorum = Eastern Cape Province.* Typically dark coloured. Cape Province and Natal.

231

(b) T.c. volkmanni (Reichenow), 1902: *Damaraland.* Lighter coloured. Size given above. South West Africa to Botswana.
(c) T.c. zambesiensis Roberts, 1922: *Zimbiti.* Zululand northwards and Mozambique. Paler than *(a)*.

322 Cinnamon Dove
Kaneel-duifie

Aplopelia larvata (Temminck and Knip), 1810: *Le pays d'Antiniquoi*
= *Knysna.*

Native Names: Indenge (X); i-Gwanjiya (G).

PLATE 33 (OPP. P. 225).
Length 25-30 cm (wing ♂ 150—153—158, ♀ 147—149—153; tail 90—105; tarsus 24—28; culmen 12,5—14. 25 specimens, 15 ♂, 10 ♀). Iris, centre dusky, rim pink; bill black; bare face pink; legs dark pink.

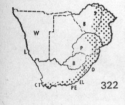

Identification: Not likely to be confused with any other dove. White face and cinnamon under-parts diagnostic. Young birds have dirty white faces and no metallic sheen; most feathers broadly tipped with rufous. A beautiful bird at close quarters.
Distribution: From Cape Town, where it is quite common, eastwards to Ethiopia.
Habits: A quiet bird, usually found on the ground in dense forests or plantations of exotic trees. More often heard than seen in its gloomy habitat, but quite common in suitably thick cover. If disturbed, flies or perches low down in the undergrowth. Usually observed scratching around in the debris under the trees. Carries its tail rather high when walking.
Food: Berries and seeds. Also small insects.
Voice: Very quiet; a peculiar low but resonant "hoo-oo", uttered with slight back and forth movement of the head, has been described. Also a rodent-like squeak, every 3 seconds, repeated 10—30 times.
Breeding: The nest is placed only just above the ground in matted creepers or bushes on the border of glades. Eggs 2, creamy white to yellowish. Average (8) 28,3 × 22,1 (26,9—29,9 × 20,9—23,6). Laid October to April in Natal, in Rhodesia July, August, December to March. Fledgeling period 21 days.

LOCAL RACE:
A.l. larvata (Temminck and Knip), 1810: *Le pays d'Anteniquoi* = *Knysna,* Southern Africa to Kenya, other races in West Africa.

Family TRERONIDAE

The Fruit Pigeons are characterized by their green or yellowish plumage, stout bill, with the basal part soft, short legs, with the tarsus feathered on the upper-part, soles of the toes broadened; they subsist upon soft berries and fruit, particularly wild figs, and when feeding are so cryptically coloured that they are not easily seen, but may usually be noticed when using their wings, with which they make a sound like a switch rapidly flicked through the air. Sensitive birds which may die of fright at the sound of a gun.

323   Green Pigeon   Papegaai-duif

Treron australis   (Linnaeus), 1771: *Madagascar.*

Native Names: Intendekwane (X); i-Jubantonto (Z); Lekhoalepa, Lephui (Ch); i-Huruti (D).

PLATE 33 (OPP. P. 225), RACES *(a)*, *(b)* AND *(c)*.
Length about 30 cm (wing ♂ 171—175—179, ♀ 162—168—174; tail 88—110; tarsus 20—25; culmen (hard part) 12—14; soft part of bill 7—9, 37 specimens, 22 ♂, 15 ♀). Iris pale blue; bill bluish grey, cere bright scarlet; legs orange to vermilion, feathered "trouser" yellow.

Identification: The only green pigeon in our area. Young birds lack the mauve wing patch. Sexes alike, female may have narrower grey collar.
Distribution: From Great Namaqualand and the eastern Cape Province northwards to the Sudan.
Habits: These beautiful birds are quite common in well-timbered areas, particularly where wild fig trees are found. They are usually found in thickly foliaged trees where they are difficult to see. While feeding they adopt all sorts of peculiar attitudes, even hanging upside down like parrots. Most often seen in parties. Flight very rapid; when high up the tails appear noticeably short. When perched in trees, if not feeding, remain perfectly still.
Food: Fruit, mainly figs, berries; Chapin records earth in the stomach.
Voice: A shrill whistling cry, quite unlike other doves. Recorded as "tweti-tweti-tweti" followed by two or three popping clicks. In the Congo as "Oh well, very well (soft); getting rich, getting rich (harsh quick), that's so, that's so (fainter, slower)".
Breeding: The nest is frail platform of sticks placed, often at some height, in a leafy tree. Eggs 2, sometimes only 1, are laid from October to January; pure white. Average (43) 30,4 × 23,6 (28,3—32,3 × 21,7—25,7).

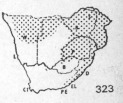

323

LOCAL RACES:
(a) T.a. delalandii (Bonaparte), 1854: *Durban, Natal.* As figured on Plate 33. Top of tail green. Size above. From Humansdorp in the eastern Cape Province northwards to Zululand, Transvaal, E. Botswana and Matopos.
(b) T.a. vylderi (Gyldenstolpe), 1924: *Queveb, Great Namaqualand.* As figured on Plate 33 No. 323. South West Africa, except the north east.
(c) T.a. schalowi Reichenow, 1880: *Diamond Fields = North-eastern Botswana.* Yellower than *(a)*, top of tail green. Northern Botswana and mid-Zambesi Valley.
(d) T.a. damarensis (Reichenow), 1901: *Nukuna, Okavango River.* As figured on Plate 33. Tip of tail green. Wing ♂ 179—183 (4), ♀ 174—180 (4). Ovamboland and the Okavango River.
(e) T.a. orientalis Gunning and Roberts, 1911: *Vila Perveista P.E.A.* Mozambique and eastern Rhodesia.
(f) T.a. ansorgei Hartert and Goodson, 1918: *Huila, S. Angola* Cunene River.

324 = 323 *(a)*

325 = 323 *(c)*

Family PSITTACIDAE

Parrots are well known as cage-birds and hardly need description: the bill is strong and curved, sharply pointed at the tip, the mandible short, stout and squared, adapted to cracking hard kernels; the maxilla is hinged at the base so that the bill can be moved up and down. In climbing about the branches of

trees the bill is used to grip the branches while the feet are being moved forward. The toes are placed two in front (the middle ones) and two behind (the outer ones) and are stout, with strong curved claws, and longer than the tarsus. The plumage is firm, usually green, though brown in one case in South Africa, with yellow and red ornamental patches. They nest in holes excavated in the trunks or branches of trees and subsist upon fruit, berries, kernels of some fruit, and even grain at times. They constitute an old family of birds, widely dispersed over the warmer parts of the world and containing many different forms.

326   Brown-necked Parrot   Knysna-papegaai

Poicephalus robustus   (Gmelin), 1788: *Patr. ignot = Eastern Cape Province.*

Native Names: Isikhwenene (X, Z and G); Chiwhangwa (D); i-Hokwe (G).

PLATE 34 (OPP. P. 240).
Length 33—35 cm (wing 214—218; tail 90—97; culmen 33—35; mandible width 17,5—20; mandible height 22—22. 5 specimens). Iris reddish brown; bill whitish brown; legs bluish grey.

Identification: The only large parrot in our area. The red forehead, chin and shoulder are distinctive. Males have no red on forehead, females may or may not have. Young birds have red on forehead but not on wings and thighs.

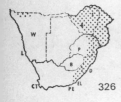

326

Distribution: Alexandria forest eastwards to Natal and Zoutpansberg; Ovamboland and Rhodesia northwards to West Africa and Tanzania.

Habits: Not uncommon, but rather restricted in its habitat, being common in some areas and rare in others quite close by. Essentially a bird of the forests and thick bush. Usually seen in small parties, either clambering about in the trees or flying high overhead with loud screams. Very regular in their visits to feeding grounds.

Food: Berries and fruits.

Voice: A single loud, harsh scream.

Breeding: Nests are placed high up in the dead trunks of trees where they are extremely difficult to reach. Eggs, glossy white, rather rounded in shape, usually 4 in number, are laid from September to October and May; March to June, October and November in Rhodesia. Average (9) 35,1 × 28,8 (32,8—39,2 × 26,6—30,2). Both sexes incubate, 24—28 days. Fledgling 67—72 days.

LOCAL RACES:
(a) P.r. robustus (Gmelin), 1788: *Eastern Cape Province.* Head greenish yellow. Size above. Alexandria to eastern Transvaal.
(b) P.r. suahelicus Reichenow, 1988: *Bagamoyo, Tanzania.* As illustrated on Plate 34. Head brownish grey often suffused with red, more so in male. Wing 210—218—227; culmen 34—42 (13). Rhodesia, Mozambique and across to Ovamboland. To the north over Central Africa.

327   Meyer's Parrot   Bosveld-papegaai

Poicephalus meyeri   (Cretzschmar), 1826: *Kordofan.*

PLATE 34 (OPP. P. 240).
Length 22—23 cm (wing 147—153—158; tail 63—75; culmen 18—22. 14 specimens). Iris red-orange; bill greenish horn; legs blackish.

Identification: Only likely to be confused with Rueppell's Parrot but rump and belly green, not blue. Sexes alike. Young birds have no yellow on forehead; little yellow on shoulder; coverts and wing-feathers edged with green and leg-feathers green.

Distribution: Transvaal and northern Damaraland northwards to the Sudan.

Habits: The common parrot of the dry thornveld. Occurs in small parties and is seldom found far from water. Flight low and fast. When disturbed in a tree they dive steeply out of it before flying off at great speed.

Food: Fruit and berries; maize and kaffir corn.

Voice: A high-pitched "chee-chee-chee"; also a double clinking call, one note higher than the other, used for "conversational" purposes.

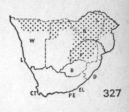

327

Breeding: Nests in holes bored into upright tree stems and lays 2 or 3 white eggs, March to August and October in Rhodesia. November also recorded in Transvaal. Average (12) 25,4 × 20 (24,7—27,8 × 19,3—21).

LOCAL RACES:
(a) *P.m. damarensis* Neumann, 1898: *Ochimbora*. Lacking the yellow frontal band and longer in the wing. Wing 160—165; tail 75—80; culmen 21—22,5. Damaraland.
(b) *P.m. transvaalensis* Neumann, 1899: *Limpopo River, W. Transvaal*. As illustrated. Size above. Western Transvaal to Ngamiland.

328 Brown-headed Parrot   Bruinkop-papegaai

Poicephalus cryptoxanthus   Peters, 1854: *Inhambane*.

PLATE 34 (OPP. P. 240).
Length 22-24 cm (wing ♂ 146—156—160, ♀ 145—153—156; tail 58—75; culmen 18—23,5. 30 specimens, 18 ♀, 12 ♀). Iris greenish yellow; bill, upper half horn, lower white; legs black.

Identification: Shows no yellow at rest but in flight under wing-coverts show bright yellow. Sexes alike. Young paler than adult, the neck suffused with dull yellow.

Distribution: Zululand, eastern Transvaal, eastern Rhodesia and Mozambique northwards to southern Kenya.

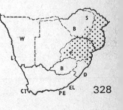

328

Habits: Quite a common species which soon attracts attention by its noisy habits. Usually seen in pairs or small parties clambering about in thick foliaged trees, where it is very difficult to see, or flying fast overhead. Sometimes perches on conspicious places such as dead tree or palm trunks. Very fond of Cashew Nut trees in Mozambique.

Food: Fruit, maize, nuts and corn.

Voice: A very loud, harsh, ear-splitting shriek.

Breeding: Nests in hollow logs during the winter, June to July. Eggs 3—4, white, shiny and rounded, measuring 33,5 × 26.

329 Rueppell's Parrot   Bruin Papegaai

Poicephalus rueppellii   (Gray), 1848: *French Guinea = Damaraland*

PLATE 34 (OPP. P. 240). ♀.
Length about 23 cm (wing ♂ 145—148—153, ♀ 135—143—147; tail 69—75; culmen 13,5—16. 18 specimens, 13 ♂, 5 ♀. Weight ♀ 120 g.

Identification: The blue rump and belly are distinctive. Male has blackish brown rump; female has blue rump. Young birds resemble the female but lack yellow on the shoulder; under wing coverts duller yellow.

Distribution: Damaraland to coastal Angola.

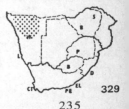

329

LOVEBIRDS

Habits: Usually encountered in pairs or small parties in the tops of tall trees where they are very difficult to see while at rest. Flight short and swift. Said to visit water twice a day.

Food: Seeds and berries; also the buds and pods of various species of *Acacia*.

Voice: A shrill intermittent cry which increases in frequency before the bird leaves its perch when disturbed.

Breeding: A nest is described in what appeared to be an old woodpecker's hole about 4 metres up in a large *Acacia* tree. The eggs, three in number were heavily incubated, ivory white and averaged 27,3 × 24; this was in February.

329X   Ring-necked Parrakeet   Ringnek-parkiet

Psittacula krameri   (Scopoli), 1769: *Senegal.*

PLATE 34 (OPP. P. 240).
Length 40 cm (wing 130—135; tail 170; tarsus 13). Iris whitish; bill red with dusky base; legs grey.

Identification: The only parrot in our area with a long graduated tail. Sexes similar but female lacks the black facial markings and pink collar. Young birds resemble the female.

Distribution: Central Africa, India, Pakistan and south-east China. In our area near Sordwana Bay, Zululand and Durban.

Habits: Little recorded here as yet; seen flying about in a flock of some 60 birds. Whether established by movement down the east coast from Zanzibar, or by the breeding up of escapees, is not known. In India moves about in parties which unite in the late afternooon to form dense flocks at established roosts.

Food: Berries, fruit and grain.

Voice: A loud scream. Particularly noisy when gathering to fly to the roosts.

Breeding: Nests in holes in trees, laying 4—5 white eggs.

LOCAL RACE:
P.k. borealis (Neumann), 1915: *Assam, India.* Northern India, Pakistan and south-east China. This is the race introduced to Zanzibar.

330   Rosy-faced Lovebird   Rooiwang-parkiet

Agapornis roseicollis   (Vieillot), 1817: *Interior of the Cape of Good Hope.*

PLATE 34 (OPP. P. 240).
Length 17—18 cm (wing 102—106—109; tail 44—52; culmen 16—18,5. 13 specimens). Iris brown; bill greenish yellow; legs grey.

Identification: The blue rump distinguishes this species from the Nyasa Lovebird, No. 332. Sexes alike. Young birds have paler faces and chests, cere brownish.

Distribution: Lower Orange River northwards to Angola.

Habits: A plentiful and sociable species where it occurs. Prefers dry, mountainous or open country, but is very dependent on water, which may be located by watching evening flights of this bird to drinking pools. At certain times of the year, when their favourite seeds are ripening, may gather in flocks

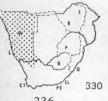

330

of many hundreds. Sometimes sleep in empty nests of the White-browed Weaver, No. 780.

Food: Berries and seeds; may do harm to crops planted near its haunts.

Voice: A harsh "shreek", uttered singly when quiet but if excited, repeated rapidly. Noisy on the wing.

Breeding: Nests are built in crevices among rocks or else compartments of Social Weaver's nests are used, the rightful owners, in some cases, probably being turned out. May also nest in roofs of houses. The nesting material is carried held in the feathers of the rump. Eggs 4—6, dull white, laid during February to April. Average (18) 23,5 × 17,3 (20,4—26,2 × 16,3—18,7). Incubation 23 days, fledgling 43 days.

LOCAL RACE:
A.r. roseicollis (Vieillot), 1817: *Interior of the Cape of Good Hope*. South West Africa. Another race in Angola.

331 Black-cheeked Lovebird   Swartwang-parkiet

Agapornis nigrigenis Sclater 1906: *Ngwezi River, Kalomo, Northern Rhodesia.*

PLATE 34 (OPP. P. 240).
Length 13—14 cm (wing 93—96; tail 36; culmen 14—15). Iris yellow in young, changing to red-brown; bill red, white at base; legs grey; ring round eye whitish.

Identification: The black cheeks prevent confusion with the next species: Sexes alike. Young birds may have some black on the mandible and are duller.

Distribution: The Caprivi east to Livingstone.

Food: Fruit and seeds.

Voice: A shrill chatter.

Breeding: As for the next species. Eggs 3—6, white 19,4—21 × 15—15,8.

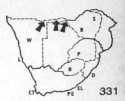

LOCAL RACE:
Sometimes considered a race of No. 332.

332 Nyasa Lovebird   Niasa-parkiet

Agapornis lilianae Shelley, 1894: *Liwonde, Nyasaland.*

PLATE 34 (OPP. P. 240).
Length 13—14 cm (wing 70—91; tail 36,5; culmen 14—15). Iris hazel; bill pale red; ring round eye bluish flesh; legs flesh.

Identification: Smaller than the Rosy-faced Lovebird, No. 330, and with green, not blue rump. Female has paler face and neck than male. Young birds resemble female.

Distribution: Malawi and north-eastern Rhodesia to the Zambesi Valley.

Habits: Rather local and subject to local movements, when they occur in large flocks. Visit water regularly. Inhabits Mopane and Acacia woodland.

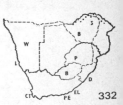

LOERIES

Food: Seeds and berries. Also flowering trees such as *Acacia*.
Voice: A shrill chatter, rather like the rattling of a chain, though shriller.
Breeding: Nest in hollows in trees. Nesting material is carried in the beak (cf. No. 330). Eggs 4—5, white. Average (9) 21,9 × 16,2 (21—22,8 × 15,6—16,6).

Family MUSOPHAGIDAE

The Loeries or Turacoes are peculiar to Africa. They are forest or savanna birds of medium size, those of the forests of beautiful plumage in green, purple and red, sometimes with white and red in the wing quills, those of the savannas plainly coloured. The red pigment has been shown to contain from five to eight per cent of copper in the pigment, and the green coloration is due to green pigment and not refraction, both peculiarities that are not found in any other birds. They lay white or greenish white eggs on frail platforms of sticks, no better than those made by doves, hidden in the branches of trees or matted creepers. They have peculiar harsh cries and feed exclusively upon berries and fruit, the species usually very local in habitat where their favourite food occurs.

333 = 336 *(d)*
334 = 336 *(e)*
335 = 336 *(c)*

336 Knysna Loerie   Knysna-loerie

> *Tauraco corythaix*   (Wagler), 1827: *Knysna*.

> Native Names: Igolomi (X); i-Gwalagwal (Z).

PLATE 34 (OPP. P. 240), RACES *(a)* AND *(e)*.
Length about 47 cm (wing 170—181—190; tail 195—228; tarsus 35—44; culmen 20—25; crest from base of culmen 45—60. 28 specimens). Iris brown; bill orange-red; legs black.

Identification: Unmistakable. Sexes alike. Young birds are duller and have less red in the wings; bill brownish.

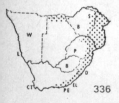

336

Distribution: From George eastwards to Natal, eastern Transvaal, Mozambique, eastern Rhodesia westwards to Angola and northwards to Central Africa.
Habits: Essentially a bird of the evergreen forests, happily still quite common where it is not harassed. In flight the beautiful red wings show to best advantage; the sight of a loerie in flight is almost a tourist attraction. Flight is buoyant but quite strong, the bird usually landing in the centre of a tree after a downward glide, and then hopping with amazing agility to the top. Also takes prodigious hops among the branches, the bird appearing as if mounted on springs, so light is the contact with the branch at the end of each bound; may also run along large branches with legs well bent, raising its tail after stopping.
Food: Mainly fruit, especially wild figs and Kaffir Plums.
Voice: A loud series of "kok, kok, kok's" slowly rising and increasing in volume and then dying slowly away. Also a rattling gargling alarm note and a quiet guttural hissing sound, the latter uttered with the head thrown right back onto the shoulders.

Breeding: The nest is a shallow platform of sticks rather like a large dove's nest and is placed in a tree or in thick creepers. Eggs 2, white and smooth shelled. Lays September to February in Rhodesia. Average (12) 38,8 × 33,3 (36—40,9 × 31,6—35,7). Incubation 22(c) days. Nestling period 20 days (Priest).

LOCAL RACES:
(a) T.c. corythaix (Wagler), 1827: *Knysna.* As figured in Plate 34. Size above. From George to St. Lucia in coastal *and* inland forests; north of St. Lucia only in inland forest.
(b) T.c. phoebus Neumann, 1907: *De Kaap, Barberton, Transvaal.* Bluer on the lower wings and back than *(a)*. Wing 172—181—185 (8). Eastern Transvaal, Zoutpansberg and Swaziland.
(c) T.c. reichenowi (Fisher), 1880: *Nguru Mountains, Tanganyika.* Similar to *(d)* but the lower back, ends of scapulars and base of tail blue instead of green. Wing 177—181—189 (6). Crest 62—83. Northern Zululand from St. Lucia to Mozambique to Tanzania.
(d) T.c. livingstonii Gray, 1864: *Manganja Highlands, Nyasaland.* Wing 170—178—186 (11); crest 66—81. North-eastern Rhodesia. Mozambique and Malawi.
(e) T.c. schalowi (Reichenow), 1891: *Novo Redondo, Angola.* As figured, Plate 34. Wing 176—181—185 (4). Crest 80—110. West of *(d)* from the upper Zambesi Valley westwards to Angola and southern Zaïre.

337 Purple-crested Loerie   Bloukuif-loerie

Tauraco porphyreolophus (Vigors), 1831: *Inland of Africa from Algoa Bay = Durban, Natal.*

Native Names: i-Gwalagwala (G); i-Hurukuru (D).

PLATE 34 (OPP. P. 240).
Length about 47 cm (wing 168—179—192; tail 180—210; tarsus 35—40; culmen 24—28. 35 specimens). Iris dark brown; bill and legs black.

Identification: The purple crest is distinctive. Sexes alike.
Distribution: From Pondoland to eastern Rhodesia and Mozambique; beyond our limits to Uganda.
Habits: A fairly common species which inhabits much drier country than the last. Typical of trees along streams but also of the grassy woodlands, heavier thorn scrub and to a certain extent the lower evergreen forests. In the drier parts such as Rhodesia it keeps to riverine forest until the rains come, when it spreads as pairs up the smaller tributaries and into the adjoining woodlands. General habits similar to the last species.

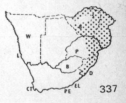

337

Food: Fruit, including wild figs, Mobola and Kaffir Plums.
Voice: A series of loud, explosive "krooks", which precede shrill wailing notes.
Breeding: The nest is similar to that of the last species. Eggs 2, glossy white. They are laid from November to January. Average (16) 37,1 × 34,5 (35—40 × 33,4—35,8).

LOCAL RACES:
(a) T.p. porphyreolophus (Vigors), 1831: *Durban, Natal.* As figured in Plate 34. Size given above. Natal and Mozambique to the Zambesi; southern Rhodesia.
(b) T.p. chlorochlamys (Shelley), 1881: *Ugogo.* Wing 174—185—199; other dimensions as in *(a)*. Lower Zambesi Valley northwards to Uganda. Birds from middle Zambesi probably intermediate between *(a)* and *(b)*.

PLATE 34

326 *(b). Poicephalus robustus suahelicus.* Brown-necked Parrot.
Knysna-papegaai.
327. *Poicephalus meyeri transvaalensis.* Meyer's Parrot. Bosveld-papegaai.
328. *Poicephalus cryptoxanthus.* Brown-headed Parrot. Bruinkop-papegaai.
329. *Poicephalus rueppellii.* Rueppell's Parrot. Bruin Papegaai. ♀.
329X. *Psittacula krameri.* Ring-necked Parrakeet. Ringnek-parkiet.
330. *Agapornis roseicollis.* Rosy-faced Lovebird. Rooiwang-parkiet.
331. *Agapornis nigrigenis.* Black-cheecked Lovebird. Swartwang-parkiet.
332. *Agapornis lilianae.* Nyasa Lovebird. Niasa-parakiet.
336 *(a). Tauraco corythaix corythaix.* Knysna Loerie. Knysna-loerie.
336 *(e). Tauraco corythaix schalowi.* Knysna Loerie. Knysna-loerie.
337. *Tauraco porphyreolophus porphyreolophus.* Purple-crested Loerie.
Bloukuif-loerie.
339. *Corythaixoides concolor concolor.* Grey Loerie. Kwêvoël.
393. *Apaloderma narina narina.* Narina Trogon. Bosloerie.
418. *Upupa africana.* African Hoopoe. Hoephoep.
419 *(a). Phoeniculus purpureus purpureus.* Red-billed Hoopoe. Kakelaar.
419 *(d). Phoeniculus purpureus damarensis.* Red-billed Hoopoe. Kakelaar.
421. *Rhinopomastus cyanomelas cyanomelas.* Scimitar-billed Hoopoe. ♂.
Swartbek-kakelaar.
455. *Pitta angolensis.* Angola Pitta. Angola-pitta.

240

326B

327

328

329 ♀

329X

330

331

332

A

E

336

339

337

418

393

421 ♂

A

D

419

455

KN

N. LIGHTON.
'38

341

340

346

345

343

344

344x

KN

347

349

358

348

353

356

355

357

354

NIGHTON.
'38

PLATE 35

340 *(a). Cuculus canorus canorus.* Cuckoo. Koekoek.
341. = **340** *(b). Cuculus canorus gularis.* African Cuckoo.
Afrikaanse Koekoek.
343. *Cuculus solitarius.* Red-chested Cuckoo. Piet-my-vrou.
344. *Cuculus clamosus.* Black Cuckoo. Swart Koekoek.
344X. *Cercococcyx montanus.* Barred Long-tailed Cuckoo.
345. *Pachycoccyx audeberti validus.* Thick-billed Cuckoo. Dikbek-koekoek.
346. *Clamator glandarius choragium.* Great Spotted Cuckoo.
Groot Gevlekte Koekoek.
347. *Clamator levaillantii.* Striped Cuckoo. Gestreepte Nuwejaarsvoël.
348. *Clamator jacobinus serratus* (white-breasted phase).
Jacobin Cuckoo. Nuwejaarsvoël.
349. *Clamator jacobinus serratus* (black-breasted phase).
Jacobin Cuckoo. Nuwejaarsvoël.
353. *Centropus grillii.* Black Coucal. Swart Vleiloerie.
354. *Centropus cupreicaudus.* Coppery-tailed Coucal. Groot Vleiloerie.
355. *Centropus sengalensis flecki.* Senegal Coucal. Senegal-vleiloerie.
356. *Centropus superciliosus loandae.* White-browed Coucal. Vleiloerie.
357. = **356** *(b). Centropus superciliosus burchellii.*
Burchell's Coucal. Vleiloerie.
358. *Ceuthmochares aereus australis.* Green Coucal. Groen Vleiloerie.

339 Grey Loerie   Kwêvoël

Corythaixoides concolor   (A. Smith), 1833: *Inland of Port Natal.*

Native Names: Mokoe, Mokoenete (Ch); u-Mdhluwe, u-Mxuwe (G)

PLATE 34 (OPP. P. 240).

Length 47—50 cm (wing 203—210—223; tail 225—260; tarsus 34—39; culmen 23—26; crest 62—79. 13 specimens). Iris brown; bill and legs black.

Identification: Sexes alike. Young birds are more ashy grey and have short crests.

Distribution: From Zululand northwards to Tanzania and Zaïre; from the Transvaal westwards to the Kalahari and South West Africa.

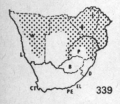

339

Habits: A common and conspicious species, well known to hunters because of its "go-away" call which it is fond of uttering when intruded upon, often following the hunter and thus alarming the animals he is bent on shooting and causing no little annoyance. Usually seen in small parties, flying rather heavily one after the other from tree to tree and slipping out on the far side often unobserved. In trees they clamber and jump about with great dexterity in seach of their food, raising and lowering their crests a great deal if alarmed. Usually found near water and thus absent from the dry central Kalahari, though it has been stated that they can live without permanent water.

Food: Fruit, flowers and other vegetable matter, insects and even small birds.

Voice: The most characteristic call is a loud drawn-out "go-away" or "kweh", hence the popular name, "Goaway Bird". Also various cat-like howls and shrieks. When angered goes "brump, brump".

Breeding: The nest is the usual dove-like structure, often so thin that the eggs can be seen from below, placed in a thorn tree or sometimes a soft-foliaged tree up to about 8 metres from the ground. Eggs 2—3, white faintly tinged with blue, smooth and slightly glossy. Average (35) 41,4 × 33,0 (38,2—44,6 × 31,5—34). Young birds leave the nest when about half-grown (2 to 3 weeks old) and clamber about in the branches near the nest. As they get older they do not even sleep in the nest. They are able to fly at about 6 weeks. Breeds throughout the year but mainly September to October and February to June.

LOCAL RACES:

(a) C.c concolor (A. Smith), 1833: *Port Natal.* With only a trace of greenish on the breast, crest shorter, sides of face less pallid grey. Size above. Zululand and eastern Transvaal.

(b) C.c. bechuanae Roberts, 1932: *Gaberones, Bechuanaland.* Slightly paler than *(a)* with a distinct suffusion of green on breast; sides of face not as pale as in *(c)*. Crest between *(a)* and *(c)*. Size slightly larger than *(a)*. Wing 207—217—224; crest 66—81 (16). Rhodesia, western and northern Transvaal and Botswana. Ngamiland.

(c) C.c. pallidiceps Neumann, 1899: *Benguela, Angola.* Very marked suffusion of green on breast, sides of face palest, crest longest. Wing 201—212—223; crest 73—88 (16). Great Namaqualand and northwards to Angola.

Family CUCULIDAE

The Cuckoos and Coucals are zygodactylous birds (that is, with the outer toe reversible to the back), with fairly strong bills, arched slightly, smooth and rather pointed, with the nostrils near the base: all have 10 primaries and 10 tail-feathers, the former usually narrowing to a point at the tip, and forming a

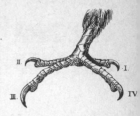

rather pointed wing in most species, but the outermost primary usually only about half the length of the longest, which is generally the third outermost primary; the tail is usually fairly broad and long, but variable in the different genera. The colour, too, varies considerably in the different genera. All the true Cuckoos have the hind claw short and curved, and correlated with this are parasitic in their nesting habits, with one exception amongst our species in the Centropine genus *Ceuthmochares*, which has a curved hind claw and makes its own nest. The true Coucals differ from the true Cuckoos in having a long, straight hind claw and build their own nests. They are put into a distinct family by some authorities, but as the gap is somewhat bridged by *Ceuthmochares* the distinction can hardly be regarded as more that that of a subfamily. The true Cuckoos feed very largely upon caterpillars, even the hairy ones that other birds may avoid, while the Coucals are more carnivorous in their diet, consuming small birds found in nests, small mammals and lower vertebrates, besides insects and larvae. They all have very distinctive call-notes, to know which is to know the species. The family is widely dispersed over the globe, with a fair number of genera and species, but never very plentiful and usually solitary in habits.

340   Cuckoo   Koekoek

Cuculus canorus   Linnaeus, 1758: *Sweden.*

PLATE 35 NOS. 340 AND 341 (OPP. P. 241).
Length 30—33 cm (wing ♂ 212—219—224, ♀ 204—206—209; tail 144—168; culmen 23—26. 16 specimens, 10 ♂, 6 ♀). Iris yellow; bill yellow with tip black (see below); legs yellow.

Identification: Two illustrated. The African cuckoo has the beak mainly yellow with a black tip; the European has only the very base of the bill greenish. The African race has complete bars across the tail-feathers. Females have a brownish wash across the chest. Young birds (African) are completely barred below, grey above with white tips to the feathers; bill black.

Distribution: Europe, western Asia and Africa. European birds migrate to Africa and African birds migrate south within Africa. In our area both races come as far south as Damaraland on the west and eastern Cape Province on the east. Also near Bredasdorp and Sedgefield.

Habits: Not a common species in South Africa and remarkably little has been recorded about it. Occurs principally in the thornveld. European birds recorded as arriving in September and departing in January (Rhodesia); African birds occur from October to March.

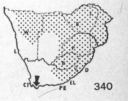

Food: Mainly hairy caterpillars.

Voice: A loud, melancholy "hoop-hoop" rather like the African Hoopoe and with the accent on the second syllable unlike the European birds which call "*Cuck*-oo"; the latter are silent in Africa.

Breeding: Little is recorded about the parasitism of the African Cuckoo. An oviduct egg is a pale green blue with mauve and brown spots and measures 24 × 18. Another oviduct egg is cream marked with irregular blotches and spots of rufous and mauve 24,8 × 17. The main host here is the fork-tailed Drongo. The young eject eggs or young of their fosterers. Breeds November-January. Nestling naked and black; mouth orange.

LOCAL RACES:
(a) C.c. canorus Linnaeus, 1758; *Sweden.* Slightly larger than *(b).* Wing ♂ 216—228, ♀ 200—223 (Europe ex *Handbk. Brit. Birds*). Europe and western Asia. Other races in east Asia. Illustrated as **No. 340.**
(b) C.c. gularis Stephens, 1815: *Camdeboo = Graaff-Reinet, Cape Province.* Size above. Africa. Illustrated as **No. 341.**
(c) C.c. subtelephonus Zarudny, 1914: *Russian Turkestan.* Much paler grey above, especially on the head. Recorded from Beira and eastern Rhodesia.

342 Lesser Cuckoo   Klein Koekoek

Cuculus poliocephalus Latham, 1790: *Srinagar, Kashmir.*

Length about 28 cm; wing 152—174; tail 134—156; culmen 19—22. Iris brown; bill black, mandible green; legs yellow.

Identification: Not figured. Similar to the previous species but much smaller and more boldly marked below.
Distribution: A single specimen recorded from Durban, Natal. It is not uncommon in East Africa. Also from eastern Rhodesia. Secretive in its habits remaining in mid forest level, usually silent.
Voice: A loud distinctive "ko-ko-ko kof".

LOCAL RACE:
C.p. poliocephalus Latham, 1790: *Srinagar, Kashmir.*

343 Red-chested Cuckoo   Piet-my-vrou

Cuculus solitarius Stephens, 1815: *Caffraria = Eastern Cape Province.*

Native Names: Pezukomkono (Z); Uphezukomkhono: um-Gubilitshane (X).

PLATE 35 (OPP. P. 241).
Length about 30 cm (wing 172—175—184; tail 145—160; culmen 20,5—23. 17 specimens). Iris dark brown; bill-maxilla blackish, mandible yellow, tip grey; legs yellow. Weight 66,5 g.

Identification: The reddish chest distinguishes this bird from the Cuckoo, No. 340. Sexes alike. Young birds have white edges to feathers of upper-parts. Chick shiny black; back flat but concave while ejecting an object; nostril round, inside of mouth orange.
Distribution: Occurs in tropical Africa south of the Sahara, migrating to South Africa from late September to March. There are winter-sight records for the Cape. Penetrates as far as Cape Town but avoids the dry west.
Habits: A species of the forests and thickly wooded kloofs which has also taken to plantations of exotic trees such as pines, gums and wattles. An extremely noisy bird, calling for hours on end, chiefly in the early morning and evening but also at any hour of the day and even in the middle of the night. In spite of its noisy habits is not often seen as it perches high up in thickly foliaged trees, keeping very still, only shaking slightly as it calls.
Food: Caterpillars, beetles, grubs and a few seeds recorded.
Voice: A loud, ringing, descending "whip . . . whip . . . wheeooo", the third note loudest and slurred downwards; uttered by the male and giving rise to popular name "Piet my vrou". Also a "kwik, kwik" seldom heard. Females make a low gurgling sound. Fledglings make a "tzeep, tzeep".

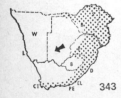

343

Breeding: Parasitic on the Chorister, Natal and Cape Robins but mainly the Cape Robin. Other recorded hosts are Cape Wagtail, Cape Rock Thrush, Kurrichane Thrush, White-throated, Swynnerton, Bearded and Starred Robin, Stone Chat and other less usual species. Only one egg per nest is deposited (2 recorded rarely), usually uniform, shiny chocolate or olive, but sometimes blotched with reddish brown. Average (15) 24,6 × 18,4 (22,8—26,4 × 17,2—19,3). Incubation period 13—15 days. The chick evicts eggs or young of its host for the first four days after it hatches. Nestling period 17½—22 days.

LOCAL RACE:
C.S. solitarius Stephens 1815: *Caffraria* = *E. Cape Province.*

344   Black Cuckoo   Swart Koekoek

Cuculus clamosus   Latham, 1801: *Cape of Good Hope.*

Native name: Unomtan'ofayo (X).

PLATE 35 (OPP. P. 241).
Length about 30 cm (wing 167—176—184; tail 141—155; culmen 22—27. 25 specimens). Iris dark brown; bill black; legs pinkish brown.

Identification: The only all-black cuckoo with no crest, cf. No. 349. Shows no white "window" in wings in flight. Occurs in what appear to be two phases, either plain black or finely barred with rufous on chest, under tail-coverts and tail. Sexes alike. Young birds lack white spots on sides of tail and are browner black than adults. Chick is dark purple; nostril *round* and prominent; back flat, not hollowed.

Distribution: Tropical Africa, migrating to South Africa from late October to March and penetrating as far as Damaraland on the west and Port Elizabeth on the east. Recently in the Cape Peninsula.

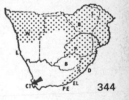

344

Habits: A bird of the open thornveld savannas and fairly thick thornbush country. Quite common in some areas, often congregating in small flocks of half a dozen. Sits boldly in the open. Shortly after arrival, begins its maddeningly monotonous call which continues all day and night for the first month or more. Many are shot by exasperated farmers who can stand the noise no longer. Flight fast and swerving. Appears hunched up when at rest, most of its body below the perch which is about at chest-level.

Food: Caterpillars and other insects.

Voice: A mournful, weary "whoo, whee" or "whoo, whoo, whee" or even "whoo, whoo, whee, whee", rising a minor third (from the whoo to the whee) and slurring into the major. Also when excited, a rapid whirling "yowyowyowyowyowyowyow" rising in pitch and volume and then dying away. Young birds asking for food make a "sweet" noise.

Breeding: Parasitic on shrikes, particular the Boubou, No. 709. Also recorded in the nests of Black Flycatcher, Black-headed Oriole and young being fed by Black-eyed Bulbul, Puff-back Shrike, Crimson-breasted Shrike and Black-crowned Tchagra. Authentic eggs are rare; an oviduct egg is described as white, tinged with grey, with small light brown and brownish violet speckles and flecks. Similar eggs have been found in nests but were not proved by being allowed to hatch. They measure 23,2—24 × 17—17,9 (3). Another fairly authentic egg is described as reddish brown with small speckles of

245

reddish brown and bluish grey concentrated at the thick end, 24 × 17, in a Boubou's nest. Accurate egg data are urgently required. Nestling period not more than 21 days. Chicks appear to eject eggs or young of the host after the first 48 hours.

LOCAL RACE:
C.c. clamosus Latham, 1801: *Cape of Good Hope.* The only race to visit South Africa; also occurs in East Africa. Other races in West Africa and in Zaïre.

344X   Barred Long-tailed Cuckoo

Cercococcyx montanus   Chapin, 1928: *Kalongi, Congo.*

PLATE 35 (OPP. P. 241).
Length 33 cm (wing 144—155). Iris brown; bill blackish above, yellowish brown below; feet and toes yellow.

Identification: A long tailed Cuckoo, brown with buff bars above. Wings and tail browner with pale edges to feather tips. Buffish below with broad bars from chin to lower chest in adult but to tail in young birds.
Distribution: From West Africa across to Uganda south. Recently collected on the Haroni-Lusitu junctions, eastern Rhodesia. Also Mozambique north of the Save River.
Habits: A lowland evergreen forest species very shy and retiring. The call is unusual.
Voice: A long call that builds up to a crescendo. First 4 to 5 "hwee-hooas" then two mellower "hwee-huoo's" then up to 25 "kwee kwews" crescendo, concluding "hwee-hwee-huy-huy".
Breeding: An egg laid in a cage measures 21 × 15; similar eggs, white with a faint band of brownish spots round the thick end have been found in Broadbill nests.

LOCAL RACE:
C.m. patulus Friedmann, 1928: *Bagilo, Tanganyika.* As above.

345   Thick-billed Cuckoo   Dikbek-koekoek

Pachycoccyx audeberti   (Schlegel), 1879: *Ambodikilo, Antongil Bay, Madagascar.*

PLATE 35 (OPP. P. 241).
Length about 36 cm (wing 215—235; tail 160—210; tarsus 24—25; culmen 26—30). Iris brown; bill black above, yellow below; eyelids and legs yellow.

Identification: The only cuckoo with white under-parts and no crest. The bright yellow eyelids are conspicuous. Note the comparatively short and barred tail. Young birds are black-and-white on the head and mantle; tips of all wing and tail-feathers white; might thus be confused with the next species, but the piebald head is distinctive and the wing-spots are three times as large.
Distribution: Malagasy; eastern Transvaal and Rhodesia northwards to Kenya and across to West Africa.
Habits: Not common; inhabits savanna woodland and fairly thick forest at low levels. Stated to be very restless, always moving about in trees or flying short distances and uttering their characteristic calls. The long wings and

345

hawklike stance lead to identification confusion in the field. Its movements are slow and deliberate. Appears to be resident.

Food: Caterpillars, mantises and other insects including grasshoppers.

Voice: A series of querulous notes like a goshawk. Expressed "Chee-cher-cher-cher Cher-cher".

Breeding: Parasitic on the Red-billed Helmet Shrike. An oviduct egg is described as thin-shelled, pale greenish blue in colour with scattered small brown and greyish brown speckles.

LOCAL RACE:
P.a. validus (Reichenow), 1879: *Muniuni, Tana River, Kenya.* As illustrated; size above. Eastern Transvaal, Rhodesia and Mozambique north to Kenya and across to Angola.

Ad.

Imm.

346

346 Great Spotted Cuckoo　　Groot Gevlekte Koekoek

Clamator glandarius (Linnaeus), 1758: *Gibraltar.*

PLATE 35 (OPP. P. 241).
Length 37—40 cm (wing 180—198—200; tail 180—201; tarsus 28—31; culmen 26—33. 29 specimens). Iris dark brown; bill blackish brown, paler at base of mandible; legs brownish.

Identification: Large birds easily identified by their crests and spotted backs. Sexes alike. Young birds resemble adults but have weak crests; forehead and crown blackish, spots on back smaller, throat and chest orange-buff; flight feathers rufous.

Distribution: Africa and southern Europe. Comes as far south as the eastern Cape Province and Damaraland. Recorded in the Kalahari National Park and Saldanha Bay.

Habits: A summer visitor to South Africa from September to April, the birds which visit us coming from Central Africa. A noisy species which flies about in the tree-tops but descends to lower levels when seeking food, even seeking it on the ground. Fairly common in suitable areas of fairly open wooded country.

Food: Hairy caterpillars.

Voice: A loud, harsh, rasping oft-repeated "keeow". Alarm note, a short "kawk". Female has a bubbling "burroo-burroo".

Breeding: In South Africa known to parasitise the Black Crow, Pied Crow, Raven, Pied Starling, Long-tailed, Pale and Red-winged Starling, Glossy Starling (*L. nitens*) and Burchell's Starling. May lay several eggs in a nest, up to 13 recorded in Rhodesia (two females). Eggs greatly resemble those of the Pied Crow, being pale greenish with evenly scattered numerous tiny speckles and some larger, irregularly disposed markings of slate-grey and slate-brown. Average (41 from Southern Africa) 30,7 × 21,6 (29—35,2 × 22,6—28). The young cuckoos do not eject the chicks of their host but are reared in amity with them but late-hatched chicks of either species may die. Nestling period at least 18 days. September to February.

LOCAL RACE:
C.g. choragium Clancey, 1951: *Hlobane, Natal.* Africa south of the Equator. As illustrated; size above. The nominate race (larger) also visits our region but does not breed here (Clancey).

347   Striped Cuckoo   Gestreepte Nuwejaarsvoël

Clamator levaillantii   (Swainson), 1829: *Senegal.*

PLATE 35 (OPP. P. 241).
Length 38—40 cm (wing 176—181—187; tail 215—237; tarsus 27—30,5; culmen 27—31. 13 specimens). Iris dark brown; bill black; legs slate-blue.

Identification: The larger size and heavy streaking of the chest should prevent confusion with the rather similarly coloured Jacobin Cuckoo, No. 348. Sexes alike. Young birds are brown above, buffy below; crest shorter than in adults and have no white tips to tail-feathers.

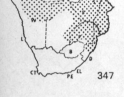

Distribution: Africa south of the Sahara. Migrates to South Africa from October to May, coming as far south as Natal, Transvaal, Botswana and Damaraland. Occasionally further south, Albany and once from Swellendam and Agulhas, but specimens required.

Habits: Not very common in our area, usually seen perched in a dense bush or tree uttering its characteristic call. Essentially a bird of deep evergreen forest.

347

Food: Caterpillars.

Voice: Normal call commences with a hollow-toned "kur, kur, kur", repeated about a dozen times, followed after a short pause by a rapid series of about twenty "kwi, kwi" notes, dying away at the end (Chapin).

Breeding: Parasitic on babblers such as the Arrow-marked and perhaps the Pied Babbler in our area. One or two other doubtful hosts have been recorded but not proved; bulbuls are also probably used. Oviduct eggs are uniform pale glossy blue to greenish blue, somewhat pitted, measuring 26,0 × 20,4. November to May in Rhodesia. The chick does not attempt to eject the host's eggs or young. Chicks are fed for at least 36 days after leaving the nest. Incubation 11 days.

348   Jacobin Cuckoo   Nuwejaarsvoël

Clamator jacobinus   (Boddaert), 1783: *Coromandel Coast of India*

PLATE 35, 2 PHASES, NOS. 348 AND 349 (OPP. P. 241).
Length 33—34 cm (wing 152—156,5—162; tail 173—182—195; tarsus 24—26; culmen 23,5—25,4—27. 27 specimens). Iris dark brown; bill black; legs dark grey.

Identification: Occurs in two phases, one black-breasted and the other white below with grey on throat and chest. Both phases may be distinguished from other cuckoos by their black crests and white wing-patches. Sexes alike, of either phase. Young birds are black or grey below *from the first plumage.* Chick black; back convex and nostrils *oblong and not protruding*; cf. No. 344.

Distribution: Southern Asia and Africa south of the Sahara. A breeding migrant which arrives in October and departs in March. Penetrates as far as Damaraland on the west and Knysna on the east, occasionally as far as Cape Town where it was reported as common, about a century ago, by Andrew Smith.

348

Habits: Quite a common species, the black or grey breasted forms appearing to be quite common in some areas and either uncommon or quite absent in others. Rather restless, does not sit on one perch and call for hours like the Black Cuckoo but spends much of its time flying about in pairs; flight straight

and swift; when entering a tree often aims low and swoops up into the branches from below.
Food: Caterpillars.
Voice: A variety of notes; a loud ringing "kleeuw-wee-wip"; an uncontrolled guttural "gee-gee-geegeegee-gee-geegee-goo"; "pewp, pewp, pewp".
Breeding: The main hosts of this species are the Sombre Bulbul, Layard's Bulbul and the Fiscal Shrike. Other minor hosts are the Forktailed Drongo, Bokmakierie, Boubou Shrike Terrestrial Bulbul, Cape Bulbul, Cape Wagtail, Cape Tit-babbler, Fiscal Flycatcher and Paradise Flycatcher; other less well authenticated hosts have been recorded. Normally 1 egg is deposited per nest, 2 are not uncommon, while 3, 4 and even 7 have been recorded. A black-breasted chick and a grey-breasted chick have been found together, fully grown in a Fiscal Shrike nest (J. Spence). Eggs are white and glossy. Average (27) 26,5 × 21,9 (24,1—28,2 × 20,8—24). Incubation period 11 days. Eviction of eggs or young of the host is weakly developed in this species; it *may* occur within the first 24 hours, but usually the young of the host merely become trodden into the bottom of the nest and die, to be removed by the parent. Nestling period 14 days.

LOCAL RACE:
(a) C.j. jacobinus (Boddaert) 1783: *Coromandal Coast of India*. Breeds in India, Burma, etc. Recorded from Rhodesia, Mozambique and Natal as non-breeding migrant.
(b) C.j. pica (Hemprich and Ehrenberg) 1833: *Ambukohl, Dougob, Sudan*. Visits northern South West Africa and Botswana. Also non-breeding recorded in Rhodesia and Transvaal.
(c) C.j. serratus (Sparrman), 1786: *Cape of Good Hope*. As illustrated, measurements of pale breasted phase, **No. 348**, given above. Black-breasted birds, **No. 349**, seem slightly smaller and shorter-beaked: wing 145—154—160; tail 165—175—192; tarsus 24—27; culmen 20—22,5—25. (16 specimens). Africa south of the Sahara.

350 Emerald Cuckoo   Mooimeisie

Chrysococcyx cupreus (Shaw), 1792: *Gambia, West Africa.*

Native Names: Bantwanyana (Z); i-Nchalayandayandai (G); Intananja (X).
PLATE 36 ♂ AND ♀ (OPP. P. 256).
Length 18—22 cm (wing ♂ 109—113—115, ♀ 106—108—111; tail ♂ 85—97, ♀ 75—81; tarsus 14—17; culmen 17—19. 16 specimens, 12 ♂, 4 ♀). Iris dark brown; bill pale green; legs lead-blue.

Identification: Males easily identified by their green chests and yellow bellies; females differ from female of Klaas's Cuckoo by being barred with *green*, not brown, below; from the female Diederik by its fine bars below and by lacking white spots on secondaries and wing-coverts. Young birds are yellowish below and resemble the female but males have white tips to the feathers of crown and nape; which avoids confusion with a young Klaas's which has brown barring on green on the crown; young females are similar to Klaas's, q.v.
Distribution: From Knysna eastwards and northwards over Africa south of the Sahara.
Habits: A species of forested areas, where it is not uncommon. The absence of winter records seems to point to the species being migratory in South Africa; however, it is usually procured by following its call-note, and if it is silent in winter it may have been overlooked. Tends to keep high up in large trees and is thus more often heard than seen. Recorded from late September to

350

January. Males sing from the same tree day after day and drive off any other males which approach. Flight rapid and somewhat undulating.

Food: Mainly hairy caterpillars but also other insects and odd seeds.

Voice: A loud, clear whistled "Pretty Georgie" or "teeu-tu-tui"; uttered as a rule from high up in a tree.

Breeding: Several hosts have been recorded in South Africa but few have been proved. The Bleating Bush Warbler has been seen feeding young. Elsewhere in Africa the Puff-back Shrike, bulbuls, sunbirds, Paradise Flycatcher, a Prinia and several species of weaver bird have been seen feeding young Emerald Cuckoos. A white egg found in a warbler's nest at Bedford hatched into a young cuckoo of this species; one oviduct egg was pure white, another was white speckled with purple. Only one egg is laid in a nest.

LOCAL RACE:
(a) C.c. cupreus (Shaw), 1792: *Gambia, West Africa.* Reaches our area along the Okavango River. Wing ♂ 105—117 but tail longer than in *(b)*, ♀ 101—131.
(b) C.c. sharpei van Someren, 1922: *Ifafa Road, Natal.* Southern Africa. As illustrated; size given above.

351   Klaas's Cuckoo   Meitjie

Chrysococcyx klaas (Stephens), 1815: *Senegal = Platte River, Cape Province.*

PLATE 36 ♂ AND ♀ (OPP. P. 256).
Length about 18 cm (wing ♂ 96—102—106, ♀ 100—104—106; tail 69—80; tarsus 14—17; culmen 16—18. 28 specimens, 22 ♂, 6 ♀). Iris brown; bill greenish brown, tip black; legs greenish.

Identification: Sexes as illustrated but female sometimes like male. Female differs from female Diederik by having *fine* barring on flanks and no white spots on secondaries and wing-coverts. Young may be distinguished from young Diederiks by having black beaks and from young Emerald cuckoos by white earpatch. See also under young of No. 350.

Distribution: Africa south of the Sahara and Arabia.

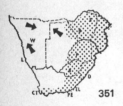

351

Habits: A common species of the savannas and rocky hills; undoubtedly a migrant in places, but there is evidence to show that it remains in the coastal lowlands as specimens have been collected in winter (July). When not calling is inconspicuous and easily overlooked. Arrives (or rather is first heard) in August or September and is usually in evidence until March to April. Females are very retiring and seldom seen but males sit in exposed situations and call interminably, particularly in Spring (October). Named in honour of le Vaillant's faithful Hottentot servant, Klaas.

Food: Caterpillars and other insects.

Voice: A rather mournful "whit jeh", repeated two or three times with pauses of 5—10 seconds between series of calls. The Afrikaans name is onomatopoeic, "Meitjie" and expresses the call pretty closely.

Breeding: In South Africa definitely known to parasitise the Cape, Pririt, Paradise and Dusky Flycatchers, Black and Marico Sunbirds, Greater Double-collared Sunbird (commonly), Bar-throated Apalis, the Crombek, Lesser-masked and Red-headed Weavers. Eggs are very variable: white or pale blue, plain or with reddish or rufous-scattered speckles; also pinkish white, heavily spotted with reddish blotches forming a fairly definite ring around the blunt end. Laid from October to March; about 18 × 13. The chicks eject young of the host.

LOCAL RACE:
C.k. klaas (Stephens), 1815: *Senegal = Platte River, C.P.* As illustrated; size above. Africa, another race in Arabia.

352 Diederik Cuckoo   Diedrikkie

Chrysococcyx caprius (Boddaert), 1783: *Cape of Good Hope.*

PLATE 36 (OPP. P. 256). ♂.
Length 18—20 cm (wing 114—118—125; tail 77—90; tarsus 16—17; culmen 16—19. 51 specimens). Iris red; bill black; legs bluish black.

Identification: Distinguishable from Klaas's Cuckoo by its barred tail, strong white eyebrow (in male), *red* eye, white spots on secondaries and lack of green areas at side of throat and chest. Females resemble males but are duller above and somewhat browner, while below they are more barred and have a reddish wash on chest and throat; eyebrow less distinct. Young birds may be immediately distinguished from young of the last two species by having *coral red bills;* otherwise they are like females but browner on the head and more barred below.
Distribution: Africa south of the Sahara. A migrant in South Africa from late September to March or even as late as April and May. Rarely over-winters in Natal.
Habits: The commonest of the glossy cuckoos in our area, favouring open country, thornveld, or stands of exotic trees such as gums. When breeding, males are very pugnacious and establish territories from which they chase any other males. Females are secretive and quiet but may sometimes be seen being fed caterpillars by males. Flies and glides about with tail spread, calling loudly.

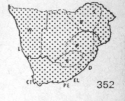

352

Food: Hairy caterpillars and other insects.
Voice: A plaintive and loud "dee, dee, deederik", repeated over and over again with a varying number of preliminary "dees"; the female answers with a "deea-deea-deea".
Breeding: The commonest hosts of this species are various birds of the weaver family, particularly the Red Bishop Bird, the Masked Weaver, the Cape Weaver, Red-headed Weaver and the Cape Sparrow. Other South African hosts include the Yellow-throated Sparrow, Lesser Masked Weaver, Golden Weaver, Cape Wagtail, Spectacled Weaver, Mountain Chat, Titbabbler, Great Sparrow and Marico Flycatcher. Oviduct eggs are unspotted light blue; pale bluish spotted with brown and grey; plain bluish white; pale cream closely freckled and speckled with pinkish brown and violet-grey, or pale-green; apparently the same bird lays similarly coloured eggs. Eggs (14) 20,9 × 14,4 (18,6—25,0 × 13,3—15,6) October to March in Rhodesia. In some cases the female cuckoo undoubtedly removes an egg of the host and usually tries to eat it; in other cases she apparently does not do so. Nestlings eject eggs or young of the host between 2nd and 4th day. Adult cuckoos have been seen feeding young cuckoos reared by their hosts.

353 Black Coucal   Swart Vleiloerie

Centropus grillii   Hartlaub, 1861: *Gabon.*

PLATE 35 (OPP. P. 241).
Length 32—37 cm (wing ♂ 158, ♀ 171, 173; tail 170—190; tarsus 35—38; culmen 25—27. 3 specimens). Iris hazel; bills and legs black.

Identification: The only coucal with a black breast. In non-breeding dress, streaked above tawny and black, below dark buff, spotted on chest and neck, wings and tail as in breeding dress. Sexes alike, female larger. Young birds resemble non-breeding adults but are barred with black on the wings.

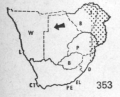

353

Distribution: Natal northwards to Ethiopia and across to Angola and West Africa.
Habits: A fairly rare species in our area, inhabiting long moist grass and in particular grassy vleis, where it tends to remain concealed, only occasionally sitting on an exposed situation, before diving into the grass again.
Food: Insects such as beetles, grasshoppers, mantises and caterpillars.
Voice: Variously described; a soft bubbling; a rapid "popop" and a ventriloquial "coick". Mostly by female. Alarm call "tuck tuck".
Breeding: Its nest is a domed structure of grass, with living strands outside, and is placed in tall grass. Breeds December to March in Rhodesia; eggs 3—6 usually 4. Three eggs taken by Mr. H. W. Bell Marley at Richard's Bay Zululand, on 27th October, 1902, measure 28—29,1 × 24,5—25,5. They are white. Incubation probably by male for the most part. Chicks hatch at intervals and so vary in size. When disturbed they defecate a foul smelling liquid, hiss and growl. Can leave the nest by eleventh day. Fluctuates in numbers apparently with rainfall.

354 Coppery-tailed Coucal   Groot Vleiloerie

Centropus cupreicaudus   Reichenow, 1896: *Angola.*

PLATE 35 (OPP. P. 241).
Length 44—50 cm (wing 210—218—230; tail 235—260; tarsus 46—55; culmen 38—44. 18 specimens). Iris red; bill and legs black.

Identification: Rather resembles Burchell's Coucal, No. 356 *(b)*, but is very much larger with coppery *violet* crown and tail. Sexes alike.

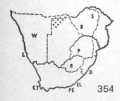

354

Distribution: From Angola to Malawi, coming within our limits on the Upper Zambesi and Ngamiland, where it is not uncommon.
Habits: Frequents the dense reed beds of swampy areas and sometimes strays into the bush adjoining. At times, takes its post on top of the reeds to sun itself and look around.
Food: Almost any small animals they can overpower.
Voice: A deep booming, bubbling sound. Also a harsh crowing note.
Breeding: Nothing recorded from our area. Elsewhere builds a large loose nest of grass and twigs, low down in a tree. Eggs white, three measure 38—38,3 × 26,7—26,9.

LOCAL RACE:
C.c. cupreicaudus Reichenow, 1896: *Angola.* As above.

252

355 Senegal Coucal   Senegal-vleiloerie

Centropus senegalensis   (Linnaeus), 1766: *Senegal.*

PLATE 35 (OPP. P. 241).
Length 35—42 cm (wing 165—179; tail 200—235; tarsus 37—41; culmen 29—32. 4 specimens). Iris red; legs and bill black.

Identification: The unbarred rump, reddish mantle and absence of an eyebrow distinguish this species from race *(a)* of the next species, which it overlaps. Sexes alike. Young birds *have* barred upper tail-coverts but the bases of the tail-feathers are not barred (see next species); head brown streaked lighter.
Distribution: From Senegal to Egypt, south to Ngamiland, northern Botswana and Rhodesia.
Habits: Not common in our area; has much the same habits as the next species, frequenting the bush, scrub and long grass in the neighbourhood of water.
Food: Beetles, grasshoppers, caterpillars, small rodents and reptiles.
Voice: A series of fifteen to twenty tooting notes, descending at first and then rising just before the end. These notes may also be repeated at the same pitch. These calls are uttered with the bill pointed downwards.
Breeding: Nests from November to March in Rhodesia, making a large, loose, domed structure of grass, sticks and leaves, well lined and placed low down in thick cover. Two eggs from Pilane, Botswana, measure 28,1 × 24,3 and 29,7 × 24,1. They are white. Incubation 18, fledging 18—20 days.

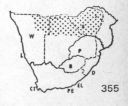

355

LOCAL RACE:
C.s. flecki Reichenow, 1893: *Nukana, Bechuanaland.* As illustrated; size above. From within our limits north to Malawi and southern Angola.

356 White-browed Coucal   Vleiloerie

Centropus superciliosus   Hemprich and Ehrenberg, 1833: *Coast of Yemen, Arabia.*
Native Names: Ubikhwe (X); u-Fookwe (Z); Makhofe (S); i-Gudugudu (D); um-Fuku (G).
PLATE 35, NOS. 356 AND 357 (OPP. P. 241).
Length 38—44 cm (wing ♂ 160—164—172, ♀ 170—176—180; tail 195—230; tarsus 37—43; culmen 28—30. 12 specimens, 6 ♂, 7 ♀). Iris red; bill and legs black.

Identification: The white eyebrow (race *(a)*) and barred upper tail-coverts distinguish this species from the last. Sexes alike but female larger. Young birds have barred bases to the tail-feathers and barred feathers on the back; head brownish black. Nestling is an extraordinary creature, pitch black and leathery with long white hairs above. Race *(b)* known as Burchell's Coucal. Breeds in partly juvenile plumage.
Distribution: From the south-west Cape eastwards to Arabia and across to Angola and the Congo.
Habits: The commonest and best known coucal in South Africa. Commonly found where there are large reed beds, but also in scrub near streams, rivers and dams. Seldom seen on account of its skulking habits but may be seen flying across open spaces with heavy or long gliding flight to the next cover. Much more in evidence when breeding, both on account of its calling

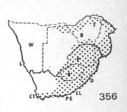

356

253

frequently and because it ventures into the open more. Does not appear to be migratory. Invariably seen singly or in pairs. Basks in the morning sun.

Food: Grasshoppers, mice and any insects or small animals it can manage to eat.

Voice: One of the most characteristic sounds of South Africa; a descending series of rapid, liquid notes, sounding like "doo, doo doo-doo-doo" (about 17 times), rising abruptly at the end; very like water running out of a bottle. Said to presage rain, hence a popular name "rain-bird". Also makes a swearing "kuch" sound.

Breeding: Constructs a large, round, untidy nest of curled broad grass blades or twigs with leaves still on them, lined often with green leaves. It is placed about 3 metres up in a thick creeper, tree or matted thorn bush. Eggs 3—5, white. Average (50) 33,6 × 26,0 (31—37 × 24,6—27,9). Breeds from September to January; also February. Incubation 18 days, starting with first egg. Chicks defecate a foul smelling liquid if threatened. They leave the nest at about 20 days, before they can fly and clamber about in the bush.

LOCAL RACES:
(a) C.s. loandae (Grant), 1915: *Ndala Tando, N. Angola*. Illustrated, as **No. 356;** size above. Zambesi Valley to Zaïre, Kenya and Angola.
(b) C.c. burchelli Swainson, 1838: *Cape Province*. Illustrated as **No. 357.** Wing ♂ 154—164—170, ♀ 167—174—187; tail 190—240; tarsus 39—43; culmen 30—35. 59 specimens, 38 ♂, 21 ♀. Cape Town eastwards to Rhodesia and north on the east to southern Tanzania.

358 Green Coucal   Groen Vleiloerie

Ceuthmochares aereus (Vieillot), 1817: *Malimbe, Portuguese Congo.*

PLATE 35 (OPP. P. 241).
Length about 33 cm (wing 116—127; tail 193—200; tarsus 27—30; culmen 28—31. 5 specimens). Iris red; bill yellow, a black patch on top near base; legs blackish.

Identification: The yellow bill is conspicuous in the field. Sexes alike. Young birds have some brown in the upper wing-coverts, brown eyes and upper mandible dusky.

358

Distribution: From Uitenhage (very rare) eastwards to Uganda and across to the Cameroons, Zaïre and Angola.

Habits: An uncommon resident in our area. A species of the bush along the coast and rivers, or larger forests, which is not often noticed on account of its assimilative plumage and shyness. Spends much of its time creeping and clambering about in thick cover.

Food: Mantises, caterpillars, tree frogs, orthoptera and other insects.

Voice: An extraordinary, loud and distinctive cry, commencing with a loud "tsick" (3 times), becoming more and more rapid "tit-tit-tit-ttt . . ." then changing to a wailing "cheer" (3 times) which also speeds up to a loud "tuk-tuk-tk-tk-tk". Calls "tsick-tsick" as it flies about.

Breeding: The nest is a loosely constructed platform of twigs, with leaves attached, and is placed in dense cover, usually about 3—5 metres up. Eggs, laid in October and November, number 2—4 and are white. Average (7) 29,2 × 21,9 (27,7—31,5 × 20,7—23,1).

LOCAL RACE:
C.a. australis Sharpe, 1873: *Natal*. As illustrated; size above. South Africa to Ethiopia. Other races to the west.

Family TYTONIDAE

The Barn Owls are kept separate from the majority of Owls on anatomical grounds, and externally on differences to be observed in the clearly marked facial disc, and the inner side of the middle toe being pectinated. Two species of this family occur in South Africa, one being the cosmopolitan Barn Owl and the other our Grass Owl; the former is a great boon to farmers in its enormous consumption of small rodents and its habit of taking up its habitation in houses, barns and other buildings. A peculiarity of this species is that it lays its eggs at intervals, so that the last egg may be laid when the eldest of the brood has already assumed its feathers, while the other Owls are more normal in that respect.

359 Barn Owl   Nonnetjie-uil

Tyto alba (Scopoli), 1769: *Friuli, Northern Italy.*

Native Name: Sephooko (S); Isikhova (X).

PLATE 37 (OPP. P. 257).
Length 30—33 cm (wing ♂ 290—298, ♀ 235—287; Tail 115—130; tarsus 58—67; culmen 18—20. 7 specimens, 3 ♂, 4 ♀). Iris dark brown; bill yellow; legs yellow.

Identification: Very similar to the next species but not as dark on the back so that there is less contrast between the back and under-parts. Face heartshaped and *pointed* below, crown little darker than face. See next species. Tail barred; also much smaller. Young birds are darker grey above and washed with buff below.
Distribution: Almost cosmopolitan; throughout our area.
Habits: Commonly found in quiet nooks in buildings when not disturbed, such as church spires, lofts with open windows; also in dark caves, mining tunnels where there are ledges, hollow trees and particularly the deserted nests of the Hamerkop, No. 72. Hunts by night but occasionally comes out on dull days. Farmers who wish to encourage this bird should make sure that there is easy access to the attics of their barns by leaving holes in the gables leading into the upper parts of the roof.

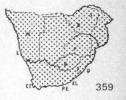

359

Food: Enormous quantities of small rodents. Up to 27% of food is birds in late Spring; Button Quail, Cape Sparrow, Masked Weaver and even Guinea fowl recorded. Undoubtedly a bird of the greatest economic value; should never be molested. Diet normally consists of 80—100% rodents.
Voice: Various ghostly sounds varying from snoring noises to loud screams. Idle superstition is responsible for the death of many of these birds because of their eerie calls; it is believed that a death will occur in a house if a Barn Owl calls on the roof, hence the Afrikaans name "Doodvoël".
Breeding: Eggs are laid on ledges in caves or mines, on bare attic floors and in Hamerkop nests, during the period March to September. They are usually, but not always, laid at intervals, so that the last egg may be fresh when the first chick hatched is nearly ready to leave the nest. They number 5—9 and are white. Average (40) 40,7 × 30,6 (37,8—44,3 × 29—32). Incubation 32—34 days, by female only (Europe). Young fly at about 3 months (Europe).

LOCAL RACE:
T.a. affinis (Blyth), 1862: *Cape of Good Hope =Cape Town.* Throughout Africa except the Sahara and Congo forests.

PLATE 36

350. *Chrysococcyx cupreus.* Emerald Cuckoo. Mooimeisie. ♂ and ♀.
351. *Chrysococcyx klaas.* Klaas's Cuckoo. Meitjie. ♂ and ♀.
352. *Chrysococcyx caprius.* Diederik Cuckoo. Diedrikkie. ♂.
440. *Indicator indicator.* Greater Honeyguide. Groot Heuningwyser.
♂, ♀ and Imm.
441. *Indicator variegatus.* Scaly-throated Honeyguide.
Gevlektekeel-heuningwyser.
442. *Indicator minor minor.* Lesser Honeyguide. Klein Heuningvoël.
442X. *Indicator meliphilus.* Eastern Least Honeyguide.
Oostelike Klein Heuningvoël.
443. *Prodotiscus regulus.* Sharp-billed Honeyguide. Skerpbek-heuningvoël.
444. *Prodotiscus zambesiae.* Slender-billed Honeyguide.
Dunbek-heuningvoël.

351♂

352 ♂

350♂

351♀

350♀

♂

440

♀

440
Imm ♂

441

442x

KN

442

443

444

359

360

365

366

370

362

361

363

A

B

364

369

367

368

KN

NIGHTON
'37

PLATE 37

359. *Tyto alba affinis.* Barn Owl. Nonnetjie-uil.
360. *Tyto capensis.* Grass Owl. Grasuil.
361. *Asio capensis capensis.* Marsh Owl. Vlei-uil.
362. *Ciccaba woodfordii woodfordii.* Wood Owl. Bosuil.
363. *Otus scops.* Scops Owl. Skopsuil. Phases A and B.
364. *Otus leucotis.* White-faced Owl. Witwanguil.
365. *Glaucidium perlatum.* Pearl-spotted Owl. Witkol-uil.
366. *Glaucidium capense.* Barred Owl. Gebande Uil.
367. *Bubo capensis.* Cape Eagle Owl. Kaapse Ooruil.
368. *Bubo africanus africanus.* Spotted Eagle Owl. Gevlekte Ooruil.
369. *Bubo lacteus.* Giant Eagle Owl. Reuse-ooruil.
370. *Scotopelia peli.* Fishing Owl. Visuil.

360   Grass Owl   Grasuil

Tyto capensis   (A. Smith), 1834: *South Africa = Cape Town*

Native name: Isikhova (X).

PLATE 37 (OPP. P. 257).
Length 34—37 cm (wing 325—342; tail 120—130; tarsus 70—78; culmen 19—23).
Iris black; bill white; legs yellow.

Identification: Larger and darker on the back than the Barn Owl; tail not barred; face rounder and crown much darker than face, giving a capped effect. Sexes alike. Young birds have reddish faces and are more golden below.

Distribution: Peculiar to the southern half of Africa, as far north as the Cameroons and Kenya.

Habits: Quite unlike the Barn Owl in habits, frequenting long grass either along streams or near vleis but also in lightly wooded country. When flushed flies a short distance and drops suddenly into the grass.

Food: Probably mainly rodents, its longer bill suggesting that it may attack larger prey than the Barn Owl, for example the Vlei Otomys.

Voice: Hisses loudly.

Breeding: Nests on the ground in long grass; the eggs are said to be laid normally and not at intervals; other authorities, however, say that the young do vary greatly in size in one brood. There is probably much variation in this habit as there is in the Barn Owl. Eggs 3—5, white, laid from October to February. Recorded in May in the Cape and Rhodesia. Average (38) 41,4 × 32,7 (37,4—45 × 30—36). Incubation period about 42 days.

LOCAL RACES:
T.c. capensis (A. Smith), 1834: *South Africa = Cape Town*. As above except in Damaraland.
T.c. damarensis Roberts, 1922: *Damaraland*. Fewer and smaller spots on underparts. Damaraland only.

Family BUBONIDAE

Members of this family are much the same as the preceding *Tytonidae* in general, except that the middle toe nail is not pectinated and the facial disc is not so clearly defined. Some species have crests, resembling ears, but others have not and the species vary considerably in size and structure, some with feathered, others with naked legs, but all of them characterized by their soft feathers and noiseless manner of flying. Most of the species have distinctive cries. None of them construct nests, the eggs being laid on the bare ground, or wood when laid in trees, or upon the nests of other birds, such as hawks and eagles. The eggs are always white and usually more rounded than in the case of the *Tytonidae*.

361   Marsh Owl   Vlei-uil

Asio capensis   (A. Smith), 1834: *Cape Province = Waaiplaats,*
Martindale.

Native Name: Chidyizimbori (D).

PLATE 37 (OPP. P. 257).
Length 36—37 cm (wing 270—285—300; tail 140—155; tarsus 47—52; culmen 16—19, to feathers 27,5—30,5. 23 specimens). Iris dark hazel; bill and legs black.

Identification: Sexes alike. Characteristic "black eyes" and barred tail easily seen. Young birds are deeper coloured than adults.

Distribution: Africa and southern Spain except in dry or heavily forested areas.
Habits: Frequents the long grass in marshy ground. A common and conspicuous species from its habit of flying round its haunts two or three hours before sunset. More gregarious than other owls, perhaps from its concentration in the restricted area of its habitat, and may be flushed in flocks of thirty or forty.
Food: Aquatic insects, frogs, lizards and mice; small birds.
Voice: A peculiar frog-like croak.
Breeding: Lays 3—4 eggs in a grassy hollow on the ground during July to August or March to April. The eggs are white, rather more rounded than those of the Grass Owl. Average (50) 40,4 × 33,7 (37,7—43 × 31,2—36,5).

361

LOCAL RACE:
A.c. capensis (A. Smith), 1834: *Waaiplaats = Martindale, C.P.* Africa as far north as southern Zaïre and Ethiopia. Other races to the north.

362 Wood Owl   Bosuil

Ciccaba woodfordii   (A. Smith), 1834: *South Africa = Knysna.*

Native Names: isi-Kova- esincani, isi-Kova-esibungwini (G).
PLATE 37 (OPP. P. 257).
Length 30—36 cm (wing 233—248—264; tail 145—160; tarsus 38—47; culmen 17—20. 29 specimens). Iris brown; bill yellow, claws black.

Identification: The only medium-sized owl which lacks "ears" (except the distinctive species Nos. 359—60). Variable in ground-colour from blackish brown to deep russet. Sexes alike. Young birds are paler.
Distribution: From Cape Peninsula eastwards to Mozambique and eastern Transvaal; eastern Rhodesia and central Africa as far north as the Sudan and West Africa.
Habits: A fairly common but localised species, frequenting the denser forests and bush; usually seen sitting in a tree or bush close to the main trunk. Has adapted to suburbs in Cape Town.
Food: Mice, small birds, frogs; but mainly insects such as grasshoppers, crickets and caterpillars. Snake once.
Voice: A distinct call note, likened by the Zulus to "weh, mameh" ("Oh, my mother!"). Other renderings are "who are you?" and "hoo-hu, hoo-hu, hu-hu".
Breeding: Nests in hollow logs usually about 3 metres up; the nest hole about 45 cm below the entrance. Sometimes *on* the ground. The same site may be used year after year. Eggs, usually 2, often only 1, rarely 3, white are laid from August to October. Average (10) 44,6 × 37,3 (43,3—46,4 × 35,5—38,4).

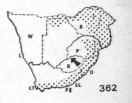

362

LOCAL RACE:
C.w. woodfordii (A. Smith), 1834: *South Africa = Knysna.* Southern Africa, north to Tanzania and Angola.

363 Scops Owl   Skopsuil

Otus scops (Linnaeus), 1758: *Italy.*

Native Names: Kharivisanyane, le-Rivisame (Ch).

PLATE 37, PHASES *(a)*, *(b)*, (OPP. P. 257).

Length 18—20 cm (wing 132—137—143; tail 60—70; tarsus 21—23; culmen 10—12. 12 specimens). Iris yellow; bill and legs bluish horn.

Identification: Might possibly be confused with the White-faced Owl which is the only other *small* eared owl. However, the Scops always shows some brown on the back, has a grey face and is much less clearly streaked above. Sexes alike. Young birds resemble adults. Brown and grey colour-phases occur, lettered *(a)* and *(b)*.

Distribution: From Swellendam eastwards to Natal, rare, northward to southern Europe and across to Angola and West Africa.

Habits: Widely dispersed in the savanna bush; it perches as a rule in trees with greyish bark that matches its plumage but also hides in holes. When alarmed during daylight it often utters a purring chirrup at intervals, and when doing so is extremely difficult to see, unless it happens to move. At dusk searches for its food on the ground.

363

Food: Apparently entirely insectivorous.

Voice: A purring chirruping trill.

Breeding: Nests in holes in trees but very little has been recorded in South Africa about their breeding habits. Eggs are white, 3 from northern Zululand measure 33 × 27—28. Recorded in June, September to November.

LOCAL RACE:

O.s. senegalensis (Swainson), 1837 = *Gambia, West Africa.* Africa south to the Sahara. Some authorities recognize no races, others up to four. There is certainly a tendency for western birds (in South Africa) to be greyer and more closely barred but odd rufous, poorly barred specimens occur among them. The matter is best left in abeyance.

364 White-faced Owl   Witwanguil

Otus leucotis (Temminck), 1824: *Senegal.*

PLATE 37 (OPP. P. 257).

Length 25—28 cm (wing ♂ 190—194—198, ♀ 195—199—206; tail 86—100; tarsus 25—26; culmen 16—19. 23 specimens, 8 ♂, 15 ♀). Iris orange-yellow; bill bluish horn; legs greyish.

Identification: The blackish ears and almost white face are distinctive. Shows a white line along edge of scapulars. See also under No. 363. Sexes alike, female larger. Young birds lack the black streaks on the crown.

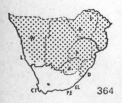

Distribution: From Durban on the east and Orange River on the west, northwards to Senegal and the Sudan. Found in the dry Kalahari.

Habits: A fairly common species of the acacia savannas. Perches during the day in thorn-trees, particularly along the banks of dry water-courses. Usually seen in pairs.

364

Food: Largely insects but many mice, other small mammals and invertebrates.

Voice: The call is a "w-h-h-h-oo-oo", the first part a stammering trill, the "oo-oo" only just audible as bisyllabic. Also makes a low "to-whit, to-wheet".

Breeding: Nests on top of old nests of hawks or other birds, laying 2—3 eggs, during August to November in Rhodesia, July to February in South West Africa and Natal. Also stated to make flimsy nests of its own. Eggs white, slightly glossy. Average (25) 39,7 × 32,8 (37,8—42,3 × 30,6—34,7).

LOCAL RACE:
O.l. granti (Kollibay) 1910: *South West Africa.* Southern Africa to Angola and Tanzania.

365   Pearl-spotted Owl   Witkol-uil

Glaucidium perlatum   (Vieillot), 1817: *Senegal.*

Native Name: Mundungulu (Z).

PLATE 37 (OPP. P. 257).
Length 18—19 cm (wing 104—107—115; tail 72—80; tarsus 20—22; culmen 11—12. 17 specimens). Iris yellow, bill greenish yellow; legs yellow, claws dusky. Weight 88 g.

Identification: The tiny size, lack of ears, and pearl spots on the back should render this species unmistakable. Sexes alike. Young birds almost lack spots on the crown and mantle.
Distribution: From Senegal to Ethiopia southwards (except the Congo forest) to the Orange River and Zululand.
Habits: Not uncommon. To some extent diurnal in habits, as it is often seen flying about in daylight, though actually more active at night. Does not take the same care to hide itself during daylight as the other small owls.
Food: Mainly large insects, small mammals and birds.
Voice: Calls mainly in the early evening, a series of notes ascending an octave and then descending in a slurred single note, "tu, *tu*, *tu*, ti, tii (then down) tia-tia tia tia". Also a 2—3 second whistle, slurring down at the end.
Breeding: Eggs are laid from September to December in holes in trees such as old barbet or woodpecker nests. They are white, usually 3 in number. Average (18) 30,6 × 25,4 (29,3—31,6 × 24—26,4).

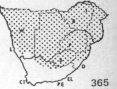

365

LOCAL RACE:
G.p. licua (Lichtenstein), 1842: *Vaal-Orange Junction.* From our area to southern Zaïre, Uganda and Ethiopia.

366   Barred Owl   Gebande Uil

Glaucidium capense   (A. Smith), 1834: *South Africa = Eastern Cape Province.*

PLATE 37 (OPP. P. 257).
Length 20—21 cm (wing 134—139—143; tail 80—89; tarsus 21—24; culmen 12—14. 15 specimens). Iris yellow; bill bluish horn; legs pale yellow.

Identification: No ears. Lacks the spots on the head and back which characterize the last species; slightly larger. Sexes alike. Young birds have the head spotted, not barred.
Distribution: Originally described from the Eastern Cape but not procured there since; from Zululand, Ngamiland and northern South West Africa (rare) northwards to Kenya.

366

Habits: A fairly common species in the denser acacia bush, especially along rivers; its distribution more restricted than that of the Pearl-spotted Owl, but it is also often seen in daylight, perching in quite conspicuous places. Its mate is often in an adjoining tree.

Food: Small vertebrates, also caterpillars and insects including grasshoppers.

Voice: A low "kroo-kroo", also a peculiar bubbling just before sunset. Alarm note a croaking purr.

Breeding: Nests in holes in trees: 3 eggs taken in Boror on 26th September measure 32—34 × 27—27,5. Recorded also in October.

LOCAL RACES:
(a) G.c. capense (A. Smith), 1834: *Eastern Cape Province.* A dark rufous form; fourteen light bars on tail. Eastern Cape, Natal and Zululand west to Angola.
(b) G.c. robertsi Peters, 1940: *Boror, P.E.A.* More rufous than *(a)*, twelve light bars on tail. Mozambique to Tanzania.

367 Cape Eagle Owl   Kaapse Ooruil

Bubo capensis   A. Smith, 1834: *South Africa = Cape Town*

PLATE 37 (OPP. P. 257).
Length 48—53 cm (wing ♂ (5) 330—357, ♀ (12) 363—392; tail ♂ (5) 155—215, ♀ (12) 169—240; tarsus 62—65; culmen 28—29. 5 specimens). Iris orange-yellow; bill and cere black; claws horn.

Identification: Not easy to distinguish from the Spotted Eagle owl, No. 368, but more heavily *blotched* in brown and white on the back and chest; is not finely barred on the belly as in that species. Sexes alike. Eye orange.

Distribution: The southern mountainous belt from Cape Town eastwards to Natal and Zululand and eastern Rhodesia. Extends through East Africa to Ethiopia.

 367

Habits: A rare species; remarkably little has been recorded about its habits. Apparently essentially a bird of mountainous and forested country. Reported to be somewhat diurnal, even attacking its prey in daylight. Data are urgently required.

Food: Any small mammals and birds which it can overpower. Said to attack animals as large as a springhare; hares and dassies mainly.

Voice: A loud, relatively high-pitched, double "whooo whooo", the first note louder than the second. Alarm note "wak wak".

Breeding: Recorded as laying in a tree, but usually on the ground. Also in caves and between rocks during August to December. Eggs 2—3, white. Average (12) 57,5 × 45,3 (46—59 × 45—48).

LOCAL RACES:
(a) B.c. capensis A. Smith, 1834: *South Africa = Cape Town.* Southern Africa. As above in size.
(b) B.c. mackinderi Sharpe, 1899: *Mt. Kenya.* Larger than *(a)* with barring on lower parts reduced. (Wing ♂ 375—402 (8), ♀ 406—428 (5); tail ♂ 184—204 (8), ♀ 200—238 (5) Rhodesia to Kenya highlands.

368 Spotted Eagle Owl   Gevlekte Ooruil

Bubo africanus   (Temminck), 1823: *Cape of Good Hope.*

Native Names: Isihuluhulu (X); isi-Kova (Z and G); Mophooe (Ch); le-Rivise,
le-Siviri (S); i-Kwikwi (D).

PLATE 37 (OPP. P. 257).
Length 43—47 cm (wing 315—340—370; tail 176—220; tarsus 60—70; culmen
20—26. 36 specimens). Iris yellow to orange; bill and legs black. Weight 685 g (20).

Identification: Greyer, and more finely barred below than No. 367. Sexes
alike. Young birds similar but with some smoky barring on head; finely barred
below.
Distribution: Cape Town to southern Arabia, the Sudan and French Guinea.
Habits: The commonest large owl in our area occurring wherever there are
hills and bush, even in fairly open country. Lies up during the day amongst
rocks or in big trees, emerging towards dusk when it may be seen in numbers
on telegraph poles or other vantage points. May become very tame if not
molested; often killed by cars at night.

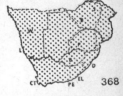

Food: Mice, moles, rats, shrews, lizards, scorpions, great numbers of insects
and very occasionally birds. Pellets measure 45—70 × 20—25 mm.
Voice: A loud "hu-hoo". The male (high) answered by female (low).
Breeding: Nests from July to December with a peak in September to October;
this applies in the Cape or Rhodesia; also rarely during May in the Cape.
Favoured sites are ledges on cliffs, in mines, old wells, houses, hollow trees,
on top of Hamerkop or Social Weavers' nests; sometimes far from cover, just
on the bare ground. Eggs 2 or 3, white. Average (83) 49,9 × 41,7 (45,4—53,2
× 38,6—44,5). Incubation period 32 days.

LOCAL RACE:
B.a. africanus (Temminck), 1823: *Cape of Good Hope.* Southern Africa north to Angola
and Uganda.

369 Giant Eagle Owl   Reuse-ooruil

Bubo lacteus   (Temminck), 1824: *Senegal.*

Native Names: Ifubisi (X); Morubisi (Ch); isi-Kova-isikulu (G); i-Kwikwi or
i-Zizi (D).

PLATE 37 (OPP. P. 257).
Length 58—65 cm (wing 425—451—470; tail 235—275; tarsus 55—63; culmen
35—38. 12 specimens). Iris dark hazel; bill ashy horn, cere bluish grey; claws blackish.

Identification: The huge size and generally pale appearance are distinctive.
Wing span up to 155 cm. Much paler and greyer than illustrated. Sexes alike.
Young has crown, wing-coverts and under-parts barred smoky grey.
Distribution: From George eastwards to Ethiopia; on the west from Orange
River to Senegal. There is an old record from Somerset West. Rare in Natal.
Habits: A widely dispersed species in the acacia savannas where there are
large trees, but nowhere common. Lies up in daylight on the limbs of tall
trees; at dusk may leave and take up its stance on a conspicuous post, uttering
its characteristic call.

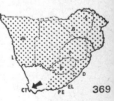

Food: Mammals such as hares, roosting birds up to the size of guinea-fowls, fruit-bats, frogs and insects. A danger to fowls which roost in the open.

Voice: A low, gruff hooting "huhu" followed by a series of "huhu" notes rising in scale. Also a weaker trembling, whistling sound repeated again and again.

Breeding: Nests from June to September, laying its eggs in old nests of other birds of prey, usually 10 metres or more up in trees and often quite conspicuous; sometimes uses a hollow tree. Also on top of Social Weaver's nests. Eggs are white, usually 2 in number, rough and pitted. Average (17) 62,6 × 50,6 (57—66 × 48,5—53,5). Incubation period 25 days.

370 Fishing Owl   Visuil

Scotopelia peli Bonaparte, 1850: *Ashanti, West Africa.*

Native Name: i-Fukesi (Z).

PLATE 37 (OPP. P. 257).

Length about 63 cm (wing 400—430; tail 230—260; tarsus 65—70; culmen 36—38). Iris dark brown, bill black, mandible grey beneath; legs pinkish white.

370

Identification: A large reddish brown owl with no horns and *bare* legs; also distinguishable by having no clearly marked facial disc. Sexes alike, male smaller. Young bird is paler with narrower barring above. Takes 15 months to reach adult plumage.

Distribution: From eastern Cape Province (very rare) northwards to Zululand, Mozambique and Rhodesia, thence to Angola and Ethiopia and across to Senegal. Common in the Okavango.

Habits: A remarkable species which frequents the larger rivers and lakes, subsisting largely on fish, to which its naked feet, long claws and rough soles seem specially adapted. Usually seen in pairs and partially diurnal, often flying about in the late afternoon. Hunts from a perch or bank.

Food: Mainly fish, up to 2 kg and crabs but also stated to take small mammals and even guineafowl.

Voice: Call a "boo-hoo" duet, male high female lower. Followed by a grunt, repeated every 10 seconds for 3-4 minutes. Also a deep snoring sound; also a staccato "kuu-ku-ku" emitted in crescendo, the final note much drawn out; "a weird screechy howl, which rises in a nerve-shattering crescendo, to peter out like a cry of a lost soul falling into a bottomless pit" apparently a contact call between parent and young.

Breeding: Nests are placed in holes in large trees from 5 to 10 metres up; the parent birds rest in the leafy upper branches during the day. An egg measures 59 × 49,2. Eggs in October, December, March and April. Two eggs are laid but only one chick is reared. Chick white with tubular nostrils.

Family CAPRIMULGIDAE

Nocturnal, insectivorous birds of wide distribution in the world, capturing their prey during dusk or darkness while in flight, and having soft plumage, much as in the Owls, but small, weak bills, a wide gape, long rictal bristles, large eyes and weak legs and feet. During daylight they lie up on the ground or flat on the branches of trees, and all are cryptically coloured, though often handsomely marked and sometimes with peculiar structural developments, such as long plumes projecting from the wing or long tails. They look much alike. All of them lay two eggs, usually on the bare ground, but sometimes on open level places on stumps or branches of trees. They get their vernacular name of Nightjar from the jarring, irritating notes that some of them utter at night; Nighthawk, from their similarity to small Hawks, and Goatsucker from their supposed habit of sucking the milk of goats at night, a fallacy founded on their wide mouths and habit of frequenting the vicinity of stockpens at night to catch the insects attracted to the animals.

371   European Nightjar   Europese Naguil ♂

Caprimulgus europaeus Linnaeus, 1758: *Sweden.*

Native Names (generic): isa-Vola (Z); Udebeza (X); le-Uvauva, Maubane, Mmapeke (Ch).

PLATE 38 ♂ AND ♀ (OPP. P. 272).
Length 25—28 cm (wing ♂ 184—198, ♀ 183—195; tail 129—138; 17—19; culmen 8—10. 12 specimens ex *Handbk. Brit. Birds.*) Iris deep umber; bill blackish brown; legs brownish.

Identification: Resembles most the next species, since both have *spots* of white at the end of the tail, on the outer two feathers. Distinguishable by its larger size, absence of orange collar and usually first 3 (rarely 2 or 4) primaries with white spots. Female has no white wing-spots; tips of tail-feathers buff.
Distribution: A migrant from Europe and Asia which does not breed here. May be expected anywhere in our area; there are several old records from the Cape. Probably absent from very dry areas of Bushmanland and Namaqualand.
Habits. Arrives in South Africa during the latter half of September and departs towards the end of March. During the day, almost invariably lies up on branches of big trees, very seldom on the ground.
Food: Beetles, moths, mantises and grasshoppers recorded.
Voice: Call in flight, "coo-ic:"; also uttered just before flight. Alarm notes: ♂, "quick-quick-quick"; ♀ "tchuck". Song a sustained, vibrant, churring trill (Europe), probably not uttered here.

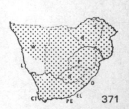

371

LOCAL RACES:
(a) C.e. europaeus Linnaeus, 1758: *Sweden.* As figured in Plate 24. Dark in colour and having a white spot on the second outermost primary which does not extend to the outer web. Inhabits Europe and western Asia, migrating to all parts of our area.
(b) C.e. unwini Hume, 1871: *Agrore Valley, Hazara, North-west India.* Paler in colour than (a); white spots on primary extends broadly across the outer web. Wing shorter, 173—198. Inhabits central Asia, migrating as far south as Natal.
(c) C.e. plumipes Przhevalski, 1876: *north bend of the Hwang ho.* Visits south-eastern Africa.

372   Rufous-cheeked Nightjar   Rooiwang-naguil

Caprimulgus rufigena   A. Smith, 1845: *Eastern Cape Province.*

PLATE 38 (OPP. P. 272).
Length 23—24 cm (wing ♂ 157—164—176, ♀ 149—160—167; tail 114—130; tarsus 17—18; culmen 9—11,5. 42 specimens, 19 ♂, 23 ♀.) Iris dark hazel; bill black; legs flesh.

Identification: Distinguishable from the European Nightjar by the collar of orange-buff round the neck; also has *four* outer primaries with white patches on the inner web, the inner three with white on the outer web. Has no bright rufous *below* the white of throat as the next species has. Female lacks white on tail and has wing-spots buff, not white. Young browner than adults.

Distribution: From the Karoo, eastern Cape Province, East Griqualand, Orange Free State, South West Africa and western Transvaal and Rhodesia. During the period mid-April to mid-September migrates north as far as Nigeria and the western Sudan.

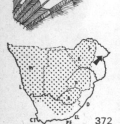

372

Habits: Essentially a bird of the drier west, being found even in desert areas almost free of vegetation. In more normal country lies up during the day among trees.

Food: Insects.

Voice: "Kow, kow, kow"; then purrs like a motorbike. When disturbed a repeated "dug-dug-dug"; also "cquew, cquew, cquewoo, cquewoo". Claps wings.

♂

Breeding: Breeds from September to January, in Rhodesia mainly in October and November. No nest is made but quartz pebbles may lie around the eggs. In South West Africa the eggs are frequently laid on red sand. They number 1 or 2, pinky white, with a thin clouding of darker pink and traces of slate. Average (9) 26,8 × 19,8 (24,7—28,6 × 19—20,6).

373   Fiery-necked Nightjar   Afrikaanse Naguil

Caprimulgus pectoralis   Cuvier, 1817: *Houtniqua* = *Knysna.*

Native Names: Muswerahope (D); i-Savolo (G); Udebesa (X).

PLATE 38 (OPP. P. 272), A AND B.
Length 23—25 cm (wing 160—165—172; tail 118—134; tarsus 15—18; culmen 10—13; length of white on outer tail-feather in ♂ 38—52, in ♀ 23—36. 31 specimens). Iris dark brown; bill and legs brown.

Identification: The most rufous form around the head, thus distinguishable from the Freckled Nightjar. Very like the last species which may have nearly as much white on tail. Sexes alike but the white areas on wing and tail are smaller in the female (see under "length" above).

♀

Distribution: South Africa northwards to Zaïre, Uganda and Tanzania.

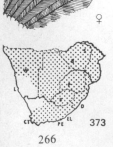

373

Habits: Perhaps our commonest nightjar, at any rate in the Cape Province where its call is one of the most characteristic sounds on moonlit nights. By day usually lies up in the shade of bushes lying lengthways on branches. At night hunts from a fixed perch and does not hawk over a wide area as other species do. Is thus largely a species of wooded areas. Prefers not to take long flights over open ground but is sometimes seen on roads and clearings. Finds exotic trees such as gums and pines very much to its liking.

Food: Insects, beetles and spiders.
Voice: Normal call a musical "wheh wheh", "whehwhehwheh", the second half descending and quavering. The rhythm of the whole phrase is aptly given by the words "Good Lord, deliver us"—hence one of its popular names "Litany Bird". Better perhaps is the Afrikaans "jag weg, die wewenaar". Is reputed to call only from branches of trees, often from quite high up, seven metres or more. Calls mainly on bright moonlit nights, at all hours, but most often just after sunset and towards dawn. Sometimes preceded by a series of rapid "kow, kow, kow's".
Breeding: Eggs are laid on dead leaves and debris under trees; several broods are reared and the same site is used year after year. Breeding occurs from September to December. Eggs 2, salmon-pink with vague markings of darker pink and brown. Very conspicuous when the bird is off them. The brooding bird sits with eyelids closed till only a thin slit remains. Sits very close. Two of race (a) measure 29,8 × 20,5 and 28,8 × 20; those of race (b) smaller, 23—27,2 × 18—19,4 (6). Incubation at least 17 days. Feigns injury when has young.

LOCAL RACES:
(a) *C.p. pectoralis* Cuvier, 1817: *Houtniqua = Knysna*. As figured on Plate 38, **No. 373** (a). Wing 161—166—170 (11). Cape Province, Orange Free State, Natal and southern Zululand.
(c) *C.p. fervidus* Sharpe, 1875: *Ovamboland*. As figured on Plate 38, **No. 373** (b). Sizes given above. North of (a) as far as Zaïre and Tanzania.

374 Freckled Nightjar   Donker Naguil

Caprimulgus tristigma   Rüppell, 1840: *Gondar*.

PLATE 38 (OPP. P. 272).
Length 27—28 cm (wing 175—185—195; tail 123—136; tarsus 15—20; culmen 10—12. 14 specimens). Iris brown; bill and legs dusky.

Identification: Resembles the last species in the amount of white on the tail but lacks the red around the neck; general colour of the back greyer. Larger than the other species except the European. Females lack white in the tail. Young birds are paler and have more rufous primaries than adults.
Distribution: From the drier mountains of the Cape, Transvaal, Rhodesia northwards to West Africa and Ethiopia. Has moved into cities.
Habits: A very localized resident which is essentially a bird of rocky outcrops. Usually found on bush-covered stony kopjes or on bare rocks under the shade of bushes. In Rhodesia is particularly fond of large whale-back granite hills, its colour matching the grey weathered granite almost exactly.
Food: Flying insects such as beetles and termites.

374

Voice: A weird "whow-whow" repeated over and over again, sometimes with three syllables, sometimes with four. Also "Wock, wock, wock" and a higher long series of "whoot-whoot-whoot" notes.
Breeding: Eggs are laid on bare rock or in slight hollows in rocks where gravel and small sticks have collected. Apparently nests on buildings in Durban. Breeds from September to November. Eggs 2, dirty white with a few fine spots of reddish chestnut scattered over the surface or with many very faint blotches of that colour, both with underlying blotches of pale bluish purple. Measurements 28—30 × 20—22. Incubation 18½ days.

LOCAL RACE:
(a) *C.t. lentiginosus* A. Smith, 1845: *Great Namaqualand*. South West Africa and Cape Province, Eastern Botswana and Transvaal.
(b) *C.t. granosus* Clancey, 1965, *48 km from Bulawayo*. Darker and greyer. Larger, wing ♂ 184—205, ♀ 185—205. Rhodesia, E. Botswana, Mozambique N. of Save.

375 Natal Nightjar   Natalse Naguil

Caprimulgus natalensis A. Smith, 1845: *Near Port Natal = Durban*.

PLATE 38 (OPP. P. 272).
Length about 23 cm (wing 150—163; tail 100—110; tarsus 19—20; culmen 9—11). Iris dark brown; bill and legs dusky.

Identification: One of the two species with the whole outer edge of the tail white in males; also has half the outer web of the *second* tail-feather white, Female similar but white of tail buff; wing-spots buff. Young resemble female.
Distribution: From East London to Natal, Zululand and again in the Caprivi; Zambia then to West Africa and Uganda.
Habits: Rare in our area. A very local, resident species found mainly near the coast in our area. Lies up during the day in the grass or dry ferns on the coastal flats, usually near patches of palms, to which it resorts to hide when disturbed. Occurs near grassy or swampy situations.
Food: Insects, particularly beetles.
Voice: A prolonged "chop, chop, chop, chop", or "chuck, chuck", not as rapid as the gurgling of the next species. Also a tremulous "wha-hu-hu-hu" uttered in flight.
Breeding: Eggs are laid on the bare ground from September to November. They number 2, pinky white, very faintly marked with slate. Measurements of two authentic eggs (the bird was shot) are 31,2 × 21,7 and 30,5 × 21,3 (Richard's Bay, in Bell Marley Coll.). Others from the same area measure 28—29,4 × 21—22,2 (4).

LOCAL RACES:
(a) *C.n. natalensis* A. Smith, 1845: *Near Port Natal = Durban*. Natal and Zululand.
(b) *C.n. carpi* Smithers, 1954: *Kabuta, Caprivi Strip*. Upper-side paler than (a); primaries more dusky, less black; buff markings on under-parts paler. Wing ♂ 155—158 (2); ♀ 156—164 (2). The Caprivi.

375

376 Mozambique Nightjar   Laeveld Naguil

Caprimulgus fossii Hartlaub, 1857: *Gaboon*.

PLATE 38 (OPP. P. 272).
Length 23—24 cm (wing 150—156—162; tail 110—119—127; tarsus 14—18; culmen 7,5—9,5. 13 specimens). Iris dark brown; bill pale, culmen and tip dusky; legs brown.

Identification: Rather similar to the last species but the outer tail-feathers only show white; there is also a pair of white patches on the chest. Females have the white wing-spots and white tail-feathers, buffy. Young birds resemble females but are less boldly marked above.
Distribution: From Zululand and Kroonstad, Ovamboland and Ngamiland, northwards to West Africa and Tanzania.
Habits: A resident tropical species which is very common in the lower areas of Mozambique. In Rhodesia commonest from December to April and

376

thus probably migratory to some extent. It is particularly common for a mile or so on either side of large rivers, where they may be seen just after dusk in clearings or sitting on dirt roads. An hour or more after sunset they appear to disperse and are more conspicuous on certain evenings than others. Hunts from a perch at dusk but mainly by flying about hawking for its prey. Essentially a "ground" nightjar, seldom perching in trees.

Food: Insects, mainly termite, beetles.

Voice: Males make a prolonged gurgling or chuckling sound while perched on the ground; a rather frog-like noise which may continue for minutes at a time with louder and quieter phases which suggest either that two birds are calling or that one is breathing in and out as it calls.

Breeding: Two eggs are laid during September to November. They are pale salmon-pink, spotted and freckled with lilac and purplish pink. 27,7 × 19,2; 26,1 × 19,2, rough. Incubation period 14—17 days.

LOCAL RACES:
(a) *C.f. mossambicus* Peters, 1868: *Inhambane, P.E.A.* As figured on Plate 38. Size given above. Zululand, Mozambique and Rhodesia.
(b) *C.f. welwitschii* Bocage, 1867: *Between Penedo and Cacoaco.* Paler than (a) and larger. Wing 157—162—170; tail 117—125—134 (21). Northern Orange Free State, Transvaal, Rhodesia, northern South West Africa, Angola and southern Zaïre.

377   Pennant-wing Nightjar   Wimpelvlerk-naguil

Macrodipteryx vexillaria   (Gould) 1838: *Sierra Leone.*

Native Name: Mwere (D).

PLATE 38 ♂ AND ♀ (OPP. P. 272).
Length 25—28 cm (wing ♂ 234—240, including streamers, 675—730; wing ♀ 190—196; tail 127—145; tarsus 19—23; culmen 8—12. 5 specimens). Iris dark brown; bill blackish; legs light pinkish brown.

Identification: Breeding males unmistakable; otherwise the large size is noticeable. Females as illustrated. Males drop the long pennants very quickly after breeding.

Distribution: A migratory species which comes south to breed as far as Rhodesia, rarely to East Griqualand, Natal and Zululand. In the non-breeding season goes north to Sierra Leone and the Sudan. Arrives in our area about the beginning of September and departs in March.

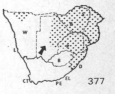

377

Habits: Locally quite common in Rhodesia and found on stony, wooded hillsides and sandy areas. Somewhat diurnal, often emerging in broad daylight during the late afternoon. Males often fly to considerable heights, perhaps pursued by a female. When flushed, usually perch lengthways on the branch of a tree.

Food: Largely flying termites but also beetles, grasshoppers, ants and other insects.

Voice: Rather silent; when breeding reported to make a faint piping or twittering squeak in flight.

Breeding: Eggs are laid on the bare ground from November to December. They are pinkish white to salmon, spotted with reddish and violet-grey. Average (15) 31,8 × 21,9 (30—34,2 × 21—23). Incubation 15—18 days.

Family MICROPODIDAE

The Swifts feed exclusively upon insects caught in flight and do not perch like the Swallows, but cling to ledges, rough surfaces of perpendicular rocks or cliffs, by all four toes. The toes are turned forwards. The family is cosmopolitan and contains some remarkable species in regard to nesting habits, such as the nest composed of a jelly-like substance which is regarded by the Chinese as such a delicacy for soup, the glued nests of the Indian Swift, the egg glued to palm leaves by the Palm Swift. They are inclined to be gregarious and are very strong fliers, with long, pointed wings and usually short tails (often forked), weak bill, but wide gape, short legs and toes, the claws short, curved and strong, and plumage usually hardened from rapid flight through the air. Some species are migratory, but all of them are conservative in respect of their nesting sites, so that small differences tend to remain constant. Much remains to be learned about them. Many species sleep in the air, never coming to the earth except to breed.

378 European Swift	Europese Windswael

Apus apus   (Linnaeus), 1758: *Europe =Sweden.*

Native Names (generic): i-Hlabankomo, i-Hlankomo (X); i-Jiyankomo, i-Hlolamvula (Z).

PLATE 39 (OPP. P. 273).
Length about 18 cm (wing 171—180; tail 68—76, shortest 43—48). Iris dark brown; bill and legs black.

Identification: Difficult to distinguish in the field from the following two black-rumped species. Uniform blackish brown on wings and body. Chin light, almost white. See under races and compare No. 380. Wing tip noticeably incurved.

Distribution: Throughout the Palaearctic and Ethiopian regions. Recorded specimens from as far south as Okahandja, South West Africa; Vryburg, Cape; Orange Free State and Natal.

378

Habits: A migrant recorded from mid-November to mid-March in the Republic and from late October to mid-March in Rhodesia. Not uncommon, occurring in large flocks. Little detail is recorded because it is practically indistinguishable in the field from the next species.

Voice: Apparently silent here.

LOCAL RACES:
(a) A.a. apus (Linnaeus), 1758: *Europe =Sweden.* Size as above. Darker race but flocks intermingle with race *(b)*. This is the common race in Rhodesia, usually leaves at the end of January.
(b) A.a. pekinensis (Swinhoe), 1870: *Peking.* A paler race; chin, lores and forehead paler. Wing coverts paler than mantle. Wing 161—170. This race is common in Botswana, rare in Rhodesia.

379 Pallid Swift   Bruin Windswael

Apus pallidus (Shelley), 1870: *Egypt*.

PLATE 39 (OPP. P. 273).
Length 18 cm (wing 161—173; tail 65—73 outer, 40—45 inner).

Identification: A mouse-coloured swift with chin and throat white; smaller than the previous species.
Distribution: Southern Europe and North Africa coming south in our summer. A female recorded from Kuruman, northern Cape.
Habits: Little recorded.

LOCAL RACE:
A.p. brehmorum Hartert, 1901: *Madeira*. The single specimen is believed to be of this race.

380 Black Swift   Swart Windswael

Apus barbatus (P. Sclater), 1865: *South Africa = Cape Province*.

Native Name: Lekhaqasi (S); Ihlankomo (X).

PLATE 39 (OPP. P. 273).
Length about 19 cm (wing 178—186; tail 71—77, shortest 47—52). Iris, bill and legs black.

Identification: Very similar to No. 378; said to differ in the following minor points: The mantle is glossier black whilst the wings are greenish bronze so that the two are in contrast. Further, the chin and throat are more streaked in this species, the feathers of the under-parts show pale edges and the tail is less forked.
Distribution: Throughout Southern Africa extending as far north as Kenya.
Habits: A resident species but subject to considerable migration. Common in large flocks during the summer; circling around and screaming as they arrive at their breeding cliffs in September and again before they depart in March at the Cape. Very often with the approach of stormy weather the flocks come lower and fly around in an excited manner at terrific speed, accompanied by shrill calls. Away from the mountains this species is more silent. Seems to turn up whenever and wherever the insect food supply is sufficient, often in company with other species of Swift.
Voice: See above.
Breeding: Recorded from September to December in the crevices of a krantz most often under an overhang. The nest is constructed of rootlets, thistledown and feathers (probably from parents). Eggs 2, white, and measure 26,5 × 17; 27,5 × 17,4.

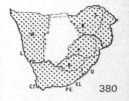

LOCAL RACES:
(a) *A.b. barbatus* (P. Sclater), 1865: *South Africa =Cape Province*. Size as above. The darker eastern race.
(b) *A.b. hollidayi* Benson and Irwin, 1960: *Victoria Falls, Rhodesia*. Paler than *(a)* and with mantle and wings the same colour. Extends south to Makarikari, Botswana.

PLATE 38

371. *Caprimulgus europaeus europaeus.* European Nightjar.

Europese Naguil. ♂ and ♀.

372. *Caprimulgus rufigena.* Rufous-cheeked Nightjar. Rooiwang-naguil.

373 *(a). Caprimulgus pectoralis pectoralis.* Fiery-necked Nightjar.

Afrikaanse Naguil.

373 *(b). Caprimulgus pectoralis fervidus.* Fiery-necked Nightjar.

Afrikaanse Naguil.

374. *Caprimulgus tristigma lentiginosus.* Freckled Nightjar. Donker Naguil.

375. *Caprimulgus natalensis natalensis.* Natal Nightjar. Natalse Naguil.

376. *Caprimulgus fossii mossambicus.* Mozambique Nightjar.

Laeveld Naguil.

377. *Macrodipteryx vexillaria.* Pennant-wing Nightjar.

Wimpelvlerk-naguil. ♂ and ♀.

390. *Colius striatus striatus.* Speckled Mousebird. Gevlekte Muisvoël.

391. *Colius colius.* White-backed Mousebird. Witkruis-muisvoël.

392. *Urocolius indicus indicus.* Red-faced Mousebird. Rooiwang-muisvoël.

392

391

390

377

375

374

376

371 ♀

371 ♂

A 373

B

372

NIGHTON
'37

387
PALM

388
MOTTLED
SPINETAIL

378
EUROPEAN

380
BLACK

386
ALPINE

389

381
BRADFIELD'S

385 x SCARCE

BOEHM'S
SPINETAIL

382
MOTTLED SWIFT

379
PALLID

385
LITTLE

383
WHITE-RUMPED

384
HORUS

K.B.NEWMAN '75

PLATE 39

378. *Apus apus apus*. European Swift. Europese Windswael.
379. *Apus pallidus*. Pallid Swift. Bruin Windswael.
380. *Apus barbatus barbatus*. Black Swift. Swart Windswael.
381. *Apus bradfieldi*. Bradfield's Swift.
382. *Apus aequatorialis*. Mottled Swift. Bont Windswael.
383. *Apus caffer.* White-rumped Swift. Witkruis-windswael.
384. *Apus horus*. Horus Swift. Horus-windswael.
385. *Apus affinis*. Little Swift. Klein Windswael.
385X. *Schoutedenapus myoptilus*. Scarce Swift. Skaars Windswael.
386. *Apus melba*. Alpine Swift. Witpens-windswael.
387. *Cypsiurus parvus*. Palm Swift. Palm-windswael.
388. *Telacanthura ussheri*. Mottled Spinetail. Boehmse Stekelstert.
389. *Neafrapus boehmi*. Boehm's Spinetail. Boehmse Stekelstert.

381 Bradfield's Swift

Apus bradfieldi (Roberts), 1926: *Quickborn, Okahandja, S.W.A.*

PLATE 39 (OPP. P. 273).
Length 18 cm (wing 169—184; tail 70—77); eye brown; bill and legs black.

Identification: Mouse-coloured but larger than 379 and with less white under chin. The primaries and tail blackish. Primaries in flight straighter than 378 and 379. Appears pale, slender and thin-winged in flight with dark streak at base of wing above.
Distribution: Mountainous regions of South West Africa down to Swakopmund and Southern Angola, across to Kuruman and Kimberley.
Habits: Little recorded.
Breeding: Nest typical of swifts in rock crevices. Made of grass, down and small feathers cemented with saliva. April. Clutch usually 2. Eggs, white 26,5 × 16,8 and 27,4 × 17,0.

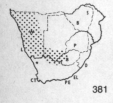
381

LOCAL RACES:
(a) A.b. bradfieldi Roberts, 1926: *Quickborn, S.W.A.* Size above. South West Africa, S. Angola.
(b) A.b. deserticolus Brooke, 1970: *Kuruman district.* Kuruman and Kimberley. Greyer than *(a)*.

382 Mottled Swift   Bont Windswael

Apus aequatorialis (von Müller), 1851: *Abyssinia.*

PLATE 39 (OPP. P. 273).
Length about 20 cm (wing 188—213; tail 85—90, shortest about 55).

Identification: About the size of the Alpine Swift, No. 386, and generally a paler version of it. Mottled below on belly, the feathers having dark brown subterminal and white terminal bands.
Distribution: Tropical Africa. Widely but locally distributed in Mashonaland and the eastern districts of Rhodesia.
Habits: A resident species; inhabits cliffs in mountainous areas but often found far from this type of habitat.
Food: Bees, flying ants and beetles.
Voice: A rather quiet scream.

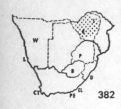
382

Breeding: Recorded in granite cliffs from north-east Rhodesia and Matopos from June to November. The nest is made of feathers of domestic fowl and guinea-fowl stuck together with saliva and placed in dry vertical rock fissures. Eggs, clutch of 2, white and elongate. 29,2 × 19,5; 29,5 × 19,2.

LOCAL RACE:
(a) A.a. aequatorialis (von Müller), 1851: *Abyssinia. Mozambique.*
(b) A.a. gelidus Brooke, 1967: *Matopos.* Granite country of Rhodesia.

383 White-rumped Swift   Witkruis-windswael

Apus caffer (Lichtenstein), 1823: *Kaffirland=Eastern Cape Province*

PLATE 39 (OPP. P. 273).
Length about 15 cm (wing 146—156; tail 70—78, shortest 40—47). Iris and bill black; feet dusky.

Identifications. Distinguished from Nos. 384 and 385 by the *long deeply forked tail* usually held closed and by the *narrow* white band across rump.

General appearance more slender than the other two white-rumped species. Blacker than No. 385.

Distribution: Eastern and Southern Africa. Throughout our area.

Habits: The status of this species is still uncertain; regarded by most as a summer-breeding visitor occurring from September to April. There are several Transvaal records from May and June, otherwise except for vagrants there are no records from May to August. Generally a bird which occurs in pairs or small family parties, often about houses or cliffs. Not afraid of man. When not attached to breeding localities mixes with other swifts, and occurs over open ground as well as near mountains.

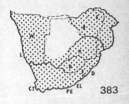

383

Breeding: Occupies crevices or holes in rocks, under eaves of buildings or deprives swallows of their closed nests for their own use. When using swallows' nests feathers are added so that they are often visible in the entrance thus indicating the swift's presence. The nest cup is lined with a few feathers. Breeds mainly September to March. Eggs 1—3, usually 2; white. Average (40) 23,2 × 14,9 (21—26 × 14,2—15,5). Double-brooded normally. Incubation 22—26 days (20). Fledgling Period 41—(46)—53 days.

384 Horus Swift   Horus-windswael

Apus horus (Heuglin), 1869: *N.E. Africa.*

PLATE 39 (OPP. P. 273).
Length about 17 cm (wing 143—161; tail 56—60, shortest 43—49). Iris brown; bill and legs dusky.

Identification: This species and the next differ from the White-rumped Swift in being *plumper and more heavily built;* the tail is not so deeply forked and there is more white on the rump. Distinguished from the Little Swift by its larger size, slightly forked tail and blacker appearance. In flight the wings appear proportionally larger than in other swifts; the *tail when spread looks almost square,* but when held normally is slightly forked. Rare records exist of black rumped birds.

Distribution: Ethiopia south to Transvaal, Orange Free State and Natal. Gradually spreading southwards; recent breeding colonies recorded from Eastern Province, Knysna and Western Province.

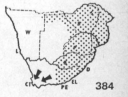

384

Habits: A migratory species recorded from October to April. Resident, not as common as other swifts. Usually colonial in breeding and so far as is known *only nests in sand-banks.* This habit is perhaps the most important clue to distinguish this species in the field. Not necessarily a swift of hilly or mountainous country. Seldom recorded except at breeding colonies where it suddenly appears out of the sky, flies rapidly about the sand-bank and then seems to fly off again.

Breeding: See under habits. The nest is composed of fibres, vegetable down and feathers placed on the floor of a 5–10 cm wide chamber at the end of a metre deep burrow. Recorded occupying old nest sites of Pied Starling, White-fronted and Carmine Bee-eaters, Banded Martin and Sand Martin. Recorded from November to March. Eggs 1—4, usually 3 or 2 white (25) 23,2 × 15,0 (21,6—24,5 × 14,5—15,7).

LOCAL RACE:
A.h. horus (Heughlin), 1869: *N.E. Africa.* Throughout our area.

275

385 Little Swift Klein Windswael

Apus affinis   (Gray), 1852: *India; Ganges valley.*

PLATE 39 (OPP. P. 273).
Length about 14 cm (wing 123—141; tail 40—49, shortest feather 38—45). Iris brown; bill black; legs brown.

Identification: See No. 384. Small size and square tail distinctive. This is a squat brownish swift with a large white rump patch. In flight the tail is square, even *slightly rounded when fanned wide open.* Wings not pointed.

Distribution: Africa, Southern Asia east to China. Throughout our area, except the dry west, only recently recorded in the south-western Cape.

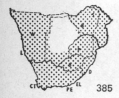

385

Habits: Resident and remains attached to the vicinity of breeding sites for most of the year; wandering mainly in June and July, especially in southern and western areas. A common, social bird attracted in towns to large buildings where it breeds under eaves and gutters; occurs in rocky areas where it breeds under overhangs and also under large bridges. At dawn and dusk they gather round the roost, accompanied by excited screeching and wheeling between buildings.

Breeding: See under habits. Nest of straw and feathers glued together against some overhang, sometimes isolated but often touching each other and overlapping. September to April. Eggs 2—3, glossy white. Average (18) 23,2 × 15,1 (21—25 × 13,8—15,7). Incubation 23 days and fledgling period 38 days (Tanzania). Both parents feed young.

LOCAL RACE:
(a) A.a. theresae Meinertzhagen, 1949: *Brandvlei.* Size above. Pale, throat unstreaked. South Africa except Natal.
(b) A.a. aerobates Brooke, 1969: *Mbandaka, Equateur Prov. Congo Kinshasa.* Smaller and darker than *(a).* Tropical Africa south to central Rhodesia and Natal. Wing 121—136.

385X Scarce Swift Skaars Windswael

Schoutedenapus myoptilus   (Salvadori), 1888: *Let Marifia, Shoa,
Ethiopia.*

PLATE 39 (OPP. P. 273).
Length about 17 cm (wing 127—141; tail 58—72, shortest feather 37—41). Iris dark brown; bill and legs dusky.

Identification: A slightly smaller, uniform, sooty-brown version of the White-rumped Swift. The chin is slightly paler than under-parts and wings have a greenish wash to the brown. A slender build with a longish deeply forked tail. Note no white on rump.

Distribution: Ethiopia to Malawi. Recently recorded from the highlands of Eastern Districts, Rhodesia.

Habits: Local, being confined to high altitudes of tropical mountains. Resident. First recorded in our area at over 2 250 metres on Inyanga by Rankine. Said to fly about high in company with other swifts. Does not spread its tail as often as the shorter-tailed species.

Breeding: Appears to breed September to December in Rhodesia. In mountain cliffs.

LOCAL RACE:
S.m. myoptilus (Salvadori), 1888: *Let Marifia, Shoa.* As above, another race in Zaïre.

276

386 Alpine Swift   Witpens-windswael

Apus melba   (Linnaeus), 1758: *Straits of Gibraltar*.

Native Name: Ubantom (X).

PLATE 39 (OPP. P. 273).
Length about 22 cm (wing 192—207—217; tail 78,7—92, shortest feather 54—66; tarsus 17,2—19,2; culmen 8,4—9,7. 16 specimens). Iris dark brown; bill black; legs brown.

Identification: Large size and white chin separated from *white belly* by a broad brown chestband distinguish this species. The sides of belly barred to a varying degree. Young birds have white edges to wing-feathers and are more mottled below.
Distribution: Southern Europe, east to India and Africa. Throughout our area.
Habits: A roving species, spending much of the year away from breeding sites though it may roost at nest-krantzes for some period. Usually found in mountainous country, but its colossal powers of flight enable it to range far and wide. Mixes freely with other swifts and sometimes even with sand martins.

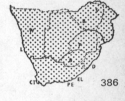

Voice: In vicinity of nesting crags utters a loud chittering in flight.
Breeding: Few details. Recorded at Colesberg breeding in crevices under rocky overhangs. Other records September to January. The nest is constructed of grass, rootlets and feathers. Eggs 1 and 2 recorded, about 31 × 19,5 (Europe).

LOCAL RACE:
(a) A.m. africanus (Temminck), 1815: *Cape Province*. Darker than nominate and with less white on the chin. Throughout except for *(b)*.
(b) A.m. marjoriae (Bradfield) 1935: *Quickborn Farm, Okahandja*. Damaraland and Great Namaqualand. Paler than *(a)*. Wing 198—208.

387 Palm Swift   Palm-windswael

Cypsiurus parvus   (Lichtenstein), 1823: *Nubia*.

PLATE 39 (OPP. P. 273).
Length about 17 cm (wing 129—135; tail 95—110). Iris brown; bill black; legs dark brown.

Identification: A slender-built, grey-brown swift with long thin wings and long deeply forked tail. Practically always in association with tall palms (see below).
Distribution: The Ethiopian region and Malagasy. Spreading southwards on the east, now recorded from Durban. Recorded from north-eastern Transvaal, Ngamiland and Ovamboland.
Habits: Resident but may wander, irregularly, from the nesting trees from March to August. Always found about palm trees and gathers there particularly at dawn and dusk. Usually near water and recently recorded breeding on girders of large bridges. Roost at night, clinging to the underside of palm leaves. Absent from Pretoria in winter—cannot tolerate cold.

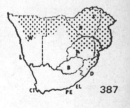

Voice: A high-pitched thin scream.
Breeding: The nest is attached to the underside of a palm leaf, composed of feathers stuck together with salivary glue; the eggs are attached to the nest

277

with salivary glue to prevent their loss during windy weather. Has recently started building nests on girders of bridges and buildings. Eggs 2, white. Average (4) 18,4 × 12,9 (17—20,6 × 12,3—13,8). Breeds all year, peak October to January.

LOCAL RACES:
(a) C.p. aemostigma (Reichenow), 1905: *S. Somalia.* A paler race than *(b).* Somalia to Natal and up Zambezi and Sabi rivers.
(b) C.p. myochrous (Reichenow), 1886: *Karema, Tanganyika.* Southern Sudan to Rhodesia and Transvaal.
(c) C.p. hyphaenes Brooke 1972: *Kumgha, Botletle R., Botswana.* Northern Botswana, Caprivi and northern South West Africa. Paler than *(b).*

388 Mottled Spinetail   Stekelstert

Telacanthura ussheri   (Sharpe), 1870: *Fort Victoria, Gold Coast.*

PLATE 39 (OPP. P. 273).
Length about 14 cm (wing 135—145; tail 30).

Identification: Similar to the Little Swift from which it is difficult to distinguish in the field. The shafts of the tail-feathers are stiffened and project beyond the tail—not a field character. The white rump is narrow, about one-third length of the very short tail. There is a small *white patch near the feet* and vent. These factors are, to a lesser degree, the larger and duller light throat-patch and slightly longer wings distinguish it from No. 385.
Distribution: Senegal and Mombasa to the Zambesi. Occurring up the Zambesi as far as Chirundu, Rhodesia, Eastern Transvaal and Mozambique, below 600 m.
Habits: A widespread resident species found in areas where there are low cliffs and bluffs especially near water. Often in association with the Little Swift.
Voice: A chatter of "zi-zick" repeated.
Breeding: Nests in holes in Baobab trees or buildings; nest of leaves and twigs stuck with saliva. Eggs 4, white 21 × 14.

388

LOCAL RACE:
T.u. benguellensis (Neumann) 1908: *Blasbalkfontein, Angola.*

389 Boehm's Spinetail   Boehmse Stekelstert

Neafrapus boehmi   (Schalow), 1882: *Rakowa=Kakoma, Tabora.*

PLATE 39 (OPP. P. 273).
Wing 108—126 (28).

Identification: Small size, apparent lack of tail and bat-like flight distinguish this species. The white of the rump is broad, as broad as the very short tail. The throat and chest are grey, contrasting with white of belly. There is a definite lobe at the outermost secondaries which are longer and broader than the other remiges.
Distribution: Northern Angola, east to the Rhodesia, Transvaal and north to Somalia. Recorded from Gorongoza, Mozambique, the Sabi Valley, and neigbhouring areas of the Kruger National Park. Also from the Caprivi Strip and northern Botswana.

389

Habits: Very local in habits and rather rare. Recorded usually in small flocks. Its apparent lack of tail and erratic flight are all that is recorded.
Voice: High-pitched "tri-tri-tri-peep" or "ti-ti-ti-peep".
Breeding: October and March breeds down disused mine borings and wells. The nest is made with leaves and twigs stuck together and against the wall with saliva with sometimes a few feathers. Eggs 3, sometimes 2. Two measure 17—19,0 × 11,9—13. Incubation ± 14 days. Fledgling period 6 weeks.

LOCAL RACE:
(a) N.b. sheppardi Roberts, 1922: *Beira.* Somalia to Southern Mozambique. Size above.

Family COLIIDAE

A family of birds peculiar to the African continent and characterized by having the outer toes on either side reversible either backwards or forwards, the claws strong and curved in adaptation to climbing about trees, legs short, bill short and rather Finch-like, but soft about the nostrils, plumage rather hair-like about the body and tail with long stiff feathers. They subsist entirely upon berries and fruit, to obtain which they creep about in the trees or bushes and resemble mice, whence the name of Mousebird. Invariably found in small parties, the individuals keeping in touch with one another by whistling notes, especially when flying from one tree or bush to another.

390   Speckled Mousebird   Gevlekte Muisvoël

Colius striatus   Gmelin, 1789: *Cape of Good Hope.*

Native Name: Indlazi (X, G and Z).

PLATE 38 (OPP. P. 272).
Length 30—35 cm (wing 88—94—102; tail 195—240; tarsus 20—24; culmen 13—14. 27 specimens). Iris dark brown; bill black above, bluish below; legs brown to dull red (see below). Weight 54 g.

Identification: Browner than the other two species in our area and without a white rump or red face; the *blackish face* is a distinctive feature. Young birds resemble adults but have the upper half of the beak bright yellowish green.
Distribution: From Cape Town eastwards to Natal and thence northwards to the Zambesi and beyond to West Africa and Ethiopia. Most characteristic of the eastern Cape, Natal and Transvaal.
Habits: An extremely common species in certain localities, frequenting thick scrub and the border of forests. Usually found in small parties clambering about like mice in thick bushes. When disturbed they take to flight one after another in a gentle dive to the next bush, alternately gliding or flying with rapid wing-beats; as they near their objective they climb steeply and crash into the bush, often clapping themselves against a branch, or hang down with their feet held level with their heads. They also sleep in this position, several birds forming a tight bunch with their heads together and bodies hanging downwards.
Food: Fruit, berries, flowers and almost any soft vegetable matter.
Voice: Normal alarm note a sharp "chick . . . chick".
Breeding: A large, softly lined cup-shaped nest is constructed, during the months July to February. It is placed from 1 to 7 metres from the ground in a

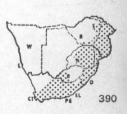
390

bush or tree. The eggs 3—4, are white and rather tough. Average (64) 21,6 × 16,5 (19,8—23,9 × 14,7—17,8). Incubation by both sexes, 11—13 days. Nestling period 17—18 days, but young leave the nest well before they are fully grown and climb about.

LOCAL RACES:
(a) *C.s. striatus* Gmelin, 1789: *Cape of Good Hope*. As shown on Plate 38. Cape Province.
(b) *C.s. minor* Cabanis, 1876: *Natal*. Throat more blackish than *(a)*. Wing 86,5—97 (10). Natal, Transvaal.
(c) *C.s. rhodesiae* Grant and Mackworth-Praed, 1938: *Umtali*. Lightly washed with cinnamon below. Legs dull red to pinkish. Eastern Rhodesia, Mozambique Highlands.
(d) *C.s. intergralis* Clancey, 1957: *Vila Luiza, Southern Mozambique*. Eastern Transvaal, Zululand, southern Mozambique lowlands.

391 White-backed Mousebird   Witkruis-muisvoël

Colius colius   (Linnaeus), 1766: *Cape of Good Hope*.

PLATE 38 (OPP. P. 272).
Length 30—34 cm (wing 88—90—95; tail 200—232; tarsus 18,5—21; culmen 11,5—13. 13 specimens). Iris black; bill bluish white, tip dark; legs red. Weight 45 g.

Identification: Easily identified, having a broad white stripe down the back, bordered by black, and a maroon rump. *Legs red*. Sexes alike. Young birds lack the colour on the rump and have beaks bright bluish green above, blackish below.

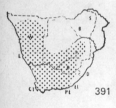

391

Distribution: The south and Karoo districts from the Atlantic coast eastwards to western Orange Free State, western Transvaal and southern Botswana as far north as Gaberones; absent from the Kalahari but present from Orange River north to Damaraland and the Okavango.

Habits: A common, sociable species, usually seen in parties wherever there are bushes or trees. In general habits very like the last species; also sleeps in bunches.

Food: Fruit and vegetable matter, quite often taken on the ground.

Voice: A rather musical "zwee, wewit". Alarm note "tzik".

Breeding: Nests are large cup-shaped structures made of dry sticks and leaves, lined with wool and vegetable down; they are usually placed between 2 and 7 metres from the ground in thick bushes or hedges. Eggs 3—4, are white and somewhat rough. Average (29) 20,9 × 16,0 (19—21,9 × 14,9—17,3). One 23,3 × 15,7. Breeds from August to November.

392 Red-faced Mousebird   Rooiwang-muisvoël

Urocolius indicus   (Latham), 1790: *India= Gamtoos River*.

Native Names: Intshili (X); um-Tshivovo, i-Shivovo (Z); le-Tsiavava, le-Katzi, le-Se (S).

PLATE 38 (OPP. P. 272).
Length 32—34 cm (wing 90—94,5—100; tail 190—250; tarsus 18—22; culmen 13—15. 31 specimens). Iris grey; bill black, base and soft cere crimson; legs rose-red.

Identification: A pale grey species with distinct red face but no white on back. Sexes alike. Young birds have the face and bill greenish.

280

Distribution: Southern Africa to southern Tanzania, except the western desert areas and thick forest.
Habits: Common, particularly in the eastern districts. For a mousebird, almost beautiful, with its soft greenish-grey plumage. A much stronger flier than the other two species; when disturbed flies for some distance and parties may often be seen flying high overhead, their tails appearing short and very pointed compared with the other species. In general habits, similar to the last two species.
Food: Fruit and berries.
Voice: A melodious call uttered frequently on the wing and also while perched in trees. Rendered as "tree-ree-ree" and responsible for several onomatopoeic names such as "Tshivovo" which matches it pretty closely.
Breeding: The nest is typical of the mousebirds but the eggs are usually scrolled with reddish or brown. Average (34) 22,0 × 16,0 (19,5—24,3 × 15—17,1). Breeds from September to February.

LOCAL RACES:
(a) U.i. indicus (Latham), 1790: *India = Gamtoos River*. As shown on Plate 38. Wing 89—96 (5). Cape Province.
(b) U.i. pallidus (Reichenow), 1896: *Kionga, Rovuma River*. Paler than *(a)*, grey with light bluish tinge; under-side much paler and tinged pink. Size given above. Natal and Transvaal to southern Tanzania, Botswana.
(c) U.i. lacteifrons (Sharpe), 1892: *Damaraland*. Paler than *(a)*; green absent on ear-coverts, and forehead creamy white. South West Africa.

Family TROGONIDAE

Beautiful tropical forest birds characterized by their soft plumage (and thin delicate skin), the feathers of the rump with hidden spines and the graduated tail-feathers having the outer ones rather pointed (both characters seen also in the *Campephagidae*); bill curved, short and inflated, the cutting edge of the mandible serrated; the first and second toes turned backwards, the other two forwards, the claws curved and strong, legs short. Usually found solitary in the depths of forests, where they are difficult to see when the green back is turned towards one and usually observed only when they take to flight. Feed on insects taken in flight or from leaves and bark of trees. Nest in natural holes in trees in midsummer and lay three or four pure white glossy eggs. Voice rather ventriloquial, probably on account of the hollow throat sac.

393 Narina Trogon   Bosloerie

Apaloderma narina (Stephens), 1815: *Anteniquoi = Knysna*.

Native Names: Intshatshongo (X); um-Jeninengu (Z); Tzoko (S).

PLATE 34 (OPP. P. 240) ♂.
Length 29—34 cm (wing 128—132—138; tail 150—175; tarsus 16—17; culmen 18—20. 25 specimens). Iris hazel; bill ashy; legs dark flesh.

Identification: Male illustrated. The female has a brown face and chest, breast pinky grey and belly red. Young bird resembles female but has mottled throat and chest, belly white with brownish markings; wing-coverts and secondaries tipped with white. Skin on throat of breeding male light blue.
Distribution: From Knysna eastwards to eastern Rhodesia and Mozambique. There is a specimen from Kasane so that it may occur right along the Zambesi

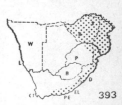

281

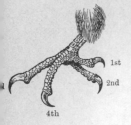

Valley. To the north extends to the southern Congo and Ethiopia and across to Sierra Leone.

Habits: This beautiful bird was named by le Vaillant in honour of a Hottentot girl whose beauty he greatly admired. It is a not uncommon resident of forests, large riverine trees and even fairly open coastal bush. It is usually seen sitting motionless in the shade in a rather hunched-up attitude and is tame and sluggish, remaining in one spot for considerable periods at a time. Creeps about the branches in search of its prey or makes short agile dashes after it in the air. Normal flight heavy, straight and soft. Frequently flies into houses at night.

Food: Insects; caterpillars, green grasshoppers and mantises in particular; fruit apparently very rarely.

Voice: Described as about eight "hoot" sounds which may be reproduced fairly accurately by "hooting" with the lips closed: "hoot! hoot! hoot! hoot-hoot! hoot-hoot!" gradually dying away, the second double note higher than the first part of the call; in tone rather like the notes of the Emerald-Spotted Dove, No. 321. When calling the bare skin of throat is blown up into a resonating sac which pulsates (Ranger).

Breeding: Nests in holes in tree trunks, no nesting material being used. Eggs 3—4, glossy white, laid from October to January. Average (12) 28,2 × 22,5 (25,9—31 × 21,2—23,2).

LOCAL RACE:
A.n. narina (Stephens), 1815: *Anteniquoi = Knysna*. As figured; size above. Southern Africa to Ethiopia and southern Zaïre.

Family ALCEDINIDAE

Kingfishers are cosmopolitan, usually resident, birds that get their name from their habit of feeding upon fish caught by diving, to which their long, stout and pointed bills are adapted; they have short legs and the third and fourth toes united for most of their length, the second united to the third at the base only. Most of the species have beautiful blue and red colours in the plumage and none of them are of large size, the largest being about the size of a Pigeon. The majority of species nest in burrows made in the banks of streams, but some species use the old nests of Barbets or Woodpeckers in trees; the eggs in all cases are glossy white, the clutches usually three to six. Their diet consists on the whole of small fish, but some species also consume any other small water animals, and several are adapted to an insectivorous diet and may live far from water.

394 Pied Kingfisher   Bont Visvanger

Ceryle rudis (Linnaeus), 1758: *Egypt.*

Native Names: isi-Quba (Z); Siunud (Ch); Seinoli (S); Isaxwila (X).

PLATE 40 (OPP. P. 288) ♂ AND ♀.
Length 28—29 cm (wing 132—140—146; tail 70—78; tarsus 9—11; culmen 53—63. 34 specimens). Iris dark brown; bill black; legs black. Weight ♂ 70—75 g.

Identification: Very distinctive. Sexes differ as illustrated. Young birds resemble adults of their respective sex but have buff edges to the white feathers of neck and chest.

Distribution: Africa to southern China.
Habits: A widely distributed and common species of streams, rivers, lakes and the seashore but particularly of the seaside lagoons so common on the South African coast. Conspicuous from its habit of hovering over the water and diving head first to capture its prey. This is carried to some favourite perch, used regularly, and is usually beaten to death before being swallowed. Often fishes in the sea off rocks. When hovering the body is held almost vertical, the head bent well forward. Raises and lowers its tail when perched.
Food: Apparently almost entirely fish but shrimps, airborne insects and crabs are reported.
Voice: A sharp "kwik kwik". A noisy species.
Breeding: Nests in a burrow in a bank, the chamber being usually about 1—2 metres from the entrance but sometimes more. No lining is used but the nest is always full of bones, fish scales, etc. Eggs are laid from August to November in the Cape; in March and from July to November in Rhodesia. They are white, rounded and glossy, 4—6 in number. Average (47) 29,7 × 23,5 (26,9—33 × 22,1—26,3). Young are fed by both sexes.

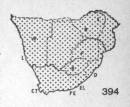

394

LOCAL RACE:
C.r. rudis (Linnaeus), 1758: *Egypt.* Africa to India. As figured; size above.

395 Giant Kingfisher   Reuse-visvanger

Megaceryle maxima   (Pallas), 1769: *Cape of Good Hope.*

Native Names: Uxomoyi (X); isi-Vuba (Z).

PLATE 40 (OPP. P. 288).
Length 43—46 cm (wing 192—202—209; tail 110—123; tarsus 13—15; culmen 86—101. 24 specimens). Iris dark brown; bill black; legs olive-brown. Weight ♀ 370 g.

Identification: Quite distinctive. Females have colours below reversed; chest spotted slate-black on white, breast rufous. Young birds have sides of chest mixed black and chestnut; under wing-coverts in young male white, in female chestnut.
Distribution: Africa south of the Sahara.
Habits: A common, widely dispersed species which frequents streams, rivers, lagoons and coastal pools. Also found in mountain streams inland, even when they are quite small but wooded. Does not visit bare dams without trees. Perches on the lower branches of trees overhanging the water, on snags, rocks or other posts whence it can watch the water below. Hovers like the last species.

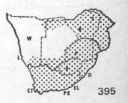

395

Food: Mainly fish and therefore looked upon with disfavour where exotic species have been introduced; also consumes crabs and other water animals to a considerable extent.
Voice: A loud ringing "kakh-kakh-kakh-kakh".
Breeding: Nests during September to January at the end of a long tunnel, at a depth of 1—3 metres. Eggs 3—4, white and glossy. Average (15) 45,5 × 35,1 (42,5—51 × 34—36,7).

LOCAL RACE:
M.m. maxima (Pallas), 1769: *Cape of Good Hope.* As figured; size above. Africa south of the Sahara except Zaïre and West Africa, where another race occurs.

396 Half-collared Kingfisher   Blou Visvanger

Alcedo semitorquata   Swainson, 1823: *Great Fish River, C.P.*

Native Names: isi-Xwiba, Chinyurahowe (D).

PLATE 40 (OPP. P. 288).

Length about 20 cm (wing 82—86—90; tail 39—45; tarsus 8—10; culmen 42—50. 27 specimens). Iris and bill black; legs red.

Identification: The only "blue" kingfisher with a black beak. Sexes alike. Young are slightly barred with black on the chest.

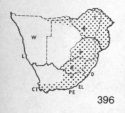

Distribution: From the south-west Cape (uncommon) eastwards to Ethiopia and from Zambia across to Angola. Apparently absent from South West Africa.

Habits: Cannot be said to be common anywhere; prefers large streams to big rivers but may even be seen in coastal lagoons. Usually seen quietly perched rather low down, on a branch or stone. Occasionally gives a quick bob, apparently a sign of agitation.

396

Food: Fish, small crabs and other water animals, including insects.

Voice: A shrill cry, "teep" or—when excited—"seek-seek".

Breeding: Nests from September to November and March, in a burrow in a sand-bank, usually between 1 and 3 metres up and only about 40 cm from the top of the bank. The passage is about 60 cm long and fouled with droppings. Eggs 3—4, white and glossy. Average (26) 23,7 × 20,0 (23—24,7 × 18,4—22).

397 Malachite Kingfisher   Kuifkop-visvanger

Corythornis cristata   (Pallas), 1764: *Cape of Good Hope.*

Native Names: i-Ntangaza (T); Isaxinila (X); Chishashero (D).

PLATE 40 (OPP. P. 288).

Length about 14 cm (wing 54—57—60; tail 24—31; tarsus 7; culmen 31—37,5. 33 specimens). Iris brown; bill and legs coral-red.

Identification: Easily mistaken for the next species, but the crested crown is *green* (barred with black) not blue and extends down to eye. Habitat also different, see below. Sexes alike. Young birds have black bills and black backs, the feathers tipped bluish; ear-coverts and chest dusky.

Distribution: Africa south of the Sahara and southern Arabia.

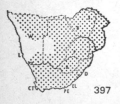

Habits: A common species on streams, vleis and marshes where there are reed beds or other forms of sheltering vegetation. Perches low down and dives for its prey in the water below. When disturbed, darts off like an arrow and streaks across the water almost skimming the surface. Sometimes bobs its head up and down while on its perch and can turn round very quickly; also raises its crest which moves sideways rather than upwards.

397

Food: Small fish, tadpoles and frogs, shrimps, beetles and grasshoppers.

Voice: A shrill "peep-peep" as it flies off. Also a weak song in the breeding season.

Breeding: Nests from September to February in banks along rivers, the tunnel being 30—90 cm long, ending in a small chamber, evil-smelling and floored with fish bones and beetle remains. Eggs 3—5, white and glossy. Average (45) 18,7 × 15,5 (17,1—20 × 15—16,3). One 21 × 16.

LOCAL RACE:
C.c. cristata (Pallas), 1764: *Cape of Good Hope.* Africa; other races on Prince's and St. Thomas Islands.

398   Pygmy Kingfisher   Natalse Visvanger

Ispidina picta   (Boddaert), 1783: *Senegal.*

Native Names: isi-Pigileni (Z).

PLATE 40 (OPP. P. 288).
Length about 13 cm (wing 51—59; tail 23—26; tarsus 7; culmen 24—28). Iris dark brown; bill and legs red.

Identification: Smaller and shorter-beaked than the Malachite, No. 397; in flight appears more violet-blue; at rest may be seen to lack a crest and has pale blue patches behind eye. Colour of crown does *not* reach eye. Sexes alike. Young birds have bills black and backs more greenish blue.
Distribution: From Kasuga River northwards to Senegal and Eritrea.
Habits: In the south this species is a migrant being present in Natal from October to May. In contrast to the last species, essentially a bird of drier country and coastal bush though it *may* be found *near* streams. Catches its prey on the ground, preferring to sit low down in the shade, watching the ground below. Rarely dives into water.
Food: Mainly insects and their larvae; also frogs, crabs and spiders.
Voice: A sharp "chip", often uttered in flight.
Breeding: Nests in burrows made in the side of wells or in river banks; even in the sides of ant-bear holes. The tunnels are only 30—60 cm long. Eggs 4—6, laid from October to November, and also in March, are white and glossy. Average (50) 17,9 × 15,6 (16,2—19,3 × 14,4—16,5).

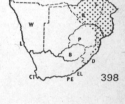

398

LOCAL RACE:
I.p. natalensis (A. Smith), 1831: *East of Cafferland = Natal.* Cape Province to Zaïre and Tanzania. Size above.

399   Woodland Kingfisher   Bosveld-visvanger

Halcyon senegalensis   (Linnaeus), 1766: *Senegal.*

PLATE 40 (OPP. P. 288).
Length 23—24 cm (wing 111—117; tail 62—69; tarsus 13; culmen 46—34). Iris dark grey; bill, upper mandible red, lower black; legs black. Weight 60—80 g.

Identification: Greatly resembles the next species but has the *lower* half of the bill, and legs *black.* Sexes alike. Young birds have dusky bills and blackish barring on neck, chest and breast.
Distribution: West Africa to Ethiopia southwards to Zululand on the east, Transvaal and across to Angola.
Habits: Apparently migratory in the south, present from October to April, occasionally May. A rather uncommon species which is found in fairly dry, wooded country, not necessarily near water. May also occur in mangroves. Usually seen perched rather low down watching for its prey on the ground beneath.
Food: Almost entirely insects such as grasshoppers, mantises, beetles, dragonflies; also lizards and young birds.

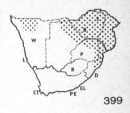

399

Voice: A noisy bird. Has a loud trilled call which is frequently uttered, especially in the breeding season. May be written as "kr-tir-r-r-r-rh!" The first note high, the others descending for about one second.

Breeding: A hole nester using old Barbet or Woodpecker nesting holes but other holes even eaves of houses or old Little Swift nests recorded. Eggs 2—4, normally 3, glossy white. Average (20) 28,0 × 24,4 (25,0—30,5 × 22,1—25,6). October to December. Incubation 13—14 days. Fledgling period 15—22 days.

LOCAL RACE:
H.s. cyanoleuca (Vieillot), 1818: *Angola*. As figured; size above. Zululand and Transvaal to Angola, northwards to Kenya and Uganda.

400 Mangrove Kingfisher   Mangliedvisvanger

Halcyon senegaloides   A. Smith, 1834: *Durban.*

Native Name: Sascula (P).

PLATE 40 (OPP. P. 288).
Length 23—24 cm (wing 100—111; tail 57—68; tarsus 11—13; culmen 48—50). Iris dark brown; bill red; legs reddish yellow.

Identification: The pure red beak and legs distinguish this species from the last; the pure white belly and *pale grey* crown prevent confusion with Nos. 401—403. At rest shows broader wing-bar than No. 399. Sexes alike. Young birds have the feathers of the underparts finely vermiculated with dusky stripes.

Distribution: Confined to a narrow coastal strip from the Kobenqaba River to the Equator.

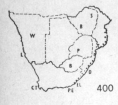

400

Habits: Confined to mangrove swamps during the non-breeding season, moving inland, up to the 300 metre contour, in October for three to four months.

Food: Crabs, small fish, lizards and insects.

Voice: In the mangroves raises its wings as it calls a racuous "chit-tchoo, tcha-tcha-tcha-tch-tch-tch" ending in a trill. When calling at breeding haunts, merely points the bill upwards and calls "cling-cling-cling-cling-cling-cling-cling-cling".

Breeding: Resorts to forested streams and apparently uses holes in trees or clay banks. October to January with birds in young plumage up to April.

401 Grey-hooded Kingfisher   Gryskop-visvanger

Halcyon leucocephala   (Müller), 1776: *Senegal.*

PLATE 40 (OPP. P. 288).
Length about 20 cm (wing 95—100—106; tail 49—65; tarsus 11—12,5; culmen 38—41. 14 specimens). Iris dark brown; bill and legs red. Weight ♂ 46, ♀ 57 g.

Identification: Belly is deep rufous, thus distinguishing this species from Nos. 399—400. Otherwise rather resembles the Brown-hooded Kingfisher, No. 402, but lacks the striped flanks and streaked head. Sexes alike. Young birds have neck and chest barred with blackish; only a trace of chestnut on the belly, and the bill black.

Distribution: From Damaraland, Transvaal and Beira northwards to Ethiopia and West Africa.

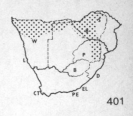

Habits: A migratory species which visits South Africa from October to March only. Frequents woodlands such as *Brachystegia* and the neighbourhood of dried-up streams or water.

Food: Mainly insects such as grasshoppers, beetles, mole-crickets and ants; also lizards.

Voice: A weak, descending "ji-ji-chi". Also a chattering call.

401

Breeding: Nests in holes in banks, usually about 30 cm from the top and with a short tunnel about 0,5 to 1 metre long. Eggs are pink when fresh, but appear white when blown. The usual full clutch is 4. Average (30) 24,8 × 21,8 (22,7—28,2 × 20,7—24,1). They are laid during October and November.

LOCAL RACE:
H.l. pallidiventris Cabanis, 1880: *Angola.* from our area to southern Zaïre and Kenya. Migrates to Uganda.

402   Brown-hooded Kingfisher   Bruinkop-visvanger

Halcyon albiventris (Scopoli), 1786: *New Guinea = Natal*

Native Names: Undozela (X); u-Nongozolo (Z); le-Inoli (S); i.Dederigwa (D).

PLATE 40 (OPP. P. 288).
Length 23—24 cm (wing 103—106—112; tail 63—70; tarsus 11,5—13; culmen 45—52. 53 specimens). Iris brown; bill red, blackish towards tip; legs dark red.

Identification: The streaked flanks distinguish it from the last two species; is larger than the next species, has a blue *back and* rump, and lacks the black eyestripe and nape. Females have brown backs. Young birds are duller, more streaked below and have blackish beaks, only red at the base.

Distribution: From Cape Town eastwards to Natal and northwards to Angola and East Africa. Absent from South West Africa.

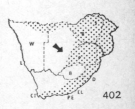

Habits: A widespread and common species found in the dry savanna veld among large trees, often far away from water. Quite often comes into gardens. Usually seen sitting motionless on a bare branch in a conspicuous position. Bobs its head continually.

Food: Insects such as beetles and grasshoppers; also lizards, crabs and even mice, young birds and small snakes.

402

Voice: Quite noisy at times uttering a loud "kik-kik-kik-kik".

Breeding: Burrows into banks for up to a metre, enlarging the end of the hole into a nest. Breeds from September to December. The nest becomes very foul with droppings, remains of insects, maggots, etc. Eggs number 4 or 5 and are white. Average (90) 27,5 × 24,1 (24,2—30,0 × 21,7—26,5). A spotted clutch has been described.

LOCAL RACES:
(a) H.a. albiventris (Scopoli), 1786: *New Guinea = Natal.* As illustrated; size above. Swellendam to southern Mozambique and western Rhodesia.
(b) H.a. orientalis Peters, 1868: *Inhambane.* Not striped below; smaller. Wing 97—101—105 (13 from Mozambique). Central and northern Mozambique, eastern Rhodesia to East Africa and Angola.

287

PLATE 40

394. *Ceryle rudis rudis.* Pied Kingfisher. Bont Visvanger. ♂ and ♀.
395. *Megaceryle maxima maxima.* Giant Kingfisher. Reuse-visvanger.
396. *Alcedo semitorquata.* Half-collared Kingfisher. Blou Visvanger.
397. *Corythornis cristata cristata.* Malachite Kingfisher.

Kuifkop-visvanger.

398. *Ispidina picta natalensis.* Pygmy Kingfisher. Natalse Visvanger.
399. *Halcyon senegalensis cyanoleuca.* Woodland Kingfisher.

Bosveld-visvanger.

400. *Halcyon senegaloides.* Mangrove Kingfisher. Mangliedvisvanger.
401. *Halcyon leucocephala pallidiventris.* Grey-hooded Kingfisher.

Gryskop-visvanger.

402 *(a). Halcyon albiventris albiventris.* Brown-hooded Kingfisher.

Bruinkop-visvanger.

403. *Halcyon chelicuti chelicuti.* Striped Kingfisher. Gestreepte Visvanger.
404. *Merops apiaster.* European Bee-eater. Europese Byvreter.
406 *(a). Merops superciliosus superciliosus.* Blue-cheeked Bee-eater.
406 *(b). Merops superciliosus persicus.* Blue-cheeked Bee-eater.

Blouwang-byvreter.

407. *Merops nubicus nubicoides.* Carmine Bee-eater. Rooibors-byvreter.
408. *Merops boehmi.* Boehms Bee-eater. Boehmse Byvreter.
409. *Melittophagus bullockoides.* White-fronted Bee-eater.

Rooikeel-byvreter.

410. *Melittophagus pusillus meridionalis.* Little Bee-eater. Klein Byvreter.
411. *Dicrocercus hirundineus hirundineus.* Swallow-tailed Bee-eater.

Mikster-byvreter.

395

396

394 ♂ ♀

KN

397

398

399

400

401

402A

403

410

A 406

B

409

407

408

411

KN

404

KN

KN

NIGHTON
35

414

412

417

426 ♂

415

413

425A ♂

424 ♀

♂

♂ 429

423 ♂

427B ♂

422

428 ♂

HIGHTON.
'37

PLATE 41

412. *Coracias garrulus garrulus.* European Roller. Europese Troupant.

413. *Coracias caudata caudata.* Lilac-breasted Roller. Gewone Troupant.

414. *Coracias spatulata.* Racquet-tailed Roller. Knopstert-troupant.

415. *Coracias naevia mosambica.* Purple Roller. Groot Troupant.

417. *Eurystomus glaucurus suahelicus.* Broad-billed Roller.

Geelbek-troupant.

422. *Bycanistes bucinator.* Trumpeter Hornbill. Boskraai.

423. *Bycanistes brevis.* Crested Hornbill. Kuifkop-boskraai. ♂.

424. *Tockus nasutus epirhinus.* Grey Hornbill. Grys Neushoringvoël. ♂ and ♀.

425 *(a). Tockus erythrorhynchus rufirostris.* Red-billed Hornbill.

Rooibek-neushoringvoël. ♂.

426. *Tockus flavirostris leucomelas.* Yellow-billed Hornbill.

Geelbek-neushoringvoël. ♂.

427 *(b). Tockus alboterminatus australis.* Crowned Hornbill.

Gekroonde Neushoringvoël. ♂.

428. *Tockus bradfieldi.* Bradfield's Hornbill. Bradfieldse Neushoringvoël. ♂.

429. *Tockus monteiri.* Monteiro's Hornbill. Monteirose Neushoringvoël. ♂.

430. See Frontispiece.

403　Striped Kingfisher　　　　　　Gestreepte Visvanger

Halcyon chelicuti　(Stanley), 1814: *Chelicut, Ethiopia.*

PLATE 40 (OPP. P. 288).
Length 28—29 cm (wing 80—83—86; tail 42—48; tarsus 11—12; culmen 29—35. 16 specimens). Iris dark brown bill, upper mandible purplish red, lower bright red; legs reddish, brown in front. Weight 42 g.

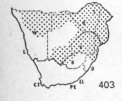

403

Identification: Easily distinguishable from Nos. 399—402 by its streaked crown and very dark eye-streak and nape; the colour pattern of the beak is also distinctive (see above). Has *only* upper tail-coverts blue, see No. 402. Sexes alike. Young birds have dark bills and buff wing-coverts.
Distribution: From Senegal to Ethiopia, thence southwards to Damaraland, the Kalahari, Transvaal and Natal.
Habits: A fairly common and widespread species, found in the dry savanna veld among large trees, often far away from water. Sits quietly on bare branches of trees, watching the ground below. Is attracted to native villages and kraals.
Food: Insects; grasshoppers, beetles, mantises, cicadas and caterpillars. Also small lizards.
Voice: One of the characteristic sounds of Africa, uttered with head bobbing up and down and wings spread; a cuckoo-clock-like "tirrrrrrrruh" or "cheer-oh". Just before sunset every kingfisher within hearing takes up the call. This call is repeated over and over again and frequently answered by others.
Breeding: Nests in old holes in trees made by barbets or woodpeckers, laying 4 or 5 white eggs which measure 24—25 × 21—22.

LOCAL RACE:
H.c. chelicuti (Stanley), 1814: *Chelicut, Ethiopia.* As illustrated; size above. Throughout the range given above except Lake Chad and West Africa.

Family MEROPIDAE

Members of this family are characterized by the long, pointed and slightly curved bill, short legs, with the front toes united, brightly coloured plumage and variously shaped tails. As the name signifies, they subsist on bees, but also on other insects, which are captured in flight, either while soaring or by darting forth at them from a perch. All the species nest in burrows in sand-banks, often in large colonies, the nests also being used at times for roosting in at night. Clutches consist of from two to seven eggs, which are always immaculate white. Several species are long-distance migrants.

404　European Bee-eater　　　　　　Europese Byvreter

Merops apiaster　Linnaeus, 1758: *Southern Europe.*

Native Names: Thlapolome (S); Makwirolwiro (Sh); i-Gwirugwiru, or i-Kwerukweru (D).

PLATE 40 (OPP. P. 288).
Length 25—29 cm (wing 137—148—157; tail 107—127; tarsus 10—12; culmen 36—41. 19 specimens from S. Africa). Iris red; bill black; legs greyish brown.

Identification: The beautiful chestnut crown and back are characteristic and distinctive. Sexes alike. Young birds have green on the nape, back and rump, and no elongated central tail-feathers; the "collar" is also faint.

290

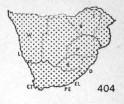

404

Distribution: Southern Europe to southern Asia. Migratory in Africa right down to Cape Town. Breeds in southern Africa but whether these are the same individuals as breed in Europe, is not known. A bird ringed in Russia recovered in Rhodesia.

Habits: Arrives in Rhodesia in September—October and stays until March, rarely until May. A single winter record 10th June, 1966, Port Alfred. In Port Elizabeth and the Cape arrives October (rarely as early as August) and departs in early February. Quite a common bird but occurs in certain areas and not others; common from Cape Town to Bushmanland and again near Port Elizabeth but not very common elsewhere. Usually seen circling high in the air, uttering their clear liquid note or perched on telegraph wires or other conspicuous posts hawking their prey. Nearly always found in flocks even when breeding. Like to sun themselves on bare trees early in the morning.

Food: Insects such as bees, dragonflies, wasps, grasshoppers, mantises, termites and butterflies.

Voice: A beautiful clear, liquid, two or three-syllabled "kwirry".

Breeding: Nests in holes in sand-banks, often in very low, almost non-existent, banks; the tunnel is long (up 2 metres) and narrow. Breeds September to December in the Cape, October to January at Port Elizabeth. Eggs 4—6, white. Average (60) 25,8 × 21,8 (23,7—28 × 20—23). Large nestlings come to the entrance of the nest-burrow to be fed.

405 See **No. 406** *(b)*

406 Blue-cheeked Bee-eater   Blouwang-byvreter

Merops superciliosus Linnaeus, 1766: *Madagascar.*

PLATE 40, 406 *(a)* AND *(b)* (OPP. P. 288).
Length 27—33 cm (wing 132—139; tail 131—162; tarsus 9—11; culmen 42—46. 5 specimens). Iris red; bill black; legs brownish.

Identification: Both races illustrated; the green back prevents confusion with the European Bee-eater while Boehm's, No. 408, is a very small bird and has no white eyebrow. Young birds lack elongated tail-feathers, top of head green and blue.

Distribution: A migrant to Africa from Persia and Malagasy. See under races.

Habits: Present from September to April. Does not sail about high up as much as the European Bee-eater, tending to hawk its prey from a fixed perch. Roosts in reed beds or mangrove swamps, flocks wheeling about at such times with powerful flight.

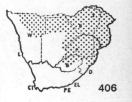

406

Food: Dragonflies, termites, bees and other flying insects.

Voice: A note scarcely distinguishable from that of the European Bee-eater.

Breeding: Race *(a)* has been found nesting in October near Gorongoza and at Mana Pools, Rhodesia. Breeds in colonies, drilling a hole in a bank. Eggs 3 or more, white, about 28 × 23, laid in October.

LOCAL RACES:
(a) M.s. superciliosus Linnaeus, 1766: *Madagascar.* As illustrated. Note top of head brownish. Size above. Malagasy, the Beira area and Kenya coast. Mainly migratory, presumably from Malagasy to Angola and north to Uganda. In our area visits the lower

Zambesi Valley as far west as Victoria Falls. Also in northern South West Africa. Visits us from September to January.

(b) M.s. persicus Pallas, 1773: *Shores of Caspian Sea.* Illustrated. Top of head blue and green. Wing 143—159; tail 125—155; tarsus 10—11,5; culmen 41—45. 6 specimens. Inhabits the area between Egypt and north-west India, where it breeds, migrating to Africa as far south as Natal and the Orange Free State; widespread in Transvaal and Rhodesia; recorded from northern South West Africa. In our area from November to April.

407 Carmine Bee-eater   Rooibors-byvreter

Merops nubicus   Gmelin, 1788: *Nubia.*

PLATE 40 (OPP. P. 288).
Length 33—38 cm (wing ♂ 145—153—160, ♀ 143—149; tail 180—220, shorter feathers 100—112; tarsus 11—13; culmen 37—46. 17 specimens, 14 ♂, 3 ♀). Iris dark brown; bill black; legs ashy brown.

Identification: Unmistakable. Sexes alike. Young birds have pink or pale bluish throats and no elongate tail-feathers.

Distribution: Zululand, Transvaal, Botswana and the Okavango northwards to Angola, Malawi and Mozambique. Migrates to Zaïre and Tanzania.

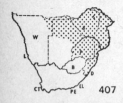

407

Habits: Occurs and breeds in our area from September to March, spending April to August in the tropics. Not a common species. At night gathers at its nesting colonies or roosts; during the day individuals scatter about the neighbourhood of rivers and marshes, taking stance on dry twigs and darting after their prey or flying about at some height often near bushfires.

Food: Grasshoppers, beetles and other insects.

Voice: A loud, deep, "terk, terk". Flocks make a harsh twittering.

Breeding: Nests in high banks on rivers, in colonies, laying in August and November. Eggs 4—5, white. Average (9) 27,0 × 22,7 (26—28,2 × 21,7—23,4).

LOCAL RACE:
M.n. nubicoides Des Murs and Pucheran, 1846: *Ouri River, South-western Transvaal.*

408 Boehm's Bee-eater   Boehmse Byvreter

Merops boehmi   Reichenow, 1882: *Bumi, nr. Kilosa, Tanganyika.*

PLATE 40 (OPP. P. 288).
Length 21,5 cm (wing 77—81; tail 125; tarsus 9; culmen 28) Iris red; bill, legs and feet black.

Identification: Smaller than No. 406 *(a)* and with no white eyebrow. Rufous area on throat also more extensive. Blue streak below eye. Sexes alike.

Distribution: From Tanzania, eastern Zaïre and Zambia south to Tete, Manica e Sofala and Rhodesia.

Habits: An uncommon, localized rather tame species which frequents the edges of thickets and riverine forest near large rivers. Usually in pairs. Behaves rather like No. 410, taking short flights after insects and not flying very high.

Voice: A shrill chirping "swee" and a liquid trill.

Breeding: The nest hole, about 2 m long, is made in a bank or sometimes on flat ground. Eggs, 3—4, white 18—19 × 15—15,2.

409 White-fronted Bee-eater
Rooikeel-byvreter

Melittophagus bullockoides (A. Smith), 1834: *South Africa=Marico District, Transvaal.*

Native Name: i-Nkota (Z).

PLATE 40 (OPP. P. 288).
Length 22—24 cm (wing 111—114—119; tail 93—105; tarsus 7,5—9,5; culmen 32—39. 16 specimens). Iris dark hazel; bill black; legs greenish black.

Identification: The square-cut tail, red throat and white forehead are distinctive. Sexes alike. Young birds have a bluish tinge on the back and the red throat is paler.
Distribution: Natal and Transvaal northwards to Kenya and the Congo. Recorded once from Swakopmund. Subject to local movement in Rhodesia.
Habits. A resident tropical species that occurs along streams and dried-up rivers. Occurs alone or in pairs and hawks continually from a few favourite perches, returning to them regularly. Roosts in large numbers in trees, on rocks, or on ledges on banks.
Food: Beetles, butterflies and other insects.
Voice: A sharp, shrill nasal "kwaank-kwani-kwani", "crekow", "chackar" or "krrrt". Twitters when roosting.
Breeding: Nests colonially in sand-banks, the burrows being a metre or more long. The nest chamber is usually floored with many regurgitated insect remains. Eggs, usually 4 in number, are laid during September and early October. They are white. Average (44) 22,7 × 18,8 (20,2—25 × 17,3—20,5).

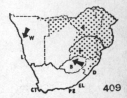

409

410 Little Bee-eater
Klein Byvreter

Melittophagus pusillus (Müller), 1776: *Senegal.*

Native Name: i-Guondwana (Z).

PLATE 40 (OPP. P. 288).
Length 17—18 cm (wing 77—81—84; tail 61—69; tarsus 7—9; culmen 23—29. 35 specimens). Iris red, brown in young; bill black; legs dusky.

Identification: The small size, square tail and black collar are diagnostic. Sexes alike. Young birds have no black collar and are pale greenish below.
Distribution: From Natal and the Vaal River northwards to Senegal, the Sudan and Ethiopia.
Habits: A common, resident species near rivers and streams, but also found at some distance from water during the breeding season. Usually seen singly or in pairs; if in larger numbers the individuals do not seem to have anything to do with one another. Perches low down on bushes or bare sticks, to which it returns after hawking its prey. Has favourite perches where it may be found day after day. A pair may often be seen sitting side by side on one of these perches.
Food: Beetles and other insects, such as butterflies and dragonflies.
Voice: Rather quiet but utters a low squeaky note.
Breeding: Does not nest colonially; eggs are laid from September to November, mainly in October, and are placed at the end of a burrow from 0,5—1,25 metres long in a low sand-bank or antbear hole. Eggs 4—6, white.

410

293

Average (100) 18,7 × 15,8 (17—20,5 × 14,4—17). Incubation begins with the first egg, 28—29 days. Nestling period 29 days. Both sexes feed the young.

LOCAL RACE:
M.p. meridonalis Sharpe, 1892: *Pinetown, Natal*. As illustrated; size above. Southern Africa to Zaïre and Uganda.

411 Swallow-tailed Bee-eater — Mikstert-byvreter

Dicrocercus hirundineus (Lichtenstein), 1793: *Orange River*.

PLATE 40 (OPP. P. 288).
Length 20—22 cm (wing 90—103; tail 90—106; tarsus 8—9,5; culmen 27—35. 10 specimens). Iris crimson; bill black; legs brown.

Identification: The very forked blue tail is distinctive. Sexes alike. Young birds lack the yellow throat but are distinguishable from all other species by the forked tail.

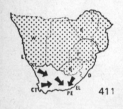

411

Distribution: From the Orange River on the west and the Limpopo on the east, northwards to Zaïre, Sudan and Ethiopia.

Habits: A species which is quite common and occurs in a wide range of habitat, from semi-desert to dry or even quite moist woodland. Usually solitary, in pairs or—when not breeding—in small restless parties, taking stance in the trees bordering pans and drier river-beds and hawking insects therefrom. Usually has its favourite perch which may be quite low down in barren country or high up where there are large trees. In winter subject to some movement, leaving the colder areas for those free from frost. Have been seen to roost, three or four deep, sitting on each other's backs.

Food: Grasshoppers, wasps and other flying insects. Said to take insects from flowers, thus getting pollen on their foreheads.

Voice: A soft "kwit, kwit", repeated several times.

Breeding: Does not breed colonially; makes burrows in sand-banks, about a metre long. Eggs are laid from September to November in South West Africa. Eggs are white, normally numbering 3 or 4. Average (15) 20,8 × 18,3 (20—21,8 × 16,8—19,5).

LOCAL RACE:
(a) *D.h. hirundineus* (Lichtenstein), 1793: *Orange River*. Southern Africa to Angola to W. Rhodesia. As illustrated; size above.
(b) *D.h. furcatus* Stanley 1814 *Mozambique*. Mozambique, S.E. Rhodesia north to Tanzania. Darker above and below, abdomen bluer; throat band broader and darker.

Family CORACIIDAE

Characterized by their medium size (about the size of a Pigeon), strong bill much like a Crow's, handsomely coloured plumage, with blue in the wings, the tail squared or with the outer pair elongate ornamentally: the front toes are united, but the outer one at the base only, so that it is reversible. Feed exclusively upon large insects, usually taken from the ground, to find which they take up stance upon some tree whence they can have a wide view. They nest in holes in trees in early summer, and lay immaculate white eggs. Peculiar in their habit, during periods of excitement, of dashing about in the air, uttering raucous screeches, especially when other birds come near their haunts, and tumbling or "rolling" about in an extraordinary fashion. Most species are residents within the tropics, but one is a migrant from southern Europe and Asia and another is a migrant within the tropics.

412 European Roller   Europese Troupant

Coracias garrulus Linnaeus, 1758: *Europe* = *Sweden.*

PLATE 41 (OPP. P. 289).
Length 30—31 cm (wing ♂ 194—198—204, ♀ 186—191—197; tail 115—135; tarsus 22—25; culmen 33—40. 18 specimens, 10 ♂, 8 ♀). Iris brown; bill blackish; legs grey.

Identification: Likely to be confused with the next species but has a *square* tail and is greener about the head and below. Sexes alike. Young birds are duller, have streaks of brown on the chest, brownish heads and uniform blue-green outer tail-feathers.

Distribution: Europe, the Middle East and western Asia. A summer migrant to Africa coming as far south as Damaraland on the west, Knysna on the east with odd specimens as far west as Mossel Bay, Somerset West and Mamre.

Habits: Arrives in Rhodesia, where it is primarily a bird of passage, in October and departs in March; reaches the Cape later, about December, and leaves in February. In some years, penetrates further southwards and in larger numbers than in others. Like most rollers is usually seen perched on telegraph wires or other conspicuous posts, flying down to catch its prey on the ground. Appears rather crow-like in posture.

Food: Grasshoppers and beetles. Also takes flying termites.

Voice: A loud harsh "rack-kack, kacker".

LOCAL RACE:
C.g. garrulus Linneaus, 1758: *Europe* = *Sweden.* As illustrated. Size above.

413 Lilac-breasted Roller   Gewone Troupant

Coracias caudata Linnaeus, 1766: *Angola.*

Native Names: le-Thakela, Mathlakela, Leclercler (Ch); Fefe (Z and T); im-Veve (G).

PLATE 41 (OPP. P. 289).
Length about 36 cm (wing 157—166—174; tail 108—128; long feathers 156—218; tarsus 20—24; culmen 29—37. 27 specimens). Iris dark hazel; bill black; legs greenish yellow.

Identification: Might easily be confused with the Racquet-tailed Roller, No. 414, but has *straight* outer tail-feathers and is much darker lilac on the chest; also has more blue in the wing. (See also No. 412.) Sexes alike. Young birds do not have the long outer tail-feathers and are brownish below.

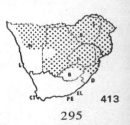

Distribution: From northern South West Africa, the Kalahari National Park, the Vaal River and Natal northwards to Zaïre, Ethiopia and Somaliland. Common in the Kruger Park.

Habits: A fairly common resident in the thornveld savannas, usually seen singly or in pairs, occasionally in family parties on trees within calling distance of each other. The blue wings are particularly beautiful in flight, hence the popular name "Blue Jay". Mosilikatze, king of the Matabele, reserved the feathers of this bird for his exclusive use and it is often known as Mosilikatze's Roller. It is quickly attracted by grass fires. During the breeding season performs various aerobatics in the air, accompanied by noisy screams, in particular performs quick rolls. Eats its prey on the ground.

Food: Very varied; locusts, grasshoppers, small reptiles, beetles, caterpillars (including the hairy varieties), ants, beetles, scorpions, centipedes and even small birds.

Voice: Various harsh screams, mainly in the breeding season.

Breeding: Nests in holes in trees, from August to December, usually at a height of 2—3 metres; the eggs lie on a little dust and dead leaves, no attempt to line the hole being made. Eggs 3, sometimes 2, are white. Average (19) 32,2 × 26 (30—34 × 24,5—28,5).

LOCAL RACE:
C.c. caudata Linnaeus, 1766: *Angola*. As illustrated; size above. Southern Africa to Kenya and Uganda.

414   Racquet-tailed Roller   Knopstert-troupant

Coracias spatulata   Trimen, 1880: *Leshumo Valley, near Victoria Falls*.

PLATE 41 (OPP. P. 289).
Length about 36 cm (wing 159—176; tail 135—157, long feathers 193—225; tarsus 20,5—21,5; culmen 30,5—35). Iris yellowish brown; bill black; legs greenish yellow.

Identification: The racquet-shaped tail-feathers are diagnostic; see also No. 413. Sexes alike. Young birds lack the elongated tail-feathers, are more lilac on the cheeks and side of breast and streaked with white, thus resembling the young of No. 413, from which they differ by having violet, not greenish blue, primary wing-coverts and brown, not green, feathers on the wing below the shoulder. Flight undulating; another way of telling it from No. 413.

Distribution: From Rhodesia and the lower Zambesi Valley northwards to Tanzania and across to Zaïre and northern Angola. Farthest south in the east Gollel.

Habits: A resident, although Matabeleland birds move east in the dry season. Inhabits rather more dense woodland than the last species but is also found in open *Brachystegia* and Mopane. General habits much the same as No. 413.

414   When breeding, displays by flying in a rapid zig-zag for some distance, then suddenly shoots straight up into the air for 5 or 7 metres with closed wings, curving gently over and descending, still with closed wings, screaming all the time.

Food: Grasshoppers, beetles and fly maggots recorded.

Voice: A high-pitched cackle.

Breeding: Nests in holes in trees during October and November. The eggs are white; 3 seems to be the normal clutch. Average (6) 32,2 × 26,2 (31,7—33,2 × 25,3—26,8).

415 Purple Roller   Groot Troupant

Coracias naevia Daudin, 1800: *Senegal*.

PLATE 41 (OPP. P. 289).
Length 36—40 cm (wing 175—189—198; tail 135—152; tarsus 22—26; culmen
37—46. 23 specimens). Iris dark brown; bill black; legs greenish brown.

Identification: Larger and much more heavily built than the other rollers;
shows a distinct white eyebrow. Sexes alike. Young birds have throat, chest
and breast brown streaked white; rump reddish brown with white shaft-stripes.
Distribution: From central South West Africa, Botswana, Orange Free State
and Zululand northwards to Senegal and Ethiopia.
Habits: Not uncommon in the savanna thornveld, like other species in pairs
or small parties, perched on the tops of trees or other conspicuous posts.
Rather more sluggish than the smaller species. Seems to be migratory, being
present in southern Mozambique from June to September; in Rhodesia from
May to December. Has the habit, in the breeding season, of rising suddenly
into the air, rocking from side to side as if its wings were beating unevenly,
and then flopping down again in the same way, crying "kra-kra".
Food: Various large insects and lizards, scorpions and small snakes.
Voice: Quieter than most rollers; various harsh grating sounds, like a knife
cutting through tough cork but louder.
Breeding: Nests in Rhodesia from September to November; young have been
found in July in South West Africa. Uses hollows in trees such as old
woodpeckers' nests or natural holes. Lays 2—3 white eggs. Average (8) 35,4
× 28,7 (34—36,6 × 27,4—29,1).

415

LOCAL RACE:
C.n. mosambica Dresser, 1890: *Mozambique = Zambesi*. As illustrated; size above.
From our area as far north as Malawi and south-east Zaïre.

416 Broad-billed Roller   Geelbek-troupant

Eurystomus glaucurus (Müller), 1776: *Madagascar*.

PLATE 41 (OPP. P. 289) NO. 417.
Length about 27 cm (wing 170—176—183; tail 92—104; tarsus 15—19; culmen
22—25,5. 22 specimens). Iris hazel; bill bright yellow; legs greenish brown.

Identification: Easily identified; the only roller with a bright yellow bill.
Sexes alike. Young are duller brown, streaked with blackish; breast to belly
greenish blue.
Distribution: From Zululand and Mozambique, the Transvaal, N. Botswana,
Rhodesia in September or October and stays till May. In Mozambique October
to December. (See under "Local Races".)
Habits: An uncommon migrant to our area, which breeds here. Prefers rather
thicker bush and forest than other rollers. Sits on a prominent perch whence it
catches its prey; also hawks insects at a considerable height. Flight wheeling
and erratic. Very aggressive, continually chasing other birds. Individuals
return to the same area year after year.
Food: Beetles, grasshoppers, ants, moths and wasps.

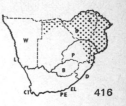

416

Voice: Extremely noisy, main call a chattering "sar a roc, sar a roc", uttered at rest or in flight.

Breeding: Nests in holes in hollow trees during October to December. Eggs 2—3, white. Average (13) 32,2 × 25,9 (30,2—33,7 × 24,3—26,6).

LOCAL RACES:

(a) E.g. glaucurus (Müller), 1776: *Madagascar.* A large race. Wing 200—210; tail 120—130; tarsus 18—20; culmen 31—33 after Reichenow. Malagasy migrating to East Africa, in our area to the Beira area from about March to September.

(b) E.g suahelicus Neumann, 1905: *Tschara, Tana River.* Upper tail-coverts blue, not greenish blue. Size above. East Africa, migrating south to Rhodesia and Mozambique, Zululand, Transvaal and Botswana. Illustrated as No. 417.

417 = 416 *(b)*.

Family UPUPIDAE

The Hoopoes are characterized by their long, rather slender, curved and pointed bills; three toes in front, the inner joined at the base and the other two for half their length, the hind toe as long as the front ones and all with rather short, sharply curved, stout, but sharp-tipped claws; in one subfamily, *Upupinae,* there is a large crest and the plumage is reddish with white across the wings, in the other subfamily, *Phoeniculinae,* there is no crest and the plumage is dark and glossy.

418   African Hoopoe   Hoephoep

Upupa africana   Bechstein, 1811: *Malimbe, Gaboon, French West Africa.*

Native Names: Ubhobmoyi (X); u-Ziningweni (Z); Pupupu, le-Remakatzaka (S); in-Zimpupu (G); Chigububu (D).

PLATE 34 (OPP. P. 240).

Length about 27 cm (wing ♂ 132—140—145, ♀ 128—135—140; tail 84—100; tarsus 16,5—21; culmen 42—56. 39 specimens, 26 ♂, 13 ♀). Iris and bill dark brown; legs grey-brown. Weight 46—49 g.

Identification: The female is slightly smaller and quite a lot duller than the male. Young birds are even duller than the female being dirty brown rather than brick-red; secondaries barred black and white.

Distribution: From Cape Town to Zaïre and Ethiopia.

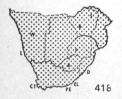

Habits: A resident, common and well-known species, usually found in the savanna veld but entering towns and gardens, becoming very tame. Restless, disappearing from some localities but not a regular migrant. Frequents lawns a great deal and spends most of its time on the ground, walking busily about probing continually with its long bill and occasionally raising its crest which is normally carried folded and not as illustrated. The large wings impart a butterfly-like quality to its flight.

Food: Caterpillars, grubs, termites, beetles, burrowing snakes, frogs and ant-lions.

Voice: An oft-repeated "hoop, hoop", audible for several hundred yards; uttered in the breeding season. Young birds after leaving the nest call "sweet, sweet".

Breeding: Nests in holes in the ground, among stones, in burrows in banks, hollow trees, attics, eaves and in termite mounds. Breeds from August to December in the Cape and Rhodesia. The nest may be lined with some grass or quite bare; it is used year after year and usually for 2 or 3 broods per year. Eggs number 4—7 and are pale blue at first but rapidly become soiled to olive-brown, the pores showing white when about to hatch. Average (43) 25,3 × 17,2 (22,2—27,5 × 16,1—18,1). Incubation by female only, 17 days; the male feeds her and continues to do so for some 7 days after the eggs hatch. Nestling period 26—32 days; both sexes feed. The nest becomes very foul and evil-smelling, even the egg-shells are not removed. More than a pair may feed young in a nest.

419 Red-billed Hoopoe   Kakelaar

Phoeniculus purpureus   (Miller), 1794: *India orientali = Eastern Cape Province.*

Native Names: Intleki'Bafazi (X); u-Nukana, u-Hlekabafazi, u-Kolukoli (Z); i-Hlebabafazi (G).

PLATE 34, RACE *(a)* ♂ AND NO. 420 = RACE *(d)* (OPP. P. 240).
Length 30—36 cm (wing ♂ 131—137—142, ♀ 125—133—137; tail ♂ 162—187, ♀ 160—170; tarsus 20—24; culmen ♂ 52—62, ♀ 41—48. 21 specimens, 9 ♂, 12 ♀). Iris dark brown; bill red; legs red. Weight ♂ 67 g.

Identification: Distinguished from the Scimitar-bill Hoopoe, No. 421, by its red beak and white spots in the tail. These are conspicuous in flight. Sexes alike but males slightly larger and longer billed. Young birds have black bills and are duller below.

Distribution: From Knysna eastwards to Ethiopia and across to Senegal; from Transvaal westwards to Damaraland and Angola.

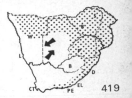

419

Habits: A resident species in the dry forests, especially along streams; quite common and very conspicuous because of its noisy habits. An essentially arboreal species, spending its time clambering around in parties examining the trunks and branches of trees for its food. The tail is used in the manner of a woodpecker and becomes very worn as the birds scramble up trunks, falling from one position to another, checking with the tail. They roost in very restricted nest-holes. Specimens held in the hand smell most disagreeable. Very restless, continually flying from one tree to the next.

Food: Beetles, millipedes, termites, caterpillars, ants and grasshoppers.

Voice: A variety of cackling noises hence the Native names which refer to the hysterical "laughter of women". General character of notes a "kak-kak-kkkkkk", usually started by one bird and quickly taken up by the rest of the flock.

Breeding: Nests in holes in trees from September to November; July and March also recorded, February to December in Rhodesia. Eggs 3—4, pale olive-green. Average (39) 24,8 × 17,1 (22,8—29,2 × 16—18,3). Incubation by female only, fed by the male or by whole parties of birds; similarly the young may be fed by parents and elder brothers and sisters (?) from previous broods. Double brooded.

LOCAL RACES:
(a) P.p. purpureus (Miller), 1794: *India orientali = Eastern Cape Province*. As illustrated; size above. Eastern Cape to Natal.

299

(b) P.p. marwitzi (Reichenow), 1906: *Makalama, Tanzania.* Small with broad white tips to bastard wing-feathers. Wing ♂ 137—142; ♀ 127—134; tail ♂ 200—225, ♀ 195—214. 5 specimens, 2 ♂, 3 ♀. Northern Zululand to Uganda and across to eastern Rhodesia in our area.

(c) P.p. angolensis (Reichenow), 1902: *Caconda, Angola.* The largest form. Wing ♂ 150—157—165, ♀ 141—152—158; tail 215—262; culmen ♂ 54—64, ♀ 41—48. 20 specimens 11 ♂, 9 ♀. Angola, northern South West Africa, Ngamiland, Transvaal and western Rhodesia.

(d) P.p. damarensis (O. Grant), 1901: *Damaraland.* Illustrated. Wing ♂ 148—157— 164, ♀ 149—152—158; tail ♂ 230—262, ♀ 210—242; culmen ♂ 44—58, ♀ 43—45. 12 specimens 8 ♂, 4 ♀. Damaraland.

421   Scimitar-billed Hoopoe   Swartbek-kakelaar

Rhinopomastus cyanomelas   (Vieillot), 1819: *Namaqualand.*

PLATE 34 (OPP. P. 240) ♂.
Length 24—28 cm (wing ♂ 110—113—122, ♀ 100—103—106; tail ♂ 125—133—147, ♀ 113—118—132; culmen ♂ 42—49, ♀ 35—42,5. 16 specimens, 8 ♂, 8 ♀). Iris brown; bill and legs black.

Identification: Easily distinguished from the previous species by its more curved *black* beak. The female resembles the male but is smaller, has a brownish throat and grey tips to flight-feathers. Young birds have throat and chest quite brown.

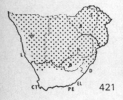

Distribution: From Natal and the Orange River northwards to Angola, the eastern Congo, Uganda and Kenya.

421

Habits: A fairly common species that inhabits drier savanna areas than the Red-billed Hoopoe, though the two are sometimes found close together. Occurs singly or in pairs, less often in small family parties than the last species and is also less noisy. Creeps about the bark of trees looking for insects and is perhaps even more agile than the Red-billed Hoopoe.

Food: Insects and their larvae; ants, flies, wasps, spiders and a few seeds and buds.

Voice: The commonest call is 3 or 4 high-pitched whistles, "whi, whi, whi", very distinctive and audible for several hundred yards; also a chattering "wha, wha, wha" and a descending twitter.

Breeding: Nests in holes in trees during September to November, laying 3 to 4 pale greenish blue eggs with distinct white pores. Average (5) 22,0 × 16,1 (21,7—22,5 × 15,3—16,5). Both sexes feed the young.

LOCAL RACES:
(a) R.c. cyanomelas (Vieillot), 1819: *Namaqualand.* As illustrated; tail short and little or not marked with white. Western Transvaal and north of the Orange River to Angola.
(b) R.c. schalowi Neumann, 1900: *Usandawe, Tanganyika.* Tail longer and more marked with white. Tail ♂ 180—185 (3), ♀ 160 (1). Natal, eastern Transvaal, Mashonaland and Mozambique north to Kenya, Uganda and Eastern Zaïre.

Family BUCEROTIDAE

The Hornbills are characterized by their large, stout, rather curved and pointed bills, usually, especially in males, with a horny casque on top that seems to be ornamental and is of various shapes; the legs are short, coarsely scaled, with the three front toes joined together at the base, the two inner ones farther forward than the outer, the claws short, much curved and with sharp edges. They are medium to large-sized and clumsy birds, easily recognized by their alternate flapping and gliding, rather heavy flight. All of them inhabit forest or savanna country, some strictly arboreal and feeding upon fruit and berries.

others partly terrestrial and taking insects and other small animals on the ground, the extreme of which is found in the Ground Hornbill that strides—or rather waddles—over the veld in search of insects, reptiles, small animals and birds. Their nesting habits are notorious, in that the hen bird is shut up in the nest—a hole in a tree or amongst rocks—with some form of plaster, during the whole period of incubation and until the young are able to fly, the male bird meanwhile providing all the food to feed the female and the young; during her incarceration the female becomes very fat and moults all her wing and tail quills. An exception to this rule is found in the Ground Hornbill. They have distinctive call-notes. Members of the family are found over the greater part of Africa, in southern Asia and islands to the south as far east as New Guinea and the Solomon Islands.

422 Trumpeter Hornbill   Boskraai

Bycanistes bucinator (Temminck), 1824: *Cape of Good Hope =*
Eastern Cape Province.

Native Names: Ilitwa (X); i-Kakamira, i-Shererakuri (G).

PLATE 41 (OPP. P. 289).
Length 58—65 cm (wing ♂ 276—289—298, ♀ 252—264—278; tail 192—235; tarsus 35—42; culmen from back of casque ♂ 140—157, ♀ 117—131; casque ♂ 125—150, ♀ 65—93. 25 specimens, 11 ♂, 14 ♀. Iris red; bare skin round eye, pink; bill and legs black.

Identification: Distinguished from the next species by its smaller casque, *pink* skin round eyes, and by having white ends to the secondaries, noticeable as a white trailing edge in flight; the black below ends on the throat. Sexes alike but female smaller with a smaller, truncated casque ending about the middle of the bill.
Distribution: From the Alexandria forest, to Kenya and Angola on the west.
Habits: Essentially a bird of forests and large trees along rivers, occasionally wandering into quite dry country to seek food. Noisy and active early in the morning and in the evenings. Usually encountered in small flocks and often mobbed by small birds.

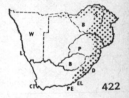

Food: Mainly frugivorous with an occasional large insect.
Voice: Makes a wide variety of wails, cat-calls, screams and braying sounds.
Breeding: Nests in holes in trees from October to December, plastering the entrance to the nest hole with mud and excrement until a narrow slit is left through which the hen is fed by her mate. The eggs are white, and 2—4 form the clutch. Average (10) 47,8 × 34,7 (45—50,2 × 33,3—36,8). The youngest and eldest chick are very different in size. The nest is said to be plastered up after use to preserve it for the following year. Also nests in crevices in rocks.

423 Crested Hornbill   Kuifkop-boskraai

Bycanistes brevis Friedmann, 1929: *Mount Lutindi, Tanganyika.*

PLATE 41 (OPP. P. 289).
Length 75—80 cm (wing 350—365; tail 270—300; tarsus 45—56; culmen from back of casque 145—210; casque ♂ 162—205; ♀ 92—115). Iris brown or crimson; bare skin round eye blue, grey or pinkish; bill brownish grey, casque yellowish.

Identification: Has casque and line at base of bill yellow; breast black and wings all black, no white trailing edge as in the last species. Female smaller and with a truncated casque. Young birds have low casques.

301

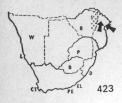

Distribution: From eastern Rhodesia and Beira northwards to Ethiopia.

Habits: A species of coastal and montane forest where it may be found in pairs or quite large flocks of fifty or so; roosts communally sometimes in hundreds. Flight straight and undulating with periods of gliding after every four or five wing-beats; the wings making a loud soughing noise.

Food: Fruit, mainly figs; also locusts.

423

Voice: A loud "quark, quark, quark" and various braying, howling and screeching sounds.

Breeding: The female immures herself in a hole high up in a tall tree, with saliva and earth brought by the male. She remains there about 4½ months and is fed by the male. Eggs 2—3, are white. Three measure 45,6—47,5 × 32,5—33,5. Breeds in our area during October.

424 Grey Hornbill   Grys Neushoringvoël

Tockus nasutus (Linnaeus), 1766: *Senegal.*

PLATE 41 (OPP. P. 289) ♂ AND ♀.
Length 43—48 cm (wing ♂ 215—223—232, ♀ 197—203—208; tail 185—209; tarsus 28—32; culmen ♂ 82—90, ♀ 66—73, 21 specimens 14 ♂, 7 ♀. Iris reddish brown; bill as illustrated; legs black.

Identification: The dark beak of the male is distinctive among the small hornbills; the female might be mistaken for a Yellow-billed Hornbill, No. 426, but the grey head, white eyebrow and brown tail should avoid confusion. Shows a white streak down the back in flight. Young birds are browner on the head but young females have still more yellow on the beak which is smaller.

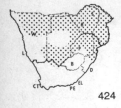

Distribution: From Zululand, Transvaal, Botswana and Damaraland northwards to Eritrea and across to Senegal.

Habits: A common species in the dry acacia, savanna bush, spending most of its time in trees and only occasionally descending to the ground. Usually seen in parties of four to five which move with dipping flight from tree to tree, usually gliding, with a few flaps as they rise to land; after landing they raise the tail. Is quickly attracted by grass fires.

424

Food: Mainly fruit; also small reptiles and insects, including termites.

Voice: A plaintive, whistled "pee-u" repeated over and over, rather reminiscent of a curlew. This is uttered with wing flaps and the bill pointing upwards and is preceded by a ticking sound.

Breeding: The female plasters herself up in a hole in a tree or rarely among rocks, leaving only a small aperture. She undergoes a complete moult while inside and when the chicks are 3 to 4 weeks old, breaks out to help feed them. The chicks then repair the hole and keep the nest clean. Both the female and the young defecate outside, through the hole. Three eggs are normally laid, during October or November. September to December in Rhodesia. They are dull white. Average (7) 37,1 × 26,6 (34,8—38,9 × 26—27,5). Incubation period 21—24 days. The young remain in the nest 21 days after the mother emerges.

LOCAL RACES:
(a) T.n. epirhinus (Sundevall), 1851: *Caffr. sup. ad lat. 24° S. = Upper Limpopo Valley. Tvl.* As illustrated; size above. Southern Africa to Kenya.
(b) T.n. dorsalis Sanft, 1954: *Onguma, S.W.A.* Paler above than *(a)*. South West Africa, western Botswana.

425 Red-billed Hornbill

Rooibek-neushoringvoël

Tockus erythrorhynchus (Temminck), 1823: *Senegal.*

Native Name: Khokhoropo (Ch).

PLATE 41 ♂ (OPP. P. 289).
Length 42—50 cm (wing ♂ 183—187—195, ♀ 162—171—182; tail 174—200; tarsus 33—41; culmen ♂ 72—79, ♀ 59—67,5. 14 specimens, 5 ♂, 9 ♀. Iris yellow; bill red, base of lower mandible black; legs dark brown.

Identification: No casque. A small species whose red beak prevents confusion with the Yellow-billed Hornbill, No. 426. The whiter neck and head together with large amounts of white in the wings should prevent confusion with Nos. 427—9. Sexes alike, but female smaller and with a shorter beak. Young birds have short bills and buffy spots on the wing-coverts.
Distribution: Swaziland, Transvaal, Botswana and Damaraland north to Ethiopia and across to Senegal. Common in the Kruger Park.
Habits: A common species of savanna woodlands and larger trees, usually found in small flocks which may enter native villages, kraals or rest camps in game reserves. Becomes very tame. Spends a lot of time on the ground, unlike the last species.
Food: Mainly insects such as beetles, grasshoppers and other larvae; also fruit and bulbs.
Voice: Its call note is characteristic: "tshu-tweetshwee" (three times), "tshutshutshu" (three times), "tshutweetshwee" (three times), "kukwee" (twice).
Breeding: Nests in holes in trees during October to January; general breeding behaviour similar to the last species. Eggs 3 to 6, white and pitted. Average (29) 39,2 × 27,9 (37,7—41,9 × 26,2—30,4).

425

LOCAL RACES:
(a) T.e. rufirostris (Sundevall), 1850: *Aapies River, Pretoria, Transvaal.* As illustrated; size above. Swaziland to Malawi, Transvaal, Botswana and southern Angola.
(b) T.e. damarensis (Shelley), 1888: *Otjimbinque, S.W.A.* Much whiter than *(a)*, feathers on the lower throat pure white at base not grey, and other parts also whiter; bill longer. Wing ♂ 181—193—200; culmen ♂ 88—93—99 (7). Northern South West Africa. The nominate may extend to the Kaokoveld.
(c) T.e. degens Clancey, 1964: *Mlaula Estates, Stegi dist. Swaziland.* Similar to *(a)* but smaller wing ♂ 166—171—179, ♂ 160—163. Zululand, eastern Swaziland, Transvaal Lowveld, eastern Rhodesia and Mozambique.

426 Yellow-billed Hornbill

Geelbek-neushoringvoël

Tockus flavirostris (Rüppell), 1835: *Taranta Mountains, Eritrea.*

Native Name: Mokhothopitzi (Ch).

PLATE 41 ♂ (OPP. P. 289).
Length 48—60 cm (wing ♂ 190—203—213, ♀ 182—191—203; tail 195—222; tarsus 34—43; culmen ♂ 71—92, ♀ 67—77. 26 specimens, 15 ♂, 11 ♀. Iris yellowish white; bill yellow; legs blackish.

Identification: Rather similar to the last species but larger and with a yellow bill. Sexes alike, female smaller. Young birds darker with bill dusky yellow.
Distribution: From Zululand and the Orange River northwards to Angola on the west, Somaliland and the Sudan. Common in the Kruger Park.

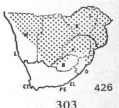
426

PLATE 42

431. *Lybius torquatus torquatus.* Black-collared Barbet.

Rooikop-houtkapper.

432. *Tricholaema leucomelas leucomelas.* Pied Barbet. Bont Houtkapper.

433. *Buccanodon leucotis leucotis.* White-eared Barbet. Witoor-houtkapper.

434. *Buccanodon whytii sowerbyi.* Yellow-fronted Barbet.

Geelbles-houtkapper.

435. *Buccanodon olivaceum.* Green Barbet. Groen Houtkapper.

436. *Pogoniulus pusillus pusillus.* Red-fronted Tinker Barbet.

Rooikop-tinker.

437. *Pogoniulus chrysoconus extoni.* Yellow-fronted Tinker Barbet.

Geelkop-tinker.

438. *Pogoniulus bilineatus bilineatus.* Golden-rumped Tinker Barbet.

Swartkop-tinker.

438X. *Viridibucco simplex.* Green Tinker Barbet. Groen Tinker.

439. *Trachyphonus vaillantii.* Crested Barbet. Kuifkop-houtkapper.

453. *Jynx ruficollis ruficollis.* Red-throated Wryneck. Draaihals.

432

433

436

431

434

437

435

KN

438

438x

KN

439

453

MIGHTON
'37

PLATE 43

445. *Geocolaptes olivaceus olivaceus.* Ground Woodpecker. Grondspegt.
446 *(a). Campethera bennettii bennettii.* Bennett's Woodpecker.
Bennettse Spegt. ♂ and ♀.
446X. *Campethera scriptoricauda.* Tanzanian Woodpecker. ♂ and ♀.
447 *(b). Campethera abingoni abingoni.* Golden-tailed Woodpecker.
Goudstert-spegt. ♂ and ♀.
447 *(d). Campethera abingoni anderssoni.* Golden-tailed Woodpecker.
Goudstert-spegt. ♂ and ♀.
448. *Campethera notata.* Knysna Woodpecker. Knysna-spegt.
449. *Campethera cailliautii fuelleborni.* Little Spotted Woodpecker.
Klein Gevlekte Spegt. ♂ and ♀.
450 *(a). Dendropicos fuscescens fuscescens.* Cardinal Woodpecker.
Kardinaal-spegt. ♂ and ♀.
450 *(e). Dendropicos fuscescens loandae.* Cardinal Woodpecker.
Kardinaal-spegt. ♂ and ♀.
451. *Thripias namaquus namaquus.* Bearded Woodpecker. Namakwa-spegt.
♂ and ♀.
452. *Mesopicos griseocephalus griseocephalus.* Olive Woodpecker.
Gryskop-spegt. ♂ and ♀.

Habits: Another common species of dry savanna thornbush and Mopane areas, rare in mountainous country. Also frequents kraals and native villages if not disturbed and becomes quite tame. Spends a lot of time on the ground.
Food: Mainly insects, including ants, winged termites and others caught in the air; also fruit, seeds and small vertebrates such as lizards.
Voice: Call note a repeated "tock-tock-tocke-tocke". The mating call is uttered with the wings up and head held right down below the feet and sounds like "tock, tock, tock, tack (rising), tschedeck-tschedeck . . .".
Breeding: Nests only in holes in trees, the entrance being cemented with clay, insect remains and any other debris in the nest. October to January, March in Rhodesia. Eggs white with conspicuous pores; 2, or more, often 3 to the clutch. Average (8) 37,9 × 27,5 (35,3—39,6 × 26,3—28,8).

LOCAL RACE:
T.f. leucomelas (Lichtenstein), 1842: *Kaffirland.* Southern Africa and Angola. As illustrated; size above.

427   Crowned Hornbill   Gekroonde Neushoringvoël

Tockus alboterminatus   (Büttikofer), 1889: *Gambos, Angola.*

Native Names: Umkholwane (X and Z); i-Goto (D); Woto (Zw).
PLATE 41 ♂ (OPP. P. 289).
Length 50—54 cm (wing ♂ 247—255—266; ♀ 232—234—237; tail 203—235; tarsus 27—32; culmen ♂ 91—99, ♀ 77—90. 9 specimens, 4 ♂, 5 ♀. Iris yellow; bill red, basal band yellow; legs dark brown.

Identification: The only medium-sized hornbill with a red beak having a casque; the dark head and chest are also characteristic except for No. 428, but that species has no casque. Sexes alike, female slightly smaller. Young birds have casque indistinct, bill orange and buff edges to wing-coverts and tail-feathers.
Distribution: From Knysna eastwards to Rhodesia and onwards to Somaliland.
Habits: A common species of forested or lightly wooded country with patches of thicker forest. May be seen in quite open fields or even in gardens of towns. Although a social species, usually seen in small or quite large flocks, pairs mate for life. They roost at several definite sites, using each for about three weeks before moving on to the next; roosting perches are usually slender twigs open to the sky above.
Food: Insects such as grasshoppers, caterpillars (including hairy ones), termites, wasps and beetles; also chameleons, small birds, fruit and seeds.
Voice: Main call a series of melancholy whistling notes. Also a bugling threat call.
Breeding: The female immures herself in a hole in a tree from 2 to 14 metres above the ground. The cement used consists of dung, bark and soil from the bottom of the nest, with saliva. October and November. Eggs, normally 4, are white. A clutch (4) measures 39,5—42,5 × 28,5—30. After about 70 days the female breaks out and the young remain 24 days or so longer, after plastering the nest up again.

427

LOCAL RACES:
(a) T.a. alboterminatus (Büttikofer), 1889: *Gambos, Angola.* Kunene and Okavango rivers. Pale. Smaller than *(b).* Wing ♂ 228—249, ♀ 211—230. Lower Zambesi, northern Mozambique to Kenya.
(b) T.a. australis (Roberts), 1932: *Riet River, Bathurst.* As illustrated; size above. Cape Province to Mashonaland and southern Mozambique.

428 Bradfield's Hornbill   Bradfieldse Neushoringvoël

Tockus bradfieldi   (Roberts), 1930: *Waterberg.*

PLATE 41 ♂ (OPP. P. 289).
Length 50—57 cm (wing ♂ 254—264—272, ♀ 230—232—234; tail ♂ 215—250, ♀ 194—230; tarsus 28—38; culmen ♂ 86—111, ♀ 77—89. 14 specimens, 8 ♂, 6 ♀. Iris yellow; bill orange; legs blackish brown. Weight ♀ 198, 204 g.

Identification: Distinguishable from the next species by having the outer tail-feathers the same colour as the inner ones; secondaries uniform with back; head and neck also paler. Lacks the casque and dark head and neck of the Crowned Hornbill, No. 427.
Distribution: Damaraland to Ovamboland and eastwards to Matabeleland.
Habits: A species of mountain slopes as well as the open *Baikiaea* woodlands and dry northern Kalahari. Usually seen in pairs and during the breeding season both sexes may be heard calling at all times of the day.
Food: Large insects, fruit and occasionally small reptiles.
Voice: Melancholy, complaining notes rather similar to the Crowned Hornbill.

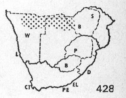
428

Breeding: A nest found in South West Africa by Hoesch, in November, was placed at the end of a hole among rocks about a metre deep. The female was plastered in and had been there for 14 days, had moulted all her tail-feathers and about half her wing-feathers and laid one egg. This was white, with distinct pores and measured 39,1 × 26,7.

429 Monteiro's Hornbill   Monteirose Neushoringvoël

Tockus monteiri   Hartlaub, 1865: *Benguella.*

PLATE 41 ♂ (OPP. P. 289).
Length 54—58 cm (wing ♂ 215, ♀ 195—215; tail 210—235; tarsus 41—49; culmen ♂ 114, ♀ 90—94). Iris reddish brown; bill red, base yellow, tip purplish; legs brown.

Identification: Easily distinguishable by the white outer tail-feathers and a lot of white on the wings which is lacking in Bradfield's Hornbill.
Distribution: Damaraland to the Benguela area.
Habits: Found mainly in mountainous areas in South West Africa, such as the Waterberg, Erongo and mountains of Kaokoveld. A shy and wary species which seeks its food on the ground more than most species of this genus; it may dig holes as much as a foot deep. The mating call is accompanied by strange up-and-down movements of the body, the head and neck maintaining an even keel.

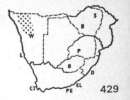
429

Food: Insects, small animals, young plant shoots, berries, pollen and wasps.
Voice: "Tak-taack, tak-taack".

Breeding: Nests in trees, the female being incarcerated as in other similar species. Eggs, white, a clutch of 5 collected in South West Africa during February measuring 39,6—42,4 × 26,3—27,7.

430 Ground Hornbill   Bromvoël

Bucorvus leadbeateri (Vigors), 1825: *Interior of South Africa =*
Lower Bushman River, C.P.
Native Names: Intsikizi, Intsingisi (X); in-Singisi (Z and G); Lekhotutu (S); Lerratakuru (Ch).
FRONTISPIECE. ♂, ♀ AND IMM.
Length about 90 cm (wing 496—535—560; tail 310—358; tarsus 112—123; culmen 180—225. 7 specimens, 6 ♂, 1 ♀). Iris pale sea-green; naked skin round eye and neck red; legs black.

Identification: Unmistakable, resembling a large black turkey. Sexes similar but female has bare skin of head blue, except round the eye where it is red; her casque is also narrower. Young birds have skin of head black, are browner and have black markings on the white of primaries and primary coverts. These white feathers are conspicuous in adults in flight.

Distribution: From the eastern Cape Province to Kenya; from Transvaal across the northern Kalahari to Angola and the Congo.

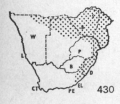

430

Habits: A southern species of a genus that has become more terrestrial than other hornbills. It is usually found in pairs or small parties that hunt separately within sight of each other, waddling slowly over the ground and calling to one another when separated. If put to flight they do not go far but may perch in trees to which they also resort for roosting. Patches of burnt ground are greatly favoured for seeking food.

Food: Insects, frogs, small reptiles, rats and mice.

Voice: A deep booming by both sexes, but different in tone. This booming has caught the imagination of the natives, who give it various interpretations, such as the female saying "I'm going, I'm going, I'm going home to my relations", and the male retorting "You can go, you can go, you can go home to your relations!" This booming is also uttered at the first sign of dawn.

Breeding: Nests in holes in trees or krantzes but the entrance is not plastered up. The male is assiduous in feeding his mate but she also leaves the nest at times and he takes her place. Two eggs are laid, white and rather rough. Average (8) 74,0 × 50,7 (67,3—77 × 46,9—55,7). More than two birds have been reported as feeding the young. Nestling period at least 82 days.

Family CAPITONIDAE

The Barbets are small birds related to the Woodpeckers, but differ from them in having soft tails and the bill not straight, but shorter, stouter and usually arched on the culmen, adapted to a frugivorous and insectivorous diet. They have very characteristic call-notes, attractive plumage in yellow, green, red, brown, black and white in the different species; nest in holes in trees excavated by themselves and lay white eggs. They are distributed in the tropical countries of Africa, Asia and America, and in Africa the family contains a large number of genera and species.

431 Black-collared Barbet   Rooikop-houtkapper

Lybius torquatus (Dumont), 1806: *Brazil = South-eastern Cape Province.*

Native Names: Isinagogo (X); isi-Kurukuru (Z); Kopaopi (S); u-Mkweboro (D).

PLATE 42 (OPP. P. 304).
Length 19—20 cm (wing 87—92—97; tail 51—63; tarsus 19—23; culmen 21,5—25, 68 specimens). Iris reddish brown; bill black; legs dark brown.

Identification: The only barbet with a red face and neck. Sexes alike. Young birds have the head blackish with odd traces of orange-red on forehead with speckled throat, notch less distinct.

Distribution: From the eastern Cape Province to Ethiopia and across to Angola and Zaïre.

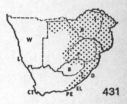

431

Habits: A common species, widely distributed in the acacia veld and open dry forests, particularly along streams and rivers where the growth of trees is greater. Usually to be seen in pairs though not always close together. Sometimes numbers gather together in the same tree and create an awful din.

Food: Fruit and insects, including termites and beetles.

Voice: One of the characteristic sounds of Africa; a duet between two birds, starting with a "skiz-skizskiz" whirring sound and then a musical "two- (first bird) puddely (second bird), two-puddely", repeated about eight times, the first note being higher than the second. The bird calling "two" sways excitedly. Also go "snaar" when annoyed; young birds make a purring sound in the nest.

Breeding: Nests are excavated, by both sexes, in upright dead trunks or in the underside of branches to a depth of 15 to 25 cm. Breeding occurs from September to December, less often in February and April. The 3 or 4 eggs are white and are laid straight on to the bare wood and chips at the bottom of the nest. Average (45) 24,3 × 17,5 (22,5—26,5 × 16,4—18,9). Incubation period 18½ days (2). Brooding commences with the first egg but all hatch at the same time. Nestling period 33—35 days.

LOCAL RACES:
(a) L.t. torquatus (Dumont), 1806: *Brazil = Eastern Cape Province.* As illustrated. Cape Province to Transvaal.
(b) L.t. zombae (Shelley), 1893: *Zomba, S. Malawi.* Head brick-red, rather than crimson. Slightly smaller. Wing 88—90 (6). From Beira and the lower Zambesi northwards to Malawi.
(c) L.t. lucidiventris Clancey, 1956: *Mchabesi, Matopos, Rhodesia.* Red of head deeper than *(a):* below less vermiculated. Southern Mozambique, Zambia and Rhodesia. Size above races *(a)* and *(c)*.
(d) L.t. bocagei (Sousa), 1886: *Caconda, Angola.* More yellow below, north-western Botswana and northern S.W.A.

432 Pied Barbet   Bont Houtkapper

Tricholaema leucomelas (Boddaert), 1783: *Cape of Good Hope.*

Native Name: se-Rokolo (S).

PLATE 42 (OPP. P. 304).
Length 17—18 cm (wing ♂ 82—84—85, ♀ 79—81,5; tail 46—53; tarsus 19—20; culmen 19—21,5. 8 specimens. 6 ♂, 2 ♀. Iris dark brown; bill black; legs blackish.

Identification: The broad black-and-white stripes on the head and red forehead are distinctive. Sexes alike. Young birds have no red on forehead, and eyebrow greenish yellow; otherwise like adults but more streaked below.

309

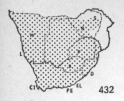

432

Distribution: Southern Africa and Angola.

Habits: The commonest and most widely distributed barbet in our area. Usually seen singly or in pairs in the tops of trees calling loudly to one another or moving restlessly from one tree to another. Flight fast and direct. Roost in nest holes or nests of weaver birds, especially the Social Weaver.

Food: Fruit and insects.

Voice: A very loud nasal, toy trumpet-like "pehp, pehp". Also a loud, ringing, hoopoe-like "poop-poop".

Breeding: Excavates its nest hole in dead tree trunks or boughs, using old euphorbia stems and even the closed nests of the Cliff and Stripe-breasted Swallows or the grass nests of the Social Weaver, where trees are too thin to bore into. Eggs 2—4, white and laid from October to January. September to March in Rhodesia. Average (20) 22,3 × 16,4 (20,5—24 × 15,5—17,6). Incubation 14—15 days. Nestling period 35 days.

LOCAL RACES:
(a) *T.l. leucomelas* (Boddaert), 1783: *Cape of Good Hope.* As illustrated; size above. Cape Province, Orange Free State, Transvaal, Botswana, northern South West Africa and Angola.
(b) *T.l. namaqua* Sclater, 1922: *Klipfontein = Little Namaqualand.* Yellower and more spotted below than (a), markings on throat smaller. Little and Great Namaqualand and Orange River.
(c) *T.l. affine* Shelley, 1879: *Weenen, Natal.* Eastern Cape Province to Natal. Slightly smaller, flanks sometimes striped but not conspicuously. Wing ♂ 78—83 (5), ♀ 78—80 (3); culmen 19—21.
(d) *T.l. zuluensis* (Roberts), 1932: *Mkusi River.* Slightly smaller, underparts more yellow and with no flank stripes. Wing 74,5—79; culmen 18—20. Zululand, eastern Transvaal and south-eastern Mashonaland.

433 White-eared Barbet   Witoor-houtkapper

Buccanodon leucotis (Sundevall), 1850: *Lower Caffraria = Umlalazi River, Zululand.*

Native Name: Sabakweba (Z).

PLATE 42 (OPP. P. 304).
Length about 19 cm (wing 90—92,5—95; tail 48—53; tarsus 20—22; culmen 19—20. 6 specimens). Iris dark sepia; bill black; legs black.

Identification: The general dark brown to blackish colour, white streak behind eye and white belly, are distinctive. Sexes alike. Young birds have base of bill whitish.

Distribution: From Natal to Kenya and Tanzania.

Habits: A fairly common species in suitable localities, inhabiting large trees and forests along rivers especially where there are wild fig trees. Several birds may roost in company, occupying holes in trees.

Food: Fruit, mainly wild figs and insects.

433

Voice: A "ho, ho, ho" answered by a high-pitched "ha". Also persistent twittering when courting.

Breeding: Nests in decayed trunks in early summer, laying 3 to 6 white eggs, October to December. Average (8) 23,3 × 18,0 (22,5—24 × 17,7—18,3). Several birds may feed the young. Nestling period 39 days.

LOCAL RACES:
(a) *B.l. leucotis* (Sundevall), 1850: *Lower Caffraria = Umlalazi River, Zululand.* As illustrated. Natal to Mozambique and eastern Rhodesia.

434 Yellow-fronted Barbet Geelbles-houtkapper

Buccanodon whytii (Shelley), 1893: *Zomba, Southern Malawi.*

PLATE 42 (OPP. P. 304).
Length about 19 cm (wing 90—92,3—96; tail 54—55—56 (26); tarsus 22; culmen 18
(1). Iris brown; bill black; legs black.

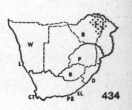

434

Identification: The yellow crown distinguishes this bird; in flight shows some
white in the wings. Sexes alike.
Distribution: Eastern and northern Rhodesia, western edge of Mozambique,
Malawi to Zaïre and southern Tanzania. Only above 900 metres in
Rhodesia.
Habits: A fairly common species in favoured localities, inhabiting forest and
thick woodlands especially where there are evergreen trees. Usually seen in
small parties of about four birds, which may roost together in the same hole in
a tree trunk.
Food: Wild fruits, particularly figs *(Ficus).*
Voice: Normally rather silent. A soft "coo" repeated about every second for
a minute or so. Also a louder, single "phew".
Breeding: Nests from September to November, also in January and May. The
eggs number 3 to 6, usually 4 and are white. They are laid at the bottom of
holes bored into dead trunks about 3—6 metres up. Average (10) 23,9 × 18,3
(22,9—25 × 17,5—19). Nestling period 49 days.

LOCAL RACES:
B.w. sowerbyi (Sharpe), 1898: *Fort Chiquaqua, Mashonaland.* As illustrated; size
above. Eastern and north-eastern Rhodesia.

435 Green Barbet Groen Houtkapper

Buccanodon olivaceum (Shelley), 1880: *Rabai, near Mombasa,
Kenya.*

PLATE 42 (OPP. P. 304).
Length about 17 cm (wing 86—90; tail 49—53; tarsus 23—24; culmen 18). Iris red,
centre dark brown; bill black; legs black.

Identification: General colour olive-green above and paler below, with a
yellow tinge at the base of primaries and tail-feathers, a large pale yellow
patch behind the eye; top of head browner olive than the back. Sexes alike.
Distribution: Zululand, northern Mozambique, Malawi, Tanzania and Kenya.
Habits: A local species, not uncommon in the Ngoye Forest and always
found in thick forested localities.
Food: Insects, slugs, moths, cockroaches and fruit.
Voice: A monotonous *"chop* (3 secs.)-*chop"*, uttered by both sexes and
repeated 5 or 6 times. Sounds rather like a cork being drawn or a Zulu "Q".
Young birds in the nest make a whirring sound.
Breeding: A hole is bored into a dead tree, both sexes participating. Breeds
from November to January, the eggs numbering 4, pure white. Measurements
22,3—22,9 × 17,5—18,0 (4).

LOCAL RACE:
B.o. woodwardi (Shelley), 1895: *Eshowe, Zululand.* Description and size above.
Apparently restricted to the Ngoye Forest.

436 Red-fronted Tinker Barbet   Rooikop-tinker

Pogoniulus pusillus   (Dumont), 1806: *Sunday's River, Cape Province.*

Native Name: Unoqandilanga (X).

PLATE 42 (OPP. P. 304).
Length about 12 cm (wing 58—59—62; tail 33—36; tarsus 14—16,5; culmen 12—13,5.
18 specimens). Iris dark brown; bill black; legs greenish grey.

Identification: The *red* forehead prevents confusion with either of the other two small Tinker Barbets. Sexes alike. Young birds lack the red on the forehead.

436

Distribution: From the eastern Cape Province (Grahamstown) eastwards to Eritrea; in our area only as far as Zululand and the Transvaal.

Habits: A common bird, usually heard more often than seen as it tends to keep in the tops of trees hidden by the foliage and its call is somewhat ventriloquial. Examines bushes and trees very thoroughly when seeking its food, jerking its head and working from one side of the tree to the other.

Food: Berries, fruit and insects.

Voice: A clinking note sounding like tapping on a small anvil. It is repeated very consistently at 120—140 times a minute and may continue for as many as 355 notes!

Breeding: Nests from October to December, boring a hole (about the size of a 10 cent coin) into a dead tree or branch, often quite low down. Eggs number 2 to 3 and are white. Average (8) 19,3 × 14,2 (18,5—20,9 × 13,7—15,2).

LOCAL RACES:
(a) P.p. pusillus (Dumont), 1806: *Sunday's River, Cape Province.* As illustrated; size of both races above. Eastern Cape to Natal.
(b) P.p. niethammeri Clancey, 1952. *Makane's Pont, Pongola River, N.E. Zululand.* Lighter and more yellow below; more striated above. Frons brighter. Zululand, Swaziland, extreme southern Mozambique and Transvaal.

437 Yellow-fronted Tinker Barbet   Geelkop-tinker

Pogoniulus chrysoconus   (Temminck), 1832: *Galam, Senegal.*

PLATE 42 (OPP. P. 304).
Length about 12 cm (wing 58—62—66; tail 31—37; tarsus 12—15; culmen 11,5—14.
26 specimens). Iris sepia, bill black, legs brown. Weight 15 g.

Identification: Distinguishable from the other two small Tinker Barbets by its *yellow* forehead; paler yellow below than the last species. Sexes alike. Young birds have no yellow on the forehead.

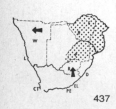

437

Distribution: From Transvaal, Botswana and northern South West Africa northwards to Senegal on the west and Ethiopia on the east. Occurs in Mozambique.

Habits: A common species which inhabits *Acacia* and other types of woodland. Easily overlooked for the same reasons as the last species. May call throughout the heat of midday. Spends much of its time in the tops of trees calling but when seeking food clambers about the branches and even the trunks of trees, almost like a woodpecker.

Food: Insects and berries, including those of the mistletoe.

Voice: Only the male calls, an anvil-like tinkling similar to the last species but slightly lower pitched and less often uttered. Also a quiet frog-like croak.

Breeding: Breeds from October to December, its general breeding habits being similar to those of the last species. The size of the nest hole has been found to be exactly that of a ten cent coin. Eggs measure 17,5—18,4 × 13,9—14,0 (3). Both parents feed the young.

LOCAL RACE:
P.c. extoni (Layard), 1871: *Kanye, Bechuanaland.* As illustrated; size above. Southern Africa northwards to southern Zaïre and Tanzania.

438 Golden-rumped Tinker Barbet   Swartkop-tinker

Pogoniulus bilineatus (Sundevall), 1850: *Caffraria inferiore = Umlalazi River, Zululand.*

PLATE 42 (OPP. P. 304).
Length about 12 cm (wing 55,5—56,5—58; tail 30—33; tarsus 14,5—16; culmen 12—14. 8 specimens). Iris dark brown; bill black, legs ashy. Weight 13—15 g.

Identification: Easily identified by its uniform black crown and back. Sexes alike. Young birds have whitish bills and green tips to the feathers of the back.
Distribution: Natal eastwards to Kenya, eastern Congo and Malawi.
Habits: A species of the coastal belt where it is quite common. In habits very similar to the last two species but prefers heavier woodland and forest. Darts straight from branch to branch with a whirr of wings.
Food: Fruits, berries and insects.
Voice: A deeper, fuller note than the Red-fronted Tinker Barbet, rather like a Zulu "Q" or "troop, troop".

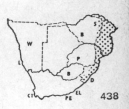

438

Breeding: Recorded breeding in November, the nest excavated in a decayed stump or on the underside of a branch, often close to the ground. October to January in Rhodesia. Eggs 4, white, measure 16,8—17,9 × 14,0—14,2 (4).

LOCAL RACE:
P.b. bilineatus (Sundevall), 1850: *Caffraria inferiore = Umlalazi River, Zululand.* As illustrated; size above. Natal to Mozambique.

438X Green Tinker Barbet   Groen Tinker

Viridibucco simplex (Fischer and Reichenow), 1884: *Pangani River, Tanganyika.*

PLATE 42 (OPP. P. 304).
Length about 12 cm (wing 49—55).

Identification: Small, green above with yellow rump and yellow wing bar. Underparts olive grey.
Distribution: Coastal Kenya to Mozambique. Recorded at Funhalouro south of Beira.
Habits: Lives in tree tops of large forests.
Voice: "Pop-op-op-op-op-op" repeated about six times sometimes ending in a trill.

313

439   Crested Barbet   Kuifkop-houtkapper

Trachyphonus vaillantii   Ranzani, 1821: *South Africa = Durban.*

PLATE 42 (OPP. P. 304).
Length about 23 cm (wing 97,5—102—107; tail 80—93; tarsus 24—28; culmen 21—26, 43 specimens). Iris reddish brown to blood-red; bill pale yellowish green, tip dusky; legs ashy. Weight 69—71—80 (24).

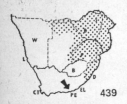

Identification: Sexes alike. Young birds are duller and browner above.
Distribution: From Natal to Tanzania, westwards to Angola and southern Zaïre.
Habits: A locally common and conspicuous species which elsewhere keeps much to the shelter of heavily foliaged trees and is consequently often overlooked. Has become quite tame in large gardens in Pretoria and Johannesburg. Is usually seen singly or in pairs, moving quietly about in bushes or small trees. Also spends a lot of its time calling.
Food: Worms, beetles, grubs, moths, grasshoppers and fruit. In other areas largely termites.
Voice: A characteristic purring trill which may continue for half a minute or longer and is repeated frequently. Sounds rather like an alarm clock with the bell removed. Nestlings also churr.
Breeding: Nests from August to February, excavating a hole in a decayed tree or bough, and laying 4 to 5 white eggs. Average (18) 27,9 × 20,4 (26—29,9 × 18,3—21,9).

Family INDICATORIDAE

The Honeyguides are a peculiar family related to the barbets. Most of the species are confined to Africa, the exception occurring in Asia. They are parasitic like cuckoos. Some species have developed the remarkable habit of leading men or animals to bees' nests, by uttering chattering cries, leading the way to them and then making a different noise or keeping quiet. They appear to do this mainly in order to eat the beeswax rather than the honey or larvae. They have very tough skins and nictitating membrane over the eyes, possibly as some protection against bee-stings. They have been found to use regular sites where the males call persistently and to which the females come to mate but otherwise the sexes live apart. The white outer tail-feathers are conspicuous in flight. Nestlings have a prominent callosity studded with scale-like tubercles on the "heel" of the leg, thus resembling barbets. They also have powerful hooks on the beak when hatched; these are used to kill the young of the host.

440   Greater Honeyguide   Groot Heuningwyser

Indicator indicator   (Sparrman), 1777: *Fish River, Cape Province.*

Native Names: Intakobusi (X); i-Ngede (Z); i-Nsedhlu (T); Tsewe (Sh) Tsese, Tsehlo, Phetlo (S).

PLATE 36, ♂, ♀ AND IMM. ♂ (OPP. P. 256).
Length 19—20 cm (wing ♂ 108—112—119, ♀ 103—107—111; tail 62—79; tarsus 14—17; culmen 12—16. 43 specimens, 25 ♂, 18 ♀. Iris brown; bill pinkish white, in females and young black; legs bluish green to grey. Weight 49—53 g.

Identification: As illustrated; young may come into breeding condition while still in the plumage shown in Plate 36.

Distribution: Africa south of the Sahara, except the great equatorial forests and the dry, treeless west of South Africa. Extends as far south as Cape Town.
Habits: A fairly common resident, favouring dense bushveld or grassy areas dotted with trees. Avoids forest unless it occurs in small patches near lighter woodland, but even then does not penetrate far. Will guide ratels (Honey-badgers), and humans to bees' nests, uttering a harsh cry (see below). Males use regular call-sites, in high trees, from which they utter their characteristic call; females come to the males and mating occurs. One well-known site is known to have been in use for 25 years. The male has a spectacular display in which he performs downward and upward swoops while flying, usually in a circle, at the same time making a "whurr-whurr" noise either with his wings or tail. It is not known if both sexes do this.

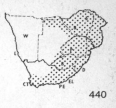

440

Food: Insects of various sorts, wax, bees and their larvae.
Voice: Note at call-site may be given as "vic-terr" or "whit-purr, whit-purr, whit-purr" preceded by a soft "purr"; often described as the "victor" call. This is repeated 7 to 11 times, every minute or so. Voice when guiding may be duplicated by rattling a half-empty matchbox *lengthwise*.
Breeding: Parasitic on the Little Bee-eater, Pied Starling, Hoopoe, and White-fronted Bee-eater; also on barbets, Yellow-throated Sparrow, wood-peckers, Kakelaar, swallows, Banded Sand Martin, kingfishers and a chat. September to January. Eggs are white; authentic specimens measure 23,0 × 18,5, 25,6 × 18,6 and 22,5 × 18,0. Some or all of the host's eggs are broken by the female. The chick has not been observed to kill the young of the host but in one case was seen ejecting the young from the nest.

441 Scaly-throated Honeyguide
Gevlektekeel-heuningwyser

Indicator variegatus Lesson, 1831: *Africa = Knysna.*

Native Name: Ndhlava (Z).

PLATE 36 (OPP. P. 256).
Length about 19 cm (wing ♂ 108—111—115, ♀ 103—105—107; tail 59—70; tarsus 15—17; culmen 12—14. 12 specimens, 8 ♂, 4 ♀). Iris dark brown; bill dark horn, base whitish; legs greenish grey. Weight 35,5—53,5 g.

Identification: The scaly appearance of the throat and chest is characteristic. Sexes alike but female slightly smaller, markings on throat and breast paler and sparser. Young birds resemble females but may be more heavily spotted below.
Distribution: From the Sudan southwards, except the Congo forests, on the east as far as Knysna.
Habits: Not common; found in thick bush and riverine forests. Guides people to bees' nests but not as often or as diligently as the previous species. Call-sites are used in the same way as in the previous species and one is known to have been used for at least 9 years.

441

Food: Insects, beeswax, bee larvae and the honey in the comb. May hawk insects like a flycatcher.
Voice: Call-site phrase a low, guttural purr, almost frog-like; may be written "ghrrr" and lasts 2—3 seconds, ascending at the end. This is audible 500 yards away under favourable conditions; when calling actively is given at intervals of 1—1½ minutes. Also has a high-pitched, whistled note like "foyt-foyt-foyt".

Breeding: Parasitic on barbets and woodpeckers. An oviduct egg measures 20,7 × 16,5; two others of reasonable authenticity measure 21,7 × 16,5 and 20 × 16,5. Recorded breeding from October to December but undoubtedly also starts earlier. Is active at call-sites longer than the other two species.

442 Lesser Honeyguide   Klein Heuningvoël

Indicator minor Stephens, 1815: *Cape of Good Hope=Zwartkops River, C.P.*

Native Names: i-Nhlalala (G); i-Shezu (D).

PLATE 36 (OPP. P. 256).

Length about 15 cm (wing ♂ 86—91—96, ♀ 84—85—87; tail 50—65,5; tarsus 12—14; culmen 10—11. 23 specimens, 14 ♂, 9 ♀). Iris dark brown; bill black; legs olive-grey.

Identification: The moustachial stripe and dark centres to feathers of back are characteristic features. Sexes alike, but female smaller. Young birds resemble adults but moustachial stripe and subocular white stripe indistinct.

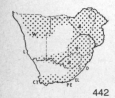

442

Distribution: Africa south of the Sahara; in South Africa absent from the treeless, western areas, the south-west Cape and Botswana.

Habits: Inhabits a variety of country from forest to sparsely wooded areas in Damaraland; is fairly common and resident. Chooses a call-site in rather dense trees and unless its call is known, is frequently overlooked. Also flies in undulating circles and produces a *single* "whurr" sound either with its tail or wings. Call-sites have been used for at least 25 years. Catches much of its food by "hawking" after flying insects like a flycatcher. Is not known to guide.

Food: Insects, beeswax, bees and honey.

Voice: Call-site note a "lew" or "klew" uttered 10 to 30 times with intervals of half a minute to three minutes between series. This note is probably uttered by the male only; audible for up to 400 metres. Nestlings make a rolling squeaky noise.

Breeding: Definitely known to parasitise the Pied Barbet, Black-collared Barbet and Yellow-throated Sparrow; other less authentic hosts include woodpeckers, a swallow, a bee-eater and other barbets. An oviduct egg measures 21,5 × 16,8 (Zaïre) while another laid in a trap measures 22,5 × 17; yet another, allowed to hatch, measured 21,4 × 17. They are pure white, oval and glossy. This species is not known to puncture eggs of the host but appears sometimes to remove an egg when laying its own. Lays September to February, mainly October to December. Incubation period estimated as 16½ days in one case, and about 12 days in another. Nestling period 38 days when reared by Black-collared Barbet. The newly-hatched chick bites the young of the host to death, using the hooks on its bill.

LOCAL RACES:

(a) I.m. minor Stephens, 1815: *Zwartkops River, Uitenhage District, C.P.* As illustrated; size above. Southern Africa (except Damaraland) north to Zaïre, Uganda and Somaliland.

(b) I.m. damarensis (Roberts), 1928: *Quickborn, S.W.A.* Males without black moustachial streak, chin grey, not white, both sexes paler on head. Wing ♂ 93, ♀ 80—86 (5). Damaraland.

442X   Eastern Least Honeyguide
Oostelike Klein Heuningwyser

Indicator meliphilus   (Oberholser), 1905: *Taveta, Kenya.*

PLATE 36 (OPP. P. 256).
Length about 13 cm (wing 71—80).

Identification: Similar but smaller than No. 442. Light mark over bill.
Distribution: Kenya south to Mozambique. Recently recorded from Beira across to the Lusitu Haroni junction on the Rhodesian border.
Habits: Little recorded but lives on forest edges.
Food: Insects.
Voice: A thin sibilant whistle.

Family PRODOTISCIDAE

Comprising one genus formerly placed in the *Indicatoridae* from which it differs in having 10 instead of 12 tail-feathers, the bill slender, arched and pointed; do not lead to bees' nests. Parasitic. White outer tail-feathers conspicuous.

443   Sharp-billed Honeyguide   Skerpbek-heuningvoël

Prodotiscus regulus   Sundevall, 1850: *Caffraria inferiori et superiore*
= *Mohapoani, Witfontein Mountains, W. Transvaal.*

PLATE 36 (OPP. P. 256).
Length 13—14 cm (wing ♂ 79—81—84; ♀ 71—76—82; tail 49—54; tarsus 10—12; culmen 11—12. 9 specimens, 5 ♂, 4 ♀). Iris greyish brown; bill almost black; legs blackish. Weight 14,3 g.

Identification: Distinguishable from the next species by its white throat and browner back. Sexes alike. Young birds have the three outer tail-feathers wholly white.
Distribution: From Knysna eastwards to the Sudan and across to Angola and West Africa (Cameroons).
Habits: A rare species in our area, found in open bushveld and in wattle and gum plantations. Rather warbler-like in habits, fluttering about after its food and frequently bobbing its head *sideways*. Might be mistaken for a flycatcher, particularly the Dusky Flycatcher, but is more restless and does not sit motionless on a perch. In flight the tail is spread, thus showing the white outer tail-feathers. Flight undulating, dipping glides alternating with periods of rapid wing-beats; jerky when "hawking".
Food: Mainly insects; also what appears to be beeswax, but may be from insects.
Voice: A low guttural "tsip" or "zeet". Also a "tseeu, tseeu" rather like a Cape Canary, known to be uttered by the female.
Breeding: A young bird has been seen being fed by Yellow-throated Sparrows. Also Neddicky. No authentic egg has yet been described.

443

317

LOCAL RACES:
(a) P.r. regulus Sundevall, 1850: *Mohapoani, Witfontein Mountains, W. Transvaal.* As illustrated; size above. Eastern Cape Province to southern Mozambique, Transvaal to West Africa and the Sudan.

444 Slender-billed Honeyguide   Dunbek-heuningvoël

Prodotiscus zambesiae   Shelley, 1894: *Zomba, Nyasaland.*

PLATE 36 (OPP. P. 256).
Length about 12 cm (wing 71—75; tail 47—50; tarsus, 11,5; culmen 8,2—9). Iris dark brown; bill blackish, corners of mouth greenish yellow; legs dark greenish grey.

Identification: More olive-green above than the last species and with a slight wash of greenish below. Sexes alike. Young similar to adults but duskier, less olive-green above. No moustachial streak, throat finely streaked.

Distribution: Ethiopia, southwards to Angola and Zambia on the west, Rhodesia and northern Mozambique.

Habits: A widely dispersed, but little known, species. Almost entirely restricted to *Brachystegia* woodland—very uncommon. Bobs its head *up and down,* sometimes displaying white feathers on either side of its rump. Does not guide to bees' nests. Creeps about the tops of trees and occasionally hawks insects in the air. Flight rapid and undulating.

Food: Insects, mainly scale insects and their waxy exudations but also other species and spiders.

Breeding: Very little recorded but is known to parasitise Flycatchers and White-eyes in Central Africa. An oviduct egg is described as white, measuring 15 × 12.

LOCAL RACE:
P.z. zambesiae Shelley, 1894: *Zomba, Nyasaland.* As illustrated; size above. From our area north to southern Zaïre and Tanzania.

Family PICIDAE

Woodpeckers have the same zygodactile toes as the preceding families, the inner and outer toes directed backwards, the two middle ones forwards, with short, curved and sharply pointed claws adapted to clinging to bark of trees. The bill is straight, stout at the base and pointed, often worn at the tip; the tail feathers have stiff, stout shafts and are sometimes pointed at the tips but wear off by being placed against the bark while the bird is clinging and rapping. They procure their food, consisting of insects and their larvae, by tapping the bark and dead wood of trees and by inserting the tongue into crevices, this organ being protruded for a considerable length and being covered with a sticky substance for extracting the insects; the back of the tongue extends in two long muscles that pass round the back of the head to the forehead above. They nest in holes pecked out of the trunks or branches of dead trees, sometimes through the green bark to the dead core within, and lay glossy white eggs. Species are found in all the warmer countries of the world, and even in the temperate regions, where they are sometimes migratory.

445 Ground Woodpecker   Grondspegt

Geocolaptes olivaceus   (Gmelin), 1788: *Cape of Good Hope.*

Native Names: Umgximde (X); Uapaleome, Mokhetle (S).

PLATE 43 (OPP. P. 305).

Length 25—29 cm (wing 129—137; tail 80—97; tarsus 24—27; culmen 34—37. 15 specimens). Iris white, sometimes tinged red or yellow; bill black; legs black.

Identification: The only woodpecker with pink belly and rump, unlikely to be confused with any other due to habitat preference. Sexes similar but female lacks red spots on "moustache". Young birds are duller and have belly mottled with olive and buffy-white.

Distribution: Confined to South Africa from Little Namaqualand south to Cape Town and eastwards to northern Transvaal.

Habits: A peculiar and unique woodpecker which has forsaken the trees for a terrestrial existence. Inhabits boulder-strewn hillsides, mountain slopes and the walls of dongas. Is usually seen in small parties of about half a dozen, sitting erect on large boulders or flying rather heavily from one rocky outcrop to the next. Occasionally sits in sturdy bushes. Hops when on the ground.

445

Food: Insects and larvae, including ants, obtained on the ground.

Voice: A loud, harsh scream like the call of a dassie or the noise produced when sharpening a saw with a file. Also a loud "chick-*scream*-chick-*scream*-chick".

Breeding: Nests from August to September in the Cape, during October to November in Natal. Three to five white eggs are laid at the end of a hole burrowed into a bank, often in road cuttings. The passage is usually about one metre long. Average (29) 28,2 × 21,8 (25—30,2 × 20,2—22,8).

LOCAL RACES:

(a) G.o. alivaceus (Gmelin), 1788: *Cape of Good Hope.* As illustrated; size above. Top of head and nape grey; bright red below; throat greyish; flanks strongly barred. Cape Province to Lesotho.

(b) G.o. prometheus Clancey, 1952: *Woodbush.* Paler above than *(a)* and with less pink below; barring on flanks very pale. Wing 127—136; tail 82—89; culmen 33—40. 10 specimens. Highlands of northern and eastern Transaal.

446 Bennett's Woodpecker   Bennettse Spegt

Campethera bennettii   (A. Smith), 1836: *Beyond Kurrichaine = Western Transvaal.*

PLATE 43, ♂ AND ♀ (OPP. P. 305).

Length 22—24 cm (wing 118—122—127; tail 62—73; tarsus 18—21; culmen 24—27,5. 17 specimens). Iris dark red; bill black; legs black.

Identification: The red moustache of the male might cause confusion with the male of the next species, but the *whole* top of the head is crimson, i.e. forehead, crown and occiput. The female has *chestnut* stripes below eye and on sides of throat thus avoiding confusion with the female of the next species. Young birds resemble the female but the young male has odd red feathers on the forehead, crown and moustache.

Distribution: From Zululand and Transvaal across to Damaraland, northwards to Tanzania and southern Zaïre. Common in Satara camp, Kruger Park.

446

319

PLATE 44

456. *Mirafra cheniana.* Singing Bush Lark. Spot Lewerik.
457. *Mirafra passerina.* Monotonous Lark. Bosveld-lewerik.
458 *(c). Mirafra africana transvaalensis.* Rufous-naped Lark.
Rooinek-lewerik.
458 *(d). Mirafra africana grisescens.* Rufous-naped Lark.
Rooinek-lewerik.
459 *(a). Mirafra africanoides africanoides.* Fawn-coloured Lark.
Vaalbruin-lewerik.
459 *(f). Mirafra africanoides sarwensis.* Fawn-coloured Lark.
Vaalbruin-lewerik.
460 *(a). Mirafra sabota sabota.* Sabota Lark. Sabota-lewerik.
460 *(g). Mirafra sabota waibeli.* Sabota Lark. Sabota-lewerik.
461 *(c). Certhilauda albescens guttata.* Karoo Lark. Karoo lewerik.
461 *(h). Certhilauda albescens erythrochlamys.* Karoo Lark. Karoo lewerik.
463. *Calendula magnirostris magnirostris.* Thick-billed Lark.
Dikbek-lewerik.
464. *Pinarocorys nigricans.* Dusky Lark. Donker Lewerik.
465. *Mirafra chuana.* Short-clawed Lark. Kortklou-lewerik.
466 *(a). Mirafra apiata apiata.* Clapper Lark. Klappertjie.
466 *(d). Mirafra apiata adendorffi.* Clapper Lark. Klappertjie. Imm
466 *(e). Mirafra apiata lewitti.* Clapper Lark. Klappertjie.
466 *(g). Mirafra apiata kalaharica.* Clapper Lark. Klappertjie.
468 *(a). Mirafra rufocinnamomea pintoi.* Flappet Lark.
Laeveld-klappertjie.
468 *(d). Mirafra rufocinnamomea mababiensis.* Flappet Lark.
Laeveld-klappertjie.

456

457

C
458
D

A
459

F

A
460

G

463

C
461

H

464

465

D
Imm

A

466

E

A

468

G

K B NEWMAN
'77

472

473

H
474
E

K

A
475
475
J

483

479

♀
484
♂

♂
485A
♀

♂
486
♀

488
Imm

490

488
E
488
G

491

492

K B NEWMAN '77

PLATE 45

472. *Botha fringillaris.* Botha's Lark. Vaalrivier-lewerik.
473. *Heteromirafra ruddi.* Rudd's Lark. Drakensberg-lewerik.
474 *(e). Certhilauda albofasciata albofasciata.* Spike-heeled Lark.
Vlakvoël.
474 *(h). Certhilauda albofasciata boweni.* Spike-heeled Lark.
Vlakvoël.
475 *(a). Certhilauda curvirostris curvirostris.* Long-billed Lark.
Langbek-lewerik.
475 *(j). Certhilauda curvirostris damarensis.* Long-billed Lark.
Langbek-lewerik.
475 *(k). Certhilauda curvirostris kaokensis.* Long-billed Lark.
Langbek-lewerik.
479. *Certhilauda burra.* Red Lark. Rooi Lewerik.
483. *Ammomanes grayi.* Gray's Lark. Namib-lewerik.
484. *Eremopterix leucotis smithi.* Chestnut-backed Finch-lark.
Rooirug-kaffertjie. ♂ and ♀.
485 *(a). Eremopterix verticalis verticalis.* Grey-backed Finch-lark.
Grysrug-kaffertjie. ♂ and ♀.
486. *Eremopterix australis.* Black-eared Finch-lark. Kaffertjie. ♂ and ♀.
488. *Calandrella cinerea cinerea.* Red-capped Lark. Rooikop-lewerik. Imm.
488 *(e). Calandrella cinerea spleniata.* Red-capped Lark. Rooikop-lewerik.
488 *(g). Calandrella cinerea niveni.* Red-capped Lark. Rooikop-lewerik.
490. *Spizocorys conirostris conirostris.* Pink-billed Lark. Rooibek-lewerik.
491. *Spizocorys sclateri.* Sclater's Lark. Namakwa-lewerik.
492. *Spizocorys starki.* Stark's Lark. Woestynlewerik.

Habits: A species of the dry *Acacia* thorn country, nowhere common. Very little has been recorded of its habits. Feeds mostly on the ground. Often follows Glossy Starlings.
Food: Insects, especially ants. Termites and their eggs.
Voice: A loud whirring chatter, high-pitched, sometimes in duet.
Breeding: Holes are bored into dead trees. The eggs usually number three and are white. September to January in Rhodesia. Average (6) 24,9 × 18,4 (24—26,5 × 18—19).

LOCAL RACES:
(a) C.b. bennettii (A. Smith), 1836: *Western Transvaal*. As illustrated; size above. Zululand, Transvaal, the eastern Kalahari and Rhodesia.
(b) C.b. capricorni Strickland, 1852: *North Damaraland*. Paler on the rump and upper tail-coverts; less spotted on breast and slightly larger than *(a)*. Wing 125—128—130 (9). South West Africa, W. Botswana and S.W. Angola.
(c) C.b. buysi Winterbottom, 1966: *Swartboois Drift, Kunene River*. More barred on mantle and wings than *(b)*; rump unbarred pale yellow, below unspotted pale yellow. Larger, wing 126—132. Northern South West Africa and S.W. Angola.

446X   Tanzanian Woodpecker

Campethera scriptoricauda   Reichenow, 1896: *Bumi, Morogoro Dist. Tanganyika.*

PLATE 43 (OPP. P. 305). ♂ AND ♀.
Length about 23 cm (wing 109—120). Iris red; bill black, yellowish at base; legs olive-green.

Identification: Very similar to No. 446 but differs by having the chin spotted in both sexes. Colour of legs differs. No brown panels on side of head in the female as in No. 446.
Distribution: Kenya to Malawi and Mozambique. Recently recorded from Inhaminga, 240 km due north of Beira.
Habits: In-its southern limit found in open Brachystegia woodland with high grass ground cover. A quiet bird and its tapping is very subdued.
Food: Mainly ants.

447   Golden-tailed Woodpecker   Goudstert-spegt

Campethera abingoni   (A. Smith), 1836: *Port Natal = Durban.*

Native Names: Kokonya, Kakuse (Ch); Chinyamdodza (D); isi-Qopumuti (G).

PLATE 43, RACES *(b)* ♂ AND ♀ AND *(d)* ♂ AND ♀ (OPP. P. 305).
Length 19—23 cm (wing 107—110—114; tail 60—66; tarsus 17; culmen 23—28. 10 specimens). Iris red; bill black; legs olive-green. Weight 64,5—71 g.

Identification: Males have red moustachial streaks like the last species, but have the forehead *black and red* thus avoiding confusion. Females lack the chestnut moustaches of the last species and both sexes are less heavily marked below than the Knysna Woodpecker which only meets this species in Natal. See also under No. 449. Young birds resemble dull versions of the female.
Distribution: Senegal to Somaliland, southwards to Damaraland, Transvaal and Natal.
Habits: A widely dispersed species in dense *Acacia* bush, particularly along

447 dry river-beds. Noisy, rapping loudly on dead tree trunks; usually seen in pairs.

An arboreal ant forager; associates with No. 450 but taps less.
Food: Insects and their larvae, but mainly ants.
Voice: A single, loud "waaa" by male.
Breeding: Nest-holes are drilled into trees. Breeds from August to December.
Eggs 2 or 3, white. Average (9) 25,1 × 17,8 (23,6—26,5 × 17,4—18,6).

LOCAL RACES:
(a) C.a. vibrator Clancey, 1953: *Newington, Eastern Transvaal.* Paler green and more heavily barred above than *(b).* Wing 112—115—121 (16). Swaziland, southern Mozambique and Rhodesia except Matabeleland.
(b) C.a. abingoni (A. Smith), 1836: *Zeerust, W. Transvaal.* Smaller, size above. Less barred above and below than *(a).* W. Transvaal, O.F.S., Botswana and Rhodesia.
(c) C.a. constricta Clancey, 1965: *Gillits, near Kloof, Natal.* Natal, Zululand, southeastern Swaziland and Maputo district.
(d) C.a. anderssoni (Roberts), 1936: *Windhoek.* As illustrated. Throat and breast black with white spots or stripes in adult males. Wing 113—116—118 (8). Northern South West Africa.

448 Knysna Woodpecker — Knysna-spegt

Campethera notata (Lichtenstein), 1823: *Kaffraria= Uitenhage.*

Native Name: Isinqolamthi (X).

PLATE 43, ♂ (OPP. P. 305).
Length 20—21 cm (wing 105—107—110; tail 67—75; tarsus 19—21; culmen 19—24. 10 specimens). Iris brown; bill and legs black.

Identification: Males resemble males of the last two species in having *red* moustachial streaks but they are much more heavily *blotched* with black below. This also identifies females which have the forehead and moustache black with yellow spots.
Distribution: The Breede River mouth area eastwards to Illovo, Natal.
Habits: A species confined to more open forest, dense bush and even comparatively open country where there are large trees. Practically nothing has been recorded about it.
Food: Ants are recorded.
Breeding: Nests in holes in trees. Two eggs from George, laid in October, measure 23,3 × 17,5 and 23,3 × 17,7; they are white (Bell Marley Collection). Another from Albany, also laid in October, measures 23,5 × 18 (R. H. Ivy).

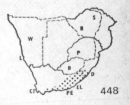

449 Little Spotted Woodpecker — Klein Gevlekte Spegt

Campethera cailliautii (Malherbe), 1849: *Mombasa, Kenya.*

PLATE 43, ♂ AND ♀ (OPP. P. 305).
Length about 18 cm (wing 91—97; tail 58—66; tarsus 15—17; culmen 14—15). Iris dark red or umber; bill black; legs olive-green.

Identification: Both sexes may be distinguished by their small size and by having neither a black nor a red moustache. Female has no red on the forehead. Young birds resemble the female but are finer-spotted on the head and more boldly spotted below.
Distribution: East Africa southwards to the Save and eastern Rhodesia.
Habits: A species which occurs over a wide range of habitat from forest to thorn-bush country and in Kenya, palm groves; Brachystegia and ever-green forest. Its tapping is a rapid and impatient sound.

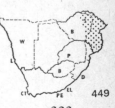

Food: Largely ants and termites. Has been seen attacking seed-pods in search of insects.

Voice: A high-pitched "hee" repeated about four times.

Breeding: Nests in holes in trees. Two eggs from Boror, taken in November 1908, measure 24,8 × 18,5 and 22,6 × 18.

LOCAL RACE:
C.c. fuelleborni (Neumann), 1900: *Langenburg N. E. Lake Nyasa.* S.W. Uganda, Tanzania, Zambia, E. Zaïre south to Beira and E. Mashonaland.

450 Cardinal Woodpecker   Kardinaal-spegt

Dendropicos fuscescens (Vieillot), 1818. *Cape Colony =*
Grootvader's Bosch.

Native Names: Phaphalikota (Ch); isi-Qopamuti, i-Nqonqonda (Z); isi-Qola, isi-Nqolanti (X).

PLATE 43, ♂ AND ♀ OF RACES *(a)* AND *(e)* (OPP. P. 305).
Length 14—16 cm (wing ♂ 89—94—97, ♀ 91—94—97; tail 44—51; tarsus 15—17; culmen 17,5—21. 15 specimens, 9 ♂, 6 ♀). Iris red to dark brown; bill black. legs olive-green.

Identification: Males are distinguishable by having *black* moustachial streaks (see also No. 451), while females have *black* (occasionally with a few red feathers) crowns and moustaches. There should thus be no confusion with the foregoing four species. Compared with the species which also has black moustaches, both sexes are much smaller, have the forehead uniform brown, not heavily spotted and are more heavily marked below. Young birds resemble the male but are duller and have the crown red but nape black.

Distribution: From Cape Town to Eritrea and across to Senegal.

Habits: Probably our commonest woodpecker occurring wherever there are trees but not in forests. In arid areas frequents the trees along dry watercourses. A pair of these birds often joins bird parties. Their drumming is rapid and not as loud and resonant as the larger species. Seeks its food in a variety of habitats; trees, reeds, mealie stalks and euphorbias. Usually lands low down in a tree and works its way upwards, then flies off to the next tree.

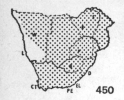 450

Food: Insects and their larvae, particularly *Coleoptera*.

Voice: A quiet chittering uttered by both sexes; a useful distinguishing feature. In emergency may scream. "Creek, creek, creek," when aggressive.

Breeding: Holes are bored into dead trunks or branches of trees, both sexes taking part in the task which lasts about two weeks. Breeds during September and October in the Cape, from July to January in the Transvaal and July to November in Rhodesia. Two or three eggs are laid (rarely four), white and glossy. Average (5) 20,3 × 16,1 (19,5—21,1 × 15,5—16,4). Incubation 10—12 days, by both sexes and beginning with the first egg. The male may feed the female at the nest. Nestling period 27 days; both sexes feed the young.

LOCAL RACES:
(a) D.f. fuscescens (Vieillot), 1818: *Cape Colony = Grootvader's Bosch.* As illustrated; the darkest race; size above. Cape Province and Orange Free State.
(b) D.f. stresemanni Grote, 1922: *Okaukweyo, South West Africa.* Similar to *(a)* but paler above, the barring more white and black. Less heavily striated below. South West Africa and western Botswana.
(c) D.f. transvaalensis Roberts, 1924: *Nylstroom.* Similar to *(f)*, but paler above, whiter below, less washed with yellowish-green; breast striae still finer. Northern Swaziland, southern Mozambique, Rhodesia and eastern Botswana.

(e) D.f. loandae Grant, 1915: *Loanda.* As illustrated. Wing 92—94—97 (23). Ngamiland to Wankie, northwards to Angola and Zaïre.
(f) D.f. intermedius Roberts, 1924: *Weenen, Natal.* Paler and more golden above than *(a),* the bars less heavy. Under-parts washed with greenish-yellow; striations finer. Natal, Zululand and southern Swaziland. Wing 92—96.

451 Bearded Woodpecker   Namakwa-spegt

Thripias namaquus (Lichtenstein), 1793: *Interior of South Africa =*
Damaraland.

PLATE 43, ♂ AND ♀ (OPP. P. 305).
Length 23—25 cm (wing ♂ 130—134—138, ♀ 127—131—137; tail 60—75; tarsus 17—21; culmen 27—36. 35 specimens, 19 ♂, 16 ♀). Iris deep red; bill greenish-grey; legs olive-grey.

Identification: The large size, boldly patterned head, very large *black* moustachial streaks, black line behind eye and finely barred under-parts should make the identification of this species easy. Note also that the forehead is boldly spotted with white (c.f. No. 450). Young birds are dull versions of the male.
Distribution: From Damaraland, eastern Cape Province (rare) and Zululand, northwards south of the Sahara, except West Africa.
Habits: A widespread and fairly common species which tends to be found in drier areas such as *Acacia* and Mopane country. A noisy species which drums loudly, each call consisting of four regular taps, by female often on the same tree, early morning, midday and late afternoon. Feeds on dead trees and usually found in pairs. Prefers larger trees, forages trunk and larger branches.
Food: Insects and their larvae.
Voice: A loud nasal scream, sounds like "hare". Also "kwik, wik, wik, wik."
Breeding: Data meagre. Breeds in South Africa during May and June; in Rhodesia from October to December. Holes are drilled in trees. Eggs 3 to 4, white. One is recorded as measuring 25 × 17,5.

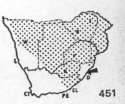

LOCAL RACE:
T.n. namaquus (Lichtenstein), 1793: *Damaraland.* As illustrated; size above. From our area northwards to Angola, Uganda and Kenya.

452 Olive Woodpecker   Gryskop-spegt

Mesopicos griseocephalus (Boddaert), 1783: *Cape of Good Hope.*

Native Name: isi-Qupamuti (Z).

PLATE 43, ♂ AND ♀ (OPP. P. 305).
Length about 20 cm (wing ♂ 105—109—114, ♀ 104—106—109; tail 60—69; tarsus 17—20; culmen 22—31. 48 specimens, 31 ♂, 17 ♀). Iris dark brown; bill bluish-black; legs greenish-grey.

Identification: Easily identified by its *uniform* olive-green colouration, *red rump* (conspicuous in flight), and grey head, the male of course with red crown and nape. Young birds are duller than adults.
Distribution: From the Cape Peninsula to Natal, Swaziland and eastern Transvaal (but not Rhodesia or southern Mozambique). Malawi northwards to Uganda and the eastern Congo.
Habits: Confined to evergreen forests and thick coastal bush where it is not uncommon. General habits similar to those of other woodpeckers. When

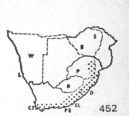

calling, shakes its head from side to side. Prefers small trees and small branches in large trees.

Food: Insects and their larvae.

Voice: A loud "wer chick", uttered with head movements as above. Also a cheerful "chi-r-r-r—re".

Breeding: Nests during October and November in the Cape, September in Zululand, drilling holes in dead trunks of trees. While pecking at the trunk, executes 4 to 5 strokes per second. Eggs 3, white, a clutch from Ingwavuma measuring 23—23,5 × 18—18,5. Both sexes incubate (Le Vaillant).

LOCAL RACE:
M.g. griseocephalus (Boddaert), 1783: *Cape of Good Hope.* Throughout our area as far north as southern Malawi.

Family JYNGIDAE

Wrynecks occupy a place between the Woodpeckers and Barbets, having the bill of the former and soft tail of the latter. They live entirely on insects and larvae and nest in crevices in trees, not excavated by themselves. Only one species occurs in South Africa.

453   Red-throated Wryneck   Draaihals

Jynx ruficollis   Wagler, 1830: *Kaffirland = Eastern Cape Province.*

PLATE 42 (OPP. P. 304).
Length 19—20 cm (wing 90—92,7—96; tail 66—74; tarsus 18—21; culmen 15,5—18. 20 specimens, 12 ♂, 8 ♀). Iris reddish-brown; bill and legs dull greenish.

Identification: The rust-red chest and throat are distinctive. Sexes alike. Young birds have duller throats. The dark stripe down the back of the neck is conspicuous from behind.

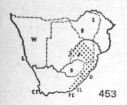

Distribution: From Uitenhage eastwards to Uganda and from Botswana northwards to the Congo. Absent from South West Africa and only one sight record (Priest) from Rhodesia. Recently in Orange Free State.

Habits: Widely dispersed over drier acacia veld, particularly in wooded gorges on hillsides and along streams, but very local in habitat and not common anywhere. Is usually seen perched in the open on dead trees often uttering its characteristic note. Seeks its food on dead branches on bark and occasionally on the ground. Probably migratory in the southern parts of its range. Roosts in hollow trunks.

453

Food: Mainly ants and their pupae.

Voice: A loud, harsh "kwik-kwik-kwik-kwik-kwik-kwik". Also a low pitched guttural note.

Breeding: Does not excavate its own nest, but uses a disused nest of a barbet or woodpecker, or a natural crevice in a tree trunk or bough; has also been known to use artificial nest-boxes and the eaves of a house. Breeds from August to December in Natal; from September to December in Transvaal. Eggs 3 or 4, white. Average (15) 22,1 × 16,4 (20,5—23,5 × 15,5—17,5). Nestling period at least 25 days. Both sexes incubate 12—15 days.

LOCAL RACE:
J.r. ruficollis Wagler, 1830: *Kaffirland = Eastern Cape Province.* As illustrated; size above.

Family EURYLAIMIDAE

Members of this family are placed in a suborder *Eurylaimi* of the Order *Passeriformes* on morphological differences not easily defined on external characters, except that the only species found within our limits has an extraordinary broad bill. The genus to which it belongs was formerly placed with the Flycatchers, but investigations by Dr. P. R. Lowe in 1924 showed that it should be placed with this suborder, of which the species previously known were confined to India, the Malay Archipelago and Philippine Islands.

454   Broadbill   Breëbek

Smithornis capensis   (A. Smith), 1839: *Towards Delagoa Bay.*

PLATE 57 (OPP. P. 465).
Length about 14 cm (wing 70—71—74; tail 48—55; tarsus 14,5—16; culmen 14,5—16. 10 specimens, 9 ♂, 1 ♀). Iris dark brown; bill black; lower mandible white; legs yellowish olive-green. Weight 22 g.

Identification: The very broad bill, black cap and heavy streaking below render this bird unmistakable. In flight displays a conspicuous white patch on the back (see below). Females have the crown grey, streaked with black. Young birds are buff above.

Distribution: From Durban northwards to Kenya, Rhodesia and Caprivi strip to Angola, Ghana and Liberia.

Habits: A bird of forest and thick coastal bush. Normally quiet and inconspicuous, perching low down and hawking its food. Sometimes feeds on the ground. Its presence is usually revealed by its call-note. Has the curious habit of suddenly performing a quick circular flight over its perch; the circle is about 60 cm in diameter and the whole performance is repeated at intervals of about a minute. It is during this display that the white bases of the feathers of the back become obvious.

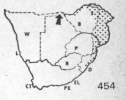

454

Food: Insects, mainly beetles, also ants, grasshoppers and spiders.

Voice: Note uttered during display is a loud frog-like "purr-rupp" which has been likened to a small old-fashioned motor horn.

Breeding: The nest is a drooping tangle of leaves, bits of bark and fibres suspended from a small branch a few feet from the ground, with a chamber in the middle lined with fibres. Eggs 2 to 3. October to February in Rhodesia. Average (11) 23,3 × 15,9 (21,3—24,9 × 14,5—16,6).

LOCAL RACES:
(a) S.c. capensis (A. Smith), 1839: *Towards Delagoa Bay = Zululand, Natal.*
(b) S.c. albigularis Hartert, 1904: *Canhoca, Angola.* Angola east to Mozambique.

Family PITTIDAE

A family of tropical birds placed in another suborder, *Tyrrani*, of the Order *Passeriformes*, upon internal morphological grounds and recognizable by being about the size of a Thrush, with the bill fairly strong and slightly arched, the legs fairly long, but tail very short, and plumage with beautiful contrasts in colour-markings.

327

455 Angola Pitta

Angola-pitta

Pitta angolensis Vieillot, 1816: *Angola.*

PLATE 34 (OPP. P. 240).
Length about 20 cm (wing 130—136; tail 50; tarsus 40; culmen 35—38). Iris dark brown; bill brown; legs pink.

Identification: Quite unmistakable. Young birds have fawn throats and are pink, not red, below.

Distribution: Tanzania, Angola and West Africa. Occurs sporadically in Rhodesia, mainly in the Eastern Districts, while on three different occasions (but all in November) birds have been picked up in Matabeleland. In South Africa odd vagrants have been found at several localities in Transvaal (Pietersburg, Pretoria and Potchefstroom) once again in November, while once a specimen appeared in Port Elizabeth during April. It is significant that birds resident in East Africa migrate south in November and return in March or April; it appears, therefore, as if some birds come too far south in November while others go the wrong way when returning north in April and end up in South Africa.

Habits: This beautiful bird inhabits thick bush particularly where evergreens are present. Spends much of its time, in the morning and evening, scratching amongst fallen leaves around anthills. When disturbed usually flies into a tall tree and hides by crouching on a branch. Hops well and quickly.

Food: Insects, termites and slugs.

Voice: Alarm note sounds like "hgg", the "g" as in Afrikaans. Also utters a "sproo" and gives a little jump as it does so. During the breeding season calls "lop, lop, lop, pleeup".

Breeding: The nest is a large, untidy, domed structure of twigs and dry leaves, the inside lined with finer twigs, tendrils and a few dry leaves, the entrance at the side. It is built into the smaller branches of thorny trees 2—4 metres from the ground. Eggs 2 or 3, white or cream with small liver-coloured and darker spots and grey undermarkings, especially at the larger end. December. Average (6) 28,0 × 23,5 (27,5—29) × (23—25).

LOCAL RACE:
P.a. longipennis Reichenow, 1901: *Ipiana, south-west Tanzania.* Tanzania to Rhodesia and Mozambique.

Family ALAUDIDAE

Larks are terrestrial birds, usually of plainly coloured plumage with short, but in a few cases, fairly long bills; the feet and claws are variable. The *back of the tarsus is scaled* and not in one plate as in the Pipits, which they otherwise closely resemble in superficial appearance and in habitat. The sexes are alike. The plumage of the young generally has the same pattern as that of the adults, but is mottled in appearance due to the light edges to the feathers of the upper-parts.

All the species nest on the ground. Some sing from the ground but many perch on trees or on conspicuous posts and many sing whilst in flight. The song and call notes are distinct and in most cases are the easiest means by which the various species may be recognized. Their diet is largely insects but some feed to a large extent on seeds. The majority of species are very local in their habitat and consequently specific and subspecific differences are frequent. The family is widespread over the tropical and warmer parts of all the continents and some islands; some species which are usually migratory extend to the temperate regions of the northern hemisphere. One third of the world's species occur in our area.

456   Singing Bush Lark   Spot Lewerik

Mirafra cheniana   A. Smith, 1843: *Latakoo, Northern Cape.*

PLATE 44 (OPP. P. 320).
Length about 12 cm (wing ♂ 71—75,5—79, ♀ 72—73,9—76; tail 43—46,5—50; tarsus 18—19,8—21,5; culmen 12—12,9—14. 17 specimens, 10 ♂, 7 ♀!). Iris brown; bill horn, yellowish below; legs flesh.

Identification: A small lark, easily confused with the next species where they occur together. Note the buffer flanks, practically the only way to separate this species from the next is that the belly and flanks are more rufous than the chin. See habits.
Distribution: Highveld grassland from East Griqualand (Matatiele) and western Natal, Orange Free State, southern Transvaal (Pretoria), northern Cape (Kuruman) and Matabeleland.
Habits: A common resident, though regarded by many as migratory because of its silence after breeding. An inhabitant of the open veld and glades where it perches freely on the ground, rocks or bushes. Ayres states that this is definitely our Skylark, rising in the air to a considerable distance, fluttering as it pours forth its hymn of praise. Where it occurs, is common and sings continuously. The males spend much time chasing others of the species, on such occasions flying low over the veld in close pursuit.
Food: Small insects.
Voice: "Kuruk-kurukureeo". Sings continuously whilst on a raised perch and in the air and is said by Roberts to imitate the calls of other birds. Own song rather monotonous.
Breeding: The nest, built when the new grass is fairly long, is a scrape in the ground lined with grass and fibres, domed and hidden between tufts of grass. November to December. Eggs 3—4, white, thickly covered with two shades of slate-brown in small spots, but variable, the marks sometimes forming a zone round the thick end. 18,3 × 13,4 and 18,3 × 13,4.

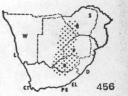

457   Monotonous Lark   Bosveld-lewerik

Mirafra passerina   Gyldenstolpe, 1926: *Mohapoani, Witfontein Mts., Western Transvaal.*

PLATE 44 (OPP. P. 320).
Length about 14 cm (wing ♂ 83—85—88; ♀ 78—80—84; tail ♂ 53—59, ♀ 51—53; tarsus 20—21,4—23; culmen 12—13,5. 18 specimens, 11 ♂, 7 ♀). Iris hazel; bill horn; legs flesh.

Identification: The flanks and belly as light as chin. See No. 456 and No. 492. May be confused with Stark's Lark, No. 492; distinguished by reddish edges of primaries. Throat appears white when singing.
Distribution: Bushveld savannas of western Matabeleland and Transvaal, to Ngamiland and Damaraland.

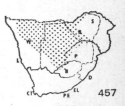

329

Habits: A common resident inhabiting open glades in thorny bush, seldom seen since it runs much on the ground. To the north it is found in mopane forest on stony ground with a sparse grass cover. Subject to movements due to rains and drought. During the breeding season the males are more bold and call continuously their monotonous note, either from the ground, when perched on the top of trees, or when fluttering about at no great height above the tree-tops in the vicinity of the nest. Sings even in the moonlight at night.
Voice: A monotonous "chloritwe"; alternatively "aquavit". Sings while perched on a small tree or bush.
Breeding: The nest is placed in between patches of grass in a hollow in the ground, which is scratched out and lined with dry grass. Recorded in December. Eggs 2—4, pale bluish ground colour, mottled and speckled all over with different shades of reddish brown and grey or slate, zoned at the large end. Average (7) 21,1 × 14,8 (18,2—22,7 × 13,8—15,3).

458 Rufous-naped Lark   Rooinek-lewerik

Mirafra africana   A. Smith, 1836: *Eastern Province of the Cape.*

Native Names: i-Gwangqa, i-Qabatule (X); u-Nongwatshi (Z).

PLATE 44 RACES *(c)* AND *(d)* (OPP. P. 320).
Length about 18 cm (wing ♂ 95—100—105, ♀ 89—92; tail 58—71; tarsus 27—32; culmen 18—23; hind claw 11—14. 14 specimens, 10 ♂. 4 ♀). Iris hazel; bill horn with edges of mandibles lighter; legs flesh.

Identification: A fairly large lark. Call note (see below) and habitat preference distinguish this species more easily than plumage. The markings: rufous-tinged nape, light eye-stripe, breast markings and rufous edges to flight-feathers, which show as a "red-wing", help to identify it. Young birds have feathers of crown, back and chest with narrow dark-brown subterminal bar and light buff terminal bar; breast marked with brownish blobs.
Distribution: South of the Sahara from West Africa and southern Sudan to the Cape Province. Absent from the south-west Cape and Namaqualand.

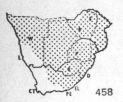

458

Habits: Resident, perhaps one of the commonest larks of savanna veld in Southern Africa. Occurs singly or in small parties. Found where there are open strips of ground bearing a thin growth of shortish grass and small trees and bushes scattered about, such as occur along the border of woodlands or open marshes. Also old lands and native gardens. The male, especially during breeding season, utters its rusty, squeaking call at fairly frequent intervals from a low perch on top of a bush, fence pole or anthill and shuffles its wings and raises nape feathers at the same time. May call on the ground and sings a short song during a low fluttering flight. When alarmed whilst feeding on the ground runs swiftly through the grass and frequently hides; if flushed utters a sharp single note.
Food: Insects; occasionally in winter it eats seeds.
Voice: A plaintive whistle "tseep-tsee-ooo", also written "chirri-too-wee" and "cher-chi-ou-ee". Silent for a period about June. Also mimics other birds. Song a string of rapid whistles, warbles and chirps.
Breeding: The nest, a shallow cup made of fine dry grass, is placed against a plant or more often in a hollow under a tuft of grass with a thinly built dome over it; sometimes cup and dome are substantially built. Eggs 2—3, elongate pinky white, less often pale cream with variable marking of light chocolate

brown, red-brown or slate colour. More usual egg closely spotted, occasionally with blotches which may be concentrated at the large end. August to March and May in Rhodesia. Average (50) 22,3 × 16,4 (20,2—24,3 × 14,9—18,2).

LOCAL RACES:
This species shows a cline from south to north from the largest and darkest in the south; birds to the west become redder or pinker with light streaking.
(a) M.a. africana A. Smith, 1836: *Eastern Province of the Cape.* From Port Elizabeth north through the eastern Cape, southern Orange Free State to central and coastal Natal. The largest and darkest race. Size above.
(b) M.a. zuluensis (Roberts), 1936: *Maputa, N.E. Zululand.* Zululand (from about St. Lucia) and Swaziland to Sabi River in Mozambique. Less rufous than *(c)* and lighter below than *(a)* and *(c)* (wing ♂ 94—97,4—101; culmen 17,5—21. 13 specimens).
(c) M.a. transvaalensis Hartert, 1900: *Rustenberg.* Northern and eastern Orange Free State, upper Natal, Transvaal, Rhodesia (see also *(b)* and *(d)*) westwards to Botswana. Lighter and redder than *(a),* less heavily streaked (wing ♂ 91—98—104; culmen 16,5—20. 35 specimens). As illustrated.
(d) M.a. grisescens Sharpe, 1902. *Tibakais Vlei, Matabeleland.* North-west Rhodesia, northern Botswana and Caprivi Strip. Paler and greyer above than *(c)* (wing ♂ 98—104; culmen 17—19. 3 specimens). As illustrated.
(e) M.a. ghansiensis (Roberts), 1932: *Gemsbok Pan, Ghanzi dist.* Central Damaraland to southern Botswana from Ghanzi to Fort Rietfontein. Very pale pinkish race with reduced markings (wing ♂ 94—99; culmen 17,5—20,5. 6 specimens).
(g) M.a. pallida Sharpe, 1902: *Elephant Vlei, Damaraland.* Northern Damaraland, Kaokoveld and Ovamboland. Palest form of all (wings 98; culmen 21).

459 Fawn-coloured Lark Vaalbruin-lewerik

Mirafra africanoides A. Smith, 1836: *Eastern Province of the Colony and Latakoo.*

PLATE 44, RACES *(a)* AND *(f)* (OPP. P. 320).
Length about 14 cm (wing 87,5—94; tail 57—65; tarsus 21—23; culmen 13—15. 9 specimens). Iris chestnut, bill yellow-brown; legs flesh. Weight 19—21,5 g.

Identification: The field impression is of rufous-fawn upper-parts and white belly. Finely streaked on head. Tail dark.
Distribution: Eastern and Southern Africa. Rare south of the Limpopo River in Mozambique. Not recorded from Natal, south eastern Transvaal, eastern Orange Free State and the Cape Province south of the Orange River, except in the vicinity of Colesberg.
Habits: Resident, local in habitat. The commonest lark of the Kalahari and dry west. Found in savanna sand-veld where there is low scrub or bushes and trees with open sandy stretches, such as dry river-beds or edges of open Acacia woodlands. The male seeks tops of medium-sized trees or bushes from which it utters its melodious, sustained song.
Food: Seeds and insects, beetles, millipedes, termites etc.

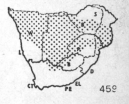

459

Voice: A long and melodious call, rendered "te-e-e-tee-ree-tee-ree-tee-ree-te-e-e". Also a trill ending with "sweet sweet".
Breeding: The nest is made of grass stems forming a neat cup and curled over to form a dome; the lining of soft fine grass. Situated in a hollow against and partly under a grass tuft. November to March. Eggs 2—3, white, closely speckled in light chocolate yellow with a few scattered blotches and a little spotting of light and dark grey, occasionally more concentrated at obtuse end. Average (11) 20,8 × 14,5 (19,4—21,8 × 13,9—15,6).

LOCAL RACES:
The species is sub-divided into colour races which show a cline from reddish birds in the south becoming paler to the north-west and greyer to the north-east. There is also a cline

331

in the feather centres and breast markings from heavy markings in the east to lighter and smaller markings towards the west.

(a) M.a. africanoides A. Smith, 1836: *Eastern Province of the Colony and Latakoo.* Griqualand West and southern Botswana. Buffy rufous above, with largish markings on breast. Size as above.

(b) M.a. austin-robertsi White, 1947:*Nylstroom.* Western Orange Free State and western Transvaal. Darker above owing to broader stripes on crown and upper-parts; breast less heavily marked than *(a)* (wing 86—90; culmen 13,5—14. 5 specimens).

(c) M.a. harei Roberts, 1917: *Windhuk, Damaraland.* Damaraland, from the Waterberg Plateau as far south as Aus. Paler, more yellowish above with less streaking; even smaller markings on breast (wing 84—94; culmen 13,1—16. 9 specimens).

(d) M.a. gobabisensis (Roberts), 1936: *Gobabis District.* To east and north-east of *(c)* from Alice and Gobabis to the Waterberg. Richer and redder than *(c)*, streaking above more pronounced (wing 84—93,5; culmen 13—16. 5 specimens).

(e) M.a. vincenti (Roberts), 1938: *Umvuma, Rhodesia.* Selukwe and midlands of Rhodesia and southern Mozambique. Less red than *(b)* with heavy black stripes; especially on head; breast more heavily spotted. Confined in its distribution to red kalahari-sand areas.

(f) M.a. sarwensis (Roberts), 1932: *Kaotwe, Botswana.* Dry central Kalahari. Light pink rufous above, lighter than *(d)* and less yellowish red than *(c)* (wing 76—91; culmen 12—15,5. 38 specimens).

(g) M.a. makarikari (Roberts), 1932: *Nkate, N.E. Botswana.* Ngamiland, eastwards to Makarikari and Wankie, Rhodesia. Less red than *(f)*, being yellowish sandy grey above (wing 87,5—91,5; culmen 13—14. 3 specimens).

(h) M.a. rubidior White, 1955: *Ozondjanche, nr. Otjiwarongo.* From a small area north of the Waterberg. Much darker and richer than *(d)*, black streaking heavier (wing 93; culmen 17).

460   Sabota Lark   Sabota-lewerik

Mirafra sabota   A. Smith, 1836: *Latakoo to the Tropic =Bechuana-land.*

Native Name: Sabota (Ch).

PLATE 44, RACES *(a)* AND *(g)* (OPP. P. 320).
Length about 15 cm (wing 76—90; tail 46—57; tarsus 19—22,5; culmen 12,2—15,8. 43 specimens). Iris brown; bill blackish; legs flesh. Weight 24,7—27 g.

Identification: A medium to smallish lark, with a speckled chest and short thickish bill; generally grey or tawny rather than rufous in colour. There is no rufous patch on the folded wings as found in the previous species.

Distribution: The dry acacia savanna of southern and south-western Africa. South West Africa, Botswana, the Cape south of the lower Orange River to De Aar, western Free State, Transvaal, northern and western Natal and southern Mozambique.

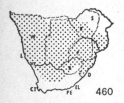

460

Habits: A common resident of the bushveld showing a preference for the wide belt of thornbush which flanks dry river-beds. Referred to as one of the tree larks because of its habit of taking refuge in a bush or tree. Feeds on the open sandy ground; when alarmed flies, with undulating flight to the nearest tree or bush and chirps its alarm note. Occurs in pairs or small parties. Sometimes sings, hovering a few yards above the ground.

Food: Small seeds and insects.

Voice: A weak call of a few notes rather harsh; song quiet uttered from perch or in flight and mimics other birds.

Breeding: The nest is said to resemble that of the previous species. October to February. Eggs 2—3, white, marked with chocolate yellow and slate, somewhat concentrated as a ring or cap at the obtuse end. Average (21) 20,8 × 15,2 (19,6—23 × 14,2—15,8).

LOCAL RACES:
Distinguished both by colour variation and bill size. Some authorities (Praed and Grant) separate the small billed races as one species from the large-billed races as another species. There is a general trend from reddish brown in the east to paler colours in the west and greyer colours centrally. There is a cline of longest and thickest bills in the south to shorter bills in the north with eastern birds having more slender bills.

(a) M.s. sabota A. Smith, 1836: *"Latakoo to the Tropics"* = *Bechuanaland*. Northern Cape and Natal into southern Mozambique, west Swaziland, eastern Transvaal and to Matabeleland west of Beit Bridge and Selukwe. Reddish brown back. Size as above. Weakest bill. Illustrated.

(b) M.s. sabotoides (Roberts), 1932: *Gemsbok Pan*. South-western Botswana from drier areas. Colour paler or grey-brown with markings on breast near *(d)*.

(c) M.s. bradfieldi (Roberts), 1928: *De Aar*. Griqualand West south to Petrusville and De Aar, north-west to Keetmanshoop. Paler red-brown back than *(a)*, breast buffish as *(a)* but very heavily marked. Heaviest bill of all; culmen length 15—16,5; height 6—6,5.

(d) M.s. herero (Roberts), 1936: *Windhuk*. Damaraland plateau see also *(e)* and *(f)*. Lighter than *(b)*, under-parts buffy white with smaller markings on breast. Bill heavy but longer; culmen length 15,5—17,5; height 5,5—6,2.

(e) M.s. naevia Strickland, 1852: *Damaraland = Otjimbinque*. West of *(d)* from Walvis Bay to Erongo. Altogether paler than *(d)* with small breast markings. Wing ♂ 87—93; culmen length 15,5—16,5; height 5,7—6 (18 specimens).

(f) M.s. hoeschi Stresemann, 1939: *Wåltersdorf nr. Grootfontein*. North-eastern Damaraland as far west as Onguma; see *(g)*. Darker brown than *(d)*, *(g)* and *(h)*. Wing ♂ 85—88; culmen length 15—16; height 5,5—6,2 (4 specimens). Illustrated.

(g) M.s. waibeli Grote, 1922: *Okaukwejo, Ovamboland*. Ngamiland and the north-western area of Etosha Pan. Very whitish upper-parts but with heavy black streaking. Wing ♂ 86—89 (4 specimens). Illustrated.

461 Karoo Lark   Karoo-lewerik

Certhilauda albescens   (Lafresnaye), 1839: *Blaauwberg, Cape*.

PLATE 44, RACES *(c)* AND *(h)* (OPP. P. 320).
Length about 17 cm (wing 82—94; tail 56—68; tarsus 21—24; culmen 15—17. 6 specimens). Iris dark brown; bill horn, lighter at base; legs grey-brown.

Identification: The colour pattern of the head is diagnostic in all races; a light eye-stripe above and below eye with a definite darker patch on the ear-coverts, well illustrated in No. 461. See under races for colour which varies from rich rufous to greyish forms. The shortish square tail appears dark in the heavy flight. Distinguished from the Red Lark by more slender bill and different song.

Distribution: South-western Cape from Swellendam north to Bloemfontein and thence westwards; northwards along the western coastal strip as far north as Walvis Bay.

Habits: A common resident which inhabits open scrub where the ground is sandy or gravelly. Spends much of its time on the ground creeping and hopping about under the bushes where it digs for food, vigorously showering sand to either side. Quite often takes a dipping aerial flight up to 50 feet or so, singing and dropping down to settle on a bush. *Frequently alights on bushes,* from which it sings. When disturbed usually runs off, mouse-like, and hides behind bushes, but if pursued will take off for a short flight.

Food: Seed and insects.

Voice: A pretty song "chip-chip-chip-chippee" often repeated. From bushes or the ground they call "eizer-eeit", a low-pitched "tchee-tchee-tchee-ch-r-r-r-r" or "chip-chee-trrrl".

Breeding: The nest is placed at the base of a bush or tuft of grass. The cup is

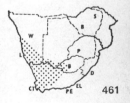

461

a shallow structure of fine grass, said to have a thin dome of long stems curled over from the cup. One record of a cup constructed in a Longclaws' nest. August to December. Eggs 2—3, white, with close freckling of chocolate-brown overlying small blotching and spotting of rust and slate-blue somewhat concentrated at larger end. Average (17) 22,0 × 15,1 (19,8—23,9 × 14,5—16,1).

LOCAL RACES:
The species shows variation in colour tone and feather pattern. The southern birds are most heavily streaked while to the north markings are practically absent. The colour varies from palest forms along the coast with rufous forms inland and to the north. See No. **479** which is considered to be the same species by some authorities.
(a) C.a albescens (Lafresnaye), 1839. *Blaauwberg, Cape.* Cape flats as far north as Berg River except at the mouth. Palest but most heavily streaked form. Size as above.
(b) C.a. codea A. Smith, 1843: *plains between Olifants and Orange River.* Coastal from Saldanha Bay to Port Nolloth. Slightly more rufous than *(a)* and less heavily marked.
(c) C.a. guttata (Lafresnaye), 1839: *Oliphant's River, S.W. Cape.* Inland from Swellendam, north-east of De Aar and west to Springbok. A rufous form, heavily streaked.
(d) C.a. karruensis Roberts, 1936: *De Aar, Cape Province.* Eastern Karoo districts, Murraysburg and De Aar. A very dark race, much darker than *(c)*.
(e) C.a. patae Macdonald, 1953: *Grootderm, Orange River.* Confined to coastal area south of the Orange River Mouth. Two colour phases like *(a)* and *(c)* but lightly streaked above and below.
(f) C.a. cavei Macdonald, 1953: *Witputs, Great Namaqualand.* Southern end of Huib Plateau. Upper-parts darker and richer (a cinnamon-brown) than *(e);* streaking similar.
(g) C.a. barlowi (Roberts), 1937: 8 *miles west of Aus, Great Namaqualand.* Vicinity of Aus. Much lighter than *(e);* streaking reduced to little more than a thin line. Bill blackish horn.
(h) C.a. erythrochlamys (Strickland), 1852: *Damaraland.* Namib sand dune area from Koichab River just north of Aus to near Walvis Bay. Illustrated, similar to *(g)* but almost lacking in streaking, more buffish white below. Bill brownish horn.

462 = 461 *(c).*

463 Thick-billed Lark   Dikbek-lewerik

Calendula magnirostris (Stephens), 1826: *South Africa; near Cape Town.*

PLATE 44 (OPP. P. 320).
Length about 18 cm (wing ♂ 102—110, ♀ 95—97; tail 58—67; tarsus 25—27; culmen 18—20, hind claw 13—17. 7 specimens, 4 ♂, 3 ♀). Iris brown; bill horn, lighter below; legs pale brown.

Identification: A largish, heavily built lark. The illustration shows long hind-claws, which are easily seen when the bird perches on wire fences. The thick, heavy bill, prominent markings on the chest and double call note are diagnostic. Predominantly grey-brown and heavily marked. A slight crest at back of head with rather a flat crown. Tail is shortish, dark and somewhat square in flight.

Distribution: The Cape Province, except for eastern littoral zone and north-east areas; Orange Free State as far north as the Vaal and Lesotho.

Habits: A common resident, usually occurring in pairs or small family parties. Its persistent double note is usually uttered from an antheap, low bush or fence wire; otherwise it spends most of its time creeping about open country where the vegetation is sparse. Also inhabits cultivated areas, the commonest lark of the south-western Cape wheatlands. During the breeding season the male sings in flight, the short song being uttered while rising in the air.

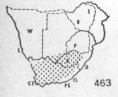

463

Food: Seeds and insects, especially beetles and plant bulbs.

Voice: A persistent double call note "teee-wheatleooo" or "too-toodle-oo". Also imitates many other birds.

Breeding: The nest is placed in a slight depression under or near some small plant, never entirely concealed. The nest cup is variable from a well constructed neat shallow hollow of rootlets and grasses to a cup with some woolly plant-down and a feather or two as lining. August to November. Eggs 2—3, white to pale cream, heavily spotted and speckled in shades of yellowish brown. Average (28) 22,7—16,7 (20,9—24,2 × 16—17,2).

LOCAL RACES:

(a) *C.m. magnirostris* (Stephens), 1826: *South Africa; near Cape Town.* Coastal areas from Springbok south to the Cape and Cape Agulhas. As illustrated, longer bill and hind-claw than *(b):* size as above.

(b) *C.m. harei* Roberts, 1924: *Phillipstown, C.P.* Inland from Namaqualand and Karoo, from higher altitudes than the coastal plains. Redder or more buffish above than last, with shorter bill and hind-claw; culmen ♂ 16—18, ♀ 15—16,5; hind-claw 9—14.

(c) *C.m. montivaga* Vincent, 1948: *Sanqubetu valley, Lesotho.* From the highlands of Lesotho. Size as *(b)* but darker above and below than that race.

464 Dusky Lark   Donker Lewerik

Pinarocorys nigricans (Sundevall), 1851: *Aprevier = Aapies River, Pretoria dist.*

PLATE 44 (OPP. P. 320).

Length about 19 cm (wing 115—118; tail 76; tarsus 26—27,5; culmen 15—15,5; hind-claw 7—8. 2 specimens). Iris hazel; bill horn; legs slaty white.

Identification: The bold thrush-like markings on the chest are conspicuous. Large and darkish in general appearance due to heavy markings but birds in worn dress appear paler. Sexes alike. The flight is buoyant and undulating.

Distribution: From northern Zululand, Transvaal, northern Botswana and South West Africa from Windhoek northwards to the Congo and Tanzania.

Habits: Common in some areas but for the most part uncommon. A species which shows partial migration, birds in the south, from September to May, move north of the Zambesi River. A few winter records in Rhodesia. Flocks of from 30 to 40 males recorded from southern Mozambique, but for the most part recorded in small flocks or singly; somewhat shy; inhabiting stony ground, open bush country and cleared ground in woodland. Somewhat thrush-like in habits. Frequently perches on trees. When walking flicks its folded wings level with the back.

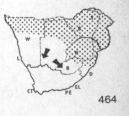

464

Food: Insects.

Breeding: Breeds in the north, Angola, Zaïre and Tanzania in the dry winter and spring. Recorded once in Zululand, a neat nest let well into the soil at the foot of a dead stump in open ground, made of grey, broad grass-blades, without lining. Eggs 2, very pale greenish blue with well-defined and distributed hair-lines of umber or dark brown. 24,5 × 15,5 and 24,1 × 15,5, in September.

LOCAL RACE:

P.n. nigricans (Sundevall). 1851: *Aprevier = Aapies River.* Pretoria dist.

465 Short-clawed Lark   Kortklou-lewerik

Mirafra chuana   (A. Smith), 1836: *Country beyond Latakoo.*

PLATE 44 (OPP. P. 320).
Length about 19 cm (wing ♂ 105, ♀ 91; tail ♂ 75—79, ♀ 66,5; tarsus 26—27,5; culmen 16,5—20,5; hind-claw 7—8,5. 3 specimens). Iris brown; bill horn coloured; tarsus flesh colour.

Identification: Similar to the Rufous-naped Lark, No. 458. Differs by having short front claws, very slender bill, the upper tail-coverts rufous and the *folded primaries not showing a rufous patch* which is characteristic of No. 458.
Distribution: Northern Cape Province, western Transvaal and eastern Botswana.
Habits: A rare, little-known species. Partial to open ground in mixed "Karee tree" and "Vaalbos" thorn-trees. Like No. 458 this species when disturbed, flies to the top of a thorn-tree nearby and utters a clear whistling call-note.
Food: Insects and grass seeds.
Voice: "Tsirioweee."
Breeding: Unrecorded.

465

466 Clapper Lark   Klappertjie

Mirafra apiata   (Vieillot), 1816: *Swartland = Malmesbury dist., C.P.*

PLATE 44, RACES *(a), (d)* IMM., *(e)* AND *(g).* (OPP. P. 320).
Length about 15 cm (wing 84—92; tail 54—63; tarsus 18—23; culmen 13,5—15,5; hind-claw 7—9. 6 specimens). Iris light-brown; bill horn; legs flesh colour.

Identification: A smallish rufous lark, cap darkish with barred mantle and scapulars. Usually distinguished by its habit of rising with a fluttering flight and clapping wings. The mantle and scapular feathers are conspicuously marked, having very dark subterminal bars with a light buffish or whitish edge. See No. 468.
Distribution. Southern Africa except Natal and Mozambique. Extending north as far as Ovamboland, Ngamiland and central Transvaal.
Habits: A common resident species, it remains quieter and less obtrusive during the non-breeding period and is thus inclined to be overlooked. Inhabits higher parts of hill slopes and undulating downland in grassland or open bush country where the vegetation is low. Shows a preference for rocky slopes. Occurs singly, in pairs or small family parties. During the breeding season the male rises steeply into the air, hovering for a few seconds, clapping its wings, then dropping straight down whistling a long drawn-out "foo-eee". Usually several birds can be heard at once. For some reason this behaviour is considered by farmers to forecast rain and hence the name "rain bird" or "misvoël".

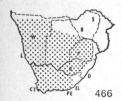

466

Food: Seeds and insects.
Voice: See above. Also sings on the ground and in flight.
Breeding: The nest is placed at the base of a plant, a very slight and loosely built structure of thin grass and plant stems lining the hollow and brought up at the back to form a thin dome. From October in the Cape to February in the Transvaal. Eggs 2—3, creamy white, closely speckled in yellowish brown except at narrow end. Average (12) 23,0 × 15,4 (21,5—26,5 × 14,3—16,4).

LOCAL RACES:
Some authorities (Praed and Grant) separate the races into two groups as separate species. This is based upon bill character—robust or slender. Variation in the species is largely in colour and degree of marking. Darker, more heavily marked birds in the south tend to become russet to the north-east and greyer to the north.
(a) *M.a. apiata* (Vieillot), 1816: *Swartland = Malmesbury dist.* From Mamre north wards to Olifants River and inland to Ceres. Drab-grey with few russet markings, no distinct cap. Flight-feathers with indistinct russet margins. Light fawn below, spots light on throat, heavy on breast. Size as above. Illustrated.
(b) *M.a. algoensis* (Roberts), 1926: *Port Elizabeth.* Riviersonderend eastwards to Grahamstown. Drab-brown, more russet than *(a)*. Russet margins to flight-feathers. Under-parts as in *(a)*. Size as in *(a)*.
(c) *M.a. marjoriae* Winterbottom, 1956: *Zoetendalsvlei, Bredasdorp.* Southern part of Cape Flats east to Bredasdorp. Lacks nuchal collar of *(a)*; darker and less russet above than in *(a)* and *(b)*. Wing 77—86; tail 51—63; tarsus 19—24; culmen 15—19. 11 specimens.
(d) *M.a. adendorffi* Roberts, 1919: *Klaver.* From Klaver northwards to Springbok. Imm. Illustrated. Upper-parts as *(a)* but with a russet cap. More cinnamon-brown under-parts, markings on breast fewer, not extending to throat. Tends to be larger than *(a)*. Wing 89—94; tail 56—61; tarsus 19—24; culmen 15—18.
(e) *M.a. hewitti* (Roberts), 1926: *Rooiberg, Transvaal.* Central Transvaal to Orange Free State and Griqualand; possibly Great Namaqualand. Illustrated. Mainly russet above; feathers above frequently edged with white. Under-parts cinnamon-brown with breast spots smaller than in *(a)*. Larger. Wing 79—94; tail 48—65; tarsus 24—27; culmen 13,5—17.
(f) *M.a. deserti* (Roberts), 1926: *Omutako Flats nr. Okahandja.* Damaraland from Okahandja to south of Windhoek and east to Gobabis. Buffy brown above; no distinct cap. Under-parts like *(a)* but markings smaller.
(g) *M.a. kalaharica* (Roberts), 1932: *Gemsbok Pan.* Northern Kalahari from around Ghanzi south-east to Kuke. Vinaceous buff above; no distinct cap. Under-parts buffish white with few smallish breast markings. Illustrated.
(h) *M.a. damarensis* Sharpe, 1874: *Ondonga, Damaraland.* Vicinity of Ondonga. Greyer above than *(g)*.
(i) *M.a. nata* Smithers, 1955: *10 mls. W. of Nata.* Eastern Botswana. Paler than *(g)* being ashy-grey above.

468 Flappet Lark   Laeveld-klappertjie

Mirafra rufocinnamomea   (Salvadori), 1865: *Northern Abyssinia.*

Native Name: u-Qaqatshe (Z).

PLATE 44, *(a)* AND *(d)* (OPP. P. 320).
Length about 15 cm (wing 75—80,7—82; tail 52—59; tarsus 21—24; culmen 13,5—15. 13 specimens). Iris brown; bill brownish; feet reddish. Weight 26 g.

Identification: An eastern and northern version of the previous species. Only in Ngamiland do the two species overlap. This bird does not call whilst on the wing as is the case with the Clapper Larks. In the hand, the rufous of the primaries is divided by a dark zone along the shaft whereas the colour is uniform rufous in No. 466.
Distribution: Zululand, Swaziland, eastern and northern Transvaal and Ngamiland northwards to Central Africa.
Habits: The only recorded difference between the general habits and habitat of this and the previous species is the lack of song—see above. After clapping its wings in a castanet-like rattle it falls to about 20 or 30 feet off the ground and swerves along level for some distance before settling.
Voice: Said to call from a tree or antheap early in the morning—a muffled rattle-like noise.

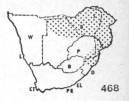

468

337

Breeding: As for the last species; one nest described by A. W. Vincent was oval rather than round in shape. October to November in the Republic, November to April in Rhodesia. Eggs 2—3, white with close streaky freckling of roan-brown and underlying spotting of ash-grey, forming a ring at thick end. Average (11) 20,6 × 14,7 (19,3—22,3 × 13,0—15,9).

LOCAL RACES:
Southern forms are distinguished by colour differences.
(a) M.r. pintoi White, 1956: *Catuane, southern Mozambique.* Zululand, Swaziland, southern Mozambique and north-east Transvaal. Upper-parts well marked, dark vinous pink in colour; underside usually strongly pigmented. Illustrated.
(b) M.r. smithersi White, 1956: *Deka farm, Matetsi, Rhodesia.* Rhodesia and northern Transvaal. Much lighter above and below than *(a).*
(d) M.r. mababiensis (Roberts), 1932: *Tsotsorogoa Pan, Ngamiland.* Ngamiland. A very pallid race. Illustrated.

469 Considered indeterminate. See page xxxii.

470 See 466 *(e)* to *(g)*

471 See 466 *(h)*

472 Botha's Lark   Vaalrivier-lewerik

Botha fringillaris (Sundevall), 1850: *"Caffraria superior"* = *North of Drakensberg, Transvaal.*

PLATE 45 (OPP. P. 321).
Length about 12 cm (wing 77, 79,5; tail 42, 44; tarsus 20, 21; culmen 11, 12; hind-claw 10, 16. 2 specimens). Bill pinkish.

Identification: This small lark can be confused with the Pink-billed Lark, No. 490. Appears darker above in the field and is distinguished by its conical bill; long practically straight hind-claw; tail with white outer tail-feathers. The first primary is long. The first primary in No. 490 is short. The blackish patch on tail appears triangular in shape with the base of the side-feathers buffish. Immature does not show a white chin.
Distribution: Confined to the upper Vaal River catchment area of Orange Free State and Transvaal.
Habits: Said to occur in pairs or small parties on the same type of veld as the Pink-billed Lark. No other notes recorded.

 472

473 Rudd's Lark   Drakensberg-lewerik

Heteromirafra ruddi (C. Grant), 1908: *Wakkerstroom, Transvaal.*

PLATE 45 (OPP. P. 321).
Length about 14 cm (wing ♂ 73,5—74,9—77,5, ♀ 69—71—74; tail 38—45; tarsus 24—26; culmen 13—15; hind-claw 12—20. 17 specimens, 10 ♂, 7 ♀). Iris grey-brown; bill horn; legs flesh.

Identification: A curious little lark; the tail is so short and thin that the bird appears tailless; the crown-feathers are long and those of the eyebrow project outwards like horns. The hind-claw is very long.

Distribution: The Drakensberg plateau from Griqualand East, upper Natal and south-east Transvaal north as far as Belfast.

Habits: An uncommon, local species frequenting the open grassveld amongst spurs of the high mountains. Three to four hover high up in the air during the breeding season, uttering a clear and distinct song, sounding like a person whistling with bubbles in the mouth and then followed by variations of clear whistling notes.

Voice: See above.

473

Breeding: The nest is made in a tuft of grass. Recorded in January near Wakkerstroom, December in the Orange Free State. Three eggs, pinkish, thickly marked with pale brown and a heavy ring of slate round the broad end. 20,7—20,9 × 15—15,2.

474 Spike-heeled Lark   Vlakvoël

Certhilauda albofasciata   Lafresnaye, 1836: *Cape of Good Hope.*

Native Names: u-Ngqembe (X); Motinyane (S).

PLATE 45, RACES *(e)* AND *(h)* (OPP. P. 321).
Length about 15 cm (wing ♂ 89—91,3—95, ♀ 80—83; tail ♂ 50—59, ♀ 43—49; tarsus ♂ 27—31, ♀ 25—28; culmen 19,5—21. 13 specimens, 9 ♂, 4 ♀). Iris brown; bill blackish; legs grey.

Identification: The upright stance, long bill, white throat-patch and short tail distinguish this species. In flight the short dark tail with white terminal fringe is conspicuous. See also habits. Female lighter and smaller than male.

Distribution: Southern Africa from the eastern Cape (Tarkastad), Orange Free State and the higher western parts of Natal westwards; in the north to the highveld of Transvaal and Pietersburg, across Botswana to Benguella in the west. Not in the dry Namib.

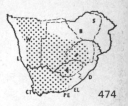

474

Habits: Resident, though small parties wander locally. Usually occurring in numbers up to six or eight. Keeps much to the ground, though when pursued may alight on low bushes. Prefers open and somewhat stony ground where there is little, or at the most, only low open vegetation but also occurs in the Kalahari dunes. Confiding but shows some little excitement when approached, calling and then flying for a short distance and alighting, usually turning round before doing so and standing very upright to keep the intruder in view. Flight undulating.

Food: Beetles.

Voice: In flight a short "twitt-twitt" or "kree-kree" and a soft musical "ploo-ploo-ploo . . .". Also "chitt-chitt-chitt-chew-chew-chew", rapidly.

Breeding: The nest is a deep cup placed under a tuft of grass or some other low plant; constructed of dry rootlets and grass and usually facing south or east. August to December. Eggs 2—3, pale greenish clouded with yellow-brown sepia and grey, with overlying scattered spots of brown concentrated as a dark ring about the thick end. Average (10) 21,1 × 15,0 (20,0—23 × 14,5—15,2).

LOCAL RACES:
The races are separated mainly by colour and pattern, ranging from more rufous and heavily marked birds in the south and east to pale and lightly-marked birds to the north-west. There is a size cline from larger birds in the south and east to the smallest in the north-west.

(a) C.a. albofasciata Lafresnaye, 1836: *Cape of Good Hope.* Central Cape Province to Natal. Chestnut-brown mottled with blackish brown. Size as above.
(b) C.a. bushmanensis (Roberts), 1937: *Road from Goodhouse to Steinkopf.* In the basin and around the perimeter of the Orange River valley between Great Namaqualand and Bushmanland. Generally lighter above and below.
(c) C.a. garrula A. Smith, 1846: *Northern parts of the Colony=Van Rhynsdorp.* North of the Olifants River to Calvinia and the Springbok area. Darker than *(a)* and size similar.
(d) C.a. subpallida (Roberts), 1932: *Marabastad, Pietersburg Dist.* Pietersburg plateau, eastern Botswana south to northern Cape Province: Somewhat resembling *(a)*; less rufous and darker on crown; chest fairly heavily marked.
(e) C.a. alticola (Roberts), 1932: *Van Wyk Mine, Boksburg.* North-eastern Orange Free State and southern Transvaal. A dark form; lighter rufous than *(a)* below, but darker above. Illustrated.
(f) C.a. bradfieldi (Roberts), 1932: *Langklip, 60 mls. west of Upington.* From west of Upington, probably in the Kalahari sandveld of Gordonia. Dark centres of feathers very much reduced, giving a more uniform colour. Wing ♂ 88—93. 6 specimens. ,
(g) C.a. arenaria Reichenow, 1904: *Rehoboth.* Southern South West Africa as far as Gobabis and Windhoek; see *(h)*, *(f)* and *(j)*. Browner and paler below than *(a)*. Size as *(a)* but becoming smaller to the north. Wing ♂ 86—94.
(h) C.a. boweni (de Schauensee), 1931: *Spitskopjie.* The semi-arid plains of the Swakopmund, Karibib and Omaruru districts. Paler than *(g)* and smaller. Wing ♂ 81—87. 16 specimens. Illustrated.
(i) C.a. erikssoni Hartert, 1907: *Okahokahana, Ovamboland.* The chalky flats of the Outjo and Ovambo districts. Generally pale grey-brown; similar in size to *(h)*. Wing ♂ 82—90. 8 specimens.
(j) C.a. kalahariae O-Grant, 1912: *Lehututu, central Kalahari.* Central Kalahari. Generally paler; vinaceous buff. Wing 88.
(k) C.a. meinertzhageni MacDonald, 1953: *Pofadder, northern Cape Province.* Bushmanland. Paler than *(c)* and narrower markings.
(l) C.a. baddeleyi Clancey, 1957: *Rietfontein, northern Cape Province.* Asbestos mountains and Ghaap plateau. Deeper russet above than other races.
(m) C.a. macdonaldi Winterbottom, 1958: *23 mls. N. of Karoopoort, Ceres.* Southern and Little Karoo. Greyer than *(a)* more vinaceous.
(n) C.a. latimerae Winterbottom, 1958: *Cofimvaba, Transkei.* Transkei and Border area. Redder above and paler below than neighbouring races.
(o) C.a. bathoeni Winterbottom, 1958: *East of Kakia, Bechuanaland.* South-eastern Botswana. Darker and redder than *(j)* and lighter than *(l)*.
(p) C.a. salinicola Clancey, 1962. *Lake Dow.* N.E. Botswana.

475 Long-billed Lark   Langbek-lewerik

Certhilauda curvirostris (Hermann), 1783: *"Le Sirli du Cap de Bonne Espérance".*
PLATE 45, RACES *(a)*, *(j)* AND *(k)*. (OPP. P. 321).
Length about 20 cm (wing ♂ 104—107,4—113; tail 73—82; tarsus 27,5—30; culmen 29,5—33; hind-claw 11—15,2. 5 ♂ specimens). Iris dark brown; bill brown; legs yellowish.

Identification: A large lark with a long bill. The prominent light eye-stripe and narrow dark tail are characteristic; see also habits. Female smaller than male, bill noticeably shorter.

Distribution: Southern Africa except the lower parts of Natal, Mozambique and eastern and northern Transvaal. Not recorded from Rhodesia.

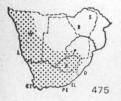

Habits: A common resident species occurring singly or in pairs, occasionally in family parties. Found on similar types of terrain to the previous species; perhaps more partial to stony ground and edges of stubble lands. Crouches when feeding and stalks rather than runs, often standing with upright stance on higher pieces of ground, looking about or calling. During the breeding season it has the characteristic habit of taking short flights, rising almost vertically

475

then plummeting down and at the same time calling its loud, plaintive, drawnout "phee-yeoo".

Food: Small insects and seeds.

Voice: See above. Also from the ground "churr-wee-wrrr", or "phee-hee-hee"; juvenile utters a "chrrr".

Breeding: The nest is placed under a tuft of grass or a stone; made of rough grass, from which a loose dome may be constructed, and lined with fine grass. September to November. Eggs 2—3, pale pinkish, lightly and evenly covered with yellowish brown and slaty markings. Average (10) 22,9 × 16,4 (21,8 × 24,8 × 15,8—17).

LOCAL RACES:
Variation in colour, markings and size separates the races; the southern birds are darker and more heavily marked as well as larger. To the north birds become paler and less marked. Along the coast the birds are grey, more heavily marked and bill length increases from Cape Agulhas to Port Nolloth.

(a) C.c. curvirostris (Hermann), 1783: *"Le Sirli du cap de Bonne Esperance"*. Western Cape coastal areas from Olifants River south to the Cape Flats. See *(b)*. Darkest and most heavily marked form with dark centre of feathers broad and edged with grey. Size above. Illustrated.

(b) C.c. brevirostris Roberts, 1941: *Zoetendals Vallei, Bredasdorp*. Bredasdorp division east to Riversdale and Mossel Bay based on few specimens, some recent material suggesting *(a)* also occurs here. Colour more ochreous above bill and tail much shorter (culmen ♂ 22,5, ♀ 20,5) but may reach the lower limits of *(a)*.

(c) C.c. falcirostris Reichenow, 1916: *Port Nolloth*. Namaqualand coast from about Port Nolloth. Similar to *(a)* but much longer bill. Culmen 30—32. 4 ♂ specimens.

(d) C.c. subcoronata A. Smith, 1843: *Karoo plains of middle and eastern districts of C.C. = Deelfontein*. Eastern districts of the Karoo (Deelfontein, Hanover, etc.). Distinctly rufous on upper-parts compared to *(a)* and less heavily marked. Bill shorter and straighter. Wing ♂ 110—114; culmen 23—26,5. 10 ♂ specimens.

(e) C.c. gilli Roberts, 1936: *Nieuveld Mountains above Beaufort West*. Western Karoo from Beaufort West to Touws River. Differs from *(c)* in having uniform crown and nape whilst being more heavily striped on back. Size as *(d)*.

(f) C.c. semitorquata A. Smith, 1836: *"Eastern Province of the Colony"*. From the eastern Cape to southern Orange Free State. A paler rufous above than *(d)* with thinner markings above and below. Wing 106—109; culmen 21—22,5. 3 ♂ specimens.

(g) C.c. daviesi Gunning & Roberts, 1911: *Matatiele*. Uplands of East Griqualand, Drakensberg, south-eastern Transvaal, Swaziland and Natal. A darker and duller form than *(f)*, always with stripes above and below, Wing 103—111; culmen 25—28. 12 ♂ specimens.

(h) C.c. transvaalensis Roberts, 1936: *Olifantshoek, Rustenberg Dist.* Southern Transvaal to southern Botswana. A brighter rufous form with stripes above and below indistinct or absent. Smaller than *(f)* or *(g)*. Wing 102—109; culmen 19—22,5. 14 ♂ specimens.

(i) C.c. bradshawi (Sharpe), 1904: *Upington*. Orange River from mouth to Upington, including Richtersveld, north to Helmeringshausen. Paler and more vinous rufous above than *(d)*; less striped above and below. Bill short and straight. Wing 103—112; culmen 27—29. 14 ♂ specimens.

(j) C.c. damarensis (Sharpe), 1904: *Tjobis, Damaraland*. Naukluft Mountains north to just south of Brandberg Mountains. More pallid than *(i)* and less marked. Wing 107—110; culmen 28—28,5. 3 ♂ specimens. Illustrated.

(k) C.c. kaokensis Bradfield, 1944: *Messum River, nr. Brandberg Mountains*. Kaokoveld from Brandberg mountains northwards to Oropembe, Kaokoveld. Darker and pinker above, more heavily spotted on the breast than *(j)*. Wing 110—114; culmen 25—28. 10 ♂ specimens. Illustrated.

476 = **475** *(c), (e)* and *(i)*

477 = **475** *(j)*

478 = **475** *(f), (g)* and *(h)*

479 Red Lark Rooi Lewerik

Certhilauda burra (Bangs), 1930: *"Bushman Flats"*.

PLATE 45 (OPP. P. 321).
Length about 19 cm (wing 101—104—107; tail 74—83; tarsus 26—28; culmen 14—16,5. 9 ♂ specimens). Iris dark brown; bill horn; legs light brown.

Identification: Two colour-phases occur; the unmarked phase illustrated. Marked phase with crown and upper-parts striped with dark brown. The marked phase practically inseparable in the field from No. 461 *(c)* except by habitat preference—see below. This species has a distinctly heavier bill and the flight and tail-feathers are darker. See under 461.
Distribution: Recorded from Kenhardt, Brandvlei, Prieska, van Wyksvlei and Carnarvon.

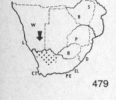

Habits: Apparently resident, confined to patches of red Kalahari sandveld which are scattered over the Bushman Flats. Sir Andrew Smith states "it soars frequently, particularly in the early part of the day and about sunrise whistles delightfully, being while so occupied generally perched upon the summit of the highest bush which exists locally".

479

Voice: Song like a Cape Canary.
Breeding: Lays 3 or 4 eggs; nest in a hole in the ground . . . made of grass, coarse outside, fine within. (A. Smith).

LOCAL RACES:
Roberts had named a race and a new species **(No. 480)** of this lark. Apart from the two colour-phases there is some variation in the amount of marking. This species appears very similar in many respects to *C.a. cavei* **(No. 461 *(f)*)**, but bill much heavier.

480 = 479

481 See 461 *(h)*

482 See 461 *(g)*

483 Gray's Lark Namib-lewerik

Ammomanes grayi (Wahlberg), 1855: *between Kuisip and Swakop Rivers, Damaraland.*
PLATE 45 (OPP. P. 321).
Length about 14 cm (wing ♂ 82—85, ♀ 76,5; tail 49; tarsus 22—23; culmen 13—16; hind-claw 8—9).

Identification: Small size and extremely pallid coloration render identity obvious. The only other species as pale as this is the Namib Chat (Plate 50, No. 571 *(c)*) which can be distinguished by its tail pattern and habit of flicking its wings. The bill of this lark is very thin.
Distribution: Confined to the Namib Desert from Aus to Oropembe.

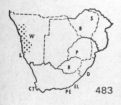

Habits: Apparently subject to a certain amount of very local movements near coastal towns, being commoner during some months than others. Very shy, but one can approach in a car to where the birds were last seen without any flying off; they then remain stationary for some time and cannot be observed until they move. The cryptic colouring blends well with the desert sand. Usually a few individuals are seen together.

483

Voice: Sings mostly at night; a series of high pitched tinkling notes combined with whirring wing beats and slurred whistles, uttered during undulating flight.
Food: Seeds and insects.
Breeding: Breeds March to July near Swakopmund. Eggs 2—3, laid in a deep cup.

LOCAL RACES:
(a) *A.g. grayi* (Wahlberg), 1855: *between Kuisip and Swakop Rivers, Damaraland.* Paler form. From Aus to Cape Cross.
(b) *A.g. hoeschi* Niethammer, 1955: *Namib west of Oropembe.* From Namib desert in the Kaokoveld. Darker above and below than last with markings more clearly defined.

484   Chestnut-backed Finch-Lark   Rooirug-kaffertjie

Eremopterix leucotis (Stanley), 1814: *Abyssinia.*

PLATE 45, ♂ AND ♀ (OPP. P. 321).
Length 13 cm (wing 78—82,8—86; tail 43—49; tarsus 14—18; culmen 10—13. 20 specimens). Iris grey-brown; bill horn-blue; legs ashy.

Identification: Distinguished in all stages by *chestnut wing-coverts* and grey under-wing. Male lacks white patch on crown of next species and the outer tail-feathers are white. Female variable, sometimes like male, sometimes as illustrated, sometimes with only wing-coverts chestnut but always with dark belly-patch. Immature and young like the last plumage of female.
Distribution: South of the Sahara as far as Zululand and Natal Highlands; Westminster, Orange Free State; Colesberg, Cape and Quickborn, South West Africa.
Habits: Resident in some areas but records indicate that between June and September flocks of up to fifty (one record of hundreds) appear to wander about out of their normal breeding areas—the movements not regular. In the breeding season separate into pairs but still occur in loose flocks, often in association with the following two species. Occurs in open flats, airfields and cultivated lands, though showing more of a preference for low vegetation than the unprotected open areas favoured by the next species. Takes to the air for short distances in a low irregular flight, dropping suddenly to earth again some yards off. May settle on tops of tall trees.
Food: Grass seeds.
Voice: Sharp rattling call "chip-chee-w". Sings beautifully, usually in fluttering flight.
Breeding: Recorded from a stony hillside, a tiny cup of dead grass beneath an aloe and amongst short grass. Also a nest at foot of a single stem sapling without cover of any kind. March to September, December and January in Rhodesia. October and January in Transvaal. Eggs 2, greyish white, freckled all over with brown, usually having a darker ring at thick end. Average (4) 18,9 × 13,8 (18—20 × 12,9—15).

484

LOCAL RACE:
E.l. smithi (Bonaparte), 1850: *South Africa.* South of the Zambesi River.

485   Grey-backed Finch-Lark   Grysrug-kaffertjie

Eremopterix verticalis (A. Smith), 1836: *Country both sides of Orange River.*

PLATE 45, ♂ AND ♀ RACE (a) (OPP. P. 321).
Length 13 cm (wing ♂ 80—83,8—85,5, ♀ 76,5—78,3—82; tail 40—48; tarsus 15—17,5; culmen 9,5—12. 37 specimens, 15 ♂, 12 ♀). Iris brown; bill bluish grey; legs brownish to bluish white.

Identification: White patch on crown and grey back distinguish the male bird. Female greyer on back than illustrated. All stages have grey on back and wing-coverts.

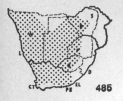

485

Distribution: The dry west from Angola to the Cape as far as Malmesbury, rarely to Bellville, east to the eastern Cape, King William's Town, in karroid veld. Southern and western Transvaal and Orange Free State except the north eastern parts.

Habits: Very much as for the last species; in the south seems to move away during winter. Less dependent upon low vegetation and particularly partial to wheatlands and neighbouring veld. When running about they frequently utter a shrill but not very loud chirp.

Breeding: Nest is cup-shaped, made of grass, built up with stones or earth and placed under a small bush or tuft of grass. One record of a nest lined with sheep's wool. December and January. Eggs 2, whitish freckled with yellowish brown and slate, slightly concentrated at the thick end. Average (6) 19,6 × 14,1 (18,8—21 × 13,3—15,4). Both sexes incubate (12) days.

LOCAL RACES:
(a) E.v. verticalis (A. Smith), 1836: *Country both sides of Orange River.* From the Cape to eastern Cape north to the Kalahari and western Transvaal. As illustrated; size above.
(b) E.v. damarensis Roberts, 1931: *Gobabis, S.W.A.* Damaraland to western limits of Kalahari, Twee Rivieren south to about Port Nolloth. Very much paler upper-parts and black not so intense. (Wing 76—85; culmen 9,5—12,5. 9 specimens).
(c) E.v. khama Irwin, 1957: *Makarikan Pan, Botswana.* North-eastern Botswana. Much paler edges to mantle feathers than other races.

486   Black-eared Finch-Lark   Kaffertjie

Eremopterix australis   (A. Smith), 1836: *Palla, Bechuanaland.*

PLATE 45, ♂ AND ♀ (OPP. P. 321).
Length about 13 cm (wing ♂ 79—80, ♀ 73—78; tail 43—48; tarsus 15,5—17; culmen 9,5—10. 6 specimens, 3 ♂, 3 ♀). Iris orange to ruby red; bill bluish white; legs flesh to dusky white.

Identification: Distinguished from two previous species by black earcoverts, *no white* anywhere and black under-wing. Bill smaller. Belly black in female as in other finch-larks.

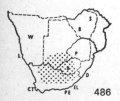

486

Distribution: Karoo areas to western Transvaal; west to Damaraland and as far south as Laingsburg.

Habits: Much as for preceding two species though not as common except in the Karoo where great flocks occur. Frequents very barren country such as the Bushman Flats.

Breeding: Nest placed under the shelter of a clump of weeds or grass, built on a base of sticks of coarse grass, slightly lined with fine roots and seed heads. Ayres records nests found within 20 yards of water. March and April, Eggs 2, whitish speckled with pink and lavender-grey, somewhat concentrated at the large end. 17,6—17,8 × 12,6—13,2. Both sexes incubate, (12) days.

487   See page xxxii.

488 Red-capped Lark
Rooikop-lewerik

Calandrella cinerea (Gmelin), 1789: *Cape of Good Hope.*

Native Names: in-Tibane, in-Tubane, in-Tutyane, in-Trutyane, u-Drutyayi (X).

PLATE 45, RACES *(e)* AND *(g)* IMM. (OPP. P. 321).
Length about 15 cm (wing ♂ 92,5—94,6—97; ♀ 86,5—90; tail 58—67; tarsus 19—21,5; culmen 12—14. 8 specimens, 5 ♂, 3 ♀). Iris hazel; bill black with brownish base, to pink; legs dark brown.

Identification: In all races the distinct rufous cap and patches at side of breast are diagnostic. Juvenile appears very speckled above and the dark spotted chest patches join in the centre.

Distribution: Throughout Southern and Eastern Africa.

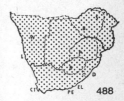

488

Habits: A common resident species occurring singly or in pairs during the breeding season. From March to August and in the north as late as November, forms small flocks of up to 20 birds or more which range about, apparently for some distance. Partial to treeless tracts generally; especially overgrazed pastures, stubble lands and open, thinly covered ground with short grass and weeds. Ground-dwelling, walking about in a busy manner calling frequently, but capable of running very rapidly over the open ground. When put to flight calls, flies off low, drops suddenly on to the ground and runs. Flocks are wary and sometimes difficult to identify, but single birds are quite confiding.

Food: Seeds of grasses and wheat.

Voice: From the ground a "cheep" or "tsheerk" and "tshee-ree" or "chirrup". In flight a short "chick". At dawn executes long aerial cruises uttering a series of short phrases, starting sibilant and ending harsh-"tcheet, tcheet, tchrreat". Mimics other bird calls.

Breeding: Placed often near a tuft of grass but quite as frequently placed in the open without any protection. A neat cup of grass lined with finer grass. August to December in the Cape; July to November in Transvaal; practically every month in Rhodesia. Eggs 1—4, usually 2; creamy white with close freckling of sepia and underlying ash-grey, some having markings indistinct. Average (30) 20,8 × 14,9 (17—22,7 × 13,2—15,3). Incubation 13—15 days (6). Nesting 10—12 days (6).

LOCAL RACES:
This species is separated into races on colour, although the northern birds do appear smaller than the southern ones. Dark and light forms have been recorded together in Western Kalahari and from east of Etosha Pan.
(a) C.c. cinerea (Gmelin), 1789: *Cape of Good Hope.* South-western Cape from Olifants River eastwards. General colour drab-brown; size as above.
(b) C.c. anderssoni (Tristam), 1869: *Otjimbingwe.* Damaraland. Darker than *(a).*
(c) C.c. saturatior Reichenow, 1904: *Kondeland, S.W. Tanganyika.* From the plateau in Rhodesia northwards. Mottled dark reddish brown and blackish above; darker than *(b).*
(d) C.c. witputzi (Macdonald), 1952: *Witputs.* From Olifants River north through Bushman flats to western Botswana and Great Namaqualand. Paler than other races, more suffused with buff.
(e) C.c. spleniata (Strickland), 1852: *Damaraland=Walvis Bay.* Illustrated. Namib Desert in South West Africa. Very pale fawn-brown.
(f) C.c. millardi Paterson, 1958: *10 mls. N.E. of Tsane, Botswana.* South-western Kalahari. Palest race with only trace of buff.
(g) C.c. niveni (MacDonald), 1952: *Gezabuzo, Natal.* Eastern Cape, Natal to S.W. Transvaal. Browner above. Illustrated.

489 = 488 *(e)*

490 Pink-billed Lark   Rooibek-lewerik

Spizocorys conirostris (Sundevall), 1850: *Upper Caffraria =Southeast Transvaal.*

PLATE 45 (OPP. P. 321).
Length about 13 cm (wing 73—76,7—81; tail 39—48; tarsus 15—19; culmen 10—12,5. 24 specimens). Iris straw-brown; bill pink, black in juveniles; legs pink.

Identification: Bill short, thick conical and pink. Underparts uniform rufous. Compare No. 472, with which it can be confused. Compare also Nos. 491 and 492, which are generally not rufous but earth-brown or grey.

Distribution: Grasslands from Cradock and Tarkastad northwards to Natal and Lydenburg, Transvaal; west to Upington, thence northward to Ovamboland and Zambia.

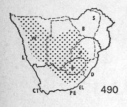

490

Habits: Common and apparently resident for the most part but regarded as migratory, June to February, in the Cape. Occurs in pairs or small family parties but flocks from June to October. Occurs in open flats, particularly old cultivated fields, where seeds are abundant, also burnt veld during winter.

Food: Insects and grass seed.

Voice: Uttered in flight or on the ground a tri- or bi-syllabic "twee-twee-twee" or "chee-chee-chee" delivered quickly.

Breeding: The nest is a cup-shaped depression, let into the ground and thickly lined with dried grasses or soft seeds. Recorded October to May. Eggs 2, white, covered with speckles of dark chocolate and slate, sometimes concentrated in a zone at thick end. Average (9) 19,1 × 13,7 (18—20,4 × 13,2—14).

LOCAL RACES:
(a) S.c. conirostris (Sundevall), 1850: *Upper Caffraria =S.E. Transvaal.* Eastern and southern parts of species range. Darkest and largest race; size as above.
(b) S.c. damarensis Roberts, 1922: *Ondongua.* Ovamboland east to Botswana. Paler than *(a)* and smaller. (wing 70—74,3—77; culmen 9,5—12. 11 specimens).
(c) S.c. barlowi Roberts, 1942: *20 mls. west of Upington.* Southern South West Africa to Upington. Paler than *(b)*, much lighter marked, especially on throat. (Wing 74, 75; culmen 11, 11,5. 2 specimens).

491 Sclater's Lark   Namakwa-lewerik

Spizocorys sclateri (Shelley), 1902: *Hauntop River; Great Namaqualand.*

PLATE 45 (OPP. P. 321).
Length about 14 cm (wing ♂ 83—86, ♀ 80—84,5; tail 42—49; tarsus 16—17,5; culmen 13—14,2. 12 specimens, 6 ♂, 6 ♀). Iris brown; bill horn-colour, darker at tip; legs pale brown.

Identification: Distinguished from Stark's Lark and No. 490 by its slightly longer, thinner bill, lack of crest and by being more earthy brown. The throat is lighter than chest and belly. Said to appear like the Lark-like Bunting, No. 871, but the bill of that species is much shorter and stouter.

Distribution: Known only from Great Namaqualand and eastwards to Philipstown District.

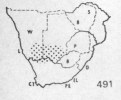

491

Habits: Little recorded. Occurs in ones and twos but flocks apparently during non-breeding periods.

492 Stark's Lark Woestynlewerik

Spizocorys starki (Shelley), 1902: *Wilsons Fountain, Great Nama-qualand.*

PLATE 45 (OPP. P. 321).
Length about 14 cm (wing ♂ 76—80,9—85, ♀ 76—77,6—79,5; tail 39—51; tarsus 14,5—18; culmen 11,5—14. 22 specimens, 14 ♂, 8 ♀).

Identification: Appearing a whitish lark in the field. Distinguished from No. 457 and others by its long crown-feathers which give a crested appearance and grey *not* reddish edges to flight-feathers. White below, slightly tinged pinkish with markings on throat.

Distribution: The arid plains of the west from Great Namaqualand and Namib Desert to Angola, Ovamboland, Botswana and western Transvaal; south to Calvinia in the north-west Cape.

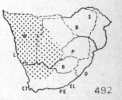

Habits: A common species in the western parts of its distribution; resident but flocking, 20—30 up to 100 birds, in non-breeding seasons; especially about Kenhardt. During drought gather by the thousand at waterholes in Damaraland. Frequents dry "pans" and open ground where the grass is short, sometimes with other larks and very shy. When flushed they fly in a wide arc to settle not far off.

Food: Seeds even to newly hatched young.

Voice: A rich melodious "prrt-prrt".

Breeding: Nests in a hollow in the ground based on stones etc. and lined with grass-blades and hair. Recorded by Bradfield, 20th April, 1921, at Okahandja. Two eggs, pinkish with numerous faint traces of darker streaks and spots darkening the whole egg; 19,6 × 14,2 and 19 × 13,7.

Family HIRUNDINIDAE

Swallows feed on insects captured in flight with the result that they spend much of their time on the wing. They are frequently confused with swifts but this family is easily distinguished by the angular wings rather than the rounded sickle-shaped wings of the swifts. The swallows perch like other passerines, and have one toe directed backwards, in this respect differing from the swifts. The bill is short, flattened and weak and the gape is wide. They vary considerably in nesting habits, some burrowing into sand-banks, others making nests of mud pellets, either in the shape of a half-bowl, open above or closed with a round entrance, or closed with a long tubular entrance. The family is cosmopolitan and contains many species.

493 European Swallow Europese Swael

Hirundo rustica Linnaeus, 1758: *Europe = Sweden.*

Native Names (generic): u-Fabele; u-Calizapolo, u-Dlihashe (X); i-Nkonyane (X and Z); Peolane, le-Fokotsane (S); Peradie (Ch).

PLATE 46 (OPP. P. 352).
Length about 18 cm (wing 121—125—127; tail 68—110, shortest feather 42—46; culmen 8—9. 10 specimens). Iris hazel; bill and legs black. Weight 19,5 g.

Identification: The reddish or *buffish throat bordered by a broad dark band* below distinguishes this species from all other swallows at any stage of its

347

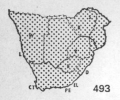

plumage. Immature birds have very pale throat-patches, upper-parts are more brownish with mottled white feathers occasionally visible.

Distribution: Breeds in Europe migrating south to India and Africa. Throughout Southern Africa.

Habits: A non-breeding migrant. The first arrivals come during the last week of August or early September, and the latest records are for the first week of May. During the period October to March the birds are very common. Winter records are rare. Birds ringed in Southern Africa have been recovered across the Palaearctic from Ireland in the west to 90° east in Siberia. Birds from eastern Europe tend to be more common in the eastern winter quarters but there are evidently no fixed wintering zones from a geographical point of view. The fastest recorded flight is a Johannesburg ringed bird recovered 34 days later 12 000 kilometres away. Longest distance recorded 12 480 kilometres. Oldest age 70 months. Widely distributed over all types of country in flocks up to several hundred. Flocks gathering to roost in reed beds have been recorded of many thousands in the Transvaal. Frequently rest in bunches on telephone wires alongside roads.

Food: Insects, especially flying termites; sand hoppers (amphipods) also recorded.

Voice: "Tswit-tswit-tswit" often run together into a regular twitter.

LOCAL RACES:
(a) H.r. rustica Linnaeus, 1758: *Europe = Sweden.* General distribution as above.

494 Angola Swallow   Angola-swael

Hirundo angolensis   Bocage, 1868: *Huilla, Angola.*

Length about 15 cm (wing 120; tail 65, shortest 45; culmen 9).

Identification: Differs from the European species in having chestnut chin extending on to chest with indistinct blue-black narrow band. Rest of underparts sooty-grey. Tail not so deeply forked.

Distribution: From Zaïre, Tanzania, south to Malawi and Angola. Recorded from within out limits once on the Cunene, along the Okavango River and Caprivi strip.

Habits: Similar to the European swallow in association with man and in breeding habits. Perhaps spends less time on the wing and more sluggish in flight than its European counterpart.

Voice: A warbling note uttered on the wing.

Breeding: Extralimital.

LOCAL RACE:
H.a. angolensis Bocage, 1868: *Huila, Angola.* The southern race.

495 White-throated Swallow   Witkeel-swael

Hirundo albigularis   Strickland, 1849: *South Africa = Cape Peninsula.*

PLATE 46 (OPP. P. 352).

Length about 17 cm (wing 126—132—138; tail 58—80, shortest 42—45; culmen 9—10. 12 specimens). Iris brown; bill black; legs dark brown.

Identification: Bright metallic blue sheen above; red just above bill and white on tail distinguish this bird. The bar across throat is broader at shoulder and sometimes tapers to a point before meeting bar of other side, though usually the bar is right across. In flight the end of wing is held more in line with the body than the European Swallow, in this way giving the appearance of a more prominent shoulder. See No. 496.

Distribution: Throughout Southern Africa as far north as Angola, southern Zaïre, Zambia and Malawi.

Habits: A common breeding migrant arriving from the middle to the end of August and departing in April or early May. Occurring singly or in pairs and after breeding in small family parties. Usually return to breed at the same spot year after year, to a bridge or culvert, a dwelling or rock face. Very swift flyers. Young quite often fall out of nests into water and are able to swim short distances. Oldest record 10 years.

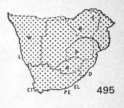
495

Food: Insects.

Voice: Call-note is a "gentle twitter". The song is a pleasant warble.

Breeding: Nest placed close to and under an overhang of natural rock or man-made structure, especially under bridges; the same nest may be used year after year. Composed of mud pellets in the form of a half-bowl and lined with fine roots and some feathers. Eggs recorded from August to late March, double brooded. Eggs 2 to 4, usually 3, white speckled with red-brown markings concentrated to a varying degree at the larger end where there are also some slate-blue markings. Average (87) 20,2 × 14,2 (18,1—23 × 13,5—15). Incubation 15½ to 16 days; nestling 20 to 21 days but returning to nest for a further 12 days.

LOCAL RACE:
H.a. albgularis Strickland, 1849: *South Africa = Cape Peninsula.* Differs from a race (*H.a. ambigua*) apparently breeding in Angola, southern Zaïre and Zambia in having longer wing and tail measurements.

496 Wire-tailed Swallow   Draadstert-swaeltjie

Hirundo smithii Leach, 1818: *Chisalla Is., Congo.*

PLATE 46 (OPP. P. 352).
Length about 13 cm (wing 103—107—109; tail ♂ 73, 75, ♀ 51—52; shortest feather 30—35; culmen 7,5—9,5. 6 specimens, 2 ♂, 4 ♀. Iris brown; bill and legs black.

Identification: The chestnut-red top of head, pure white under-parts and incipient band across the lower abdomen make identification easy. The female has shorter outer tail-feathers. Young much duller, head is brown and the throat and neck is washed reddish-buff. See also below.

Distribution: Ethiopian and Indian regions to Central Asia. Extending south, along the coast to Durban, to north-eastern Transvaal, Rhodesia and Ngamiland.

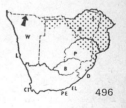
496

Habits: Resident at all levels in Rhodesia but further to the south-east, is a breeding migrant; arriving in April and departing by the end of October immediately after breeding. Like the last species found singly or in pairs near dwellings or bridges. In flight resembles the last species and except for smaller size, might be mistaken for that bird until the reddish top of head is seen.

Voice: Seldom heard, a sharp double chirp.

Breeding: Like the last species, it often nests under the eaves or even inside the rooms of houses, constructing a similar half-bowl shaped nest against the wall. Recorded June to October in the south, July to November and again

349

February to April in Rhodesia. Eggs 3—4, similar in marking to the previous species: Average (26) 18,4 × 13,0 (17—19,5 × 12,5—14,2). Incubation 14½—18½ days (5). Nestling 18—22 days (4). Female only broods.

LOCAL RACE:
H.s. smithii Leach, 1818: *Chisalla Is., Congo.* Found over the greater part of the Ethiopian region.

497 Blue Swallow   Blou Swael

Hirundo atrocaerulea   Sundevall, 1850: *Lower Caffraria = Umvoti, Natal.*

PLATE 46 (OPP. P. 352).
Length about 25 cm (wing 115, 119; tail 145, 160; shortest feather 41, 44; culmen 7, 7,5. 2 specimens). Iris dark hazel; bill black; legs dark brown.

Identification: Wholly steel-blue with very long outer tail-streamers especially in the male. Mottled with a few white feathers on flank not easily seen and shafts of primaries and tail-feathers white. Young duller and has a yellow gape.

Distribution: From parts of Rhodesia above 1 000 metres and in the higher grassland areas on the eastern side of the Drakensberg north of Zoutpansberg. Migrates as far north as Uganda during the non-breeding season.

Habits: Occurs from September in Rhodesia, October in Natal to April in the southern breeding areas. A very local species, nowhere common. Recorded in parties of up to 9. Hawks diligently for flies over the grass usually around sheltered nooks near bush and water.

497

Voice: A wheezy mono- or bi-syllabic note. Song of six to eight clear notes in a monotone likened to the alarm call of the Wattled Plover from a distance.

Breeding: Nests always placed in holes in the ground, mine shafts, animal holes and watercourses, sometimes up to 6 metres from the entrance. The nest, composed of mud and fine grass, is half-bowl shaped and lined with grass, rootlets or a little vegetable down, placed on the vertical walls or roof of the hole. Recently taken to breeding on buildings. September to March. Eggs 2 to 3, white, delicately marked with yellowish-brown, brown and slate-blue. Average (5) 18,4 × 13,2 (18—19 × 12,8—13,7). Double brooded.

498 Pearl-Breasted Swallow   Pêrelbors-swaeltjie

Hirundo dimidiata Sundevall, 1850: *Upper Caffraria = Leroma, Transvaal*

PLATE 46 (OPP. P. 352).
Length about 14 cm (wing 100—104—108; tail 57—70, shortest feather 40—44; culmen 7—7,5. 8 specimens). Iris brown; bill and legs black.

Identification: Small size, *no white on tail* and absence of chestnut colouring on head distinguish this species from No. 495. The sides of rump may be slightly mottled with white, but rump otherwise dark; see No. 507. The flight of this swallow is more like the European Swallow than the White-throated Swallow. Immature, brownish mottled with irregular iridescence.

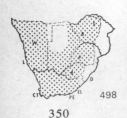

Distribution: Over the greater part of Southern Africa and to Angola, Zambia, southern Zaïre, Malawi and south-western Tanzania. Absent from the eastern areas north of the Kei River, east of the line of mountains forming the edge of the escarpment from Drakensberg northwards.

498

SWALLOWS

Habits: A common breeding migrant to the Cape Province arriving late August or early September and departing in early March (see under Breeding) in the west; a month later in the east; apparently migrating during the non-breeding season (records from February to November) to the Transvaal highveld. A resident breeding species in South West Africa and Rhodesia. Usually occurs in pairs or family parties and is partial to human habitation, principally in the drier areas.

Food: Insects.

Breeding: Tradition says that it may occupy sparrow or house swallows' nests but no recent record suggests anything other than that it builds its own half-bowl-shaped structure. Nest sites in houses, barns or farm sheds, against cliffs, in road culverts, wells and even in disused antbear holes. Nest constructed of pellets of mud and lined with fine rootlets or horsehair. August to December in the Cape, to March in the eastern Cape and later to April, starting in July, in Rhodesia. Eggs 3—4, pure white. Average (16) 16,4 × 12,4 (14,8—17,5 × 11,9—13). Double brooded, using the same nest. Incubation 16—17 days (4). Nestling 20—23 days.

LOCAL RACES:
(a) H.d. dimidiata Sundevall, 1850: *Upper Caffraria = Leroma, Transvaal.* Southern race occurring to Cunene River. Size as above, as illustrated.
(b) H.d. marwitzi Reichenow, 1903: *Usafua, south-western Tanzania.* More greyish below than *(a)* and slightly smaller to the east. Occurs from Angola to Malawi and south-western Tanzania. Recorded from Rhodesia.

499 Grey-rumped Swallow   Gryskruis-swaeltjie

Pseudhirundo griseopyga   (Sundevall), 1850: *Port Natal.*

PLATE 46 (OPP. P. 352).
Length about 14 cm (wing 91—95,4—101; tail 63—90, shortest feather 35—42; culmen 6. 9 specimens). Iris brown; bill brown; legs pale brown.

Identification: A small dullish swallow. No white on tail. White above the black lores. The grey rump contrasts with the blue of back, although not as strongly as in the House Martin, No. 507, which has a *white* rump. The young may be confused with No. 504 because the throat and fore-neck are buff-coloured; the rump, back and wing-coverts are narrowly edged with reddish-brown and tail is forked. A marked superciliary stripe contrasting with black-brown lores and ear coverts.

Distribution: The Ethiopian region. Recorded as far south as northern Natal and Swaziland. Few sight records from northern Transvaal. Also Ngamiland and Rhodesia.

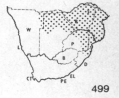

499

Habits: Apparently resident but subject to local movements especially during the rainy season. Common in Rhodesia but uncommon to the south. Occurs in pairs and small parties, *partial to vleis and open grassland* or burned ground.

Voice: A grating "chraa" in flight.

Breeding: Occupies rodent holes burrowed in open flat ground, also old Kingfisher and Little Bee-eater nest holes. Soft fibres are added to form a lining to the nest. Recorded May, July to September and December. Eggs 3—4, pure white and glossy. Average (17) 16,1 × 11,9 (14,5—17 × 11—12,8).

LOCAL RACE:
P.g. griseopyga (Sundevall), 1850: *Port Natal.* As described above.

351

PLATE 46

493. *Hirundo rustica rustica.* European Swallow. Europese Swael.
495. *Hirundo albigularis albigularis.* White-throated Swallow.
Witkeel-swael.
496. *Hirundo smithii smithii.* Wire-tailed Swallow. Draadstert-swaeltjie.
497. *Hirundo atrocaerulea.* Blue Swallow. Blou Swael.
498. *Hirundo dimidiata dimidiata.* Pearl-breasted Swallow.
Pêrelbors-swaeltjie.
499. *Pseudhirundo griseopyga.* Grey-rumped Swallow. Gryskruis-swaeltjie.
500. *Cecropis senegalensis monteiri.* Mosque Swallow. Moskee-swael.
501. *Cecropis semirufa semirufa.* Red-breasted Swallow. Rooibors-swael.
502. *Cecropis cucullata.* Greater Striped Swallow. Groot Streepswael.
503. *Cecropis abyssinica unitatis.* Lesser Striped Swallow.
Klein Streepswael.
504. *Petrochelidon spilodera.* Cliff Swallow. Familieswael.
504X. *Phedina borbonica.* Mascarene Martin.
506. *Ptynoprogne fuligula fuligula.* Rock Martin. Kransswael.
507. *Delichon urbica urbica.* House Martin. Huisswael.
508. *Riparia riparia riparia.* European Sand Martin. Europese Oewerswael.
509. *Riparia paludicola paludicola.* African Sand Martin.
Afrikaanse Oewerswael.
510. *Riparia cincta cincta.* Banded Sand Martin. Gebande Oewerswael.
511. *Psalidoprocne holomelaena holomelaena.* Black Saw-wing Swallow.
Saagvlerk-swael.
512. *Psalidoprocne orientalis percivali.* East African Saw-wing Swallow.
Tropiese Saagvlerk-swael.

SWALLOWS & MARTINS

493 495 496 497 498 499 500 501 502 503 504 506 507 508 509 510 504x 511–512

500 MOSQUE

501 RED-BREASTED

502 GREATER-STRIPED

503 LESSER-STRIPED

493 EUROPEAN

495 WHITE-THROATED

499 GREY-RUMPED

498 PEARL-BREASTED

504 CLIFF

496 WIRE-TAILED

497 BLUE SWALLOW

507 HOUSE MARTIN

510 BANDED SAND MARTIN

506 ROCK MARTIN

511 BLACK SAW-WING

504x MASCARENE MARTIN

508 EUROPEAN SAND MARTIN

509 AFRICAN SAND MARTIN

512 EAST AFRICAN SAW-WING

K B NEWMAN 1970

513 ♂   ♂ 513 ♂   516   515

517   518   519   Imm.

520   Imm.

521X   KN   523X   KN   521   Imm.

523   524   522

NIGHTON
'38

PLATE 47

513. *Campephaga phoenicea flava.* Black Cuckoo-Shrike.
Swart Katakoeroe. ♂ and ♀.
514. = **513** *Campephaga phoenicea flava.* Black Cuckoo-Shrike.
Swart Katakoeroe. ♂.
515. *Coracina pectoralis.* White-breasted Cuckoo-Shrike.
Witbors-katakoeroe.
516. *Coracina caesia caesia.* Grey Cuckoo-Shrike. Blou Katakoeroe.
517. *Dicrurus adsimilis adsimilis.* Fork-tailed Drongo. Mikstert-byvanger.
518. *Dicrurus lugwigii ludwigii.* Square-tailed Drongo. Klein Byvanger.
519. *Oriolus oriolus oriolus.* European Golden Oriole. Europese Wielewaal.
Adult and Imm.
520. *Oriolus auratus notatus.* African Golden Oriole.
Afrikaanse Wielewaal. Adult and Imm.
521. *Oriolus larvatus larvatus.* Black-headed Oriole. Swartkop-wielewaal.
Adult and Imm.
521X. *Oriolus chlorocephalus.* Green-headed Oriole. Groenkop-wielewaal.
522. *Corvus albus.* Pied Crow. Witbors-kraai.
523. *Corvus capensis.* Black Crow. Swart Kraai.
523X. *Corvus splendens.* House Crow. Huiskraai.
524. *Corvultur albicollis.* White-necked Raven. Withals-kraai.

500 Mosque Swallow   Moskee-swael

Cecropis senegalensis   (Linnaeus), 1766: *Senegal.*

PLATE 46 (OPP. P. 352).
Length about 23 cm (wing ♂ 142—145, ♀ 137—142; tail 83—117, shortest feather 45—50; culmen 10—11. 7 specimens). Iris brown, bill black, yellow inside mouth; legs black.

Identification: Large size. Rufous under-parts merging gradually to white chin, throat and sides of face distinguish this from the next species. Under wing-coverts white, faintly washed with buff. The lethargic flight, reminding one of that of a Bee-eater, is characteristic of this species. See also No. 501.

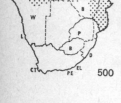

Distribution: Within our limits from just north of the Limpopo River mouth in Mozambique and in Mashonaland east of a line from Sabi River to Salisbury and Sinoia. Up the Zambesi valley to Ovamboland; thence north to Ethiopia and west to Senegal.

Habits: A somewhat uncommon, resident species. Subject to local movement, when parties of up to half a dozen may be seen. Mainly a species of large timbered woodland, though usually near water. Flies high above the vegetation level, gliding much of the time. Apparently attracted to human habitation.

Voice: A guttural croak.

Breeding: Constructs a closed nest of mud pellets, with a long tubular entrance, against the roof of lateral crevices in large trees, or under eaves of buildings. February to July, December to April in Rhodesia. Eggs 3—4, pure white. Average (11) 21,7 × 14,7 (21—22,1 × 14—15). (Malawi eggs 23,6 × 16,4). Double brooded.

LOCAL RACE:
C.s. monteiri (Hartlaub), 1862: *Angola.* From central Kenya and Zaïre south. White on inner webs of tail feathers on all except centre feathers.

501 Red-breasted Swallow   Rooibors-swael

Cecropis semirufa   (Sundevall), 1851: *Upper Caffraria = Magalies-berg, Transvaal.*

PLATE 46 (OPP. P. 352).
Length about 24 cm (wing 129—135—139; tail 123—153, shortest feather 51—57; culmen 8—11. 14 specimens). Iris dusky; bill black; legs dusky.

Identification: A large swallow with rump and under-parts chestnut-red. Differs from the last species by having lores and ear-coverts glossy black, no white on chin and throat and the under-wing pale buff. The young are browner above, paler below with shorter outer tail-feathers.

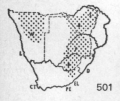

Distribution: From Senegal to Kenya southwards extending through Rhodesia and Transvaal to the high parts of northern Natal; Orange Free State as far south as Reddersburg, and northern Cape from Hopetown; Damaraland and Ngamiland on the west.

Habits: A common but widely dispersed breeding migrant, arriving in late August and departing in April with a few individuals as late as May in Rhodesia. Somewhat solitary in habits, usually occurring in open country and found near breeding sites. The flight is heavy and lazy but they seem to glide with greater purpose than the previous species. Reported feeding off the ground.

Breeding: Nests in hollow termite mounds, antbear holes, the roofs of holes in high banks and under culverts; seldom over water. The nest is a thick-walled chamber lined with feathers, having a funnel entrance 12—20 cm long. September to March but especially November and December in Rhodesia. A month later in the Transvaal. Eggs 3, occasionally 4, pure white. Average (25) 22,5 × 15,2 (20,8—24,1 × 14,6—15,8).

LOCAL RACE:
C.s. semirufa (Sundevall), 1851: *Upper Caffraria = Magaliesberg, Transvaal.* As far north as southern Zaïre. Richer rufous below and longer in the wing than northern races.

502 Greater Striped Swallow   Groot Streepswael

Cecropis cucullata   (Boddaert), 1783: *Cape of Good Hope.*

PLATE 46 (OPP. P. 352).
Length about 20 cm (wing 117—125—131; tail 90—108, shortest feather 46—54; culmen 8—9. 8 specimens). Iris brown; bill black; legs brown.

Identification: Striped under-parts distinguish this and the next species from other swallows. May be confused with No. 503 but the under-parts are tinged with fawn and the stripes are so narrow that from a distance it is not easy to see them. The ear coverts are whitish. The larger size and call-note aid identification.
Distribution: Throughout the southern parts except Mozambique. North to Angola, western Zambia and southern Zaïre.
Habits: A common breeding migrant, arriving in mid-August, September in the Cape, and departing in May—earlier in the south. One July record for the Transvaal. Migrates to Angola and southern Zaïre for the non-breeding season. Perhaps the best-known Swallow in our parts owing to its confiding nature and close association with human habitation. Flocks of 20 to 30 observed on arrival and after breeding; otherwise occurring in pairs, though several pairs may nest on one building. Returns year after year to the same site. Recorded age 80 months.

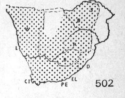

502

Voice: A pleasant twitter "chissick".
Breeding: Builds under the roof of verandahs, open buildings, lofts, culverts and bridges. Constructs nest of mud, the chamber lined with fine roots, feathers and down, with a long tubular entrance. August to April. Eggs 2 to 4, glossy white. Average (50) 22,0 × 15,2 (19,1—24 × 14,1—16,5). Incubation 16—20 days. Nestling period 20—21 days, returning to the nest for a further 9 days. Double brooded. Sometimes three clutches laid.

503 Lesser Striped Swallow   Klein Streepswael

Cecropis abyssinica   (Guérin), 1843: *Abyssinia.*

PLATE 46 (OPP. P. 352).
Length about 16 cm (wing 102—109—117; tail 73—120, shortest feather 41—48; culmen 6—8. 29 specimens). Iris dark brown; bill and legs black. Weight 17,0 g.

Identification: Can be confused with the last species. Differs mainly by its more *silky-white under-parts* with heavy streaks which are apparent from some

355

distance; the rufous ear-coverts, slimmer build, smaller size and call. Head and rump brighter but before the post-nuptial moult, this fades. Sexes alike. Young birds paler and duller, mottled on breast but otherwise patterned as adult.

Distribution: West Africa to Ethiopia southwards to eastern Cape Province and lowlands of Transvaal; in the tropics westwards to Ngamiland.

Habits: A resident species in the tropics and Mashonaland; south of Matabeleland and Mozambique occurs as a common breeding migrant for the summer only. Occurs in pairs or small parties and may be found near cliffs, bridges and dwellings, attracted to these localities by its nesting habits. A slow-flying swallow, gliding frequently and calling.

503

Food: Insects, largely beetles.

Voice: A series "tee-tee-tee" or "turr-turr-turr". Also a pleasant song.

Breeding: The nest, made of mud pellets, is built under an overhang or roof. Against tree trunks where there are no rocks or houses. The cup is lined with feathers but the long entrance tunnel is unlined. Often nests in colonies. July to November, to April in the Transvaal. May, July to December in Rhodesia. Eggs 2—4, white; occasional clutches are finely speckled with reddish-brown forming a ring at the obtuse end. Average (50) 19,7 × 13,7 (17,3—21,3 × 12,9—14,8). Incubation about 14 days. Nestling 17 to 28 days. Double brooded; both sexes feed young.

LOCAL RACE:
C.a. unitatis (Sclater and Praed), 1918: *Pinetown, Natal.* Streaked rather more broadly than other extralimital races.

504   Cliff Swallow   Famllleswael

Petrochelidon spilodera   (Sundevall), 1850: *Caffraria = Mooi River, Transvaal.*

PLATE 46 (OPP. P. 352).
Length about 15 cms (wing 111—114—117; tail 51—58, shortest feather 48—54; culmen 8—9,5. 9 specimens). Iris dusky; bill black; legs dusky.

Identification: Mottled chin and throat and the *square tail* distinguish this swallow. The degree of mottling varies. The young lack gloss on upper-parts, generally a dull colour.

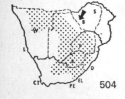

Distribution: From Grahamstown and the Sundays River west to Calvinia, northwards to the uplands of Natal and Transvaal. West through the Kalahari, in Damaraland, Windhoek and north as far as the Congo River.

Habits: A very common social breeding migrant, arriving in August and departing in April. Single records in the Transvaal in May and July. Winters in southern Zaïre; a ringed bird from the Transvaal recovered in Zaïre, 2 272 km.

504

Colonies of from fifteen to twenty to as large as four hundred nests may be found, with attendant birds seldom wandering far from the breeding site—see below. Known age 99 months.

Breeding: Nest on krantzes, under bridges, railway water tanks, eaves of buildings, particularly churches and public buildings where they become a nuisance from the untidy accumulations of dirt dropped to the ground below. The nests are round structures of mud pellets, built one against the other, with the entrances near the top facing outwards; the interior is lined with fibres and feathers. September to February. Eggs 2—4, practically always 3, white, finely spotted and blotched with reddish-brown or ink purple markings, more numerous towards the larger end. Average (50) 20,7 × 14,2 (19,1—22,7 × 13,1—14,8). Double brooded. Incubation 14 days. Nestling 24½ days.

504X Mascarene Martin

Phedina borbonica (Gmelin), 1789: *Bourbon, Reunion.*

PLATE 46 (OPP. P. 352).
Length about 12 cm (wing 102—108—113,5; tail 50—55; tarsus 13—14; culmen 6—7. 9 specimens).

Identification: Generally a brownish martin with blackish wings and tail, streaked with black on upper parts and lower parts to lower breast. White lower belly. Darker on side of face and neck.
Distribution: Western Indian Ocean islands, apparently wintering in the west. Now recorded within our limits: Inhaminga, 100 miles north of Beira, Mozambique.
Habits: A non-breeding visitor recorded in June and July, in open recently-cut woodland areas adjacent to African cultivated areas. Flight is rather slow, somewhat fluttering with a good deal of gliding on set-wings. In company with other swallows and swifts.
Voice: Phree-zz.

LOCAL RACE:
P.b. madagascariensis. Hartlaub, 1860: *Malagasy.* As above.

505   See under **No. 506,** race *(d).*

506   Rock Martin   Kransswael

Ptynoprogne fuligula (Lichtenstein), 1842: *Kaffirland = Eastern Cape Province.*

Native Names: u-Nongubendala, u-Nongubende (X); le-Kabelane (S).

PLATE 46 (OPP. P. 352).
Length about 15 cm (wing 127—131; tail 56—60, shortest feather 53—55; culmen 9—10. 3 specimens). Iris brown; bill black; legs brown.

Identification: Generally dull brown above and below. The white "windows" in the tail also distinguish this species.
Distribution: From Nigeria to Ethiopia southwards. Throughout southern Africa.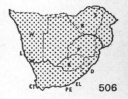
Habits: A common resident species. Has adapted itself to human dwellings where pairs or small colonies may breed, but for the most part is found in pairs in the neighbourhood of crags, or quarries, usually near water. Sometimes in lonely rugged country. Flocks may be seen in association with swallows, martins and swifts. The flight is somewhat slow and interspersed with frequent twisting and turning so that the tail is fanned and the white windows are easily seen. Quite active at dawn and dusk, flying about in half-light.
Voice: A melodious twitter.
Breeding: Nests against an overhang, gable of a house, or bridge or sometimes under eaves, very often next to some sort of ledge where the birds can rest. The nest is a half-bowl-shaped structure of mud pellets lined with rootlets and feathers. August to January, February in the Transvaal and to March in Rhodesia. Eggs 3 to 4, white with evenly scattered speckles of

reddish-brown and slate. Average (50) 20,6 × 14,2 (18,8—23,8 × 13,5—15). Double brooded, three clutches may be laid. Incubation 17 days. Nestling 25—30 days.

LOCAL RACES:
(a) P.f. fuligula (Lichtenstein), 1842: *Kaffirland = Eastern Cape Province.* Eastern Cape, Natal, O.F.S. and western Transvaal. Dark above, rufous below. Size as above.
(b) P.f. anderssoni (Sharpe and Wyatt), 1887: *Damaraland.* South-western Cape to Mossamedes, Angola. Pale above and lighter below.
(c) P.f. pretoriae Roberts, 1922: *nr. Pretoria.* Pretoria, Drakensberg and western Mozambique. Dark above and darker below than *(a).*
(d) P.f. fusciventris Vincent, 1933: *Namuli Mt. north Mozambique.* Paler above and below. Rhodesia and Zambia north to Tanzania.

507 House Martin   Huisswael

Delichon urbica (Linnaeus), 1758: *Europe = Sweden.*

PLATE 46 (OPP. P. 352).
Length about 14 cm (wing 109—112—116; tail 55—62, shortest feather 42—46; culmen 7—8. 7 specimens). Iris brown; bill black; legs feathered to toes, white. Weight 19,8 g.

Identification: Under-parts, *rump* and most of upper tail-coverts *pure white;* rest of upper-parts glossy blue-black. *Tail forked.* Young browner and with yellow gape. See also No. 499.

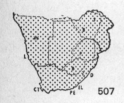

507

Distribution: Europe, east to the Himalayas, wintering to India and Africa. Recorded throughout Southern Africa. Rare in the southern Cape. A ringed bird recovered at Ceres came from Russia.
Habits: An irregular and somewhat uncommon migrant, for the most part non-breeding. It occurs singly or in flocks of as many as 100 in the drier districts. Often in association with other swallows, particularly with European Swallows, and swifts.
Voice: A single "chirrup" (Europe).
Breeding: First recorded, a pair in Cape Town, December, 1892. Subsequently at Otjiwarongo Station in May, 1928; evidently it "had bred there for some years and may still (1946)". Also in January, 1946, from Keiskama Hoek, the last of a small colony which had bred there for some years; December 1967 Kokstad and September, October 1969 Somerset West. The nest is situated against a wall, a closed upright oval with an entrance at the top or side, lined with dry grass and feathers. Young were recorded in all instances. Eggs 4—6, white. Average (100) 19,4 × 13,4 (Europe).

LOCAL RACE:
D.u. urbica (Linnaeus), 1758: *Europe = Sweden.* The only race recorded in Southern Africa.

508 European Sand Martin   Europese Oewerswael

Riparia riparia Linnaeus, 1758: *Europe = Sweden.*

PLATE 46 (OPP. P. 352).
Length about 12 cm (wing 105, 106; tail 47, 49, shortest feather 41; culmen 6,5 7,5. 2 specimens). Iris hazel; bill brown-black; legs dark brown.

Identification: May be confused with the next species, from which it differs by its definite band across chest, separating white belly from white chin and throat. See No. 509. In the hand distinguished by tuft of feathers behind the toe.

Distribution: Europe and Asia south in winter. Recorded as far south as Quickborn, South West Africa; a sight record from Swakopmund needs confirmation. Vryburg, northern Cape; Potchefstroom, Transvaal; and Durban in Natal.

Habits: A rare and irregular non-breeding migrant. Little recorded; probably similar in habits to the next species. Usually near water and on open plains.

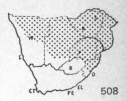

508

LOCAL RACE:
R.r. riparia Linnaeus, 1758: *Europe = Sweden.* Another race in eastern Asia.

509 African Sand Martin   Afrikaanse Oewerswael

Riparia paludicola (Vieillot), 1817: *South Africa.*

Native Names: le-Kabelane; le-Kavelane (S).

PLATE 46 (OPP. P. 352).
Length about 13 cm (wing 101—106—110; tail 49—59; shortest feather 41—50; culmen 6—7. 15 specimens). Iris hazel; bill and legs black.

Identification: Chin and throat never white, though they may be a pale mouse-brown. The mouse-brown extends from bill to chest, usually white from belly to under tail; rarely the under-parts are wholly brown. In the hand has no tuft of feathers on tarsus above hind toe. See No. 508.

Distribution: From the Sahara, south to the Cape and Malagasy.

Habits: A common resident, subject to some local movement and in the Cape occurring as a summer breeding migrant with few winter records. In some areas only recorded during the winter months. It frequents streams and rivers where flocks hawk insects. Usually occurs in localities where there are sand-banks for breeding. Roosts in large flocks in reeds during the non-breeding season; small populations roost in old breeding holes.

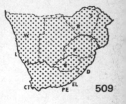

509

Breeding: Nests may be solitary or in colonies of up to 500 birds. Usually situated in a sand-bank, in burrows 45—60 cm deep excavated by themselves and, if colonially, close together. Lining is added after the eggs are laid. August to October and February in the Cape, June to September in Natal, February to October in the Transvaal and June to September and December in Rhodesia. Eggs 3 to 4, usually 2, pure white. Average (25) 17,2 × 12,3 (16,0—18,7 × 11,2—13,8).

LOCAL RACE:
R.p. paludicola (Vieillot), 1817: *South Africa.* Extending north to Benguela in the west and Lake Malawi on the east.

510 Banded Sand Martin   Gebande Oewerswael

Riparia cincta (Boddaert), 1783: *Cape of Good Hope.*

PLATE 46 (OPP. P. 352).
Length about 17 cm (wing 126—130—133; tail 58—66; culmen 9—10. 11 specimens). Iris dark hazel; bill and feet black.

Identification: Large size, neat chest band and square tail distinguish this Martin from others. The black lores and white line from above the eye to the

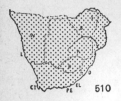

510

base of the bill are conspicuous characters. The young has feathers of upper-parts margined with rust colour.

Distribution: The Ethiopian region. Throughout our area.

Habits: A breeding migrant; locally distributed but generally uncommon. Arriving mid-August and departing in April. It is usually solitary or in pairs. Although they may be met with in dry areas they show a preference for the neighbourhood of water such as the banks of streams or vleis and their flood plains. The flight is slow and deliberate, frequently interspersed with rests on some convenient perch.

Voice: A loud chattering note, called in flight. A short "chuk".

Breeding: Nests in isolated burrows 60—90 cm deep in sand-banks. Usually made by the parents but old Kingfisher holes may be used. Recorded breeding in company with Pied Starlings and parasitised by the Greater Honeyguide. The nest pad is made of dry grass or grass roots and lined with feathers. Recorded from August to October in southern Cape, September to February in Rhodesia. Eggs 3—4, pure white. Average (22) 21,1 × 15,1 (19—22,7 × 14,6—15,7).

LOCAL RACE:
R.c. cincta (Boddaert), 1783: *Cape of Good Hope.* Ranging as far north as Angola, Zambia and Malawi.

511 Black Saw-wing Swallow   Saagvlerk-swael

Psalidoprocne holomelaena   (Sundevall), 1850: *Port Natal.*

Native Name: u-Nomalahlana (X).

PLATE 46 (OPP. P. 352).
Length about 15 cm (wing 105—108—110; tail ♂ 82—89, ♀ 63, shortest feather ♂ 40—44, ♀ 39; culmen 5,5—6,3. 6 specimens, 5 ♂, 1 ♀. Iris dark brown; bill black; legs purplish.

Identification: A slenderly built, wholly black swallow with deeply forked tail. Female slightly smaller with tail less forked and lacking the serrations on the first primary. Young lacks green gloss.

Distribution: The moister districts of the south and east from the Cape Peninsula north to Uganda and Kenya.

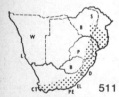

511

Habits: Not an uncommon resident species. Usually occurs singly or in pairs in forested localities especially where dark trees overhang water. Occasionally wanders from wooded kloofs but nearly always near water. In flight very swift and graceful, flitting between the trees with great dexterity hawking insects.

Voice: Seldom calls. A soft chirp when alarmed.

Breeding: Burrows in sand-banks, even in small road cuttings less than 45 cm high; the hole is about 25 mm in diameter and 45 cm long, sloping upwards. Also uses other birds nesting holes. The nest is a pad of grassblades, pine needles or "old man's beard" tree moss. November to February. Eggs 1 to 3, white. Average (6) 18,4 × 12,9 (17,9—19,2 × 12,4—14,3).

LOCAL RACE:
P.h. holomelaena (Sundevall), 1850: *Port Natal.* Another race occurs in the Ruwenzori Mountains. Recorded along the littoral to Inhambane and as far north as Zoutpansberg and east of the rift valley in Kenya. Recorded at Bikita in Rhodesia west of the Sabi River.

512 East African Saw-wing Swallow
Tropiese Saagvlerk-swael

Psalidoprocne orientalis Reichenow, 1889: *Lewa, Dodoma Dist.,*
Tanganyika.

PLATE 46 (OPP. P. 352).
Length about 15 cm (wing 103—106; tail 80—86, shortest feather 40—42; culmen 6. 3
specimens). Iris brown; bill black; legs dusky. Weight 11,9 g.

Identification: Easily distinguished from the previous species by the conspi-
cuous white under wing-coverts.
Distribution: Ethiopia south to eastern highland districts of Rhodesia and
Gorongoza in Mozambique.
Habits: Much the same as previous species. A not uncommon resident.
Breeding: The nest and nest site as for previous species. Recorded south of
the Zambesi in February, March, July, October and November. Eggs 2, white,
about 18,5 × 13 (Kenya).

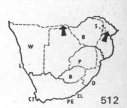

512

LOCAL RACES:
(a) *P.o. percivali* Ogilvie-Grant, 1899: *Ruo R. south Malawi.* As above. Malawi to
Inyanga highlands, Rhodesia and Gorongoza, Mozambique.
(b) *P.o. reichenowi* Neumann, 1904: *Chinchoxo, Portuguese Congo.* Angola, recorded
from the Caprivi Strip. A browner bird and under wing-coverts greyish not white.

Family CAMPEPHAGIDAE

A family of Passerine birds having roughly the appearance of Cuckoos,
whence the name of Cuckoo-Shrike—peculiar in respect of the feathers of the
lower back having stiff shafts for part of their length, the ends soft, so that the
tips of the shafts can be felt by running the fingers against them. The family
occurs in Africa, southern Asia, eastwards to Australia, two genera within our
limits. They subsist upon insects and construct shallow bowl-shaped nests in
the fork of branches, surrounding the outside with lichen, and lay normally
two greenish and spotted eggs. Their cries are peculiar, but not often heard.

513 Black Cuckoo-Shrike   Swart Katakoeroe

Campephaga phoenicea (Latham), 1790: *Gambia, West Africa.*

Native Names: u-Singa-olumnyama, ♀ um-Bamxo, u-Sasa (X).

PLATE 47. 513 ♂ AND ♀ AND 514 ♂ (OPP. P. 353).
Length 22 cm (wing ♂ 100—105—113, ♀ 97—103—109; tail 95—105; tarsus 18—21;
culmen 14—16. 46 specimens, 25 ♂, 21 ♀. Iris dark brown; bill black; swollen skin of
gape yellow-orange; legs black.

Identification: Males may or may not have a yellow shoulder, see Plate 47. In
either dress they may be distinguished from other similar black birds by the
swollen, *bright yellow-orange gape and rounded tail*. Females are quite
different (see Plate), while young birds resemble females, but have blacker
throats, more barring below and pointed tail-feathers.

361

Distribution: From Cape Town (rare) eastwards to the Transvaal and across to Angola and north over all Africa south of the Sahara.
Habits: A fairly common species but quiet and unobtrusive and thus frequently overlooked. Spends much of its time in thick bush, either seated quietly on a perch or creeping through the undergrowth. May also be seen flying from one patch of bush to the next; flight very flapping thus differing from the Black Flycatcher or Square-tailed Drongo. Occasionally hawks insects in the air but usually feeds off leaves or on the ground.

513

Food: Caterpillars, including hairy ones, insects and fruit.
Voice: A low insect-like trilling note, uttered in flight or at rest, "wheeo-wheeo-eee-ee-e", or a high-pitched trill "kkkkkkrrrrrererereeeee", also a low chirp. A metallic "cha-cha-chee-turut".
Breeding: The nest is a small structure placed on a branch or in a small fork and easily overlooked as it is covered and lined with lichens; built by female. Breeds from October to December. September to February in Rhodesia. The eggs number 2 or 3 and are shiny bluish or yellowish green, with numerous speckles of olive-brown, brown and purplish-slate, rather more massed at the obtuse end. Average (23) 23,9 × 17,1 (21,5—26,1 × 16,3—18). Incubation by female only, 20 days. Both sexes feed the young but female only broods them, 20—23 days (7) (Skead).

LOCAL RACE:
C.p. flava Vieillot, 1817: *South Africa* = *Gamtoos R.* South Africa to Zaïre and Sudan.

514 = 513.

515 White-breasted Cuckoo-Shrike   Witbors-katakoeroe

Coracina pectoralis   (Jardine and Selby), 1828: *Sierra Leone.*

PLATE 47 (OPP. P. 353).
Length about 27 cm (wing ♂ 136—141—149, ♀ 138—141—146; tail 107—117; tarsus 22—24; culmen 18—21. 18 specimens 13 ♂, 5 ♀. Iris dark brown, bill black; legs dark grey.

Identification: The only Cuckoo-Shrike with a white breast. Female has chin to neck paler than male. Young birds general colour white, spotted below, barred and spotted above; pointed outer tail-feathers; white edge to flight feathers and coverts. Is illustrated too large (Plate 47).

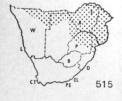

Distribution: From Senegal to Ethiopia and southwards to Ovamboland, Ngamiland and Transvaal.
Habits: Not very common; usually found in pairs, perched in trees at a fair height and flitting thence after insects in flight or searching the trunks of trees. Makes long hops through the foliage and peers short-sightedly at leaves and twigs.

515

Food: Caterpillars, ants, grasshoppers and other insects.
Voice: A loud whistling warble of "duid-duid" in the male and "tche-e-e-e-e" by the female. Also various squeaking sounds.
Breeding: The nest, built by the female, is placed high up in tall trees from 6—20 m. up. It is a shallow bowl about 10 cm across and 20 mm deep, well

hidden by lichens and cobwebs. Eggs are laid from September to November; they number 2, sometimes only 1, pale bluish-green or dull green, heavily freckled with shades of sepia and underlying ash-grey. Average (8) 27,6 × 19,7 (26,5—30 × 18,9—20,1). Incubation 23 days. Nestling 22—24 days.

516 Grey Cuckoo-Shrike   Blou Katakoeroe

Coracina caesia (Lichtenstein), 1823: *Kaffraria = Eastern Cape Province.*

Native Names: u-Singa, um-Simpofu, um-Swinkobe (X); Mmaselakhoasa (S).

PLATE 47 (OPP. P. 353).
Length 27 cm (wing ♂ 129—131—133, ♀ 126—128—131; tail 107—118; tarsus 22—25; culmen 18—21. 20 specimens, 9 ♂, 11 ♀. Iris brown; bill and legs black.

Identification: Note the ring round eye and the black mark at base of bill; the latter is lacking in the female, which is also paler. Young birds have their feathers edged with black and white.

Distribution: From Swellendam eastwards to Ethiopia and across to the Cameroons. Confined to the eastern districts of Rhodesia.

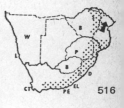

Habits: A species of the evergreen forests, usually seen singly or in pairs, clambering about the trunks and thicker branches of trees searching for insects; also sits for long periods on one twig. Flight weak but may catch insects on the wing.

Food: Caterpillars and other insects such as grasshoppers and beetles.

516

Voice: Utters a thin mammal-like squeak.

Breeding: Nest like that of the preceding species; eggs of a rather clear green, with numerous light olive-coloured, often rather elongate markings. Two from Mokeetsi, laid in November, measure 26,2 × 19,5 and 26,7 × 19,2.

LOCAL RACE:
C.c. caesia (Lichtenstein), 1823: *Kaffraria = Eastern Cape Province.* Southern Africa. As illustrated; size above.

Family DICRURIDAE

The Drongos are black birds with broad, short, rather arched bills and numerous long rictal bristles, the tail forked in most species. Members of the family extend from Africa eastwards through India to Australia. They are found in savanna and forest country, perching on trees and particularly conspicuous posts from which they hawk passing insects, including honey-bees; rather vicious in habits and fond of mobbing, with wild cries, other birds like Hawks or Owls that intrude upon their domain. When not excited they have a variety of whistling notes, which serve to relieve the silence of their habitats. Their nests are shallow, saucer-shaped, composed of twigs and fine roots, webbed together and slung between the diverging twigs of a horizontal forked branch, usually well away from the tree trunk and difficult of access. Clutches in South Africa consist of two or three eggs, which are white to pink and variable in colour.

363

DRONGOS

517 Fork-tailed Drongo Mikstert-byvanger

Dicrurus adsimilis (Bechstein), 1794: *Duywenhoks River, Southern Cape Province.*

Native Names: in-Tengu (X and Z); Theko, Thekuana (S); in-Tengu, Indunaye-zinyone (G); i-Ndhenguri (D).

PLATE 47 (OPP. P. 353).
Length 25 cm (wing ♂ 126—135—142, ♀ 126—132—138; tail 113—126; tarsus 21—24; culmen 19—23. 38 specimens, 24 ♂, 14 ♀. Iris red; bill and legs black. Weight 51,0 g.

Identification: Sexes alike, female's tail less forked. Young birds are dull black with grey edges to the feathers.

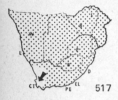

517

Distribution: From Senegal to Somaliland southwards to the Orange River on the west and Swellendam on the east. A few odd birds recorded as far west as Cape Town.

Habits: A common and very conspicuous bird which perches boldly in pairs or alone on prominent vantage points. Parties may be seen when numbers are attracted by quantities of insects such as flying termites emerging from the ground or when grass is being burnt. Like all drongos is noisy and aggressive, swooping at hawks, small carnivora, etc. Inhabits open bush-country, not thick forest.

Food: Insects, including termites, grasshoppers, mantises, butterflies and bees. A captured insect may be held down with the foot while being eaten in the manner of a hawk.

Voice: A variety of twanging, creaking, rasping metallic sounds; also imitates other birds' calls.

Breeding: The nest is a small, shallow saucer of twigs, rootlets and tendrils bound together with spiders' web. It is placed from 2—12 metres up and nearly always at the end of a long thin branch on the outside of a tree. Little attempt is made to conceal it and it may be so flimsy that the eggs can be seen through the bottom. Eggs are laid from September to December but mainly in October and November. They are very variable, white, cream or buffy-pink with red-brown, pink or black spots, the markings being usually of one colour. Clutch 2 to 4, also variable in size. Average (100) 24,9 × 18,4 (21,2—29 × 17,1—19,5). Incubation period 16 days; the young leave the nest after about 14 days. May have 2 to 3 broods in a season.

LOCAL RACE:
D.a. adsimilis (Bechstein), 1794: *South Africa = Duywenhoks River, Southern Cape Province.* Cape Province to Angola and south-east Zaïre, Uganda and Kenya. Birds from Natal and to Tanzania are somewhat smaller.

518 Square-tailed Drongo Klein Byvanger

Dicrurus ludwigii (A. Smith), 1834: *Port Natal = Durban.*

Native Names: in-Tengwana (Z); Thekoana (S); in-Tengu (G).

PLATE 47 (OPP. P. 353).
Length about 19 cm (wing 97—101—106, tail 88—93; tarsus 14—17; culmen 17—19. 11 specimens. Iris red to orange; bill and legs black.

Identification: The tail is actually slightly forked, not square. May be differentiated from the last species by its smaller size and *comparatively*

364

square-looking tail; from the Black Flycatcher, No. 664, by its *red eye*, or if that is not visible, by its *slightly forked tail* when seen from below. For difference from No. 513, see that species. Female duller than male. Young birds resemble the female but are greener above.

Distribution: From the eastern Cape Province (Bathurst), through eastern Transvaal and Rhodesia to the Sudan and West Africa.

Habits: Very local in habitat and not very common. Occurs in denser bush and forest than the last species and is shyer and quieter. Although it may emerge and sit on conspicuous posts in the open, it normally prefers to remain within the cover of trees in the shade. May swoop at intruders who approach its nest.

518

Food: Insects, caught mainly on the wing. Nectar. May harass other birds for food.

Voice: Various strident calls and may mimic other species.

Breeding: The nest is a small cup slung hammock-wise at the end of a branch. It is constructed of lichens, twiglets, stalks and cobwebs. Breeds from September to December. Eggs 2 or 3, white, plain or spotted and speckled with violet-brown and grey. Average (34) 21,3 × 15,7 (19,8—22,5 × 15—16,4).

LOCAL RACE:
D.l. ludwigii (A. Smith), 1834: *Port Natal = Durban.* As illustrated; size above. South Africa to south-eastern Zaïre and Malawi.

Family ORIOLIDAE

Passerine birds characterized by their fairly long, strong and slightly arched bills, usually pinkish or reddish coloured, and the plumage of adults bright yellow, with some black as a rule in contrast. They are widely distributed over Africa, Europe and Asia, some as long-distance migrants, some as migrants within the continent and others apparently residents. They live in large trees and forests, and their loud, clear notes, together with their striking, conspicuous yellow plumage, cause them to be well known wherever they occur.

519 European Golden Oriole   Europese Wielewaal

Oriolus oriolus (Linnaeus), 1758: *Sweden.*

PLATE 47, AD. AND IMM. (OPP. P. 353).
Length 24 cm (wing ♂ 150—155, ♀ 144—147; tail 80—87; tarsus 20—23; culmen 25—27,5. 6 specimens, 3 ♂, 3 ♀. Iris dark crimson, brown in young; bill dark pink, brown in young; legs slate.

Identification: The black wings of the male prevent confusion with the next species (see Plate 47). Black line on face ends *at* eye. Female is yellower on flanks, head and under tail-coverts than the immature bird illustrated but not nearly as yellow as the immature of the next species.

Distribution: Europe and Asia, migrating to Africa. Widespread in suitable habitat throughout except for arid Namib.

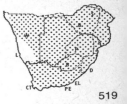

Habits: Quite a common visitor from the north, arriving in October and leaving again in March. Usually seen in small parties flying about in the tops of tall trees; a high percentage of visiting birds in immature plumage. Frequents rather dry woodlands, and particularly areas with high trees such as windbreaks among orchards.

Food: Insects and fruit.

519

Voice: A loud and striking call sounding like "weela-weeo" or "who-are-you". Alarm note a harsh rattling "chrrr".

LOCAL RACE:
O.o. oriolus (Linnaeus), 1758: *Sweden:* As illustrated. Only this race so far recorded from Southern Africa. Another race in India has black spot behind eye.

520 African Golden Oriole   Afrikaanse Wielewaal

Oriolus auratus Vieillot, 1817: *Africa = Gold Coast.*

PLATE 47, AD. AND IMM. (OPP. P. 353).
Length 24 cm (wing 132—143; tail 78—84; tarsus 21—23; culmen 26,5—28). Iris red; bill deep brownish-pink; legs bluish-grey. Weight 71 g.

Identification: Males have yellower wings than the last species and yellow tail-feathers except the central four; note also black line extending *through* eye, even in immature. Female is greener above and less bright below than male. Immature bird as illustrated.

Distribution: From Senegal to Ethiopia southwards to Damaraland, Rhodesia, Transvaal and Mozambique.

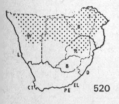

520

Habits: Seems to be migratory in the south of its range but some individuals certainly stay throughout the year; also appears sporadically in some areas. In Rhodesia arrives in September or October and departs in late February and March. Keeps to thick bush often along the base of small hills and is very difficult to see in spite of its brilliant plumage.

Food: Flying ants, caterpillars, insect eggs and wild berries.

Voice: Rather like the Black-headed Oriole but lasting longer, "fee-you-fee-you-fee-you" or "weer-er-er-wul".

Breeding: In Rhodesia breeds from September to December but mainly in October and November. The nest is slung at the end of a small slender branch, 5—13 m from the ground. It is cup-shaped and constructed of lichens, grass stems, cobwebs and woolly plant-down. Eggs are very beautiful, being buff-pink suffused with deeper rose-colour near the markings, which consist of bold spots of chestnut- and chocolate-brown and shellmarks in the form of large and small spots of slate-grey. Average (12) 29,7 × 20,9 (27,5—32,9 × 20—21,8).

LOCAL RACE:
O.a. notatus Peters, 1868: *Tete, Portuguese East Africa.* As illustrated; size above. Southern Africa to southern Zaïre; to Uganda and Kenya, in the non-breeding season.

521 Black-headed Oriole   Swartkop-wielewaal

Oriolus larvatus Lichtenstein, 1823: *Eastern Cape Province.*

Native Names: um-Xo, um-Qokolo (X); um-Goqonga (Z); Khulon (S); Chimku-rioku (D).

PLATE 47, AD. AND IMM. (OPP. P. 353).
Length about 25 cm (wing 132—138—145; tail 90—105; tarsus 21—24; culmen 26—30. 18 specimens). Iris crimson; bill brownish-pink; legs grey-blue.

Identification: Unmistakable on account of the black or blackish head in all plumages. Females resemble males. Young as illustrated.

Distribution: From the Sudan and Ethiopia southwards through East Africa to the southern Cape Province as far as Great Brak River.

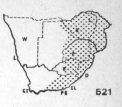

Habits: A fairly common and well-known species in well-wooded localities such as the forests, thick coastal bush and woodlands of our eastern regions. Favours high trees, spending much of its time, particularly in the early morning, uttering its loud liquid notes from the highest perch available. Flight slightly undulating, swift and direct. Seems to be somewhat migratory in some areas.

Food: Caterpillars, fruit, berries, beetles, mantises, locusts, termites, etc.

Voice: Most common call a very loud, liquid, whistled "pheeeoooo" which descends abruptly. Also a harsh "kweeer".

Breeding: Nest a bag of "old-man's-beard" slung at the end of a long slender branch, from 5—13 m up, in a tall tree. The nest is well hidden by beard-lichen which may be attached to the surrounding twigs with cobweb and also hangs in streamers below the nest. Has taken to gum tree and wattle plantations. Breeds from September to December but mainly in October and November. The eggs are beautiful, pinky in ground-colour with a few marks which are more concentrated in a ring round the thick end, of olive-brown, brown and slate, the marks often in the form of streaks or wavy lines. Average (46) 29,0 × 20,5 (27,5—32,7 × 19,2—22,3). Nestling 14½ days.

LOCAL RACES:
(a) O.l. larvatus Lichtenstein, 1823: *Terr. Caffrar, Eastern Cape Province.* As illustrated; size above. Cape Province to Rhodesia where it begins to intergrade with *(b).*
(b) O.l. angolensis Neumann, 1905: *Malandje, Angola.* Smaller and brighter than *(a).* Angola to Tanzania, Kenya, Uganda and Zaïre. Enters our limits in Ngamiland. Culmen 24—28.

521X Green-headed Oriole   Groenkop-wielewaal

Oriolus chlorocephalus   Shelley, 1896: *Mt. Chiradzulu, Nyasaland.*

PLATE 47 (OPP. P. 353).
Length about 24 cm (wing ♂ 133—141, ♀ 129—132).

Identification: The head, mantle, rump and tail moss green with a conspicuous yellow hind collar connected at side to yellow underparts. Sexes alike. Young distinguished by greenish-yellow hind collar and throat and streaked underparts.

Distribution: High montane regions of eastern Tanzania, Malawi and Mozambique extending south to Gorongoza at 1 500 metres above sea level.

Habits: Found in temperate forested areas; said to occur with No. 521 and probably similar in habits.

Food: Forest fruits, flowers—especially *Grevillea*, insects.

Call: Similar to 521. Distinctive "heee-eee-aaa".

Nest: Typical Oriole type of nest.

LOCAL RACE:
O.c. speculifer Wolters and Clancey, 1969: *Mt. Gorongoza, Mozambique.*

Family CORVIDAE

The Crows are characterized by being the largest of our Passerine birds, with glossy black or black-and-white plumage, bill stout, but variable, the nostrils

367

PLATE 48

525. *Parus afer afer.* Grey Tit. Piettjoutjou.
526. *Parus griseiventris.* Northern Grey Tit. Noordpietjoujou.
527. *Parus niger niger.* Southern Black Tit. Suidelike Swart Mees. ♂ and ♀.
528. *Parus leucomelas.* Black Tit. Swart Mees. ♂ and ♀.
529. *Parus rufiventris pallidiventris.* Rufous Tit. Swartkop Mees. ♂.
530. *Anthoscopus caroli hellmayri.* Grey Penduline Tit. Grys Kapokvoël.
531. *Anthoscopus minutus minutus.* Cape Penduline Tit. Kaapse Kapokvoël.
532. *Salpornis spilonota salvadori.* Spotted Creeper. Boomkruiper.
533. *Turdoides jardineii jardineii.* Arrow-marked Babbler. Pylvlek Katlagter.
534. *Turdoides melanops melanops.* Black-faced Babbler.
Swartwang-katlagter.
535. *Turdoides leucopygia hartlaubii.* White-rumped Babbler.
Witkruis-katlagter.
536. *Turdoides bicolor.* Pied Babbler. Wit Katlagter.
537. *Aethocichla gymnogenys.* Bare-cheeked Babbler. Kaalwang-katlagter.
538. *Pinarornis plumosus.* Boulder Chat. Swart Katlagter.
539. *Achaetops pycnopygius.* Damara Rock-jumper. Damara-bergkatlagter.
540 *(a).* *Chaetops frenatus frenatus.* Rock-jumper. Bergkatlagter.
540 *(b).* *Chaetops frenatus aurantius.* Rock-jumper. Bergkatlagter. ♂ and ♀.

528 ♂ ♀ 530 531 525 526 527 532 529 539 540ʙ ♂ ♀ 538 540ᴀ 534 536 537 535 533

Nlighton '38

544

543

542

548

547

546A

545D

549

550A

551A

725

♂
559

♀

562
♂ ♀

725

560 ♀
♂

561
♂ ♀

553A

553E

557

552A

556

558

Nighton.
39'

PLATE 49

542. *Lioptilus nigricapillus.* Bush Blackcap. Rooibek-tiptol.
543. *Pycnonotus capensis.* Cape Bulbul. Kaapse Tiptol.
544. *Pycnonotus nigricans.* Red-eyed Bulbul. Rooioog-tiptol.
545 *(d). Pycnonotus barbatus layardi.* Black-eyed Bulbul. Swartoog-tiptol.
546 *(a). Phyllastrephus terrestris terrestris.* Terrestrial Bulbul. Boskrapper.
547. *Phyllastrephus flavostriatus flavostriatus.* Yellow-streaked Bulbul.
Geelstreep-boskruiper.
548. *Phyllastrephus debilis debilis.* Slender Bulbul.
Klein Geelstreep-boskruiper.
549. *Andropadus milanjensis milanjensis.* Stripe-cheeked Bulbul.
Streepwang-willie.
550 *(a). Chlorocichla flaviventris flaviventris.* Yellow-bellied Bulbul.
Geelbors-willie.
551 *(a). Andropadus importunus importunus.* Sombre Bulbul. Willie.
552 *(a). Turdus libonyanus libonyanus.* Kurrichane Thrush. Rooibek-lyster.
553 *(a). Turdus olivaceus olivaceus.* Olive Thrush. Olyf Lyster.
553 *(e). Turdus olivaceus smithi.* Olive Thrush. Olyf Lyster.
556. *Turdus gurneyi gurneyi.* Orange Thrush. Gurneyse Lyster.
557. *Turdus litsipsirupa litsipsirupa.* Groundscraper Thrush. Gevlekte Lyster.
558. *Turdus fischeri natalicus.* Natal Thrush. Natal-lyster.
559. *Monticola rupestris.* Cape Rock-Thrush. Kaapse Kliplyster. ♂ and ♀.
560. *Monticola explorator.* Sentinel Rock-Thrush. Langtoen-kliplyster.
♂ and ♀.
561. *Monticola brevipes.* Short-toed Rock-Thrush. Korttoon-kliplyster.
♂ and ♀.
562. *Monticola angolensis.* Angola Thrush. Angola-lyster. ♂ and ♀.
725. *Nicator gularis.* Yellow-spotted Nicator. Geelvlek Nicator.

hidden by long bristles. They have loud cawing notes, usually occur in pairs, though often congregating together in large numbers, are omnivorous, though mainly carnivorous, and construct large nests of sticks.

522   Pied Crow   Witbors-kraai

Corvus albus   Müller, 1776: *Senegal.*

Native Names: i-Gwamgwa, Kwahube, Gwahube (X); Lokhokuba, Mohakajane, Lefokuba, Molhakavane, Mmankhoro (S); Chigombe (D).

PLATE 47 (OPP. P. 353).
Length 46—52 cm (wing 328—356—388; tail 175—200; tarsus 55—61; culmen 51—58. 17 specimens). Iris dark brown, bill and legs black. Weight 546 g.

Identification: The white chest and collar are distinctive. Sexes alike; young birds are duller black, particularly below.

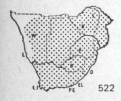

Distribution: Africa south of the Sahara except dense forested regions. In South Africa only absent from very barren areas such as Bushmanland.
Habits: A common, widespread but localized species, usually seen in pairs, or small parties when numbers are attracted by a source of food. Around towns has taken to scavenging in refuse dumps and near abattoirs; along roads finds food in the shape of animals run over by cars. In some areas has learnt to follow trains for scraps. Is generally very unpopular among farmers because of its habit of attacking weakened sheep. Nevertheless seems to be increasing in numbers and extending its range because of its wariness and ability to look after itself.
Food: Almost anything in the shape of an animal diet and also some vegetable matter.
Voice: A loud, nasal "kwahk". May be taught to talk well.
Breeding: Constructs a large stick nest in high 5,7—13,6 metres, often isolated, trees, telegraph poles or occasionally on a krans. Breeds from September to October, with odd records for August, November and January. Eggs number 1 to 7 usually 4 light green, blotched and freckled with olive, pale violet-grey and blackish-brown. Average (100) 45,0 × 30,5 (41,2—51 × 27,4—32). Incubation 18—19 days. Nestling 35—45 days. Three-quarters of incubation by female.

523   Black Crow   Swart Kraai

Corvus capensis   Lichtenstein, 1823: *Cape of Good Hope.*

Native Names: u-Nomyayi, i-Dakatye (X); i-Gwababane (Z); Mmamokhomelo, le-Khoava, Mokhoabane, le-Khoa (S).

PLATE 47 (OPP. P. 353).
Length 48—53 cm (wing ♂ 320—330—350, ♀ 293—321—338; tail 163—200; tarsus 62—70; culmen 54—63. 14 specimens, 8 ♂, 6 ♀. Iris dark brown; bill and legs black.

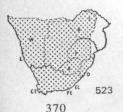

Identification: All black. Even in flight the beak appears long and narrow. Sexes alike. Young birds duller with little gloss.
Distribution: From Cape Town northwards and eastwards to Angola and Zambia; again in the Sudan and Ethiopia but not Zaïre or West Africa.

Habits: A common but localized species which replaces the Pied Crow in some areas; in general occurs in open country such as grain-lands and the Karoo. It may be seen in small numbers or in flocks of up to fifty, the flocks being composed of young and unmated birds. Mated pairs stay attached to a territory of about 70 ha. When calling, usually from a high tree, puffs the feathers of the head and neck out and makes a hideous din. Often roosts in numbers on telegraph poles.

Food: Omnivorous; carrion, insects, frogs, grain, berries, fruit, etc. May do considerable damage to grain crops.

Voice: A very noisy species, uttering a high-pitched "kah" and also a bubbling alarm note.

Breeding: The nest is a large platform of sticks, often incorporating wire, placed in a tree or aloe, on the ledge of a krans, or, most commonly, on a telegraph pole, 3,4—8,4 metres. The nest may be quite low down in desert areas or as high as 20 m. It is lined with feathers, dung, rags, string, hair or wool. Eggs 1 to 6, mean 3,5, pink with darker pink, purplish-grey and red-brown freckles and small blotches. Average (100) 44,9 × 31,0 (40,6—53 × 28,3—34,3). Incubation by both sexes, 18—19 days. Nestling period 38—39 days. The young may be fed for 3 months after leaving the nest and remain with their parents for 6 months. Breeds from July to March, mainly August to December. Both sexes incubate.

523X   House Crow   Huiskraai

Corvus splendens   Vieillot, 1817: *Bengal.*

PLATE 47 (OPP. P. 353).
Length about 43 cm (wing ♂ 266—284, ♀ 252—282; tail 154—175; tarsus 44—51; bill from skull 45—56. from Ali and Ripley). Iris brown, bill black, legs black. Weight 266—304 g.

Identification: Smaller than 523. Forehead, crown and throat contrasting glossy black. Dusky grey nape, upper back, neck and upper breast. Juvenile lacks gloss on black and is mouse-grey rather than dusky-grey.

Distribution: India extending down African coast along the Indian Ocean. Introduced to Zanzibar from which it apparently came south on board ships. First recorded in Durban 14 September 1972. One recorded at East London November 1975, otherwise only in Durban.

Habits: Associated with man and his environment. Intelligent, inquisitive and impudently familiar, yet wary and alert at all times. Gregarious and roost communally. Flight with unhurried shallow wingflaps often with fantastic aerobatics. Walks with a perky gait and sidling hops, often flicking the wings. This species has taught the Mynah to tear open plastic bags for food.

Food: Omnivorous.

Voice: A shrill, "quah quah".

Breeding: First recorded in 1975 Durban. An untidy platform of sticks and twigs placed in a fork of a branch 3 to 4 metres up. Not colonial but may be 3 to 4 nests in a tree. October. Eggs 3—4 pale blue green speckled and streaked with brown. Average (200) 37,2 × 27 mm (India). Both sexes incubate. Incubation 16—17 days (Ali and Ripley).

524   White-necked Raven   Withals-kraai

Corvultur albicollis   (Latham), 1790: *Africa = Cape Town.*

Native Names: i-Hlungulu, um-Fundisi, i-Hwababa (X); i-Gwababa, Luabai (Z); Lekhoaba (S); i-Qugwana (G); i-Gungu (D).

PLATE 47 (OPP. P. 353).
Length 50—54 cm (wing 376—430; tail 180—183; tarsus 72—79; culmen 61—66. 4 specimens). Iris dark brown; bill black with whitish tip; legs black.

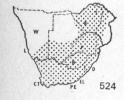

524

Identification: The deep, heavy beak and white collar prevent confusion with the Pied Crow, No. 522. Female has a smaller bill. Young birds are duller black with some black on white collar. In flight when white collar is not visible, the heavy beak distinguishes it from the Black Crow.

Distribution: From Cape Town northwards to Great Namaqualand and eastwards to Rhodesia and beyond to Kenya, Uganda and eastern Zaïre.

Habits: Essentially a bird of mountainous country though it may stray quite far from the nearest hills, does not occur in open country even if heavily wooded. Near its haunts it is regarded as an unmitigated pest as it is an inveterate thief, plundering poultry runs of chickens and eggs and even destroying lambs and sick sheep; is always the first to arrive at the carcass of a dead animal, tearing out the eyes before the vultures arrive. Is very wary, however, and well able to take care of itself and as a consequence survives in numbers, even forming quite large flocks. Finds much of its food on tarred roads, eating small animals which have been run over.

Food: Insects, carrion, in fact almost anything in the way of animal food; also fruit.

Voice: A deep-throated "kraaak"; also a high-pitched nasal note. May be trained to talk.

Breeding: Its nest is placed on the ledge of a precipice 11—32 metres up. Eggs number 1 to 6 normally 4, in colour very similar to those of the Pied Crow, pale green but rather more heavily *streaked* with olive, violet-grey and brown. Four measure 47—55,5 × 32,8—35. Recorded breeding July to November, once in April. Incubation 19—21 days.

Family PARIDAE

The Tits are small insectivorous birds with rather short and fairly strong bills, having the nostrils hidden by bristles. Members of the family occur throughout Africa, Asia, Europe and North America, one genus and five species occurring within our limits in South Africa.

525   Grey Tit   Piettjoutjou

Parus afer   Gmelin, 1789: *Cape of Good Hope.*

Native Name: Sekhakha (S).

PLATE 48 (OPP. P. 368).
Length 15 cm (wing 69—73—77; tail 53—60; tarsus 17—21; culmen 13—15. 13 specimens). Iris dark brown; bill black; legs lead. Weight 19,6 g.

Identification: Distinguished by the broad white streak below eye down side of neck. Longer billed than 526 and more tawny coloured above, grey below. Young have flight feathers edged with buff.

Distribution: Cape Province to the Orange Free State, Transvaal, Great Namaqualand and beyond to Angola, eastern Zaïre and Somaliland.
Habits: Widespread in the south but further north is confined to acacia trees. A species of drier country where it searches for its food among small trees or low bushes, creeping about the branches, uttering its loud call from time to time and generally moving on in a restless manner. Usually seen in pairs or family parties.
Food: Caterpillars and insects.
Voice: A scolding "titsikrur-krur-krur" and various ringing calls such as "give-ear, give-ear" or "t'wit, t'wit, t'wit". Other onomatopoeic renderings are "petitjoutjou" or "Piet Rossouw".
Breeding: Nests are made in any convenient hole in a bank, rock, tree or fence pole; they are warmly lined with horse-hair or other soft material. Breeds from August to October in the Cape on to December in Rhodesia. Eggs 3 to 4, white dotted with red, violet and grey. Average (10) 18,1 × 14,1 (17,1—19,5 × 13,6—14,6).

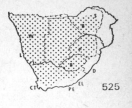
525

LOCAL RACES:
(a) P.a. afer Gmelin, 1789: *Cape of Good Hope.* Illustrated as No. 525, size above. Cape Province and Great Namaqualand.
(b) P.a. cinerascens Vieillot, 1818: *Camdeboo = Orange River.* Wing 72—79—84; tail 55—64; tarsus 17—20; culmen 12—14. Angola, northern South West Africa across to Transvaal, Natal and southern Mashonaland.

526 Northern Grey Tit   Noordpietjoujou

>*Parus griseiventris* Reichenow, 1882: *Kakoma, Tabora dist., Tanganyika.*

PLATE 48 (OPP. P. 368).
Length 15 cm (wing 74—82; tail 56—63; tarsus 18—20; culmen 11,0—12,5). Iris dark brown; bill black; legs lead.

Identification: Called the Small-billed Grey Tit because of a shorter and stouter beak than 525. Paler than 525 with grey above and slightly buffy on belly. Little or no white on nape.
Distribution: From northern Mashonaland north to Zaïre and Tanzania.
Habits: Confined to well-developed Brachystegia woodland from 900 to 1 800 metres in north-eastern Rhodesia. Thus ecologically separated from the previous species. Similar in habits to 525 but reputed to have a different call note.
Breeding: As 525.

526

527 Southern Black Tit   Suidelike Swart Mees

>*Parus niger* Vieillot, 1818: *Sundays River, Eastern Cape.*

Native Names: isi-Cubujeje, isi-Cukujeje (X).

PLATE 48, ♂ AND ♀, (OPP. P. 368).
Length 16 cm (wing ♂ 81—85—89, ♀ 77—80—84; tail 63—80; tarsus 17—21; culmen 10—12. 53 specimens, 32 ♂ 21 ♀. Iris brown; bill and legs black.

Identification: See next species.
Distribution: Eastern Cape Province and Natal across to northern South West Africa and northwards to Senegal and the White Nile. Common in the Kruger Park.

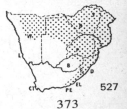
527

Habits: Haunts forest, thick bush, mopane forest and even quite scrubby woodland where it hunts about, from ground level to the tree tops, in search of its food. A conspicuous bird and males frequently sit on an exposed perch and call loudly.

Food: Mainly caterpillars and insects; also fruit and seeds.

Voice: A harsh cry of "twiddy-zeet-zeet-zeet", the first syllable shrill, the last three rasping. Also a shrill, buzzing twitter "zeu-zeu-zeu-twit".

Breeding: Nests are built at the bottom of cracks or holes in hollow trees or stumps, the nest itself being a soft pad of grass and lichens. Eggs 3 to 4, white with numerous light reddish speckles of red, brown or grey, mainly at the big end. Average (26) 18,4 × 14,2 (16,6—21,2 × 13—14,8). Breeds from October to December, rarely as early as August. Incubation 15, nestling 24 days (Skead).

LOCAL RACE:
P.n. niger, Vieillot, 1818: *Sundays River, Cape Province.* Eastern Cape Province to Malawi, westwards to Damaraland.

528 Black Tit   Swart Mees

Parus leucomelas   Rüppell, 1840: *Lake Zwai, Abyssinia.*

PLATE 48, ♂ AND ♀ (OPP. P. 368).
Length 15 cm (wing ♂ 86—94 (10), ♀ 84—92 (5) after MacDonald).

Identification: The male shows much more white on the wing than the previous species. Undertail coverts black. The female is duller in colour than the male.

Distribution: West Africa across to Ethiopia and southwards to Angola, Zambia and Malawi. Occurs within our limits in northern South West Africa south to Windhoek.

Habits: As the previous species.

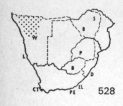

LOCAL RACE:
528 *P.l. carpi* MacDonald & Hall, 1957: *Warmquelle, Kaokoveld.* Southern Angola and highlands of Damaraland. Considered by some authorities as races of 527. Sexual dimorphism of 527 distinguishes that form from this species.

529 Rufous Tit   Swartkop Mees

Parus rufiventris   Bocage, 1877: *Caconda, Angola.*

PLATE 48, ♂ (OPP. P. 368).
Length 14—15 cm (wing 73—85; tail 60—70; tarsus 18—20; culmen 10—11. After Reichenow). Iris yellow; bill black; legs light bluish-grey.

Identification: Male illustrated. The rufous belly and black head, lacking the white stripe below the eye of No. 525, are distinctive. The yellow eye is very noticeable. Sexes alike. Young birds have iris brown, are duller and have wing-feathers edged with yellowish.

Distribution: From north-eastern Rhodesia and Ovamboland northwards to Zaïre and Tanzania.

Habits: Not very common in our area; in Rhodesia inhabits well developed *Brachystegia* woodlands, spending most of its time high in the branches, usually in pairs or small parties.

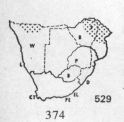

529

Food: Caterpillars.
Voice: A call of "chick-wee"; also a rasping note. Alarm note a sweezy "chweerr-chweerr-chweerr".
Breeding: Nests in cavities in dead or living tree trunks, usually fairly low (from 1 to 2 m), but also as high as 7 metres up. The nest is a soft pad of vegetable fibres. Eggs 2 to 4, usually 3; white or cream speckled or heavily marked with chestnut-brown, ashy-grey or violet-grey. September to December in Rhodesia. Average (12) 17,2 × 13,4 (15,8—19,5 × 12,8—14,1. (Zaïre).

LOCAL RACES:
(a) P.r. rufiventris Bocage, 1877: *Caconda, Angola.* Belly deep rufous, darker above than *(b).* Size above. Ovamboland to Zaïre.
(b) P.r. pallidiventris Reichenow, 1885: *Kakoma, Tanzania.* As illustrated; belly and back pale. Wing 75—87. North-eastern Rhodesia to Mozambique and Tanzania.

Family REMIZIDAE

These tiny birds are often placed in the *Paridae,* on account of the nostrils being covered with bristles, but they differ considerably in having a sharply pointed bill and, furthermore, construct extraordinarily compact nests of woolly fibres, which are slung to the projecting branches of small trees, with a protruding entrance that closes easily, and below it an open pocket, *supposed* to mislead snakes and other enemies seeking to find their way into the nest. So strongly woven are these nests that they are torn with difficulty.

530 Grey Penduline Tit   Grys Kapokvoël

Anthoscopus caroli (Sharpe), 1871: *Ovaquenyama, Ovamboland.*

PLATE 48 (OPP. P. 368).
Length 8—9 cm (wing ♂ 50—51—52,5 ♀ 49,5—51—52; tail 27—28,5; tarsus 12,5—13,5; culmen 7,5—9. 15 specimens, 9 ♂ 6 ♀). Iris brown; bill and legs slate. Weight 6,2 g.

Identification: Lacks the black forehead of the next species. Sexes alike. Young similar to adults.
Distribution: From Damaraland across to Transvaal and Natal northwards to Uganda and East Africa.
Habits: General habits similar to those of the next species, usually found in pairs or small family parties working through bushes and trees in search of their food. When disturbed they stream after each other to the next bush. They also explore large flowers. Commonest in dry *Acacia* woodland in the southern areas, but also in *Brachystegia* in the north.
Food: Insects.
Voice: A faint "cheep". Song, a squeaky "tseewhee" repeated five or six times, the first note higher than the second.
Breeding: The nest is made of woolly vegetable down and is very similar to that of the next species. Eggs, white 4 to 6. Average (21) = 4,3 × 9,6 (12,8—15 × 9,3—9,9; one 16,6 × 10,5 perhaps of a parasite). Young are fed by both sexes. Breeds from October to December; August to February in Rhodesia.

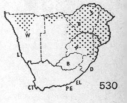

LOCAL RACES:
(a) A.c. caroli (Sharpe), 1871: *Ovaquenyama, Ovamboland.* Axillaries and under wing coverts buff. Northern South West Africa and Okavango swamps to Francistown, Botswana.
(b) A.c. hellmayri Roberts, 1914: *Mapagone, north-eastern Transvaal.* As illustrated, size above. Natal, eastern Transvaal, southern Mozambique to the Sabi Lundi area in Rhodesia.
(c) A.c. robertsi Haagner, 1909: *Villa Pereira, Boror, Mozambique.* Lower belly and under tail-coverts warmer buff. Wing 51—58. Mozambique from Inhambane north to eastern Zambia and Tanzania.

531 Cape Penduline Tit Kaapse Kapokvoël

Anthoscopus minutus (Shaw and Nodder), 1812: *Heerenlogement, Western Cape.*

Native Names: u-Notoyi (X); le-Soarelela (S).

PLATE 48 (OPP. P. 368).

Length 9—10 cm (wing ♂ 47—51—53, ♀ 47—50—52; tail 33—37; tarsus 13—15; culmen 7—9. 26 specimens, 17 ♂, 9 ♀). Iris yellowish-brown; bill dark; legs slate blue.

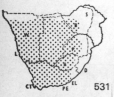

Identification: The black forehead and spotted chin prevent confusion with the last species. Sexes alike. Young birds resemble adults.
Distribution: The drier parts of Cape Province northwards to southern Angola on the west and Transvaal on the east.
Habits: Quite a common species usually seen in family parties of 10 to 20, searching bushes for insects and flitting away after each other when disturbed. Members of these parties call to each other continually to keep in touch. The remarkable nests (see below) are used for roosting when breeding is not going on, and a dozen or more birds may pack into one nest for the night, closing the entrance behind them. Known to roost in weaver nests.

Food: Small insects, their larvae and eggs; also berries.
Voice: A "crickling" which may be written "trrit, trrit".
Breeding: The nest is made of fine woolly substances from plants and animals which are felted into a tough cloth-like material. The nest is oval with a tubular entrance about 25 mm long near the top but projecting horizontally for about 25 mm, the entrance hole being also about the same in diameter. The nest may be placed from 30 cm—5 m from the ground but is usually at about 2 to 3 metres up. Breeds from June to December in the Cape; October to February in Rhodesia. Eggs number 3 to 6 and are pure white. Average (20) 14,3 × 9,6 (13,2—15,3 × 9,3—10). Larger numbers of eggs 9, 12 are probably due to two females. Incubation period 13—14 days, nestling 22 days.

LOCAL RACES:
(a) A.m. minutus (Shaw and Nodder), 1812: *Oliphant's River = Heerenlogement, Western Cape Province.* As illustrated; size above. South Africa.
(b) A.m. damarensis Reichenow, 1905: *Damaraland.* Upper-parts light grey without olive tinge, below light yellow. Wing 48—50—52 (16). Damaraland and the Kalahari.

Family CERTHIIDAE

A family that is widely distributed in the northern hemisphere, of which only one species extends southwards into our northern limits. It is characterized by its rather long, slightly curved bill, short legs but long hind toe and claw, the latter much curved, and sharp, the combined hind toe and claw as long as the tarsus; the plumage is brown and mottled and banded, in that respect differing from that of the Sunbirds, which the Creepers somewhat resemble in the bill.

532   Spotted Creeper   Boomkruiper

Salpornis spilonota   (Franklin), 1831: *Vindhyian Hills, India.*

PLATE 48 (OPP. P. 368).

Length about 15 cm (wing 87—94; tail 50—60; tarsus 16; culmen 17—20. After Reichenow). Iris dark brown; bill dusky brown; legs greyish. Weight 16 g.

Identification: The spotted plumage and long thin, curved bill, combined with characteristic habits (see below), are diagnostic. Sexes alike. Young resemble adults but are slightly duller.

Distribution: From Angola, Rhodesia and Mozambique northwards south of the Sahara and India south of the Himalayas. Sight record in northern Kruger National Park needs confirmation.

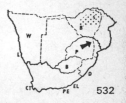

532

Habits: Not uncommon in Rhodesia, particularly above 800 metres, being strictly confined to *Brachystegia* woodland and apparently never in *Acacia* or mopane. Sight record in the Kruger Park refers to occurrence on dense deciduous *Androstachys johnsoni* forest. Usually seen singly or in pairs and very often as members of a "bird party"; flies to the lower parts of a tree and works its way upwards to the top, rather like a woodpecker does but without spreading its tail, and then flies off to the next tree to repeat the process. Flight undulating, again like a woodpecker. Is frequently overlooked as it takes care to climb tree on the blind side away from an observer.

Food: Moths, caterpillars, beetles, ants and woodborers.

Voice: A rapid series of shrill, wisping whistles, "sweepy-swip-swip-swip-swip", and less often, five or six high croaking notes, "keck, keck".

Breeding: The nest is cup-shaped and made of grass bound together with cobwebs and covered with lichen and bark. It is placed on a horizontal branch usually against a vertical stem and has been recorded from 3,5 to 12 m up. Eggs laid in Rhodesia August to October, 2 in number; pale bluish-green, somewhat glossy, the larger end tinged with buff, freckled with brown or with coalescing blotches of greyish-lilac, mostly in a zone at the large end. Rhodesian eggs 18,7 × 13,5 (18,0—19,5 × 12,9—13,8). The female incubates and is fed by the male.

LOCAL RACE:
S.s. salvadori (Bocage), 1878: *Caconda, Angola.* As illustrated; size above. Rhodesia to Angola, Tanzania and Kenya.

Family TIMALIIDAE

Members of this family resemble the Thrushes in many respects, but are kept apart on morphological grounds; their definition on external characters is not simple. At one time the Bulbuls were associated with them, but have now been placed apart either as a subfamily or distinct family, while the Tit-babblers have also been placed with them or separated as a sub-family, or placed in other families, such as the Tits or Flycatchers.

377

533   Arrow-marked Babbler   Pylvlek Katlagter

Turdoides jardineii (A. Smith), 1836: *North-western Transvaal.*

Native Names: Sekhanokha (Ch.); i-Dhlekwana (G).

PLATE 48 (OPP. P. 368).
Length 23—25 cm (wing 103—110—116; tail 105—111; tarsus 31—33; culmen 23—25. 42 specimens). Iris red round a ring of orange *or orange with yellow inner ring*; bill black; legs brown. Weight 70 g.

Identification: Might be mistaken for White-rumped Babbler, No. 535 (which see). Sexes alike. Young birds are much plainer with no arrow-marks on chest.

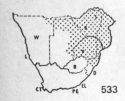

Distribution: From Natal to Kenya and across to eastern Zaïre, south to Ngamiland and Natal.

533

Habits: A common and conspicuous bird of woodlands, riverine reed beds or forest underbush, usually seen in parties of about 7 individuals which clamber about low down in thick bushes moving on to the next bush one after the other with fluttering flight followed by a glide into cover. Social breeders, all members of a flock will feed chicks but at this time they are much more quiet and inconspicuous than during the rest of the year. Individuals constantly keep in touch with one another by uttering their strange call (see below). Feed mainly on the ground.

Food: Insects such as termites, grasshoppers, caterpillars, crickets and ants; also spiders, lizards and snails. Seeds.

Voice: Normal call a grating churr which is uttered by all the birds in a party one after the other. The effect is of a whirring, grating, crescendo of sound, getting louder and louder as each bird joins in and dying away as they stop one by one.

Breeding: The nest is a mass of grass and twigs placed in a tree, often among driftwood along a river, at any height from 0,5 to 3,5 m up; there is a bowl-shaped cavity in the top lined with fibres and rootlets. Nests are quite often placed among reeds. Parasitised by the Striped Cuckoo. Eggs number 3 or 4 and are pale uniform greenish-blue. Average (32) 25,8 × 18,7 (24—27,4 × 17,4—19,7). Breeds mainly during October but recorded in all months except March and April.

LOCAL RACES:
(a) T.j. jardineii (A. Smith), 1836: *Rivers beyond Kurrichane = North-western Transvaal.* As illustrated; size above. Western Transvaal to southern Kalahari.
(b) T.j. natalensis Roberts, 1908: *Weenen, Natal.* Smaller than *(a).* Wing 96—104,5—109; tail 86—96; tarsus 30—32; culmen 19,5—21. 13 specimens. Natal, eastern Transvaal, Sabi-Lundi junction area of Rhodesia and southern Mozambique.
(c) T.j. kirkii (Sharpe), 1876: *Mazzaro, Portuguese East Africa.* Underparts more buffy; size still smaller. Wing 90—97; tail 87—94; tarsus 30—32; culmen 19—21 (4). Northern Mozambique, the Zambesi Valley as far west as the Senyati River, Malawi, north-eastern Zambia to Tanzania.
(d) T.j. affinis Bocage, 1869: *Quilengues, Angola.* Northern Botswana to southern Angola. Greyer on upper parts than *(a).*

534   Black-faced Babbler   Swartwang-katlagter

Turdoides melanops (Hartlaub), 1867: *Damaraland.*

PLATE 48 (OPP. P. 368).
Length 28 cm (wing 115—123; tail 118—125. After Chapin; tarsus 32; culmen 19—26). Iris light yellow; bill and legs black.

Identification: Unlikely to be confused with any other babbler due to its restricted distribution in our area. Light yellow eye is a good field character.

The black face and absence of arrow-markings should avoid confusion with the last species. Sexes alike. Young birds are less clearly marked than adults.
Distribution: Northern Damaraland and Angola to Tanzania, Kenya and Uganda.
Habits: Somewhat rare and shy birds which keep to thick cover such as elephant grass, where they creep about near the ground searching for food, often scratching about among fallen leaves. Is usually encountered in small parties of about five birds.
Food: Mainly insects but reptile remains are also recorded; also fruit.
Voice: Call note a nasal "pă-pă-pă" which may be combined into a chatter of the same petulant quality. Also a nasal "wha-u".
Breeding: Nests are cup-shaped structures made of twigs and roots, lined with softer materials. Eggs greenish blue, smooth at the extremities but quite rough in the centre, with numerous little tubercles.

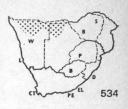

LOCAL RACE:
T.m. melanops (Hartlaub), 1867: *Damaraland.* As illustrated; size above. Northern Damaraland to Ovamboland.

535 White-rumped Babbler   Witkruis-katlagter

Turdoides leucopygia (Rüppell), 1840: *Coast of Eritrea.*

PLATE 48 (OPP. P. 368).
Length 26 cm (wing 105—117—121; tail 105—124; tarsus 35—39; culmen 21—24. 23 specimens). Iris red with yellow round pupil; bill black; legs brown, feet darker. Weight 71 g.

Identification: Rather similar to the Arrow-marked Babbler, No. 533, but rump white; more scaly about the head and chest. Sexes alike but males seem to be browner on the throat. Young birds are paler on the throat.
Distribution: From Ngamiland northwards to Angola, Tanzania, Eritrea and the Sudan. Recorded from the Okavango River and extreme westerly tip of Rhodesia.
Habits: A common bird in Ngamiland where it may be seen in large parties of up to a score searching for food on the ground or in the trees along rivers. They roost and find refuge in the reed beds. Flight a rapid flutter and glide.
Voice: No noisier bird could be imagined. Normal call a petulant nasal "pă, pă, pă" rather like the last species.
Breeding: Nest similar to that of the Arrow-marked Babbler. Eggs 3, fairly deep greenish-blue, about 25—28 × 19—20,5. Little recorded for our area.

LOCAL RACE:
T.l. hartlaubii (Bocage), 1868: *Huilla, Angola.* As illustrated; size above. Ngamiland, the Cunene, Angola, eastern Zaïre to Tanzania.

536 Pied Babbler   Wit Katlagter

Turdoides bicolor (Jardine), 1831: *South Africa = Kuruman.*

PLATE 48 (OPP. P. 368).
Length 26 cm (wing 108—113—118; tail 106—117; tarsus 33—36; culmen 24—25,5. 10 specimens). Iris reddish orange; bill black; legs brown.

Identification: Unmistakable. Sexes alike. Young birds are more or less uniform olive-brownish, with dark wings and tail and take on the white feathers gradually.

536

Distribution: The Molopo River northwards to Damaraland and across the Kalahari to western Transvaal and south-western Matabeleland.
Habits: Essentially a bird of dry bushveld. Like other babblers it is gregarious, as many as a dozen consorting together. Even in the nesting season it is not solitary as a rule, though apparently monogamous, the nests being placed in neighbouring trees.
Food: Insects and caterpillars.
Voice: A challenging note like a kakelaar (Priest).
Breeding: Nests are placed in thorn-trees and are composed of sticks and straw, the bowl-shaped cavity above lined with hair and fine fibres, kept down with fine rootlets. Breeds from October to January. Eggs, 2 to 5, usually 3, pale bluish white with a more or less noduled surface. Average (10) 26,0 × 19,3 (24—27,9 × 18,7—20).

537   Bare-cheeked Babbler   Kaalwang-katlagter

Aethocichla gymnogenys   (Hartlaub), 1865: *Benguella.*

PLATE 48 (OPP. P. 368).
Length 24 cm (wing 110—117; tail 100—110; tarsus 33—36; culmen 24—25. 6 specimens). Iris yellow; bill and bare skin of face black; legs dusky-grey.

Identification: Unmistakable. Sexes alike.
Distribution: Southern Angola and northern South West Africa.
Habits: Lives in the bush along dry water-courses and in dry open plains and hillsides where there are trees. A social species, found in parties often with other species such as shrikes.

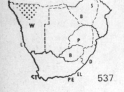

537

Breeding: A nest found by R. Jensen was placed in a tamboetie tree in an upright multiple fork. A fairly bulky but loosely-constructed, deep bowl of dry grass, with no lining.
Eggs: 2, glossy turquoise, completely smooth. 26,6 × 20,2; 26,4 × 20,2. Laid in December.

538   Boulder Chat   Swart Katlagter

Pinarornis plumosus   Sharpe, 1876: *Matopos, Rhodesia.*
PLATE 48 (OPP. P. 368).
Length 23—27 cm (wing 110—118; tail 114—132; tarsus 27—31; culmen 18,5—20,5. 3 specimens). Iris umber; bill and legs black.

Identification: Uniform sooty brown with white tips to outer three tailfeathers. Sexes alike. In flight shows a line of white spots on inner webs of primaries. Also on edge of tail. Plumage is soft.
Distribution: Rhodesia below 1 800 metres northwards to Fort Jameson and Petauke districts.
Habits: Found in boulder-strewn localities, particularly where there are large boulders on the side of a hill. Very large bare masses of rock do not seem to attract it. A beautifully agile bird, running over huge rocks, half-flying, half-gliding from rock to rock, rather in the manner of a Rock-jumper. Raises and then lowers its tail on alighting.

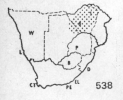

538

Food: Beetles, small lizards and grasshoppers recorded.

Voice: A monotonous squeaking "ink, ink, wink, wink" like an unoiled pram. Also a clear piping whistle, uttered with the bill held vertically.
Breeding: Nests are placed in large cracks in rocks. Breeds from September to December. Eggs 2, or more commonly 3, greenish-blue profusely covered with red, brown and purplish markings. Average (8) 26,2 × 18,4 (25,5—27,5 × 17,6—19,5).

This species is considered to be member of the Thrush family.

539 Damara Rock-Jumper*   Damara-bergkatlagter

Achaetops pycnopygius (P. Sclater), 1852: *Omaruru River, Damara-land.*

PLATE 48 (OPP. P. 368).
Length about 23—27 cm (wing 66—69—73 (19); tail 69—82; tarsus 23,5—25; culmen 17,5—19. 11 specimens). Iris brown; bill horn; legs brown.

Identification: Unmistakable moustachial stripe, rufous flanks and rump conspicuous. Sexes alike.
Distribution: Mountains of Damaraland and Kaokoveld as far south as the Auas mountains and north to Angola.
Habits: A species of mountains and inselbergen even extending far into the Namib desert. Keeps to the undergrowth and the ground between boulders especially bordering dry water courses. In the early mornings and evenings, both sexes take up their station on top of a high boulder or bush and sing beautifully. It is shy, hiding away in crevices upon the least alarm, but when not disturbed is a lively bird.
Food: Small beetles and grasshoppers recorded.
Voice: A beautiful warbling "tip tip tootle titootle tootle too".
Breeding: The nest is built entirely of grass usually situated in the centre of large grass tufts. Recorded breeding in December and March. Eggs 2 or 3, pale buffy pink and small dark red-brown spots. Average (14) 21,4 × 15,4 (22,7—20,9 × 16,3—15,0). Young birds leave the nest very early and scuttle about among the grass and rocks like mice.

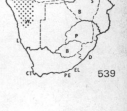

539

540 Rock-Jumper   Bergkatlagter

Chaetops frenatus (Temminck), 1826: *South Africa = River Zonder Einde Mountains, Cape.*

PLATE 48, 540 (a), 540 (b) ♂ AND ♀ (OPP. P. 368).
Length 20—25 cm (wing 90—96; tail 100—115; tarsus 38—40; culmen 20—21). Iris red; bill and legs black.

Identification: Unmistakable. Sexes as illustrated. Plumage soft, loose and fluffy.
Distribution: Confined to South Africa, from the western Cape Province (but not the Peninsula) eastwards to Lesotho and Natal.
Habits: Quite a common species in favoured localities such as boulder strewn mountain slopes above 600 metres over most of its range, but much lower, even to sea-level, in the Cape. Occurs in pairs or small family parties which may be seen taking prodigous hops from rock to rock or flying rather weakly, usually down hill. Feeds by digging in the ground and by scratching about in

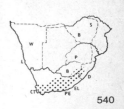

540

* This species is considered to be related to the Grassbird 618.

dead leaves. Normal progression is by a fast run over the rocks, frequently disappearing and emerging again some way off.

Food: Grasshoppers and other insects. Also gekkos.

Voice: "Pee, pee, pee, pee, pee . . ." repeated rapidly about twelve times and descending rather like an alarm-clock running down. Also various calls such as "peeeu-pip" or "pee-tee-teep".

Breeding: A large untidy cup-shaped nest is built under stones, or rarely under a lump of palmiet, of dry grass, moss and lichens, lined with hair. It is built by both sexes and eggs are laid from September to November. They are pure white in colour and the clutch is nearly always 2, but 3 have been recorded. They measure 26,5—27,6 × 19,8—20,2 (4).

LOCAL RACES:
(a) *C.f. frenatus* (Temminck), 1826: *South Africa = Rivier Zonder Einde Mountains, Cape Province*. Illustrated as **No. 540** *(a);* size above. From the Cedarberg mountains near Clanwilliam eastwards to Knysna and probably beyond.
(b) *C.f. aurantius* Layard, 1867: *Graaff-Reinet, Cape Province*. Illustrated as **No. 540** *(b)*. Wing ♂ 89—95, ♀ 84—88; tail 80—100; tarsus 36—41; culmen 18—23,5. 8 specimens, 5 ♂, 3 ♀. Eastern Cape Province, Natal and Lesotho.

541 = 540 *(b)*

Family PYCNONOTIDAE

The Bulbuls are frugivorous small birds that are sometimes also insectivorous, the majority of species inhabiting bush or forest country. Members of the family are numerous in Africa and others occur in Asia and southern Europe. The characters of the bill vary considerably in different genera, so that a comprehensive diagnosis is difficult and the student must be guided by the coloured figures. The species make cup-shaped nests in trees or bushes and lay from two to four eggs. Most of them have loud whistling cries by which they can be identified.

542   Bush Blackcap   Rooibek-tiptol

> *Lioptilus nigricapillus*   (Vieillot), 1818: *Bruintjies Hoogte, Somerset East, Cape Province.*

PLATE 49 (OPP. P. 369).
Length 26—28 cm (wing 76—81—88; tail 68—83; tarsus 22—25; culmen 12—15. 17 specimens). Iris hazel; bill orange-pink; legs flesh.

Identification: The black crown and nape and orange-pink bill are distinctive. Sexes alike.

Distribution: Peculiar to South Africa, from the Eastern Cape Province to the higher regions of Natal and thence to the Zoutpansberg.

Habits: Uncommon. Essentially a bird of thick bush and forest. Is usually seen on the borders of forests, clambering about the trees and creepers in search of its food. Rather sluggish and deliberate in its actions.

Food: Berries and fruit.

Voice: During the breeding season utters quite a lively series of notes, rather like a bulbul but in greater variety. Sings mainly during the period October to January.

Breeding: Nests in midsummer in eastern Transvaal, forming a small cup-shaped nest of twigs and a little moss, lined with rootlets, in the fork of

542

some tree on the edge of, or in openings in the forest, usually one to two metres from the ground, preferably in trees growing in marshy patches. Eggs are dull white with rather elongate markings of light brown over the whole egg, rather more at the obtuse end, where there are also underlying marks of slate-colour, forming a dark zone, and measuring 24,3 × 17.

543 Cape Bulbul   Kaapse Tiptol

Pycnonotus capensis   (Linnaeus), 1766: *Cape of Good Hope.*

PLATE 49 (OPP. P. 369).
Length 19—21 cm (wing 86—96; tail 82—92; tarsus 20—23; culmen 18—20). Iris black; wattle round eye white; bill and legs black. Weight 46 g.

Identification: The *white* wattle round eye prevents confusion with the next species; in life appears more crested than illustrated, more like the next species. Is also much darker than illustrated and the uniform dark under-parts readily distinguish it from the Black-eyed Bulbul, No. 545, quite apart from the presence of the eye-wattle. Sexes alike. Young birds resemble adults but the white wattle takes two or three months to develop. Albinos recorded.
Distribution: Confined to the Cape Province, from Springbok in the north-west, eastwards to the Sundays River.
Habits: A common species found in all regions of coastal scrub or bushes along rivers. One of the few local birds which has taken to the dense thickets of exotic wattles which have spread over the southern Cape Province. A noisy, lively and conspicuous bird which is usually seen in pairs flying about or perching on the tops of low bushes or trees. May become very tame and feeds at bird-tables, becoming almost gregarious at such places or anywhere that an abundant source of food is available. Is not too popular in fruit orchards. Oldest record 79 months.

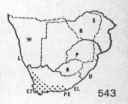

Food: Mainly fruit and berries; also feed at flowers, their foreheads becoming red or yellow with pollen.
Voice: A cheerful liquid call of "pietmajol" or "piet-piet-patata".
Breeding: The nest is a shallow bowl composed of twigs, roots and other vegetable matter, lined with finer rootlets and placed in a bush from one to 4 metres from the ground, usually well concealed. Breeds from September to November and also in March. Eggs number 2 or 3, pinky-white with reddish and some underlying slate markings. Average (38) 23,8 × 16,9 (21,7—26 × 15,9—18). A very sensitive bird while nesting, the most cursory inspection by humans often leading to desertion and destruction of the eggs.

544 Red-eyed Bulbul   Rooioog-tiptol

Pycnonotus nigricans   (Vieillot), 1818: *Goodhouse, Orange River.*

PLATE 49 (OPP. P. 369).
Length 19—21 cm (wing ♂ 90—97—109, ♀ 84—91—97; tail 74—96; tarsus 19—23; culmen 16—20. 39 specimens, 22 ♂, 17 ♀). Iris orange or red-brown, wattle round eye red; bill and legs black. Weight 35—38 g.

Identification: The *red* wattles round eye are distinctive; shows a lot of contrast between colour of head and body. Sexes alike, female smaller. Young birds are dull versions of adults with pink eye-wattles.

383

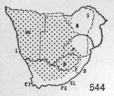

Distribution: Dry inland areas of Cape Province, Lesotho, southern and western Transvaal across to the west coast and north to southern Angola.

Habits: Generally speaking a bird of drier country than the Cape Bulbul but otherwise very similar in habits. In the very dry parts of the west coast, is only found near waterholes, living in the bush along dry watercourses and resorting to wells and the larger rivers for water. Anting recorded.

544 **Food:** Fruit and berries. Also takes insects.

Voice: Very like the last species.

Breeding: Nests are built from one to four metres up, in small trees or bushes, often in thorn-trees and are shallow cups built of twigs and grass-lined with rootlets. Eggs nearly always number 3 (cf. Cape Bulbul), pinkish-white, marked all over with red, red-brown and purplish, with underlying grey, speckles and small blotches. Average (21) 22,2 × 16,1 (19,7—24 × 14,7—17,1, one 18,2 × 14). Incubation period 11—12 days (2); nestling period 13 days. Incubation by female only; both parents feed the young. Breeds from November to March.

LOCAL RACES:
(a) P.n. nigricans (Vieillot), 1818: *Goodhouse, Orange River.* As illustrated. Occurs on west of range Angola, Botswana south-west to Kenhardt.
(b) P.n. superior Clancey, 1959: *Mamathe's Lesotho.* Darker and larger than *(a)*. Eastern Karoo, O.F.S. and Transvaal highveld eastwards.

545   Black-eyed Bulbul   Swartoog-tiptol

Pycnonotus barbatus   (Desfontaines), 1787: *Near Algiers.*

Native Names: i-Kwebula (X); i-Potwe (G and Z); le-Koete, Rrankhoitsili, Rirampyokholi (S); i-Gweturi (D).

PLATE 49 (OPP. P. 369).

Length 20—22 cm (wing ♂ 96—99—104, ♀ 89—95—99; tail 83—92; tarsus 20—23; culmen 16—19. 55 specimens, 26 ♂, 29 ♀). Iris dark brown; bill and legs black. Weight 37—44 g.

Identification: Lacks the eye-wattles of the previous two species; dark colour of head extends lower on to chest. Sexes alike. Young birds are dull. Albinos recorded.

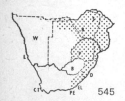

Distribution: From the Sunday's River eastwards and from the Orange Free State and the Okavango River northwards over Africa south of the Sahara; north of the Sahara in Morocco and Tunisia.

Habits: An extremely common bird, particularly in Natal and Mozambique, wherever there are trees and fairly thick bush. Usually seen in pairs though 545 many may gather at a good source of food. A friendly and cheerful bird, always uttering its characteristic call and when disturbed sitting on a conspicuous perch and watching the intruder. Is very demonstrative when a snake, cat or small carnivore is sighted, numbers gathering and keeping up a ceaseless chatter. Does quite a lot of hawking for insects in the air.

Food: Soft fruit, berries and insects.

Voice: Usually given as "come back to Calcutta". At sunrise keeps up a monotonous double note repeated over and over "chit-chit" or "gwit-gwit".

Breeding: The nest is a cup of twiglets lined with hair, roots and fine grass. It is usually about 2 but may be as high as 9 or 12 metres up. Breeds from

August to November. Eggs number 2 to 4 but nearly always 3. They are white, the ground-colour being almost obscured by spots of purplish-red, reddish, pinkish-brown and underlying grey and pale lilac. Average (100) 23,3 × 16,6 (20,8—26 × 15,3—18,2. One 27,6 × 16,0, another 20,3 × 17,2). Incubation period 12—14 days in the south. Nestling 10—12 days in the south, 13½ in Rhodesia.

LOCAL RACES:
(a) *P.b. tricolor* (Hartlaub), 1862: *Angola*. Crown, cheeks and chin brown, not black. Damaraland to Angola.
(b) *P.b. ngamii* O. Grant, 1912: *Lake Ngami*. Forepart of face black, changing gradually to greyish-brown on throat, neck and back. Ngamiland. Wing 100—105; tail 91—94; tarsus 21—23; culmen 16—19,5. 12 specimens.
(c) *P.b. pallidus* Roberts, 1912: *Boror, Mozambique*. Paler above and below, clearer white in the centre below; yellow of under tail-coverts extending faintly upwards on the belly. Slightly smaller, wing 90—97. Lower Zambesi Valley northwards to northern Mozambique.
(d) *P.b. layardi* Gurney, 1879: *Rustenberg, Transvaal*. As illustrated, rather darker, with black cap well defined. Size above, Rhodesia, Transvaal, Natal and Eastern Cape Province.

546 Terrestrial Bulbul   Boskrapper

Phyllastrephus terrestris Swainson, 1837: *Auteniquoi = Knysna*.

Native Names: i-Kalakandle; um-Nqu; u-Gwegwegwe (X).
PLATE 49 (OPP. P. 369).
Length 20—22 cm (wing ♂ 91—94—100, ♀ 84—86—87; tail 87—106; tarsus 24—26; culmen 20—23. 19 specimens, 9 ♂, 10 ♀). Iris light to dark red; bill brownish; legs grey. Weight 25,2—35,9 g.

Identification: May be distinguished by its white throat contrasting with dark head, chin and brownish chest. Habitat preference and call are also aids to identification. Sexes alike. Young birds resemble adults but wing-coverts are edged with reddish; iris grey.
Distribution: From Swellendam to Knysna, eastwards to Kenya and across to Ngamiland and Zambia.

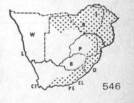

Habits: A fairly common species of forest and thick bush. Has the habit of creeping about in search of its food among the leaves on the ground in family parties, maintaining a quiet chattering all the time. May be found even in very dense, gloomy undergrowth where few other birds go. Perches only low down in the trees and spends most of its time on the ground. It is consequently difficult to see and is more often heard scratching about in dry leaves. When alarmed parties set up a cackle and move even deeper into the depths of the undergrowth.
Food: Mainly insects and snails.
Voice: A quiet but grating churr when alarmed. Also a short warbled song.
Breeding: Nests on projecting branches of small trees, only about a metre from the ground as a rule. The nest is slung between the twigs and is a shallow bowl composed of black fibres externally, lined with rootlets. The clutch is 2 or 3, glossy white marked with blotches and lines of grey and dark olive-brown, often zoned at the obtuse end. September, November to February in Rhodesia. Average (9) 22,6 × 16,2 (21—23,8 × 14,7—17), race (a).

BULBULS

LOCAL RACES:
(a) P.t. terrestris Swainson, 1837: Auteniquoi = Knysna. Upper-parts and flanks darkest; largest, size above. Knysna to Natal, Zululand and Transvaal. Transvaal birds smaller; wing ♂ 80—92 (13), ♀74—83 (10). As illustrated.
(b) P.t. intermedius Gunning and Roberts, 1911: Noome, Umbelluzi River, Mozambique. Lighter coloured, particularly on the under tail-coverts; size smaller, wing ♂ 90—96—98, ♀ 78—83—86 (15 ♂, 8 ♀). North-east Zululand, Botswana, Rhodesia and Mozambique. Eggs measure 19,7—20,5 × 14,2—16,2 (5).

547 Yellow-streaked Bulbul   Geelstreep-boskruiper

Phyllastrephus flavostriatus (Sharpe), 1876: *Macamac, Transvaal.*

PLATE 49 (OPP. P. 369).
Length 18—21 cm (wing ♂ 95—97—100, ♀ 81—85—88; tail ♂ 78—91, ♀ 73—83; tarsus 20—24; culmen 17,5—21,5. 24 specimens, 9 ♂, 15 ♀). Iris brown to hazel; bill black; legs bluish slate-grey. Weight (20) 21,4—39,8 g.

Identification: Distinguishable by its pale yellow streaking below. Sexes alike but female very much smaller, even distinguishable in the field. Young birds are yellower below and chest dusky-olive.

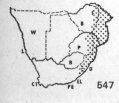

Distribution: From Zululand to eastern Rhodesia and across to Zaïre; up the east coast to Uganda.

Habits: A not uncommon species which keeps to the trees, often in the highest branches, in forest and thick bush. Searches the bark and mossy growths for its food and also clambers about in creepers, shaking up the bundles of dead leaves caught up in them. May cling to the trunks of trees, even hanging upside down. Has the characteristic habit of flipping one wing open and then the other.

547

Food: Grasshoppers, beetles, bugs, spiders, insect eggs and larvae; also berries.

Voice: Commonest call sounds like "chip! Chap! chop!—chip! Chap! chop!" with some variation.

Breeding: The nest is a bowl-shaped structure of twigs and rootlets, covered outside with moss, placed in tangled creepers or amongst leaves. Eggs number 2, and are pink or purplish-pink in ground-colour, with spots of red-brown, dark slate and dark brown. They measure 22,5—24 × 16—17.

LOCAL RACES:
(a) P.f. flavostriatus (Sharpe), 1876: Macamac, Transvaal. As illustrated; size above. Pondoland to Rhodesia.
(b) P.f. dendrophilus Clancey, 1962: Chimanimani Mountains. Eastern highlands of Rhodesia. Darker, greyer forehead and crown; lighter below.

548 Slender Bulbul   Klein Geelstreep-boskruiper

Phyllastrephus debilis (W. Sclater), 1899: *Near Inhambane.*

PLATE 49 (OPP. P. 369).
Length about 14 cm (wing ♂ 66—67,5, ♀ 62—63; tail 60—64; tarsus 16,5—18; culmen 13,5—15. 5 specimens, 2 ♂, 3 ♀). Iris red-brown; bill dusky, lower mandible lighter. Weight 12,5—15,5 g.

Identification: A smaller bird than the last species with a paler grey crown, nape and cheeks. Sexes alike, female smaller. Young birds have the crown and face washed with green.

Distribution: From Inhambane northwards along the coast to south-eastern Kenya, where it occurs farther inland. Just extends into Rhodesia at the confluence of the Haroni and Lusitu Rivers and Chimanimani Mountains.

Habits: In habits, rather like a warbler, creeping about in the undergrowth and lower parts of creepers in search of its food.

Food: Insects.

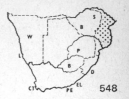

548

Voice: Alarm note a throaty gurgle. A warbling song with sudden bursts of loud phrases.

Breeding: The nest is a neat cup of lichens, grassheads and ferns bound overall with spider-web. Situated 2 metres up on outer branch of underbush in forests. October and January in Rhodesia. Eggs 2, light blue ringed at broad end with dark brown and lighter blotches and spots. 18,9 × 14,1.

LOCAL RACE:
P.d. debilis (W. Sclater), 1899: *Near Inhambane.* Inhambane to southern Tanzania.

549 Stripe-Cheeked Bulbul   Streepwang-willie

Andropadus milanjensis (Shelley), 1894: *Mlanje, Nyasaland.*

PLATE 49 (OPP. P. 369).
Length 19—21 cm (wing ♂ 90—94—98, ♀ 90—93; tail 78—89; tarsus 22—24; culmen 17,5—19. 15 specimens, 13 ♂,2 ♀). Iris umber; bill black; legs brown. Weight (20) 32,8—48,9 g.

Identification: Has a ring of white feathers around the eye, most noticeable above it, and clear white streaks on the ear-coverts. Sexes alike. Young birds have the grey of the head washed with greenish.

Distribution: From eastern Rhodesia and northern Mozambique to Malawi, Kenya and Tanzania. Common on Mount Selinda and Gorongoza Mountain.

Habits: A solitary and retiring bird, frequenting dense foliage and only venturing out after rain on the outskirts of forests in pursuit of insects. May be found moving quietly about low down or in the higher foliage of tall trees. When disturbed, dives down into the thick undergrowth.

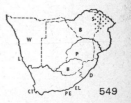

549

Food: Fruit and insects including beetles.

Voice: A loud and unmusical "cha-cha-cha-cha-cha-cha". Also described as "ukker-ukkeri-ukkeri". May also attempt to sing.

Breeding: The nest, situated from 4—7 m up, is usually placed on thin saplings or branches; it is a thin but neatly rounded cup of coarse twigs, roots and grass, lined with tree-fern fibres. Breeds October to January, March. Eggs are dull white, densely mottled, spotted and streaked with chocolate, brown and underlying grey. One nest contained only one but 2 have been recorded. Four measure 24,3—25 × 16,5—17,6.

LOCAL RACE:
A.m. milanjensis (Shelley), 1894: *Mlanje, Nyasaland.* Malawi, northern Mozambique and eastern Rhodesia.

550   Yellow-bellied Bulbul   Geelbors-willie

Chlorocichla flaviventris   (A. Smith), 1834: *Near Port Natal =*
Durban.

PLATE 49 (OPP. P. 369).
Length 20—23 cm (wing ♂ 100—105—109, ♀ 95—98—100; tail 87—105; tarsus
21—25; culmen 18—21. 18 specimens. 8 ♂, 10 ♀). Iris red; bill dark slate; legs grey.
Weight 42,7 g.

Identification: Closely resembles race *(c)* of the next species *(q.v.)* but has a
conspicuous *red*, not *white*, eye. Also has a narrow, white ring round eye.
Sexes alike, female smaller. Young birds have paler heads, the same colour as
the back.

Distribution: From coastal Natal to Kenya and across to Angola and south-
eastern Zaïre. Throughout Rhodesia except the Mashonaland Plateau.

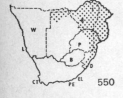

Habits: Skulking birds which keep to dense coastal bush or tangles along
river banks. Quite a common species where it occurs but difficult to observe as
it makes for the thickest cover when alarmed.

550   **Food:** Berries, flowers and insects.

Voice: A high-pitched, laughing, nasal "pao-pao-pao", which is answered by
another bird. A noisy species.

Breeding: Nests are situated in leafy trees, rather low down, cup-shaped and
composed of twigs and fibres, rather loosely constructed and lined with finer
material. Eggs number 2, whitish or cream, almost hidden by splashes and
dots of olive, light and dark brown and underlying grey, all more concentrated
at the thick end. Average (8) 25,1 × 17,8 (24—26,8 × 16,8—18,9).

LOCAL RACES:
(a) C.f. flaviventris (A. Smith), 1834: *Near Port Natal = Durban.* As illustrated. Wing
♂ 103—105 (3). Natal to southern Mozambique.
(b) C.f. occidentalis Sharpe, 1881: *Angola.* Clearer and deeper yellow below. Size
above. Transvaal, Rhodesia to Angola, south-eastern Zaïre to Tanzania and northern
Mozambique.

551   Sombre Bulbul   Willie

Andropadus importunus (Vieillot), 1818: *Auteniquoi Forest =*
Knysna.

Native Names: i-Nkwili (X); i-Wili (Z); i-Chwikijori (D).

PLATE 49 (OPP. P. 369).
Length 19—23 cm (wing ♂ 87—92—95, ♀ 83—88—95; tail 86—95; tarsus 22—25;
culmen 14—17. 18 specimens, 11 ♂, 7 ♀). Iris pale cream, almost white; bill black; legs
dusky. Weight 33,1—38,3 g.

Identification: Might be mistaken for the last species *(q.v.).* Sexes alike.
Young birds are dull editions of adults but the iris is *grey.*

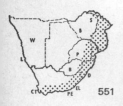

Distribution: From Cape Town eastwards and northwards in coastal areas to
551   Kenya; inland in our area as far as eastern Transvaal and the Haroni-Lusitu
confluence area of Rhodesia.

Habits: A very common species of forests and coastal bush. Although it can be heard on all sides it is seldom seen as it remains hidden well inside the bushes of its haunts; even if exposed, as it often is while calling, it is difficult to see on account of its cryptic colouration and tendency to keep very still. Occasionally ventures forth and may even perch on exposed situations such as telegraph wires. Most of its time is spent, when not calling from the upper branches of a bush or tree, in clambering about the branches and creepers in search of its food. Is usually found singly or in pairs but is common enough for many to be present in the same general area.

Food: Fruit, berries and insects.

Voice: Probably the most characteristic sound of South African coastal areas; a loud "*peet*-chuke-achuke-achuke . . . pheeeoooo", the last note a descending whistle. Also written "Willie . . . Quickly run around the back of the bush . . . pleeease." This call is kept up all day and at all seasons of the year but of course more in spring. Also has a short but attractive song.

Breeding: The nest is a thin basin of twigs, rootlets and fibres and is usually placed in a rather slender bush or tree, often at the edge of a clearing with little attempt at concealment, in contrast to the birds' normally rather secretive ways. It is placed from 1 to 4 metres up. Breeds October to January. Eggs number 2, buff with scattered blurred spots and scrolls of greenish, slate and brown. Average (30) 24,3 × 17,2 (21—26,9 × 16,2—18,7). The incubating female may be very tame and can sometimes almost be touched. Incubation period 15—17 days; nestling 14—16 days.

LOCAL RACES:

(a) A.i. importunus (Vieillot), 1818: *Auteniquoi = Knysna.* As illustrated; size above. Cape Province to eastern Transvaal (Barberton).

(b) A.i. noomei Roberts, 1917: *Haenertsberg, Transvaal.* With a small amount of yellowish about the belly and under tail-coverts. North-eastern Transvaal to eastern Rhodesia.

(c) A.i. hypoxanthus Sharpe, 1876: *Tete, Portuguese East Africa.* Brighter yellow below and more yellowish above than *(a)*. Closely resembles race *(a)* of the last species but differs in the nicking of the bill behind the tip of the maxilla and in the colour of the iris. Northern Zululand to Mozambique and the lower Zambesi Valley.

Family TURDIDAE

The true thrushes are arboreal birds that largely seek their food on the ground, but related to them are a number of smaller birds of the bush, forests, plains, open mountains and hills, so that to furnish a comprehensive definition in words is difficult. They have fairly long and slender bills, slightly arched above not flattened, with short rictal bristles; the legs and feet are fairly stout in true thrushes, more slender in the robins being adapted to terrestrial as well as arboreal habits. Many of them are good singers. Their nests are always cup-shaped and their eggs are usually some shade of bluish green and more or less spotted. The diet consists of insects, worms and small molluscs and often berries and small fruits. The young are always spotted, usually with light buffish tips to the feathers of the upper-parts and darkish brown tips to the feathers of the under-parts.

552 Kurrichane Thrush   Rooibek-lyster

Turdus libonyanus (A. Smith), 1836: *near Kurrichane, West Transvaal.*

PLATE 49 (OPP. P. 369).

Length about 22 cm (wing 110—116—125; tail 90—105; tarsus 26—31,5; culmen 20—22,5—24. 24 specimens). Iris brown with orange fleshy rim round eye; bill orange; legs fleshy to pale yellow. Weight 69—82,2 g.

Identification: The orange beak, streak down side of throat and greyish back distinguish the adult bird. Sexes alike. Young bird has a yellowish bill with dark tip, chest speckled with rounded marks but chin white; throat with dark streaks down either side distinguish it.

Distribution: Senegal to Egypt southwards to northern Damaraland, Botswana, Transvaal and Natal.

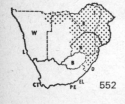

552

Habits: A common resident species. Somewhat shy, inhabiting the acacia bush of savannas, occurring usually near streams and rivers, but may also be found in dry forest regions. It haunts the streams and their neighbourhood where larger trees abound, searching on the ground for food, otherwise keeping to the trees. It runs rapidly, comes to a full stop, appears to listen and then plunges its beak in the ground. Also pecks about fallen leaves.

Food: Worms, spiders, caterpillars, grasshoppers and flies.

Voice: A loud whistling note; song rather poor, mainly heard from September to October. Excellent mimic.

Breeding: May nest semi-colonially. The nest is situated 1—7 metres up in the fork of a branch or against the trunk of a tree. A basin-shaped structure glued with mud to the branch and composed of twigs, grass, roots, dried leaves, string, etc., bound with mud when available and lined with finer roots and thistle. August to March. Eggs 2 to 3, rarely 4, pale greenish, finely speckled or spotted all over with pinky-brown. Average (100) 26,2 × 19,8 (23—29,9 × 18,5—21,6). Several brooded.

LOCAL RACES:

Races are separated by colour variation from rich colouring in the east to paler less olive above, buff on flank to the west. There is also some difference in size.

(a) T.l. libonyanus (A. Smith), 1836: *near Kurrichane, W. Transvaal.* Eastern Botswana, Transvaal and Natal. Upper-parts greyish olive-brown, flanks pale buff-orange. Size as above. Illustrated as **No. 552** *(a).*

(b) T.l. chobiensis (Roberts), 1932: *Kabulabula, Botswana.* Ngamiland and Chobe River. Lighter and less olive above than *(a)* but flanks about the same. Size as *(c).*

(c) T.l. tropicalis Peters, 1881: *Inhambane, P.E.A.* Rhodesia except north-west (see *(b)*), Matabeleland and Mozambique. Upper-parts more yellowish, flanks richer buff-orange. Smaller: wing 107—111—117, tail 86—93,1—99, culmen 19—20,8—22,5 (10 specimens).

(d) T.l. verreauxi Bocage, 1869: *Caconda, Angola.* Southern Angola and northern Damaraland. Upper-parts olive-greyish brown, flanks slightly buff-orange. Wing up to 115, tail to 90.

553   Olive Thrush

Olyf Lyster

Turdus olivaceus   Linnaeus, 1766: *Cape of Good Hope.*

Native Names: um-Swi (X); u-Muswi (Z).

PLATE 49 *(a)* AND *(e)* (OPP. P. 369).
Length about 24 cm (wing 120—124; tail 89—94; tarsus 32—34; culmen 22—23,5. 3 specimens). Iris brown; bill yellow; darker above; legs yellow-brown. Weight (17) 72—78,6—90) g.

Identification: Dark upper-parts and dusky-olive breast shading to a varying degree to orange rufous belly and flanks distinguish the species. Yellowish bill is conspicuous. Sexes alike. Young has white chin and spotted chest but yellow gape and light streaks on feathers of upper-parts indicate its young plumage.

Distribution: From the Cape north to the Orange River, eastern Rhodesia and the higher western parts of Mozambique and Gorongoza. Beyond to Ruwenzori Mountains and Ethiopia.

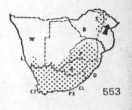

553

Habits: A common resident. In moister areas is found in thick bush and mountain forests, only at higher altitudes to the north-east. In dry parts it frequents the bush only along streams and rivers and is consequently found locally. Usually occurs singly or in pairs. Fond of scratching among the fallen leaves under bushes, spending much of its time on the ground. When alarmed flies up with a loud alarm note and perches in the nearest bush, very still but hopping along the branch if danger threatens.

Food: Worms, snails, grasshoppers, caterpillars, etc., seeds and fruit.

Voice: Call-note a loud "chink" or "tschuck". Song a melodious but short, "wheety-wheety wheet". Excellent mimic.

Breeding: The nest is a large untidy structure placed in a fork in a branch or against the trunk of a tree from 2—5 metres up, occasionally up to 10 metres. Made of straw, leaves, twigs and moss in a ragged manner, the cup is neatly and closely lined with fine dry grass. Rarely bound with mud. Recorded throughout the year with peaks in the Cape in September and October and again in February. Eggs 2—3, rarely 4, usually greenish-blue, boldly dotted and blotched with brownish slate and chestnut brown; rarely with ground colour cream tinged greenish or pinkish. Average (100) 29,3 × 21,6 (27,3—33,5 × 19,6—23,9). Incubation 14 days (2). Nestling 16 days.

LOCAL RACES:
(a) T.o. olivaceus Linnaeus, 1766: *Cape of Good Hope.* South-western Cape to about Grahamstown. Less buff-orange below, the flanks partly olive. Size as above. Illustrated as **No. 553** *(a).*
(b) T.o. pondoensis Reichenow, 1917: *Pondoland.* Transkei north to Natal and Swaziland. Yellow under-parts brighter and extending over flanks. Wing 119—129—133; tail 90—100; tarsus 30—34; culmen 23—27. 14 specimens.
(c) T.o. transvaalensis (Roberts), 1936: *Woodbush, Transvaal.* Northern Transvaal mountain forests. Differs from *(b)* only by its darker upper-parts and breast-band. Wing ♂ 126—128, ♀ 121; tail 88—97; tarsus 29—33; culmen 23—25,5. 12 specimens, 10 ♂, 2 ♀.
(d) T.o. swynnertoni Bannerman, 1913: *Chirinda Forest, Rhodesia.* Higher evergreen forests of eastern Rhodesia. Wing ♂ 112, ♀ 107; tail 77, 87; tarsus 28; culmen 23. 2 specimens.
(e) T.o. smithi Bonaparte, 1850: *S. Africa.* Little Namaqualand, central and northern Cape, Orange Free State, southern and western Transvaal. Illustrated as **No. 553** *(e),* very much less buff-orange below. Wing 119—124—132; tail (91) 95—105; tarsus 28—33,5; culmen 22,5—26,5. 16 specimens.

391

554 = 553 *(d).*

555 = 553 *(e).*

556 Orange Thrush   Gurneyse Lyster

Turdus gurneyi   Hartlaub, 1864: *near Pietermaritzburg, Natal.*

PLATE 49 (OPP. P. 369).
Length about 23 cm (wing 107—110—113; tail ♂ 87—88, ♀ 77—86; tarsus 31—32,5; culmen 20—21. 6 specimens, 3 ♂, 3 ♀). Iris hazel; bill dark brown; legs flesh-coloured.

Identification: Unmistakable with rich chestnut lower-parts, olive-brown upper-parts and primary coverts black and white. White ring around eye prominent in adult bird. Young marked with buff above and under-parts mottled black and chestnut; wing pattern as adult.

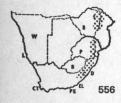

556

Distribution: In the higher forested areas from Stutterheim and the Pondo-land coast, Natal interior, eastern to northern Transvaal and eastern districts of Rhodesia. North to the Equator.
Habits: A rare tropical species. Occurs in the depths of the forests and utters a wild song at dusk from these retreats, but is otherwise so shy and elusive that it is seldom recorded. Spends much of its time on the ground.
Voice: A hissing trill. Song undescribed.
Breeding: A nest recorded by Bell Marley is a deep cup of dried grass blades mixed with bracken and *Metalasia*; lined with fine grass roots and tendrils. Placed in a small bush. Belcher records the nests as large masses of green moss with a lining of black fibre, set conspicuously in the fork of a slender shrub. Recorded November to January. Eggs 2—3, turquoise spotted with red-brown and underlying lilac blotches, sometimes more concentrated at broad end. Belcher records more unspotted eggs from Malawi than spotted ones. Average (4) 25,5 × 19,4 (24—28,5 × 19,2—19,5).

LOCAL RACES:
(a) T.g. gurneyi Hartlaub, 1864: *near Pietermaritzburg, Natal.* Pondoland to eastern Transvaal. As illustrated. Size above.
(b) T.g. otomitrus (Reichenow), 1904: *Bulongwa, N.E. of Lake Nyasa.* Woodbush, northern Transvaal, north through Rhodesia to Malawi. Darker above and below.

557 Groundscraper Thrush   Gevlekte-lyster

Turdus litsipsirupa   (A. Smith), 1836: *between the Orange River and the Tropic.*

Native Name: le-Tshutshuroopoo (Ch.)

PLATE 49 (OPP. P. 369).
Length 22 cm (wing 120—128—136; tail 63—76; tarsus 31—35; culmen 22,5—27—30,5. 39 specimens). Iris red-brown, juvenile brown; bill brown; legs fleshy to yellow-brown. Weight 75 g.

Identification: Conspicuously spotted on breast but lacks the bold markings on the wing of the next species. Also distinguished by the orange "window" in the primaries which is easily seen in flight and the orange axillaries. Appears squat because of its shortish tail. Young have lighter brown upper-parts; the wing-coverts with light buff tips.

392

Distribution: Rare and local in Natal and Mozambique. Widely distributed north of the Vaal River, Rhodesia, Kalahari and Damaraland northwards to Ethiopia. Recorded from Kroonstad, Orange Free State, Colesberg and Kimberley, Cape Province.

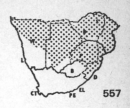

557

Habits: Resident. Not uncommon, but local in habit, being a species of the drier acacia veld. Partial to big trees especially near cattle kraals, and often scratching among fallen leaves. Flight is strong. Has a habit of flicking one wing at a time.

Voice: Calls from trees; an onomatopoeic "litsipsirupa", hence the Sechuana name. Alarm note of four or five sharp notes between a chuckle and a whistle. Song "li-tlo-li-tlolik, tlo-tlo-teetlo-tleederik".

Breeding: A heavy nest is placed in a fork of a tree from 2—6 metres up; built of grasses, weeds, everlasting plants and lined with down, leaves and sometimes feathers. September to January. Eggs 2 to 4, usually 3, ground colour turquoise or bluish white spotted with red-brown and blotched with lilac. Average (61) 27,8 × 20,3 (25,7—31 × 18,6—21,5).

LOCAL RACE:
T.l. litsipsirupa (A. Smith), 1836: *between the Orange River and the Tropic*. Throughout our area; other races from Zambia and Malawi northwards.

558   Natal Thrush   Natal-lyster

Turdus fischeri   Hellmayr, 1901: *Pangani River, Tanganyika.*

PLATE 49 (OPP. P. 369).
Length about 23 cm (wing ♂ 118—121—125, ♀ 110—116—120; tail 89—97; tarsus 29—31,5; culmen 22—24. 10 specimens, 4 ♂, 6 ♀). Iris dark brown; bill black, ochre at base of lower mandible; legs pale flesh.

Identification: Heavily spotted chest and black-and-white pattern of wing-coverts distinguish this from the last species. Under-wing is whitish, not buff.

Distribution: Coastal region from Pondoland to St. Lucia, beyond our limits to Malawi and Tanzania. Sight records from Naqa Naqa Forest in the vicinity of East London by Miss M. Courtenay-Latimer.

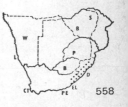

558

Habits: A very local and somewhat rare species. In recent years found commonly, in chosen localities in Natal, only during the winter from March to September. Apparently breeds in Pondoland and winters in Natal and southern Zululand. Occurs singly or in pairs. To be found on banks of small streams at the bottom of valleys, and the basal portions of the steep slopes on either side within the canopy of coastal forests. At all times inconspicuous, keeping to the lower branches of the leafy trees or else on the ground scratching and feeding amongst rotting vegetation.

Food: Grubs and insects.

Voice: Quiet "tree-troo". Song heard from the upper branches of a leafy tree is beautiful and rich with a flute-like quality; with "thu-whu-wheewer" an oft-repeated phrase.

Breeding: A heavy nest with mud, small twigs, grasses and moss, lined with feathers and tendril leaves. Recorded November, December near Durban, January in Pondoland. Eggs 3, resemble those of the Cape Thrush, but with rather darker markings. Average (6) 26,7 × 19,9 (25—28,6 × 19,3—20,5).

LOCAL RACE:
T.f. natalicus Grote, 1938: *Durban, Natal*. Distributed as above. Other races from Malawi and Tanzania, possibly now extinct.

393

559 Cape Rock-Thrush   Kaapse Kliplyster

Monticola rupestris (Vieillot), 1818: *near Cape Town* = *Table Mountain.*

Native Names: i-Kwelamatshani (Z); Mmarataseilo (S).

PLATE 49, ♂ AND ♀ (OPP. P. 369).

Length about 21 cm (wing ♂ 110—113—119, ♀ 106—109—115; tail 72—88; tarsus 28—31; culmen 21—25. 33 specimens, 21 ♂, 12 ♀). Iris brown; bill black; legs dusky black.

Identification: In the male the blue-grey is confined to the head and neck. Immature is heavily streaked below with white and brown, appearing almost scaly, otherwise much as female. Young spotted with buff and brown.

Distribution: The Cape Province, eastern Orange Free State, Lesotho, Natal and locally in south-eastern and northern Transvaal as far as the Zoutpansberg. Also at Kanye, Botswana.

Habits: A common resident. Usually observed perched on the tops of rocks or peaks of bushes, aloes or trees whence it utters a wild whistling note. Not very shy and has even adapted itself to human habitation. Not only recorded from wild mountainous country, occurring right down to the seashore in the southern Cape. Has the habit of flicking wings after landing on a rock.

Food: Various insects, spiders, millepedes, centipedes, small molluscs and small frogs. Also seeds (of *Acacia*) and berries.

Voice: Loud clear whistle "chir*ee*woo; chirri, *wee*roo".

Breeding: Situated in a crevice or on a ledge of rock beneath an overhang, the nest is a large untidy structure made of loose vegetation, old grass, twigs and peaty matter with a shallow cup-shaped cavity in the middle lined with fine roots. October to February. Eggs 3 to 5, pale blue, sometimes quite plain but usually marked with spotting of rust colour. Average (39) 26,9 × 19,9 (25,1—30,8 × 19,1—20,8) one 26,6 × 18,3. Both parents feed young. Recorded as host to the Redchested Cuckoo and reputed to act as host to the Greater Honeyguide.

560 Sentinel Rock-Thrush   Langtoon-kliplyster

Monticola explorator (Vieillot), 1818: *"mountains of the Cape of Good Hope."*

Native Name: um-Ganto (X).

PLATE 49, ♂ AND ♀ (OPP. P. 369).

Length about 18 cm (wing 97—102—108; tail 56—65; tarsus 32—35; culmen 19—22,5. 16 specimens). Iris dusky brown; bill black; legs dusky brown.

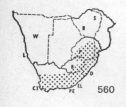

Identification: Smaller than the last species. The male has blue-grey extending on to back and upper-breast. Female with whiter throat and chest. See Nos. 561 and 562. The immature similar to No. 559.

Distribution: The Cape Province, higher parts of Natal, and locally in eastern and northern Transvaal, Swaziland and just within southern Mozambique.

Habits: Not as common as the last species, both occurring in similar habitats although this bird has not adapted itself to human habitations. It is found more often on open hillsides and is more lively in manner. In the northern Lebombo mountains occurs as an irregular visitor in May and June. Said to move to lower levels in the winter in Natal. This species has a habit of drawing itself bolt upright on its look-out post.

Food: Insects, especially ants and beetles; also seeds and berries.
Voice: Similar to No. 559, less deliberate and quieter.
Breeding: Like the last species but the nest is smaller. Also recorded nesting on the ground under a rock. September to December. Eggs 3—4, similar to those of No. 559 but smaller and rounder. Average (9) 26,4 × 19,5 (25,7—28,2 × 19—20,4). Incubation 13—14 days. Nestling 16 days.

561 Short-toed Rock Thrush   Korttoon-kliplyster

Monticola brevipes (Waterhouse), 1838: *'Tans Mt., near Walvis Bay.*

PLATE 49, ♂ AND ♀ (OPP. P. 369).
Length about 18 cm (wing 97—108; tail 60—67; tarsus 25—27; culmen 20—22). Iris dark brown; bill black; legs black.

Identification: In the male the broad white eyebrow or crown distinguishes this species from the last, although there is no recorded overlap in distribution. Some birds have crown the same colour as back, others have whitish crowns; birds to the west show a greater tendency to white than those in the east but the character is not constant.
Distribution: A western species from the Orange River northwards and east to northern Cape, Orange Free State as far as Welkom, and western Transvaal. One specimen from Stegi in Swaziland.
Habits: Not uncommon on isolated mountains and kopjes. Frequents the stony kopjes that are covered with trees, upon which it habitually perches rather than on rocks. Also found about abandoned dwellings.
Food: Insects and scorpions; also seeds.
Voice: A musical whistling note. Mimics freely.
Breeding: The nest is situated under a rock, made of dried grasses and rootlets lined with finer material. Eggs 3, uniform greenish blue. Average (7) 22,7 × 18,3 (21,1—24,2 × 17,1—18,3).

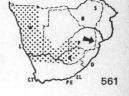

561

562 Angola Thrush   Angola-lyster

Monticola angolensis Sousa, 1888: *Caconda, Angola.*

PLATE 49, ♂ AND ♀ (OPP. P. 369).
Length about 18 cm (wing 94—100—108; tail 59—69; tarsus 23—28,5; culmen 19,5—22,5. 32 specimens). Iris sepia; bill black; legs black.

Identification: Black mottling on blue-grey crown, mantle and back distinguishes the male from other rock thrushes. The female is similarly mottled, perhaps with finer black markings on yellowish-brown. Immature plumage like that of female but only centre of chin white and with buff edges to the wing-coverts.
Distribution: From southern Tanzania to the Zambesi and west to Angola. Found within our area in Mashonaland and the Eastern Districts of Rhodesia, also from north-east Matabeleland.
Habits: Widely but sparsely distributed. Its name Rock Thrush is a misnomer, as it frequents the open, dry forests and not rocky country. However, it is usually found in broken and hilly areas of *Brachystegia* woodland. Has the habit when disturbed of flying up into one of the surrounding trees and sitting there motionless for some minutes before flying off.

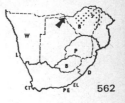

562

CHATS

Food: Mainly termites and ants.
Voice: A rather high-pitched song in the breeding season. Mimics freely.
Breeding: The nest is variable, a slight flycatcher-like structure placed in a hollow, eggs sometimes laid straight on the rotten wood, at other times makes a typically thrush nest. Usually on a branch but are recorded in holes. August to December. Eggs 3 to 4, turquoise blue, usually plain, sometimes finely spotted with red-brown. Average (7) 25,1 × 18,3 (24,5—26 × 17,5—19). Nestling 20 days.

563 Wheatear   Tapuit

Oenanthe oenanthe (Linnaeus), 1758: *Europe = Sweden.*

PLATE 50, ♀ (OPP. P. 400).
Length about 15 cm (wing ♂ 94—98, ♀ 89—96; tail 52—60; tarsus 25—27; culmen 16—18. 12 specimens. *Handbk. Brit. Birds).* Iris sepia; bill and legs black.

Identification: The male is darker on back than illustrated and the ear-coverts form a dark brown patch. This bird is separated from all other chats in our area by the *white on the tail* which is *not graduated;* upper tail-coverts white. Can be confused with 568 juvenile but with more slender bill and tarsus. Also lacks chestnut edge to inner secondaries and tertiaries. See 568.
Distribution: Europe and Asia, south to central Africa. Recorded from within our limits by Capt. B. Alexander on the Zambesi River and south of the Zambesi in Rhodesia by Wilde. Sight records for Barberspan, Transvaal and South West Africa. Three more recent records from Rhodesia.
Habits: A very rare migrant. Usually seen singly in Africa. Found in all types of open country. Known to overwinter in Zambia.

LOCAL RACE:
O.o. oenanthe (Linnaeus), 1758: *Europe = Sweden.* The southern race also occurs in Tanzania but is not yet recorded as far south as this one.

564 Mountain Chat   Bergwagter

Oenanthe monticola Vieillot, 1818: *Namaqualand.*

Native Names: Khaloti, le-Tsoanafeki (S).
PLATE 50 ♂, ♂ AND ♀ (OPP. P. 400).
Length 17—20 cm (wing ♂ 106—109—112, ♀ 102, 103; tail ♂ 70—76, ♀65, 67; tarsus 28—31; culmen 17,5—20. 8 specimens, 6 ♂, 2 ♀). Iris dark hazel; bill and legs black.

Identification: Males are very variable in colour but all have the same pattern of *white rump and outer tail-feathers* and white shoulder patch. Young male resembles female. Female should not be confused with other chats since it is generally darker above and below.
Distribution: Found only in southern Africa; Cape Province, Natal, Transvaal to the Zoutpansberg, north to Angola on the west.
Habits: A common resident. Shows a preference for hilly country, found generally in dry and arid localities often far from man but also adapts itself to human habitation. Usually in pairs or small parties. A bold bird which perches

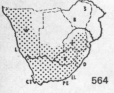
564

on conspicuous rocks or antheaps from which it soars a short distance, drops suddenly and then flies off low for some distance.

Food: Insects, especially young grasshoppers. Also attracted to bird tables.

Voice: Beautiful song uttered very early or late, sometimes even on moonlight nights.

Breeding: Normal nesting site is under stones on hillsides. Nowadays also in stone kraals, on top of gutters, under verandah roofs and also in nesting boxes. The nest is a rough and clumsy affair of old grass and other vegetable matter or wool, with a bowl-shaped cavity lined with fibres and hair. It is built by female only in 4 to 14 days. Recorded from June to March but mainly September to January. Eggs 2 to 3, greenish-blue with clouding of pinky-rufous specks, more concentrated round the thick end. Average (83) 23,2 × 16,2 (20,9—25,9 × 15,8—18,2). Incubation 13—14 days by female only; nestling 16½ days, fed by both parents. Two or three broods per annum.

LOCAL RACES:
(a) *O.m. monticola* Vieillot, 1818: *Namaqualand.* From the western Cape to Griqualand West, north to Kaokoveld. Size as above. Formerly a race *O.m. atmorii* (Tristram) was described from Damaraland on colour difference due to whiter crown but these phases intermingle.
(b) *O.m. griseiceps* Blandford and Dresser, 1874: *Colesberg, Cape Province.* Eastern Karoo and Drakensberg to Transvaal and southern Botswana. Larger; wing ♂ 109—116, ♀ 104—113; tail 72—80; tarsus 28,5—33; culmen 17—20 (8 ♂, 6 ♀ specimens).

565 See **571** *(c).*

566   Karoo Chat   Karoowagter

Cercomela schlegelii   (Wahlberg), 1855: *Onanis, Damaraland.*

PLATE 50, *(a)* AND *(d)* (OPP. P. 400).
Length 15—18 cm (wing ♂ 94,5—95,6—97, ♀ 83,5—86,7—90; tail ♂ 65—68, ♀ 59—62; tarsus 26—30; culmen 13—16,5. 11 specimens, 6 ♂ 5 ♀). Iris brown; bill and legs black.

Identification: Size and build of the Mountain Chat, No. 564, but with *grey rump*. It is also distinguished by having under-parts lighter than upper-parts. The entirely dark centre tail-feathers distinguish this species from the smaller chats. See No. 564—also under Habits.

Distribution: From Little Namaqualand, east to Hanover and Colesberg, north to Bloemfontein and north-west to Rehoboth, Erongo and along the Namib to Angola.

Habits: The commonest chat of the Karoo. Widespread and resident throughout. Similar in habits to the Mountain Chat but very fond of sitting on telegraph wires, or perching on the top of bushes to call. When alarmed it makes off rapidly in a wavy flight.

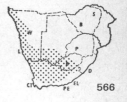

566

Food: Insects and seeds.

Voice: A rattling note, "tirr-tit-tat" or "tirr-tit-tat-tut".

Breeding: The nest is situated on the ground under a bush or tuft of grass. Constructed of grasses and vegetable down. October to February. Eggs 2 to 3, pale greenish-blue, rather thickly covered with pale reddish freckling. Average (15) 20,0 × 15,0 (19,1—21,5 × 14,3—16,5).

LOCAL RACES:

(a) C.s. schlegelii (Wahlberg), 1855: *Onanis, Damaraland.* Along the Namib, south to the northern part of Great Namaqualand. The lightest and smallest form; size as above. Illustrated as **No. 566** *(a).*
(b) C.s. namaquensis (W. Sclater), 1928: *Great Namaqualand.* Great Namaqualand. Larger than *(a);* wing ♂ 103—107—112. (5 specimens).
(c) C.s. benguellensis Sclater, 1928: *Huxe.* Slightly darker than nominate and smaller (wing 85—90). Coastal Kaokoveld and S.W. Angola.
(d) C.s. pollux (Hartlaub), 1866: *"Karoo" = Traka, Willowmore dist., C.P.* Southern and eastern extension of its range. Largest and darkest race. Wing ♂ 102—107—112. 6 specimens. Illustrated as **No. 566.** *(d).*

567 = 566 *(d).*

568   Capped Wheatear   Skaapwagter

Oenanthe pileata (Gmelin), 1789: *Cape of Good Hope.*

Native Names: isi-Xaxabesha, in-Kotyeni (X); Thoromeli (S).

PLATE 50 AD. AND IMM. (OPP. P. 400).
Length about 18 cm (wing ♂ 91—98—104, ♀ 88—90—92; tail ♂ 57—68, ♀ 50—59; tarsus ♂ 29—34, ♀ 26—32; culmen 15—16; 36 specimens, 27 ♂, 9 ♀). Iris dark brown; bill and legs black.

Identification: The white of rump and sides of tail is conspicuous in flight; the white does not extend the full length of the tail as in No. 563. The brown upper-parts and handsome black-and-white pattern of face and chest make this species easy to identify. Sexes alike. Young has no or a speckled breast-band and wing-coverts. Juvenile has strikingly larger head than 563 (see 563).
Distribution: From Kenya to Angola southwards to the Cape.

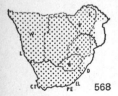

568

Habits: A common resident except in the south-eastern coastal areas where it is uncommon during the colder months. A dry season visitor to Rhodesia from May to November. A familiar species on old camping sites and around cattle kraals where the ground is almost bare or the grass short; hops about with much excited wing-flicking and jerking of the tail; also perches on stones or low bushes. Very friendly about homesteads where not disturbed. Known as the Koggelaar from its antics on the wing when it towers up and about with outbursts of song.
Food: Insects, including flies, locusts and ants. Also lucerne butterflies and caterpillars.
Voice: Readily imitates other bird calls and even farmyard animals. Utters a pretty variety of notes which are sustained until dusk, giving it the name "Nagtegaal" or "Rossignol".
Breeding: Makes a padded nest of straw and soft materials from 30 cm to 1 metre inside a gerbille or rat burrow in open ground. September to January. Eggs 3 to 5, pale greenish or bluish-white either unmarked or faintly marked with pink speckles. A clutch recorded of one pale greenish egg and two white ones. Average (25) 23,8 × 17,7 (22—27 × 16,8—20,4).

LOCAL RACES:
Due to its migratory habits and wide variation in colour, no satisfactory races can be admitted.

569 Buff-streaked Chat   Bergklipwagter

Myrmecocichla bifasciata   (Temminck), 1829: *"Caffrerie"* = *Eastern Cape Province.*

Native Name: le-Tsonafika (S).

PLATE 50, ♂ AND ♀ (OPP. P. 400).
Length 17 cm (wing ♂ 86—91—98, ♀ 82—86—91; tail 53—65; tarsus 27—31,5; culmen 16,5—19. 26 specimens, 18 ♂, 8 ♀). Iris dark brown; bill and feet black.

Identification: In the field has a conspicuous buffish-white "V" from the rump through the shoulders. Female not quite so reddish as illustrated. Note wholly black tail and light buff rump in both sexes. Immature has an orange rump, the feathers of back, chin and breast edged with dark brown.
Distribution: The eastern Cape from Grahamstown and East London, to Graaff-Reinet and northwards to the Drakensberg and environs, upper parts of Natal, southern and eastern Transvaal to Zoutpansberg.
Habits: Confined to hills and mountainous regions; seldom seen away from stony or rocky localities. A very lively and attractive bird, which dances about on the rocks and seems to take a special delight in chirping and displaying when approached. Is not shy, but very wary when alarmed. Frequents cattle kraals and farm-houses.

569

Food: Insects.
Voice: Imitates other birds and also animals. Loud and pleasant song.
Breeding: Builds a large and untidy nest under large stones, or in a hole in a rock or well. Nest built of soft tow-like grass, dry grass and horsehair. September to December. Eggs 3 or 4, white with a faint blue tinge freckled with pinkish-brown, with usually a richer coloured ring at the big end. Some eggs have only a few spots apart from a ring or cap at big end. Average (23) 23,5 × 16,5 (21—25,4 × 15,5—17,3).

570 Familiar Chat   Spekvreter

Cercomela familiaris   (Stephens), 1826: *S. Africa* = *Cape Peninsula.*

Native Names: Phophorokhosa, le-Tlerenyane, le-Terenyane (S).

PLATE 50 (OPP. P. 400).
Length about 15 cm (wing ♂ 85—88—92, ♀ 79—82—85; tail 55—68; tarsus 22,5—26; culmen 13—16. 46 specimens, 22 ♂, 24 ♀). Iris brown; bill and legs black. Weight 19,5—21 g.

Identification: Very similar to Nos. 571 and 572 but distinguished by the *centre tail-feathers* being *wholly dark brown* such that the folded tail appears uniform brown; further, the rufous colouring is not graduated as in the next two species. Immature is darker above and below; generally more rufous. Young speckled on chest and on wing-coverts otherwise as immature.
Distribution: All over Southern Africa northwards to the Sahara Desert. Generally absent from the moister coastal areas from Natal north.
Habits: A resident species and one of the commonest chats in our area. Occurs on the rocky slopes of mountains, and about homesteads, attracting attention by its friendly manner and habit of flicking its wings. An active but silent bird which becomes very tame if encouraged. Oldest record 74 months.

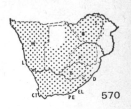

570

Food: Insects, especially flies. Used to eat grease from wagon wheels without fear—hence the name "Spekvreter".

PLATE 50

563. *Oenanthe oenanthe oenanthe.* Wheatear. Tapuit.

564. *Oenanthe monticola monticola.* Mountain Chat. Bergwagter.

Two ♂, and ♀.

566 *(a). Cercomela schlegelii schlegelii.* Karoo Chat. Karoowagter.

566 *(d). Cercomela schlegelii pollux.* Karoo Chat. Karoowagter.

568. *Oenanthe pileata.* Capped Wheatear. Skaapwagter. Ad. and Imm.

569. *Myrmecocichla bifasciata.* Buff-streaked Chat. Bergklipwagter.

♂ and ♀.

570. *Cercomela familiaris familiaris.* Familiar Chat. Spekvreter.

571 *(a). Cercomela tractrac tractrac.* Tractrac Chat. Woestynspekvreter.

571 *(c). Cercomela tractrac albicans.* Tractrac Chat. Woestynspekvreter.

572. *Cercomela sinuata.* Sickle-wing Chat. Vlaktespekvreter.

573. *Thamnolaea cinnamomeiventris cinnamomeiventris.* Mocking Chat.

Dassievoël. ♂ and ♀.

574. *Myrmecocichla arnoti arnoti.* Arnot's Chat. Arnotse Swartpiek.

♂ and ♀.

575. *Myrmecocichla formicivora.* Ant-eating Chat. Swartpiek. ♂ and young ♀.

576. *Saxicola torquata torquata.* Stone Chat. Bontrokkie. ♂ and ♀.

577. *Saxicola rubetra.* Whinchat. Het Paapje.

660. *Namibornis herero.* Herero Chat. Herero-spekvreter.

570

577

576 ♂ ♀

563

660

572

C

571

A

566 A D

573 ♀ ♂

Imm

568

569 ♂

♀

564 ♂

♀

575 ♀

♂

574 ♂

♀

KN

NIGHTON.
'38

590

591

593 x

593

588

Imm

589

592

591 x

KN

586

584

KN

583

KN

585

582

KN

579

KN

578

581

580

KN

LIGHTON.
'39

PLATE 51

578. *Cossypha dichroa.* Chorister Robin. Lawaaimaker.
579. *Cossypha natalensis.* Natal Robin. Natal-lawaaimaker.
580. *Cossypha heuglini euronota.* Heuglin's Robin. Heuglinse Lawaaimaker.
581. *Cossypha caffra caffra.* Cape Robin. Janfrederik.
582. *Bessonornis humeralis.* White-throated Robin. Witkeel-janfrederik.
583. *Erythropygia coryphaeus coryphaeus.* Karoo Scrub Robin.
Slangverklikker.
584. *Tychaedon signata signata.* Brown Robin. Bruin Janfrederik.
585. *Erythropygia quadrivirgata wilsoni.* Bearded Robin.
Gebaarde Janfrederik.
586. *Erythropygia paena paena.* Kalahari Scrub Robin. Wipstert.
588. *Erythropygia leucophrys leucophrys.* White-browed Scrub Robin.
Gestreepte Wipstert.
589. *Pogonocichla stellata stellata.* Starred Robin. Witkol-janfrederik.
Ad. and Imm.
590. *Swynnertonia swynnertoni.* Swynnerton's Robin.
Swynnertonse Janfrederik.
591. *Sheppardia gunningi gunningi.* Gunning's Robin.
Gunningse Janfrederik.
591X. *Alethe fuelleborni.* White-breasted Alethe.
592. *Luscinia luscinia.* Thrush Nightingale. Lyster-nagtegaal.
593. *Cichladusa arquata.* Morning Warbler. Môrelyster.
593X. *Cichladusa ruficauda.* Red-tailed Morning Warbler.
Rooistert Môrelyster.

Breeding: Usually nests in a hole or under a stone in rocky areas but around homesteads builds in holes in walls, in kettles, old tins, petrol funnels and even in a car top in the open. The nest is a fairly deep cup loosely and roughly made of chaffed grass and rootlets, lined with hair, feathers and sometimes wool. August to April. Eggs 2 to 4, usually 3. One record of 6, probably two females. Greenish blue with scattered rufous speckles, mainly in a zone around the thick end. On some eggs there is no concentration at the big end and in others the markings are dull and indistinct. Average (100) 20,6 × 15,2 (18,9—22,5 × 13,9—16,1). Incubation 13—15 days (6). Nestling 15—18 days (4).

LOCAL RACES:
(a) C.f. familiaris (Stephens), 1826: *S. Africa = Cape Peninsula.* Southern and eastern Cape Province. As illustrated. Size as above.
(b) C.f. hellmayri (Reichenow), 1904: *Limpopo north of Pietersberg, Transvaal.* Northern Orange Free State, Transvaal, eastern Botswana and Rhodesia—see *(c)* and *(d)*. Darker above and below than *(a)*.
(c) C.f. modesta (Shelley), 1897: *Karonga, N.W. shore of Lake Nyasa.* In the low country of the Zambesi as far west as Sebungwe area and northwards, Zambia, Malawi and northern Mozambique. More grey than *(a)* or *(b)*.
(d) C.f. galtoni (Strickland), 1852: *Otjimbinque, Damaraland.* Little Namaqualand, northern Cape north to Damaraland; also western Botswana. Very pale, more whitish above and below.
(e) C.f. angolensis Lynes, 1926: *Huxe, Benguella.* Kaokoveld and Ovamboland north to Mossamedes. Whiter belly and under tail-coverts than *(d)* with little or no pinkish tinge on breast. Also slightly smaller than *(d)*.

571   Tractrac Chat   Woestynspekvreter

Cercomela tractrac (Wilkes), 1817: *Auteniquois country = Orange River.*

PLATE 50, *(a)* AND *(c)* (OPP. P. 400).
Length 14—15 cm (wing 81—83—85; tail 50—55; tarsus 26—29,5; culmen 13—16,5. 13 specimens). Iris brown; bill and legs black.

Identification: Where distribution overlaps Nos. 570 and 572, confusion with these two species is likely. Generally this is a smaller and lighter bird (especially above) than either No. 570 or 572. *The rump is pale buff, almost white.* Young like that of No. 572 but more heavily white-tipped on crown.
Distribution: From the drier regions just south of Olifants River in south-west Cape, along the Orange River to Aliwal North in the east. North to the Kaokoveld.
Habits: Much the same as those of the Familiar Chat, No. 570. Occurs in more open ground, indeed, one race lives under the most arid desert conditions. Said to be quite tame. Spends much of its time on the ground and is able to run with great swiftness.

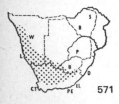
571

Food: Insects.
Breeding: Nests under a stone or bush, a nest similar to that of the Stone Chat. Eggs 2 to 3, greenish-blue, rarely finely marked with red-brown. Average (9) 22,2 × 16,1 (19,5—24,2 × 15—16,9).

LOCAL RACES:
(a) C.t. tractrac (Wilkes), 1817: *Auteniquois country = Orange River.* Little, and eastern Great Namaqualand, south to Olifants River, east to Middelburg and Aliwal North. The darkest race. Illustrated as **No. 571** *(a).*
(b) C.t. barlowi (Roberts), 1937: *Aus, S.W.A.* Western Great Namaqualand. Paler than *(a)* but darker than *(c).*

(c) C.t. albicans (Wahlberg), 1855: *Walvis Bay.* The Namib from Cape Cross to about Luderitz. A very pale form. Illustrated as **No. 571** *(c).*
(d) C.t. hoeschi (Niethammer), 1955: *Kaoko-Namib west of Orupembe.* Kaokoveld Namib. Darker and slightly larger than *(c).*
(e) C.t. nebulosa Clancey, 1962: *McDougall Bay, Port Nolloth.* Coastal Namaqualand. Has a redder rump and greyer, less white underside than *(b).*

572   Sickle-Wing Chat   Vlaktespekvreter

Cercomela sinuata   (Sundevall), 1857: *Capetown = Saldanha Bay.*

PLATE 50 (OPP. P. 400).
Length about 15 cm (wing ♂ 78,5—80,6—85, ♀ 72—76,1—78,5; tail 48—57; tarsus 26—30; culmen 13—16. 15 specimens, 8 ♂, 7 ♀). Iris brown; bill and legs black.

Identification: Easily confused with the last two species. Generally plumper in form and darker above, contrasting with the under-parts, and decidedly *more rufous on rump than* No. 571. In flight shows the brighter chestnut rump and base of tail. Immature spotted above, feathers of under-parts having brown edges. In the hand the second primary has a pronounced attenuated tip.
Distribution: The Cape Province from Saldanha Bay to Orange River on the west, to Humansdorp and Kei Road on the east, northwards to Lesotho, Orange Free State and northern Cape. Also from Waterberg, Transvaal.
Habits: One of the commonest birds of the Hanover district and generally a common Karoo species. Frequents rather bare ground having sparse short growth and scattered stunted bushes; also ploughed fields, grazing lands and the borders of cultivation. In habits, resembles the Stone Chat, No. 576, flying from one low perch to another and dropping down occasionally to peck about for food. More in the habit of flicking its wings than the Familiar Chat.
Breeding: The nest is situated on the ground at the base of a tiny bush or plant. It is a neat cup of dry grasses and moss, lined with fine tendrils and woolly plants. September to January. Eggs 2 to 3, though said to lay up to 5. Greenish blue usually with indistinct streaky freckling of pale rust forming a zone or ring at the big end sometimes with richer red-brown and a few pale lilac spots. Rarely said to be unmarked (Symons). Average (16) 20,1 × 14,7 (19—22,1 × 13,7—15,6).

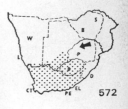

LOCAL RACES:
(a) C.s. sinuata (Sundevall), 1857: *Cape Town = Saldanha Bay.* As above.
(b) C.s. hypernephela Clancey, 1956: *40 mls. east of Maseru, Lesotho.* Darker than *(a).* Confined to Lesotho.

573   Mocking Chat   Dassievoël

Thamnolaea cinnamomeiventris   (Lafresnaye), 1836: *Cape of Good Hope = Cape Province.*

PLATE 50 ♂ AND ♀ (OPP. P. 400).
Length 20—23 cm (wing ♂ 109—115—122, also 104, 106, ♀ 103—109—115; tail one ♀ 83, 90—100; tarsus 27,5—31,5; culmen 18—22. 30 specimens, 17 ♂, 13 ♀). Iris dark brown; bill and legs black.

Identification: Unmistakable; a dark bird with rich chestnut belly, upper and under tail-coverts and rump. The male is easily distinguished by the white shoulders. Immature like female.

403

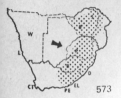

573

Distribution: Eastern Cape Province from just south of Baviaanskloof to Natal, Orange Free State and Transvaal northwards to Ethiopia.

Habits: A very local species, common and resident where found though tending to wander after breeding. Confined to steep cliffs and kloofs, preferably with tumbled boulders at the base and thick bushes. Usually occurs in small parties. It is shy in places, but in others becomes remarkably tame and comes about homesteads in a friendly way, being not only handsome but lively, attractive and somewhat noisy. Flight is usually close to the ground or bushes interspersed with many glides; always glides on to a perch or rock and then raises its tail up and down slowly.

Food: Insects and fruit.

Voice: A capable mimic; recorded as imitating 15 birds during 20 minutes of singing covering a wide range of species from hawks to warblers. The song is loud and attractive, interspersed with some mimicked call every now and then. Recorded to mimic 22 species. Call a whistled "mzee-ho" and a melodious "see-pee". Alarm a harsh "krät".

Breeding: Usually uses Lesser Striped Swallows' nests where the entrance tunnel has been broken, lining the nests with hairs of dassies and buck. Known to oust swallows from their nests. August to December. Eggs 3, one record of 4, pale greenish, bluish-white to pure white freckled with pale reddish lilac sometimes rather concentrated at the thick end to form a cap. Average (54) 24,4 × 18,1 (23,8—27,6 × 17—19,2). Two measurements of 22,5 × 17,2 and 35,6 × 16.

LOCAL RACES:
(a) T.c. cinnamomeiventris (Lafresnaye), 1836: *Cape of Good Hope.* Cape Province, O.F.S., Lesotho, Botswana and S. Transvaal.
(b) T.c. odica Clancey, 1962: *Inyanga.* Montane areas N. Transvaal, Rhodesia and Mozambique.
(c) T.c. autochthones Clancey, 1952: *Ingwavuma, Lebombo.* Coastal from Pondoland to Mozambique. Smaller, no white on chest.

574   Arnot's Chat   Arnotse Swartpiek

Myrmecocichla arnoti (Tristram), 1869: *Adam Kok's New Land =*
Victoria Falls.

PLATE 50 ♂ AND ♀ (OPP. P. 400).
Length about 18 cm (wing 97—102—107; tail 63—76; tarsus 26—30; culmen 14—17. 14 specimens). Iris red-brown; bill and legs black.

Identification: Does not occur in the same localities as the Mountain Chat with which it could be confused; wholly *black* tail and rump would distinguish this species. Immature birds have head and neck black, but the white shoulder-patch is present; some immature males show odd white feathers on crown; similarly immature female shows odd white feathers on chin and breast.

574

Distribution: The low country of north-eastern Transvaal, through Rhodesia westwards to Ngamiland and Ovamboland; beyond our limits to Tanzania.

Habits: Extremely localized and restricted, though invariably abundant where occurring. Occurs in park-like forests, especially Mopane and *Brachystegia* areas. It is a lively bird that commonly occurs in small parties under the shade of the big trees, usually keeping low down about gnarled trunks, where it searches for insects. Somewhat thrush-like, spending less time on the ground than on the trees looking for food.

Food: Small insects, ants.
Voice: A quiet musical "fick". A loud song of squeaking and rasping notes.
Breeding: Situated in holes or natural hollows in trees from 2—4 metres up, the nest is a shallow saucer-shaped structure of dead leaves and old cobwebs lined with grass and feathers. Eggs 3, bluish-green thickly and evenly speckled with pale rusty brown. Average (8) 22,5 × 17,1 (22,4—24 × 16,2—17,5).

LOCAL RACE:
M.a. arnoti (Tristram), 1869: *Adam Kok's New Land = Victoria Falls.* Another race in Angola.

575 Ant-eating Chat   Swartpiek

Myrmecocichla formicivora (Vieillot), 1818: *"Pays des Cafres" = Sundays River, Eastern Cape.*

Native Names: isa-Nzwili (X); Thume (S).

PLATE 50, ♂ AND YOUNG ♀ (OPP. P. 400).
Length about 18 cm (wing ♂ 98—101—107, ♀ 93—96—97; tail ♂ 58—66, ♀ 56—58; tarsus 30—35; culmen 16—20. 25 specimens, 13 ♂, 12 ♀). Iris dark brown; bill and legs black.

Identification: Old females also attain white lesser wing-coverts. Young males and females are like the female illustrated. Immature is redder brown. Flies about with a peculiar fluttering of rapidly beating wings when the blur of *white "windows" in the wings* identifies the species immediately.
Distribution: Little Namaqualand, across the Karoo to Humansdorp, northwards to the highveld, over the Drakensberg into upper Natal, Transvaal; general on the west over the Kalahari to Ngamiland and Ovamboland. Once recorded in Rhodesia from Wankie Game Reserve.

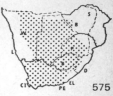

575

Habits: A common resident found on open ground, especially where there are antheaps. It perches on antheaps, on tops of bushes and on fence poles. Has a habit of hovering and either dropping down on to its perch or bouncing up again, flying about with a wavy action and fluttering wings. The stance is very upright.
Food: Termites.
Voice: A sharp "peek" or "piek".
Breeding: Situated in burrows excavated by itself in banks, or more often in the roof, a few feet from the entrance, of an antbear burrow, the nest is formed of a padding of grass lined with rootlets in a chamber at the end of a 45—90 cm tunnel. October to January, as early as July in the Transvaal. Eggs 3 to 4, usually pure white but one egg recorded with a few fine light brown speckles at rounded end. Average (26) 23,9 × 17,9 (23,3—25,4 × 16,9—19,2); one egg 22 × 17.

576 Stone Chat   Bontrokkie

Saxicola torquata (Linnaeus), 1766: *Cape of Good Hope.*

Native Names: i-Ncape, isa-Ngcape (X); is-Ncapela, isi-Qawane, isi-Nqawana, si-Cequ, u-Sagwebe (Z); Hlatsinyane, Thisa (S); Mucherechedzabadga (I).

PLATE 50, ♂ AND ♀ (OPP. P. 400).
Length 14 cm (wing 67—69,7—74; tail 47—55; tarsus 20,5—24; culmen 12—14. 8 specimens). Iris black; bill and legs black. Weight 15,8 g.

Identification: This handsome little bird, black and white with reddish breast, is well known; the dull female is readily identified by means of the white

405

shoulder-patches and whitish rump. The immature male differs from female by having black sides to face. Young birds have speckled upper-parts and breast but have the white wing and rump patches.

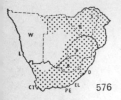

576

Distribution: Extends from the Cape northwards to the Sahara and beyond to Europe and Asia. Not in South West Africa.

Habits: Common. In some milder areas it is resident throughout the year but in many places, especially the eastern coastal areas from Zululand and Mozambique (also Beaufort West and Fort Beaufort) it is only recorded from April to September. It inhabits treeless country, where there is low scrub, especially along streams, and moist flats where grass prevails. Generally to be seen perched low on the tip of a dry twig or grass stem, now and then hopping to the ground to pick up an insect, or catching insects flying past.

Food: Insects, including dragonflies and flying termites.

Voice: Generally silent; a weak note; a short bright song.

Breeding: The nest is usually well concealed on the ground under a branch, or in a bunch of low grass or reeds; rarely in the open. Also recorded in dry reeds standing in water. A neat nest of dry grass and rootlets, lined with finer material often with a few feathers or bits of vegetable down. July to December. Eggs 3—4, pale green finely speckled with reddish markings, slightly concentrated at the thick end. A. W. Vincent records eggs from Zaïre as light Cambridge blue, both unmarked and indistinctly marked. Average (71) 19,2 × 14,5 (17,5—22,3 × 13,5—15,8). Smaller to the north—average (24) 18,5 × 14,1 from Zaïre. Incubation 14 to 15 days (2). Nestling 13 to 16 days (4). Double brooded.

LOCAL RACES:
(a) S.t. torquata (Linnaeus), 1766: *Cape of Good Hope.* Size as above. As illustrated. Throughout range except for *(b)* and *(c)*.
(b) S.t. clanceyi Latimer in Clancey, 1961: *Wallekraal.* Lamberts Bay to Alexander Bay. Whiter than nominate.
(c) S.t. stonei Bowen, 1931: *Vila Machado, Angola.* Southern Angola, the Okavango River and N. Botswana. Buff flanks, chestnut confined to chest band.

577 Whinchat   Het Paapje

Saxicola rubetra (Linnaeus), 1758: *Europe = Sweden.*

PLATE 50 (OPP. P. 400).
Length 13—14 cm (wing 78; tail 47; tarsus 22; culmen 12. 1 specimen). Iris brown; bill and feet black.

Identification: Summer plumage illustrated. White on base of tail, not rump. Also *two* white patches on wing, lesser coverts and bastard wing. Note that it is heavily streaked above and may be streaked on breast. Winter plumage like that of female Stonechat but having a white chin bordered by a dark line and with a white eye-stripe.

Distribution: Breeds in Europe and migrates to Africa, south to Malawi and rarely Zambia. One record from Swakopmund by R. D. Bradfield. Recent sight records from Himeville, Umfolozi in Natal, Salisbury, Rhodesia, and Okavango, South West Africa need confirmation.

Habits: A vagrant. Found typically in open grassland and farm patches with a scattering of shrubs and small trees. Occurs singly.

LOCAL RACE:
S.r. rubetra (Linnaeus), 1758: *Europe = Sweden.* As above.

578 Chorister Robin — Lawaaimaker

Cossypha dichroa (Gmelin), 1789: *South Africa.*

Native Names: u-Gaga-sisi (X); Mananda, i-Binda (Z); Tsakha (S).

PLATE 51 (OPP. P. 401).
Length about 20 cm (wing ♂ 97—102—105, ♀ 93—97—101; tail 80—92; tarsus 27,5—32 (one ♂ 26); culmen 16,5—19 (one ♀ 14). 30 specimens, 20 ♂, 10 ♀). Iris brown; bill black; legs yellow-brown.

Identification: The black sides of face and head distinguish this bird. Centre and outer webs of outer tail-feathers brown. Immature has upper-parts and wing-coverts spotted, whilst feathers of the under-parts have black tips; this is lost by the end of April.

Distribution: Along the coast from George to Pondoland, thence inland through the Natal and Zululand interior to the eastern and north-eastern Transvaal as far north as Zoutpansberg.

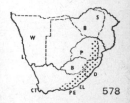

578

Habits: A not uncommon forest species, for the most part resident, though in Natal and southern Zululand many birds migrate from the inland to the coastal forests from April to September. The most arboreal of our robins, spending most of its time in the mid stratum of the forests and only feeding regularly on the ground during winter months. A very noisy bird, fond of mocking the calls of other birds, but not often seen on account of its shyness.

Food: Beetles, ants and termites, berries in autumn and winter.

Voice: A harsh ratchet-like alarm note; call is a double whistle "toy-toy" to "peep-borrow"—the first note high, the second quiet. Song, heard from August to May, consists mainly of imitations interspersed with its own bubbling phrases and is uttered from tops of forest trees.

Breeding: Usually the nest is situated in a hole in a tree, as high as 7 metres; it is a shallow cup of rootlets. October to January. Eggs 2 or 3, uniform chocolate to olive. Average (6) 23,5 × 17,8 (22,6—25,5 × 16—19). Often uses the same nest year after year. Host to the Red-chested Cuckoo, the eggs of which are a perfect match of this species.

579 Natal Robin — Natal-lawaaimaker

Cossypha natalensis A. Smith, 1840: *near Port Natal = Durban.*

PLATE 51 (OPP. P. 401).
Length 18—20 cm (wing ♂ 88—92,3—95, ♀ 85—87,7—91; tail ♂ 72,5—80, ♀ 68—75; tarsus 23—28; culmen 14,5—17. 18 specimens, 11 ♂, 7 ♀). Iris brown; bill black; legs dull brown. Weight 27,1—32,7 g.

Identification: Predominantly rufous with speckled blue-grey on wings and back. The crown and nape variable and contrast strongly with under-parts. Tail pattern as in last species. Juvenile spotted on top and sides of head, mantle and wing-coverts; underside mottled with black.

Distribution: Along the littoral from about East London, rarely from Grahamstown, northwards to East Africa thence westwards to Zaïre and Angola. Also from thick scrub in the Eastern Districts of Rhodesia and along the Zambesi as far west as Chirundu.

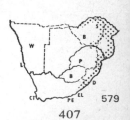

579

Habits: A resident of the dense forests. An elusive bird which is more often heard than seen; it keeps to the undergrowth of the forest, only venturing into the tree-tops when certain berries ripen. Hunts insects on the ground and becomes very active at dusk when it forsakes cover and may be seen hopping in open glades and drives.

Food: Insects and berries.

Voice: Alarm note is a guttural "gur"; call-note "trrree-trrirr", rising then falling, monotonously repeated for long intervals at a time. Song excels in mimicry even the previous species, with which it is easily confused; uttered from the undergrowth or midstratum.

Breeding: A hollow stump is a favourite site for the nest though it may also be found in a rocky crevasse, on the ground, or suspended in hanging foliage. It is constructed of dead leaves and twigs, the cup coarsely lined with fine fibres. October to January. Eggs 2—3, from chocolate-brown through olive-green to turquoise blue. Average (47) 22,5 × 16,8 (20,5—25 × 16—17,8). Both sexes feed the young. Parasitised by the Red-chested Cuckoo.

LOCAL RACES:
This species is locally migratory and there is considerable variation between individuals so that recognition of races is not clear cut.
(a) C.n. natalensis A. Smith, 1840: *near Port Natal* = *Durban*. From East London north to southern Mozambique. As above.
(b) C.n. intensa Mearns, 1932: *Taveta, Kenya.* Ethiopia south to northern Mozambique and Zambesi River west to Angola. Differs from *(a)* in having crown more cinnamon-rufous.

580 Heuglin's Robin — Heuglinse Lawaaimaker

Cossypha heuglini Hartlaub, 1886: *"Keren"* = *Wau, Bahr el Ghazal.*

PLATE 51 (OPP. P. 401).
Length 19—20 cm (wing ♂ 95—98—99, ♀ 88—91—95; tail ♂ 83—93, ♀ 76—88; tarsus 27—30,5; culmen 15—18. 13 specimens, 6 ♂, 7 ♀). Iris light brown; bill black; legs brownish. Weight 38,5 g.

Identification: The white eyebrow distinguishes this bird from Nos. 578 and 579. Sexes alike, though female is slightly smaller and has a browner mantle. Tail pattern as in previous two species. The crown is sometimes dark blue-grey rather than black. Juvenile attains a white or light stripe over eye even at the spotted stage; otherwise similar to young, No. 578, but redder below.

Distribution: Ethiopia west to Darfur and south on the east to northern Zululand, eastern Transvaal and the plateau of Rhodesia; on the west to Angola, Ngamiland and Zambesi Valley.

Habits: A not uncommon resident. Frequents the low matted bush along streams and rivers or forests, where it spends much of its time on the ground. While it may be secretive in habit, it is also found in gardens about towns. Often associated with No. 582, where both occur together.

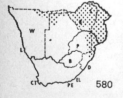
580

Food: Spiders, flies, termites, beetles and ants.

Voice: Call likened to "don't you *do*-it" or "pip-pip-uree". The remarkable song, regarded by many as the finest of all African birds, is both emotional and ventriloquial; occasionally sings in duet; sometimes repeats a phrase such as "fetch-my-potion, fetch-my-potion" or "think-of-it", etc., becoming louder and more rapid. Sings at dawn and dusk, sometimes at night.

Breeding: Situated in forested shaded gullies, the nest is placed in the hollow top of an old tree stump or a small cavity in a bank; not hidden, but is most inconspicuous because it is constructed of dark materials. Also recorded in a brick wall. Female builds nest. The nest is loosely built of large twigs, dead leaves or bark, with an inner structure of moss and rootlets. August to February. Eggs 2, ground colour variable from pale buff-olive, pale buff to cream, almost entirely obscured by a suffusion of red-brown, with a zone of reddish brown at the obtuse end; sometimes unmarked. Average (9) 23,0 × 16,6 (21,5—25 × 16—17). Incubation from 15 to at least 17 days (2). Nestling 15—17 days (3). Host to the Red-chested Cuckoo.

LOCAL RACES:
There is no agreement by authorities on races.
(a) *C.h. euronota* Friedmann, 1930: *Lumbo, Mozambique.* Northern Zululand, eastern Transvaal, Rhodesia and Mozambique. Slightly smaller and more olivaceous than other races.

581 Cape Robin   Janfrederik

Cossypha caffra   (Linnaeus), 1771: *Cape of Good Hope.*

Native Names: u-Gaga (X); u-Gaka (Z); Mokhofe (S).

PLATE 51 (OPP. P. 401).
Length about 18 cm (wing ♂ 82—86,2—91, ♀ 75—80,3—84; tail ♂ 72—85, ♀ 69—77; tarsus 27—31,5; culmen 14—17. 25 specimens, 15 ♂, 10 ♀). Iris brown; bill and legs black. Weight 23,8—40 g.

Identification: The light eye-stripe, orange throat and upper breast with bluish grey under-parts are distinctive. Sexes alike. Young is uniform brown, lightly spotted above and below; this plumage is lost in about 14 weeks; tail and rump as adult.

Distribution: From the Cape Province northwards to southern Great Namaqualand, Transvaal and Natal. Upper parts of the Eastern Districts of Rhodesia to the highlands of Kenya. Vagrant in southern Mozambique.

Habits: A common resident, but young birds move to lower levels in Natal and Zululand from April to September. In the south widely distributed; in the dry west confined to the shelter of bush along streams and rivers; to the north-east found mainly in the cool forests and bush of higher levels. It has adapted itself to towns, where it occurs commonly in gardens where shrubberies afford retreat. It is always suspicious, venturing out into the open with a nervous jerking of its reddish tail and slipping back to shelter directly it senses danger.

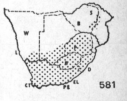

581

Food: Insects, spiders, worms, small frogs and lizards; berries and small fruits.

Voice: Normal call is rendered "*Jan*-Fred-erik". Alarm note "wadeda". A pretty short song, which often mimics other birds.

Breeding: The nest is placed in the heart of some thick bush; often in a bank of a stream overgrown with ferns and other plants that partly hide the nest. Also in crevices, holes in trees or poles, in tins, or under plants in flower-pots, forks of trees, in flood debris or on piles of dead brush. From ground level to 3 metres up. The nest is a loose mass of grass, bark, twigs, leaves, etc., with a neat cup lined with fine roots or horsehair. July in the Cape, otherwise September to January. Eggs, usually 2, sometimes 3 in the Cape; 2, 3, occasionally 4, in the Transvaal. Usually a pinky white with more or less of a greenish tinge, thinly marked with fine pinky speckles; sometimes cream, obscured by a suffusion of light red-brown; light green with only a circlet of rust-red markings at large end and even immaculate pale blue (A. W. Vincent). Average (100) 23,0 × 16,6 (20,5—25,8 × 15—17,9). Incubation 13—19 days (5) by female only. Nestling 14½—18 days (5); feeding by both parents. Host to the Red-chested Cuckoo.

LOCAL RACES:
(a) *C.c. caffra* (Linnaeus), 1771: *Cape of Good Hope.* South-western to eastern Cape. White eyebrows thinner and not extending much behind eye. Size as above.
(b) *C.c. namaquensis* W. Sclater, 1911: *Klipfontein, Little Namaqualand.* Little and Great Namaqualand, Orange River system and western Transvaal. White eyebrow broader and extending back over the ear-coverts. Wing ♂ 88,5—92,1—99 (12); ♀ 87.
(c) *C.c. drakensbergi* (Roberts), 1936: *Wakkerstroom, S. Transvaal.* Drakensberg and adjoining foothills on the east to central Transvaal. Intergrading with the next race in eastern Rhodesia. Colour similar to (a) but larger; wing ♂ 86—93,6—100 (16), ♀ 81—86,1—91,5 (6).
(d) *C.c. iolema* Reichenow, 1900: *East Africa = Kilimanjaro.* Kenya south to Malawi and Mozambique, including Gorongoza. Intergrades with (c) in eastern Rhodesia. Darker above than (c) and smaller. Wing ♂ 84—87,3—90 (16), ♀ 78,5—83—86 (14).

582   White-throated Robin   Witkeel-janfrederik

Bessonornis humeralis   A. Smith, 1836: *Marikwa (Marico) River, W. Transvaal.*

PLATE 51 (OPP. P. 401).
Length 16—18 cm (wing ♂ 77—81—85, ♀ 73—74,5—76; tail ♂ 70—79, ♀ 63—70; tarsus 26—29; culmen 15—17. 18 specimens, 14 ♂, 4 ♀). Iris red-brown; bill and legs black. Weight 23,8—24,6 g.

Identification: White chin and throat with dark sides of face and neck distinguish it from similar species. Note the narrow black terminal band at tip of tail. Young is recognizable by the adult tail-pattern and white patch on wing-coverts, though brown and spotted elsewhere as other young robins.
Distribution: Confined to the area Rhodesia to Zululand, extending along the coast from the Tugela River to Maputo. General in Rhodesia, absent in Zambesi Valley and parts of north and west Mashonaland.
Habits: A fairly common resident. Inhabits the thorn-bush and overgrown dongas and gullies along streams and rivers in dry areas. Feeds mainly on the ground where it moves with quick hops. Unlike other members of its family is most conspicuous and vociferous during the winter months.

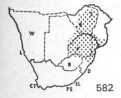

582

Voice: A querulous call "pee-you-wheet" followed by a low chuckle. Alarm note a sharp "cheep" and a guttural "berg". A good mimic.
Breeding: The nest is situated between the roots of a tree, under a bank or low branch on the ground. Placed level with the ground and made with dead leaves, it is lined with leaf stems and grass, rarely feathers, and is perfectly concealed. Nests also recorded in thick bush 45 cm off the ground. September to January. Eggs 2—3, cream or pinkish cream or almost uniform red-brown freckled with darker red-brown and pale ash grey which may form a dark ring at big end. Average (25) 21,2 × 14,8 (19,7—22,5 × 14—15,1). Host to the Red-chested Cuckoo and Diederik Cuckoo.

583 Karoo Scrub Robin   Slangverklikker

Erythropygia coryphaeus (Lesson), 1831: *Cape of Good Hope =*
Sundays River, Cape.

PLATE 51 (OPP. P. 401).
Length about 17 cm (wing 71—75,5—79; tail 67—79; tarsus 26—28,5; culmen
13—15,5. 9 specimens). Iris light brown; bill and legs dusky.

Identification: A nondescript grey-brown bird distinguished by the white
eye-stripe and in flight by *dark fan-shaped tail with white tips* to the feathers.
See also under habits. Not streaked on chest as No. 588, which it otherwise
resembles in colour and habits. Young has a *mottled* chest, back is more
barred than mottled; eye-stripe present.

Distribution: The Karoo, north to Lesotho and southern and western Orange
Free State; southern Botswana and Great Namaqualand.

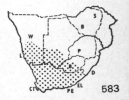

583

Habits: One of the commonest species of the dry south-western areas.
Resident. Spends most of its time on the ground, looking for food or creeping
about in the lower branches of brush. A lively bird like all the Robins when it
shows itself, flicking open its tail and dancing about excitedly before betaking
itself to shelter; often perches on the tops of the bushes as well; when
disturbed always takes to the lower part of another bush. Rather inquisitive
and bold. A noisy bird, fond of making a great fuss when snakes, cats, etc.,
are observed.

Food: Insects and berries.

Voice: A short call. Alarm call a harsh grinding note.

Breeding: Nests on the ground under the shelter of a bush or some prostrate
plant, well concealed. The nest is made of dry grass, rootlets and moss, lined
with finer material even occasionally with plant-down. July to December. Eggs
2—3, rarely 4, pale greenish blue much marked with speckles of red-brown
and rather elongate spots of purplish slate. Average (38) 20,0 × 14,7
(19—21,8 × 13,7—15,3); one egg 16,6 × 14,5. Incubation 14—15 days (2);
nestling 13—14½ days (2).

LOCAL RACES:
(a) *E.c. coryphaeus* (Lesson), 1831: *Cape of Good Hope = Sundays River, Cape.*
Throughout species range except west coastal strip—see *(b)*. Browner than *(b)*. As
illustrated. Size above.
(b) *E.c. cinereus* MacDonald, 1952: *Port Nolloth, Little Namaqualand.* Cape Agulhas
north along a narrow coastal belt to Orange River. Greyer than *(a)*. Wing 69,5—77. (7
specimens).

584 Brown Robin   Bruin Janfrederik

Tychaedon signata (Sundevall), 1851: *Caffr. Inf. = Umhlanga,*
Natal.

PLATE 51 (OPP. P. 401).
Length 18—19 cm (wing ♂ 81—86,5—92, ♀ 79—81,6—88; tail ♂ 73,5—83, ♀ 67—76;
tarsus 24,5—29,5; culmen 18—22. 21 specimens, 11 ♂, 10 ♀). Iris brown; bill black;
legs light brown.

Identification: A bigger bird than the last and one that occurs in completely
different habitat so that there should be no confusion. The white eye-stripe,
white tips to tail and black-and-white primary coverts are diagnostic. Chin
white and sometimes there is white below the eye above a dark malar stripe.

411

See No. 585. Young is similar to adult, having buff tips to feathers of upper-parts and being speckled on breast.

Distribution: From Humansdorp in the eastern Cape, locally distributed through coastal forests of Pondoland, Natal and Zululand. North of the Tugela river ranges into the interior of Zululand. Recently recorded from Woodbush in north-eastern Transvaal.

Habits: Not uncommon. It is found only in areas of well-developed and undisturbed forest, among the thinner growths where trees are large, but never straying far from the vicinity of some dense undergrowth to which it can retire if disturbed. It feeds entirely on the ground where its sombre plumage makes it very difficult to detect.

584

Food: Insects, including millipedes.

Voice: Alarm note a harsh "zeet-zeet-zeet-zeet" often repeated many times. A very fine songster, often singing from high perches. The song reminiscent of that of the Cape Robin in that it begins every phase with the same note; song could be confused with Gurney's Thrush.

Breeding: The nest is situated in old stumps of trees, up to 3 m in thick bush. November. Eggs 2, whitish or very pale greenish blue, variably smeared and blotched or speckled with dark brown and purplish. Average (12) 21,3 × 15,8 (19—22,5 × 15—16,6).

LOCAL RACES:
(a) *T.s. signata* (Sundevall), 1851: *Caffr. Inf.* = *Umhlanga, Natal*. Eastern Cape to Natal. As illustrated; size above.
(b) *T.s. tongensis* Roberts, 1931: *Mangusi Forest, Maputa, N.E. Zululand*. North-east Zululand. Lighter brown above and below. Bill shorter, only 17,5.
(c) *T.s. oatleyi* (Clancey), 1956: *Woodbush Forest Reserve, Northern Transvaal*. North-eastern Transvaal. Darker and redder above and more dusky below than (a). Culmen 22,5—23.

585 Bearded Robin   Gebaarde Janfrederik

Erythropygia quadrivirgata (Reichenow), 1879: *Kapini, Lower Tana, Kenya.*

PLATE 51 (OPP. P. 401).
Length about 16—18 cm (wing 78—85; tail 66—79; tarsus 26—29; culmen 16—18). Iris brown; bill brown; feet pale mauve.

Identification: Shows a blackish stripe above the white eye-stripe; the malar stripe conspicuous. Could be confused with the last species but separated by the blackish tail, browner under-parts and contrasting black-and-white pattern of head and neck. Note white wing bar at base of primaries. Young has similar pattern but is mottled on upper-parts and on chest.

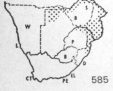

Distribution: From southern Somaliland down the coast as far as St. Lucia, north-eastern Zululand, ranging inland at lower levels along the Sabi, Limpopo and Zambesi river systems.

Habits: A tropical species, resident in more or less dense, dry forest such as Mopane woods, in dense Baikiaea forest, riparian forest or even thickets on

585

anthills. It is not often seen, but has a loud, rather scolding but not unmusical whistling song, usually uttered at daybreak or dusk, or on cloudy days; one bird usually starting and others vying with it until large numbers may be heard at the same time. Feeds low in bushes or on the ground where it scuffles about in dead leaves like a thrush.

Food: Insects, including worker and soldier termites.

Voice: Call-note a low "chuck". Alarm note "tchek-tchek-tcherrrrr". Whistling song similar to No. 588 but more musical and varied.

Breeding: Nest in a shallow hollow in a tree. October to November. Eggs 2—3, aquamarine heavily spotted and blotched with bright russet-brown. Average (11) 20,6 × 14,9 (18,8—21,6 × 14,3—15,6).

LOCAL RACES:
This species has been separated from a western bird on minor colour differences.
(a) E.q. rovumae Grote, 1921: *Mbarangandu River, S. Tanganyika.* As above.
(b) E.q. wilsoni Roberts, 1936: *Mosie, near Maputa, southern Zululand.* Extreme southern race confined to the Republic. Duller, more earth brown than *(a)*.
(c) E.q. interna Clancey, 1962: *15 mls. W. of Victoria Falls.* Western race from middle Zambesi westwards. Lighter and warmer above and brighter more orange rump.

586   Kalahari Scrub Robin   Wipstert

> *Erythropygia paena*   A. Smith, 1836: *between Latakoo and the Tropic*
> = *N. of Kuruman.*

Native Name: Tshwietle (Ch.).

PLATE 51 (OPP. P. 401).
Length about 16—17 cm (wing ♂ 67—70,7—74, ♀ 67—69,3—72; tail 60—69; tarsus 22—27; culmen 14—16,5. 22 specimens, 15 ♂, 7 ♀). Iris dark brown; bill dusky black; legs slate-grey. Weight 19—19,8 g.

Identification: Readily identified by broad black band across rufous tail and white tips on outer tail-feathers, showing as white triangles in flight. The eye-stripe is lighter over the eye than illustrated. Young have light spotting on under-parts.

Distribution: Kalahari scrub from northern Cape, western Orange Free State, Transvaal, western and south-western Matabeleland; west to Damaraland and Angola.

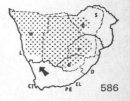

Habits: Common in more or less open, low scrub typical of the Kalahari, especially bordering pans. Has the same habit as the Karoo Scrub Robin, No. 583, of suddenly spreading its tail with a sideways movement when on the ground or perched on low bushes. A noisy bird at dusk and dawn. Spends much of its time on the ground.

Voice: A low scolding note. Song a wild whistling.

Breeding: Nests in the heart of matted bushes, or in the grass mixed with thorn bushes, close to the ground usually at the base of a tree. One nest recorded in a clump of mistletoe about 2,5 m up a tree standing on burnt ground. A cup-shaped structure of grass, smoothly lined with rootlets and horsehair. September to January. Eggs 2—3, dull white much speckled with purplish slate, red-brown and brown. Average (5) 20,1 × 14,4 (18,4—22,3 × 13,5—15,8). Parasitized by Diederik.

LOCAL RACE:
E.p. paena A. Smith, 1836: *between Latakoo and the Tropic* = *N. of Kuruman.* Another paler race occurs in Benguella, southern Angola. Birds of Damaraland are variable and intermediate. Size as above.

413

587 See 588 *(d)*.

588 White-browed Scrub Robin   Gestreepte Wipstert

Erythropygia leucophrys (Vieillot), 1817: *Gamtoos River, E. Cape.*

Native Name: 'Mtcheliswali (Z).

PLATE 51 (OPP. P. 401).

Length about 15 cm (wing 64—69,2—73; tail 57—73; tarsus 22—26; culmen 14—16. 19 specimens). Iris red-brown; bill dark brown; legs ash-brown. Weight 18,8—20 g.

Identification: The rufous rump and base of tail, the white tips to tail and the striped breast are diagnostic. The amount of rufous and markings on rump varies according to the races—see below. The young bird has the same tail and wing markings but is mottled below and above.

Distribution: In the thorn scrub bush from Knysna in the southern Cape, eastwards to Natal and then northwards to Mozambique, Transvaal, Rhodesia, Ngamiland, Ovamboland, Angola and Zaïre.

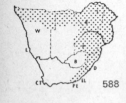

588

Habits: A common resident. Shows a preference for scattered scrub and secondary growth with a little rough tufty grass among the bushes rather than dense bush or forest. Rather shy and skulking, keeping out of sight in the thick of a bush, it suddenly slips away to the next cover, flying close to the ground. Fans its tail jerkily like all scrub robins. Food usually taken on the ground, sometimes in the air as it flits from bush to bush.

Food: Insects; also seeds in winter.

Voice: A few penetrating notes constantly repeated. Sings at dawn and dusk from tree-tops.

Breeding: Nests on the ground or in matted bush very low down. The site varies tremendously but most often in some mass of low vegetation or brushwood. The nest is roughly constructed and is a bulky cup of coarse grass with stems left sticking out with a neat lining of tendrils or finer grass. October to December. Eggs 2—3, white, evenly and well freckled with light brown, some heavier ashy markings at thicker end sometimes forming a ring. Average (83) 19,9 × 14,4 (17,5—22,9 × 13,5—15,8).

LOCAL RACES:

(a) E.l. leucophrys (Vieillot), 1817: *Gamtoos River, E. Cape.* Southern Cape Province to Natal. The darkest form, most heavily striped below. As illustrated.

(b) E.l. pectoralis A. Smith, 1836: *between Orange River and Kurrichane.* Transvaal, Swaziland and Mozambique extending to the extreme south-west of Rhodesia. More rufous above and less striped.

(c) E.l. zambesiana Sharpe, 1882: *Tete, lower Zambesi.* Zambesi Valley including the whole of the north-eastern Rhodesia, southern parts of Zambia and Malawi.

(d) E.l. makalaka Neumann, 1920: *Makalakaland.* The north-western part of Rhodesia and Ngamiland. Under-parts still less striped, especially in females; flanks and breast more rufous.

(e) E.l. ovamboensis Neumann, 1920: *Ombongo, Ovamboland.* Damaraland, Kaokoveld Ovamboland and Botswana. Stripes below as in *(d)* but flanks and breast, hind-neck and back paler.

(f) E.l. simulator Clancey, 1964: *Panda, S. Mocambique.* Coastal Mozambique. Paler and greyer than *(a)*.

589 Starred Robin   Witkol-janfrederik

Pogonocichla stellata   (Vieillot), 1818: *Plettenberg Bay.*

PLATE 51 (OPP. P. 401).
Length 15—17 cm (wing 75—78,5—85; tail 58—68; tarsus 23—26,5; culmen 12—14.
15 specimens). Iris dark brown; bill brown; legs light olive-yellow. Weight 21,5—
24,2 g.

Identification: In the field the white throat and lore spots are normally
concealed. In flight the tail shows orange "windows", with a broad blackish
line down the centre, sides and across the tip. The young moult into *an olive
stage* which appears capable of breeding. This stage has upper-parts uniform
green; under-parts light olive-yellow; gape orange and tail as adult. Young is
"spangled", similar to olive stage but heavily spotted on upper-parts, the
feathers having yellow spots on quill and brown edges, under-parts with brown
edges to feathers; tail not as well marked as adult with yellow-olive not orange
patches.

Distribution: Confined to forests from George, eastwards to Natal thence
northwards in mountain forests of Zululand, Swaziland, eastern Transvaal and
Rhodesia to Kenya.

589

Habits: A common species. Some birds, especially young ones, move from
the high interior forests to the warmer river valleys from March to September.
In Natal they move to the coastal belt but not usually so far east in
Mozambique. A quiet, but not shy, solitary bird usually seen foraging on the
ground among leaves or searching lower branches of forest trees. Rather
flycatcher-like in its habits of catching much of its prey on the wing.

Food: Insects, berries, ants.

Voice: A guttural "zit" or "gut" and a double note "ee-tchoo" or
"too-twee". The song flute-like; two notes, a pause followed by six whistling
notes higher pitched. "Peep peep peep pooee".

Breeding: The nest is placed on the ground, usually on a steep slope or at the
base of a small tree or rock. It is dome-shaped with an elliptical entrance hole
in the side and is constructed of large dead leaves and moss, lined with finer
fibres and hairs. October to February. Eggs 3, creamy white, plentifully
freckled with red-brown, especially at the larger end. Average (14) 21,6 ×
16,3 (20,4—22,8 × 16,1—16,8), one egg 25,0 × 16,8.

LOCAL RACES:
(a) P.s. stellata (Vieillot), 1818: *Plettenberg Bay.* From southern Cape to southern
Zululand. Edges of remiges blue-grey. Size as above.
(b) P.s. transvaalensis (Roberts), 1912: *Woodbush, Transvaal.* Swaziland to eastern
parts of Rhodesia. Wing-coverts with edges white.

590 Swynnerton's Robin   Swynnertonse Janfrederik

Swynnertonia swynnertoni   (Shelley), 1906: *Chirinda, S. Rhodesia.*

PLATE 51 (OPP. P. 401).
Length about 14 cm (wing 67—68,9—72, tail 46—52,5; tarsus 24—26,5; culmen
13—14. 6 specimens). Iris dark brown; bill black; legs pale pink-grey.

Identification: As illustrated, female slightly more olive above. Young has
head brown with terminal pale rufous spots to the feathers, rest of upper-parts
greyer and spotted; chest and belly white.

415

PLATE 52

603. *Acrocephalus arundinaceus.* European Great Reed Warbler.
Europese Groot Rietsanger.
604. *(a). Calamocichla gracilirostris gracilirostris.* Cape Reed Warbler.
Kaapse Rietsanger.
604 *(c). Calamocichla gracilirostris leptorhyncha.* Cape Reed Warbler.
Kaapse Rietsanger.
604Y. *Calamocichla rufescens.* Rufous Reed Warbler. Rooibruin Rietsanger.

606. *Acrocephalus baeticatus baeticatus.* African Marsh Warbler.
Klein Rietsanger.
607. *Acrocephalus palustris.* European Marsh Warbler.
Europese Rietsanger.
608. *Acrocephalus schoenobaenus.* European Sedge Warbler.
Europese Vleisanger.
609. *Bradypterus baboecalus baboecalus.* African Sedge Warbler.
Kaapse Vleisanger.
610. *Bradypterus barratti barratti.* Scrub Warbler. Ruigtesanger.
611. *Bradypterus sylvaticus.* Knysna Scrub Warbler. Knysna-ruigtesanger.
612. *Bradypterus victorini.* Victorin's Scrub Warbler.
Rooibors-ruigtesanger.
613. *Euryptila subcinnamomea.* Cinnamon-breasted Warbler.
Kaneelbors-sanger.
614. *Camaroptera fasciolata fasciolata.* Barred Warbler. Gebande Sanger.
615. *Camaroptera stierlingi.* Stierling's Barred Warbler.
Stierlingse Gebande Sanger.
616. *Schoenicola brevirostris brevirostris.* Fan-tailed Warbler.
Breëstert-sanger.
617. *Melocichla mentalis orientalis.* Moustache Warbler.
Breëstert-grasvoël.
618. *Sphenoeacus afer afer.* Grassbird. Grasvoël.

603

604

A

C

604 Y

KN

606

607

608

609

612

613

614

615

611

610

618

617

616

NIGHTON
'39

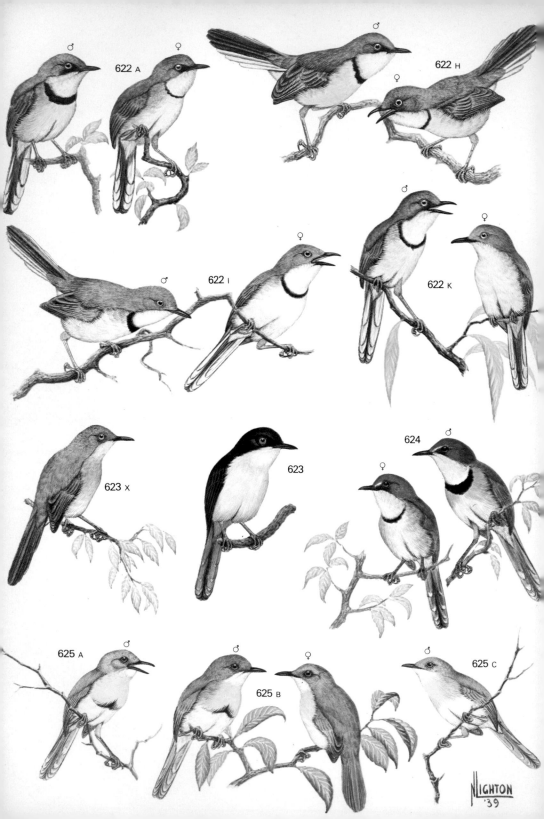

622 A ♂ ♀

622 H ♂ ♀

622 I ♂ ♀

622 K ♂ ♀

623 X

623

624 ♀ ♂

625 A ♂

625 B ♂ ♀

625 C ♂

NIGHTON
'39

PLATE 53

622 *(a). Apalis thoracica thoracica.* Bar-throated Apalis.
Bandkeel-kleinjantjie. ♂ and ♀.

622 *(h). Apalis thoracica spelonkensis.* Bar-throated Apalis.
Bandkeel-kleinjantjie. ♂ and ♀.

622 *(i). Apalis thoracica arnoldi.* Bar-throated Apalis.
Bandkeel-kleinjantjie. ♂ and ♀.

622 *(k). Apalis thoracica rhodesiae.* Bar-throated Apalis.
Bandkeel-kleinjantjie. ♂ and ♀.

623. *Apalis melanocephala.* Black-headed Apalis. Swartkop-kleinjantjie.

623X. *Apalis chirindensis.* Chirinda Apalis. Chirinda-kleinjantjie.

624. *Apalis ruddi.* Rudd's Apalis. Ruddse Kleinjantjie. ♂ and ♀.

625 *(a). Apalis flavida flavida.* Yellow-breasted Apalis.
Geelbors-kleinjantjie. ♂.

625 *(b). Apalis flavida neglecta.* Yellow-breasted Apalis.
Geelbors-kleinjantjie. ♂ and ♀.

625 *(c). Apalis flavida florisuga.* Yellow-breasted Apalis.
Geelbors-kleinjantjie. ♂.

590

Distribution: Confined to the higher forested areas of eastern Rhodesia and neighbouring Mozambique. From Mount Selinda to Umtali district and Gorongoza Mountain.

Habits: A not uncommon resident. Alert, inquisitive and tame, usually to be found on or near the forest floor where it hops about the leaves and fallen logs with quick movements and frequent flicks of the wings and tail. It becomes shy during the breeding season. In flying about in thick underbush it has rather noisy wing-beats.

Voice: A quiet "si-si". Also a medium pitched shivering trill.

Breeding: Placed one or two metres from the ground in a thick tree, on a stump or bush, the nest is composed of moss, leaves, roots and a few twigs and grass blades. The cup is neatly lined with fine roots and fibres. Eggs 2, rarely 3, pale blue-green with numerous red-brown freckles usually denser at the thick end, but may be marked only at the large end; (20—23 × 14—15).

591 Gunning's Robin   Gunningse Janfrederik

Sheppardia gunningi   Haagner, 1909: *Mzimbiti, near Beira.*

PLATE 51 (OPP. P. 401).
Length 13 cm (wing 69,5, 71; tail 51, 54; tarsus 20, 23; culmen 12,5, 13. 2 ♂ specimens). Bill dark brown, light at lower base. Legs pale pink.

Identification: As illustrated, but may be paler below and the eye-stripe is not always so distinct. Female, smaller and paler below. Young of northern race has head and mantle spotted tawny and black and chest-feathers have dark edges.

Distribution: Coastal areas from Beira to Kenya.

Habits: A local species, about which little has been recorded. Forest birds which spend much of their time seeking food on the ground, and in creepers in the mid-stratum of the forest. Not shy.

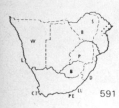

591

LOCAL RACE:
S.g. gunningi Haagner, 1909: *Mzimbiti, near Beira.* More rufous below and less olive green above than the northern race.

591X White-breasted Alethe

Alethe fuelleborni   Reichenow, 1900: *Between Poroto Mts. and Tandala, s-w Tanganyika.*

PLATE 51 (OPP. P. 401).
Length about 22 cm (wing 102—112; tail 79; tarsus 32; culmen 23. 1 specimen). Iris brown; bill black; legs pinkish-flesh.

Identification: About the size of a Thrush, white below with distinct greyish-olivaceous line below eye down sides of neck to merge onto the flanks. Upper parts olivaceous-brown. Tail and rump russet. Wing coverts white.

Distribution: Tanzania to Malawi and Mozambique. Occurs within our region near Dondo, Beira.

Habits: Little recorded, a skulking species of tangled undergrowth and evergreen forests.

Food: Beetles.

LOCAL RACE:
A.f. xuthura Clancey and Lawson, 1968: *Dondo near Beira.* South of the Zambesi, Mozambique. White below, less olivaceous on flanks and tail less chestnut. Two races formerly recognized, this race named from only one specimen.

592 Thrush Nightingale — Lyster-nagtegaal

Luscinia luscinia (Linnaeus), 1758: *Europe = Sweden.*

PLATE 51 (OPP. P. 401).
Length 16—18 cm (wing ♂ 84—92, one 95, ♀ 83—90; tail 63—71; tarsus 25—28;
culmen 16—17. 12 specimens ex *Handbk. Brit. Birds*). Iris brown; bill dark brown; pale
horn at base of lower mandible; legs fleshy brown.

Identification: Distinguishable from similar warblers by *russet upper tail-coverts and tail*. Distinguished from the European nightingale by mottling on lower throat and chest.

Distribution: Scandinavia to western Siberia, wintering to the south in Arabia and Central Africa. Recordings widespread although uncommon in Rhodesia. Sight records extend distribution to Pretoria, Transvaal and Durban, Natal.

Habits: Uncommon but appear to be attracted to thickets of *Lantana camara*—a somewhat straggling bush about a metre high with heads of small white, yellow or red flowers. In areas where this shrub has run wild it is recorded as very common. Unlike the famous European Nightingale, which is silent in Africa, this species is said to sing in its winter quarters.

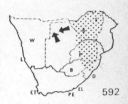

593 Morning Warbler — Môrelyster

Cichladusa arquata Peters, 1863: *Sena, on the Zambesi.*

PLATE 51 (OPP. P. 401).
Length about 20 cm (wing 86—88,6—91; tail 85—92; tarsus 25—27; culmen 16—17. 5
specimens). Iris brown to straw coloured; bill black; legs slate-brown.

Identification: The pattern on throat and the rufous of wings, longish tail and rump make identification easy. Sexes alike. Young has indication of orange chin and throat patch but is otherwise mottled below.

Distribution: From East Africa to the Zambesi; recorded in the Zambesi drainage area below 750 metres as far west as Victoria Falls and from the lower Sabi River.

Habits: A common species, resident and closely associated with palms; frequently resorts to areas of human habitation. Usually met with in small parties which creep about palms, almost mouse-like. Descend to the ground to forage where they behave like thrushes, *hopping* about with tail erect. Clap wings in flight making "prrup, prrup" sound.

Food: Insectivorous.

Voice: A staccato but melodious song interrupted by chat-like cries of "wheet-chuk" or "cur-lee-chuk-chuk". Sings mostly at dawn and dusk.

Breeding: Nests are normally situated in a palm at the junction of a frond with the trunk; also often adhering to walls under balconies of houses. The nest is a semi-circular shell of mud and grass roots, containing a cup of woven fibres stripped from dead mid-ribs of palm leaves somewhat like a swallow nest. October, November and February, March. Eggs 2, sometimes 3, bluish white sparingly spotted all over with red-brown.

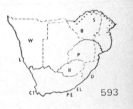

593X   Red-tailed Morning Warbler   Rooistert Môrelyster

Cichladusa ruficauda   (Hartlaub), 1857: *Gabon.*

PLATE 51 (OPP. P. 401).
Length about 17 cm (wing 85—95). Iris red-brown; bill black; legs purplish-slate.

Identification: Similar to No. 593 but smaller and lacks black "bib" edge line around buff on chin and throat. Crown and back more rufous, nape greyer.
Distribution: Gabon to Angola. Recently recorded at Swartbooi's Drift on the Cunene River.
Habits: Habitat associated with Borassus or oil palms. Usually occur in pairs.
Voice: Loud and melodious whistled phrases repeated by both birds of a pair, often almost in unison. Also mimics.
Food: Entirely insectivorous.
Breeding: A cup nest built in a palm crown, on a baobab or even a ledge of a building. 2 eggs, pale greenish-white with dull rufous speckles at large end, October to April.

Family SYLVIIDAE

The distinction between Warblers and Thrushes is not well defined, and some genera might be allocated to either, or even to separate families. They are smaller birds than the Thrushes and not terrestrial, but live in trees, bushes, marshy vegetation and grasslands, constructing either open cup-shaped or closed nests, which are usually suspended from branches, reeds or grass, according to their habitat. There is a great number of genera, most of the birds having distinctive calls and some warbling songs. All of them live on insects so that in the text the item on food is usually left out. Only a few of the arboreal species are known to eat fruit.

594   Whitethroat   Witkeel-sanger

Sylvia communis   Latham, 1787: *England.*

PLATE 56 (OPP. P. 464).
Length about 15 cm (wing 70,5—72,3—74; tail 57—64; tarsus 20—22; culmen 11—11,5. 7 specimens). Iris brown; bill brown, paler at base of lower mandible; legs brownish flesh.

Identification: Chin and throat white and distinct against light buffish chest; there is no white eye-stripe as illustrated, the greyish crown extending below the level of the eye. Eye-ring white. Note also reddish brown edgings to secondaries and wing-coverts and white outer tail-feathers. Has the habit of raising the crown-feathers slightly, which gives a characteristic peaked appearance to the head.
Distribution: Europe and North Africa moving south to Central Africa. Recorded as far south as Okahandja in South West Africa, Vryburg in the northern Cape and just south of Pretoria in the Transvaal. A sight record from Mooi River, Natal needs confirmation.
Habits: A non-breeding migrant recorded from November to April. It is not common, though generally to be discovered during mid-summer in thorny brakes in more or less open veld. Here it is usually found as a quick-moving

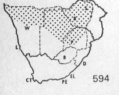

594

bird in the bushes, active in catching insects in flight or searching for them in the branches and leaves. Recorded as singing in Kenya in October.

Voice: Full song recorded in February in Transvaal.

LOCAL RACES:
(a) S.c. communis Latham, 1787: *England*. Probably general but details not known, see *(b)*.
(b) S.c. icterops Ménétriés, 1832: *Talysch, Caspian Sea*. This race, which is greyer above with lighter edges to flight-feathers, is considered more common than *(a)* in Rhodesia. Status elsewhere undetermined.

595   Garden Warbler   Tuinsanger

Sylvia borin   (Boddaert), 1783: *France*.

PLATE 56 (OPP. P. 464).
Length about 15 cm (wing 80—81,9—84; tail 54—60; tarsus 18,5—21; culmen 11—12,5. 7 specimens). Iris brown; bill horn-brown, lighter at base of lower mandible; legs pale brown. Weight (50) 15,1—29,2 g.

Identification: Illustration should be somewhat browner, near No. 594 in general colour, but lacking white throat. Edges to secondaries and coverts same colour as back. Outer tail-feathers not white. A nondescript, slightly plump warbler.
Distribution: Europe and western Asia coming south to Central Africa as far as Okahandja in South West Africa, southern Transvaal and on the east recorded as far south as Uitenhage, although rare at Matatiele.
Habits: A non-breeding migrant recorded from October to April. Occurs in *Acacia* trees and *Brachystegia* woodland, especially along watercourses and rivers; also shows a distinct preference for Lantana bushes. It is a tree warbler, usually seen actively searching for insects, though occasionally eating soft fruit like berries and figs. But for the bird calling it would probably be overlooked, as it is skulking in habits.
Voice: A soft babbling sub-song continuously uttered by male.

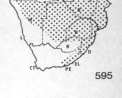

595

LOCAL RACES:
(a) S.b. borin (Boddaert), 1783: *France*. As above.
(b) S.b. woodwardi (Sharpe), 1877: *Berea Hills, Durban, Natal*. From eastern Europe and Asia migrating to winter in eastern Africa. Paler and greyer above than *(a)* and slightly larger. First described from a specimen collected in its winter quarters.

596   Icterine Warbler   Spotvoël

Hippolais icterina   (Vieillot), 1817: *France*.

PLATE 56 (OPP. P. 464).
Length 14—15 cm (wing 69,5—75,7—81; tail 51—56; tarsus 19—22; culmen 13—14,5. 7 specimens). Iris brown; bill brown, lower mandible yellow; legs lead-grey. Weight 14,5 g.

Identification: Yellow under-parts are quite distinct, upper-parts are browner than illustrated. Slightly larger than No. 599, with which it can easily be confused—see that species. The bill in this species is wider and the interior of the mouth is orange.
Distribution: Europe and western Asia southwards to Africa. Recorded as far south as Okahandja in South West Africa, Vryburg and Kuruman in northern Cape, southern Transvaal, Beira and Natal.

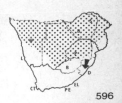

596

421

Habits: A non-breeding migrant recorded from November to February. Like the last two species it is partial to *Acacia* trees. It searches for insects creeping along and hopping from branch to branch with a quick action, singing much of the time as it works its way about.

Voice: A remarkable, long-sustained and varied jumble of melodies and discordant notes, each repeated several times and interspersed with jarring notes.

597   Olive-tree Warbler   Olyfboomsanger

Hippolais olivetorum   (Strickland), 1837: *Zante.*

PLATE 56 (OPP. P. 464).
Length 16—18 cm (wing, one of 80, 85—87,9—90; tail 65—70; tarsus 22—23; culmen 15,5—17,5. 10 specimens). Iris brown; bill horny brown, much paler on lower mandible; legs yellowish horn.

Identification: Tips of outer tail-feathers white. The bill is longer than in other similar species. White lores and eye-ring. Generally more olive-grey than Nos. 594 and 595.

Distribution: Balkan Peninsula and Asia Minor south to Africa. Recorded from within our limits at Bulawayo, Rhodesia, Vaal River and Blaauwberg in the Transvaal. Also Tshane in south west Botswana.

Habits: Apparently a very localised non-breeding migrant, so far recorded only in the months of February and March. Found to be plentiful in February at Blaauwberg, where they were heard warbling and singing at all times of the day amongst the densely foliaged trees, in which they were found feeding on insects and wild fruit. Found in *Acacia* woodlands and scrub.

598   River Warbler   Sprinkaan Rietsanger

Locustella fluviatilis   (Wolf), 1810: *Danube, near Vienna.*

PLATE 56 (OPP. P. 464).
Length about 15 cm (wing 72; tail 57; tarsus 21; culmen 12). Iris pale brown; bill dark brown, paler below; legs pale horn-brown.

Identification: As illustrated; note the light eye-stripe, the streaked chest and the *graduated tail.*

Distribution: Central and eastern Europe south to Africa. Recorded from the Zambesi and Caprivi; near Rustenburg, Pretoria district and Umtali; also Transkei.

Habits: A very rare non-breeding migrant recorded in December and January. It frequents the vegetation along streams and rivers but not necessarily the reed beds, rather the bushes and trees or the short grass in *Brachystegia* woodland. A skulking and secretive species, feeding near the ground.

599   Willow Warbler   Hofsanger

Phylloscopus trochilus   (Linnaeus), 1758: *England.*

PLATE 56 (OPP. P. 464).
Length 12 cm (wing 61—66,4—70; tail 44—54; tarsus 17—20; culmen 9,5—11,5. 11
specimens). Iris hazel; bill brown, lighter at base of lower mandible; legs brown. Weight
6,6—8,2 g.

Identification: Call-note easily distinguishes this bird. A smaller tree warbler
than the previous species. Yellowish below but rarely as far as belly.
Distribution: Europe and Asia to Africa extending to the Cape and to
Okahandja in South West Africa. Also the Kaokoveld.
Habits: A common non-breeding migrant recorded from September to April,
rarely in May. Usually heard before being seen, in trees, in gardens and
plantations, as it actively searches the foliage for insects. Found along rivers,
acacia veld and in *Brachystegia* woodland. Appears to spend most of its time
amongst the middle or upper foliage of trees.

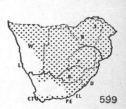

Voice: Usual note a single plaintive "kweet", "foowee" or "tsweep". Song
a simple but pleasing liquid warble written "Se-se-se-se-see-see-su-
su-suit-suit-sueet-sueeeteu". In February attains full song but may be heard in
partial song throughout its sojourn here.

LOCAL RACES:
(a) P.t. trochilus (Linnaeus), 1758: *England.* Throughout Southern Africa. Size as
above.
(b) P.t. acredula (Linnaeus), 1758: *Uppsala, Sweden.* Recorded from Matabeleland,
Midlands and north-west Mashonaland in Rhodesia; less common than *(a).* A paler
bird.
(c) P.t. yakutensis Ticehurst, 1935: *Eastern Siberia.* From Natal, Namib, Rhodesia and
Botswana. A grey-brown bird; no yellow except under wings. Slightly larger than *(a).*

600   Yellow-bellied Eremomela   Geelpens-bossanger

Eremomela icteropygialis   (Lafresnaye), 1839: *Orange River.*

PLATE 56 (OPP. P. 464).
Length 9—10 cm (wing 54—55,8—59; tail 34—42; tarsus 16,5—18; culmen 9—11. 13
specimens). Iris light red; bill dark brown; legs dark brown.

Identification: May be confused with No. 602 and with the White-eyes, Nos.
775-777, especially since this species has a *narrow* white ring around the eye.
This white ring distinguishes it from Nos. 601 and 602; the grey throat and
chest and rufous tinge to lesser wing-coverts separate it from these species and
the White-eyes. Female slightly smaller.
Distribution: The Karoo northwards to Eritrea. Recorded from Brandvlei in
western Cape, Oudtshoorn and Grahamstown northwards.
Habits: Not an uncommon species but little recorded. Found in pairs or family
parties searching for insects in bushes and trees especially in scrub about pans
or watercourses in drier areas. Frequents the upper and outer branches of
vegetation. A lightly built, active little bird which also works its way about the

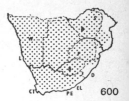

lower parts of bushes and low scrub.
Voice: A distinctive little jingle of four syllables "tchitchu". Song similar to,
but not as loud as the Grassbird, No. 618.

Breeding: The nest is usually situated in a bush in open veld, from 60 to 270 cm above the ground. It is a neat, delicate cup-shaped structure made of dry grass and fibres bound with cottony fibre and spider webs; the bottom of the cup is thicker with wool- and vegetable-down. August to January and March. Eggs 2—3, glossy white, with scattered minute and larger spots of greenish brown forming a zone at the larger end. Average (34) 15,6 × 11,4 (14,2—16,8 × 10—12,2).

LOCAL RACES:
(a) E.i. icteropygialis (Lafresnaye), 1839: *Orange River.* On the west, Little Namaqualand to Kaokoveld and throughout central and south-western Kalahari. Much lighter than others. Size as above.
(b) E.i. saturatior O. Grant, 1910: *Deelfontein, Cape.* Karoo Districts north to the Orange Free State. Chest fulvous grey, abdomen darker yellow—as illustrated.
(c) E.i. polioxantha Sharpe, 1883: *Swaziland.* Zululand northwards through eastern Transvaal to Matabeleland and Mashonaland; beyond to Malawi and Tanzania. Chest greyish white, abdomen sulphur-yellow and extending on to lower-breast. Tail slightly shorter, 31—35; tarsus 15—17.
(d) E.i. viriditincta White, 1961: *15 mls. W. of Victoria Falls.* Chobi-Caprivi area, southern Barotseland. Duller green and less yellow below.

601   Burnt-necked Eremomela   Bruinkeel-bossanger

Eremomela usticollis Sundevall, 1850: *"Caffraria superiore"* = *Leroma, Transvaal.*

PLATE 56 (OPP. P. 464).
Length about 12 cm (wing 52,5—54,3—59; tail 38—45; tarsus 18,5—21; culmen 10—11,5. 37 specimens). Iris yellow; bill brown, lighter below; legs flesh-coloured. Weight 8,0 g.

Identification: The chestnut throat-bar is variable and may even be absent. The under-parts are uniform and slightly yellower than illustrated. Generally light grey above—see No. 602.

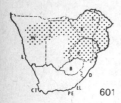

Distribution: From the acacia thornveld of Damaraland and Ngamiland, south-eastwards to western Transvaal and northern Zululand, northwards to western Zambia, central Malawi and neighbouring Mozambique.
Habits: Little recorded except that it is much the same in habits as the closely related Bush-Warblers and the White-eyes and is often found in association with them. Creeps about in search of insects in the topmost branches of acacia trees. Usually found in pairs or small family parties. Displays considerable activity in flight.
Voice: "Zip-zip-zip", a musical "di-di-di-di" or "dyup-dyup-dyup-dyup".
Breeding: A small thin walled cup slung between leafy branches 3—6 metres up Acacia trees. Nests of soft felt-like vegetable down. 52 mm wide, 36 mm cup 41 mm deep. Nest covered with chips of acacia leaves or praying mantis egg capsules bound by silky web. Eggs very pale green with a few scattered light brown spots. October to April in Rhodesia. Eggs 2—4, 15,9—16,2 × 11,5—11,6.

LOCAL RACES:
(a) E.u. usticollis Sundevall, 1850: *"Caffraria superiore"* = *Leroma, Transvaal.* As above.
(b) E.u. rensi Benson, 1943: *Fort Johnston.* Darker above. Extends south to Zambesi valley.

601

602 Greencap Eremomela Donkerwang-bossanger

Eremomela scotops Sundevall, 1850: *"Caffraria superiore"* = *Mohapoani, Bechuanaland.*

PLATE 56 (OPP. P. 464).
Length 12 cm (wing 54—57,3—61,5; tail 43—51; tarsus 16—19,5; culmen 11—12, one 9. 23 specimens). Iris pale yellow; bill black; legs pallid flesh.

Identification: Similar to the previous two species but easily distinguished by yellow underparts, blue-grey upper-parts and by the grey lores which contrast with the yellow below and greenish yellow crown.
Distribution: Uganda southwards to Natal on the east, Transvaal, north-east Botswana and Angola.
Habits: Apparently not uncommon except in the extreme south. Little has been recorded from our area. Usually found in small parties actively searching for insects in trees and calling while doing so; could easily be overlooked as a flock of White-eyes. It is inclined to fly out after flies, catching them in flight with a decisive snap. At times joins into bands of a dozen birds which go through a peculiar performance, becoming very excited and chasing each other about.

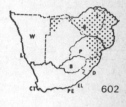

602

Voice: A loud chirring note. Breeding birds sing monotonously before sunrise.
Breeding: Nesting described by Newby-Varty. A small cup-shaped structure placed 6—7 metres up in bunches of leaves at the end of branches of a tree. Made of vegetable-down and binding cases of Matuti buds. July, September to November and January. Eggs 2—3, greenish blue lightly covered with lilac and reddish brown spots concentrated at the thick end. 15—17 × 12—12,5.

LOCAL RACES:
(a) E.s. scotops Sundevall, 1850: *"Caffraria superiore"* = *Mohapoani, Bechuanaland.* Rhodesia, southern Mozambique southwards. The yellow of the breast continues as a wash over the abdomen.
(b) E.s. pulchra (Bocage), 1878: *Caconda, Angola.* Southern Angola, southern Zaïre and Zambia. A specimen from Panda Matenga, 40 miles south of Victoria Falls is reputed to be of this race. Whitish abdomen and lower-breast sharply demarcated from yellow upper-breast.

603 European Great Reed Warbler
Europese Groot Rietsanger

Acrocephalus arundinaceus (Linnaeus), 1758: *N. Europe = Danzig, Germany.*

PLATE 52 (OPP. P. 416).
Length about 20 cm (wing ♂ 96—99—10; ♀ 89—90,2—96; tail 71—83; tarsus 27—29; culmen 17—20. 10 specimens, 4 ♂, 6 ♀). Iris brown; bill dark brown above, yellowish brown below; legs flesh-coloured. Weight 22—34 g.

Identification: Relatively large size and song distinguish this reed warbler. The bill is relatively heavy for this group. Plain back, light eye-stripe and graduated tail are features to note. The inside of mouth is bright orange-red. Sexes alike.
Distribution: Europe and western Asia, south to Africa. Extending to Okahandja, South West Africa; Philipstown, northern Cape; Orange Free State and Natal to Flagstaff, Pondoland.
Habits: A not uncommon non-breeding migrant from November to March. A solitary bird usually found in the vegetation along streams and rivers, espe-

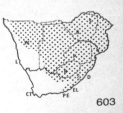

603

cially tall (3—3,5 m) grasses and high reeds. More prone to perch on trees or telegraph wires than other reed-warblers and may be found in hedgerows. The song usually attracts one's attention; otherwise is a slightly larger and more clumsy version of the next species.

Voice: A loud crackling song—"tuckle-tuckle-tuckle" or "karra-kara-karra-keek", "gurk-gurk-gurk", interspersed with shriller notes. A capable ventriloquist, so that the sound is always varying. Sings throughout its stay.

LOCAL RACES:
(a) *A.a. arudinaceus* (Linnaeus), 1758: *N. Europe = Danzig, Germany.* Widespread. As above. Twice as abundant as *(b)*
(b) *A.a. zarudnyi* Hartert, 1907: *Djarkent, Turkestan.* Recorded from Makarikari, Natal, Transvaal and Rhodesia. Paler above, less rufous, paler below.

604   Cape Reed Warbler   Kaapse Rietsanger

Calamocichla gracilirostris   (Hartlaub), 1864: *Natal.*

PLATE 52 (OPP. P. 416).
Length 17—18 cm (wing ♂ 71—73,6—78, ♀ 64—67,7—69; tail ♂ 64—76, ♀ 57—64; tarsus ♂ 25—30, ♀ 24,5—25; culmen 14—17. 16 specimens, 12 ♂, 4 ♀). Iris hazel; bill brown with base pinkish buff; legs darkish brown.

Identification: Perhaps slightly less rufous than illustrated. Note light eye-stripe and dark legs; this in conjunction with habitat and song distinguish this species. Most likely to be confused with the next two species or with No. 609. This bird is larger than the Marsh Warbler and much more rufous than the Sedge Warbler.

Distribution: Recorded generally throughout Africa south of the Sahara. In South West Africa only occurs in northern Damaraland.

Habits: A common resident in large reed beds on lagoons, rivers, streams and permanent marshes. *Usually to be seen in open reeds* growing on the border of open water, searching for insects as it glides up and down or from one to the other of the reeds. Most inquisitive and is attracted by anything unusual.

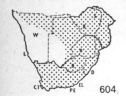

604

Food: Though insectivorous recorded as taking small frogs.

Voice: A loud and cheerful song, a short but brilliant burst of mellow notes, "krrrrip-krrrp-krrrp-krrip, krrp, krrp, krrip, krrip . . .''; unlike the next species because the song is short and complete—see No. 606.

Breeding: The nest differs from No. 606 in that it is a *cone-shaped* structure (see No. 606) and from No. 609 by the fact that it is *plaited* around reed stems for support in the classical reed-warbler style. Practically always placed over water, from 20—120 cm, in growing upright reeds or rushes, very often near or under a larger bird's nest or even near an observation hide. Constructed of reeds and grass, the cone is built about the deep cup and lined with finer material. September to December in the Cape and to March in Rhodesia. Eggs 2—3, white or white tinged with green or bluish grey thickly covered with minute spots in black to pale sepia-brown with some underlying ashy freckling. Average (20) 20,0 × 14,6 (18—23,3 × 13,9—15,3).

LOCAL RACES:
(a) *C.g. gracilirostris* (Hartlaub) 1864: *Natal.* Cape Province to Natal and Transvaal. The largest and most rufous form. Size as above. Illustrated.
(b) *C.g. cunensis* Hartert, 1903: *Cunene River, Angola.* From type locality northwards in Angola. Also Ngamiland. Said to be greyish brown above. Similar in size to *(a).*

(c) C.g. leptorhyncha (Reichenow), 1879: *Tschra, Mouth of Tana River, Kenya.* Northern Zululand, Rhodesia northwards. Illustrated. Considerably smaller than *(a)*. Wing ♂ 67, ♀ 56; tail 56—63; tarsus 23—26,5; culmen 15—15,5. 3 specimens, 2 ♂, 1 ♀.

604X   See page xxxii

604Y   Rufous Reed Warbler   Rooibruin Rietsanger

Calamocichla rufescens (Sharpe & Bouvier), 1876: *Landana, Portuguese Congo.*

PLATE 52 (OPP. P. 416).
Length about 18 cm (wing 82; bill 17). Iris light reddish brown; bill dusky brown above, yellower at base; legs bluish grey, yellow soles.

Identification: Similar to No. 604 but larger than the local race of that species. More olive above and less rufous below. No stripe from bill to eye.
Distribution: Lake Chad to Angola and Zambia. Recently recorded from the Okavango Swamps, Botswana.
Habits: A bird that is primarily found in papyrus reeds, keeping within the vegetation, hopping or climbing about on the tall stalks in search of insects. Secretive in habits like the Scrub Warblers, and seldom seen.
Voice: A loud gurgling "churr-churr, chirrup, chuckle."
Breeding: Not yet recorded within our limits. Deep cup-shaped nest placed in the middle of a papyrus head. Eggs 2—3, white finely speckled with brown and larger markings at the blunt end, 20,3—21,2 × 15,1—15,5.

LOCAL RACE:
C.r. ansorgei Hartert, 1906: *Malange, Angola.*

605   See 604 *(c)*

606   African Marsh Warbler   Klein Rietsanger

Acrocephalus baeticatus (Vieillot), 1817: *South Africa = Knysna, Cape Province.*

PLATE 52 (OPP. P. 416).
Length 12—13 cm (wing 55—58,2—63; tail 47,5—54, one 57; tarsus 20—22; culmen 12—13,5. 22 specimens). Iris pale brown; bill brown, paler below; legs yellow-ash-coloured. Weight (23) 9—10,5—12 g.

Identification: Similar to No. 604, slightly more buff below and smaller. The legs of this species are light and there is no distinct light eyebrow.
Distribution: Over the greater part of the Ethiopian region in suitable localities. Throughout our area but more restricted in the dry west.
Habits: A common species occurring as a summer breeding visitor over the greater part of our area from August to March or April; is resident in the tropics. Less often found in marshes *in open vegetation* near water in the Cape; also frequents the open wattle bush of the Cape Flats, *often some distance from a vlei*. It is a tame bird and is often *found about gardens*. Also occurs in reeds along rivers, usually in sparsely growing reeds and quite often in those that are not standing in water.
Voice: A pretty song, somewhat slow and conversational since the bird (prior to nesting) sings for remarkably long periods at a time. Too varied to record, but "churr" and "chirruc" notes frequently used; mainly heard during the first month after its arrival.

606

427

Breeding: The nest is more often recorded in low weeds and bushes than in reeds. It is a small deep cup, bound on to some support but not tapering in the same way as in No. 604, giving it a flatter appearance. It is built of dry grass, reeds or leaves and lined with finer material. September to November in the Cape, October to February in the Transvaal. Eggs 2, usually 3, sometimes 4, slightly rounder than the last, pale greenish or bluish white dotted and blotched with olive-brown and with underlying pale slate markings, somewhat concentrated at larger end. Average (34) 17,8 × 13,3 (16,9—18,7 × 12,8—14,3), one as long as 19,3. Incubation 12½—14 days. Nestling 14 days (Skead).

LOCAL RACES:
(a) A.b. baeticatus (Vieillot), 1817: *South Africa = Knysna, Cape Province.* Throughout our area but replaced by the next along the Zambesi. Size as above.
(b) A.b. suahelicus Grote, 1926: *Zanzibar.* Coastal, Natal northwards. Darker than *(a)* and deeper buff below wing 54—56.
(c) A.b. cinnamomeus Reichenow, 1908: *Lake Edward.* Rhodesia, Angola to Malawi. Darker above than *(a).* Wing 52—57.
(d) A.b. hallae White, 1960: *Brandberg, South West Africa.* South West Africa, Botswana. Paler and greyer than *(a)* and whiter below.

607   European Marsh Warbler   Europese Rietsanger

Acrocephalus palustris   (Bechstein), 1798: *Thuringia.*

PLATE 52 (OPP. P. 416).
Length about 14 cm (wing 66—67—71; tail 53—55; tarsus 20,5—22; culmen 13—13,5. 7 specimens). Iris olive-brown; bill dark brown, lighter below; legs brownish flesh-colour. Weight 11 g.

Identification: Practically indistinguishable from the last species except in the hand. It is less rufous above and there is a pale yellow-buff wash over the underparts; also darker on flanks. Separated from the African species by wing formula; note illustration of the longer second primary (first primary very short and not shown).
Distribution: Europe and western Asia southwards to Central Africa. It is found only in the warmer districts extending throughout Rhodesia, south to the Transvaal thornveld and Natal as far as Matatiele, north-eastern Cape. Also Windhoek in March.
Habits: A non-breeding migrant, widespread from December to March. Said to be more active in its movements than the African species. Some observers consider there is a difference in call-note and warble between this species and the last; utters a quiet but distinct "tuc" as it works through the undergrowth. Also a slightly nasal "tcherr". Sometimes warbles to itself.

607

608   European Sedge Warbler   Europese Vleisanger

Acrocephalus schoenobaenus   (Linnaeus), 1758: *Europe = S. Sweden.*

PLATE 52 (OPP. P. 416).
Length 13—14 cm (wing 64—65,2—69; tail 47—53; tarsus 20—21,5; culmen 12. 6 specimens). Iris brown; bill brown, paler below; legs pale brown. Weight 13 g.

Identification: Distinguished from other Sedge, Reed and Marsh Warblers by the markings on the head and by mottled back and mantle. See illustration and under Habits below.

Distribution: Europe and western Asia southwards to our areas. Recorded from Walvis Bay, Otjimbinque in Damaraland, widespread through Rhodesia, Transvaal, Orange Free State, Natal and Eastern Cape.

Habits: A non-breeding migrant from November to April. Recorded once in September. It is not uncommon in the coarse grasses and water vegetation, though not necessarily the reed beds, growing on open streams and rivers. It has a characteristic clicking note, not easily described. Said to sing often in Kenya but to be somewhat silent in Zaïre.

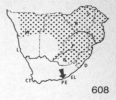

608

609 African Sedge Warbler   Kaapse Vleisanger

Bradypterus baboecalus (Vieillot), 1817: *South Africa = Knysna,*
Cape Province.

PLATE 52 (OPP. P. 416).
Length 14—19 cm (wing 58—60,6—63; tail 67—75; tarsus 20—23; culmen 13—16. 7 specimens). Iris dull brown; bill black, lighter at base; legs brownish.

Identification: A darker, more skulking bird than any of the previous species. The tail is much broader, longer and more rounded than in No. 604 and others; the centre tail-feather being twice as wide as in that species. The throat is usually faintly streaked. Habits and call are distinctive.

Distribution: From the western Cape Province, eastwards and northwards to Transvaal, Ngamiland and Angola, north to Central Africa.

Habits: A retiring but fairly common resident in the permanent marshes. It is seldom seen on account of its skulking habits. Always found over water and *in matted rushes or weeds through which it can creep about*. Rather inquisitive, and if one conceals oneself in the reeds the bird will come very close but remain well hidden.

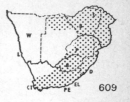

609

Voice: A loud call—like a stick held to the spokes of a revolving wheel, "tirr-tuk-tuk-tuk" or "crack-crack-crack-crack-crack", ending with a bubbling trill and a "pirrring" made with the wings.

Breeding: A loose, almost untidy nest when compared with the Reed Warbler's, this nest is a plaited cone usually situated in a mass of rushes and supported by them rather than by being bound to any reed. A cone-shaped structure, but the cup appears small because of its wide rim; the nest is composed of dry rush or weed leaves curled around and lined with rootlets. September to November in the south December to March in Rhodesia. Eggs 2, very pale cream closely and finely spotted with yellowish brown and pale ashy colour, more boldly and densely at the big end. Average (5) 19,7 × 14 (19—20,6 × 13,4—14,4).

LOCAL RACES:
(a) B.b. baboecalus (Vieillot), 1817: *South Africa = Knysna, Cape Province.* Western Cape to Natal and Transvaal and Mashonaland. Size as above; the Transvaal specimens have shortest bills.
(b) B.b. tongensis Roberts, 1931: *Kosi Bay, Zululand.* North-east Zululand, northwards to northern Mozambique. More rufous tinged below on flanks and under tail-coverts; shorter culmen 13—14,5.
(c) B.b. msiri Neave, 1909: *Msiri village, Bunkeya Katanga, Belgian Congo.* From Lake Ngami, Botswana northwards to Zaïre. Darker and with a shorter bill than *(a)*.

429

610 Scrub Warbler   Ruigtesanger

Bradypterus barratti Sharpe, 1876: *Macamac, Transvaal.*

PLATE 52 (OPP. P. 416).
Length 15—16 cm (wing 61—63,3—64; tail 68—73; tarsus 21—22; culmen 13—14. 4 specimens). Iris brown; bill black; legs dusky brown.

Identification: Rather similar to the previous species except that its habitat is entirely different. This bird is more spotted on the throat. The tail does not appear as slender as illustrated—see No. 609.

Distribution: Confined to the scrub in coastal kloofs from eastern Cape to Zululand, inland to higher ground from the Drakensberg northwards to the eastern highlands of Rhodesia.

Habits: A not uncommon but very local species. Occurs in thick moist undergrowth in well-forested areas. A skulking species; usually all that is to be seen is a shadowy figure moving about the ground or in the branches low down. Keeps to the depths of the tangles and seldom shows itself. Presence easily detected by its song.

610

Voice: Recorded as a trilling call—a quavering whistling note, loud and arresting.

Breeding: Placed in the heart of a matted bush, the nest is a bowl-shaped structure of dry grass and leaves. November. Eggs 2, pinky white, thinly speckled yellowish brown over a slate-blue; 20 × 15,3.

LOCAL RACES:
(a) B.b. barratti Sharpe, 1876: *Macamac, Transvaal.* Eastern and northern Transvaal. Darker than *(b)* or *(c)* and more heavily spotted on throat and chest. Size as above.
(b) B.b. priesti Benson, 1946: *Vumba, Rhodesia.* Eastern districts of Rhodesia and adjacent Mozambique above 1 500 metres. Spotting on throat only; more white on belly. Wing ♂ 63—64—65, ♀ 60; tail ♂ 67—71; culmen 13—13,5. (4 specimens, 3 ♂, 1 ♀).
(c) B.b. cathkinensis Vincent, 1948: *Cathkin Peak, Natal.* South-eastern Transvaal and Natal border areas. Paler and less red than *(a)*, lighter below and spotting on throat only. Larger, wing ♂ 66—66,8—68, ♀ 63; tail 69—76; culmen 13—14,5. (5 specimens, 4 ♂, 1 ♀).
(d) B.b. godfreyi (Roberts), 1922: *Pirie, Eastern Cape.* From Albany district north to Zululand and extreme south of Mozambique and Swaziland. Darker than *(a)* and *(c)*, flanks darker and throat spotting as *(c)*. Wing ♂ 63, ♀ 62; tail ♂ 68; culmen 12.

611 Knysna Scrub Warbler   Knysna-ruigtesanger

Bradypterus sylvaticus Sundevall, 1858: *Knysna.*

PLATE 52 (OPP. P. 416).
Length 14—15 cm (wing ♂ 60, ♀ 57; tail ♂ 61, ♀ 57; tarsus 19,5, 19; culmen 13. One ♂, one ♀). Iris dark hazel; bill pinkish brown, lighter below; legs olive-brown.

Identification: Very similar to the last; uniform below and with short rounded tail. Chin of young birds speckled with white. Slight variation in tones have been used to distinguish races but there is variation.

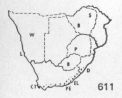

Distribution: Known only from Table Mountain, Knysna to near Port Elizabeth, and from Pondoland to southern Natal.

Habits: A rare, very locally distributed species. Inhabits dense gloomy tangles of undergrowth and forest debris; on Table Mountain occurs on the damper south-eastern slopes in bramble thickets. May only be detected by its song which, although being loud and clear, is uttered from dense growth and thus may not be heard from far off.

611

Voice: Heard from August to January in the Cape. A beautiful song; high-pitched notes are uttered at first at short intervals, then lower notes which are speeded up, increasing to a blurred trill, "tsip-tsip-tsip-trip-tsiptsiptsiptsiptrrrrrill", concluding with a bubbling trill.
Breeding: The nest is situated off the ground in a thicket just below the leafy outer canopy. A large bowl shaped nest built of dried vegetable matter lined with finer fibres. September. Eggs 3, pinky-white finely marked with red spots. 19,8 × 15,0, 20,0 × 14,9, 19,6 × 14,8. Incubation 19 days. Nestling 13—14 days.

612 Victorin's Scrub Warbler   Rooibors-ruigtesanger

Bradypterus victorini Sundevall, 1858: *Knysna*.

PLATE 52 (OPP. P. 416).
Length 15—17 cm (wing 53—55; tail 74—77; tarsus 21—22; culmen 13—13,5. 4 specimens). Iris red-brown; bill brown, paler below; legs ash-brown.

Identification: Well illustrated, showing the more cinnamon coloration than other Scrub Warblers. Habitat differs markedly from previous species. Song distinctive but could be confused with that of the Grassbird, No. 618; this species has a more varied rhythm whilst the Grassbird is uniform, merely trailing down at the end.
Distribution: Confined to the mountains of southern Cape, from the northern Cedarberg and French Hoek east to Uitenhage.
Habits: A common species in restricted localities. It occurs on mountain slopes which are often wet and misty, where scrub and cover is fairly thick, especially in rocky kloofs and along mountain streams. Not as skulking as other Scrub Warblers but nevertheless not seen as much as it is heard. When suddenly disturbed the bird scuttles through the grass at great speed and is then easily mistaken for a mouse. They are tame and rather inquisitive. It does not sit in a prominent position to sing as does the Grassbird but otherwise similar in habits.

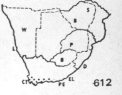

Voice: A varying number of phrases from low- to high-pitched notes, "twiddy twee twit, twiddy twee . . . ." gaining in rapidity and ending in four or five low sucking notes. Alarm a loud "purrr".
Breeding: The nest is well hidden about 30 cm above the ground among grassy vegetation. The nest has a roughly woven grass base, then a lining of bark and dead leaves and finally a deep cup of fine grass. September and October. Eggs 2, pinkish white spotted with red, mainly at the large end. 21 × 15 and 20,8 × 15,3.

613 Cinnamon-breasted Warbler   Kaneelbors-sanger

Euryptila subcinnamomea (A. Smith), 1847: *Kamiesberg, Little Namaqualand.*

PLATE 52 (OPP. P. 416).
Length 13—14 cm (wing 53—54; tail 57,5—58; tarsus 19—20,5; culmen 12,5—13. 3 specimens). Iris light greenish; bill and legs black.

Identification: The cinnamon forehead, breast and tail-coverts distinguish the species. Sexes alike. The black tail is a useful field key in view of the fact that the tail is usually held cocked up.

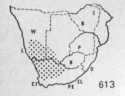

613

Distribution: Peculiar to the Karoo scrub round kopjes from Greys Pass east to Verwoerd Dam, north in the west to Naukluft, South West Africa.

Habits: A somewhat rare species to be found in rocky areas strewn with big boulders. Remarkably swift in flight and action; flies low over the bush and lands on a rock, tail up, then hops on, either to another rock or into cover, where it remains well concealed. Sometimes appears to bound from boulder to boulder. Sir Andrew Smith remarks "for some time before it was shot it was beheld flitting from bush to bush, occasionally perching on their summits, at other times hopping rapidly to and fro among their branches, as if engaged in quest of insects, which were found to constitute its food."

Food: Grasshoppers and other small insects.

Voice: Occasionally utters a whistled "düii, düii", rather resembling a Diederik Cuckoo.

Breeding: Nests in the grass or restio at the foot of a big rock on a kopje, surrounded by thick bush. The nest is composed chiefly of spider's webs; it is thick walled, oval with entrance near the top. Also made of grass stems padded with vegetable and animal wool. Eggs 2 or 3, sometimes 4, palish white with numerous dots and small spots of lilac, with larger dots most visible near the big end. July and August. 19 × 13,8.

614 Barred Warbler   Gebande Sanger

Camaroptera fasciolata (A. Smith), 1847: *N.E. of Latakoo, Northern Cape.*

PLATE 52 (OPP. P. 416).
Length 13—15 cm (wing ♂ 60—62,1—64, ♀ 54—56,9—59; tail ♂ 52—57,5, ♀ 47—52; tarsus 20—23; culmen 12—14,5. 20 specimens, 11 ♂, 9 ♀). Iris grey; bill brown-black; legs flesh-coloured. Weight 13,1 g.

Identification: As illustrated—see No. 615 for difference. The non-breeding plumage has duller brown underparts and is distinct from the breeding plumage. Sexes alike, but breeding males have spotted chin, uniform brown throat and upper chest.

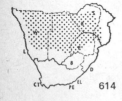

614

Distribution: Widespread in the dry Kalahari and central Transvaal, also in South West Africa from Mariental and the Fish River. North to Angola and Tanzania. Absent below 900 metres in Rhodesia.

Habits: A common but local species, it keeps to the thorny trees and bushes. See under 615. A restless species, wren-like in habits creeping about in undergrowth, usually with its tail up. Characteristically when hunting invariably starts at the bottom of a bush, gradually works its way up to the top and then flies to the next bush to start from the bottom as before. When in small parties they usually keep in touch with a high-pitched cry. The male has a pretty aerial flight display during breeding period.

Breeding: The nest is well concealed, built in large-leaved trees growing along streams or on small kopjes near streams or vleis. Situated at one to three metres from the ground, it is roughly oval with the side-top entrance sewn within growing leaves by loops of vegetable-down poked through numerous tiny holes pecked in the leaves. The entrance is almost hidden by the leaves.

The nest is made of plant-down with soft grass and rootlets. October to January. Eggs 2—3, either pale blue or cream, evenly speckled with lilac and pale violet-grey. Average (23) 17,1 × 11,9 (16—19 × 11,9—12,8).

LOCAL RACE:
C.f. fasciolata (A. Smith), 1847: *N.E. of Latakoo.* Western Transvaal, Botswana, Damaraland and southern border of Rhodesia. Size above.

615 Stierling's Barred Warbler
Stierlingse Gebande Sanger

Camaroptera stierlingi Reichenow, 1901: *Songea, south-western Tanganyika.*

PLATE 52 (OPP. P. 416).
Length 14 cm (wing ♂ 57,5—60—64, ♀ 54,5; tail 40—49; tarsus 19,5—22; culmen 12—13). Iris orange; bill black; legs flesh-coloured.

Identification: Much whiter below than the previous species. Eye colour differs. This bird has no non-breeding plumage.

Distribution: Occurs in Sabi-Limpopo valley in Rhodesia, extending into eastern Transvaal. Occurs further up the Limpopo and extends into eastern Botswana. Also Zululand.

Habits: Where this species overlaps distribution with 614 this species occurs mainly in *Mopane, Brachystegia* and *Baikiaea* type of woodland whereas 614 prefers *Acacia* and *Commiphora* trees.

Voice: "Twi-diet" or "biririt-biririt" uttered at one- to two-second intervals for long periods. A "Tsik" call. See also under Habits—cry is like "maa".

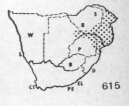

615

LOCAL RACES:
(a) C.s. irwini Smithers and Patterson, 1956: *Umvuma, Rhodesia.* Malawi, Zambia to Rhodesia. As above.
(b) C.s. pintoi Irwin, 1960: *Umbeluzi near Lourenco Marques.* From lower eastern areas of Mozambique extending into eastern Transvaal lowveld. Barring better defined than *(a)* and white below.

616 Fan-tailed Warbler
Breëstert-sanger

Schoenicola brevirostris (Sundevall), 1850: *"Caffraria inferiore"* = *Umlazi River, Natal.*

Native Name: Um-vokontshi (X).

PLATE 52 (OPP. P. 416).
Length 15—16 cm (wing ♂ 60—61,6—63, ♀ 56—62; tail 69—81; tarsus 16,5—19,5; culmen 10—12,5. 10 specimens, 7 ♂, 3 ♀). Iris brown; bill black above, ash-coloured below; legs flesh-coloured.

Identification: The large fan-shaped tail of broad black feathers tipped with white distinguishes this species. Sexes alike. See Habits. Flanks slightly darker than illustrated.

Distribution: Recorded from Pondoland to Natal, thence northwards to Zoutpansberg, eastern areas of Rhodesia over 900 metres as far west as Salisbury; beyond our limits to Angola, Central Africa, Uganda and Kenya.

Habits: A not uncommon species in moist areas of reeds and flooded grassy marshes. A summer breeding visitor to higher plateau country, resident in low

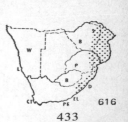

616

country normally. A bird that keeps very much to the tangled vegetation of its haunts, but often ventures to perch on the top of reeds or grasses, especially early in the morning. It has rather a jerky flight, bobbing as though weighed down by its voluminous tail. When alarmed creeps about until nearly stepped on; flies only a few metres before dropping into the tangle. Performs a display flight in circles up to 15 metres high, singing and making a noise with its wings.

Food: Insects, mostly beetles; also grasshoppers.

Voice: Male has a weak metallic "cheep, cheep, cheep, cheep". Female a harsh chick. Alarm note a persistent rasping note.

Breeding: J. Vincent describes the nest as bowl-shaped, composed of dry strips of grass loosely interwoven and placed near the ground in a tuft of coarse grass. Eggs, pale cream finely freckled with red-brown forming a cap or ring where there are also ash-grey markings. February to March. Clutch 2—3. 18,6 × 13,9, 18,9 × 13,6 and 17,9 × 13,5, 18,3 × 13,7.

LOCAL RACE:
S.b. brevirostris (Sundevall), 1850: *"Caffraria inferiore"* = *Umlazi River, Natal.* The Southern race; from our area extending as far as southern Malawi. Replaced in Angola and Zambia by a darker race.

617 Moustache Warbler   Breëstert-grasvoël

Melocichla mentalis   (Fraser), 1843: *Accra.*

PLATE 52 (OPP. P. 416).
Length 18—20 cm (wing 75—77; tail 84; tarsus 28—29; culmen 17. 2 specimens). Iris light yellowish buff; bill black, bluish grey below; legs bluish grey.

Identification: Note the rufous edge to wings and the heavy bill. This bird might easily be mistaken for a Thrush rather than a Warbler.

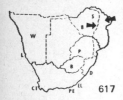

617

Distribution: West Africa to Ethiopia southwards from Angola to the Lower Zambesi Valley. Recorded only from Inyanga and Mount Selinda, eastern Rhodesia and Gorongoza mountain in southern Mozambique.

Habits: A tropical species which occurs in rank grass in or near open woodland and along edges of forested gullies where the grass is taller. Named the "Tropical Grassbird" on account of its general resemblance to the next species. Sometimes seen sunning itself on the top of the grass, but usually keeping well hidden in rank vegetation.

Food: Insects; mantises, grasshoppers and beetles.

Voice: A melodious song, from a prominent perch, "chirp-chirp-chirp-chirp, doesn't it tickle you?" or "tip-tip-twiddle-iddle-eee".

Breeding: Nest is placed in the middle of a tussock of grass about 30 cm from the ground. A somewhat large flat cup, outwardly composed of what looked like dead banana sheathing, the lining of long, thin pieces of dead grass and rootlets (Belcher). Eggs 2, pinkish white, marbled with rufous tending to form a cap at the larger end. 21,5 × 16; 22,4 × 16,1; 24 × 16,5.

LOCAL RACE:
M.m. orientalis (Sharpe), 1883: *Pangani River, Usambara, Tanzania.* From Kilimanjaro south to our limits.

618 Grassbird   Grasvoël

Sphenoeacus afer (Gmelin), 1789: *Cape of Good Hope.*

Native Names: itshitshi, u-dwetya, (X).

PLATE 52 (OPP. P. 416).
Length 19—23 cm (wing 64—67,8—70; tail 98—106; tarsus 21—23,5; culmen 15—17,5. 8 specimens). Iris reddish brown; bill black; legs lead-grey. Weight 27,0—32,3 g.

Identification: The handsomely marked head, well marked upper-parts and the long tail with pointed tips to the feathers make identification quite easy. The habits and song are also characteristic.
Distribution: Southern Cape Province eastwards to Natal and northwards to Zoutpansberg and eastern Rhodesia.
Habits: A common resident, haunting coarse hillside vegetation and flat country usually along open streams. Often seen perched on the grass or weeds sunning itself or singing from a prominent position. Otherwise remains low and creeps about the long grass; when flushed flies off a short distance, its pointed tail easily recognizable and its flight awkward with short rounded wings.

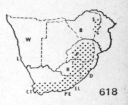

618

Voice: A musical burst, very much as recorded for previous species. See also No. 612.
Breeding: Situated in the heart of a grass tuft, the nest is a bowl-shaped structure of curled grass-blades with a finer, loosely-woven grass cup. Sometimes the nest is quite visible from above, but more often it is very well concealed. July to December in the Cape; September to April in the Transvaal. Eggs 2 or 3, pale grey or dull white with slate-coloured dots sometimes forming a concentrated dome at the top end. Average (24) 22,1 × 16,3 (21,2—23,3 × 15,1—16,7). Incubation 14—17 days; nestling 14—16 days. Female only builds nest; both parents feed young.

LOCAL RACES:
(a) S.a. afer (Gmelin), 1789: *Cape of Good Hope.* Southern Cape Province, northwards to Olifants River, east to Knysna. Flanks, upper and under tail-coverts striped. Size as above.
(b) S.a. intermedius Shelley, 1882: *Kaffraria.* Eastern Cape. Only the flanks striped. Wing 69—71,9—76; tail 97—113; tarsus 22—25; culmen 16—18. (18 specimens).
(c) S.a. natalensis Shelley, 1882: *Natal = Newcastle.* Natal to south-eastern Transvaal and westwards to Rustenburg district. Even the flanks not striped. Wing 70—75,5—80; tail 92—108, one 115; tarsus 21—26; culmen 16—19. (13 specimens).
(d) S.a. transvaalensis C. Grant, 1908: *Woodbush, Transvaal.* Northern Transvaal and eastern Rhodesia above 1 350 metres. Colour as *(c)*; wing 71—72; tail 83—84; tarsus 25—26; culmen 15—16. (3 specimens).

619 Rufous-eared Warbler   Rooioor-kleinjantjie

Malcorus pectoralis A. Smith, 1829: *Karoo, to north of Olifant's River, C.P.*

PLATE 56 (OPP. P. 464).
Length 14—16 cm (wing 48,5—51; tail 75—80; tarsus 19,5—20; culmen 10—12,5. 4 specimens). Iris reddish hazel; bill black; legs flesh-coloured.

Identification: The rufous ear-coverts, the narrow black collar on white chest and the long thin tail, characteristically held upright, make identification very easy. The ear-coverts are slightly lighter in the female.

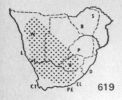

619

Distribution: Peculiar to the dry areas from Olifants River (has been recorded from Table Mountain) in western Cape, northwards to Damaraland, eastwards to Grahamstown, thence north to Westminster in the Orange Free State.

Habits: A common resident species. Occurs usually in small parties or pairs where the vegetation is sparse and for the most part low. It resembles a Prinia but spends most of its time on the ground searching for food and the tail is nearly always held upright. Has the habit of darting from one bush to another, then dropping to the ground out of sight.

Voice: A quiet "chit-it" and "chrit". Also a loud, penetrating "tee, tee, tee, tee" about twice a second.

Breeding: Situated in a small bush, near the ground, the nest is a very neat oval structure of dead grass lined with silky seeds and a few feathers. Breeds any time after rain October to May. Eggs 3—7, pale blue to white, unspotted. 14,7—16,5 × 10,9—11,2. Incubation 12—13 days.

LOCAL RACES:
(a) M.p. pectoralis A. Smith, 1829: *Karoo, to north of Olifant's River, C.P.* Cape and Karoo. Size as above.
(b) M.p. ocularius (A. Smith), 1843: *Northern Cape Colony.* Northern Cape to W. Transvaal. Underparts whitish, black band narrower and flanks unstreaked.
(c) M.p. etoshae (Winterbottom), 1965: *Etosha Pan.* From Ovamboland to Damaraland. A more pallid race.

620   Redwing Warbler   Rooivlerk-tinktinkie

Heliolais erythroptera (Jardine), 1849: *Western Africa = Gold Coast.*

PLATE 56 (OPP. P. 464).
Length about 14 cm (wing ♂ 49,5—52, ♀ 48, 49; tail 50—64; tarsus 20—21,5; culmen 13—15. 6 specimens, 4 ♂, 2 ♀). Iris yellowish brown; bill light brown; legs yellowish buff.

Identification: Non-breeding plumage is illustrated. At all stages the rufous edges of wing-feathers and coverts form a good field character. The breeding plumage is quite different; the crown, mantle and back are smoky grey, the bill black.

620

Distribution: From West Africa to Ethiopia and southwards to the Zambesi River. Recorded from the Eastern Districts of Rhodesia and as far south as Inhambane in Mozambique. Heard in Kruger Park?

Habits: An uncommon species in our area, recorded throughout the year. Occurs in *heavily grassed woodlands* or in savanna where there is long grass and similar vegetation beneath the trees. A restless little bird, occurring in pairs or family parties of up to half a dozen. Always on the move and drawing attention to itself by constant calling.

Voice: A melodious tinkling.

Breeding: Once recorded in our area. December to March in Malawi. The nest is a thin-walled oval composed of fine dead grass with lining of feathery grass heads. Eggs 2, greenish clouded all over with pinkish fawn. 17,5 × 12,5.

LOCAL RACE:
H.e. rhodoptera (Shelley), 1880: *Usambara Hills, Tanganyika.* From western Kenya southwards to our area.

621 Crombec

Stompstert

Sylvietta rufescens (Vieillot), 1817: *Africa = Olifant's River, Western Cape.*

Native Name: Ndibilitshe (Z).

PLATE 56 (OPP. P. 464).
Length 10—12 cm (wing ♂ 60—63,1—66, ♀ 57—59—61,5; tail ♂ 27—33, ♀ 24—29; tarsus 18—20,5; culmen ♂ 14,5—15,9—17, ♀ 13—15. 15 specimens, 7 ♂, 8 ♀). Iris pale brown; bill dusky brown, lighter below; legs yellowish brown. Weight 10,0—11,9 g.

Identification: The very short tail and comparatively long bill easily distinguish this species. Easily confused with the next—see that species. See also under Races.

Distribution: Throughout our area northwards to Zaïre and Ethiopia.

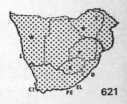

Habits: A common resident. Occurring in the dry thornveld areas and scrub and open savanna. Usually in pairs or small family parties, searching for insects amongst the leaves and twigs, uttering a twittering note and when moving from tree to tree, darting rapidly. Creeps about the outer branches, often quite high up in the tops of open trees but usually near the ground.

Voice: A pretty, shrill call, "peep-peep-peep". The phrase used for another species of crombek is equally good for this species "richi-chichi-chichirrr" or "krrip, kooop kripkrip kreee" (Skead).

Breeding: The nest is suspended from the inside branches of a wattle or thorn-tree, or outer edge of a drooping branch in secluded areas. The nest is built in the shape of an open bag or purse, constructed of dry grass, fibres and cottony material in a somewhat fragile form; lined inside with a little vegetable-down and covered outside with spider webs and similar materials. August to November in the Cape to January in Transvaal and March Rhodesia. Eggs 2, rarely 3, white with dull markings of greenish slate and brown; A. W. Vincent records eggs of race *(e)* with either reddish or brownish spots. Average (30) 18,7 × 12,6 (17,5—19,6 × 12,2—13,1); two rather long eggs 22,4 × 12,5 and 20,1 × 12,5 (A. W. Vincent). Incubation 14 (± 1) days. Nestling 14 days.

LOCAL RACES:
(a) S.r. rufescens (Vieillot), 1817: *Oliphant's River, Western Cape.* From the south-west Cape northwards to South West Africa, intermediate with *(b)* in the northern Cape and western Botswana. As illustrated. Size above.

(b) S.r. flecki (Reichenow), 1900: *Mutschumi (Machumi Pan) south of Lake Ngami, Botswana.* Ngamiland, eastern Botswana. Orange Free State, Transvaal and Rhodesia. Colour as *(a)* but bill shorter; culmen ♂ 12—14—15.

(c) S.r. diverga Clancey, 1954: *Doornhoek Farm, Cradock, Eastern Cape.* Karoo districts from about Matjesfontein in the west to southern Orange Free State. Darker above than *(a)* and richer cinnamon below. Wing ♂ 59—62; culmen ♂ 14,5—14,8—15. (4 specimens).

(d) S.r. resurga Clancey, 1953: *Weenen, Natal.* Confined to Natal and parts of southern Zululand. Similar to *(c)* but upper-parts much lighter, more bluish grey. Wing ♂ 58—64; culmen ♂ 13—13,9—15. (10 specimens).

(e) S.r. pallida (Alexander), 1899: *between Tete and Chicowa, on the Zambesi, Portuguese East Africa.* From northern Zululand through Mozambique, including low-lying areas of extreme eastern Transvaal. Much lighter than other races and with a definite light eye-brow. Smaller. Wing ♂ 53,5—55; culmen 12. (2 ♂ specimens).

621X   Red-faced Crombec

Rooiwang-stompstert

Sylvietta whytii   (Shelley), 1894: *Zomba, Nyasaland.*

PLATE 56 (OPP. P. 464).
Length about 10 cm (wing 60—65). Iris hazel; bill dark brown, paler below; legs reddish brown.

Identification: Very similar to the previous species; bill shorter. Differs by having more rufous under-parts right across breast and flanks, whilst lores and ear-coverts show as a rufous patch; shows no light stripe above eye as the local race of No. 621 does. The upper-parts are more grey.

Distribution: Central Africa southwards to Rhodesia where it occurs across the plateau from Wankie to eastern districts, mainly in higher areas. As far south as Inhambane in Mozambique.

Habits: Tends to occur in higher trees and in the canopy and often in bird parties. Especially associated with *Baikiaea* woodland.

Breeding: October to December in Rhodesia. Nest suspended from end of a twig. A deep cup covered with bark etc. Eggs, 2 white with red spots. 17 × 12.

LOCAL RACE:
(a) S.w. whytii (Shelley), 1894: *Zomba, Malawi.* The coastal race. Wing 56—60.
(b) S.w. nemorivaga Clancey, 1966: *Charaman Plateau, N. W. Rhodesia.* Inland race. Wing 60—65.

621Y   Red-capped Crombec

Rooikroon-stompstert

Sylvietta ruficapilla   Bocage, 1877: *Caconda, Angola.*

PLATE 56 (OPP. P. 464).
Length 12 cm (wing 65—70). Iris yellow; bill horn; legs reddish-brown.

Identification: As illustrated, ear coverts chestnut. Upper parts ashy grey; throat whitish, under-parts light buff.

Distribution: Angola, Zaïre, Zambia to Malawi. Occurs within our region in Rhodesia west of the Victoria Falls.

Habits: Occurs in *Brachystegia* woodland along the Zambesi Valley. Nowhere overlapping with 621X within our area.

Breeding: The nest is a purse of grass ornamented with leaves and flowers. Eggs, 2, white about 18 × 11, October.

LOCAL RACE:
S.r. chubbi Ogilvie-Grant, 1910: *Broken Hill.* This race has grey crown, ear coverts rust and the rust patch on upper breast is in the centre only.

622   Bar-throated Apalis

Bandkeel-kleinjantjie

Apalis thoracica   (Shaw and Nodder), 1811: *"Interior of Africa"* = *Grahamstown, Cape Province.*

Native Names: Ugxakhweni (X); Setholemoru (S).

PLATE 53, ♂ AND ♀, RACES *(a), (h), (i)* AND *(k)*. (OPP. P. 417).
Length about 13 cm (wing 50—52,4—54; tail ♂ 56—59, ♀ 52—54; tarsus 18—22; culmen 12—13,5. 10 specimens, 7 ♂, 3 ♀). Iris pale yellow; bill black; legs pinkish.

Identification: This variable little warbler is distinguished by light under-parts with a neat black collar below throat and greyish to greenish upper-parts.

438

Distinguished from any other Apalis by the light eye and white outer tail-feathers. Female is usually duller. See under Local Races for variation in colour.

Distribution: From the south-western Cape to eastern Cape and Natal, Zululand northwards to Transvaal; Rhodesia and beyond to Malawi, Mozambique and Tanzania.

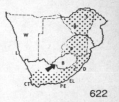

622

Habits: A common resident. Partial to heavily wooded kloofs and the bush adjoining, spreading thence along wooded streams; to the north of its range occurring only at higher altitudes. Creeps about amongst the trees and bushes in search of insects, sometimes in quite open bushes but more often in thick growth. Discloses its presence by its loud whistling note. Not at all shy; perhaps a little inquisitive, but appears quite unconcerned about one's presence and continues to creep about the branches.

Food: Insects, especially caterpillars.

Voice: Call-note "pil-pil" or "pilly-pilly-pilly"; the mate usually answers with a softer version of the same note. Also a long drawn out "chwee-chwee".

Breeding: The delicate nest may be situated in a low thinly-leafed bush or long matted grass; but a favourite site is in hanging creepers or overhanging growth on the side of a bank. It is a slightly pear-shaped oval with a side-top entrance, composed of fibres, fine grass and some soft silky material; externally decorated with moss and spider webs; lined with rootlets and sometimes vegetable-down. August to December in the Cape, to February in Transvaal and Rhodesia. Eggs 3, sometimes 4, pale greenish blue, sometimes pinky white spotted with red-brown often in a zone at the thick end. Average (68) 17,1 × 12,5 (16,1—18,6 × 11,5—13,2), one egg 16 × 10,5 (Swynnerton). Incubation 14—15 days (1) (Skead). Nestling 17—18 days (2) (Skead). Parasitised by Klaas's Cuckoo.

LOCAL RACES:
(a) A.t. thoracica (Shaw & Nodder), 1811: *Grahamstown, Cape Province.* Eastern Cape Province. Illustrated as 622 *(a)*. Size above.
(b) A.t. claudei W. Sclater, 1910: *Plettenberg Bay, Cape Province.* Knysna. Much like *(a)* but whiter below down the middle; flanks and under tail-coverts olive-brown. Wing 50; tail 57; tarsus 20; culmen 13.
(c) A.t. capensis Roberts, 1936: *Paarl, Cape Province.* Western Cape Province. Greyer crown and white belly. Wing 49—51; tail ♂ 53—56, ♀ 49; tarsus 19—20,5; culmen 13. (2 ♂, 1 ♀ specimens).
(d) A.t. venusta Gunning & Roberts, 1911: *Port St. John, Cape Province.* Pondoland to coast of Natal. More yellowish above and below; faintly yellowish on white of throat. Wing 48—53; tail ♂ 48—56, ♀ 48—49; tarsus 19—21; culmen 12—14. (7 ♂, 4 ♀ specimens).
(e) A.t. lebomboensis Roberts, 1931: *Ubombo, Zululand.* Forests on Lebombo Mountains. Much as *(g)* but small. Wing 49—54; tail ♂ 50—53, ♀ 42,5—47; tarsus 18—21; culmen 12—14. (7 ♂, 5 ♀ specimens).
(f) A.t. darglensis Gunning & Roberts, 1911: *Dargle, Natal.* Dargle district, Natal midlands. Much as *(d)* but more olive, especially on flanks, and larger. Wing 52—54; tail 48,51; tarsus 20,21; culmen 12,5, 13. (2 ♂ specimens).
(g) A.t. drakensbergensis Roberts, 1937: *Nelsburg, near Barberton, Transvaal.* Heights of Drakensberg in eastern Transvaal (Wakkerstroom and Carolina districts). Grey crown, throat and belly cream. Larger. Wing 54—59; tail ♂ 53—57,5, ♀ 50—56; tarsus 21—23; culmen 13,5—15. (4 ♂, 3 ♀ specimens).
(h) A.t. spelonkensis Gunning & Roberts, 1911: *Groot Spelonken, Transvaal.* Zoutpansberg to Woodbush. Illustrated as 622 *(h)*. Wing 49,5—55; tail ♂ 49—55, ♀ 46—52,5; tarsus 18—22; culmen 12—14,5. (10 ♂, 8 ♀ specimens).

439

(i) A.t. arnoldi Roberts, 1936: *Mt. Selinda, Rhodesia.* Eastern districts of Rhodesia. Illustrated as 622 *(i)*. Wing 51, 51,5; tail ♂ 52, ♀ 46; tarsus 20,21; culmen 12, 13. (1 ♂, 1 ♀ specimen).

(j) A.t. flaviventris Gunning & Roberts, 1911: *Wonderboom, Pretoria, Transvaal.* Western Transvaal. Intermediate between *(i)* and *(k)*. Wing 52—58; tail ♂ 53—57, ♀ 51—53,5; tarsus 19—21; culmen 13—14,5. (10 ♂, 6 ♀ specimens).

(k) A.t. rhodesiae Gunning & Roberts, 1911: *Matopos, Rhodesia.* Rhodesia from the Matopos to Inyanga district. Illustrated as 622 *(k)*. Wing 51,5—53,5; tail ♂ 52—53, ♀ 48,5; tarsus 20—20,5; culmen 11,5—12,5. (2 ♂, 1 ♀ specimens).

(l) A.t. quarta Irwin, 1966: *Gorongoza, Mocambique.* Darker above, paler below. Isolated on Mt. Gorongoza.

(m) A.t. griseopyga Lawson, 1965: *Kersefontein Berg R.* Grey above and flanks paler not olive. S.W. Cape up western reaches.

623   Black-headed Apalis   Swartkop-kleinjantjie

Apalis melanocephala (Fischer & Reichenow): 1884: *Pangani, Tanganyika.*

PLATE 53 (OPP. P. 417).
Length 13 cm (wing 48). Iris yellowish brown; bill black; legs flesh.

Identification: Blacker above than 623X, face uniform black. The long tail with white tips to outer feathers and habits typical of the Apalis aid identification. When calling, the black inside of mouth is distinctive.

Distribution: Mozambique, Eastern Districts of Rhodesia, north to East Africa.

Habits: A common resident typical of lowland forested areas. Characteristic of the higher branches of trees in the forest interior and coming to lower reaches on forest edges and along thick bush near streams. As with all species of Apalis, creeps about the foliage, picking here and there under leaves and from the twigs, hopping rather than flying as it moves through the canopy.

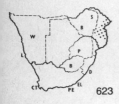

623

Voice: A loud reiterated "pee-pe-pe" or "pinks", 20 or 30 times each with the briefest pause between; also described as a clockwork motor running "durr-ir-ir-ir", etc. Often with a second bird answering the first. Call-note a quiet "seet".

Breeding: A rounded thick-walled nest built of moss and lichen, lined with seed-down. Entrance high on the side. November, December and February. Eggs 2—3, deep blue-green heavily spotted and blotched with red-brown or chocolate colour, rather more at large end. 19 × 13 (2).

LOCAL RACE:
A.m. lightoni Roberts, 1938; *Zimbiti near Beira.* Inhambane north, and S.E. Rhodesia. Buffish below.

623X   Chirinda Apalis   Chirinda-kleinjantjie

Apalis chirindensis Shelley, 1906: *Chirinda Forest, Rhodesia.*

PLATE 53, ♂ (OPP. P. 417).
Length about 13 cm (wing 47,5—49; tail 53,5—59; tarsus 18—19,5; culmen 11—12. 4 specimens). Iris pale orange-brown; bill blackish; legs pale pinkish brown. Weight 7,5—8,9 g.

Identification: As illustrated. Lower parts with a grey tinge.
Distribution: Eastern Rhodesia and adjacent Mozambique highlands.

440

Habits: Occurs in montane forested area and medium level forest. Found with 623, only at Haroni-Lusitu junction.
Voice: Said to be different from 623.

624 Rudd's Apalis   Ruddse Kleinjantjie

Apalis ruddi C. Grant, 1908: *Coguno, Inhambane, Portuguese East Africa.*

PLATE 53, ♂ AND ♀ (OPP. P. 417).
Length about 13 cm (wing ♂ 47,5—50, ♀ 48; tail ♂ 54—56, ♀ 49; tarsus 18,5—22; culmen 11—13. 5 specimens. 4 ♂, 1 ♀). Iris black; bill black; legs dark flesh.

Identification: The yellowish green sides of chest more extensive than illustrated, reaching almost right across breast in some birds. The back is greenish (as illustrated for No. 622 *(h)*). Note that only the tips of the tail-feathers are white or yellowish white.
Distribution: Confined to lower level inland forests from the northern shores of St. Lucia northwards as far as Inhambane, Mozambique.
Habits: A rare species. It is partial to certain trees covered with lichens and drooping "old-man's-beard". Has the habits of No. 623. Its call-note is distinctive and resembles No. 623, serving to guide one to the birds in the tangled bush.
Breeding: A nest found by Com. R. B. Wilson was placed in the fork of a tree. It was composed of tree lichens woven together with dried grasses and lined with vegetable matter. October. Eggs 2, bright turquoise-blue boldly marked with large rusty spots of varied sizes, more at the larger end. 16,8 × 12,8; 17,4 × 12,6.

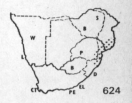
624

625 Yellow-breasted Apalis   Geelbors-kleinjantjie

Apalis flavida (Strickland), 1852: *Damaraland.*

PLATE 53, RACES *(a), (b)* AND *(c)* (OPP. P. 417).
Length 12—13 cm (wing 47—52,5; tail ♂ 50, ♀ 46,5; tarsus 17—19; culmen 10,5—11,5. 3 specimens, 1 ♂, 2 ♀). Iris yellowish brown; bill dark brown; legs light brown.

Identification: The white chin, yellow breast terminating in a neat black bar in the male of some races, and the green upper-parts and tail make identification easy. The under tail-coverts are yellow. The male loses the black breast band in non-breeding plumage and then resembles the female according to Stark & Sclater.
Distribution: From Cameroons and Somaliland southwards to north-eastern Damaraland, Ngamiland, east to northern Transvaal and down the coast to eastern Cape.
Habits: Not uncommon. Frequents the moister thick bush and evergreen forests; often found on the sunny sides of the forests. Usually occurs in pairs or family parties. A typical Apalis in its behaviour of creeping through the vegetation and searching for insects. The call is also distinctive.
Voice: The singing note is described as "chee-chee-chwerr-chwerr"; duet, "skee-skee-skee, chiz*zick* chiz*zick*, chiz*zick*", replied to by mate rather more slowly "krik-krik-krik". Alarm note almost a buzzing "churr", or rapid "crit-crit-crit . . .".

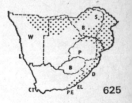
625

Breeding: The nest is situated on the outer branches of a tree, or bush, up to 5,6 metres above the ground. It is placed in a fork of supporting branches, is built of lichens and mosses bound with cobwebs, and is oval in shape with a side-top entrance. Also recorded in hanging "old-man's-beard", *Usnea*, with hardly any nest. January and February. Eggs 2 and 3, pale greenish or white with rufous marks and sometimes with slate-greyish under-markings, mostly at big end. Average (9) 16,2 × 11,7 (15—18 × 10,5—12,5).

LOCAL RACES:
Some authorities separate the races given below into two distinct species. The distinguishing feature in such cases is the presence or absence of black chest mark, the length of tail, the colour of the crown and the amount of yellow on the tail. However, these are geographical variations and do not warrant specific distinction.
(a) *A.f. flavida* (Strickland), 1852: *Damaraland*. Northern South West Africa to Ngamiland. Top of head entirely grey. As illustrated. Size as above.
(b) *A.f. neglecta* (Alexander), 1900: *S.E. Africa = Zambesi River*. Zambesi Valley southwards in riverine forests in Mashonaland, Sabi Valley, north-eastern Transvaal, Mozambique and Zululand. Only the fore-part of crown grey as illustrated. Wing 47—52; tail ♂ 45—53, ♀ 44—49; tarsus 18,5—22; culmen 11—12,5. (3 ♂, 8 ♀ specimens).
(c) *A.f. florisuga* (Reichenow), 1898: *"Kaffirland" = Eastern Cape*. From Gamtoos River north to Natal. Less grey on forehead as illustrated. No black on chest. Wing 46—50; tail ♂ 48—53,5, ♀ 47—48; tarsus 19,5—21; culmen 11—12. (4 ♂, 4 ♀ specimens).

626 Karoo Green Warbler Groen Bossanger

Eremomela gregalis (A. Smith), 1829: *Northern dist. of Little Nama-qualand.*

PLATE 56 (OPP. P. 464).
Length 12 cm (wing 51—54; tail 48—52; tarsus 16,5—18,5; culmen 8—10. 9 specimens, 6 ♂, 3 ♀). Iris bright yellow; bill black; legs flesh-coloured.

Identification: Easily confused with other Bush Warblers. The underparts are whitish *contrasting* with the green and grey of upper-parts of head, see No. 628. The tail-coverts are yellowish green. The feathers at base of tarsus are sooty grey. The bill is shorter than that of the next two species.

Distribution: Confined to the Karoo scrub from Clanwilliam, east to Oudtshoorn, Colesberg; through Great Namaqualand to Swakopmund.

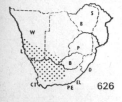

626

Habits: Not very common and local in habits. Andersson records that it occurs in small families of from two to six individuals amongst the widely scattered dwarf vegetation; it hops slowly and systematically amongst the branches, searching diligently for small insects, which constitute its sole food, and uttering all the while a low but distinct chirp.

Voice: A wailing, bleating note like "quee, quee-quee." Also a call-note like that of a Black-cheeked Waxbill.

Breeding: The nest is situated in a grasstuft. A nest is described as like that of a White-eye. December and August. Eggs pale blue spotted at the obtuse end with small dry blood-coloured spots.

LOCAL RACES:
(a) *E.g. gregalis* (A. Smith), 1829: *Northern dist. of Little Namaqualand*. Karoo areas of Cape Province west. As illustrated. Size above.
(b) *E.g. damarensis* Wahlberg, 1855: *Swakop River, Great Namaqualand*. More pallid than (a) and yellower on rump.

627 Bleating Bush Warbler   Kwêkwêvoël

Camaroptera brachyura (Vieillot), 1820: *Pampoen-Kraal near Knysna, Cape Province.*

Native Names: Unome, Unomanyuka (X); i-Mbuzana (Z).

PLATE 56 (OPP. P. 464).
Length 12—13 cm (wing 49—53,5—58; tail 34—45; tarsus 21—23; culmen 11,2—13. 15 specimens). Iris rich brown; bill black; legs flesh coloured.

Identification: Rather similar to the previous species but has a longer bill, the grey of crown merges gradually with the light under-parts and the feathers around base of tarsus are buff. This bird has a greyish white ring around eye. The call is very characteristic.

Distribution: In the lower forests of the south and east, from George eastwards along coastal areas to Natal, thence inland to Woodbush and northwards through Mozambique, eastern areas of Rhodesia to Somaliland.

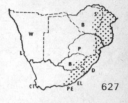

627

Habits: A common species. Occurs in forests, extending outside where there is dense bush on streams and rivers. Found singly or in pairs, attracting attention by a weak, bleating note. Creeps about among the undergrowth or on the ground, keeping its tail erect and often drooping its wings.

Voice: Typically a bleating "kwê" likened to the bleating of a lost kid. Call a loud "whit-whit-whit". Whilst nesting the male dances in a loop over a branch, making a vibrant, aggressive, whirring sound.

Breeding: The nest is a round ball of cottony fibres and coarse fibres bound inside broad leaves of bushes or trees, on the ground or as high as 6 metres up, on the outer branches. October to January. Eggs 2, 3 or 4, white, occasionally dotted with small reddish dots. Average (8) 17,1 × 12,4 (16,5—19 × 12—13,8).

LOCAL RACES:
(a) C.b. brachyura (Vieillot), 1820: *Pampoen-Kraal near Knysna, Cape Province.* From George eastwards to Natal. As illustrated. Size above.
(b) C.b. constans Clancey, 1952: *Gwaliweni Forest, Lebombo Mountains, N.E. Zululand.* From Zululand to Swaziland, eastern parts of Transvaal and Mozambique south of Maputo. Paler and more yellowish above and paler below.
(c) C.b. bororensis Gunning & Roberts, 1911: *Ngomwe, Boror, Portuguese East Africa.* From Maputo northwards, including eastern Rhodesia to Tanzania. Brighter yellow above than *(b)*.

628 Grey-backed Bush Warbler   Grysrug-bostinktinkie

Camaroptera brevicaudata (Cretzschmar), 1831: *Kordofan.*

PLATE 56 (OPP. P. 464).
Length 12—13 cm (wing 52,5—54,5—57,5; tail 38—45; tarsus 19,5—22; culmen 12,5—13,5. 10 specimens). Iris pale red; bill blackish, lighter below; legs flesh colour.

Identification: Distinguished by the contrasting green of wings against upper- and under-parts in all stages. Also the feathers at base of tarsus are yellow-ochre. Note that the grey of head merges gradually with light under-parts. Note summer and winter plumage as illustrated.

Distribution: A tropical species from Senegal and the Sudan southwards. In the Kaokoveld south to Kaukurus in South West Africa, Ngamiland, central Transvaal and north-eastern Zululand.

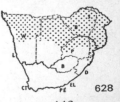

628

Habits: Common and resident, though not frequently recorded from the western-central Transvaal areas. Similar in habits to the last species, but frequenting denser, drier bush.

Voice: A gentle bleating note. Male utters a high-pitched "pee" while displaying, followed by bill-rattling.

Breeding: The nest is the same as for the preceding species, being constructed in a broad-leaved bush or tree and neatly sewn in. November, December and May. Eggs 3, pale greenish blue, well marked with underlying and overlying blotches of red-brown. Average (14) 17,5 × 12,4 (16,6—18,5 × 11,7—12,8).

LOCAL RACES:
(a) *C.b. sharpei* Zedlitz, 1911: *Damaraland.* Damaraland north to Okavango River, east to Ngamiland. Crown in the male in summer paler grey. As illustrated. Size above.
(b) *C.b. noomei* Gunning & Roberts, 1911: *Pongola River, Northern Zululand.* Zambesi Valley, Zambia, southwards to northern Transvaal and north eastern Zululand. Darker crown in the breeding plumage of the male.

629　Fantail Cisticola　　　　　　　　Landery-tinktinkie

Cisticola juncidis (Rafinesque), 1810: *Sicily.*

Native Names: Unonzwi (X); Mtantasane, mo-Tintinyane, mo-Teane mo-Tinyane (S); u-Dogwe (Z).

PLATE 54, ♂ BR. AND ♂ N- BR. (OPP. P. 448).
Length 10—12 cm (wing ♂ 52—53,5—55, ♀ 46—48—50; tail ♂ summer 33—36, winter 40—45, ♀ summer 31—35, winter 35—38; tarsus 17—19; culmen 9,5—10,5. 21 specimens, 13 ♂, 8 ♀). Iris hazel; bill grey; culmen brown; legs flesh.

Identification: Likely to be confused with the next four species but identifiable by plumage, habits, call and its unique nest (see below). Tail shows a pattern of sub-terminal spots from *above and below*, plus white tips. Male illustrated; female like non-breeding male. Young birds are lightly sulphured below.

Distribution: Almost all Africa (except deserts), Portugal right across to Japan, Sunda Islands and northern Australia.

Habits: A common species which frequents open grasslands, especially on the borders of damp places where the grass is longer; also old lands, edges of cultivated fields and flat areas of rank weeds. Seems to have extended its range as a result of the planting of lucerne fields in terrain, such as the Karoo and lower Orange River, which otherwise would be quite unsuitable for it. In the breeding season, males are conspicuous and easily identified by their habit of flying around at a height of about 15 m, uttering a note like "klink" or "tzit", dipping as each note is uttered. There is an interval of one to two seconds between the sounds.

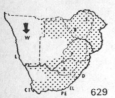

629

Food: All Cisticolas eat minute insects.

Voice: Alarm note an excited succession of "zit zit zit zit . . .". See also under habits.

Breeding: The nest is unique in being of the soda-water bottle type, with the entrance at the *top* and is composed of cottony or silky strands woven into upright strands of living grass, these being drawn together into a sort of spiral completely hiding the nest and entrance, making the whole very difficult to find. The inside is lined with bits of downy material, largely added after the eggs are laid, so that new nests are thin-walled but thicken by the addition of material until the young are hatched. Eggs 3—5, are laid from November to March. They are white to pale blue, marked, speckled or spotted with a variety of shades of red, rust and secondary grey. Average (20) 15,2 × 11,3.

LOCAL RACE:
C.j. terrestris (A. Smith), 1842: *Near Kurrichane, N. Cape Province.* From Cape Town eastwards and northwards to Tanzania and Zaïre. As illustrated. Size above.

630 Desert Cisticola   Woestyn-tinktinkie

Cisticola aridula   Witherby, 1900: *Gerazi, White Nile, Sudan.*

PLATE 54, ♂ BR. AND ♂ N- BR. (OPP. P. 448).
Length 10—12 cm (wing ♂ 50—51—52 (12), ♀ 47—52 (5); tail ♂ summer 35—40, winter 39—45, ♀ summer 33—35, winter 41—43; tarsus 17,5—19,5; culmen 10—11,5). Iris hazel; bill grey; culmen brown; legs flesh.

Identification: Likely to be mistaken for the last species, since it has a tail of the same length, but longer than in the next three species which it also resembles. However, is paler on the back than No. 629 and shows the tail-pattern from *below* only. From the next three species is best distinguished by having the tail longer, almost as long as the wing, and by its habits. Males illustrated. In winter more striped than mottled above, the light edges to feathers broader. Young are mealy editions of winter adults; not sulphured.
Distribution: Africa south of the Sahara except West Africa and the south-west, southern and eastern Cape Province.
Habits: Frequents the same type of veld as No. 629, but extends over drier country such as the Kalahari. Quite common but local in distribution. During the breeding season performs low aerial cruises without any very characteristic antics. If alarmed by an intruder, the male flies about in an erratic fashion, alternated with rapid downward swoops, and utters sharp ''tuc, tuc'' sounds and *snaps* its wings during the swoops. (No. 629 *never* snaps its wings.) The sound is similar to that made by ''snapping'' the finger and thumb, and in this species is only done during these threatening swoops and *not* as part of the courtship display (cf. Nos. 634 and 635).
Voice: A monotone repetition of a single, high-pitched, tinkling ''ting (½ sec.) ting . . . ting . . .'', uttered from the top of a low shrub, tall grass or while cruising.
Breeding: The nest is of the ball type, with the entrance at the side but near the top. It might thus be mistaken for a nest of the last species but is always made of *dry* material. The roof is rather loosely made and the entrance is large. It is usually about 30—60 cm from the ground in a tuft of grass. Eggs are laid from November to March, very variable in colour; white to pale blue, plain, or speckled or spotted with purplish red or purplish brown. Average (34) 14,6 × 11,4.

LOCAL RACE:
C.a. kalahari O. Grant, 1910: *Molopo River, Brit. Bechuanaland.* South Africa; other races to the north.

631 Cloud Cisticola

Gevlekte Klopkloppie

Cisticola textrix (Vieillot), 1817: *Cape of Good Hope.*

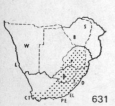

631

PLATE 54, NOS. 631 *(a)* ♂ BR. AND ♂ N- BR, 631 *(b)* ♂ BR. (OPP. P. 448).
Length about 10 cm (wing ♂ 53—54—57, ♀ 47—48—49; tail ♂ summer 25—28, winter
35—37, ♀ summer 26—28, winter 31—34; tarsus ♂ 21—22,5, ♀ 18,5—20; culmen
10—11,5. 20 specimens, 10 ♂, 10 ♀). Iris hazel; bill lead-grey; culmen brown; legs
flesh.

Identification: One of three *very* short-tailed species and except for race *(a)*
which is immediately recognizable by having spotted under-parts, likely to be
confused with Nos. 634 and 635. In the field they are easily separable in the
summer by their characteristic habits (q.v.). Appears thicker-set and longer-
legged than No. 634 and has a shorter tail than No. 635; these facts are of less
value than habits in field identification. Males as illustrated. Breeding female
mottled on crown. In winter both sexes have dark centres of feathers narrower,
giving streaked rather than mottled effect. Young resemble winter adults,
lightly sulphured below.

Distribution: From Cape Town eastwards and northwards to the highveld of
Transvaal eastwards to Zululand.

Habits: In the Cape favours flat, bare marshy ground, particularly near the
sea at the mouths of rivers; inland occurs in open country covered with short
grass and in grassy vleis. Performs remarkable high aerial cruises in the
breeding season; the male rises from the grass with whirring wings at an angle
of 45 degrees and mounts so high as to become almost invisible. He then
cruises back and forth in random circles making loud "B, B, chick-chick" or
"see see seesee chick chick chick" calls, repeated every two or three seconds;
starting on the climb up, from 6 m or so onwards. Descends in a headlong
nose-dive but checks and throws up just before reaching the ground and then
descends gently into the grass. Usually varies the high cruising with sudden,
jerky swerves and downward swoops. *Does not snap* its wings as it descends,
only repeats the "chick chick" very rapidly.

Voice: As above.

Breeding: Nests in the Cape from August to November; in Transvaal from
November to March. The nest, of the ball type with the entrance at the side, is
placed almost on the ground and is covered over with a bower of green grass
blades woven into and around the roof. The nest is unfortunately indistinguishable from that of the next species which often nests in the same area. Eggs 4,
pale greenish speckled with dark brown; 15,5 × 12 (4). Nestling 15½ days.

LOCAL RACES:
(a) C.t. textrix (Vieillot), 1817: *Cape of Good Hope.* Western Cape Province to Algoa
Bay. As illustrated. Wing ♂ 51,5—52,5—54, ♀ 45—48—50; tail 27—30; tarsus 19—22;
culmen 9—11. 23 specimens, 13 ♂, 10 ♀.
(b) C.t. major (Roberts), 1913: *Grahamstown.* Eastern Cape through to the Orange Free
State, Transvaal and upper parts of Natal. As illustrated. Size given above. Under-parts
not spotted as in *(a)*.
(c) C.t. marleyi (Roberts), 1936: Manaba, Zululand. Zululand. Wing ♂ 50—
51,5—52,5, ♀ 45—47—48,5; tail summer 25—28; tarsus 19—22,5; culmen 10—11,5.
11 specimens, 8 ♂, 3 ♀.

632 = 631 *(b)*

633 = 631 *(c)*

634 Ayres's Cloud Cisticola   Kleinste Klopkloppie

Cisticola ayresii Hartlaub, 1863: *Natal.*

Native name: Iqgaza.

PLATE 54, ♂ BR. AND ♂ N- BR. (OPP. P. 448).
Length 9—11 cm (wing ♂ 49—50,5—52, ♀ 42—46—48; tail ♂ summer 24—27, winter 34—35, ♀ summer 24—28, winter 33; tarsus ♂ 18,5—19,5, ♀ 17,5—18,5; culmen 9—10,5. 21 specimens, 10 ♂, 11 ♀). Iris hazel; bill lead-grey; culmen brown; legs flesh.

Identification: Very similar to Nos. 631 and 635; best identified in the field while breeding. More lightly built than the former and with a proportionately shorter tail than the latter. Also somewhat darker above than No. 631. In winter plumage males become brighter and streaked, rather than mottled above; tail becomes longer. Female resembles male but non-breeding crown mottled. Young birds resemble winter adults, sulphured below.

Distribution: Eastern Cape Province, Orange Free State and Natal northwards to Kenya, Uganda and Gaboon; absent from Mozambique.

Habits: A common species of highveld grassland and open, short grass areas even near sea-level. Prefers thicker and longer grass than the last species. Executes the same type of high-level cruises as the last species (q.v.) but does not call until high up and makes a very different sound—a thin, squeaky note which may be written as "squeaky-squeaky" or "see see-se see-se se". When it throws up, or darts about, at the end of its nose-dive, makes a series of *physical, crackling wing-snaps* (cf. No. 631).

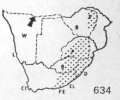

634

Voice: See under Habits.

Breeding: The nest is of the ball type, placed in a bunch of grass, close to or on the ground. Eggs 3—5, laid in December, October to March in Rhodesia; very variable but usually pale greenish, speckled minutely with red-brown. A clutch of 3 averages 17,5 × 11,4.

LOCAL RACE:
C.a. ayresii Hartlaub, 1863: *Natal.* Southern Africa to Gaboon and Tanzania. As illustrated. Size above.

635 Pale-crowned Cloud Cisticola
Bleekkop-klopkloppie

Cisticola brunnescens Heuglin, 1862: *Godofelasi, South Eritrea.*

PLATE 54, ♂ BR. AND ♀ BR. (OPP. P. 448).
Length 10—11 cm (wing ♂ 53—55, ♀ 48—50; tail summer 32—35; tarsus ♂ 20,5—21,5, ♀ 18—20; culmen 10—12). Iris hazel; bill lead-grey; culmen brown; legs flesh.

Identification: Male in breeding dress may be distinguished from the two previous species by its pale crown. In all other plumages practically indistinguishable in the field. Female in summer is more mottled on crown and nape (see illustration). Male in winter more like female. Young are mealy editions of winter adults and are brightly sulphured below.

Distribution: From Pondoland, Natal and eastern Transvaal, eastern Rhodesia through East Africa to Ethiopia and Cameroon highlands.

Habits: Inhabits rather damper situations than the last two species and is local and uncommon, except perhaps in Natal where it is still, however, rarer than

635

PLATE 54

629. *Cisticola juncidis terrestris.* Fantail Cisticola. Landery-tinktinkie.

♂ Br. and ♂ N-Br.

630. *Cisticola aridula kalahari.* Desert Cisticola. Woestyn-tingtinkie.

♂ Br. and ♂ N-Br.

631. *(a). Cisticola textrix textrix.* Cloud Cisticola. Gevlekte Klopkloppie.

♂ Br. and ♂ N-Br.

631 *(b). Cisticola textrix major.* Cloud Cisticola. Gevlekte Klopkloppie. ♂ Br.

634. *Cisticola ayresii ayresii.* Ayres' Cloud Cisticola.

Kleinste Klopkloppie. ♂ Br. and ♂ N-Br.

635. *Cisticola brunnescens egregia.* Pale-crowned Cloud Cisticola.

Bleekkop-klopkloppie. ♂ Br. and ♀ Br.

636. *Cisticola brachyptera isabellina.* Shortwing Cisticola.

Kortvlerk-klopkloppie.

637 *(a). Cisticola fulvicapilla fulvicapilla.* Neddicky. Neddikkie.

637 *(d). Cisticola fulvicapilla ruficapilla.* Neddicky. Neddikkie.

♂N-Br

629

♂Br

♂N-Br

630

♂Br

♂Br

631A

♂N-Br

♂Br

634

631B

♂N-Br

636

♂Br

635

636

A

♀Br

D   637

638

639 ♂ Br

♂ N-Br

641 ♂

643 ♂

644 ♂

642 ♂ N-Br

♂ Br

♀ Br

646 ♂

645 ♂

645 x
♂ Br

KN

648 ♂

♀ Br

647 ♂ N-Br

♂ Br

MLIGHTON
'39

PLATE 55

638. *Cisticola subruficapilla subruficapilla.* Grey-backed Cisticola.
Grysrug-tinktinkie. ♂.

639. *Cisticola lais lais.* Wailing Cisticola. Huilende Tinktinkie.
♂ Br. and ♂ N-Br.

641. *Cisticola rufilata rufilata.* Tinkling Cisticola. Rooiagtige Tinktinkie. ♂.

642. *Cisticola chiniana chiniana.* Rattling Cisticola. Bosveld-tinktinkie.
♂ Br. and ♂ N-Br., ♀ Br.

643. *Cisticola cantans muenzneri.* Singing Cisticola. Singende Tinktinkie. ♂.

644. *Cisticola erythrops nyasa.* Red-faced Cisticola. Rooiwang-tinktinkie. ♂.

645. *Cisticola galactotes galactotes.* Black-backed Cisticola.
Swartrug-tinktinkie. ♂.

645X. *Cisticola pipiens.* Chirping Cisticola. Piepende Tinktinkie. ♂ Br.

646. *Cisticola tinniens tinniens.* Le Vaillant's Cisticola. Vleitinktinkie. ♂.

647. *Cisticola natalensis natalensis.* Croaking Cisticola. Groot Tinktinkie.
♂ Br., and ♂ N-Br. and ♀ Br.

648 *(a). Cisticola aberrans aberrans.* Lazy Cisticola. Luie Tinktinkie. ♂.

the last two. Performs the same type of aerial cruise as No. 631 but when aloft utters only a thin, wispy single note, "tsee tsee tsee . . .", sometimes with another scarcely audible sound thus—"tsee tsee tsee ti ti ti ti ti ti ti ti tsee tsee tsee". In our area does not give wing snaps, although it does elsewhere. The nose-dive descent seems also to be silent and *without* wing snaps; if any sound *is* made it is the song rapidly repeated.

Voice: See under Habits.

Breeding: Nest similar to that of No. 634 but often in moister situations. Eggs 4—5, variable, white to pale blue, spotted with rust-red, purple-brown, dark brown and underlying grey. November to April in Rhodesia. Average (14) 15,5 × 11,6.

LOCAL RACES:
(a) C.b. egregia (Roberts), 1913: *Wakkerstroom.* Pondoland to northern Transvaal. As illustrated. Size above.
(b) C.b. cinnamomea Reichenow, 1904: *Ngomingi, Tanganyika.* Zaïre, Tanzania south to Mashonaland. Darker than *(a)* and less tawny.

636 Shortwing Cisticola   Kortvlerk-klopkloppie

Cisticola brachyptera (Sharpe), 1890: *Volta River, Gold Coast.*

PLATE 54 (OPP. P. 448).

Length 11—12 cm (wing ♂ 48—52; tail summer 32—36, winter about 39; tarsus 21; culmen 11). Iris hazel; bill, upper mandible brown, blackish at base, lower greyish flesh; legs dark flesh.

Identification: Not very like any other *Cisticola*; might be mistaken for the next species but differs in habits and at rest appears broader-tailed. Female in breeding dress is more streaked on the mantle than male; in winter male is also streaked on mantle and head. Young birds are sulphured below, otherwise like winter adults.

Distribution: From Melsetter and Beira northwards to Ethiopia and across to West Africa.

Habits: Essentially a bird of the savannas, trees being apparently essential to it for singing perches. The male has the habit of cruising overhead, with tail held fan-wise, taking off from a tree and climbing to a height of a hundred metres, much like the Cloud-scrapers. Then follows a thunderbolt dive with a final upward swoop just before landing. Most of the male's time, in the breeding season, is spent perched, 1,5—15 m up, on the dead branch of a tree or other conspicuous post. From this vantage point he utters a feeble song, a sniffling, descending "see, see, see" or longer, up to nine "see's". This may be described as "mississippi-ing".

Voice: As above; alarm note a weak "chick".

Breeding: Nests rather late November to May. Nest of the ball type, placed low, about nine inches off the ground and lacking a bower. Eggs 3—4, plain white or greenish blue, freckled with rust-red. Average (3) 15,4 × 11,7.

LOCAL RACE:
C.b. isabellina Reichenow, 1907: *Songea, Southern Tanganyika.* Rhodesia to Tanzania.

636

637 Neddicky

Neddikkie

Cisticola fulvicapilla (Vieillot), 1817: *Camdeboo, Cape Province.*

Native Names: Incede (X); u-Gigi, i-Ncede (Z).

PLATE 54, RACES *(a)* AND *(d)*. (OPP. P. 448).
Length 10—11 cm (wing ♂ 47—49,5—51, ♀ 44—46—48,5; tail 39—46; tarsus 16,5—18,5; culmen 10—11,5. 20 specimens, 14 ♂, 6 ♀). Iris hazel; bill greyish flesh; legs flesh. Weight 10—12 g.

Identification: Races *(a)* to *(c)*, having grey under-parts, combined with rufous crowns, should not be confused with other species. Race *(e)* might be confused with the last species but has crown more rufous and back plainer; in the field shows a longer and more slender-looking tail, even at a distance. Sexes alike in summer. Both sexes little different in winter. Young not sulphured below; like adults.
Distribution: From the south-west Cape eastwards to Tanzania and across to northern South West Africa and Angola.
Habits: One of the commonest and most familiar birds in South Africa. Inhabits gardens, thornveld, plantations and any fairly open country with bushes or trees. During the breeding season the male takes up his song-perch on a bush, tree or a telegraph wire and repeats his monotonous little song almost all day long. This is a loud, resonant, ventriloquial, slightly mournful "weep, weep, weep, weep . . .", rising slightly in pitch and volume and repeated *ad lib*. When alarmed in grass, flies into the nearest bush or tree and quietly watches the intruder.
Voice: Alarm note a rapid clicking, very like the noise produced by running one's fingers across the teeth of a comb. For song, see under Habits.
Breeding: The nest is an oval of broad grass blades, lined with finer soft material, the entrance at the side near the top. There is one record of an open cup-shaped nest—abnormal. It is placed in a tuft of grass, usually beside or amongst the twigs of a bush, on the ground or up to 30 cm above it. Breeds September to December in the Cape; November to February in the north. Eggs 3—5, very variable, bluish, greenish or pure white marked with various reds in almost any variety of pattern. Average (40) 15,3 × 11,4 (14,6—16 × 10,4—11,6). Incubation 12—14½ days. Nestling 12—14 days (4).

LOCAL RACES:
(a) C.f. fulvicapilla (Vieillot), 1817: *Camdeboo, Cape Province.* Knysna to Natal. As illustrated. Size above.
(b) C.f. silberbaueri (Roberts), 1919: *Groot Drakenstein, Cape Province.* Western Cape Province. Crown hardly differentiated from the back, under-parts more extensively blue-grey.
(c) C.f. lebombo (Roberts), 1936: *Ubombo, Zululand.* Lebombo mountains. Crown sharply differentiated from the back, below blue-grey but whiter on the belly in the male, less blue-grey below in female; smaller, wing ♂ 48,5, ♀ 45; tail 37; tarsus 18 and 16,5; culmen 10,5.
(d) C.f. ruficapilla (A. Smith), 1843: *Interior of South Africa.* Transvaal and Rhodesia. As illustrated; blue-grey hardly noticeable or absent; larger; wing ♂ 51—51,5, ♀ 45—51; tail ♂ 43—47, ♀ 37—45; tarsus 16—18; culmen 10—11. 16 specimens, 8 ♂, 8 ♀.
(e) C.f. muelleri Alexander, 1899: *Mesanangue, P.E.A.* Lower Zambesi Valley area of Mozambique northwards to Tanzania. Below buffy white, still smaller; wing ♂ 47,5—49; tail 37—39; tarsus 17—18; culmen 10—11.
(f) C.f. hallae Benson, 1955: *Tsotsoroga Pan, Bechuanaland.* Southern Angola and Zambia, north-east Botswana and north-west South West Africa. Paler than *(e)*.

637

638   Grey-backed Cisticola   Grysrug-tinktinkie

Cisticola subruficapilla (A. Smith), 1843: *South Africa = South-western Cape Province.*

PLATE 55, ♂ (OPP. P. 449).

Length 11—13 cm (wing ♂ 53—55—59, ♀ 47—49,5—52; tail ♂ 51—59, ♀ 46—55; tarsus ♂ 17—19, ♀ 16—18; culmen ♂ 11—12, ♀ 10—11. 57 specimens, 32 ♂, 25 ♀). Iris dark hazel; bill lead-grey; culmen brown; legs flesh.

Identification: Likely to be confused with the next species, the Wailing Cisticola and also with le Vaillant's Cisticola, both of which occur in the same areas. From the latter it is easily distinguished by having a grey back, *streaked* with black, not heavily blotched; the crown, also, is streaked and not very rufous (see Plate). From the Wailing Cisticola, No. 639, is best distinguished by habits and habitat preference (see below); it is also slightly smaller, but in colour is almost indistinguishable from race *(b)* of No. 639. Sexes alike; summer and winter plumages the same. Young resemble adults, slightly sulphured on face.

Distribution: From Cape Town northwards to the Kaokoveld and eastwards to De Aar, Cradock and Port Elizabeth.

Habits: A common species found in a variety of habitats; from coastal sand-dunes, estuarine flats and the Karoo in the Cape Province; also in mountainous country in South West Africa.

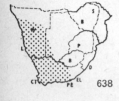

638

Voice: Normal call a loud, ringing "proueeee, tseep, tseep, tseep". Song, during the breeding season, is uttered from a low perch or top of a bush— "weesisee chizzarizzaree chichichoo", in descending scale, sometimes with a prelude of quick confused notes. Alarm note a piping "tee, tee, tee"; in extreme urgency a soft grating "churr".

Breeding: The nest is of the ball type, placed on the ground or low down in a small bush, generally well ingrown with grass, which is incorporated in the walls. It is lined with soft plant material and has the entrance at the side near the top. Eggs 3—4, pale blue, fairly well marked with reddish, brownish or purplish freckles and spots but very variable. Average (44) 15,8 × 11,8 (14,7—17,1 × 11,5—12,8). Breeds August to November.

LOCAL RACES:

(a) C.s. subruficapilla (A. Smith), 1843: *South Africa = S.W. Cape Province.* South-west Cape. As illustrated. Size above.

(b) C.s. namaqua Lynes, 1930: *Klipfontein, Little Namaqualand.* Little Namaqualand eastwards to Deelfontein and Fauresmith. Above paler throughout, but chiefly due to the markings being small, fainter and softer, below and face plain, spots and freckles absent or at most obsolete. Wing ♂ 51—57 (6), ♀ 48—50 (4).

(c) C.s. jamesi Lynes, 1930: *Cradock, Cape Province.* Karoo of eastern Cape Province. from Port Elizabeth and Albany to Cradock and De Aar districts. Above scarcely different from *(a)*, but below rather more buffy than greyish, not, or very faintly, spotted below and very little freckled on face.

(d) C.s. karasensis (Roberts), 1937: *Kochena, Great Karas Mountains.* Great Namaqualand and Damaraland. Paler than *(b)*, whiter below and very little striped on the back, crown slightly striped and not rufous in contrast with the back. Wing ♂ 55—57—59 (5), ♀ 52—53 (3).

639 Wailing Cisticola   Huilende Tinktinkie

Cisticola lais   (Hartlaub and Finsch), 1870: *Natal.*

Native Names: u-(*or* i-) Qobo; i-Hlatsinyane (Z); Iqobo (X).

PLATE 55, ♂ BR. AND ♂ N-BR. (OPP. P. 449).
Length 11—14 cm (wing ♂ 60—66, ♀ 51—55; tail ♂ 55—66, ♀ 44—54; tarsus ♂ 20—22,5, ♀ 17,5—20,5; culmen 11,5—13, ♀ 10,5—12. 30 specimens, 17 ♂, 13 ♀). Iris hazel; bill lead-grey; culmen sepia; legs flesh; palate black. Weight 11—15,5 g.

Identification: In the south, very easily confused with the last species but is larger, more boldly patterned above and in summer shows more contrast between a light reddish crown and light grey back; below buff tinted, *not grey*. See also Habitat and Voice. Sexes alike, female smaller. In winter plumage redder and marks thinner.

Distribution: From Angola, Malawi and Uganda south to eastern Rhodesia, Transvaal, Natal and Cape Province as far as George. Status in the western Cape obscure but reported from Piketberg.

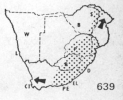
639

Habits: A species of hills and mountains, frequenting streams and rocky, well-grassed localities often near patches of thick bush or forest. Usually found in pairs but in winter in small parties; when alarmed sidles up the taller grass-stems to watch an intruder.

Voice: Alarm note a loud wailing "hweeet" or "to-wee-yeh" increasing in volume. The song is a variety of notes, but always associated in some way with the wailing note; it is uttered from the top of a bush or tall grass-stem.

Breeding: Nest of the ball type, is built of green blades in a tuft of green grass. Breeds November to February. Eggs are variable, plain white, or white or pale blue speckled with purplish and dark brown. About 17,2 × 12,5. October to February in Rhodesia.

LOCAL RACES:
(a) C.l. lais (Hartlaub and Finsch), 1870: *Natal.* Eastern Cape, Natal and north-eastern Free State, eastern Transvaal. As illustrated. Size above.

(b) C.l. maculata Lynes, 1930: *Berg River, Cape Province.* Originally found at the Berg River near Piquetberg by Layard but not recorded there since. Similar birds occur eastwards to Port Elizabeth. Slightly smaller than *(a)* and sometimes striped below. Wing ♂ 55,5—58,5—61, ♀ 49—51—53; tail ♂ 53—64, ♀ 46—58. 35 ♂, 32 ♀.

(c) C.l. monticola Roberts, 1913: *Six-mile Spruit, Pretoria.* Southern Transvaal. ♂ summer and ♂ winter. Top of head redder than *(a)* and back less heavily marked; in winter top of head striped, striping of back narrower than in summer. Wing ♂ 60—61—63, ♀ 54—57—60; tail ♂ 57—64, ♀ 51—60. 6 ♂, 6 ♀.

(d) C.l. mashona Lynes, 1930: *Chirinda, Rhodesia.* North-eastern Transvaal and Mashonaland. Like *(c)* but top of head always dappled, never plain; back more boldly mottled. Wing ♂ 58—60, ♀ 50—53; tail ♂ 50—58, ♀ 50—55. 4 ♂, 5 ♀.

(e) C.l. oreobates Irwin, 1966: *Gorongoza, P.E.A.* Confined to higher parts of Gorongoza Mountain. Crown darker, less richer chestnut upper parts and white less buff below than *(d).*

640 = 639 *(c)*

641 Tinkling Cisticola   Rooiagtige Tinktinkie

Cisticola rufilata (Hartlaub), 1870: *Elephant Vlei, Damaraland.*

PLATE 55, ♂ (OPP. P. 449).
Length 13—14,5 cm (wing ♂ 54—57—60, ♀ 51—52—53; tail ♂ 51—60, ♀ 48,5—57; tarsus 18—22; culmen 11—13,5. 26 specimens, 15 ♂, 11 ♀). Iris hazel; bill black, lower edge grey; legs flesh; palate black.

Identification: Is sometimes confused with *C. chiniana*, No. 642, but is altogether a redder bird with narrow, reddish tail-feathers. The heavily mottled back avoids confusion with Nos. 643 and 644. Is very like the previous species, which it overlaps near Pretoria, but the crown is plainer, tail redder and with bolder black spots; eyebrow conspicuous and sub-loral spot grey; cheeks redder. Sexes alike in summer, sub-loral spot smaller in female. In winter only slightly different, becoming lighter and redder generally and more striped than mottled above; sub-loral spots disappear. Young are dull editions of winter adults; not sulphured.

Distribution: Damaraland, Botswana, western Transvaal, Rhodesia northwards to Angola and Malawi and south-eastern Zaïre.

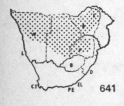

641

Habits: An inhabitant of the more or less open, dry scrub of the Kalahari and similar areas. It is a shy species, quiet and always alert; difficult to get to know as it dives into cover at the least alarm.

Voice: Alarm note "dee dee du du e e e"; song "very pretty, each note ending like the resonance of a small silver bell".

Breeding: The nest is described as of the ball type, made of grey dry grass-blades, lined with white and a little brownish plant-down, and concealed in a dense bush of green weeds, about 30 cm from the ground. Eggs 3, white or pale blue with a mass of pinky brown spots and freckles at the thick end, overlying a few purplish slate marks, more scattered towards the greatest diameter and absent at the thin end. Average (59) 17 × 12,6 (16—18,8 × 11,4—13,2). Breeds September to February in Rhodesia.

LOCAL RACE:
C.r. rufilata (Hartlaub), 1870: *Elephant Vlei, Damaraland.* Damaraland across to Transvaal and north to Malawi. As illustrated. Size above.

642 Rattling Cisticola   Bosveld-tinktinkie

Cisticola chiniana (A. Smith), 1843: *Kurrichane, Transvaal.*

Native Names: i-Nqoba (Z); le-Khere (Ch).

PLATE 55, ♂ BR., ♂ N- BR. AND ♀ BR. (OPP. P. 449).
Length 13—16 cm (wing ♂ 64—66,5—71, ♀ 55,5—56—57,5; tail ♂ 60—69, ♀ 53—58; tarsus ♂ 21—24, ♀ 19,5—20; culmen 12—15. 19 specimens, 14 ♂, 5 ♀). Iris hazel; bill blackish, base of lower mandible grey; legs dark flesh; palate black in ♂ summer, otherwise brown to rosy. Weight 17—18,5 g.

Identification: As illustrated. Very similar to the Grey-backed Cisticola, No. 638, but fortunately the two do not occur in the same areas (compare maps). Otherwise is most like the Wailing Cisticola, No. 639, but habitat and habits are completely different (see below). For differences from the last species, see under No. 641. Sexes alike, female smaller. In winter both sexes become much redder and striped rather than blotched above and palate colour changes from black in male (see above). Young birds resemble winter adults; no sulphuring below.

Distribution: From Natal northwards to southern Ethiopia; from Transvaal, Botswana and Damaraland northwards to Angola and Zaïre.

Habits: A common and conspicuous species in the dry savanna bush. In summer the male sits on the very top of a tree, or highest point of a dead branch, and utters his very characteristic song. His black palate is conspicuous while singing. In winter small parties may be met with moving through the thorn bushes. They are inquisitive birds and always come to swear at intruders. Females are very unobtrusive and seldom seen.

Voice: Alarm note a harsh, swearing "chair-chair". Song consists of two or three whistling notes followed by a churring trill which gets longer as the breeding season advances: "chee, chee, chichi, chirrrrrrrrrr".

Breeding: Nests are of the ball type, placed in grass mixed with thorn bushes, usually about a foot or less from the ground. Eggs are laid from November to March. They number 3 and are very variable; white or pale blue, plain or variously speckled and blotched with red-brown and secondary purple-grey. Average (34) 18,2 × 12,9 (16,7—19,1 × 12,3—13,8). Incubation by female only. Nestling 14 days.

642

LOCAL RACES:
(a) C.c. chiniana (A. Smith), 1843: *Kurrichane, Transvaal.* Eastern Botswana, Transvaal and Rhodesia. As illustrated. Size above.
(b) C.c. campestris (Gould), 1845: *Australia = coastal South-eastern Africa.* Natal, Swaziland, southern Mozambique, eastern Transvaal and south-east corner Rhodesia. A darker race, especially above in summer plumage. Wing ♂ 59—64—67, ♀ 52—54—58; tail ♂ 53—68, ♀ 49—54; tarsus ♂ 21—23, ♀ 19—21; culmen 12—15. 27 specimens, 20 ♂, 7 ♀.
(c) C.c. frater Reichenow, 1916: *Damaraland.* Damaraland, Botswana and upper Zambesi Valley. A decidedly paler race at all seasons. Wing ♂ 63—66—69, ♀ 51—54—56. 20 ♂, 16 ♀.
(d) C.c. procera Peters, 1868: *Tete.* Lower Zambesi Valley. Above darker with the markings less pronounced, the head-top and wing-edging both a trifle redder; tail shorter by 2 or 3 mm.
(e) C.c. smithersi Hall, 1956: *Panda Matenga, N.E. Botswana.* N.E. Botswana. Above greyer, red head top duller, under-parts greyer, less buff.

643 Singing Cisticola   Singende Tinktinkie

Cisticola cantans   (Heuglin), 1869: *Gondar, Ethiopia.*

Native Names: Chitiwa (D); i-Tsiyana (G).

PLATE 55, ♂ (OPP. P. 449).
Length 11,5—14 cm (wing ♂ 53—58; tail summer 44—48, winter 52—58; tarsus 21,5; culmen 14,5). Iris hazel; bill black; legs brownish flesh. Weight 11 g.

Identification: Very similar indeed to the next species but has the crown and edges of wing-feathers *red*, a conspicuous white eyebrow, and no red on face (Plate 55 is too red in this respect). Sub-loral spot black. Sexes alike. In winter becomes brighter and rustier above. Young birds are dull faded editions of winter adults. The plain back of this species avoids confusion with the other red-faced species, No. 641, which it only meets in central Rhodesia.

Distribution: Rhodesia, east of Selukwe—Salisbury, southern Mozambique northwards to the Sudan and West Africa.

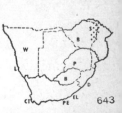

643

Habits: A species of rank grass and weed growths in open bush country where it keeps very much to the shelter of the undergrowth, being more often heard than seen. Likes soft, more or less luxuriant bushes, not hard thorny types.

Voice: Song-calls are uttered from a perch on top of a bush, tree, patch of jungle, or from the lower branches of a small tree. The most characteristic call is "jhu ee" or "wheech oo" and less important calls are "teu teu", "k weck", "o ki wee" and a sibilant cicada-like "srrt srrt srrt"; alarm note a small "tsit tsit".

Breeding: Nests are of the tailor type, sewn into the leaves of a soft-leaved herb or sapling, generally 60—90 cm above the ground, of the same type as the next species. Eggs 2 or 3, white to light turquoise-blue, marked boldly with blotches, and hardly any spots, of various dull reds and secondary greys. They are laid from November to March in Rhodesia. Average (36) 16,8 × 12,4.

LOCAL RACE:
C.c. muenzneri Reichenow, 1916: *Sanya, Mahenge, S. Tanganyika.* From Rhodesia to Malawi and southern Tanzania. As illustrated. Size above.

644   Red-faced Cisticola   Rooiwang-tinktinkie

Cisticola erythrops   Hartlaub, 1857: *West coast of Africa, between Liberia and Nigeria.*
Native Name: u-Msiaan (Z).

PLATE 55, ♂ (OPP. P. 449).
Length 12—14,5 cm (wing ♂ 51—55,5—57, ♀ 48—50,5—54; tail 47—62; tarsus 19—23; culmen 13—15. 15 specimens, 9 ♂, 6 ♀). Iris bright hazel; bill blackish, lower mandible grey; legs brownish flesh.

Identification: Very similar to the last species but the crown and edges of wing-feathers do not contrast strongly with the back, i.e., they are not so red; face pale red (white in the last species), eyebrow less conspicuous. Slightly more buff on chest and flanks than illustrated. For difference from Nos. 639, 640 and 641 note the plain back. Sexes alike. In winter plumage the upper-parts become rich umber-brown; the tawny wash below deepens so that the face in particular shows no white. Young birds are dull equivalents of winter adults.

Distribution: Africa south of the Sahara as far south as eastern Transvaal and Natal, rare south of the Tugela River.

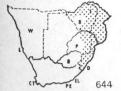

644

Habits: A widespread species in tropical marshes where there are reed beds and also the reeds and vegetation along streams and rivers. Sometimes found a considerable distance away from water. Rather wary birds but easily located on account of their loud call-notes. Perch a great deal on reed stems.

Voice: Utters various *very* loud and cheerful notes, the most characteristic being a "wink, *wink*, WINK" or cheer, *cheer*, CHEER". When less excited the song consists of a tinkling, rather harsh "tink tink tink tink twee twee twee twee" then much louder, rich and metallic "CHEWIP CHEWIP CHE WE WE WE" or "peet peet peet wink WINK WINK" in a crescendo.

Breeding: Nests are of the tailor type, stitched, or rather plugged, inside broad leaves of herbs or saplings. Eggs 2—4, usually 3, are greenish blue with reddish brown blotches more numerous at the obtuse end. Average (26) 17,3 × 12,7. Breeds October to March in Rhodesia.

LOCAL RACE:
C.e. nyasa Lynes, 1930: *Ruo, Chiromo, Nyasaland.* Natal to Tanzania and across to south-eastern Zaïre, Zambia and Malawi. As illustrated. Size above.

645 Black-backed Cisticola   Swartrug-tinktinkie

Cisticola galactotes (Temminck), 1823: *New Holland = South Africa = Natal.*

PLATE 55, ♂ (OPP. P. 449).
Length 10,5—15 cm (wing ♂ 55—59—62, ♀ 52—53,5—55; tail ♂ summer 47—54 ♂ winter 57—63; tarsus 20—23; culmen 12—14. 17 specimens, 10 ♂, 7 ♀). Iris hazel; bill black; centre of lower mandible grey; legs flesh; palate black.

Identification: Might be confused with No. 646, but edges of feathers of back are grey not brown and top of tail in summer is grey and black, not red (see also under Habits below). In winter tail is longer and upper-parts become redder and more narrowly marked with black. Sexes alike. Young are mealy, rusty editions of winter adults, strongly sulphured below.
Distribution: From Natal northwards to Ethiopia on the east across to Zaïre and south to the Okavango. Absent from the west of South Africa.
Habits: A fairly common species which frequents open marshy growth in the low country, living and nesting in the luxuriant growth of reeds and grass at the edges of rivers, lakes and estuaries. Rather a quiet, undemonstrative bird.
Voice: Commonest call is a monotonous, feeble, rasping sound like winding up a watch, "zreeeee" or a harsher "rraaare", uttered with the black mouth conspicuously open; may also call while flying slowly, low over the reeds. Makes various other chirping sounds such as "chit, chit, chit" or "trrrp, trrrp, trrrp". When alarmed "tee, tee", or if very agitated a loud piping "PRRRIT PRRRIT PRRRIT" (compare with No. 646).
Breeding: The nest is of the ball type, placed in grass, sedges and water weeds, about 0,6 to 1,2 metres above floor-level, more or less hidden by overtwined grass and often decorated with cocoons, coloured bits of plants, etc. Eggs 3—4, laid in summer, are very distinctive, being always plain, glossy, deep terra-cotta or brick-red. Size 16—17 × 12,5.

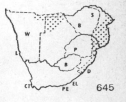

645

LOCAL RACE:
C.g. galactotes (Temminck), 1823: *New Holland = South Africa = Natal.*

645X Chirping Cisticola   Piepende Tinktinkie

Cisticola pipiens Lynes, 1930: *Huambo, Angola.*

PLATE 55, ♂ BR. (OPP. P. 449).
Length about 12,5—15 cm (wing ♂ 60—66; tail ♂ 61—64). Iris brown; bill brown; legs flesh.

Identification: Similar to the previous species but tends to be more black brown than buff, and certainly less streaked on crown. Larger than the previous and differs in song.
Distribution: Southern Zaïre, Zambia and Angola, south to northern Botswana, and in particular the Okavango Swamps from Sepopa in the west to Mababe in the east.
Habits: Very similar to the last species but seems almost entirely confined to papyrus swamps in our area. Seldom goes far from the swamp edges. Male sits

on top of tall reeds to utter song. At least in the breeding season not likely to be overlooked with its extraordinary flight and noticeable song. Flight jerky; tail appears loose, flopping from side to side.

Voice: A croaking or twanging strophe of four notes "trrrit trrit trree-treeeee" or a bubbling "tic-tic-turr".

Breeding: Nest similar to that of 645. Eggs 3—4, glossy pink marbled and clouded with terra-cotta. Average (10) 17,8 × 12,7 (15,7—19,1 × 12—13). October to April in Zaïre.

LOCAL RACE:
C.p. congo Lynes, 1936: *Kinshasa, Zaïre.* As above.

646 Le Vaillant's Cisticola   Vleitinktinkie

Cisticola tinniens (Lichtenstein), 1842: *Kaffirland = Eastern Cape Province.*

Native Name: Umvila (X).

PLATE 55, ♂ (OPP. P. 449).
Length 11,5—15 cm (wing ♂ 50—53,5—58, ♀ 46—49—51; tail ♂ 51—66, ♀ 46—60 all seasons; both sexes short in summer; tarsus 17,5—20; culmen 10—12. 57 specimens, 37 ♂, 20 ♀). Iris hazel; bill black; basal two-thirds lower mandible grey; legs dark flesh.

Identification: See under No. 645 and under Habits below. Black back is diagnostic where No. 645 does not occur. Sexes alike, but female usually slightly more dappled on nape and hind-neck. In winter crown becomes streaked and back more streaked than blotched with black. Young birds are rustier editions of winter adults, top of head darker, more heavily marked; sometimes sulphured about face and breast.

Distribution: From the south-west Cape eastwards to Natal, Transvaal, Rhodesia and Mozambique. Thence northwards to Angola and Zambia and appearing again in Kenya.

646

Habits: A common species which frequents marshes, particularly the fairly short reeds or weeds on the fringes of such areas. Is also found in taller reeds but seldom along rivers. When disturbed makes a lot of noise and perches on the highest point available or flies overhead, keeping the intruder in view.

Voice: Alarm note a moderately loud "tee, tee, tee". Main call during the breeding season "chee chee" (small opening notes) . . . "cherrueee" (loud warble). Note that the Grey-backed Cisticola, No. 638 utters a similar call but the "chee" notes come *after* the warble.

Breeding: Nests are oval balls of rootlets and grass, softly lined, or sometimes completely constructed of plant-down and usually placed in the weeds or short reeds and grass on the banks of streams and marshes. An abnormal cup-shaped nest has been found being used once. Eggs are laid from August to October in the Cape; from September to March in Transvaal and Rhodesia. They vary greatly in colour, being white to greenish or bluish, freckled, blotched or spotted with reds and secondary grey. Pink erythristic eggs also occur. They number 3, 4 or 5. Average (100) 16,1 × 12,1 (14,6—18 × 11,1—13). Nestling period 14 days.

LOCAL RACE:
C.t. tinniens (Lichtenstein), 1842: *Kaffirland = Eastern Cape Province.* As shown on the accompanying map. As illustrated. Size above.

647 Croaking Cisticola   Groot Tinktinkie

Cisticola natalensis (A. Smith), 1843: *Port Natal* = *Durban.*

Native Names: Uboyiboyi (X); u-Boyu (Z); i-Diwamatoro (D).

PLATE 55, ♂ AND ♀ BR., ♂ N-BR. (OPP. P. 449).
Length 13—17,5 cm (wing ♂ 69—72—76, ♀ 58—60,5—63; tail ♂ summer 48—57, winter 59—72; ♀ summer 46—60, winter 56—66; tarsus ♂ 27—30, ♀ 23,5—27; culmen 12—15,5. 40 specimens, 21 ♂, 19 ♀). Iris brown; bill ♂ blackish, ♀ flesh; legs dark flesh; palate ♂ black, ♀ flesh.

Identification: Easily identified by its large size and streaked hind-neck and crown which is *not* red as it is in most cisticolas. Sexes alike but female much smaller, slightly more buff above and with a flesh-coloured bill. In non-breeding dress both sexes grow longer tails and become much more buff above and more boldly streaked (see Plate 55). Young birds are mealy, rusty equivalents of winter adults; brightly sulphured below.
Distribution: Africa south of the Sahara except the great forests, deserts and the southern and western parts of South Africa.

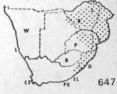

Habits: A common species of rank, open, grassland, or grass country with scattered bushes or trees, more often in dry country than wet but also along the borders of cultivation and small marshes. The males perch on top of bushes and trees, keeping a look-out. They also perform butterfly-like flights over the nesting females, zig-zagging to and fro with bounding wing-beats, uttering peculiar clucking noises.

647

Voice: Alarm note a frog-like croak, generally preceded by a chirp—"tee YRRR" or "chip MUNK" or "ee PRRRK". These notes are repeated over and over again. The female may join in, giving an answering trill after the male's croak.
Breeding: Nest of the ball type, placed in a thick bushy tuft of grass which is intertwined into a bower to hide the nest. It is placed low down almost on the ground. Eggs are laid from December to March in Rhodesia. They are variable in colour from white to pale blue, with scattered spots of red, browns and violet or grey. Average (48) 19,0 × 13,8 (17,6—21 × 12,8—14,6).

LOCAL RACES:
(a) C.n. natalensis (A. Smith), 1843: *Port Natal* = *Durban.* From our area northwards to Malawi and Tanzania. As illustrated. Size above.
(b) C.n. holubi (Pelzeln), 1882: *Panda Matenga, Bechuanaland.* North-eastern Botswana and extreme south-western Rhodesia. Paler, more ashy grey than *(a)* with lighter margins to feathers of upper parts.

648 Lazy Cisticola   Luie Tinktinkie

Cisticola aberrans (A. Smith), 1843: *Near Port Natal* = *Durban.*

Native Name: Ungxengezi, Uqume (X).

PLATE 55, RACE *(a)* ♂ (OPP. P. 449).
Length 13—15 cm (wing ♂ 53—56—59, ♀ 48—51,5—54; tail ♂ 61—72, ♀ 56—64; tarsus 19—23; culmen 11—13. 26 specimens, 14 ♂, 12 ♀). Iris hazel; bill greyish flesh; culmen brown; legs yellowish flesh; palate black.

Identification: In the field appears plain-backed, thus looking rather like a Neddicky, No. 637 *(d)*, but with a very *long tail*, longer even than Nos. 643 and 644, with which it might also be confused; but note that the tail is *plain* below or has only small spots in race *(c)*. Sexes alike. In winter the crown becomes redder, the back rustier and slightly more clearly marked; the mottling becoming stripy. Young birds are dull equivalents of winter adults.

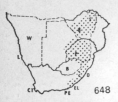

Distribution: From the eastern Cape Province northwards to Malawi and across to eastern Botswana, Rhodesia and Zambia.

Habits: An extremely localized species which favours rank grass and weeds along streams and hillsides, particularly where there are rocks under trees; keeps low down in the vegetation or hops about on the rocks almost like mice, flirting its tail almost like a *Prinia*. In the breeding season cocks emerge and sing from some conspicuous perch. Rather lethargic, not performing any aerial displays.

648

Voice: Song rather feeble, a gabbled strophe of fairly loud metallic ''tu-hwee tu-hwee tu-hwee'' notes uttered as a crescendo and repeated with variations. Other call-notes are ''chu-ip'', ''k-weee'' or ''kwee-et''.

Breeding: Nest of the ball type, placed in the base of a bunch of grass, the tops of which are curled over. Three or four eggs are laid from September to March. They are pale greenish blue, finely spotted with various shades of brown and red: 17,3—17,7 × 12,4—12,8.

LOCAL RACES:
(a) C.a. aberrans (A. Smith), 1843: *Near Port Natal = Durban.* Transvaal. As illustrated. Size above.
(b) C.a. minor Roberts, 1913: *Port St. Johns, C.P.* Eastern Cape to Zululand. Smaller: Wing ♂ 50—51,5—55, ♀ 45—47—50; tail ♂ 55—69, ♀ 51—59; tarsus 19—22; culmen 11—12,5.
(c) C.a. nyika Lynes, 1930: *Nyika Plateau, Malawi.* Eastern Rhodesia to Malawi. Size as in *(a)* but crown darker and usually spots on tail.

Family PRINIIDAE

A small group of birds commonly associated with the Warblers, which they closely resemble, but differing from them in having only 10 tail-feathers. The true Prinias construct oval nests that are woven of strips of green grass or fibres, like those of Weaver Birds, and placed and concealed in bushes or weeds near the ground, seldom at a height of more than 1½ metres, and their eggs are easily distinguished from those of the Warblers. They range through Africa to southern Asia.

649   Tawny-flanked Prinia   Bruinsy-langstert-tinktinkie

Prinia subflava   (Gmelin), 1789: *Senegal.*

Native name: Ungcuze (X).

PLATE 56 (OPP. P. 464).

Length 10—15 cm (wing ♂ 48—51—53, ♀ 45—48—50; tail ♂ summer 54—57, winter 65—81, ♀ summer 47—53, winter 64—70; tarsus 19—22; culmen 10—12,5. 48 specimens, 26 ♂, 22 ♀). Iris light brown; bill black; legs flesh. Weight 8,1—9,0 g.

Identification: The plain under-parts distinguish this *Prinia* from others except the next species in non-breeding dress; the reddish wings are then distinctive. Sexes alike. Young birds are yellowish below and have yellowish bill. Southern birds become much more rufous in the winter.

Distribution: From the eastern Cape Province northwards over most of Africa south of the Sahara and southern Asia as far east as Java.
Habits: A widespread species, found commonly in the coarse vegetation and scrub along rivers and streams. Is usually encountered in pairs or small parties.
Food: Insects such as small beetles, larvae and small flies and moths.
Voice: Alarm note a characteristic "weeping"; song a monotonous "przzt, przzt, przzt". Also utters a loud challenging note.

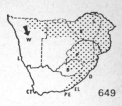

649

Breeding: The oval nest is made of fine strips of reed blade or grass and is lined with fine grass (not down). It is placed in shrubs, reeds over water or weeds, from 75—180 cm up. It also, frequently, has the surrounding leaves sewn into it and a slight porch over the side entrance. Breeds from December to early April in Transvaal; mainly November to March in Rhodesia. A July record near Windhoek. Eggs number three or four; ground-colour varies from cream to blue or greenish, with spots, small blotches and wavy streaks of brown, from liver-brown to chestnut or black, mainly in a zone round the thickest part of the egg. Some eggs have the ground-colour a light reddish brown. Average (150) 15,9 × 11,5 (14,5—17,7 × 10,8—13; one 14 × 11). Nestling period 13—17 days.

LOCAL RACES:
(a) P.s. pondoensis Roberts, 1922: *Port St. John's, Pondoland.* Eastern Cape Province, Natal and Zululand. Outer margin of primaries only slightly reddish, rump, upper tail-coverts and base of tail not reddish, or only slightly so in winter.
(b) P.s. affinis (A. Smith), 1843: *Interior of South Africa = Rustenburg, Transvaal.* Transvaal to south-eastern Zaïre. As illustrated. Size above.
(c) P.s. ovampensis Macdonald, 1941: *Ovaquenyama, Ovamboland.* Northern South West Africa and adjacent Angola. A paler race. A record from Windhoek.
(d) P.s. bechuanae Macdonald, 1941: *Mababe Flats, Bechuanaland.* Northern Botswana, Caprivi, southern Zambia and adjacent Angola.

649X Forest Prinia   Woudtinktinkie

Prinia robertsi Benson, 1946: *Vumba, Southern Rhodesia.*

PLATE 56 (OPP. P. 464).
Length 14—15 cm (wing 50; tail 57—60; culmen 15,5 from base of skull. 2 specimens, 1 ♂, 1 ♀). Iris yellowish brown; bill black; legs brown. Weight 8,3—9,5 g.

Identification: Crown, forehead, sides of head to below the eye brownish slate, merging into dull olive-brown on the mantle, wing-coverts, back, rump and upper tail-coverts. Flight-feathers and tail dark brown. Chin and throat grey, chest greyish rufous, flanks rufous, belly white. Sexes alike.
Distribution: Known only from the eastern regions of Rhodesia, above 1 500 metres.

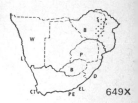

Habits: Quite a common species where it occurs, frequenting the dense scrub, bracken and borders of forest-patches but avoiding the main forests. Spends most of its time creeping about the dense undergrowth but occasionally ascends into the branches of trees. Apparently forms large parties when not breeding.

649X

Food: Small flies, a caterpillar and a beetle recorded.
Voice: A very noisy species, uttering a harsh, rather shrill chatter "cha, cha, cha cha, cha", the *a* as in *bad*.

Breeding: The nest is placed about one metre up and is made of the stripped inflorescences of fine grasses; dome-shaped with a side entrance. It is lightly attached to the plants at the side with cobwebs. Reported breeding in October to February. Eggs 2—3, bright turquoise, boldly marked with large round spots of chocolate and underlying greyish lilac. Three measure 17,5 × 13; 17,6 × 13 and 17,2 × 12,9.

650   Black-chested Prinia
Swartband-langstert-tinktinkie

Prinia flavicans   (Vieillot), 1820: *South Africa = Namaqualand.*

Native Name: Tontobane (Ch).

PLATE 56 (OPP. P. 464).

Length 13—15 cm (wing ♂ 51—53—57 (30), ♀ 48—50—53 (25); tail ♂ summer 62—68, winter 72—94, ♀ summer 50—58, winter 76—81; tarsus 19,5—22; culmen 9—11,5. 39 specimens, 23 ♂, 16 ♀. Iris brownish yellow; bill black; legs flesh. Weight 9,4—10 g.

Identification: In breeding dress easily distinguished by the well-defined broad black bar, as shown. In winter may show no bar or only a few spots; then resembles No. 649 but lacks the reddish wings. Sexes alike. Young birds yellower below, the black bar showing as a brown patch.

Distribution: From the Orange River to Transvaal, the Kalahari, Damaraland and Benguella.

Habits: Usually found in or near patches of short tangled thorn bushes in fairly open ground. In the Kalahari frequents the neighbourhood of pans and is quite common. Feeds mainly in bushes above the ground.

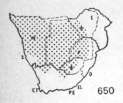
650

Food: Insects.

Voice: Alarm note a weeping sound. The male makes a clapping warbling sound of five or six seconds' duration. "Chip-chip-chip-chip-chip-chip" or "chrrrrrt" or "zrrrrrrt".

Breeding: The nest is an oval structure of grass or reed-blades and is placed 90—150 cm up in grass, shrubs, weeds or even in orange trees. It is lined with vegetable-down, much of it added after the eggs have been laid. A nest was observed to take 11 days to build. Breeds from September to March in Transvaal; December to March in South West Africa and as late as May in the Kalahari. Eggs 3—4, usually blue or blue-green but also light blue, pale olive or pale fawn, with overlapping blotches of brown, grey, purple-grey and black, sometimes with scrolls at the thick end. Average (100) 16,0 × 11,5 (14,7— 17,4 × 10,5—12,4; two 13,7 and 14 × 10,5). Incubation period 12—13 days.

LOCAL RACES:
(a) P.f. flavicans (Vieillot), 1820: *South Africa = Namaqualand.* Cape from Kenhardt, South West Africa except in the north and Botswana. As above.
(b) P.f. ortleppi (Tristram), 1869: *Colesberg, Cape.* From Colesberg north Orange Free State and the Transvaal. More sulphur-yellow below and warmer above.
(c) P.f. ansorgei Sclater, 1927: *Huxe, Southern Angola.* Southern Angola to Kaokoveld. Distinctly white and paler with chest band almost absent when compared with *(a)*.

462

651   Karoo Prinia   Karoo-langstert-tinktinkie

Prinia maculosa   (Boddaert), 1783: *Cape of Good Hope.*

Native Name: Ujiza (X).

PLATE 56 (OPP. P. 464).
Length 13—15 cm (wing ♂ 47—53—58, ♀ 48—50,5—53; tail 60—80; tarsus. 19—22; culmen 10,5—12. 28 specimens, 16 ♂, 12 ♀). Iris light brown; bill black; legs pale brown.

Identification: The long narrow tail and streaked breast are distinctive. Sexes alike. Young birds are more heavily streaked below.
Distribution: Cape Province to Zoutpansberg on the east and Great Namaqualand to the north.
Habits: A very common species of Karoo veld, coastal scrub and mountain slopes, often about streams. An active and excitable bird which creeps about the undergrowth or on the ground in search of its food. When alarmed takes up its stance on top of a bush and scolds the intruder; when too closely approached dives into the undergrowth and slips away on the far side of a bush. Flirts its tail up and down a great deal. May hawk insects in the air. Males have a dipping display flight.

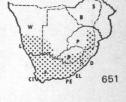
651

Voice: A noisy species which utters a variety of notes. During the male's display he goes "cheeuk, cheeuk". Call-note "ting, ting".
Breeding: The nest is placed fairly low down, from 30 cm to 1 m up in a small bush or clump of grass. It is oval with the entrance at the side and is constructed of green grass and plant-down and well lined with white, woolly plant-down. Recorded having built within old nests of the Red Bishop (No. 808) and Cape Widow (No. 810). But this is rare. Eggs 2—5, usually 4. Mainly August to December; also July through to April rarely. They are pale blue to bluish white, with spots and blotches of liver-brown and lilac with a few marks of deep chestnut-brown and black, mostly concentrated at the thick end. Average (135) 16,5 × 11,8 (14,9—20,0 × 11,0—12,8). Incubation by both sexes 13—14—17 days (17). Nestling 13—14—16 days (14).

LOCAL RACES:
(a) P.m. maculosa (Boddaert), 1783: *Cape of Good Hope.* Cape Province, Great Namaqualand, Orange Free State and Lesotho. Illustrated as **No. 651** *(a).* Size above.
(b) P.m. hypoxantha (Sharpe), 1877: *Eland's Post, Cape Province.* Eastern Cape Province, Natal to Zoutpansberg. Illustrated as **No. 651** *(b).* Wing ♂ 50—51,5—53, ♀ 49—51—53; tail 53—80; tarsus 20—23; culmen 11—13. 21 specimens, 10 ♂, 11 ♀.

652 = 651 *(b)*

653   Namaqua Prinia   Namakwa-langstert-tinktinkie

Burnesia substriata (A. Smith), 1842: *Oliphant's River, Cape Province.*

PLATE 56 (OPP. P. 464).
Length 13—14 cm (wing 52—56; tail 65—78; tarsus 20—22; culmen 11—12,5). Iris grey; bill blue-black; legs flesh.

Identification: The striping extends lower on to the breast than shown on the Plate. May be distinguished from the Karoo Prinia, No. 651, by its redder back and flanks and *plain* tail below. Sexes alike.
Distribution: Confined to the Karoo areas from Little Namaqualand eastwards to Cradock.

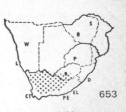
653

PLATE 56

594. *Sylvia communis communis.* Whitethroat. Witkeel-sanger.
595. *Sylvia borin.* Garden Warbler. Tuinsanger.
596. *Hippolais icterina.* Icterine Warbler. Spotvoël.
597. *Hippolais olivetorum.* Olive-tree Warbler. Olyfboomsanger.
598. *Locustella fluviatilis.* River Warbler. Sprinkaan Rietsanger.
599. *Phylloscopus trochilus trochilus.* Willow Warbler. Hofsanger.
600. *Eremomela icteropygialis icteropygialis.* Yellow-bellied Eremomela.
Geelpens-bossanger.
601. *Eremomela usticollis.* Burnt-necked Eremomela. Bruinkeel-bossanger.
602. *Eremomela scotops scotops.* Greencap Eremomela.
Donkerwang-bossanger.
619. *Malcorus pectoralis pectoralis.* Rufous-eared Warbler.
Rooioor-kleinjantjie.
620. *Heliolais erythroptera rhodoptera.* Redwing Warbler.
Rooivlerk-tinktinkie.
621. *Sylvietta rufescens rufescens.* Crombec. Stompstert.
621X. *Sylvietta whytii.* Red-faced Crombec. Rooiwang-stompstert.
621Y. *Sylvietta ruficapilla.* Red-capped Crombec. Rooikroon-stompstert.
626. *Eremomela gregalis gregalis.* Karoo Green Warbler.
Groen Bossanger.
627. *Camaroptera brachyura brachyura.* Bleating Bush Warbler.
Kwêkwêvoël.
628. *Camaroptera brevicaudata sharpei.* Grey-backed Bush Warbler.
Grysrug-bostinktinkie. Br. and N-Br.
649. *Prinia subflava affinis.* Tawny-flanked Prinia.
Bruinsy-langstert-tinktinkie.
649X. *Prinia robertsi.* Forest Prinia. Woudtinktinkie.
650. *Prinia flavicans.* Black-chested Prinia. Swartband-langstert-tinktinkie.
Br. and N-Br.
651 *(a). Prinia maculosa maculosa.* Karoo Prinia. Karoo-langstert-tinktinkie.
651 *(b). Prinia maculosa hypoxantha.* Karoo Prinia. Karoo-langstert-
tinktinkie.
653. *Burnesia substriata.* Namaqua Prinia. Namakwa-langstert-tinktinkie.

594

595

598

599

597

602

601

600

596
KN

619

621 Y
KN

621

620

621 X
KN

626
KN

N-Br

628

Br

653

649

627
KN

KN

651 A

651 B

649 X
KN

650

Br

N-Br

KN

654

655

655 x ♀ ♂

KN

671

454

666

679

668

670

656

657

664

658

659

667 ♀

KN

663

661

662

665 ♂ ♀

NLIGHTON
'39

PLATE 57

454. *Smithornis capensis capensis.* Broadbill. Breëbek.
654. *Muscicapa striata striata.* Spotted Flycatcher. Europese Vlieëvanger.
655. *Muscicapa adusta adusta.* Dusky Flycatcher. Donker Vlieëvanger.
655X. *Muscicapa albicollis.* White-collared Flycatcher. Withals-vlieëvanger.
♂ and ♀.
656. *Muscicapa caerulescens caerulescens.* Blue-grey Flycatcher.
Blougrys Vlieëvanger.
657. *Myioparus plumbeus orientalis.* Grey Tit-babbler.
Waaierstert-vlieëvanger.
658. *Parisoma subcaeruleum subcaeruleum.* Tit-babbler. Tjeriktik.
659. *Parisoma layardi.* Layard's Tit-babbler. Layardse Tjeriktik.
661. *Bradornis mariquensis.* Marico Flycatcher. Marico-vlieëvanger.
662. *Bradornis pallidus murinus.* Mouse-coloured Flycatcher.
Muiskleur-vlieëvanger.
663. *Bradornis infuscatus infuscatus.* Chat Flycatcher. Groot Vlieëvanger.
664. *Melaenornis pammelaina ater.* Black Flycatcher. Swart Vlieëvanger.
665. *Sigelus silens.* Fiscal Flycatcher. Fiskaal-vlieëvanger. ♂ and ♀.
666. *Chloropeta natalensis natalensis.* Yellow Warbler. Geel Sanger.
667. *Bias musicus.* Black and White Flycatcher. Swartwitpens-vlieëvanger.
♂ and ♀.
668. *Hyliota australis australis.* Mashona Flycatcher.
Mashona-vlieëvanger. ♂ and ♀.
670. *Hyliota flavigaster barbozae.* Yellow-bellied Flycatcher.
Geelbors-vlieëvanger.
671. *Seicercus ruficapilla ruficapilla.* Yellow-throated Warbler.
Geelkeel-Sanger.
679. *Erythrocercus livingstonei livingstonei.* Livingstone's Flycatcher.
Rooistert-vlieëvanger.

Habits: A rather rare species which is described as being a restless, rapidly moving little bird which occurs in the scrub along the banks of rivers and streams. Little else seems to have been recorded of its habits.

Voice: Call a distinct "tchit churrrrr"; also "eez-eez-eez" and "che-kee-kee". Song consists of a series of "tik, tik, tik" notes which are run together into a trill rather like a stick held in the spokes of a revolving wheel; this song is higher pitched than that of No. 651.

Breeding: Nest variously described; as an oval constructed of dead grass, leaves, bits of bark and rubbish, lined with feathers, fine roots, and sometimes a little hair; also as a cup-shaped structure. It is placed about 45 cm off the ground, sometimes in a tuft of tall grass or in long weeds, but the most common site is in a heap of rubbish left by floods against small bushes on river banks. Breeds in October. Eggs 2—4, pale to beautiful deep blue, either with small blotches and spots of dark reddish brown, fairly evenly scattered, or with large confluent blotches and a few lines of liver-colour and deep grey, confined mostly to the larger end. Average (9) 16,3 × 10,8 (16—17 × 11—12,7).

Family MUSCICAPIDAE

The Flycatchers are small insectivorous birds which usually have more rictal bristles and flatter bills than the Warblers, most of the species being in the habit of catching their prey in flight from the trees of their habitat. They all construct cup- to saucer-shaped nests in the branches of trees or bushes, sometimes in open clefts or behind loose bark of trees, or, even in one case, inside holes in trees. All the species are insectivorous and a few of them have fairly loud trilling or clapping notes, but most of them are rather silent or small-voiced. Some are plainly coloured but others are beautifully coloured or ornamented. Most are very local in habitat but a few are migratory, the most notable being the Spotted Flycatcher which migrates from Europe to South Africa.

654 Spotted Flycatcher   Europese Vlieëvanger

Muscicapa striata   (Pallas), 1764: *Holland.*

PLATE 57 (OPP. P. 465).
Length 14—15 cm (wing ♂ 85—87,8—91, ♀ 86—87,4—92; tail 58—63; tarsus 13—16; culmen 11,5—14,5. 29 specimens, 17 ♂, 12 ♀). Iris dark red-brown; bill black; legs ashy. Weight 16,1 g.

Identification: Easily confused with the next species but slightly larger, more reddish brown and the markings on head, throat and chest are bolder. The chin is usually off-white and marked. In Southern Africa this is more a species of open areas than the next. Its more pointed wings assist in distinguishing it from other resident species.

Distribution: Europe and western Asia, south to Africa. Occurs throughout Southern Africa, though locally absent from some areas, sparingly distributed in the Cape Province.

Habits: A common non-breeding migrant recorded from late September to early April. A bird ringed in West Finland was recovered near Johannesburg. It is usually found perched low down under trees *bordering open spaces,* or

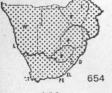

654

even in scattered trees or on wire fences and the like, from which it darts at insects in flight. It has a habit of flicking out its wings a little way when perched.

Voice: A thin sibilant "sep" and a harsher note of alarm "chirrrt".

LOCAL RACES:
(a) M.s. striata (Pallas), 1764: *Holland*. This race is the common one found in our parts.
(b) M.s. balearica Jordans, 1913: *Mallorca Is., Balearica*. A single specimen of this race is recorded by Hoesch and Niethammer from Bullspoort, South West Africa. Distinguished by the faint streaking on the chest and the wide light edges on the feather of the forecrown.
(c) M.s. neumanni Poche, 1904: *Loita Mountains, Kenya*. Western Asia wintering in East Africa—extends to Botswana to central Kalahari. Paler than *(a)*, more ashy below with narrow streaks.

655   Dusky Flycatcher   Donker Vlieëvanger

Muscicapa adusta   (Boie), 1828: *Auteniquoi = Knysna*.

Native Name: Unomaphelama (X).

PLATE 57 (OPP. P. 465).
Length 12—13 cm (wing 63,5—66,5—69; tail 48—55; tarsus 14,5—16,5; culmen 10—12. 26 specimens). Iris dark brown; bill black; tarsus ashy. Weight 9,6 g.

Identification: Smaller and more grey brown than the previous species. The uniformly coloured crown and white chin, contrasting slightly with marked greyish throat, also distinguish this from the last species. See also under Habits. Young is heavily spotted with buffish markings on upper-parts and mottled across breast.

Distribution: From West Africa, Ethiopia southwards to the Cape down the eastern moister areas.

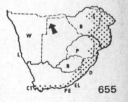

655

Habits: A locally common species for the most part resident; in southern Mozambique recorded only from April to August, whilst Godfrey records it absent from Blythswood, Transkei, during the winter. A bird of the moister-forested areas, it is found under big trees or on the edge of forest glades, perching fairly low down and darting at passing insects. When perched it sometimes flicks its wings like the last species. Usually singly or in pairs. Somewhat quiet, almost secretive and might be passed unnoticed but for its call which reveals its whereabouts.

Voice: A quiet sibilant "z-z-z-st" or "tsirit, tsit, tsirit".

Breeding: The nest site varies from moss-covered rocks to holes in banks, tree trunks and branches up to 9 metres above the ground. The nest is neat, well hidden and composed of bark, fibres, roots, lichens and mosses, neatly lined with horse-hair, rootlets and small feathers. Sides of nest thick and bulky compared to those of a Batis. September to January. Eggs 2—4, usually 3, pale greenish white, profusely speckled and spotted with pinkish to reddish brown, sometimes more concentrated at larger end. Average (30) 18,0 × 13,6 (16,4—19,3 × 12,8—14,5). The egg of a Red-chested Cuckoo has been recorded in a nest of this species. Incubation 14—15 days.

LOCAL RACES:
(a) M.a. adusta (Boie), 1828: *Auteniquoi = Knysna*. From the Cape, eastwards and northwards as far as the Limpopo River, to the north only in the low-lying areas of south-eastern Rhodesia and Mozambique.

(b) M.a. subadusta (Shelley), 1897: *Nyika Plateau, Nyasaland.* Replaces the nominate race to the north in Rhodesia, Zambia, Malawi and northern Mozambique. More buffy grey than *(a)* and smaller. Wing 61—67,5; tail 46—51; tarsus 11—14; culmen 10—11.

655X   White-collared Flycatcher   Withals-vlieëvanger

Muscicapa albicollis   Temminck, 1815: *Waltershausen, Thuringia, Germany.*

PLATE 57 (OPP. P. 465).

Length about 13 cm (wing 80—85). Iris dark brown; bill and legs black.

Identification: A small black-and-white flycatcher; white below, upper-parts black with forehead white; a broad white collar and patch on wing-coverts. Young birds lack white on collar and are brown.

Distribution: Central Europe to Persia, south to Africa. A few records from Zambia. Recorded from Matopos, Rimuka (near Gatooma) Salisbury, in Rhodesia, the Transvaal and South West Africa.

Habits: A vagrant in our area; there are single records for November and January. In habits similar to the previous species. When hunting insects does not always return to the same perch.

656   Blue-grey Flycatcher   Blougrys Vlieëvanger

Muscicapa caerulescens   (Hartlaub), 1865: *Natal*

PLATE 57 (OPP. P. 465).

Length 14—15 cm (wing ♂ 72—76,7—82,5, ♀ 70—73; tail 56,5—62; tarsus 15,5—17; culmen 11—12. 18 specimens, 14 ♂, 4 ♀). Iris brown; bill and legs black.

Identification: Distinguished from the next species by having no white on tail and by a black spot in front of eye. The white line over the eye and lores is easily seen. The blue-grey colour differentiates it from the previous two species. Sexes alike. Young is mottled below as far as belly and has speckled upper-parts and wing-coverts; tail as adult (see No. 657).

Distribution: A tropical species; from West to East Africa extending southwards to Ovamboland, Ngamiland, northern and eastern Transvaal and the eastern littoral through Natal to East London in the eastern Cape.

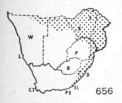

656

Habits: A widely distributed resident, common at lower altitudes. It has much the same quiet ways and habitat of the Dusky Flycatcher except that it occurs in drier forests. Usually occurs in pairs, sometimes in association with mixed bird parties. Unlike the next species it darts into the air after insects in typical flycatcher fashion.

Food: Insects.

Voice: A tripping, sibilant, non-musical loud call "tsip tsip tsip tsip tse tslipsip", or a husky "zayt".

Breeding: Situated in the niche of a tree trunk or branch of a Euphorbia, the nest site is similar to that of the Dusky Flycatcher; the nest differs from that species by being composed of matted fibres and stringy green mosses. September to December. Eggs 2—3, creamy or pale buff covered with minute pale grey and yellowish brown markings. Average (24) 19,4 × 14,4 (18—20,5 × 13,3—15).

LOCAL RACES:
(a) M.c. caerulescens (Hartlaub), 1865: *Natal*. Eastern Cape Province northwards to eastern Transvaal and southern Mozambique. Darker above and below than *(b)*. As illustrated. Size above.
(b) M.c. cinereola Finsch and Hartlaub, 1870: *Usaramo, Dar-es-Salaam, Dist. Tanganyika*. Eastern Rhodesia and Mozambique north of the Save River. Lighter above and white below.
(c) M.c. impavida Clancey, 1957: *14 mls. W. of Victoria Falls*. Inland from northern Botswana, Zambia and Angola. Less bluish, paler above and whiter below than *(b)*.

657 Grey Tit-babbler   Waaierstert-vlieëvanger

Myioparus plumbeus (Hartlaub), 1858: *Casamanse, Senegal*.
PLATE 57 (OPP. P. 465).
Length about 14 cm (wing ♂ 65—66,8—69, ♀ 61—63,4—66; tail 56—67; tarsus 16—18, culmen 11—12. 23 specimens, 11 ♂, 12 ♀). Iris red-brown; bill black; legs slate.

Identification: Distinguishable by the white outer tail-feathers which are easily seen because of its habit of raising and lowering its longish tail and fanning it at the same time. Chin is uniform with throat. See also under Habits. Sexes alike. Young very similar to the last species but tail as adult.
Distribution: From Senegal to Ethiopia southwards to Rhodesia, Swaziland, Natal as far as the Tugela River and northern Lesotho.
Habits: Sparsely distributed and somewhat uncommon. Usually occurs in pairs and often joins bird parties. Occurs along the edges of dry forests where the latter adjoin clearings. Creeps about the middle layers of foliage in search of its food, more suggesting a warbler than a flycatcher. The habit of raising and lowering the tail, see above, and spasmodically flicking the wings is very characteristic.

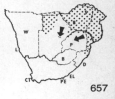

657

Food: Caterpillars and small beetles.
Voice: A loud musical "tee-ry-tee".
Breeding: Nests in old barbet or woodpecker nests or in holes in decayed branches of *Brachystegia*; up to 6 metres high. The nest is padded with a few fine straws, roots and shredded bark. September to December. Eggs 2, greenish white, thickly covered with olive and some slate-brown speckles. 17 × 13, 17 × 13,3, 17,5 × 12,5.

LOCAL RACES:
(a) M.p. orientalis (Reichenow and Neumann), 1895: *Kibwesi, Kenya*. From Kenya southwards on the east.
(b) M.p. grandior Clancey, 1962: *35 mls. W. of Nangweshi, Barotseland*. Zaïre, Tanzania south to the Okavango River—mainly west of *(a)*. Slightly paler than *(a)* but larger. Wing ♂ 70—73,5; ♀ 65—69,5; tail ♂ 63—69; ♀ 58—63 (10 ♂, 12 ♀).

658 Tit-babbler   Tjeriktik

Parisoma subcaeruleum (Vieillot), 1817: *Gouritz River, Cape Province*.
PLATE 57 (OPP. P. 465).
Length 14—16 cm (wing ♂ 62—66,9—71, ♀ 62—64,9—69; tail 62—74; tarsus 19—23; culmen 10—13,5. 46 specimens, 29 ♂, 17 ♀). Iris white to cream; bill black; legs dusky. Weight 15,6 g.

Identification: The well-marked spotted chin and throat and the rufous under tail-coverts are diagnostic; the white tips to outer tail-feathers also aid in

identifying this species. The female is said to be duller, the throat with narrower streaks.

Distribution: From the Cape north to southern Angola, Ngamiland and Rhodesia except southern Mashonaland and Eastern Districts; extending eastwards to the Drakensberg.

Habits: A common resident usually seen singly or in pairs. To be found creeping about larger bushes, thickets and thorn trees, especially those along dongas or sheltered hillsides. Searches for its food while creeping and hopping about within thickets, keeping out of sight; works its way through bushes then suddenly flies to the next bush and dives in.

Food: Insects, spiders, grubs and berries.

Voice: A loud "cheriktiktik" answered by the mate. An explosive run of sharply uttered ticks, often followed by a burst of song consisting of a few lovely clear ringing notes "chuu-ti, chuu-ti, chuu-chuu". Song is variable and often imitative of other birds.

Breeding: The nest is frequently situated up to 3 metres but usually under 1,2 metres from the ground in a thorn bush, but may be in a thicket or in a cluster of parasitic plants; Roberts records a clutch of this species taken from a Sparrow-Weaver's nest. Situated within the foliage near the end of a branch, the nest is a delicate bowl-shaped nest of fibre and rootlets bound together with cobwebs amongst the twigs, lined with plant-down or even fine dry grass only. August to December in the Cape, a month later in the Transvaal and to February in South West Africa and Rhodesia. Eggs 2—3, white with markings of greenish brown or sepia and underlying markings of blue-grey mostly at the thick end; some eggs with black and no sepia markings. Average (83) 18,3 × 13,8 (16,3—20 × 12,7—14,8). Incubation 13—15 days (2). Nestling 14—15 days (2).

LOCAL RACES:
(a) P.s. subcaeruleum (Vieillot), 1817: *Gouritz River, Cape Province.* Southern Cape Province, Orange Free State, higher parts of the Natal interior, Transvaal and Botswana. Darker than *(b)*. As illustrated. Size above.
(b) P.s. cinerascens Reichenow, 1902: *Hereroland.* South West Africa east to Matabeleland, Midlands and Beatrice in Rhodesia. Whiter under-parts than *(a)*.

659   Layard's Tit-babbler   Layardse Tjeriktik

Parisoma layardi   Hartlaub, 1862: *Zwartland, Malmesbury Dist.*

PLATE 57 (OPP. P. 465).
Length 14—16 cm (wing ♂ 64—65,7—67, ♀ 64—66,5; tail 61—64; tarsus 18—21; culmen 10,5—12. 10 specimens, 7 ♂, 3 ♀). Iris white; bill black; legs dark brown.

Identification: Distinguished by its spotted chin and throat, light eye and *white* under tail-coverts. Sexes alike. Young are said to be browner above and the throat less distinctly streaked.

Distribution: Generally from Olifants River, western Cape, northwards to Brandberg in South West Africa; east to Excelsior in the Orange Free State, Lesotho and Pirie forest in the eastern Cape. The Malmesbury area, not commonly met with along the coast until north of Berg River.

Habits: A rather uncommon resident. In South West Africa it occurs especially on the slopes and ravines of the mountains. Similar in habit and habitat preference to the last species.

Voice: A fine song interspersed with rattling sounds.
Breeding: Placed in a matted bush, similar to that of the preceding. November. Eggs 3, similar to the last species but less glossy, the markings less greenish and covering the egg more completely. Average (6) 17,6 × 13,1 (17,2—18,0 × 13—13,5).

LOCAL RACES:
(a) P.l. layardi Hartlaub, 1862: *Zwartland, Malmesbury Dist.* As above. S.W. Cape.
(b) P.l. barnesi Vincent, 1948: *Lekhalabaletsi Valley, Basutuland.* Darker above.
(c) P.l. aridicola Winterbottom, 1959: *Noisabis, Richtersveld.* Paler above. L. Namaqualand, north and east to O.F.S.

660 Herero Chat   Herero-spekvreter

Namibornis herero (de Schauensee), 1931: *Damaraland: Usakos.*
PLATE 50 (OPP. P. 400).
Length about 17 cm (wing ♂ 90—95 (4), ♀ 89—91 (6); tail 69, 72; tarsus 21, 22; culmen 14, 15. 2 specimens).

Identification: The rufous tail and white eye-stripe distinguish this Chat. Observations on the biology and ecology as well as anatomical evidence indicate that this species belongs to the thrushes *Turdidae* and not the flycatcher as was formerly believed.
Distribution: Confined to the "randberge" of western Damaraland from the Erongo Plateau south to just beyond the Naukluftberge. Extends into the Namib seasonally. Also southern Angola.
Habits: A local species, not uncommon but rather shy. During the rainy season they go further into the Namib than is normal. Recorded in groups of up to five during the dry season. Found for the most part on steep cliffs which have few bushes and small trees, also in hilly regions. Usually perches on the ground or in the lower branches of small trees and according to Hoesch and Niethammer never observed on rocks. When it lands, flicks its wings much as the Familiar Chat, No. 570.
Food: Ants and berries.
Voice: Often repeated and loud "ti-tu-tii".
Breeding: Found breeding in March. Nest a bulky cup built in a bush. Eggs, 1—2, pale blue with reddish spots.

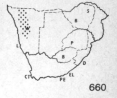

660

661 Marico Flycatcher   Marico-vlieëvanger

Bradornis mariquensis A. Smith, 1847: *South Africa = Marico River, Transvaal.*
PLATE 57 (OPP. P. 465).
Length about 18 cm (wing 80—85,4—92; tail 71—81; tarsus 19—24; culmen 12—14. 32 specimens). Iris dark brown; bill and legs black. Weight 24,1 g.

Identification: Distinguished from the next species by the lighter underparts which contrast with the fawn-brown upper-parts; thus the breast is conspicuously light grey. The edges to the wing-feathers are lighter, buff when seen at a reasonable range. A dark spot in front of eye. Both species have light buff rim around eye and line from eye to bill. Young birds are spotted above and underparts have feathers edged with brown.

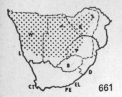

661

Distribution: The drier western areas of South West Africa south to the Naukluft mountains, the Kalahari to northern Cape, western and northern Transvaal and Rhodesia.

Habits: A common resident. Found singly or in pairs but often in small parties. Occurs in open acacia thornveld and may be seen perching on the outer, lower branches of trees from which it hunts. Sometimes flies after insects but usually drops on to the ground after prey. When on the ground the longish tail is held up, the head and breast are also held high. Habitually flicks its tail when settling.

Food: Insects.

Voice: Alarm note is a loud chattering series of "churrs".

Breeding: Situated in open sites 1,2 to 4,2 metres from the ground in small thorn trees, sometimes in clusters of parasitic plants, the nest is a ragged and frail cup-shaped structure built of rootlets, dry plant stems and soft grass, lined with soft vegetable matter, wool or feathers. July to January. Eggs 2—3, pale greenish with very faint indications of speckles sometimes forming an indistinct ring at the larger end. Average (50) 19,9 × 14,4 (18,5—21 × 13,2—15,3).

LOCAL RACES:
(a) B.m. mariquensis A. Smith, 1847: *South Africa = Marico River, Transvaal.* Southern and eastern part of the species distribution. As above.
(b) B.m. acaciae Irwin, 1957: *Ohopoho, Kaokoveld.* Northern S.W.A. and adjacent Angola. Much yellower than *(a)* and larger. Wing ♂ 86,5—89—91, ♀ 84,5—87,7—90,5; tail ♂ 76—78,5—81, ♀ 73,5—77,9—80,5; culmen ♂ 16,5—17,5—18,5, ♀ 17—17,5—18,5 (10 ♂, 10 ♀) after Lawson 1963.

662 Mouse-coloured Flycatcher
Muiskleur-vlieëvanger

Bradornis pallidus (v. Müller), 1851: *Ethiopia and Kordofan = Kordofan.*

PLATE 57 (OPP. P. 465).

Length 15—17 cm (wing ♂ 89—92,8—96, ♀ 83—87,2—94; tail ♂ 68—73, ♀ 60—74; tarsus 17,5—21; culmen 13—15. 40 specimens, 20 ♂, 20 ♀). Iris chestnut-brown; bill and legs dusky black.

Identification: Generally an earth-brown above, underparts not conspicuously lighter, with throat, chest and flanks buffish grey. See previous species. Young with light triangular-shaped spots and broad buff edges to wing-feathers.

Distribution: Over most of the acacia savanna of the Ethiopian region except the southern parts. From the Tugela River, Zululand, Swaziland and northern Transvaal northwards. Also in South West Africa on the Waterberg Plateau.

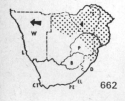

662

Habits: A common resident species found in acacia savannas and dry thorn scrub. Habits the same as for the last species, catching insects more off the ground than in the air.

Voice: Alarm a soft "churr".

Breeding: The nest is situated in small trees in scattered thorn scrub placed against the trunk or out on a branch 1,5—4 metres up. The nest is very similar to the last species. August to March. Eggs 2—3, greenish white closely freckled with yellowish or reddish brown and violet-grey underlying spots, more heavily marked at the thick end and sometimes forming a ring. Average (80) 19,7 × 14,7 (17,8—22,7 × 12,9—16,5).

LOCAL RACES:
There is difference of opinion on the racial status of this species. Five races have been used in reviews since the 1957 revision of this book.
(a) B.p. murinus Finsch and Hartlaub, 1870: *Caconda, Angola.* Throughout our area. Size above. As illustrated.

663 Chat Flycatcher   Groot Vlieëvanger

Bradornis infuscatus (A. Smith), 1839: *between Olifant's and Orange River.*

PLATE 57 (OPP. P. 465).
Length about 20 cm (wing 109—113—119; tail 75—91; tarsus 27—32; culmen 19—21. 5 specimens). Iris dark brown; bill and legs black.

Identification: The largest of the flycatcher group, this bird is distinguished by its size and uniform colouring. The light edges to wing-feathers are easily seen in the field. Female slightly more rusty brown than male.

Distribution: Peculiar to certain types of Karoo scrub and the dry west from Olifants River, western Cape, northwards to Angola. Extends eastwards to western Transvaal and Orange Free State (Boshof), and to Somerset East in the eastern Cape.

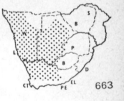

663

Habits: A widely distributed, somewhat uncommon resident in dry open country. Sits on some prominent perch, a bush or telegraph wire, from which it looks out for insects. Flies down with a rather clumsy action, dropping onto the insect on the ground. Though similar in habits to the last two species, this bird was placed with the Chats because of its general appearance.

Food: Grasshoppers, ants.

Voice: Usually silent; a low chatter recorded.

Breeding: Situated in an open bush, usually rather low, the nest is a large cup-shaped structure of grass and rootlets lined with vegetable-down. October to December. Eggs 2—3, greenish blue boldly marked with reddish spots and elongate marks and slaty underlying marks mainly at the larger end. Average (15) 23,0 × 17,1 (20—25 × 16,2—18).

LOCAL RACES:
(a) B.i. infuscatus (A. Smith), 1839: *between Olifant's and Orange River.* From Berg River mouth along the coast, general from Olifant's to Orange River. Recorded as far south as Malmesbury. Dark above, paler below. As illustrated. Size above.
(b) B.i. seimundi O. Grant, 1913: *Deelfontein, Cape.* From Somerset East to Griqualand West. Darker above and below. Smaller.
(c) B.i. benguellensis Sousa, 1886, *Benguella.* Damaraland and Southern Benguella. Paler above and below. Size much as in *(b).*
(d) B.i. namaquensis Macdonald, 1957: *Aanhoup, South West Africa.* Southern Great Namaqualand east to the Kalahari.
(e) B.i. placidus Clancey, 1958: *Kakia, Botswana.* Western Orange Free State and Transvaal, south to north-east Botswana.

473

664 Black Flycatcher

Swart Vlieëvanger

Melaenornis pammelaina (Stanley), 1814: *Abyssinia = Mozambique.*
PLATE 57 (OPP. P. 465).

Length 19—22 cm (wing ♂ 104—107—114, ♀ 97—102—106; tail 84—102; tarsus 20,5—25; culmen 13,5—15. 24 specimens, 15 ♂, 9 ♀). Iris dark brown; legs and bill black.

Identification: This species is distinguished with difficulty from the other similar, wholly black species, the Square-tailed Drongo, No. 518, and Black Cuckoo-Shrike, No. 513, see under habits. The eye is *dark brown* and the base of the bill is *black.* Compare Nos. 513 and 518. Tail squarish at tip. The plumage is glossier than the Black Cuckoo-Shrike. Immature has spotted upper-parts, browner and mottled below.

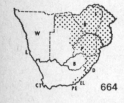

664

Distribution: Eastern and eastern-southern Africa. Comes down the littoral as far as Bushmans River mouth, extending to the west through Transvaal and Ngamiland.

Habits: A widely but sparsely distributed resident, except in the extreme south-east where it occurs during the summer only. Usually seen singly or in pairs; family parties of up to five recorded. It has a habit of perching on the projecting branches of a large tree in semi-open areas and resembles the previous species in hawking insects or dropping to the ground to pick them up. Is thus not confined to dense and shady forests as is the Square-tailed Drongo, nor always on the move searching for insects on leaves and branches as the Black Cuckoo-Shrike. This species shows a preference for Fever Trees in Mozambique.

Food: Insects.

Voice: A low sibilant "swee"; "swee, swee-ur", or "thew-thew, zt-zt, pew".

Breeding: The nest is placed in a niche or crevice in a tree trunk, tree stump or wall; also encountered among the bases of the leaves of an aloe and in an old Thrush nest. It is usually situated 60—240 cm up, although recorded up to 9 metres. The nest is a shallow cup of rootlets, fibres and soft dry vegetable material. Sometimes uses the same nest year after year. September to January. Eggs 2—4, usually 3, greenish white heavily obscured by overlying small markings of reddish and slate-brown, occasionally with markings indistinct. Average (54) 21,6 × 16,0 (19,5—24 × 15—16,8). Nestling 15 days.

LOCAL RACES:
(a) M.p. pammelaina (Stanley), 1814: *Abyssinia = Mozambique.* Extending southwards as far as the lower Zambezi. A smaller race; wing ♂ 102—105, ♀ 96; tail 81—91.
(b) M.p. ater (Sundevall), 1851: *Durban, Natal.* Eastern Cape Province, northwards to Mozambique and west to Transvaal, Ngamiland and Rhodesia. As illustrated. Size above.

665 Fiscal Flycatcher

Fiskaal-vlieëvanger

Sigelus silens (Shaw), 1809: *forests of Auteniquois = Knysna.*

Native Name: Icola (X).
PLATE 57, ♂ AND ♀ (OPP. P. 465).

Length 17—20 cm (wing ♂ 91—95,6—98, ♀ 87—89,8—93; tail 73—89; tarsus 21—24,5; culmen 13,5—17,5. 32 specimens, 24 ♂, 8 ♀). Iris hazel; bill and legs black. Weight 25,2—27,9 g.

Identification: Frequently confused with the Fiscal Shrike, No. 707, because of its superficial resemblance and its habit of perching in a prominent position on a bush or telephone pole. This species has a shorter tail, with conspicuous white windows on either side visible in flight; the bill is thin and flat; the white on the wing is on the flight-feathers, not coverts. See No. 707. Female as illustrated. Immature like female. Young has wing and tail-pattern of adult but is spotted above and mottled below.

Distribution: Peculiar to Southern Africa; extending to just north of Maputo in Mozambique, the Transvaal and Tati in northern Botswana.

Habits: A common species, somewhat sedentary; said to be a winter visitor to Pondoland and Natal and a winter invasion recorded in Mozambique. Usually found single or in pairs. Found in low open bushy areas and savanna country. Frequents gardens in towns and villages, perching on some prominent site and hawking insects or picking them up from the ground. Said to dive at other birds, though never harming them.

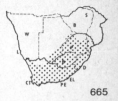

665

Food: Insects, occasionally seeds and fruits.

Voice: Feeble but protracted; a sibbling note; a "wheeze" followed by "chat chat". Said to mimic other birds. Alarm note "skisk" also "kirr-kirr-kirr".

Breeding: The nest is a rather bulky, shallow bowl placed in the fork of a small tree or at the base of an aloe leaf up to 6 metres above the ground. Composed of twigs, straw, weeds and with rootlets or vegetable-down as lining. August to January and one record in March. Eggs 3, occasionally 2 or 4, pale greenish blue with a thin suffusion of minute speckles of reddish, mostly at the thick end. Average (50) 21,5 × 15,8 (20,1—24,2 × 15—17). Incubation 13—15 days (3).

666 Yellow Warbler   Geel Sanger

Chloropeta natalensis A. Smith, 1847: *Port Natal = Durban.*

PLATE 57 (OPP. P. 465).
Length 14—15 cm (wing ♂ 59—61,6—64, ♀ 59—60—61; tail 57—62; tarsus 19,5—23; culmen 11—13. 24 specimens, 17 ♂, 7 ♀). Iris grey-brown; bill brown, yellowish below; legs slate.

Identification: This bird is regarded as a warbler since in appearance and habits it is like a reed warbler—it is thus unmistakable. Female a little duller coloured. Young is more orange-yellow below, the edges to the feathers of the rump, wings and tail buff.

Distribution: From Cameroon to Ethiopia southwards to Angola on the west, eastern Rhodesia, southwards on the eastern side of the Drakensberg and Zoutpansberg to Natal and Transkei (Coffee Bay). Also King William's Town.

Habits: A local and not very common species found singly or in pairs. Occurs in small upland valleys near water, where it inhabits grass, reeds, bracken and scattered scrub, usually near evergreen forests. Also riverine bush in flat country. Searches through the upright stems in a horizontal position, snapping up disturbed insects from the vegetation and not flying out into the open as flycatchers do.

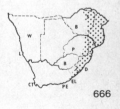

666

Food: Insects, chiefly *Coleoptera.*

Voice: A loud characteristic call; somewhat variable "chudlee-chudlee-wupdudlee-dudlee"; a triple series "trip-trip-trel-el-el-el-el-el-el". Alarm note a sharp "chip".

Breeding: The nest is attached to upright reed stems, bracken or in the fork of a small shrub situated up to 2,7 m high in rank vegetation near a stream. It is like that of a reed warbler, bound around the stems with bark shreds, grasses and rootlets, the cup lined with finer grass. October to February. Eggs 2, white, sometimes uniform but usually beautifully marked with a few pink or pinky brown streaks or dots and a number of similarly coloured specks at the obtuse end. Average (18) 18,1 × 13,4 (17,3—19 × 12,8—14).

LOCAL RACE:
C.n. natalensis A. Smith, 1847: *Port Natal* = *Durban*. As far north as Malawi. As illustrated. Size above.

667 Black and White Flycatcher
Swartwitpens-vlieëvanger

Bias musicus (Vieillot), 1818: *Malimbe, Cabinda.*

PLATE 57, ♂ AND ♀ (OPP. P. 465).
Length about 16 cm (wing 82,5, 84; tail 49, 50; tarsus 12, 13; culmen 20,5, 21. 2 specimens). Iris yellow; bill black; feet dull yellow. Weight 30 g.

Identification: The black-and-white pattern with black extending down to chest is unmistakable. In the treetops and from below the white basal portions of the primaries are a conspicuous feature. Female has a rust-coloured tail, lower back and wings; males also recorded like females. Young differ markedly; upper-parts and tail rust-coloured with head streaked brown, primaries brown and underparts white. Intermediate plumage with head and neck black, throat mottled.

Distribution: A tropical species from West Africa to Uganda southwards to Angola and coming within our limits on the north-eastern littoral as far south as Inhambane and Eastern Districts of Rhodesia.

667

Habits: Rare within our limits. A restless species found singly or in pairs frequenting the higher parts of tall trees along the borders of forests and strips of savanna bush, especially near streams. Moves from branch to branch or tree to tree with deliberate flight likened to the display flight of the Cape Widow Bird, No. 810.

Voice: A loud harsh "tchi-ki*k*-you" or "we-chip! chip-chip!" often repeated and sometimes winding up to an excited series of calls.

Breeding: Not recorded in our area. The nest is a shallow cup placed on a stout horizontal bough and is composed of strips of bark, rotten wood bound with silky fibres, and lined with stems of leaves or flowers. Eggs 2, pale bluish green with small spots of brown and grey with a zone of larger blotches at large end. 21 × 16. Probably breed in February in Malawi.

LOCAL RACE:
B.m. changamwensis van Someren, 1919: *Changamwe.*

668 Mashona Flycatcher
Mashona-vlieëvanger

Hyliota australias Shelley, 1882: *Hartley Hills, Umvuli River, Rhodesia.*

PLATE 57 (OPP. P. 465).
Length about 12 cm (wing 69—71,6—76; tail 44—50; tarsus 16—19,5; culmen 11—12,5. 9 specimens). Iris brown; bill black, bluish grey below; legs black.

Identification: May be distinguished from the next species, by its browner upper-parts and no white on tertiaries. Female is brownish grey above. Young lighter than female.

Distribution: Eastern Zaïre to eastern Tanzania southwards to Rhodesia and Mozambique as far south as Inharrime.

Habits: Somewhat uncommon, occurring singly or in pairs, sometimes joining bird parties. Restricted to *Brachystegia* especially the flat-crowned mountain acacia, *B. tamarindoides*, and where this tree is common it is invariably to be found. Frequents the tops of trees, seldom in the lower levels, seeking insects from bark or leaves but also catches insects in the air. Flight is rapid and zig zag invariably ending up behind a tree trunk.

Voice: Pleasant little chippering whistles followed sometimes by a sweet trilling warble.

Breeding: The nest is placed in the topmost branches of a tree, 6—7,5 metres up, and built in a fork. It is a neat, cup-shaped structure made of lichens, similar to that of the Puff-backed Shrike. August to January. Eggs 3, pinky white with very small spots of reddish brown and slate scattered all over with a concentration at the thick end. 17 × 13, 17 × 12,5 and 15 × 11,5.

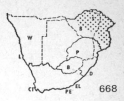

LOCAL RACE:
H.a. australis Shelley, 1882: *Hartley Hills Umvuli River, Rhodesia.* Throughout the species range except in Kenya and Tanzania. The largest race.

669 = 668

670   Yellow-bellied Flycatcher   Geelbors-vlieëvanger

Hyliota flavigaster   Swainson, 1837: *Senegal.*

PLATE 57 (OPP. P. 465).
Length about 13 cm (wing 65—68,8—74; tail 42—50; tarsus 17—19; culmen 11—12. 5 specimens; after Hartlaub). Iris dark brown; bill black, bluish grey below; legs bluish grey. Weight 11,7 g.

Identification: More rufous below than the previous species, the upper-parts metallic blue. The white on wing extends on to tertiaries. Female is grey above with a bluish tinge. Young has finely barred upper-parts and light edges to the feathers.

Distribution: A tropical species that extends from West Africa to Ethiopia and southwards to Angola and the lower Zambesi Valley. Recorded from Chimonzo and Panda in Mozambique.

Habits: Much as for the last species.

Breeding: Similar to last species.

LOCAL RACE:
H.f. barbozae Hartlaub, 1883: *Caconda, Angola.* The southern race.

671   Yellow-throated Warbler   Geelkeel-sanger

Seicercus ruficapilla   (Sundevall), 1850: *Caffraria Inf. = Durban.*

Native Name: um-Besi (X).

PLATE 57 (OPP. P. 465).
Length 10—12 cm (wing 49—52,8—56; tail 38—45,5; tarsus 18,5—20,5; culmen 10—11,5. 9 specimens). Iris brown; bill brown, lighter below; legs pale brown.

Identification: The yellow throat, eye-stripe and under tail-coverts make identification rather easy. The flanks are slightly darker grey than illustrated. Sexes alike. Young birds have breast greenish yellow.

477

671

Distribution: Ranging in evergreen forests from Swellendam, eastwards to Natal thence northwards east of the Drakensberg to Zoutpansberg, eastern border of Rhodesia and northwards to Malawi and Tanzania.

Habits: A common species occurring singly or in pairs, often joining foraging bird parties, especially in association with White-eyes. It occurs in forests and along forest edges in the upper levels of the vegetation, usually revealing its presence by its plaintive monosyllabic call. In appearance and habits rather like the Willow Warbler, jumping restlessly about the branches after insects, flitting out at insects or hovering to take an insect off a leaf.

Voice: A plaintive "tieuu" repeated for long periods, or a high-pitched "zit-zit" or metallic "tsit-sop-sop". Duet call "tsee" replied by "tsik". A song, largely of "cheefer-cheefer-cheefer" repeated in succession.

Breeding: The nest is situated in a small shrub, more usually on a moss-covered bank or slope, well concealed and domed by naturally growing moss, but if this is not available is built entirely of loose moss. Bell-Marley records a nest (specimen collected) in a solitary weaver's nest. The nest cup is lined with a little grass and a few feathers. October, November and young still being fed in April. Eggs 3, a delicate pale pink spotted and freckled in light red. 15,1 × 11; 16,4 × 12,5.

LOCAL RACES:
(a) S.r. ruficapilla (Sundevall), 1851: *Caffraria Inf.* = *Durban.* Natal and eastern Transvaal. As illustrated. Size above.
(b) S.r. voelckeri Roberts, 1941: *Cradocksbush, Knysna.* Southern and eastern Cape. Differs from *(a)* by having yellow extending to lower breast and flanks, only slightly greyish on remainder of flanks.
(c) S.r. johnstoni W. Sclater, 1927: *Kombi, Masuku Mountains, Nyasaland.* Eastern Rhodesia highlands north to Malawi. Yellow confined to throat and edge of upper breast.

672 Cape Batis   Bosbontrokkie

Batis capensis   (Linnaeus), 1766: *Cape of Good Hope.*

Native Name: Ingedle (X).

PLATE 58, ♂ AND ♀ (OPP. P. 480).
Length 12—13 cm (wing ♂ 57—60,3—63, ♀ 56,5—60,3—63; tail (39) 42—48,5; tarsus 18—22; culmen 12—15. 38 specimens, 19 ♂, 19 ♀). Iris yellow, red in ♂ in breeding condition; bill and legs black. Weight (25) 9,3—14,2 g.

Identification: The male is the only *Batis* having rufous flanks and wing-coverts; the width of the black chest band is variable. The female is distinguished by rufous on the wing-coverts and the white line extending only from the bill to the eye; the belly is usually white. Young male resembles female. Fledgling is grey above, head striped and mantle spotted with buff; chin and throat tinged buff, otherwise white below.

Distribution: Confined to Southern Africa, from the southern and eastern Cape Province, Natal, Zululand, the mountain forests of Swaziland and its vicinity, and eastern Transvaal. In Rhodesia confined to the eastern border and the Matopos. Also occurs in Malawi.

Habits: A common resident species; in the north of its range is confined to higher levels of forest and consequently has become isolated in many areas. Found generally in pairs, often in company with other species, this flycatcher is partial to moister forests, kloofs and the marginal vegetation of these areas.

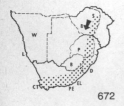

672

Many birds may gather together in a small area, calling and behaving excitedly. Active little birds that hop about the branches searching for insects, also flying out at insects, and when alarmed creating a noisy whirr of air through their wings with each beat. Incubating birds usually very tame.

Food: Insects.

Voice: Alarm note is a grinding "prritt, prritt", like two stones rubbed together. Call a repeated single "reep reep, reep"; also a rolling call "*wee*-warrawarra" and a soft "foo-foo-foo-foo".

Breeding: The nest is situated in the fork of a projecting twig, sometimes near the trunk of a large tree, or even in the fork of a smaller tree amongst the undergrowth; not usually hidden but in the poor light under the canopy of upper foliage it is difficult to find. The nest is a very neat bowl of fibres and other dry material covered externally by lichens smoothed against the twigs. Also recorded using an old canary nest once. September to December. Eggs 2—3, pinky or greenish white, sometimes salmon-pink in ground colour, with spots and large blotches forming a broad zone at the thicker end, of slaty brown and pinky red or reddish brown. Average (36) 17,9 × 13,8 (16,3—21 × 12,7—14,8). (Eggs from Natal being 1 to 2 mm smaller than those from the western Cape.) Incubation 17 days by ♀ only (Broekhuysen); both sexes feed. Nestling 16 days.

LOCAL RACES:

(a) *B.c. capensis* (Linnaeus), 1766: *Cape of Good Hope.* Throughout the species range south of the Limpopo River. As illustrated, somewhat olive-brown above. Size above.
(b) *B.c. erythropthalma* Swynnerton, 1907: *Chirinda Forest, Eastern Rhodesia.* Eastern Districts of Rhodesia and adjoining highlands of Mozambique. This race is more grey-brown above than (a) and slightly larger.
(c) *B.c. kennedyi* Smithers and Paterson, 1956: *Matopos, Rhodesia.* Matopos area, south of Bulawayo, Rhodesia. Greyer still than (b) and paler. Larger average wing ♂ 65,7, ♀ 62,5.

673 Chin Spot Batis   Witsy-bosbontrokkie

Batis molitor   (Hahn & Küster), 1850: *Kaffirland, South Africa.*

Native Names: i-Ncuaba, Matoobane (Z); Undyole (X).

PLATE 58, ♂ AND ♀ (OPP. P. 480).
Length about 13 cm (wing ♂ 57,5—60,5—65, ♀ 56—59,2—62,5; tail 42—52; tarsus 16—20; culmen 11—14,5. 124 specimens, 60 ♂, 64 ♀). Iris scarlet; bill and legs black. Weight 10,2—12 g.

Identification: The male has no rufous-coloured plumage and is distinguished by its pure white flanks, see No. 674. The female is distinguished by its *neat* rufous chin spot and breast-band. Immature male has a buff chin spot and the breast-band is buff and black.

Distribution: Eastern Cape northwards to Kenya and Uganda. Transvaal, eastern Botswana and Ovamboland. Absent from coastal Mozambique.

Habits: A common resident, in drier forest savannas and bush than the last species. Usually occurs along the banks of dry river beds in pairs, which often join bird parties. Habitat varies; not a very shy little bird, hunts actively and has similar habits to the last species.

Voice: Several calls; "chi-chirr"; "cheer-chir-chir" an insect-like buzz and a loud, piping "choi-choi-choi"; usually three notes, descending.

Breeding: The nest is like that of the last species but is not nearly so deep or bulky and contains no moss; the situation is similar, not being hidden by

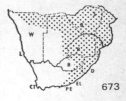

673

479

PLATE 58

672. *Batis capensis capensis.* Cape Batis. Bosbontrokkie. ♂ and ♀.
673. *Batis molitor molitor.* Chin Spot Batis. Witsy-bosbontrokkie. ♂ and ♀.
674. *Batis pririt.* Pririt Batis. Pririt-bosbontrokkie. ♂ and ♀.
675. *Batis soror.* **Mozambique Batis. Mosambiek-bosbontrokkie.** ♂ and ♀.
676. *Batis fratrum.* Woodward's Batis. Woodwardse Bosbontrokkie. ♂ and ♀.
677. *Platysteira peltata peltata.* Wattle-eyed Flycatcher.
Beloog-bosbontrokkie. ♂ and ♀.
678. *Stenostira scita.* Fairy Flycatcher. Fee-vlieëvanger.
680. *Trochocercus cyanomelas cyanomelas.* Blue-mantled Flycatcher.
Bloukuif-vlieëvanger. ♂ and ♀.
681. *Trochocercus albonotatus.* White-tailed Flycatcher.
Witstert-vlieëvanger.
682 *(a). Terpsiphone viridis granti.* Paradise Flycatcher.
Paradys-vlieëvanger. ♂ and ♀.
682 *(b). Terpsiphone viridis plumbeiceps.* Paradise Flycatcher.
Paradys-vlieëvanger. ♂.

672

673

674

675

676

677

678

680

681

682A

682B

HIGHTON
39

685

B
686

A

688

B
689
C

694

688

692

693

698

695

696

697

699

700

704

701

705 A

703

Lighton
'36

KN

PLATE 59

685. *Motacilla aguimp aguimp.* African Pied Wagtail. Bont Kwikstert.
686 *(a). Motacilla capensis capensis.* Cape Wagtail. Kwikkie.
686 *(b). Motacilla capensis simplicissima.* Cape Wagtail. Kwikkie.
688. *Motacilla clara torrentium.* Long-tailed Wagtail. Bergkwikstert.
689 *(b). Motacilla flava thunbergi.* Yellow Wagtail. Geel Kwikkie.
689 *(c). Motacilla flava lutea.* Yellow Wagtail. Geel Kwikkie.
692. *Anthus novaeseelandiae rufuloides.* Richard's Pipit. Gewone Koester.
693. *Anthus similis nicholsoni.* Nicholson's Pipit. Nicholsonse Koester.
694. *Anthus leucophrys leucophrys.* Plain-backed Pipit. Donker Koester.
695. *Anthus vaalensis vaalensis.* Buffy Pipit. Vaal Koester.
696. *Anthus lineiventris.* Striped Pipit. Gestreepte Koester.
697. *Anthus crenatus.* Rock Pipit. Klipkoester.
698. *Anthus trivialis trivialis.* Tree Pipit. Boompieper.
699. *Anthus caffer.* Bushveld Tree Pipit. Bosveld-koester.
700. *Anthus brachyurus brachyurus.* Short-tailed Pipit. Kortstert-koester.
701. *Anthus chloris.* Yellow-breasted Pipit. Geelbors-koester.
703. *Macronyx capensis colletti.* Orange-throated Longclaw. Kalkoentjie.
704. *Macronyx croceus vulturnus.* Yellow-throated Longclaw.
Geelkeel-kalkoentjie.
705. *Macronyx ameliae.* Pink-throated Longclaw. Rooskeel-kalkoentjie.

foliage, but well concealed in open shaded branches. Breeds September to January. Eggs 2 or 3, pale green or pale greenish blue fairly evenly freckled in red-brown with underlying slate-grey markings, usually more concentrated as a ring at the larger end. Average (46) 17,3 × 13,2 (15,6—19 × 12,5—14,2). Female only incubates; both sexes feed. Incubation 16—17 days (2) (Skead). Nestling 18 days (Skead).

LOCAL RACES:
(a) B.m. molitor (Hahn and Küster), 1850: *Kaffirland, South Africa.* Eastern Province to Pondoland where it inter-grades with *(b).* As illustrated. Size much as in *(b).*
(b) B.m. palliditergum Clancey, 1955: *Sand River east of Newington, eastern Transvaal.* Natal, Swaziland, Transvaal, Rhodesia, eastern and northern Botswana, Ovamboland and Etosha area. Crown paler grey. Size above.

674 Pririt Batis   Pririt-bosbontrokkie

Batis pririt (Vieillot), 1818: *Lower Orange River.*

PLATE 58, ♂ AND ♀ (OPP. P. 480).
Length about 12 cm (wing ♂ 55—56,4—58, ♀ 52—55—57,5; tail 43—47; tarsus 16—19; culmen 10,5—13,5. 45 specimens, 23 ♂, 22 ♀). Iris yellow; bill and legs black.

Identification: Very similar to the last species; for the most part the distributions of the two are separate. Slightly smaller than the previous species, flanks with black and white markings. The female is buff from chin to breast except a lighter area on the lower neck, see No. 673.
Distribution: Confined to the more arid regions from the Karoo near Grahamstown west to Little Namaqualand, to eastern Orange Free State, southern and central Botswana and north in South West Africa to Etosha Pan.
Habits: A common resident. The habits and voice are practically indistinguishable from the last species.
Voice: As No. 673. Also a deep "tuck" warning note like a Thrush.
Breeding: Similar to the previous species but nest apparently lacking the lichen outer covering. September and October. Eggs 2, ivory white, faintly spotted brown with grey-blue undermarkings forming a ring at large end. Average (4) 16,4 × 12,9 (16—16,7 × 12,1—13,2).

 674

675 Mozambique Batis   Mosambiek-bosbontrokkie

Batis soror Reichenow, 1903: *Quelimane, Portuguese East Africa.*

PLATE 58, ♂ AND ♀ (OPP. P. 480).
Length about 12 cm (wing 54—58,5; culmen 12—14; 5 specimens). Iris yellow; bill and legs black.

Identification: Does not occur in the same areas as No. 673, from which it can be distinguished by narrower chest bands. In the male the back is more speckled and lighter. In the female there is no distinct chin spot.
Distribution: Coastal plains from Inhambane, Mozambique, north to Kenya.
Habits: Considered by some authorities as a race of No. 673 because of similarity of plumage. Considered a distinct species because it is ecologically separated. Habits similar.
Voice: Two calls, one a slow pipe of four notes, and the other a harsh and jarring one—an alarm note, distinct from No. 673.

 675

676 Woodward's Batis   Woodwardse Bosbontrokkie

Batis fratrum   (Shelley), 1900: *Zululand.*

PLATE 58, ♂ AND ♀ (OPP. P. 480).
Length 11—12 cm (wing 57—58,8—60; tail 32—35; tarsus 17,5—19; culmen 12—14.
8 specimens). Iris yellow; bill and legs black.

Identification: The male is distinguishable by rufous breast and flanks and white wing-coverts. The female is similar to No. 672 but white line over the black band through eye distinguishes this bird. Immature male differs from adult female in having rufous-olive instead of black eye-stripe and buff superciliary. Cannot be confused with No. 672 because they occur far apart.
Distribution: Along the littoral from Mtunzini, Zululand, northwards through Mozambique beyond the Zambesi. Confined to lower altitudes and extending westwards to the low-lying parts of eastern Rhodesia and Tete.
Habits: Extremely local, confined to very dense, moist forests with thick undergrowth; generally remains low down. Usually occurs in pairs and often joins bird parties.
Voice: Said to differ slightly from Nos. 672 and 673.
Breeding: The nest is like that of the White-flanked Flycatcher, No. 673; made up of fine grass, spider webs and moss; well concealed. November. Eggs 2 or 3, creamy white sparingly spotted and blotched with light brown and a zone of chocolate-coloured blotches and grey spots at the larger end. Average (8) 18,1 × 13,1 (16,3—19,3 × 12,5—14,1).

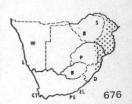

676

677 Wattle-eyed Flycatcher   Beloog-bosbontrokkie

Platysteira peltata   Sundevall, 1851: *Caffraria inferiore, Umlaas.*

PLATE 58, ♂ AND ♀ (OPP. P. 480).
Length about 18 cm (wing 62,5—63,5—64; tail 51—54; tarsus 17—19; culmen 14—16.
5 specimens). Iris inner white ring with dark mauve outer ring with a crimson wattle about eye; bill black; legs slate-coloured. Weight 16,1 g.

Identification: The *male* has a white chin and throat with a narrow black band across the chest; the female has spot on chin white, throat and upper-breast black. This handsome little bird is easily identified by colour and call. See under Habits. Young has a small wattle; brownish grey above, chestnut wings, tail and flanks.
Distribution: A tropical species from Kenya south to Natal and Angola. In our area as far south as Durban, through Mozambique, extending into Rhodesia at levels below 1 500 metres in Mashonaland and Eastern Districts.
Habits: Not common in our area and locally confined to trees and bushes in the marshy belt along low-lying streams and rivers; sometimes, however, along similar vegetation near dry river-beds. Mangrove swamps also form some attraction. Occurs in pairs or solitary as a rule and has much the appearance and habits of the *Batis* flycatcher.
Voice: Call-note a guttural "chak-chak"; a scolding "ch ch ch ch ch ch ch" when displaying. A tinkling song "er-er-fee, er-er-fee-fu".
Breeding: Nest is similar to that of the *Batis* flycatchers built of fine grasses and tendrils and placed as high as 6 metres up. October to January. Eggs 2; white smudged and spotted with dark slate, sometimes forming a ring at broad

677

end (Bell-Marley). 18,2 × 13,6, 18,2 × 14 Zululand; 19,5 × 14 (6) Rhodesia. Both sexes incubate.

LOCAL RACE:
P.p. peltata Sundevall, 1851: *Caffraria inferiore, Umlaas River nr. Durban.* Natal northwards to the middle Zambesi.

678   Fairy Flycatcher   Fee-vlieëvanger

Stenostira scita   (Vieillot), 1818: *Lower Orange River.*

PLATE 58 (OPP. P. 480).
Length about 12 cm (wing 47—51,3—55; tail 49—57; tarsus 16—19; culmen 9—11. 23 specimens). Iris dark brown; bill and legs black.

Identification: This dainty little flycatcher is unmistakable. The white outer tail-feathers and wing-bar are conspicuous in the field. Female not so dark as male. Young have the pattern of adults but are browner and not so dark.

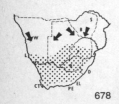

678

Distribution: Confined to the dry parts of Southern Africa. From southern Cape, except for the moister coastal areas, north to the Orange River area; one record from Quickborn, Okahandja, in South West Africa; through southern Botswana and Transvaal and extreme southern Mozambique. Two recent records from Rhodesia.

Habits: A common distinctive species subject to definite migration movements, though in the south is recorded all the year. Birds in the Karoo areas decrease in numbers from April to August and records for the Transvaal are from April to October. Occurs in Natal Drakensberg from March to September. The records from southern Mozambique (May 1911) are unusual and none has been found recently. Favours mimosa trees and thornbushes growing in the neighbourhood of and along the banks of rivers. Occurs singly or in pairs. Its long tail gives it the appearance of a warbler, as it creeps about amongst the branches of trees and low bushes.

Voice: Described as a twitter like that of a sunbird—"kisskisskisskiss"; also "cheep-cheep".

Breeding: The nest is situated on a low branch of a bush, a neat cup-shaped structure, constructed of fine twigs, grass and rootlets lined with vegetable or sheep wool and the hair of hares or buck, externally covered with lichen and cobwebs. October to December. Eggs 2—3, creamy-coloured tinged with green and very minutely speckled so that they appear yellow-brown, darker at the large end. Average (6) 14,9 × 11,5 (14,5—15,3 × 10,8—11,9). Female only builds; nest completed in four days. Incubation 17—18 days.

679   Livingstone's Flycatcher   Rooistert-vlieëvanger

Erythrocercus livingstonei   G. R. Gray, 1870: *Zambesi, P.E.A.*

PLATE 57 (OPP. P. 465).
Length about 12 cm (wing 45—47; tail 48; tarsus 15; culmen 8). Iris brown; bill brown; paler below; legs flesh-coloured.

Identification: Illustration should show central tail-feathers with a broad, dark brown, subterminal bar. Sexes alike. Young birds have crown uniform; yellow-green of the back and bar on tail almost absent.

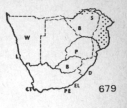

Distribution: A tropical species from Tanzania southwards to the Zambesi River as far west as Chirundu and down the coast as far as Inhambane, Mozambique.
Habits: Rare in our area. These birds inhabit dense forests with ample undergrowth, especially along streams, rivers and moister localities. Usually seen in mixed feeding parties. Resemble the *Eremomela* Bush-Warblers in habits, creeping and hopping from branch to branch; they have the habit of flitting down branches with tail fanned as in the next species. The reddish tail is always in motion.

679

Voice: A sharp "chip chip". Also a short wheezy song.
Breeding: Not recorded in our area. Constructs a domed nest with a side entrance, made of leaves bound together with spiders' webs, lined inside with soft grass. January to March in Nyasaland. Eggs 2, white, finely marked with chestnut and lilac undershading.

LOCAL RACE:
(a) E.l. livingstonei G. R. Gray, 1870: *Zambesi, P.E.A.* From Zambia southwards. Inland down to Tete. As illustrated.
(b) E.l. francisi Sclater, 1898: *Inhambane.* Coastal Mozambique. Greener, less yellow. Subterminal tail spots better developed to form a bar.

680 Blue-mantled Flycatcher   Bloukuif-vlieëvanger

Trochocercus cyanomelas (Vieillot), 1818: *Auteniquoi = Knysna, Cape.*

Native Name: i-Gotyi (X).
PLATE 58, ♂ AND ♀ (OPP. P. 480).
Length 17—18 cm (wing ♂ 64—66,6—69, ♀ 63—64,4—65; tail 71—84; tarsus 16—19; culmen 10—13. 11 specimens, 8 ♂, 3 ♀). Iris dusky; bill and legs slate-coloured.

Identification: The male is easily distinguished with its metallic throat and high crest. The female is identified from the next species by the white patch on wing-coverts and uniform tail—see No. 681. Immature male has the chin and throat dark with white spots and is slightly metallic on the crown; grey above with white tips to the coverts. Young is buff on chest and edges of wing-coverts otherwise as female.

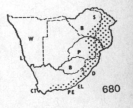

Distribution: A tropical species from Kenya southwards extending along the eastern areas to Natal, thence along the narrow coastal belt as far as Swellendam in the Cape.
Habits: A somewhat uncommon species occurring in the larger forests and thick coastal bush where it frequents the more open shady patches, especially near streams and consequently not often observed. A solitary bird; extraordinarily active with a rapid flight, sweeping through the tangles with remarkable facility. Hunts insects in the middle and top levels of the trees. Has an attractive habit of pirouetting from one side of a branch to the other, at the same time fanning the tail open and shut.

680

Voice: Resembles the Paradise Flycatcher, a rasping "zi, za". The male has an astonishing song—a loud high-pitched "kwew-ew-ew-ew" often followed by a series of four loud clicks.
Breeding: The nest is placed in a low tree or shrub, a metre or so from the ground, in a fork where two or three branches diverge and well hidden by the leaves above. It is a cup-shaped, thick-walled structure, composed of bark,

fibres and fine grass held together with moss and spiders' webs. October to January. Eggs 2—3, white with rufous to purplish slate, scattered speckles, most at the thick end. Average (5) 18,9 × 14,1 (17,3—20,6 × 12,8—14,9); three collected by Bell-Marley measure 21,7—22,9 × 14,8—15,1.

LOCAL RACES:
(a) *T.c.* cyanomelas (Vieillot), 1818: *Auteniquoi* = *Knysna, Cape.* From Swellendam east and north to Natal and eastern Transvaal. Having a much shorter crest than (b). As illustrated. Size above.
(b) *T.c.* bivittatus Reichenow, 1879: *Muniuni, Tana River, Kenya.* The lower levels of eastern Rhodesia and Mozambique, north to Kenya. A longer crest. Wing 63,5; 66; tail 68, 74; tarsus 16,5, 17; culmen 12,5, 13 (2 specimens).

681 White-tailed Flycatcher   Witstert-vlieëvanger

Trochocercus albonotatus Sharpe, 1891: *Mt. Elgon, Kenya.*
PLATE 58 (OPP. P. 480).
Length 14—15 cm (wing ♂ 63,5, 65; ♀ 60, 61,5; tail 67—74; tarsus 16—18,5; culmen ♂ 11, 12; ♀ 8,5, 9. 4 specimens, 2 ♂, 2 ♀). Iris sepia; bill and legs black. Weight 7,0—8,3 g.

Identification: This species is often seen high up in the canopy of the forest when the longish, fanned tail shows white outer edges to the feathers quite conspicuously.
Distribution: From East Africa southwards in mountain forests to the Eastern Districts of Rhodesia and adjoining higher parts of Mozambique.
Habits: A common forest bird of the higher level forests where it occurs both in the canopy and in open scrub bordering such forests. Confiding and active, they are usually seen in pairs. It has lively and sometimes acrobatic actions in pursuit of its prey; also has the habit of the two preceding species of working up or down branches fanning its tail and calling. Fans its tail frequently.

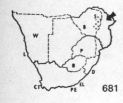

681

Food: Small beetles and flies.
Voice: "Chrrit-tit-tit" in rapid succession.
Breeding: The nest, situated 60—360 cm above the ground, is placed in the fork of a branch and is made of moss, closely felted. December and January. Eggs 3, "dirty white, blotched and spotted with greenish olive and grey chiefly at the larger end, which, in one egg, was surrounded by a distinct zone". 14,2 × 11,7, 15,9 × 12,3, 16,3 × 13,1. (C. W. Benson).

LOCAL RACE:
T.a. swynnertoni Neumann, 1908: *Chipete, Rhodesia.* As above.

682 Paradise Flycatcher   Paradys-vlieëvanger

Terpsiphone viridis (Müller), 1776: *Senegal.*

Native Names: Ujejane (X); Uve (Z); mo-Thoapea, mo-Lioroane (S and Ch); Chinyantambo, i-Zwewi (D); Ive (G).
PLATE 58, ♂ AND ♀ (OPP. P. 480).
Length including tail 23—41 cm (wing ♂ 79—81,9—85, ♀ 76—77,6—80; tail, to outer tail-feather, ♂ 67—80, ♀ 68—70; longest tail-feather ♂ 185—300 (see below), ♀ 83—102; tarsus 14—16; culmen 15—17,5. 16 specimens, 11 ♂, 5 ♀). Iris red-brown, with a blue wattle; bill black, bluish at base; legs pale slate. Weight 13,6—16,7 g.

Identification: Unmistakable. Breeding males have been recorded without the long central tail-feathers, in which case the slightly longer tail of the male may only be noticed when both sexes are together. Female may also have a long tail. Young similar to female.

Distribution: South of the Sahara from Cameroon to Ethiopia, southwards to the Cape. Found throughout our area except in the dry west of Little Namaqualand, western Karoo, southern Botswana and South West Africa as far north as the Waterberg.

682

Habits: A common migratory species in the south, becoming resident in the north-east of our area; for details see under Races. A species of the forests and big trees along streams and rivers where its long red tail-feathers at once attract attention. Catches its prey on the wing, always actively calling and flitting about with an undulating flight. Becomes quite tame and is frequently met with in gardens in settled areas.

Food: Small insects, especially small flies.

Voice: A sharply uttered "swee-swer" or "zwa-i-zwer". The song is brief, like a ripple of tiny laughter, "whee-wheeo-whit-whit", repeated twice. (A northern race.)

Breeding: Generally situated 1,5—4,5 metres up over water, the nest is placed in the fork of a tree or on a cross branch, always in the shade but never concealed in leafy vegetation. It is a neat basin-shaped structure of bark, fibres and fine roots, neatly bound together with webby material and with lichens stuck on the outside to disguise it. October to January in the Cape, as late as March to the north. Eggs 3, less often 2, cream-coloured lightly tinged with rose, small reddish chestnut spots, more about the large end. Average (36 of race *(a)*) 18,8 × 14,4 (16,9—21,5 × 13—14,5). (50 of race *(b)*) 18,7 × 14,1 (17—20 × 13—15,5). Incubation 13—14 days (4) by both sexes 17 days in Western Cape; nestling 10—12 days; both sexes feed.

LOCAL RACES:
(a) T.v. granti Roberts, 1948: *Duivenhoek River, Swellendam, Cape.* Cape Province, east and north to Mozambique and eastern Transvaal; also in the low-lying parts of eastern Rhodesia. Recorded from October to March in the Cape; in the Albany district and Natal there are occasional winter records and in Mozambique they occur all the year round. Size as above. Illustrated as **No. 682.** *(a).* Note glossier green on head and lighter belly than *(b).*
(b) T.v. plumbeiceps Reichenow, 1898: *Milange, Angola.* Northern Damaraland, Ovamboland, Rhodesia and Transvaal highveld north. Recorded in the Transvaal from September to June and scattered records from Rhodesia between May and August. This race is recorded as far north as Cameroon and northern Zaïre during the winter. Size much as *(a).* Illustrated as **No. 682** *(b).* More uniform head and neck and darker down to belly.

683 = 682 *(b)*

Family MOTACILLIDAE

This family embraces the Wagtails, Pipits and Longclaws, the first of which are well known to everybody from their friendly way of frequenting gardens and open streams. The Wagtails are usually black and white or yellow below and have a way of swinging their tails up and down as they run about on the ground, whence they get their name; the Pipits also have this habit but are mostly plainer-coloured, with two exceptions—yellow below, never black and white. The Longclaws are larger birds which look more like Larks, with the under-parts yellow, orange or pink, and with a black band across the lower throat. All the species feed on insects, though the Wagtails are fond of frequenting kitchen doors to pick up small scraps of cooked food, such as bread, porridge, meat, etc. They have, in most cases, characteristic call-notes, sometimes even a song, and build cup-shaped nests. All but the Yellow Wagtails are residents, the exceptions being migrants from the northern hemisphere which do not breed here. They are more slender than Larks (with which they are often confused by the tyro) and differ in having the back of the tarsus in a single plate on each side, only the front being scutellated.

The pipits are difficult to distinguish. The most important characteristic is the habitat occupied. For field characters note whether there is streaking on crown and back or either and the extent of white on outer tail-feathers.

Note identification in the hand is aided by wing formula—the first primary is minute and ignored in the wing formula used here.

684 = 685 *(b)*

685   African Pied Wagtail   Bont Kwikstert

Motacilla aguimp   Dumont, 1821: *Lower Orange River.*

Native Names: Umcelu, Umventshane (X); um-Vemve (Z); mo-Selakatane, mo-Khafepitzoana (S. and Ch.).

PLATE 59 (OPP. P. 481).
Length about 20 cm (wing 91—95,3—98; tail 96—103; tarsus 23—26; culmen 13,5—15,5. 7 specimens). Iris brown; bill and legs black.

Identification: Adults unmistakable; male distinctly blacker on upper-parts than female. Winter plumage has a brownish tone to the black. Young, brownish above and could be mistaken for the next species but white of wing-coverts is distinctive.

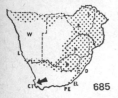

685

Distribution: Widely distributed from the tropics south of the Sahara, to within our limits from Ngamiland to the Limpopo River, southwards to Natal and eastern Cape Province and the entire Orange River system. Vagrants recorded from the Cape Peninsula area; reaching only as far as Port Elizabeth regularly.

Habits: A common resident except in the Transvaal and eastern Cape where it is very local; in the eastern Cape a summer-breeding visitor and in the Transvaal recorded from April to August (with records also for February and October). Usually near water but not necessarily, being quite common in gardens where extensive lawns supply ample food. Frequents the sand-banks and rock of rivers of larger size but not the smaller streams.

Food: Insects.

Voice: A short shrill "tu wheee".

Breeding: Situated in nooks in the banks of the river, on piles of flood debris and even in a thatched roof of a native hut, the nest is a rough and rather bulky structure loosely constructed of various soft materials with a neat cup of fine dry grass and small feathers. June to August in Transvaal and Mozambique, later to January in Orange Free State. Eggs 3—4, cloudy white with markings of sepia and a few underlying faint ashy. Average (20) 22,1 × 15,9 (20,9—22,9 × 15,1—16,5), one 24 × 15,2. Parasitised by Diederik Cuckoo.

LOCAL RACES:
(a) M.a. aguimp Dumont, 1821: *Lower Orange River*. Valleys of the Orange and Vaal Rivers. Darker flanks than (b). Size above. Illustrated.
(b) M.a. vidua Sundevall, 1851: *Syene = Assouan, Upper Egypt*. Eastern Cape Province north on the east; Rhodesia and Ngamiland and Kaokoveld in the west. Whiter flanks and with more white on the head. Wing ♂ 89—98, ♀ 85—98; culmen 14—17 (27 specimens, 16 ♂, 11 ♀).

686   Cape Wagtail   Kwikkie

Motacilla capensis   Linnaeus, 1766: *Cape of Good Hope*.

Native Names: mo-Tjoli, mo-Letasake (S. and Ch.); u-Mvemve (Z); Umcelu, Umventshane (X).

PLATE 59 (a) AND (b) (OPP. P. 481).
Length about 18 cm (wing ♂ 77—82,5—87, ♀ 77—82,1—86; tail 77—91; tarsus 21—24,5; culmen 13—15. 25 specimens, 14 ♂, 11 ♀). Iris brown; bill and legs brownish.

Identification: This common bird is unmistakable with its grey-brown upper-parts, dark band across chest and white outer tail-feathers. Note no white on secondaries; see Nos. 685, 688 and 689. Sexes alike. Young has the head brown like the back, under-parts brownish and wing-coverts tipped white.
Distribution: From Kenya and eastern Zaïre southwards to the Cape.
Habits: A common resident, one of our best known birds and a general favourite that is protected everywhere by common consent. It has adapted itself to human habitation, especially gardens, where it is seen chasing insects on the ground and in the air with great agility and dexterity. Found along the coasts and inland wherever there is water with a certain amount of shelter; often to be seen in cities, towns, villages and on farms. Somewhat uncommon and not so tame beyond the limits of the Republic. Usually seen singly, in pairs or family parties but when not breeding recorded roosting in numbers together, even in the courtyards of busy hotels.

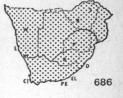

686

Food: Mainly insects, sandhoppers and food scraps about houses. Recorded hunting moths on tree trunks by beating wings against the bark.
Voice: Very varied, loud and clear; usually a "chis-sek" or "tseep".
Breeding: Nests in any safe place about houses, such as in creepers on the walls, or scaffolding holes, on tree stumps and even in matted hedges or trees; in the wilds usually selects as a nesting site any nook hidden by weeds, or tuft of grass in the bank of a stream or river. Very often an old nest is used and re-lined. The nest is a bulky structure having a neat deepish cup of fine roots and hair. July to April. Eggs 2—4, usually 3, up to 5 and 7 have been recorded; dull yellowish more or less indistinctly finely speckled with brown-ish. Average (100) 21,1 × 15,4 (19,3—25,5 × 14—16,5). Incubation by both sexes 13—14 days. Nestling 14—21½ days; both parents feed. Two broods a year recorded in the Cape, three in the Transvaal. Nest building 6—10 days.

LOCAL RACES:
(a) M.c. capensis Linnaeus, 1766: *Cape of Good Hope*. Cape, S.W.A., Transvaal, Botswana, Natal, Rhodesia and Mozambique. As illustrated. Size above.
(b) M.c. simplicissima Neumann, 1929: *Chipepe, Bailundo, Angola*. Ngamiland north to Angola and Zambia. Differing from (a) only in having a spot instead of a bar on the breast. Illustrated.

687 = 686 (b)

688 Long-tailed Wagtail   Bergkwikstert

Motacilla clara Sharpe, 1908: *Simen, Abyssinia.*

Native Name: Umcelu, Umventshane (X).

PLATE 59 (OPP. P. 481).
Length about 20 cm (wing 76—79—81,5; tail 90—103; tarsus 20—22; culmen 14—15,5. 11 specimens). Iris brown; bill black; legs greyish brown.

Identification: The soft blue-grey upper-parts, white under-parts and large amount of white on wing and *long tail* distinguish this wagtail. Sexes alike. Young browner; throat-mark narrower; white wing-marks less distinct.

Distribution: From West Africa to Ethiopia southwards, occurring in our areas in the eastern Districts of Mashonaland in Rhodesia, neighbouring high parts and Lebombo Mountains in Mozambique, high parts in north-western Transvaal, Natal and down to lower ievels as far as Albany and Bathurst districts in the eastern Cape. Common at Victoria Falls.

688

Habits: A resident species confined to fast-flowing rivers or streams, and since these conditions exist for the most part in mountainous areas, the birds are confined to mountainous or hilly regions. Usually occurs in pairs. When startled, flies low along the bed of the stream for some distance. A beautiful and graceful species to be found tripping over the pebbles by the side of the stream, or flitting over its surface in pursuit of insects. Frequently occurs near waterfalls. Fond of perching on favourite rocks.

Food: Insects, chiefly larvae of dragonfly and mosquitoes.

Voice: A loud "chirrup" or "chissk" almost invariably uttered when they take to flight. Also a pretty short song "ti-tuu-ui-tui-tui".

Breeding: The nest is placed on a ledge of rock or on the ground beside a stream, usually amongst moss, hidden by overhanging ferns. Rather a bulky structure, externally of dead leaves, moss and dried grass with a neat deep cup lined with fine rootlets and hair. September to December. Eggs 2—3, grey, freckled with irregular brown markings at the large end; more heavily marked than the previous species. Average (18) 20,2 × 15,2 (18,2—21,9 × 14,2—16).

LOCAL RACE:
M.c. torrentium Ticehurst, 1940: *Ngoye Forest, Zululand.* Eastern Cape Province northwards on the east.

689 Yellow Wagtail   Geel Kwikkie

Motacilla flava Linnaeus, 1758: *Europe = South Sweden.*

PLATE 59 *(b)* AND *(c)* (OPP. P. 481).
Length about 18 cm (wing ♂ 80—83—87, ♀ 75,5—78; tail 67—73; tarsus 21,5—23,5; culmen 12—13,5. 11 specimens). Iris brown; bill and legs black.

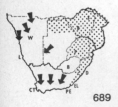

Identification: The yellowish under-parts and greenish upper-parts distinguish the species. For details of the variation of head pattern and colour, as well as a note on the taxonomy of the species, see under Races. The females are duller and may be confused with the Cape Wagtail, but yellow tinge to back and belly and shorter tail distinguish them.

Distribution: The Palaearctic region south to Malaya, India and Africa. Extends to the Transvaal, eastern Cape and Damaraland. Two records for the south-west Cape.

689

Habits: A non-breeding migrant occurring from late October to early April in Rhodesia and Mozambique (see also under Races) but to the south somewhat uncommon and less regular. Records in May eastern Province, and June Cape Peninsula. Occurs in flocks with several races where it is regularly found, elsewhere usually singly. Favours wet open grassy areas such as short grass near lakes, lawns and sewerage farms.

Food: Insects.

Voice: Somewhat like the Cape Wagtail; a brief "tseep".

LOCAL RACES:
This species, because of its wide variation in head colour-pattern and apparent intermingling of the races, has led to considerable taxonomic confusion. Modern opinion is divided between lumping into one species, two (yellow-headed and "grey"-headed groups) or seven species. Until the matter is solved the conservative opinion of one species is followed. Juveniles are practically indistinguishable.
The grey-headed group:
(a) *M.f. flava* Linnaeus, 1758: *Europe = South Sweden.* Rhodesia, Transvaal and Natal uncommon, in Mozambique the commonest race, occurring from November to early April. A distinct white stripe above eye and below dark facial patch, for this race, and crown light.
(b) *M.f. thunbergi* Billberg, 1828: *Lapland.* Recorded somewhat uncommonly in South West Africa (Waterberg), Rhodesia, Mozambique and Natal (Durban). As illustrated, no white above eye but white below dark facial patch.
The yellow-headed group:
(c) *M.f. lutea* (Gmelin), 1774: *Astrakhan, Southern Russia.* Recorded from Rhodesia (Salisbury), Transvaal (Wakkerstroom), Mozambique and eastern Cape. As illustrated, with pale forehead and facial markings; sometimes difficult to distinguish from (d).
(d) *M.f. flavissima* Blyth, 1834: *England.* The commonest race in Rhodesia occurring from October to March; flocks in Mashonaland but recorded in ones and twos in Matabeleland. Not yet recorded to the south. Differs from (c) in having darker forehead and crown and more distinct facial patch showing up the entire eye-stripe.

691 See page xxxii

692 Richard's Pipit   Gewone Koester

Anthus novaeseelandiae (Gmelin), 1879: *New Zealand.*

Native Names: Icelu, Icetshu (X); um-Ngcelu, um- (or isi-) Celekeshe (Z).

PLATE 59 (OPP. P. 481).
Length about 18 cm (wing 81—89—95; tail 58—70; tarsus 23—28,5; culmen 12,5—15,5; hind claw 10—13, one 8,5. 52 specimens). Iris brown; bill brown; legs yellowish. Weight 23,4 g.

Identification: This and the following three species are practically indistinguishable in the field. The colour patterns are similar and, to add to the confusion, the breeding and non-breeding plumages are almost as different as the species. *Generally* this bird shows darker and more distinct chest-spots, white outer tail-feathers and more boldly patterned upper-parts—a tawny-coloured pipit. In non-breeding plumage the upper-parts are only lightly mottled and edges to wing-coverts are lighter. In the hand this species is identified by wing formula. The 1st primary is the longest, the first four diminish in size very slightly and the 5th is much shorter than the 4th. The 2nd, 3rd and 4th outer primaries emarginate.

Distribution: Throughout the Palaearctic, Ethiopian, Indian and Australasian regions.

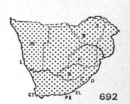

692

Habits: The commonest pipit in our region. A resident but subject to local movement. Occurs in open grassland, especially short grass near marshes or moist ground although seems to prefer long grass to the north, in the drier areas only where there is permanent water. Shows a preference for cultivated lands. Spends most of its time on the ground, but does perch on bushes or trees. Display flight in dipping undulations usually in a circular pattern calling loudly at each dip.

Food: Insects.

Voice: A loud "chis-sik" or "chizzi", also "tiset" and "pip-pit". A pretty song uttered in flight "tinkle tinkle thinkle tinkle", etc., or a rapid series of "chizzies".

Breeding: The nest is placed on the ground under or next to a tuft of grass, where a basin-shaped structure is made of dry shreds of grass, lined with rootlets and hair. October to December in the Cape, August to March in Rhodesia. Eggs, usually 3, rarely 2 or 4; pale cream closely freckled with deep sepia or umber-brown and light grey, some markings being rather streaky. Average (50) 20,9 × 15,6 (19,3—23,4 × 14,7—16,9).

LOCAL RACES:
This species is rather variable in details of colour-pattern and this has led to considerable confusion in naming races. For convenience and until the problem is resolved we have followed Roberts.
(a) *A.n. rufuloides* Roberts, 1936: *Grahamstown.* South of the Zambesi River, replaced on the west by *(b)* less patterned than the races to the north of the Zambesi.
(b) *A.n. bocagii* Nicholson, 1884: *Humbe, S. Angola.* Angola, Ovamboland, northern Damaraland and northern Botswana. A more pallid race with less streaking on breast.

693 Nicholson's Pipit — Nicholsonse Koester

Anthus similis Jerdon, 1840: *S. India = Jalna.*

Native Name: Icelu, Icetshu (X).

PLATE 59 (OPP. P. 481).
Length about 19 cm (wing ♂ 96—98,7—104, ♀ 90—93,4—98; tail 70—83; tarsus 24—30; culmen 14—16,5; hind claw 7,5—11. 20 specimens, 11 ♂, 9 ♀). Iris brown; bill brown; legs pinkish.

Identification: Darker and more *grey* brown than the tawny-brown of the last species. Boldly marked above and with buff outer tail-feathers. Habitat differs slightly. Strongly resembles the previous species. In the hand the 1st primary is shorter than the 2nd and 3rd and is equal in length to the 5th; the 6th primary is noticeably shorter than 5th. The 2nd to 5th outer primaries emarginate.

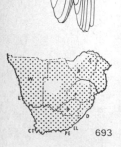

693

Distribution: Eastern and southern Africa to eastern Asia. Throughout area in suitable localities.

Habits: Widely dispersed, most commonly found on stony ground around kopjes. A woodland species in Rhodesia. May be recorded on the same ground as the previous species but is usually in hilly areas especially where there is open vegetation. Commonly perches on a tree or bush. Calls for long spells usually from top of a tree, bush or rock. Usually found in pairs.

Food: Grasshoppers, beatles, ants, crickets, mantis, etc. and spiders.

Voice: The call is a metallic, clear and ringing "kilink" or "choop", *also* written as "tsee-tsee"; an unmusical song "kliddle-kliddle" or better "chreep chrroop".

Breeding: The nest is similar to that of the last species and may be found in similar places as well as under rocks. August to March. Eggs 2, usually 3, said to be separable from the previous species by a pinkish tinge; speckles, spots and blotches over whole egg, more at the obtuse end, of dark olive, reddish brown and some slate-grey. Average (5) 21—22 × 16—16,4.

LOCAL RACES:
(a) A.s. nicholsoni Sharpe, 1884: *Sigonell, Vaal River.* Cape Province and Natal northwards to the Zambesi. As illustrated. Size above.
(b) A.s. leucocraspedon Reichenow, 1915: *Windhoek.* Damaraland. Distinguished by longer bills.
(c) A.s. petricolus Clancey, 1956: *Mamathes, Basutoland.* Lesotho. Darker and more heavily streaked above.

694 Plain-backed Pipit Donker Koester

Anthus leucophrys Vieillot, 1818: *Cape of Good Hope.*

Native Names: Tholapula (S); Icelu (X).

PLATE 59 (OPP. P. 481).
Length about 18 cm (wing ♂ 92—98,6—105, ♀ 92—94,4—98; tail (61,5) 64—80; tarsus 25,5—29; culmen 14—17; hind claw 8,5—14. 21 specimens, 14 ♂, 7 ♀). Iris brown; bill brown; legs yellowish.

Identification: Distinguished from the previous two species by its more uniform upper-parts which lack definite markings; by indistinct or absence of chest markings and by narrow buff outer tail-feathers. Very similar to the next species, see No. 695. In the hand the 1st primary is just shorter than the 2nd; the 5th is much shorter than the 4th. The 2nd to 5th outer primaries are emarginate.
Distribution: Cape Province, Transvaal, Natal and Mozambique northwards to Ethiopia and west to Senegal. Record from Erongo Mountains S.W.A. needs confirmation.
Habits: A true ground bird of open terrain where the grass is short, often in mountainous areas. A resident in most localities but flocks may be found from July to September and recorded from the mountainous areas of southern Mozambique only during that period. In habits like Richard's Pipit and also shows the same dipping flight. Often attracted in large numbers where grass has been burnt off.

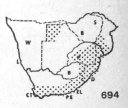

694

Voice: Usually calls from the ground "jhreet-jhroot". Utters a "chisik" note when in flight and a tripping "ttt-tit" when flying up.
Breeding: The nest is placed on the ground against or beneath an overhanging grass tuft; also recorded between two clods of earth in a recently ploughed field. October to December. Eggs 2—4, usually 3, white or clouded in yellowish brown, closely freckled in raw umber and much dark and light ash-grey. Average (12) 21,4 × 15,3 (19,3—24,8 × 14,3—16,5).

LOCAL RACE:
A.l. leucophrys Vieillot, 1818: *Cape of Good Hope* Cape Province, Natal, Transvaal and locally in the mountainous areas of southern Mozambique.

493

695 Buffy Pipit   Vaal Koester

Anthus vaalensis   Shelley, 1900: *Newcastle, Upper Natal.*

PLATE 59 (OPP. P. 481).
Length about 19 cm (wing 95—98,1—101; tail 73—77; tarsus 25,5—29; culmen 13,5—15,5; hind claw 8—11. 10 specimens). Iris brown; bill brown; legs pinkish.

Identification: Lighter coloured and more buffy above than No. 694; its hind claw shorter and more curved. Slightly bigger and heavier in build. There is variation in the amount of buff and in the spotting on the chest. Considered by many as conspecific with the preceding species but its smaller hind claw and feet are quite distinct in our area.

Distribution: Ethiopia to Malawi to Angola and south. Found widely distributed throughout our area except in the southern Cape and Mozambique. One recent record from near Calvinia.

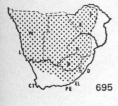

695

Habits: Its habits are much the same as No. 692 but it seems to be imbued with the same restlessness at times, moving about in flocks as No. 694. It has the habit of running or flying off and invariably makes for, and perches upon (for a brief spell), any little hummock, stone or other point on which it will be a little above the general ground level. Also perches on fences and telegraph wires. After walking or running stands very upright (with chest out) when stopped.

Voice: An occasional "chisik" in flight.

Breeding: The nest is a bulky and loosely built cup, irregular in shape, constructed of chaffed grass and coarse grass stems and lined with fine grass and very fine rootlets. August to December. Eggs 2—3, white, closely freckled and speckled in various shades of light brown and underlying dark and light ashy. Average (16) 21,6 × 15,1 (20,4—23,9 × 14,9—17,2).

LOCAL RACES:
(a) A.v. vaalensis Shelley, 1900: *Newcastle, Upper Natal.* Natal and eastern Transvaal to South West Africa. Size above. As illustrated.
(b) A.v. daviesi Roberts, 1914: *Matatiele.* Eastern Cape from Albany and south of Lesotho, westwards to De Aar and Niewoudtville. Larger in wing length.
(c) A.v. chobiensis (Roberts), 1932: *Kabulabula, Chobe River.* Ngamiland. Smaller in size; wing 90—99; tail 69—75.
(d) A.v. neumanni Meinertzhagen, 1920: *Ambaca N. Angola.* Paler below. Northern S.W.A.

696 Striped Pipit   Gestreepte Koester

Anthus lineiventris   Sundevall, 1851: *Limpopo River, Mohapoani, Botswana.*

Native Name: i-Ntsasana (X).

PLATE 59 (OPP. P. 481).
Length about 19 cm (wing 80—84,8—89; tail 66—71,5; tarsus 26—29; culmen 14,5—17; hind claw 7—9,5. 15 specimens). Iris brown; bill brown above, yellowish below; legs yellowish. Weight 31,8—34,8 g.

Identification: The larger size, yellow edges to wing-feathers and heavily streaked under-parts readily identify this pipit. Outer tail-feathers white and conspicuous.

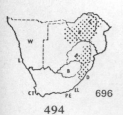

696

Distribution: Tanzania to Angola, southwards in our limits to Rhodesia, Mozambique, eastern and central Transvaal, Swaziland and Natal.

494

Habits: A somewhat uncommon resident, locally distributed in hilly areas where there are open areas with rocks and trees. Found along stony ridges and often near streams. Usually solitary or in pairs. Runs rapidly among the stones and when alarmed flies to the nearest tree. Has the curious habit of perching parallel to the branches on occasions.
Food: Insects, including grasshoppers.
Voice: Calls from a tree, a startlingly loud whistling song.
Breeding: The nest is the usual pipit structure placed under the lee of a rock or tuft of grass, one recorded so well covered as to be to all intents a domed site. October to December. Eggs 3, creamy white tinged with pink and evenly freckled in reddish brown with underlying scattered spots of dark and light slate-grey (much resembling a bulbul's egg). Average (12) 22,3 × 16,7 (19,7—24,4 × 15,9—17,5).

697   Rock Pipit   Klipkoester

Anthus crenatus   Finsch and Hartlaub, 1870: *near Cape Town.*
PLATE 59 (OPP. P. 481).
Length about 18 cm (wing ♂ 82,5—87,7—93, ♀ 79—82,1—85; tail ♂ 65—71, ♀ 62—69; tarsus 27—29,5; culmen 15,5—18; hind claw 9—11,5. 15 specimens, 11 ♂ 4 ♀).
Iris hazel; bill brown, yellowish below; legs flesh-coloured.

Identification: Not a very distinctive species. Has plain, dull under-parts, lightly marked chest; yellow edges to wing-coverts and flight-feathers; outer tail-feathers dull buff.
Distribution: Confined to the hills and mountains of the southern and eastern Cape extending as far north as Philipstown, Pondoland and Wakkerstroom in eastern Transvaal.
Habits: A fairly common resident species in more hilly areas. Frequents the grass-covered hills and perches on the bare rocks, whence the male utters a whistling song and at the same time stands erect and points its beak skywards. Sclater also describes the bird singing whilst hovering. Near De Aar is known as the ''kopje-lark'' because it inhabits the flat-topped kopjes.
Food: Spiders, grasshoppers and a few grass seeds.
Voice: A clear whistling song of two loud pipes followed by half a dozen quivering notes; a curious long drawn-out note.
Breeding: The nest is situated under a tuft of grass or a stone on a hillside. November. Eggs 3, white with numerous fine speckles and some larger ones and spots of pale olive to reddish brown and slate-grey, more at the thick end. Average (5) 21,4 × 15,2 (21—21,7 × 15—15,5).

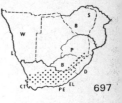
697

698   Tree Pipit   Boompieper

Anthus trivialis   Linnaeus, 1758: *Sweden.*
PLATE 59 (OPP. P. 481).
Length about 14 cm (wing 83—86,2—91,5; tail 57—64; tarsus 20—22; culmen 12,5—14; hind claw 7—9. 10 specimens). Iris dark brown; bill dark brown, lighter below; legs flesh-coloured. Weight 21,4 g.

Identification: Illustration shows the typical light, unmarked throat and the heavy radiating chest-markings. Appears short billed in the field.

495

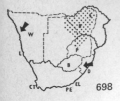

Distribution: The palaearctic region south to India and Africa. Extends to Rhodesia and Transvaal, as far south as Pretoria and Rustenburg. Recorded also from Swakopmund in South West Africa and Kloof, Natal.

Habits: A non-breeding migrant, not uncommon in Rhodesia from October to April; elsewhere rare. Recorded singly and in pairs also in flocks on migration. Occurs in light woodland and in scattered trees and bushes in grassveld usually along edge of tree line. When disturbed flies into trees. Shows preference for non-indigenous vegetation in eastern Rhodesia.

Food: Beetles, insect larvae, termites, weevils, moths and bugs.

Voice: Alarm note a sharp "tick-tick-tick".

698

LOCAL RACE:
A.t. trivialis Linnaeus 1758: *Sweden.* Another race occurs in Asia.

699　Bushveld Tree Pipit　　　　　　　　　Bosveld-koester

Anthus caffer　Sundevall, 1851: *Limpopo River = Mohapoani Berg, Botswana.*

PLATE 59 (OPP. P. 481).
Length about 14 cm (wing 70—73,4—78; tail 49—56,5; tarsus 16—19; culmen 10—13; hind claw 5—7. 25 specimens).

Identification: A small pipit, likely to be confused with the previous species but chin off-white and markings on breast tend to merge and run on to each other whilst in No. 698 they are distinct. After the moult (early March in Mozambique) the birds are darker, giving a reddish brown tone to the plumage.

Distribution: From Kenya southwards to Natal, Transvaal and Botswana.

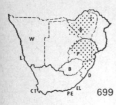

Habits: A common species of the dry savanna but elsewhere rather local and generally considered uncommon. Shows a preference for thorn bushes and fever trees. Usually found on the ground where the grass is short or thinly dispersed, when disturbed flies to the nearest tree from which it may call or sing. When flushed jumps up and makes off with erratic flight much like the next species.

699

Voice: Calls from the ground a low "tseeeer".

Breeding: The nest is concealed under a tuft of grass. October to March. Eggs 3, white with a quantity of small clear spots of pale reddish, brown and slate-blue. Average (8) 18,6 × 14,2 (17,6—19,7 × 13,2—14,8).

LOCAL RACE:
A.c. caffer Sundevall, 1851: *Limpopo River = Mohapoani Berg, Botswana.* As above.

700　Short-tailed Pipit　　　　　　　　　Kortstert-koester

Anthus brachyurus　Sundevall, 1851: *near Port Natal = Durban.*
PLATE 59 (OPP. P. 481).
Length about 13 cm (wing 62—64,6—66; tail 39—41; tarsus 16—17,5; culmen 10—11,5; hind claw 5—6,8. 5 specimens). Iris hazel; bill brown above, yellowish below; legs brown.

Identification: A small pipit, very dark above and more heavily marked below than the previous species. See also Habits.

Distribution: Recorded from scattered localities in Natal and Zululand and in southern and eastern Transvaal. Found again from Angola, Zaïre to Uganda.
Habits: Apparently uncommon and little recorded. Sclater states only plentiful during the summer months in Natal and probably all the year round in the Transvaal. A terrestrial species never alighting on any twig or stem of grass though it may seek some elevation, even an antheap, from which to sing. Generally rises from the grass close to one's feet and flits about at fair height before settling, after which it runs some little way and unexpectedly pops up again at another place. Flight is both strong and very erratic.
Food: Small insects and grass seed.
Voice: A buzzy nasal "bzzht". Song is short.
Breeding: Concealed under a tuft of grass. October to December. Eggs 2 or 3, pinky white, thinly sprinkled with fine speckles of pale olive-brown and slate-grey. Average (6) 17,5 × 13,6 (16,1—19,2 × 13,2—14,3).

LOCAL RACE:
A.b. brachyurus Sundevall, 1851: *near Port Natal = Durban*. Replaced by another race from Angola northwards.

---

701   Yellow-breasted Pipit   Geelbors-koester

Anthus chloris   Lichtenstein, 1842: *"Kaffirland" = Eastern Cape.*

Native Names: Iguruguru (X); 'Ntasare (S).

PLATE 59 (OPP. P. 481).
Length about 16—18 cm (wing ♂ 84,5—87,4—89, ♀ 80—84,2—87,5; tail ♂ 65—72, ♀ 61—72; tarsus 22,5—26; culmen 13—14,5; hind claw 10—13,5. 16 specimens, 7 ♂, 9 ♀). Iris brown; bill pale brown; legs yellowish brown.

Identification: Adult illustrated, sexes alike. Immature has buffish sides of belly with a yellow tinge to the centre and is streaked. The axillaries and under wing-coverts at the wing joint are bright yellow as in the adult.
Distribution: Found locally from the eastern Cape, northwards to the Orange Free State, southern Transvaal and higher western districts of Natal and Pondoland.
Habits: A not uncommon resident, where it occurs, in the shorter grass of the flats and valleys especially in mountainous areas. Seeks concealment in the grass more than other pipits, especially when pursued, lying close and being consequently often difficult to flush a second time. Usually seen singly or in pairs. The males sing from the tops of ant-hills. Creeps through the grass and runs quickly through the open spaces.
Food: Mantises and beetles.
Breeding: The nest, placed in a large tuft of grass, is cup-shaped and lined with fine grass. September to January. Eggs 3, a pale greenish white with scattered marks of brown and slate-grey; some heavily marked in a zone at thick end. Average (11) 21,0 × 15,8 (20—22 × 15—16,6).

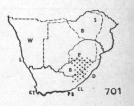

702   See page xxxii

703 Orange-throated Longclaw   Kalkoentjie

Macronyx capensis (Linnaeus), 1766: *Cape of Good Hope.*
Native Names: Inqilo (X); i-Qomfi (Z); le-Kolo, le-Thoeële (X).

PLATE 59 (OPP. P. 481).
Length about 20 cm (wing ♂ 97—100—105, ♀ 91—95,5—100; tail 61—73; tarsus 31—37; culmen 17—20; hind claw 14—22. 36 specimens, 24 ♂, 12 ♀). Iris brown; bill dark brown; legs pale brown.

Identification: The bright orange throat, separated by a black gorget from the orange-yellow breast and belly are conspicuous and distinctive features of this species. After breeding the upper-parts become darker and more spotted. In flight (see below) the white tips to tail-feathers are useful aids to identity. Sexes alike. Immature has gorget markings brown and throat ochre-buff; belly yellow.

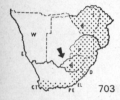

703

Distribution: From south-western Cape Province eastwards and northwards to Natal, Zululand, Orange Free State, Transvaal, Botswana and Rhodesia. Rare in the drier parts of the central Cape. Usually found in pairs, either on the ground, or sometimes perched on tufts of grass or low bushes. The flight is rather slow, heavy with quail-like, almost noisy wing-beats, the bird uttering as it goes, what Layard aptly calls, a "mewing" note which reminds one of the cry of a kitten. Does not fly for long stretches.

Food: Beetles, grasshoppers, weevils, stink bugs, termites, etc., and a few grass seeds.

Voice: See above; a nasal mewing "me-yii". Also a far-reaching whistle.

Breeding: The nest is placed on the ground or in the depths of a large tuft of grass; thickly built of grasses and compactly lined with rootlets. August to December in the Cape, as late as April to the north. Eggs 3—4, dull creamy white, rather heavily marked with olive-brown or olive-reddish and some slate-grey, as speckles, spots or even blotches at the thicker end. Average (100) 24,1 × 17,9 (22,1—26,7 × 16,7—19,1) one runt egg 15,2 × 13.

LOCAL RACES:
(a) M.c. capensis (Linnaeus), 1766: *Cape of Good Hope.* Cape Province to Natal. More darkly shaded on the breast and having streaking on breast below gorget. Size above.
(b) M.c. colletti Schouteden, 1908: *Zululand.* Zululand, Orange Free State, Transvaal and extending into the south-west of Matabeleland as far as the Matopos. Paler than *(a).* As illustrated.
(c) M.c. stabilior Clancey, 1952: *Salisbury. Rhodesia.* Mashonaland and Matabeleland. More contrasted pattern of upper-parts and brownish suffusion to the sides of breast.

704 Yellow-throated Longclaw   Geelkeel-kalkoentjie

Macronyx croceus (Vieillot), 1816: *Java = Senegal.*
Native Name: i-Qomvi (Z).

PLATE 59 (OPP. P. 481).
Length about 20 cm (wing 92—97,7—106; tail 67—86; tarsus 32—38; culmen 16,5—20; hind claw 16,5—23,5. 28 specimens). Iris brown; bill dark brown; legs pale brown.

Identification: The yellow under-parts with black gorget are unmistakable. The habits and brownish upper-parts distinguish the group (see Bokmakierie, No. 722). The Golden Pipit, No. 702, has a black band only, not a gorget.

Sexes alike. After the moult (about April) upper-parts appear more spotted; this becomes more uniform in summer. Immature is practically indistinguishable from that of No. 703 but this species (No. 704) is darker above and there is more yellow on the edges of the wing-feathers.

Distribution: Over the greater part of the Ethiopian region, extending within our limits on the east through eastern Districts of Rhodesia, the low country of Transvaal, Mozambique, Natal and Zululand as far south as Port St. Johns.

Habits: A common resident species. Occurs in moist areas in similar habitat to the previous species, which it much resembles in habits and call-notes. Resorts to trees quite frequently, to call or hawk insects.

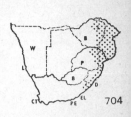

704

Breeding: The nest is placed on the ground, under, or partly concealed by, grass; it is a bulky structure of grass or reeds *(Carex)* lined with finer grass or rootlets. October to February in Natal, later to May in Mozambique. Eggs 3—4, white with streaky speckles and a few spots of yellowish brown and underlying pale ash-grey. Average (14) 24,3 × 18,3 (22,4—26,3 × 17,2—19,3).

LOCAL RACE:
M.c. vulturnus Friedmann, 1930: *Natal.* Throughout our area, replaced by another race in Nigeria.

705 Pink-throated Longclaw   Rooskeel-kalkoentjie

Macronyx ameliae   de Tarragon, 1845: *Port Natal = Durban.*

PLATE 59 (OPP. P. 481).
Length about 20 cm (wing 89—94; tail 74—80; tarsus 30—32; culmen 16,5—17; hind claw 15—17. 4 specimens). Iris brown; bill dark brown above, paler below; legs yellowish.

Identification: This beautiful bird is unmistakable. The female is slightly duller. The immature has buffish throat, the gorget is incomplete, pink on lower breast and belly, and no yellow on wings.

Distribution: Limited to a belt of country along the coast, from Durban northwards to the highlands of Mashonaland (Selukwe, Salisbury, Rusape). Once recorded from the Mababe Flats, Ngamiland. A sight record from Wankie Game Reserve needs confirmation. Extends beyond our limits to Kenya, Tanzania and Zambia.

705

Habits: Extremely local; usually found around the edge of marshy areas in medium and short grass. It is shy and lies low in the grass when approached, making off when flushed to hide again in the grass a short distance away. Flight is more irregular than the other Longclaws and once on the ground does not run about so much. Said to alight on fences and ant-hills but not recorded to perch on trees or bushes.

Voice: Alarm note similar to other Longclaws. Call-note sharply uttered, a plaintive note differing from No. 703.

Breeding: The nest is placed on the dry ground or on some vegetation, often between swamp grasses and sometimes well hidden with a short runway approach. It is a neatly built nest with a thick base of old thin grasses in the shape of a deep cup. October to January. Eggs 3, white, tinged with pale green, heavily and closely freckled in sepia and underlying ashy shades, with denser markings at the thick end. Average (19) 22,1 × 16,8 (20,1—23,8 × 15,9—17,5).

Family LANIIDAE

The Shrikes are well known from the familiarity of some species in coming into towns, and the Fiscal in particular for its raids upon Canaries and other cage birds. The bill is stout and hooked at the tip in the more carnivorous species, and the true shrikes (represented by the first three species below) have a slight tooth-like projection behind the hook, rather as in a Falcon as distinguished from other hawks. The majority of species are insectivorous rather than carnivorous and the bill is not so hooked. As compared with the Flycatchers and Warblers the bill is deeper and stouter, more rounded above and the rictal bristles are not so well developed (in the great majority) as in the former. There is a great variety in the species and the family is spread over all continents, though particularly well represented in Africa, where some occur in forests; whereas the true Shrikes and some of the others frequent the savannas and even the open plains where there are trees. All construct open, cup-shaped nests and lay speckled eggs.

706 Lesser Grey Shrike   Europese Grys Laksman

Lanius minor   Gmelin, 1788: *Italy.*

PLATE 61 (OPP. P. 513).
Length 20—22 cm (wing 110—116—122; tail 85—94; tarsus 23—26; culmen 16—18. 20 specimens). Iris brown; bill and legs black. Weight 28,6—30 g.

Identification: Resembles the Fiscal Shrike but has grey on crown and back and lacks the conspicuous white bar on the wing of that species. Distinguished from other similar shrikes to the north by its black forehead. Sexes alike. The immature lacks black forehead. See below.
Distribution: Middle southern Europe and eastern Asia southwards to Africa. Extending as far south as Windhoek and Gobabis in Damaraland, to Vryburg in northern Cape, Kroonstad in the Orange Free State and from Umbeluzi near Maputo, Mozambique. A bird of passage in Rhodesia.
Habits: A fairly common non-breeding migrant present from October to April. Occurs in the more open drier thornveld, perching on a conspicuous post, whence it watches for large insects and small animals it can overpower on the ground below. It avoids settled areas. The flight is faster than the Fiscal Shrike. Andersson records several birds perched on one tree, though normally more solitary.

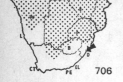 706

707 Fiscal   Fiskaal

Lanius collaris   Linnaeus, 1766: *Cape of Good Hope.*

Native Names: Inxanxadi (X); i-Qola, i-Lunga (Z); le-Tzoka, Manako, Tsemeli (S); Mutungadzorera (D).

PLATE 61, ♂ AND ♀, (OPP. P. 513).
Length about 23 cm (wing 98—99,7—103; tail 100—113; tarsus 25—30; culmen 16—19. 10 specimens). Iris brown; bill and legs black. Weight 43—58 g.

Identification: One of our commonest and most familiar birds. Its habit of sitting and waiting for prey in full view in some exposed position distinguishes it from other black-and-white shrikes. The amount of black and white, especially on head and tail, is variable; see details under Races. The female, in the Cape, is distinguished by its chestnut-coloured flanks as illustrated. The young is ash-brown above, finely barred, and light greyish brown below with fine cross-bars; tail and wing-feathers are edged with buff. See also Nos 709 and 665.

Distribution: Over the greater part of the Ethiopian region. Throughout our area except the central, sandy Kalahari.

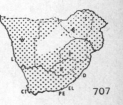

Habits: A very common resident species, found in most localities but commoner in the savanna and more open country where trees are scattered. Quite adapted to human habitation and gardens where its well-known habit is to take up watch upon the highest part of a tree or post and pour forth a harsh, grating challenge, often crudely imitating the cries of other birds, fowls, etc. Usually seen singly, perched on the top of a bush or tree whence it can survey the neighbourhood for its prey. The Fiscal does not tolerate other birds in its haunts and even carries its raids into neighbouring gardens and destroys anything that is too slow to avoid it. Has the habit of impaling some of its prey on thorns or barbs of wire fences; both sexes keep the "larder" all the year round.

707

Food: A great variety, from insects, especially beetles and grasshoppers, to lizards, small snakes, chameleons, frogs and birds, both adult and young; boldly takes nestlings even of quite large birds such as the Bokmakierie. Notorious for the number of tame Canaries and other cage birds it destroys by scaring them so that they flutter against the bars where they are seized by the head and killed.

Voice: See above. A grating "gertchagertcha-gertchagertcha" or "skiza, skiza, skizazskiza" (Skead).

Breeding: The nest is situated in the fork of a well-foliaged bush or tree from 1—4 metres up, occasionally more. A warm nest made of dry grass, twigs and grass, lined with whitish-coloured weeds, wool, rags, feathers, rootlets and even string. July to January. Eggs usually 4, 3—5, pale cream or pale greenish with scattered speckles and spots of dim pale olive and grey often forming a ring round the thicker part. Average (100) 23,7 × 17,9 (21,5—26,5 × 16,7—19,8). The nest is built by the ♀, although ♂ gathers some material. Eggs laid on consecutive days. Incubation 15—16½ days by ♀ only. Nestling 17—21 days, both sexes feed but ♀ more than ♂. Same nest is used for several broods.

LOCAL RACES:
(a) L.c. collaris Linnaeus, 1766: *Cape of Good Hope.* Western and eastern Cape Province replaced on the west by *(b)* and on the east by *(c)*. Breast freckled grey, no white eyebrow, rump grey. As illustrated. Size above.
(b) L.c. subcoronatus. A. Smith, 1841: *Latakoo.* South West Africa, except along the dry Namib—see *(d)*, northern Cape, Botswana, Orange Free State, western Transvaal and Rhodesia. Breast white, eyebrows broadly white, rump mainly whitish.
(c) L.c. predator Clancey, 1953: *Ingwavuma, N.E. Zululand.* Natal, Zululand, Mozambique and neighbouring low-lying areas of south-east Rhodesia northwards.
(d) L.c. aridicolus Clancey, 1955: *Swakopmund, S.W.A.* The Namib, dry coastal desert strip of South West Africa. Paler and greyer above than *(b)*; silky white under-parts and more white on tail. The female with chestnut-coloured flanks. Shorter more rounded tail 96—107 (14).

501

708   Red-backed Shrike   Rooirug-laksman

Lanius collurio   Linnaeus, 1758: *Europe = Sweden.*

PLATE 61, ♂ AND ♀ (OPP. P. 513).
Length about 18 cm (wing 89—92,3—95; tail 71—81; tarsus 22—25; culmen 13—17.
12 specimens). Iris brown; bill and legs black.

Identification: The male is easily identified by its grey forehead to nape and
rump, and its russet back and wing-coverts. The female and immature are
similar, but the fine vermiculations of the latter are more prominent. See also
under Habits.

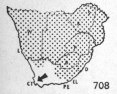

708

Distribution: The greater part of Europe and Asia southwards to India and
Africa during the non-breeding season. Extends southwards to the Orange
River in the west and to the Cape Province except the southern and south-
western portions.

Habits: A common non-breeding migrant, present from October to May; less
common at the more southerly parts of its range. Found in most types of
country but most commonly in open thorn or bush country especially near
watercourses, also in scrub-woodland. Perches on top of small trees and
bushes or on the lower projecting branches, whence it watches for its prey in
the vicinity, and especially on the ground.

Food: Mainly large insects. Has been recorded to impale prey on thorns in
our area.

Voice: A harsh "chak-chak". Song recorded in March in the Transvaal.

LOCAL RACES:
(a) L.c. collurio Linnaeus, 1758: *Europe = Sweden.* From South West Africa east to the
eastern Cape northwards. The russet extensive on upper-parts. As illustrated. Size above.
(b) L.c. kobylini (Buturlin), 1906: *Kurais, Caucasus.* On the east from Natal north,
commoner than *(a)* in Rhodesia. Russet of upper-parts duller and less extensive.
(c) L.c. pallidifrons Johansen, 1952: *Tomsk, W. Siberia.* Recorded from near Kimberley,
one specimen. Paler forehead.

708 X   Souza's Shrike   Souzase Laksman

Lanius souzae   Bocage, 1878: *Caconda, Angola.*

PLATE 61 (OPP. P. 513).
Length about 18 cm (wing 76—88; tail 72—87; tarsus 19—23; bill 12,5—14). Iris
brown; bill black; legs black. Weight 33 g.

Identification: Rather like a small brown fiscal shrike. Ashy brown on head
and nape, russet brown back, but easily distinguished from No. 708 in all
plumages by the broad white scapular bar on the wings. Female has tawny
flanks.

Distribution: Congo to Tanzania south to Malawi, Zambia and Angola.
Recorded from Mayara, Cunene River, South West Africa. Also Chobe.

Habits: Very similar to the Red-backed Shrike in habits; our records having
been collected in typical habitat of thin Kalahari woodland. This species
apparently shows local migratory movements.

LOCAL RACE:
L.s. souzae Bocage, 1878: *Caconda, Angola.* As above.

709 Boubou   Waterfiskaal

Laniarius ferrugineus   (Gmelin), 1788: *Cape of Good Hope.*

Native Names: Igqubusha (X); i-Boboni (Z); Pzempzete (S); i-Civana (G).
PLATE 61, ♂ AND ♀, RACE *(a)* AND ♂ *(g)* (OPP. P. 513).
Length about 23 cm (wing ♂ 95—99,9—101, ♀ 92—94,5—97; tail 91—104; tarsus
33—37; culmen 22,5—26; height of bill 8,8—10. 19 specimens, 9 ♂, 10 ♀. Iris brown;
bill black; legs lead-coloured. Weight 54 g.

Identification: Similar in appearance to the Fiscal Shrike but quite different in
habits, this bird creeps through the bushes for food, not watching from a
prominent perch. The tail is shorter and more rounded. The white on wings,
which is variable in this species, differs markedly from the Fiscal. South of the
Limpopo has distinct cinnamon-buff flanks, belly and rump, while the female
is duller than the male. Immature usually has white tips to outer tail-feathers
but some adults are similar.

Distribution: The whole of the Ethiopian region. In our limits absent from
the drier areas of South West Africa, Botswana except the swamps of
Ngamiland, the dry parts of Little Namaqualand and the Karoo in the Cape.

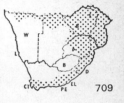

709

Habits: A common resident species occurring wherever there is tangled bush
of any extent, especially along watercourses. It creeps and hops through
bushes, often on the ground and is very inquisitive, coming to investigate any
strange noises or alarm calls. Quite often comes into gardens where it may be
seen in the open. Usually occurs in pairs and their duet, uttered from
concealment, is a familiar sound.

Food: Insects.

Voice: A duet of "ko-ko" replied by "kweet" or "boo-boo" replied to by
"whee oo"; often reversed thus "too, whee" answered by "boo-boo". The
alarm note a guttural "cha-chacha" or "bizykizzkizz".

Breeding: The nest is usually well hidden in some dense vegetation and is
difficult to find; they do sometimes build in quite exposed sites. Situated from
1—4, rarely up to 8 metres above the ground, the nest is placed on a branch or
in thick creepers; it is a shallow basin-shaped nest built of fine roots or twigs
with or without a lining of fine dry grass. August to April. Eggs 2, usually 3,
pale greenish white with numerous fine speckles of reddish brown and slate
rather more at the larger end forming a ring. Average (72) 24,4 × 18,0
(22—27 × 16,8—19). One egg 26,0 × 19,5 (Cuckoo?). Incubation 16 days
(1) (Skead). Nestling 16 days (1) (Skead).

LOCAL RACES:
This species has been separated into two closely allied species by some modern workers.
The more conservative opinion is followed here. Races *(f)* and *(g)* are sometimes
considered to belong to *L. aethiopicus.*
(a) L.f. ferrugineus (Gmelin), 1788: *Cape of Good Hope.* Southern Cape Province from
east to west. As illustrated. Size above.
(b) L.f. pondoensis Roberts, 1922: *Port St. Johns, Pondoland.* Coast of Pondoland.
Similar in all respects to *(a)*, except that it has the upper-parts more olive-yellowish.
(c) L.f. natalensis Roberts, 1922: *Weenen, Natal.* Natal to southern Lebombo Mountain
forests. Male rather paler below, ♀ darker above than *(a)*; bill averaging weaker.
(d) L.f. tongensis Roberts, 1931: *Manaba, Zululand.* North-eastern Zululand littoral to
southern Mozambique. Male mainly white below, with only a little rufous buffy about
the abdomen, ♀ paler rufous buffy than *(c)*. Size smaller, bill weaker; wing ♂ 89—95, ♀
82—92; tail 84—94; tarsus 29—34,5; culmen 23—25; height of bill 7,7—9,2 (11
specimens, 4 ♂, 7 ♀).

(e) L.f. transvaalensis Roberts, 1922: *Louws Creek, near Barberton*. The southern part of the Transvaal from east to west. Male less white on throat and breast, not so much differentiated from ♀ as *(a)*, thus ♀ darker above. Bill height 8—9.

(f) L.f. limpopoensis Roberts, 1922: *Lilliput, Sand River, Zoutpansberg dist*. Limpopo River Valley. Both sexes buffy rufous below, tail rather longer than wing; sexes alike.

(g) L.f. mossambicus (Reichenow), 1880: *Mozambique*. Rhodesia, Zambia, Mozambique except the south and Malawi. As illustrated. The pinkish buff suffusion on under-parts lighter than *(d)*; sexes alike.

(h) L.f. savensis Rosa Pinto, 1963: *Panda P.E.A.* Northern Sul do Save area Mozambique.

710   West African Boubou

Laniarius bicolor   (Verreaux), 1857: *Gaboon*.

PLATE 61 (OPP. P. 513).
Length 23—25 cm (wing 90—96, also ♂ 110, ♀ 104; tail 95—110; tarsus 32—34; culmen 24—25. 4 specimens). Iris brown; bill black; legs slate-blue.

Identification: Similar to No. 709 but lacks any pink tinge even to the base of breast feathers. Distinguished by its call and non-skulking habits.

Distribution: Gabon to Angola. Occurs within our area, along the Kunene and Okavango rivers in South West Africa; Chobe, Botletle rivers and Okavango swamps in Botswana and Caprivi.

Habits: Much more conspicuous than the last, perching boldly in pairs on top of papyrus, or exploring the large riverine forest trees.

Voice: Louder and more challenging call than the preceding, less musical. The female replies with a harsh short "kick-ick". A dominant bird sound where it occurs.

LOCAL RACE:
L.b. sticturus Finsch and Hartlaub, 1870: *Lake Ngami, Botswana*. As above, larger than the northern race.

711   Crimson-breasted Shrike   Rooibors-fiskaal

Laniarius atrococcineus   Burchell, 1822: *junction of Vaal and Orange Rivers*.

Native Names: Palamafsika (Ch); i-Billibomvu (T).

PLATE 60 (OPP. P. 512).
Length about 23 cm (wing ♂ 98—100—105, ♀ 93—97—101; tail 90—109; tarsus 30—34; culmen 20,5—26. 36 specimens, 23 ♂, 13 ♀). Iris brown; bill and legs black.

Identification: This beautiful species is unmistakable. Sexes alike. Young ash grey below, finely cross-barred with black; buff edges to feathers of upper parts; the under tail-coverts are the first to assume the crimson of the adult. Individuals with yellow breast instead of crimson, and "lavender" iris, are sometimes met with, this being due apparently to defect in the pigment. Young develop adult colour in 35 days.

Distribution: South West Africa as far as the Orange River, northern Cape, northern Orange Free State, Botswana; the western and the north-western half of the Transvaal and Matabeleland as far east as Gwelo.

Habits: A common resident species found in the drier acacia thornveld, where there is matted bush in which it can find refuge. Not very shy but very quick and on the ground, moving with long hops. Usually found singly or in

711   pairs.

Food: Insects, apparently not preying on small vertebrates.
Voice: Usually in duet, a challenging, whistled, "quot-quot" or "ter-tju-terrtju" by ♀, followed by "tju" of ♂. Alarm a snorting "tarr".
Breeding: The nest is placed in the fork of a thorn tree 1—4 metres from the ground. A shallow basin-shaped structure of curled strips of dry bark, other fibres and rootlets. September to January, later in South West Africa, October to February, April and July. Eggs 2, usually 3, pale greenish white with clearly defined spots and blotches of brown and slate-blue, sometimes forming a zone at larger end. Average (44) 23,6 × 17,6 (22,9—25,5 × 16,6—18,7). Incubation 16—17 days. Fledging 18—20.

712 Puffback Shrike   Sneeubal

Dryoscopus cubla   (Shaw), 1809: *Knysna*.

Native Names: Unomaswana, Ingqibitshane, Intak'embila (X); um-Hlope kas (Z).

PLATE 61, ♂ AND ♀ (OPP. P. 513).
Length about 18 cm (wing ♂ 78—83—88, ♀ 76—78—80; tail 66—76; tarsus 21—24; culmen 17,5—21. 31 specimens, 26 ♂, 5 ♀). Iris orange or red; bill black; legs light ashy. Weight ♀ 23—26 g (2), ♂ 27—30 g (4).

Identification: This shrike is distinguished from other black-and-white shrikes by its wholly black upper-parts except for white rump, whitish wing and pure white under-parts. The white rump is not always visible, especially when the wings are folded above the rump. The female is duller. The young resembles the female but is browner above and more fulvous on the rump and under-parts.
Distribution: From eastern Zaïre and Kenya southwards. Absent only from the south-west Cape, drier areas of the Karoo, Orange Free State, southern Botswana and Great Namaqualand.
Habits: A common resident species widely distributed wherever there is more or less matted bush or forest although absent from *Acacia*. Found creeping quietly about in the larger trees, often in pairs or family parties or together with other species in bird parties, in search of insects. The flight is heavy, dipping, with audible flapping of wings. When excited puffs out the white plumes of the back, so that it looks like a white snowball, hence the name "Sneeubal".

712

Food: Beetles, larvae and grasshoppers.
Voice: "Chick-weeu, chick-weeu" repeated as many as 10 times, sometimes with an answering weaker replica. Also a tearing "tsssssrrrrr" or harsh "chikerrr".
Breeding: The nest is situated at the top of trees in the fork of small outer branches, from 2 to as much as 12 metres above the ground, sometimes well concealed by foliage. A neat compact cup of roots, grass and wood shavings bound by cobweb and cocoon webbing and vegetable-down, lined with fine grass. August to March. Eggs 2, usually 3, somewhat variable but mainly white or pale cream, finely speckled with sepia and chocolate-brown and underlying slate, the latter more condensed at thick end; some eggs having a ring at larger end. Average (41) 21,6 × 15,9 (19,3—23,3 × 14,9—16,8), one egg 24,4 × 17,7. Parasitised by Klaas's Cuckoo.

505

SHRIKES

LOCAL RACES:
(a) D.c. cubla (Shaw), 1809: Knysna. Cape Province, from Knysna northwards to Transvaal and Natal. As illustrated. Size above.
(b) D.c. chapini Clancey, 1954: Malamala, Tvl. Eastern Transvaal and Mozambique to East Africa. Whiter below than (a).
(c) D.c. okavangensis Roberts, 1932: Maun, Ngamiland. Ngamiland, Ovamboland, Kaokoveld and northern Damaraland. Showing much white on the wings and the black of the back more restricted; in the ♀ more so than in ♂, and with the forehead flecked with grey.

713   Tchagra   Tjagra-laksman

Tchagra tchagra   (Vieillot), 1816: *Gamtoos River.*

PLATE 60 (OPP. P. 512).
Length about 22 cm (wing 79—81,2—83; tail 83—96; tarsus 26—30; culmen 24—26,5. 9 specimens). Iris dark brown; bill and legs blackish brown.

Identification: Distinguished by its largish size compared to the next species, rufous forehead and crown, no black above the buff eye-stripe and brown on hind and sides of neck. Under-parts whitish. The brown of upper-parts with an olive tinge. Sexes alike. Young has wing-coverts buff-red, the eye-stripe duller and the under surface fulvous-grey.

Distribution: From the western Cape, eastwards over the southern Karoo and through the littoral of Natal, Zululand to Swaziland and the top of the Lebombo Mountains opposite. Two records from Transvaal just north of Pretoria.

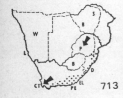

713

Habits: A fairly common resident species, frequenting the drier thorn scrub areas as well as the thicker coastal bush. Singly or in pairs, this bird creeps about the lower branches, often on the ground, and is a reluctant flyer. Call is loud and frequently draws attention to a bird which might otherwise have been overlooked. Performs a display flight like the next species.

Food: Berries, beetles and insects.

Voice: A loud rattle followed by a rapid stuttering "chchchch . . ." ended by "tew, a-tew, a" repeated about a dozen times (Skead). Also a loud whistle.

Breeding: The nest, placed about one metre up in the fork of a bush or open shrub, is a shallow cup of fibres and roots. August to September in the Cape, to December in the eastern Cape. Eggs 2—3, white with dark red-brown and purplish slate speckles and scroll marks. 23,6—27,5 × 17,8—18,5.

LOCAL RACES:
(a) T.t. tchagra (Vieillot), 1816: Gamtoos River. Southern and south-eastern Cape. As illustrated. Size above.
(b) T.t. natalensis (Reichenow), 1903: Durban. Eastern Cape northwards. Crown lighter and more rufous-brown.

714   Three-streaked Tchagra   Driestreep-laksman

Tchagra australis   (A. Smith), 1836: *north of Kurrichane = Rustenburg dist.*

PLATE 60 (OPP. P. 512).
Length about 20 cm (wing 75—76,5—81; tail 90—99; tarsus 23—26; culmen 16,5—19. 17 specimens). Iris hazel; bill and legs brownish black. Weight 33,6 g.

Identification: This species is distinguished by its brown forehead and crown and by having black lines, above (narrow) and below (broader) the light stripe

506

over the eye. Chin white, rest of under-parts buffish. The back is light brown almost fawn. Sexes alike. The young bird is duller than adult but otherwise similar in pattern.

Distribution: Throughout the greater part of the Ethiopian region. Absent in our areas from Great Namaqualand, Cape Province and southern Orange Free State and Natal except in northern Zululand.

714

Habits: A widely dispersed, not uncommon, species, which frequents the thorn bush. Occurs singly or in pairs; one of the species frequently found in bird parties. It often feeds on the ground under bushes and trees, and when disturbed hops into the lower branches to obtain a view of the intruder; when approached it creeps into the thickest tangles on the far side of a bush. In the breeding season the male flies, with quivering wings, into the air just above the trees, and floats down in a circle, uttering a shrill and pretty string of trilling notes "tui-tui-tui-tui-tui" running down the scale.

Food: Insects.

Voice: See above. Alarm note a guttural "charrr".

Breeding: The nest, usually situated in a thin clump of low growth, or in the fork of a branch up to 3 metres from the ground, is a shallow basin of roots and twigs bound together firmly with cobwebs—a flimsy structure. October to January, September to March in Rhodesia. Eggs 2—3, white with scattered fine spotting and blotching of slate and dark brown tending to concentrate at the thick end. Average (74) 21,6 × 16,2 (20—25 × 15—17,7). Nestling 14½ days.

LOCAL RACES:
(a) T.a. australis (A. Smith), 1836: *north of Kurrichane = Rustenberg dist.* Western Transvaal and Botswana; extreme south of Rhodesia. As illustrated. Largest race. Size above.
(b) T.a. damarensis (Reichenow), 1915: *Windhoek, South West Africa.* Damaraland, Ovamboland and Kalahari. In general rather paler above and clearer buffy below. Size as *(a)*.
(c) T.a. rhodesiensis (Roberts), 1932: *Kabulabula, Chobe River, Ngamiland.* Ngamiland and north-western area of Rhodesia, including Wankie. Rather light coloured above and below; wing ♂ 72—77; tail ♂ 92—101 (8 specimens).
(d) T.a. tongensis (Roberts), 1931: *Manaba, North Zululand.* North-east Zululand to Gazaland and southern Mozambique. Still lighter coloured, below greyish and white; wing ♂ 68—78; tail ♂ 80—85 (7 specimens).
(e) T.a. minor (Reichenow), 1887: *Kagehi, Mwanza dist., Tanganyika.* Lower Zambesi Valley as far west as Chirundu and east to Mtoko, north to Tanzania. Above more rufous, below clearer white; wing ♂ 70—75; tail ♂ 74—83.

715 Black-crowned Tchagra   Swartkroon-laksman

Tchagra senegala (Linnaeus), 1766: *Senegal.*

Native Names: Umgupane, Imbombo (X); i-Nqupane (Z); um-Qubana (G); Samora (D).

PLATE 60 (OPP. P. 512).
Length 20—23 cm (wing ♂ 82—86,6—93, ♀ 82—86,4—90; tail 91—112; tarsus 26—31; culmen 20,5—25. 69 specimens, 36 ♂, 33 ♀). Iris hazel; bill black; legs brown.

Identification: The black crown above the eye-stripe and the whitish under-parts distinguish this species. Sexes alike. Young has blackish brown crown and bill is horn-coloured.

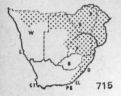

Distribution: Throughout the Ethiopian region except the drier parts of our area. Absent from Great Namaqualand, southern Botswana, Orange Free State and the western Cape Province.

Habits: A common resident species, well known because of its lack of fear of people, although it spends most of its time creeping about in thorn bush and smaller trees. Found singly or in pairs. The flight is heavy, rather hurried from one bush to the lower branches of another nearby. Hunts for its food low down, sometimes on the ground.

715

Food: Insects.

Voice: A characteristic call, variable but easily fitted to words; thus "he's-a-jolly-good-fellow" or "nothing today", "go back", or "inkos induwe tchwa-ita". Also "krok-krok-krokkrakror".

Breeding: The nest is placed in a fork or on a horizontal branch of a tallish, somewhat open tree or shrub, 2—4 metres above the ground. It is a shallow basin of roots and twigs firmly bound together. October to January in the south, September to March in Rhodesia. Eggs 2—3, white or pale pinkish white with streaks, scrolls and spots of light chestnut-brown intermingled with slate-grey markings more heavily concentrated at the big end. Average (100) 26,4 × 18,2 (22,1—26,9 × 17—19,5), one runt 15,5 × 13,2.

LOCAL RACES:

(a) T.s. confusa (van Someren), 1922: *Umfolosi, Zululand.* Eastern Cape Province to Natal and northwards to the Limpopo and eastern Rhodesia. As illustrated. Size above.
(b) T.s. mozambica (van Someren), 1921: *Lumbo, Mozambique.* Mozambique southwards to Beira, Zambesi Valley west to Sengwe River. Upper-parts richer rufous-chestnut, including the ear-coverts and sides of neck; whiter below. Smaller wing 83—85; tail 94—97; tarsus 28—29; culmen 22—24.
(c) T.s. kalahari (Roberts), 1932: *Mabeleapudi, Ngamiland.* Ngamiland to the north-west sector of Matabeleland. Lighter above and below.

716 Blackcap Tchagra   Swartkop-laksman

Antichromus minutus (Hartlaub), 1858: *Ashantee.*

PLATE 60 (OPP. P. 512).
Length about 18 cm (wing 75—78; tail 80—85; tarsus 19—21; culmen 24—26). Iris rose pink; bill black; legs lead-grey.

Identification: The black cap and uniform buffish upper-parts distinguish this species. The female differs only in having a narrow white line above the black lores. The young has blackish brown cap, bill horn-coloured.

Distribution: From Ethiopia to West Africa southwards to Angola, Rhodesia and Mozambique. Found within our limits in the eastern districts of Rhodesia and neighbouring Mozambique.

Habits: A resident, uncommon species which is restricted to rank grass and marshy vegetation. A rather more stolid bird than the previous species; less of a skulker, often perching on the conspicuous top of a low bush or tall grass stem, such as elephant grass. Flies short distances at a time.

716

Food: Dragonflies, grasshoppers and beetles.

Voice: Shorter than the previous species, a phrase which suggests the words "today or tomorrow".

Breeding: The nest is placed low down in a bush or in rank grass. It is a neat cup of rootlets and fibres. November to March in Rhodesia. Eggs 2—3, rarely one, white with few small round purple spots mainly at the large end. Average (5) 23,3 × 16,7 (22,8—23,9 × 16,4—17,2). One egg 26,6 × 18,9 according to Bell-Marley's collection.

LOCAL RACE:
A.m. remota (Clancey), 1959: *Vumba, Rhodesia.*

717   Olive Bush Shrike   Olyf Boslaksman

Chlorophoneus olivaceus   (Shaw), 1809: *Algoa Bay.*

Native Name: Umthethi (X).

PLATE 60. TWO PHASES, ♂ AND ♀ (OPP. P. 512).
Length 18—19 cm (wing 76—84,7—87; tail 75—86; tarsus 23—27; culmen 16—18,5. 42 specimens). Iris pale to dark brown; bill black; legs lead-grey. Weight 26—38 g.

Identification: *Olive phase:* Distinguished by its olive-green upper-parts including upper-parts of head, and by the black and yellow of under tail-feathers. The male has a black patch about the ear-coverts and *lores are yellow. Ruddy phase:* Distinguished from other blue-grey-crowned bush shrikes by pale, whitish under-parts with a rufous wash on breast and by the black and yellow under tail-feathers. The male has a black line from eye to ear-coverts, lores whitish. Young birds are olive-green with barring on under-parts and mottled above.

Distribution. Peculiar to the large evergreen forests, from Sir Lowry's Pass and Knysna eastwards to Natal and northwards including eastern Transvaal and eastern Rhodesia to Malawi.

Habits: A common resident species which frequents the higher bush and trees; in the eastern Cape also found in drier but thickish thorn scrub. Usually in ones or twos. On one occasion, one of each colour phase recorded feeding in the same bush (Skead). Secretive and usually remaining concealed in vegetation, but inquisitive. Creeps about the mid- and top-levels of bushes searching for insects.

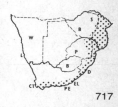

717

Food: Insects.

Voice: A high note followed by about six quickly repeated, liquid notes an octave lower. Also an attractive trilling call.

Breeding: The nest is placed in a low tree, up to 3 metres above the ground, and is a flimsy structure of mixed bents, roots, etc. October to January. Eggs 2, like a Cape Sparrow's but less streaked, pale greenish white with elongate markings of purplish brown with underlying markings of bluish grey. Average (17) 21,6 × 16,1 (19,2—23 × 14,4—17).

LOCAL RACES:
(a) C.o. olivaceus (Shaw), 1809: *Algoa Bay.* From the eastern Cape to the Transvaal and Mozambique. As illustrated. Size above.
(b) C.o. makawa Benson, 1945: *Chirobwe Mt. Ncheu, dist. Nyasaland.* Rhodesia and Malawi west of the Shire valley. Flanks brighter olive than birds from the south.

718 = 717

719 Orange-breasted Bush Shrike
Oranjebors-boslaksman

Chlorophoneus sulphureopectus (Lesson), 1831: *no locality = Senegal.*

PLATE 60 (OPP. P. 512).
Length 18—19 cm (wing 84—88,3—94; tail 81—96; tarsus 24—29; culmen 14,5—17,5. 37 specimens). Iris brown; bill and legs black.

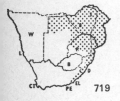

719

Identification: The *yellow forehead* and stripe over eye, coupled with the *black lores*, distinguish this attractive species. The yellow throat and orange breast are also distinctive. The young has forehead and eye-stripe grey, and is whitish where the adult is black on line from bill to ear-coverts; the chin and throat are white and contrast with the uniform yellow breast.
Distribution: The greater part of the Ethiopian region. Extends within our limits on the east as far as Grahamstown, Transvaal and Ngamiland.
Habits: A common, resident species which frequents tangled thorn bush, especially along streams and rivers. Usually in pairs and not as shy as some bush-shrikes. Agile birds, progressing upwards through the trees with springing hops.
Food: Ants and small beetles.
Voice: A musical call "pipit-yz! pipit-yz!" A monotonous liquid repetitive "poo poo poo poo . . ." or "wik wik wik . . .". Also a harsh clashing call.
Breeding: The nest is placed in the fork of a thorn tree or bush, up to 4 metres up, and is a flimsy structure of twigs and roots forming a shallow basin. So thin that the eggs may be seen from below. October to December. Recorded for the periods September to December and February to March in Rhodesia. Eggs 2, dull greenish white, heavily covered with rather elongate markings of a muddy brown overlying some markings of slate-blue. Average (32) 22,1 × 16,0 (19,8—23,9 × 15—17). Nestling 12 days.

LOCAL RACE:
C.s. similis (A. Smith), 1836: *north of Kurrichane = Rustenberg dist., Transvaal.* The southern and east African race.

720 Black-fronted Bush Shrike   Swartoog-boslaksman

Chlorophoneus nigrifrons (Reichenow), 1896: *Marangu, Kilimanjaro.*

PLATE 60, ♂ AND ♀ (OPP. P. 512).
Length about 19 cm (wing 87,5—93; tail 83—85; tarsus 25—26; culmen 17,5—19). Iris dark red; bill and legs black.

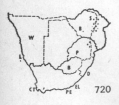

720

Identification: The black patch between eye and base of bill, with the blue-grey of crown extending right down the forehead distinguish this species from the last. Sexes as shown. Immature has forehead, lores and ear-coverts grey; greenish yellow or buffish white below.
Distribution: From Kenya southwards; recorded in our region only from the higher parts of the eastern border of Rhodesia and neighbouring Mozambique and at Woodbush in northern Transvaal. Sight record from Nduma needs confirmation.
Habits: Uncommon in our region where it frequents the mountain forests, especially the larger trees. Generally explores the canopy and the creepers but not the undergrowth. Little has been recorded. Has been observed accompanying foraging bulbuls.

Voice: Soft hooting "oo-poo" sometimes answered by a "screeee" or a clicking "chitick". Also a double "click-clack".

Breeding: Not recorded in our area. Situated at some height from the ground, the nest is a flimsy, shallow cup of twigs and tendrils placed in creepers or trees. October to November. Eggs 2, pale greenish with elongate smears of dark brown and chocolate as well as greyish shell markings. 22,4 × 17 and 22,3 × 17,3.

LOCAL RACE:
C.n. sangroundi Bangs 1931: *Mount Selinda, Rhodesia.*

721   Gorgeous Bush Shrike   Kongkoit

Telophorus quadricolor   (Cassin), 1851: *Port Natal = Durban.*

Native Names: u-Gongoni (Z); i-Ghiya-ngehlangu (Ng).

PLATE 60, ♂ AND ♀ (OPP. P. 512).
Length about 19 cm (wing 78—81—85; tail 81,5—88,5; tarsus 23—28; culmen ♂ 19—21,5, ♀ 17—19. 17 specimens, 13 ♂, 4 ♀). Iris brown; bill black; legs lead-coloured.

Identification: This beautiful bird is quite distinctive. The young has a yellow throat and an entirely green tail; see young of No. 722.

Distribution: Eastern and Southern Africa. Within our limits extending down the lower altitudes of eastern Rhodesia, eastern Transvaal and Natal as far south as Umkomaas.

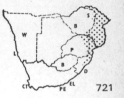

Habits: A not uncommon resident but so retiring that it remains unseen, but heard, in the depths of the tangles of matted thorn bush or dense riverine thickets. It is difficult to see as it creeps through the bushes.
Food: Insects.
Voice: One of the pleasantest bush sounds, a cheerful "kong-kong-koit", and variations.
Breeding: The nest is placed low down in a bush or amongst twigs and vines of a small tree. It is a loosely constructed shallow basin of dry grass, weed stems and twigs lined with dry leaf stalks. October, November. Eggs 2, pale greenish blue with scattered speckles and spots of red-brown and purplish slate. Average (12) 23,6 × 16,9 (22,9—24,6 × 16,4—18,3).

LOCAL RACE:
T.q. quadricolor (Cassin), 1851: *Port Natal = Durban.* Extends from the southern limits to beyond the Zambesi River.

722   Bokmakierie   Bokmakierie

Telophorus zeylonus   (Linnaeus), 1766: *Cape of Good Hope.*

Native Names: i-Ngqwani (X); Pjempjete (S).
PLATE 60 (OPP. P. 512).
Length about 23 cm (wing ♂ 97—100—104, ♀ 92—98—105; tail 92—105; tarsus ♂ 32—36, ♀ 29—34; culmen 21—26,5. 25 specimens, 13 ♂, 12 ♀). Iris hazel; bill black; legs lead-coloured. Weight 64—76 g.

Imm.

Identification: The black gorget around the yellow throat and the yellow belly are distinctive. The young has crown greenish; the under-parts yellowish or

511

PLATE 60

711. *Laniarius atrococcineus.* Crimson-breasted Shrike. Rooibors-fiskaal.
713. *Tchagra tchagra tchagra.* Tchagra. Tjagra-laksman.
714. *Tchagra australis australis.* Three-streaked Tchagra.
Driestreep-laksman.
715. *Tchagra senegala confusa.* Black-crowned Tchagra.
Swartkroon-laksman.
716. *Antichromus minutus remota.* Blackcap Tchagra. Swartkop-laksman.
717. *Chlorophoneus olivaceus olivaceus.* (Olive phase) Olive Bush Shrike.
Olyf Boslaksman. ♂ and ♀.
717. *Chlorophoneus olivaceus olivaceus.* (Ruddy phase) Olive bush Shrike.
Olyf Boslaksman. ♂ and ♀.
719. *Chlorophoneus sulphureopectus similis.* Orange-breasted Bush Shrike.
Oranjebors-boslaksman.
720. *Chlorophoneus nigrifrons.* Black-fronted Bush Shrike.
Swartoog-boslaksman. ♂ and ♀.
721. *Telophorus quadricolor quadricolor.* Gorgeous Bush Shrike.
Kongkoit. ♂ and ♀.
722. *Telophorus zeylonus zeylonus.* Bokmakierie.
723. *Malaconotus hypopyrrhus.* Grey-headed Bush Shrike. Spookvoël.

714

715

713

711

717
(RUDDY PHASE)

♂

721
♂

♀

716

717
(...VE PHASE)

♂   ♀

719

722

723

720
♀   ♂

MIGHTON
'36

A
731
B

724

729

728

726

727

730

♂
712

♀

A ♀
G
709
710
A ♂

♂
708 x
KN

♀
707
♂
708
♀
706

NIGHTON
'36

PLATE 61

706. *Lanius minor.* Lesser Grey Shrike. Europese Grys Laksman.

707. *Lanius collaris collaris.* Fiscal. Fiskaal. ♂ and ♀.

708. *Lanius collurio collurio.* Red-backed Shrike. Rooirug-laksman. ♂ and ♀.

708X. *Lanius souzae.* Souza's Shrike. Souzase Laksman.

709 *(a). Laniarius ferrugineus ferrugineus.* Boubou. Waterfiskaal. ♂ and ♀.

709 *(g). Laniarius ferrugineus mossambicus.* Boubou. Waterfiskaal.

710. *Laniarius bicolor sticturus.* West African Boubou. ♂ or ♀.

712. *Dryoscopus cubla cubla.* Puffback Shrike. Sneeubal. ♂ and ♀.

724. *Urolestes melanoleucus melanoleucus.* Long-tailed Shrike.
Langstert-laksman.

726. *Lanioturdus torquatus.* White-tailed Shrike. Kortstert-laksman.

727. *Prionops plumata poliocephala.* White Helmet Shrike.
Wit Helmlaksman.

728. *Sigmodus retzii retzii.* Red-billed Helmet Shrike. Swart Helmlaksman.

729. *Sigmodus scopifrons scopifrons.* Chestnut-fronted Helmet Shrike.
Stekelkop-helmlaksman.

730. *Eurocephalus anguitimens.* White-crowned Shrike. Kremetart-laksman.

731 *(a). Nilaus afer brubru.* Brubru Shrike. Bontrok-laksman.

731 *(b). Nilaus afer nigritemporalis.* Brubru Shrike. Bontrok-laksman.

greenish buff, the throat greyer; the tips of the tail-feathers are yellow, as in adult, and this distinguishes it easily from the young of the last species.

Distribution: Throughout the Cape Province and Orange Free State. In Natal common in the higher western areas, extending as far as Pinetown in the lower sections. Southern Transvaal and South West Africa as far north as Angola.

Habits: A common resident species which is conspicuous both from its familiar call and beautiful plumage. Frequents scattered patches of bush in open country, but not in the large forests. Somewhat terrestrial in habits running about on the ground in and around its haunts searching for food; otherwise found perched in the bushes and trees. Quite adapted to gardens around homesteads. Calls usually from some conspicuous perch and is nearly always accompanied by a mate with which a duet is carried on.

Food: Caterpillars, spiders, insects, chameleons, small lizards and frogs.

Voice: The onomatopoeic "bok, makierie"; "kok-o-vik" or "bok bok-chit". Also "pirrapee-pirrapoo". Also a joyful "wit wit wit wit". Alarm note a quiet "tock-tock-tock" or "krrrr".

Breeding: The nest is well hidden in closely matted bush or rushes and is usually placed fairly close to the ground. A fairly large compact basin-shaped structure of dry-grass, twigs and roots, often with green asparagus leaves on the outside. July to October in the Cape, throughout the year in the Transvaal but mainly September to December. Eggs usually 3 or 4, greenish blue with scattered speckles and spots of reddish brown. Average (89) 25,6 × 19,3 (23,1—27,3 × 17,0—20,2). Incubation 14—17 days (4). Nestling 17—19 days (3). Both parents feed young.

LOCAL RACES:
(a) T.z. zeylonus (Linnaeus), 1766: *Cape of Good Hope.* Cape Province to Transvaal and east. As illustrated. Size above.
(b) T.z. phanus (Hartert), 1920: *Farta Bay near Benguella town.* Great Namaqualand north. Paler than *(a)*.
(c) T.z. restrictus Irwin, 1968: *Chimanimani Mountains, Rhodesia.* An isolated population recently found in the Chimanimani Mountains. Darker than *(a)*.

723   Grey-headed Bush Shrike   Spookvoël

Malaconotus hypopyrrhus   Hartlaub, 1844: *Durban, Natal.*

Native Names: Umbankro (X); u-Hlaza (Z).

PLATE 60 (OPP. P. 512).

Length about 27 cm (wing 107—114—121; tail 106—117; tarsus 29—35; culmen 26—31. 30 specimens). Iris yellow; bill black; legs ash-brown.

Identification: The large size, grey of upper-parts of head and neck, and the large heavy bill distinguish this species easily. Note light iris and yellow tips to wing-feathers. Sexes alike. Young has horn-coloured bill.

Distribution: Over the greater part of Africa. Extends down the eastern areas including Rhodesia, eastern Transvaal, Natal and eastern Cape as far as Port Elizabeth.

Habits: A somewhat uncommon and sparingly distributed, resident species. Frequents trees and bushes, particularly near streams and rivers, where it may be heard uttering its challenging note and often seen as it searches the

branches for its prey or while flying from one tree to another. Small birds view its movements with considerable suspicion. Flight unwieldy.

Food: Mainly grasshoppers and other insects, but an entire mouse, a young 12 cm puffadder, lizards, chameleons and birds also recorded.

Voice: A loud, long ghostly and monotonous whistle, somewhat oriole-like, and frequently repeated.

Breeding: The nest is situated in the upper branches of a bush or small trees, in the fork of a stem, or placed where there is a spread of many supporting twig. A loosely built basin-shaped structure of stout twigs lined with rootlets and fine creeper stems. September to November in Natal, October to February in Rhodesia. Eggs 2—4, deep cream or pale buff suffused with many speckles of slate-grey and pale reddish often marked as a ring at the larger end. Average (31) 29,3 × 21,1 (27,3—31,5 × 19,8—22,3).

LOCAL RACE:
M.h. hypopyrrhus Hartlaub, 1844: *Durban, Natal.* The only race within our limits, extending to the Zambesi and Malawi.

724 Long-tailed Shrike   Langstert-laksman

Urolestes melanoleucus   (Jardine), 1831: *Orange River.*

Native Names: i-Kongqeli (Z); mo-Tziloli (Ch).

PLATE 61 (OPP. P. 513).
Length 40—50 cm (wing 122—134—143; tail ♂ 225—350, ♀ 215—340; tarsus 31—35,5; culmen 16,5—20,5. 42 specimens, 25 ♂, 17 ♀). Iris hazel; bill and legs black.

Identification: Quite distinctive. The female has whitish flanks, more prominent white tips to tail-feathers, and the tail is up to three inches shorter. The young is more bronzy brown above and below, and grey on rump.

Distribution: Eastern and southern Africa. Extending south to Matubatuba in Zululand, the Transvaal, western Orange Free State (also one recorded at Westminster). Old records to the Orange River.

Habits: A common resident of the thorn veld savannas. Usually in small family parties, sometimes singly, perched on the top or outer branches of thorn bushes from which passing insects are espied. The flight, influenced by the long tail, is somewhat dipping but is higher than most shrikes, fast and straight. When excited they raise their crests and spread out the tail.

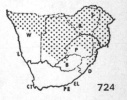

724

Food: Insects, especially grasshoppers and small reptiles.

Voice: A melancholy "kee-o" whistling note, several sometimes calling at the same time. Also written "needle-boom, needle-boom".

Breeding: The nest is placed at the extremity of a branch of a thorn-tree, up to 6 metres above the ground. A firm, large bowl-shaped nest of twigs and grass stems, lined with roots and creeper stems. August to March. Eggs 4 or 5, 6 also recorded; buffish or stone-yellow with scattered speckles and spots of reddish brown and slate-blue, sometimes concentrated at larger end. Average (26) 26,2 × 19,3 (23,1—27,5 × 18,3—20,4). Up to 28,7 recorded.

LOCAL RACE:
U.m. melanoleucus (Jardine), 1831: *Orange River.* Another race north of the Zambesi.

725 Yellow-spotted Nicator Geelvlek Nicator

Nicator gularis Hartlaub and Finsch, 1870: *Tete, Nyasaland.*

PLATE 49 (OPP. P. 369).
Length about 23 cm (wing ♂ 104—109—111, ♀ 89—92—95; tail ♂ 102—112, ♀ 88—95; tarsus ♂ 27—31, ♀ 25—28; culmen ♂ 20—22, ♀ 18,5—20. 12 specimens, 8 ♂, 4 ♀). Iris brown; bill black; legs lead-coloured. Weight 40—50 g.

Identification: The yellow-spotted wing, the yellow under-wing and under tail-coverts and heavy bill aid identification. Sexes alike, female sometimes lacks white above lores. Young paler with narrower yellow tips to wing-feathers, and outer tail-feathers more pointed. The young nestling is curious for its unfeathered, naked face.

Distribution: From West Africa to Kenya southwards to the Zambesi Valley, and down the littoral to Mkusi River, Zululand. Extends inland to the Lebombo Mountains and lower portions of Sabi River to within the boundaries of Rhodesia.

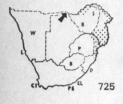

725

Habits: Not uncommon but not often seen unless searched for. Frequents the low-veld savanna bush. Appears to spend much of its time creeping about in the thicker parts of the bush, hopping from branch to branch.

Food: Insects.

Voice: Alarm note a low "churr"; sings October to January in Zululand— very loud, short phrases of a rapid warble with some rattling notes "chi-chi-chip-rrupp-chi-chi-chi", uttered from the higher branches of large trees growing in the thorny tangles.

Breeding: The nest is well hidden, made of a few light twigs in the fork of a low bush and is lined with moss. November and January. Eggs 2, elongate, pale blue with brown spots heavily overlaid with dark brown. Average (7) 25,6 × 17,8 (24,4—27 × 17—19,5).

726 White-tailed Shrike Kortstert-laksman

Lanioturdus torquatus Waterhouse, 1838: *Bull's Mouth Pass, inland from Walvis Bay.*

PLATE 61 (OPP. P. 513).
Length about 15 cm (wing 82—85,3—92; tail 43—59; tarsus 28,5—30; culmen 18—19,5. 5 specimens). Iris greenish yellow; bill black; legs dark brown.

Identification: This handsomely marked bird is regarded as a flycatcher by many authorities. Its markings are distinct and its peculiar appearance, the long wings when closed reaching nearly to the end of the short tail, render identification easy. Young has nape mottled. In flight the white wing patches are conspicuous.

Distribution: Found only in the Naukluft Mountains and Damaraland to southern Angola.

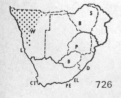

726

Habits: A common species occurring paired or in small parties, usually in more or less open thorn bush. On fringes of mopane, acacia and mixed woodlands. An active little bird, shy and restless, seeking the thickest part of the trees or bush. Its flight is slow and for short distances only. Sometimes it searches for its food on the ground or among rocks, at other times in trees, up to 25 m high, even creeping about like the Puffback Shrike amongst the matted foliage.

Food: Insects.
Voice: Call is loud clear and distinct (somewhat reminiscent of a Black-headed Oriole or Boubou) "huo-huo-huo". Other notes include querulous, churrs, croaks and scolds. Recorded to duet. Alarm note "squee, squee".
Breeding: The nest is placed fairly high up in the fork of a tree; it is a neatly woven deep cup of straws and cottony bark bound with whitish and light brown cobweb strands and lined with fine grass stems. January, February. Eggs 2, rounded, dull white to ashy blue with a zone of spots of light and dark brown at the larger end: 20 × 17.

727 White Helmet Shrike   Wit Helmlaksman

Prionops plumata (Shaw), 1809: *Senegal.*

Native Names: i-Pemvu (Z); im-Takabazana (Sw); Nariganyama (D).
PLATE 61 (OPP. P. 513).
Length about 20 cm (wing 103—109—117; tail 82—97; tarsus 19—23; culmen 12—14, one 15,5. 40 specimens). Iris bright yellow surrounded by orange eye-wattle; bill black; legs orange. Weight 33 g.

Identification: This social species with its conspicuous black-and-white flight pattern is easily identified. In flight each wing shows two white lines and the outer edges of the tail are broadly edged white. The bright orange eye-wattle and legs are noticeable. Sexes alike. Young has ashy or brownish crown and white edges to primary coverts.
Distribution: From West Africa to Kenya southwards to Angola, Kaokoveld, Ovamboland, Ngamiland and Botswana, Transvaal and Zululand extending as far south as the Tugela River.
Habits: A common social species which is always in parties numbering from four to twelve. Usually inhabits open woodland and savanna country. Other birds often join the wandering feeding parties. When flying they are usually silent but as soon as they settle they immediately begin to chatter. Searches for food among the branches and frequently darts on to the ground to pick up food. See under Breeding for social behaviour. Sleep bunched up together on the same branch like Mousebirds.

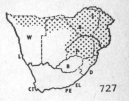

727

Food: Insects.
Voice: "Ishgwe" repeated four or five times in a chatter. Normal call a low "chow-chow".
Breeding: While they may break up into pairs for breeding, many nest in the vicinity of each other and several birds usually share the brooding and feeding of the young. The nests, in groups of five and six in neighbouring trees, are situated 3—6 metres from the ground on horizontal branches or forks. They are neatly built, deep cups of fine grasses, fibres of leaves and rootlets, with shreds of bark, externally smoothed and bound with cobwebs. September to December. Eggs 3 or 4, pale greenish, blotched and spotted with smoky purplish red, bluish and underlying slate-grey, usually more concentrated in a ring at the thick end. Average (32) 20,6 × 16,1 (19,4—22 × 15,5—17,3).

LOCAL RACE:
P.p. poliocephala (Stanley), 1814: *no locality = Mozambique.* The entire southern range extending south from Zaïre and Kenya.

728 Red-billed Helmet Shrike Swart Helmlaksman

Sigmodus retzii (Wahlberg), 1856: *Doughe = Okavango River.*

PLATE 61 (OPP. P. 513).
Length about 23 cm (wing 127—134—138; tail 98—107; tarsus 22—23; culmen 20—25. 5 specimens). Iris light orange with orange-red eye-wattle; bill orange-red; legs orange to scarlet. Weight 49 g.

Identification: This red-billed, blackish bird is unmistakable. Sexes alike, young is uniform dusky brown; the feathers of lesser wing-coverts scapulars and under-parts fringed with whitish.

Distribution: Eastern and southern Africa extending within our limits to Ovamboland, Ngamiland, Transvaal and Swaziland; absent from southern Mozambique.

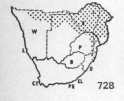

728

Habits: A common social species very similar in habits to the last. Apparently more restricted to *Brachystegia* and Mopane woodland, seemingly not in acacia savannas. In flocks of six to twelve.

Voice: Conversational chippering and snapping of bill as in No. 727. Call "chiwi-rew" repeated; also "chirt-ku-chirr, chirt, chirt . . .".

Breeding: The nest-site and nest are very similar to the last species. They also breed in proximity to each other but more than two adults have not been recorded at a nest. September to December. Eggs 3—4, larger than the last and less smoky in appearance, being pale greenish sparingly spotted with brown and a broad zone of reddish brown and grey blotches at the large end. Average (8) 23,8 × 17,0 (22,7—24,5 × 15,6—18). Both sexes incubate and feed young.

LOCAL RACES:
(a) *S.r. retzii* (Wahlberg), 1856: *Doughe = Okavango River.* From South West Africa east to the Transvaal and Rhodesia. As illustrated. Size above.
(b) *S.r. tricolor* (Gray), 1864: *Tete.* Coastal low-lying areas of Mozambique. Lighter grey-brown on the back and smaller wing 116—128.

729 Chestnut-fronted Helmet Shrike
Stekelkop-helmlaksman

Sigmodus scopifrons Peters, 1854: *Mozambique.*

PLATE 61 (OPP. P. 513).
Length about 19 cm (wing 97—102; tail 75—79; tarsus 18—20; culmen 17—18,5). Iris golden; eye-wattles dull blue; bill and legs coral-red.

Identification: The red bill and chestnut forehead are conspicuous characteristics. The general black-and-white pattern is common to both sexes which are alike. The young has forehead blackish; the tips of the bastard wing white.

Distribution: East Africa extending within our limits along coastal Mozambique to Ndumu in northern Zululand and Lebombo Mountains in Swaziland; also the Melsetter district of Rhodesia.

729

Habits: Little is recorded of this apparently uncommon species. Its habits are much the same as the previous two species but tends to remain more in tree tops than under the canopy as in other helmet shrikes.

Breeding: Not recorded in our area. The nest and nest-site are similar to the previous. Also, as in No. 727, at least three birds recorded feeding young, the third an immature male. Eggs undescribed.

LOCAL RACE:
S.s. scopifrons Peters, 1854: *Mozambique*. Other races exist to the north of Kenya.

730   White-crowned Shrike   Kremetart-laksman

Eurocephalus anguitimens   A. Smith, 1836: *North of Latakoo*.

PLATE 61 (OPP. P. 513).
Length 23—25 cm (wing 130—136—143; tail 100—116; tarsus 22—26; culmen 15—20. 22 specimens). Iris brown; bill dusky horn-colour; legs pale brown.

Identification: This large white-headed Shrike with contrasting black line from bill to beyond the ear-coverts is easily identified. Sexes alike. Young has crown brownish white and black areas at side of head are flecked with white. Flight strong, almost dove-like.

Distribution: From north-eastern Africa south to Angola; within our area to Windhoek, Damaraland, Ngamiland, Botswana, Transvaal to Pretoria and Komatipoort and in southern Mozambique. Widely distributed in Rhodesia.

Habits: A species common in open woodland and often associated with Boabab trees. A very noticeable bird owing to its habit of perching on the top or on the outermost branches of trees. Usually in small parties scattered about within call of each other. Always calls when taking to wing, the flight straight with short rapid wing-beats.

730

Food: Insects, especially caterpillars and grasshoppers. Berries.

Voice: A curious bleating "pep-pep" or "kwee-kwee" repeated when alarmed.

Breeding: The nest is like that of the helmet shrikes, placed on a horizontal bough some height from the ground. It is a thick-walled, basin-shaped structure composed of grass stems very firmly woven together and neatly plastered outside with cobwebs. September to March. Eggs 3—5, white, with clearly defined spots of various sizes of slate-blue and brown with a tinge of green. Average (17) 26,5 × 20,4 (23—29,1 × 17—22,2).

731   Brubru Shrike   Bontrok-laksman

Nilaus afer   (Latham), 1801: *Senegal*.

PLATE 61, RACES (a) AND (b) (OPP. P. 513).
Length about 15 cm (wing 80—84—91; tail 52—63; tarsus 20—24; culmen 14—17,5. 60 specimens). Iris reddish brown; bill black, slate at base of lower mandible; legs slate.

Identification: This species has been placed among the flycatchers by some authors because of its similarity in appearance. The black upper-parts with mottled white on back, white under-parts and rufous flanks, are distinctive. The female is brownish black where male is black. The young is similar to the female and has cheeks, throat and breast narrowly streaked and not cross-barred.

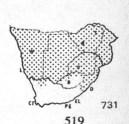

Distribution: From Senegal to Ethiopia south to Natal and the Orange River. Recorded from Vredefort, Orange Free State, and general in the Transvaal.

731

Habits: A common, active species found in dry acacia veld and forested areas. Usually observed in pairs assiduously hopping about and searching the branches of trees for insects and calling at the same time. Often joins bird parties.

Food: Insects, caterpillars, ants and beetles.

Voice: A prolonged "keerrr"; also onomatopoeic. Call a clear flute-like whistle, "tiooo tiooo tiooo", uttered from a prominent perch.

Breeding: The nest is usually situated in the upper saddle of a forking, slanting branch; it is small and difficult to see. It is a mere rib of fibres, bits of bark and webby material smoothed over and made to match the site. October to December. Eggs 2—3, light greenish white, usually thickly marked with rather elongate markings of dull slate-blue and greenish brown. Average (11) 19,7 × 16,2 (17,7—20,9 × 13—16,8).

LOCAL RACES:
(a) *N.a. brubru* (Latham), 1801: *Cape of Good Hope = Orange River.* South West Africa, Transvaal and Rhodesia. As illustrated. Size above.
(b) *N.a. nigritemporalis* Reichenow, 1892: *Ngoma.* From north-east Zululand north along the lower portions of Mozambique and neighbouring Rhodesia. Illustrated. Wing 77—81,3—86; tail 47—57; tarsus 20—22,5; culmen 15—17 (14 specimens).

732 = 731 *(b)*

Family STURNIDAE

The Starlings are birds of about twenty to thirty-five cm in length, with fairly long, usually slightly arched bill, the nostrils exposed, legs and feet fairly strong and in most species with a glossy green or bluish coloration. They are to some extent gregarious, if not found in flocks during the day at any rate congregating in large flocks in the evening, before going to roost performing wonderful manoeuvres in the air. They lay greenish blue eggs, usually spotted, but sometimes immaculate, in nests in holes, in a few cases constructing clumsy nests of masses of sticks. The species are widely distributed over the Old World, and several have been introduced from other countries into South Africa under the mistaken idea that they would become useful, though they have become a nuisance, if not an actual pest, owing to their great increase in numbers and destroying fruit.

733 European Starling   Europese Spreeu

Sturnus vulgaris Linnaeus, 1758: *Sweden.*

PLATE 62, ♂ AND ♀ (OPP. P. 528).
Length about 20 cm (wing 128—134; tail 64—68; tarsus 28—30; culmen 22—25). Iris brown; bill greyish or greenish brown, yellow when breeding; legs reddish brown.

Identification: Sexes as illustrated; cannot be mistaken for any other starling in the area in which they occur. Young birds are brownish above, throat whitish flecked with brown, breast and flanks brownish.

Distribution: From Cape Town northwards to Oranjemund, Beaufort West and eastwards to East London, Umtata and Port St. Johns.

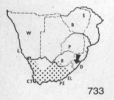

733

520

Habits: This bird was introduced at Cape Town by Cecil Rhodes in 1899; it has spread rapidly, reaching Clanwilliam in 1950 and Port Elizabeth in 1955, King William's Town in 1961 and East London in 1966. A common and familiar bird which is very attached to towns and villages, spending most of its time stalking about on lawns and grassy fields or raiding fruit trees. It roosts and breeds on buildings or tall trees in built-up areas, gathering in large flocks at dusk, creating a lot of noise which may continue throughout the night. It is not popular because it is believed to drive indigenous birds away. Economically it is probably beneficial but its habit of breeding under eaves makes it unpopular because it brings "lice" into dwellings. In winter forms huge flocks, often with Cape Weavers.

Food: Insects and soft fruit.

Voice: Normal note a grating "cheerr"; song, uttered from a high tree, gutter or chimney, is a grating, lively chatter of creaking musical whistles and imitations of other birds; it is not very loud.

Breeding: Favourite nesting sites are holes under eaves, gutters or hollow knot-holes in trees such as oaks. A little nesting material such as a few grass stems or pine-needles is added. Breeds from September to December. Eggs 3—5, pale blue. Average (50) 29,6 × 21,5 (27,5—32,9 × 20,5—22,4).

LOCAL RACE:
S.v. vulgaris Linnaeus, 1758: *Sweden.* The birds introduced appear to belong to this race.

734 Indian Myna   Indiese Spreeu

Acridotheres tristis (Linnaeus), 1766: *Philippines.*

PLATE 62, ♂ AND ♀ (OPP. P. 528).
Length about 24 cm (wing ♂ 150, ♀ 140; tail ♂ 94, ♀ 88; tarsus ♂ 38, ♀ 36; culmen 23—25). Iris brown; bill, legs and bare face yellow.

Identification: Unmistakable. Sexes alike. In flight shows a large white patch in the wings and a white fringe round tail.

Distribution: A species of India and the Far East, introduced at Durban from India. Is now found over most of Natal to Port St. Johns and has spread to Johannesburg, Germiston and Pretoria.

Habits: Essentially a bird of towns and human habitations, where it struts about the streets, market-places and gardens or sits chattering from the roof-tops. Is usually seen in pairs but gathers in fair numbers at night to roost and may then chatter late into the night.

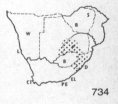

734

Food: Insects, including millipedes, snails and fruit.

Voice: A variety of rather harsh notes but also a pleasant, lively song. Has been taught to imitate the human voice in captivity.

Breeding: Nests in holes in trees, under eaves, gutters and broken street lamps, making an accumulation of rubbish with a bowl-shaped hollow in the centre. Breeds from October to May in Natal, October to January in Transvaal. Eggs 4—5, highly glossed, pale to dark greenish blue. Average (9) 30,7 × 21,2 (28,8—32,9 × 20,2—22). Incubation period about 17 days. Nestling period 24 days (Burma).

735   Wattled Starling   Lel-spreeu

Creatophora cinerea   (Menschen), 1787: *Cape of Good Hope.*

Native Names: Uwambu (X); le-Fokori (S).

PLATE 62, ♂ BREEDING AND NON-BREEDING DRESS (OPP. P. 528).
Length about 21 cm (wing ♂ 118—122—127, ♀ 114—117—120; tail 61—71; tarsus 27—30; culmen 21—24. 32 specimens, 15 ♂, 17 ♀). Iris dark brown; bill pinkish; legs brown. Weight 71 g (7).

Identification: Some males and occasionally females lose the feathers of the face and top of the head during the breeding season. The female resembles the male in non-breeding dress but has the primary-coverts black whereas they are usually white in adult males. Young birds resemble the female but young females are much browner than young males.

Distribution: From Arabia and Ethiopia southwards to Cape Town, on the west as far north as Zaïre.

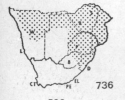

735

Habits: A locally abundant species which moves restlessly about the country in small parties or very large flocks. May appear in a certain area for a short time and then vanish, perhaps for many years. Follows locust swarms but if these fail frequents pastures, slaughter poles and garbage heaps, often in company with Pied Starlings. Feeds on the ground or pursues locusts in the air.

Food: Locusts—hence the popular name "locust-bird"—grasshoppers, crickets, termites, snails and fruit.

Voice: A rasping, squeaky whistle.

Breeding: Nests colonially, many hundreds or even thousands building in the same restricted area. The nests, made of sticks and thorny twigs, are usually placed in thorn bushes. Some may be large structures of two or three chambers and as many as a dozen double or triple nests may be found in the same tree at no great height from the ground. Breeds in areas where locusts have laid their eggs, but if this food supply fails whole colonies of eggs and young birds may be deserted, the adults moving off to better food supplies. Eggs are pale greenish blue, sometimes with a few speckles. They number 4 when conditions are very favourable, but if the rains are poor or locusts scarce, only 3 may be laid. Average (24) 28,0 × 20,4 (26,4—31,9 × 19,6—21,3).

736   Plum-coloured Starling   Witbors-spreeu

Cinnyricinclus leucogaster   (Gmelin), 1789: *Whidah, Dahomey.*

PLATE 62, ♂ AND ♀ (OPP. P. 528).
Length 18—19 cm (wing ♂ 104—108—113, ♀ 104—109; tail 57—64; tarsus 19—22; culmen 13—17. 60 specimens, 57♂, 3♀). Iris yellow; bill and legs black. Weight 47—48 g.

Identification: Males unmistakable; the heavy streaking below of the female is distinctive. Young birds resemble the female but have iris brown, ringed with yellow.

Distribution: Senegal to Ethiopia and western Arabia, southwards to South West Africa, Botswana, Transvaal, Natal and the eastern Cape as far as Port St. Johns.

Habits: A fairly common species of the warm bushveld. When not breeding occurs in large flocks often of females, with single male or small parties of

736

males wandering about nearby. Such flocks keep to open country, then pair off to breed, retiring to thicker woodland or large trees along water-courses in otherwise dry country. Also flocks with Wattled and Glossy Starlings. Is migratory in our area, recorded from October to April. Flight very swift.

Food: Insects and fruit.

Voice: A few chippering notes followed by a slurred whistle "tipu-tipu-teeuu".

Breeding: Nests in natural holes in trees, 1—10 metres up, usually about 2 metres from the ground. The cavity is lined with dung and perhaps a little dry grass, but *always* some fresh green leaves. Breeds from October to January in South Africa, mainly in October and November. Eggs 3—4, pale greenish blue with scattered reddish brown spots and blotches and underlying purplish markings somewhat concentrated at the thick end. Average (33) 24,4 × 17,7 (22,9—26,1 × 15,5—19,2).

LOCAL RACE:
C.l. verreauxi (Bocage), 1870: *Caconda, Angola.* As illustrated; size above. Breeding range, southern Africa as far north as Zaïre and Kenya. Goes as far north as the Sudan and Ethiopia when not breeding.

737   Cape Glossy Starling   Klein Glansspreeu

Lamprotornis nitens   (Linnaeus); 1766: *Angola.*

Native Names: Inyakrini (X); i-Kwinsi (Z); le-Foli (Ch).

PLATE 62 (OPP. P. 528).
Length 23—26 cm (wing ♂ 143—146—148, ♀ 130—134—140; tail 84—96; tarsus 32—36; culmen 21—26. 18 specimens, 8 ♂, 10 ♀). Iris orange-yellow; bill and legs black. Weight 81,5—85,5 g.

Identification: Difficult to tell from the next species but is greener below and more uniformly coloured about the head. See also under No. 738. Sexes alike. Young birds have the iris grey and are duller, slightly glossy on wings, mantle and head.

Distribution: From Gabon southwards through Angola and South West Africa, Botswana, Matabeleland, Transvaal and Natal to the eastern Cape Province as far as Humansdorp. Occurs in the *southern* Kruger Park.

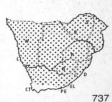

737

Habits: Quite a common and familiar species which occurs mainly in acacia thornveld. Usually seen singly or in *small*, loose parties, perched on the tops of trees where insects are taken in passing or from the ground below. Enters large towns at certain times of the year and in general seems to move about quite a lot.

Food: Insects, berries and fruit, occasionally doing some damage when the birds are plentiful.

Voice: A fairly deep note like "turr-weeu". Also sings very well throughout the year, a pleasant series of warbling, whistling phrases.

Breeding: Nests in natural holes in trees, occasionally in roofs, the cavity being lined with grass, dung and snake-skins. Both sexes construct the nest. Breeds from August to February in Transvaal, November to January in Natal and November to February in South West Africa. Eggs 3—4; in South West Africa 3 in poor years and 4 when the rains are good; they are pale greenish blue, sparingly speckled with light red. Average (64) 28,5 × 20,0 (26,1—31,8 × 18,2—21). Nestling period 19—20 days (2).

523

LOCAL RACES:
(a) L.n. culminator (Clancey and Holliday), 1951: *Addo.* Size above. Eastern Province to upper Natal. As above—larger than *(b).*
(b) L.n. phoenicopterus Swainson, 1838: *Orange River, near Prieska.* As illustrated. Smaller than *(a).* Wing ♂ 130—134—139 (40), ♀ 120—126—131 (26).

738 Blue-eared Glossy Starling   Blouoor-glansspreeu

Lamprotornis chalybaeus Hemprich and Ehrenburg, 1828: *Dongola, Sudan.*

PLATE 62 (OPP. P. 528).
Length 21—23 cm (wing ♂ 132—137—140, ♀ 123—127—130; tail 82—98; tarsus 30—33,5; culmen 18—21. 19 specimens, 13 ♂, 6 ♀). Iris orange; bill and legs black.

Identification: Very difficult to tell from the last species but is bluer below and greener about the head so blue mark on ear-coverts stands out. Practically indistinguishable from the next species in the field. Sexes alike, but female smaller. Young birds are sooty black below with some greenish wash above and below, brightest on the wings; eye dark grey.
Distribution: From Ngamiland, eastern Transvaal to Pongola River and the Lebombo, northwards to Ethiopia and across to West Africa.
Habits: Very similar to those of the last species. Gathers in larger flocks when not breeding. Is subject to some local movement. Its wings creak very loudly in flight. Common in mopane veld of *northern* Kruger Park.
Food: Fruit, berries and insects.
Voice: Normal call a loud nasal "squeare, squeare"; also various chirps and whistles and a warbling note when going to roost.
Breeding: Nests in holes in trees, fence poles or other similar places, the hole being lined with grass, sometimes also with bits of snake skin. The nest may be from as low as 1 metre, to 6 m or so. Breeds September to January in Rhodesia. Eggs 3—4, occasionally 5, pale blue sparingly speckled or with a few larger spots as well, of burnt umber and a little lilac, mostly at the larger end. Average (13) 28,8 × 19,2 (25,5—30,7 × 18,3—20).

LOCAL RACES:
(a) L.c. sycobius (Hartlaub), 1859: *Tete, Portuguese East Africa.* As illustrated; size above. Transvaal to Tanzania and eastern Zaïre.
(b) L.c. nordmanni (Hartert and Neumann), 1914: *Mossamedes, Angola.* Ngamiland to Angola.

739 Lesser Blue-eared Glossy Starling
Klein Blouoor-glansspreeu

Lamprotornis chloropterus Swainson, 1838: *Western Africa.*

PLATE 62 (OPP. P. 528).
Length about 20 cm (wing ♂ 120—126, ♀ 112—115; tail 68—72; tarsus 24—27; culmen 17—19. 5 specimens, 3 ♂, 2 ♀). Iris golden-yellow; bill and legs black.

Identification: Practically impossible to distinguish in the field from the last species, differing only in being smaller. In the hand the inner webs of the primaries show no sinuation, merely a slight narrowing, whereas in the last

738

species they show a strong V-shaped indentation, just over half-way along. Sexes alike. Young birds have greyish eyes and are dull ashy above and *light rufous* below with some iridescence above and on the tail.

Distribution: From West Africa to Eritrea, southwards to southern Rhodesia and the lower Limpopo Valley.

Habits: Very similar to those of the last species; particularly gregarious when not breeding, often roosting in flocks numbering several hundred birds. Occurs mainly in *Brachystegia*. Is subject to local movements.

Food: Insects, seeds, fruit and the bases of flowers.

Voice: Various warbling whistles and trills said to differ from the last species.

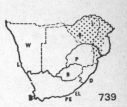

739

Breeding: Nests in holes in trees during September and October in Rhodesia. Eggs from Malawi, which probably belong to this species, measure 25,5—26 × 18,5—19,5.

LOCAL RACE:
L.c. elisabeth (Stresemann), 1924: *South Ufipa, Tanganyika.* As illustrated; size above. From within our limits to Tanzania.

740 Black-bellied Glossy Starling
Swartpens-glansspreeu

Lamprotornis corruscus Nordmann, 1835: *Kaffirland = Thornhill, Eastern Cape Province.*

Native Names: Intenenengu (X); i-Kwintsi, i-Kwezi (Z).

PLATE 62 (OPP. P. 528).
Length 20—21 cm (wing ♂ 106—110,5—112, ♀ 99—105,5—110; tail 72—82; tarsus 21,5—24; culmen 16,5—19. 14 specimens, 6 ♂, 8 ♀). Iris golden yellow; bill and legs black.

Identification: Recognizable in the field by its duller black plumage and more slender build than the last three species. Females duller below than males. Young birds are even duller than females and have dark grey eyes.

Distribution: Confined to a narrow belt near the coast from Knysna to Kenya, where it extends further inland.

Habits: A common species which occurs more or less in pairs when breeding, but otherwise in small or quite large flocks which fly about the dense indigenous bush keeping up a continuous musical chatter. Appears to migrate northwards, from the southern parts of its range, during the winter but positive data are lacking.

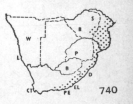

740

Food: Berries and wild fruits; also insects such as termites.

Voice: A pleasantly noisy species when in flocks.

Breeding: The nest is made inside a natural hole in a tree, or sometimes in an old Barbet or Woodpecker nest, the bottom of which is lined with a little grass, hair or feathers. Breeds from November to January. Eggs 3—4, pale greenish blue with the barest trace of brown markings. Average (24) 25,5 × 18,9 (24,2—26,8 × 17,9—19,8).

LOCAL RACES:
(a) *L.c. corruscus* Nordmann, 1835: *Kaffirland = Thornhill, Eastern Cape Province.* As illustrated. Size above. Knysna to southern Mozambique.

525

741 Sharp-tailed Glossy Starling
Spitsstert-glansspreeu

Lamprotornis acuticaudus (Bocage), 1870: *Huilla, Angola.*

Length about 21—25 cm. (wing 112—126; tail 90—100; tarsus 28—30; culmen 20—22). Iris bright red, inner rim brown; bill and legs black.

Identification: Distinguishable by its wedge-shaped tail and *red* eye in the male, orange in the female; otherwise resembles the Blue-eared Glossy Starling, No. 738. Young birds are *grey below*, the feathers edged with buffish; thus easily distinguished from the young of Nos. 737, 738 and 739. Not easily distinguished from 738 and 739, but the two central tail-feathers are definitely longer than rest of tail.
Distribution: From Ovamboland to Angola, Zambia and eastern Zaïre.
Habits: Very little recorded.
Breeding: Nothing appears to have been recorded in spite of the fact that this species is described as the commonest starling near Lubumbashi.
Voice: Reputed to be similar to 738 and 739.

742 Long-tailed Glossy Starling
Langstert-glansspreeu

Lamprotornis mevesii (Wahlberg), 1857: *Doughe R. = Okavango River.*

PLATE 62 (OPP. P. 528).
Length 30—34 cm (wing ♂ 145—149—154, ♀ 135—139—143; tail ♂ 185—210, ♀ 182—190; tarsus 31—40; culmen 17,5—20,5. 21 specimens, 14 ♂, 7 ♀). Iris brown; bill and legs black.

Identification: Easily distinguishable by the long narrow tail; female smaller and duller than male. Young birds duller, greener above and not coppery below.
Distribution: From Kaokoveld, Ngamiland and Rhodesia northwards to Angola, Zambia and Malawi.
Habits: A locally common species of Mopane veld and river systems, usually seen in flocks or small parties, flying overhead or searching for food on the ground. Roosts at night in large reed beds; before retiring, flocks of these birds go through manoeuvres in the air. Moults before breeding.

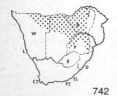

742

Food: Insects during the breeding season; otherwise fruit and berries.
Voice: A loud "kow-kow". A whistling call and a "churring" alarm note.
Breeding: Recorded as nesting colonially in holes in live *Acacia* trees, the holes being sometimes on the *underside* of the branches, and lined with fibre from decayed Baobab or Euphorbia branches. The female digs the nest hole. Breeds December to March in Rhodesia. Eggs 3—4. Nestling 22 days.

LOCAL RACE:
L.m. mevesii (Wahlberg), 1857: *Doughe R. = Okavango River.*

743 Burchell's Glossy Starling   Burchellse Glansspreeu

Lamprotornis australis   (A. Smith), 1836: *Kurrichane.*

PLATE 62 (OPP. P. 528).
Length 30—34 cm (wing ♂ 175—185—191, ♀ 161—169—173; tail ♂ 150—175, ♀ 142—157; tarsus 40—49; culmen 20—23,5. 14 specimens, 10 ♂, 4 ♀). Iris hazel; bill and legs black.

Identification: A large, broad-winged, heavily built species with a proportionately shorter tail than the last species. Sexes alike but female smaller. Young birds are duller and brown below.
Distribution: From the Pongola River northwards, west of the Lebombo to eastern and western Transvaal, Botswana and Namaqualand northwards to southern Angola and Ngamiland. Occurs in the Kruger Park.
Habits: A bird of dry country found singly, in pairs or in large parties. Occurs near water, which seems to be essential for it. Flight rather heavy. Roosts in large flocks in reed-beds after performing aerial gyrations.
Food: Insects and fruit.
Voice: Loud and harsh; the noise when large numbers are roosting is almost deafening.

743

Breeding: Nests in holes in trees during November, December and March in South West Africa. The holes are usually fairly high up but may be as low as 2 metres; they are lined with a few blades of green grass. Eggs 3—4, bright sky-blue sparingly speckled with reddish purple, somewhat concentrated at the thick end. Average (13) 29,7 × 20,9 (28—32,6 × 20,1—21,7).

LOCAL RACES:
(a) L.a. australis (A. Smith), 1836: *Kurrichane.* As above except in the lowlands of the eastern areas as below.
(b) L.a. degener Clancey, 1959: *Malamala, Transvaal.* Northern and eastern Transvaal, Swaziland and adjacent areas. Smaller than *(a).*

744 Pale-winged Starling   Bleekvlerk-spreeu

Onychognathus nabouroup (Daudin), 1800: *Kamiesberg, Little Namaqualand.*

PLATE 62 (OPP. P. 528).
Length 26—28 cm (wing ♂ 140—145—154 (17), ♀ 133—141—148 (14); tail 98—112; tarsus 30—33; culmen 21—26. 21 specimens, 11 ♂, 10 ♀). Iris orange-red; bill and legs black.

Identification: Similar to the next species but the pale, almost white windows in the wings are distinctive. Sexes alike, female smaller. Although the primaries are externally reddish, they appear white in flight but reddish when at rest.
Distribution: From the Karoo districts of Cape Province to Taungs and Orange Free State, westwards and northwards to Angola.
Habits: A species of rocky hills and mountains which is quite common in suitable localities. Occurs in small parties or flocks, even when breeding.
Food: Fruit, berries and insects.
Voice: Similar to the next species.
Breeding: Nests in crevices of precipices, laying 3—4 eggs on a shallow basin of plant and grass stems. The eggs are pale greenish blue, sparingly speckled

744

PLATE 62

733. *Sturnus vulgaris vulgaris.* European Starling. Europese Spreeu. ♂ and ♀.
734. *Acridotheres tristis.* Indian Myna. Indiese Spreeu.
735. *Creatophora cinerea.* Wattled Starling. Lel-spreeu.
♂ breeding and non-breeding.
736. *Cinnyricinclus leucogaster verreauxi.* Plum-coloured Starling.
Witbors-spreeu. ♂ and ♀.
737. *Lamprotornis nitens phoenicopterus.* Cape Glossy Starling.
Klein Glansspreeu.
738. *Lamprotornis chalybeus sycobius.* Blue-eared Glossy Starling.
Blouoor-glansspreeu.
739. *Lamprotornis chloropterus elisabeth.* Lesser Blue-eared Glossy Starling.
Klein Blouoor-glansspreeu. Ad. and Imm.
740. *Lamprotornis corruscus corruscus.* Black-bellied Glossy Starling.
Swartpens-glansspreeu.
742. *Lamprotornis mevesii mevesii.* Long-tailed Glossy Starling.
Langstert-glansspreeu.
743. *Lamprotornis australis.* Burchell's Glossy Starling.
Burchellse Glansspreeu.
744. *Onychognathus nabouroup nabouroup.* Pale-winged Starling.
Bleekvlerk-spreeu.
745. *Onychognathus morio morio.* Red-winged Starling. Rooivlerk-spreeu.
♂ and ♀.
746. *Spreo bicolor.* Pied Starling. Witgat-spreeu.
747. *Buphagus africanus africanus.* Yellow-billed Oxpecker.
Geelbek-renostervoël.
748. *Buphagus erythrorhynchus.* Red-billed Oxpecker. Rooibek-renostervoël.
749. *Promerops cafer.* Cape Sugarbird. Suikervoël. ♂.
750. *Promerops gurneyi gurneyi.* Gurney's Sugarbird. Rooibors-suikervoël.
♂.

750 ♂

749 ♂

748

747

746

742

743

♀

744

745 ♂

Imm.

739

740

738

737

735

736 ♂

♀

Br. ♂

733 ♂

♀

734

NIGHTON.

'39

KN

KN

PLATE 63

751. *Nectarinia famosa famosa.* Malachite Sunbird. Jangroentjie.
$\male$ Br. and N-Br.

752. *Nectarinia kilimensis arturi.* Bronze Sunbird.
Bronskleur Suikerbekkie. $\male$ and $\female$.

753. *Anthobaphes violacea.* Orange-breasted Sunbird.
Oranjebors-suikerbekkie. $\male$ and $\female$.

754. *Cinnyris cupreus cupreus.* Coppery Sunbird. Koperkleur Suikerbekkie.
$\male$ and $\female$.

755. *Cinnyris mariquensis mariquensis.* Marico Sunbird.
Marico-suikerbekkie. $\male$ and $\female$.

756. *Cinnyris bifasciatus microrhynchus.* Purple-banded Sunbird.
Purpurband-suikerbekkie. $\male$ and $\female$.

757. *Cinnyris shelleyi shelleyi.* Black-bellied Sunbird.
Swartpens-suikerbekkie. $\male$ and $\female$.

758. *Cinnyris afer afer.* Greater Double-collared Sunbird.
Groot Rooibors-suikerbekkie. $\male$ and $\female$.

760. *Cinnyris chalybeus chalybeus.* Lesser Double-collared Sunbird.
Klein Rooibors-suikerbekkie. $\male$ and $\female$.

761. *Cinnyris neergaardi.* Neergaard's Sunbird. Neergaardse Suikerbekkie.
$\male$ and $\female$.

763. *Cinnyris talatala.* White-bellied Sunbird.
Witbors-suikerbekkie. $\male$ and $\female$.

764. *Cinnyris fuscus.* Dusky Sunbird. Namakwa Suikerbekkie. $\male$ and $\female$.

770. *Anthreptes longuemarei nyassae.* Violet-backed Sunbird.
Blou suikerbekkie. $\male$ and $\female$.

with reddish brown. Three measure 32,2 × 22,0; 33,5 × 22,2 and 32,2 × 22,5.

LOCAL RACES:
O.n. nabouroup (Daudin), 1800: *Kamiesberg, Little Namaqualand.* As illustrated, size above. South Africa to Southern Angola.
There is a cline from smaller (wing ♂ 132—140) and paler in the north to larger and darker in the south.

745 Red-winged Starling   Rooivlerk-spreeu

Onychognathus morio   (Linnaeus), 1766: *Cape of Good Hope.*

Native Name: Isomi (X).

PLATE 62, ♂ AND ♀ (OPP. P. 528).
Length 27—28 cm (wing ♂ 144—151,5—160, ♀ 138—146—154; tail 115—138; tarsus 31—35; culmen 27—30. 50 specimens, 24 ♂, 26 ♀). Iris dark brown, outer edge red; bill and legs black.

Identification: Similar to the last species but has *red* windows in the wings. Female differs from male as illustrated. Young birds have *black* heads like males.

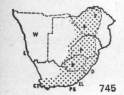

745

Distribution: From the Cape Province to Ethiopia westwards to Nigeria and Cameroon.

Habits: A common species of mountainous and hilly country, occurring as resident pairs or in large roving flocks which may number several hundred birds. Enters towns and cities, raiding gardens and nesting on the buildings. Paired birds remain mated for life and are seldom found far apart, being very companionable.

Food: Is mainly frugivorous, eating dates, various indigenous berries and the red aril of the Australian wattle, which is spread by this species as the seed is not digested; also grapes, apricots, plums, figs, etc. Eats fair numbers of insects, particularly stick-insects, also caterpillars, millipedes, termites and earthworms. Frequently probes flowers for nectar, the bird's forehead becoming dusted with pollen. Seen to perch on Klipspringer for ticks.

Voice: Commonest call is plaintive, drawn-out "spreeu", also "ti-ju". Sings quite well, a variety of warbling whistled phrases. Alarm call a harsh, jarring "tchorr".

Breeding: Places its nest in a crevice in rocks of cliffs; sometimes on ledges in caves or mining shafts, holes in buildings, or under the eaves of houses. The nest is a fairly substantial basin of sticks and grass, plastered together with mud and lined with horsehair. Breeds from October to March in the Cape, usually having two broods, one in October and another in December; November to December in Natal. Eggs 3—5, usually 3; pale greenish blue, sparingly spotted with reddish markings. Average (72) 33,4 × 23,0 (29,8—36,6 × 20,3—24,8). Incubation almost entirely by female, 12½—16—23 days (14). Nestling period 22—26—28 (14).

LOCAL RACE:
O.m. morio (Linnaeus), 1766: *Cape of Good Hope.* As illustrated. Size above. Cape to Malawi and Mozambique.

746 Pied Starling   Witgat-spreeu

Spreo bicolor   (Gmelin), 1789: *Cape of Good Hope.*

Native Names: Igiyogiyo (X); le-Holi, se-Kholi (S).

PLATE 62 (OPP. P. 528).
Length about 25—27 cm (wing 147—154—163; tail 91—106; tarsus 37—40; culmen 21—25. 11 specimens, 6 ♂, 5 ♀). Iris pale yellow; bill black, the base yellow; legs black.

Identification: The oily brown plumage and white vent are distinctive. Sexes alike. Young birds resemble adults but have the base of the bill buff.
Distribution: From Cape Province northwards to the highveld of Transvaal on the east, and on the west as far north as the Orange River.
Habits: A locally common species of the open veld or where there are scattered trees, but not in forest or thick bush. Is usually found in flocks at all times of the year, walking about on the ground with characteristic upright posture. Frequents open ground such as ploughed fields or grassy meadows, particularly near dongas or dry river beds, in the banks of which it nests. Often flocks with European or Wattled Starlings.

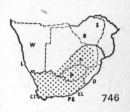

746

Food: Mainly insects, particularly ants, which other birds do not eat; also grubs, beetles, crickets and a few seeds. Often follows cattle, even perching on their backs, either to catch the disturbed grasshoppers or to pick off ticks. Also very partial to soft fruit such as figs.
Voice: A rather soft "squeer, squeer" or "squeerky-week". Alarm note a harsh, grating hiss.
Breeding: Nests either in holes in walls, under the eaves of houses, or most commonly burrows into the soft banks of ditches, wells, streams or dongas, making a padded nest at the end, usually about a metre in. Breeds from August to December in the Cape and Natal; throughout the year in Transvaal but mainly from September to March. Eggs are bluish green, about half being plain, the rest faintly spotted with brown or russet. They number 4—6, larger numbers such as 11 presumably being due to two females. Average (100) 30,6 × 21,2 (28—33,7 × 18,8—22,5).

Family BUPHAGIDAE

A family comprising two species peculiar to Africa, by some systematists placed with the Starlings *(Sturnidae)*, but differing from them in respect of the shape of the bill and the feet and claws, the last short, sharply curved and sharp. They are called Oxpeckers from their habit of perching upon, and clambering about over, large game mammals and domestic large stock to procure the ticks, upon which they subsist: in the case of domestic animals, such as horses that have chafed backs, these birds also keep the wounds open by pecking at them and stock owners consequently often dislike them, despite the good work accomplished in destroying the parasites. They clamber over the backs of animals like woodpeckers, even hanging on the sides or bellies. When resting they squat on their tarsi. In the case of big game, they are not beloved of the hunter as they are sharp to note the presence of the hunters and warn the animals of their approach. They nest in crevices of rocks or trees, under modern conditions where not disturbed under the eaves of houses, where a pad of hair and other soft material is placed. The eggs are three to five in number, white or bluish white, immaculate or spotted.

747 Yellow-billed Oxpecker   Geelbek-renostervoël

Buphagus africanus   Linnaeus, 1766: *Senegal.*

Native Names: i-Hlalanyati (X); isi-Hlalanyati (Z); Tsomi (S); um-Blanda (T); i-Landa (G); i-Deirangambe (D).

PLATE 62 (OPP. P. 528).
Length about 22 cm (wing 130—tail 100; tarsus 22; culmen 16). Iris bright orange or scarlet; tip of beak red, base yellow; legs brown.

Identification: The yellow beak with its lower mandibles widened at the base and absence of a wattle round the eye, and pale rump, distinguish this species from the next. Sexes alike. Young birds have dusky brown bills.

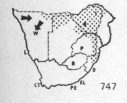

Distribution: Senegal to Ethiopia and southwards to Ovamboland on the west and Zululand on the east. Also recorded from eastern Cape Province but is extremely rare if present today, throughout our area.

747

Habits: Usually found near game animals or on domestic large stock, upon which it clambers about in search of ticks, the animals not objecting. Keeps out of sight by hanging on the far side of the animal and peering over the beast's back. Has been badly decimated by cattle-dipping. Is particularly fond of buffaloes, even returning to them after they have been shot. When approached, flies up with a warning rattling note and either flies about above the animals or away. Scattered birds may all gather on one beast before flying away as a flock.
Food: Ticks.
Voice: A hissing "kriss, kriss".
Breeding: Nests in natural holes in trees, making a pad of grass, animal hair and feathers. Recorded breeding in October and November. Eggs 2—3, white or very pale blue, sometimes spotted with deep chestnut, brown and violet. Average (5) 24,8 × 17,4 (23,4—26,6 × 16,6—18).

LOCAL RACE:
B.a. africanus Linnaeus, 1766: *Senegal.* As illustrated. Size above. Range as above except Zaïre, where a smaller race occurs.

748 Red-billed Oxpecker   Rooibek-renostervoël

Buphagus erythrorhynchus   (Stanley), 1814: *Ethiopia.*

PLATE 62 (OPP. P. 528).
Length 20—22 cm (wing ♂ 113—119—121, ♀ 116—118—120; tail 87—91; tarsus 18—21; culmen 16—18. 10 specimens, 5 ♂, 5 ♀). Iris yellow to red, narrow bare wattle round eye yellow; bill red; legs blackish brown.

Identification: Has a *red* bill, with no enlargement of the lower mandible, and a bare wattle round the eye. Sexes alike. Young are more sooty brown above with middle of beak yellow, tip olive.

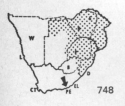

Distribution: An eastern species extending from Eritrea and Ethiopia southwards to Botswana, Transvaal and Natal.
Habits: A much commoner species than the last, but otherwise similar in habits. Roosts at night in large companies in reed beds or trees.
Food: Ticks and blood-sucking flies. Moreau found 2 291 of the former in 58

748

stomachs. Like the previous species is accused of opening up sores on animals' backs, presumably to get at the blood. On balance, the good they do probably outweighs the harm.

Voice: A hissing "churr" rather starling-like. Also a "tzik, tzik". Twitters shrilly in flight.

Breeding: Nests from October to December, either in stone embankments or in holes under the eaves of houses. The eggs number 2—3 and are pinky white, fairly heavily marked with scattered small spots of reddish brown, purple and lilac. Average (24) 23,3 × 17,2 (22,5—25,5 × 15,8—18,5; two are only 15 and 15,1). Incubation period 11—12 days. Nestling period 28—29 days. One pair incubates but other adults help feed the young.

LOCAL RACE:
B.e. africanoides Smith, 1831: *Natal.*

Family PROMEROPIDAE

The Sugarbirds represent the only family of birds peculiar to South Africa, as they do not extend beyond Rhodesia in a northerly direction. It had been suggested that they are related to the Australian Honeyeaters *(Melithreptidae)*, but they are now considered to be related to the Starlings. They are peculiar in having a rather plainly coloured plumage, long, curved bill, elongate tail-feathers and in size larger than the Sunbirds *(Nectariniidae)*. Their nests are cup-shaped, not closed like those of Sunbirds. Diet consists mainly of insects and nectar, especially of proteas.

749 Cape Sugarbird   Suikervoël

Promerops cafer (Linnaeus), 1758: *Cape of Good Hope.*

PLATE 62, ♂ (OPP. P. 528).
Length ♂ 37—44 cm, ♀ 24—29 cm (wing ♂ 90—93—98, ♀ 80—82—84; tail ♂ 222—320, ♀ 111—155; tarsus 21—24; culmen 30—36. 11 specimens, 7 ♂, 4 ♀.) Iris dark brown; bill and legs black.

Identification: Unmistakable. The female has a shorter tail than the male; young birds resemble the female. Fifth primary has wide bulge.

Distribution: Confined to the southern mountainous region from Cedarberg mountains in the north to Amatola mountains in east Cape.

749

Habits: A remarkable bird which occurs usually where proteas are in bloom, along mountain slopes mainly, but also on level ground. A territorial species while breeding, which disperses at other times and may be seen in small parties. The males spend a lot of their time perched on high bushes, calling and singing or dashing off after other intruding males. They have a curious display flight in which the male flies about with its tail held over the back and clapping its wings violently. Spends a lot of time catching insects in the air.

Food: Probably mainly insects, also nectar found by probing in proteas.

Voice: Difficult to describe, the song is a series of jangling metallic gratings and churrings. Alarm call rather like the squeak of a rusty gate.

Breeding: The nest, built by the female alone, is an accumulation of dead twigs, grass and other vegetable matter, with a neater bowl lined with fibres and dry protea-down; it is usually about 1—2 metres up but sometimes higher,

533

and is usually in a protea bush. Breeds during the winter months from March to August, but occasionally as early as February. The normal clutch is 2 eggs, light buff to reddish brown, more or less covered with blotches, scrawls and zig-zag markings of deep purplish black or with finer spots and lines of brown. Average (100) 23,4 × 17,5 (21,4—25 × 16,5—18,7). Incubation by female only, 16—17 days (11); nestling 17—21 days; both sexes feed the young.

750 Gurney's Sugarbird   Rooibors-suikervoël

Promerops gurneyi   Verreaux, 1871: *Natal.*

PLATE 62, ♂ (OPP. P. 528).
Length ♂ 25—29 cm, ♀ 23 cm (wing ♂ 92—99, ♀ 87; tail ♂ 137—170, ♀ 107—148; tarsus 20—22; culmen 25—30. 6 specimens, 4 ♂, 2 ♀). Iris dark brown; bill and legs black.

Identification: Shorter-tailed and redder on the chest and crown than the last species. Females have shorter tails than males.

Distribution: From Elliotdale in the eastern Cape, through Natal to the north-eastern Transvaal; occurs again in eastern Rhodesia.

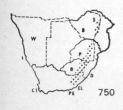

750

Habits: A fairly common species, habits much the same as for Cape Sugarbird.

Food: Small insects and nectar.

Voice: Three or four ascending notes, the last repeated several times.

Breeding: Unlike the previous species, this bird nests in early summer, from September to February. Eggs normally 2, cream-coloured, speckled and scratched with dark brown. Average (7) 22,8 × 16,7 (22,5—23,4 × 16,3—16,9).

LOCAL RACES:
(a) P.g. gurneyi Verreaux, 1871: *Natal.* As illustrated; size above. Natal to north-eastern Transvaal.
(b) P.g. ardens Friedmann, 1952: *Melsetter, Rhodesia.* Pectoral band brighter and darker, rump and upper tail-coverts less yellowish, more greenish. Size similar to *(a).* Eastern Rhodesia, above 1 000 metres.

Family NECTARINIIDAE

The Sunbirds comprise numerous species widely distributed over Africa, southern Asia and eastwards on various islands to Australia. All of them have long, more or less curved bills, strong and finely pointed for the purpose of puncturing flowers to get at the nectar when this cannot be extracted from the front, and the tongue is hollow, long and can be protruded for some distance. They are beautifully coloured in the males, and quite often in the females as well, though the latter are usually plainly coloured. They feed upon insects as well as the nectar of flowers. Very often they utter a pretty warbling or whistling song, but usually not a loud one, so that it can be heard only from close quarters. They normally lay only two eggs, which vary considerably as between the species, and the nest is a warm, oval-shaped structure of grass, fibres and bits of bark, often plastered outside with cobwebs, with the entrance at the side near the top under a projecting hood, and slung at the end of a drooping branch.

751 Malachite Sunbird   Jangroentjie

Nectarinia famosa (Linnaeus), 1766: *Cape of Good Hope.*

Native Names: Ingcungcu (X); i-Ncwincwi (Z); Taletale, se-Noavolapi Tsek-hane, Manitsoane (S).

PLATE 63, ♂ AND ♀ (OPP. P. 529).
Length ♂ 23—25 cm, ♀ 15 cm (wing ♂ 76—77—79, ♀ 66—70; tail ♂ 118—142, ♀ 46—48; tarsus 15—16; culmen 29—34. 21 specimens 17 ♂, 4 ♀. Iris dark brown; bill and legs black. Weight ♀ 11,5—15; ♂ 14,3—16,5

Identification: Males unmistakable in breeding dress; in eclipse plumage they resemble females but are somewhat greener, retain metallic wing-coverts, rump and upper tail-coverts, and may have the long tail-feathers for part of the time. Young birds resemble females.

Distribution: From Cape Town to Ethiopia, the Sudan and eastern Zaïre; on the west as far north as Great Namaqualand.

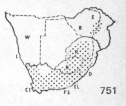

Habits: A conspicuous and fairly common species in the south, becoming rarer in Transvaal and Southern Rhodesia. The male is a dashing bird usually seen flying very fast, often chasing other males or sitting on top of a conspicuous post such as the head of an aloe and uttering its loud call. Hawks insects in the air quite a lot, and may hover in front of flowers or perch on them.

751

Food: The nectar of flowers, particularly those of *Aloe, Kniphofia, Leonotis.* Spiders, diptera and minute Coleoptera and Lepidoptera (small moths) are the main insects eaten.

Breeding: Cape, May to January; Transvaal, August to February and Rhodesia, August to March. The nest is usually placed over water but often on the bank of a dry donga, gully or small valley from 30 cm to about 3 metres from the ground. It is an oval structure of grass, twiglets, leaves and fronds of the plant in which it is built, lined with feathers and plant-down. The same nesting site is often used year after year and two or three broods may be raised each year, often using the same nest more than once; at other times building new nests for successive broods. Eggs number 2, very rarely 3, cream, densely freckled and mottled with olive, brownish and underlying grey. Average (85) 19,6 × 13,6 (17,9—21 × 13—15). Nest-building and incubation by female only, the former taking about 7 days, the latter 13 days. Nestling 18—21 days. Young are fed at first by female, later by both sexes but mainly by female. The young return to the nest at night for a day or two after leaving.

LOCAL RACES:
(a) *N.f. famosa* (Linnaeus), 1766: *Cape of Good Hope.* As illustrated; size above. Cape Province to Rhodesia.
(b) *N.f. major* Roberts, 1936: *Weenen, Natal.* Birds from Natal, Transvaal and Lesotho are larger than (a). Wing ♂ 78—82—85 in 17 specimens.

752 Bronze Sunbird   Bronskleur Suikerbekkie

Nectarinia kilimensis Shelley, 1884: *Kilimanjaro.*

PLATE 63, ♂ AND ♀ (OPP. P. 529).
Length ♂ about 23 cm, ♂ 15 cm (wing ♂ 70—74, ♀ 67—69; tail ♂ 102—120, ♀ 59—63; tarsus 18—19; culmen ♂ 27,5—29, ♀ 24,5—26. 14 specimens, 10 ♂, 4 ♀). Iris dark brown; bill and legs black. Weight 15,5 g.

Identification: Resembles the Malachite Sunbird in form but colour quite different. Female as illustrated; has yellower breast with distinct darker

535

streaks, clearer white eyebrow and a shorter, more curved beak than the female Malachite. Young birds resemble the adult female but are dusky on throat and lack breast streaking.

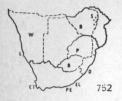

Distribution: Kenya and Uganda southwards to Malawi and the eastern border of Rhodesia above 1 350 metres.

Habits: A locally common species which inhabits thick vegetation such as briars and bracken on mountains, cultivated areas where there are trees, etc. Rather resembles the last species in habits but frequents trees more. Also hawks insects in the air.

752

Food: Flying ants, flies, small beetles and gnats; also feeds at *Leonotis, Erythrina* and other flowers.

Voice: A loud shrill "chee-oo, chee-oo" or "pea-view, pea-view", uttered by both sexes.

Breeding: The nest is deep, made of grass stems and lined with vegetable-down; it is usually within reach but may be as high as 7 metres. Breeds from September to April. Eggs, one in a clutch, are white, slightly chalky in texture, with a number of small sepia spots scattered over the larger end, chiefly in a zone, with underlying spots and blotches of brownish grey. One measures 20 × 13,5.

LOCAL RACE:
N.k. arturi P. Sclater, 1906: *Melsetter.* As illustrated; size above. Eastern Rhodesia to southern Tanzania.

753 Orange-breasted Sunbird   Oranjebors-suikerbekkie

Anthobaphes violacea (Linnaeus), 1766: *Cape of Good Hope.*

PLATE 63, ♂ AND ♀ (OPP. P. 529).
Length 13—17 cm (wing ♂ 52,5—54—57, ♀ 50; tail ♂ 68—82, ♀ 42—46; tarsus 15—16,5; culmen 20—23. 15 specimens, 13 ♂, 2 ♀). Iris dark brown; bill and legs black.

Identification: The long tail and *orange* breast render the male unmistakable; females are greener than females of the Lesser Double-collared Sunbird, which occurs in the same areas. Young birds resemble the female.

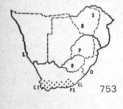

Distribution: From Cape Town northwards to the Khamiesberg and eastwards to King William's Town.

Habits: A common species of mountain slopes and plateaus, particularly where there are heaths and proteas. Occurs usually in pairs and may be found from sea-level to the tops of the highest and bleakest Cape mountains. A noisy and active species, males perching on conspicuous points and uttering their

753

characteristic chirp. Hawks insects in the air occasionally.

Food: Flies, spiders and other insects and the nectar of *Erica, Protea* and other flowers.

Voice: A very characteristic, harsh almost wheezy "tsearp" and a double "teer-turp". The male has a high-pitched song.

Breeding: Nests during the winter, normally from May to August, also January—February, but recorded in all months except November—December. The nest is placed low down, usually about 25 cm to one metre up in a small bush. Sometimes makes a nest at the top of a tall tree. It is constructed by the female of twigs, *Protea*-down and grass, very warmly lined with vegetable-down. Eggs number 1 or 2 and are whitish, heavily freckled with greyish brown, more concentrated at the thicker end. Average (120) 16,5 × 12,4 (15,1—18,2 × 11,5—13,5). Incubation by female only, 14½ days. Nestling 19—22 days (11); young are fed by both sexes, but more by the female.

754 Coppery Sunbird   Koperkleur Suikerbekkie

Cinnyris cupreus (Shaw), 1811: *Malimba, Portuguese Congo.*

PLATE 63, ♂ AND ♀ (OPP. P. 529).
Length about 12 cm (wing ♂ 55—65, ♀ 50—53; tail ♂ 43—53, ♀ 35—40; tarsus 15—16; culmen 16—20. After Reichenow). Iris dark brown; bill and legs black. Weight 10,3 g.

Identification: Might be confused with the Purple-banded Sunbird, No. 756, but is more coppery in colour and lacks the purple band across the breast. The female is olive-green above and *yellowish* below; tail blackish, with pale edges to outer-feathers. Young resemble adult females but males have dark throats. Adult male has a period of eclipse plumage from April to August in northern Rhodesia and then resembles female, but retains black wings and tail and metallic wing and upper tail-coverts.
Distribution: Senegal to Ethiopia southwards to eastern Rhodesia.
Habits: Little recorded from our area; in Zaïre tends to keep to rather marshy spots and clearings in fairly thick woodland.
Food: Spiders, insects, caterpillars and nectar from flowers; this is often obtained by piercing the bottom of the tube of a large flower.
Voice: A hoarse "chit-chat". Male has a soft, warbling song.
Breeding: The nest is oval or pear-shaped, placed about one half to two metres from the ground and constructed of fibres, grass and plant stems, woolly plant-down and lichens, thickly lined with vegetable-down. Eggs 3, cream with scattered streaky spots of chocolate and brown; in other forms with ashy or charcoal grey, the spots having a penumbra with blackish brown centres and tiny swirls over them. December to February. Average (9) 16,5 × 11,8 (15,6—17 × 11—12,2). Incubation 13 days. Nestling 16 days.

LOCAL RACE:
C.c. cupreus (Shaw), 1811: *Malimba, Portuguese Congo.* As illustrated; size above. Range as above, except Angola.

755 Marico Sunbird   Marico-suikerbekkie

Cinnyris mariquensis A. Smith, 1836: *North of Kurrichane =*
Marico.

PLATE 63, ♂ AND ♀ (OPP. P. 529).
Length ♂ 13—14 cm, ♀ 12—13 cm (wing ♂ 64—67,5—72. ♀ 60—62—63, tail ♂ 46—52, ♀ 42—43; tarsus 15—18; culmen 20—24. 45 specimens, 40 ♂, 5 ♀). Iris dark brown; bill and legs black. Weight 10,3—12 g.

Identification: Very like the next species but is larger and comparatively longer-billed in both sexes. Young birds resemble the female; young males have dark throats. Males have no eclipse plumage.
Distribution: From Damaraland, Botswana, Transvaal and Zululand northwards to East Africa and Ethiopia.

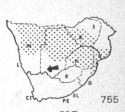

Habits: A locally common bird which is mainly found in dry acacia thorn savannas but also ranges to the drier country of the east coast.

Food: Mainly spiders; also insects, including flies, lepidopterous larvae and small hymenoptera; the nectar of flowers such as *Acacia, Leonotis, Aloe* and *Erythrina.*

Voice: A loud "chip-chip" which may be accelerated into a stuttering series. Song a brief, but loud warble.

Breeding: Suspends its nest, low down or up to 5 metres, from the branches of *Acacia* or sometimes other more leafy trees; the material used is largely white down and feathers, partially concealed by bits of bark and seeds stuck on the outside. The building is done entirely by the female, usually accompanied on each trip by the male who may even carry some material for her. Eggs number 2, greyish white very thickly marked with small streaks and smears of pale brown, olive and dark grey. Average (13) 18,3 × 12,0 (16,8—20 × 11—12,8; one 18 × 13,6). Recorded breeding from December to April in Transvaal; September to November in Rhodesia and January in South West Africa.

LOCAL RACE:
C.m. mariquensis A. Smith, 1836: *North of Kurrichane = Marico District, western Transvaal.* As illustrated; size above. Southern Africa as far north as Malawi and Rhodesia.

756 Purple-banded Sunbird   Purpurband-suikerbekkie

Cinnyris bifasciatus (Shaw), 1811: *Malimba, Portuguese Congo.*

PLATE 63, ♂ AND ♀ (OPP. P. 529).
Length ♂ 12 cm, ♀ 10 cm (wing ♂ 55—57—59,5, ♀ 51—52—53; tail ♂ 37—43, ♀ 30—34; tarsus 12,5—14; culmen 15,5—17. 14 specimens, 8 ♂, 6 ♀). Iris dark brown; bill and legs black.

Identification: Very like the last species but smaller and with a relatively shorter beak. Female less yellowish below than the female Marico. Male has dull non-breeding dress resembling the female but with dark wings, blackish throat and metallic wing-coverts and upper tail-coverts. Young birds resemble the female but have dark throats.

Distribution: From Gabon to Somalia, southwards to Angola, Caprivi and Zululand. In our area common in coastal Mozambique.

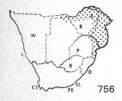

756

Habits: Frequents the larger trees in the savannas and open coastal bush, where it is usually seen in pairs exploring the flowers of creepers and bushes. In eastern Rhodesia appears from September to December and breeds, apparently retiring to lower levels during the rest of the year.

Food: Small flies and termites are recorded; is probably mainly insectivorous but also drinks the nectar of flowers, especially of acacias.

Breeding: The nest is suspended from the projecting branches of small trees, at a height of 1—4 metres, and is constructed of dry grass, plant-fibres, vegetable-down and cobwebs, covered on the outside with lichens, chips of wood, leaves and seeds. It is lined with feathers. Breeds in September to November. Eggs 1 or 2, purplish or slate-grey, owing to an even distribution of a suffusion of that colour hiding the ground colour, sometimes with a zone of darker grey round the large end. Average (16) 16,0 × 10,9 (15—17,8 × 10,4—11,8).

LOCAL RACES:
(a) C.b. microrhynchus Shelley, 1876: *Dar-es-Salaam, Tanganyika.* As illustrated; size above. Rhodesia to Kenya, and Tanzania across to Angola and eastern Zaïre.
(b) C.b. strophium Clancey and Williams, 1957: *Manhica, P.E.A.* Tail longer than *(a).* Eastern Zululand north.

757 Black-bellied Sunbird   Swartpens-suikerbekkie

Cinnyris shelleyi Alexander, 1899: *Sixty miles below Kafue-Zambesi Junction.*

PLATE 63, ♂ AND ♀ (OPP. P. 529).
Length 12—13 cm (wing ♂ 61—68, ♀ 56—59; tail 37—41; tarsus 11; culmen 18—20) Iris dark brown; bill and legs black.

Identification: In the field the male appears as a bright green sunbird with an outstandingly red breast-band. May be distinguished from the Greater and Lesser Double-collared Sunbirds, Nos. 758 and 760, by its black belly; from Neergaard's, No. 761, by its *green*, not blue, rump and by its much longer bill. Females resemble female Marico Sunbirds but are smaller and more dusky below. Young birds (of both sexes) have black throat and upper-breast and dark markings on breast and flanks.
Distribution: From the lower Zambesi Valley, as far south as Beira, to Zambia, Malawi and Tanzania. Rhodesian records require confirmation.
Habits: Little recorded in our area but further north is locally common in open woodlands, where it searches for food in the upper branches of the trees. It is especially attracted to *Loranthus* flowers.
Food: Spiders, diptera and minute hymenoptera; also nectar.
Voice: A quick diminuendo "chitter"; song a nasal "chibbee-cheeu-cheeu".
Breeding: Nest usually 2—3 metres up in leafy shrub or tree. It is made of cobwebs holding together old leaves, bits of bark and the like; lined with feathers. Eggs 2, pale drab with a few fine specks of purple all over or with broad band at broad end. August to November. 17,5 × 11,5 and 17,0 × 12,0. Two broods from one nest recorded.

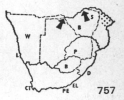

757

LOCAL RACE:
C.s. shelleyi Alexander, 1899: *Sixty miles below Kafue-Zambesi Junction.* As illustrated; size above. Lower Zambesi River to Malawi and south-western Tanzania.

758 Greater Double-collared Sunbird
Groot Rooibors-suikerbekkie

Cinnyris afer (Linnaeus), 1766: *Cape of Good Hope.*

Native Name: Ingcungcu (X).
PLATE 63, ♂ AND ♀ (OPP. P. 529).
Length 14—15 cm (wing ♂ 63—67—70, ♀ 58—60—61; tail ♂ 50—61, ♀ 42—47; tarsus ♂ 17,5—19, ♀ 16—17; culmen ♂ 26—29, ♀ 24—26. 54 specimens, 46 ♂, 8 ♀). Iris dark brown; bill and legs black.

Identification: Very like the next species but is larger, red chest-band roughly twice as broad, bill heavier and longer; with practice the calls can be distinguished. Female as illustrated. Young birds resemble females. No eclipse plumage in male.

539

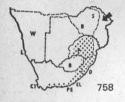

758

Distribution: From Swellendam eastwards to Natal and Transvaal. An isolated population on Gorongoza Mountain, Mozambique. Occurs again on the mountains of Central Africa and Angola.

Habits: A common species found on the borders of forest or in forest scrub in sheltered valleys, wherever there are flowers to be found, at all seasons but subject to local fluctuations in numbers. Gathers in small parties when not breeding.

Food: Spiders, beetles, diptera, scale insects and other insects; also nectar from flowers, particularly those of *Aloe, Schotia, Cotyledon* and *Erythrina* plants; may also suck the juice from soft fruits at times.

Voice: Alarm note of chattering "skiz, skiz, skiz". Male also goes "cheet, cheet" and when displaying "chert, chert"; also a rasping "skirt". Has a loud, pleasant warbling song.

Breeding: Suspends its nest from drooping vines on krantzes or from bushes or trees from 2—4 metres up. It is built by the female. Breeding recorded for all months except January to March, but mainly in October and November. Roughly the same site is used year after year. Eggs 2, sometimes only 1, are white, clouded thinly with olive, slate-grey and here and there spots or dots and some streaks of olive-brown and greyish. Average (10) 18,4 × 12,4 (17—19,5 × 11,8—13,1). Incubation by female only, 15 or 16 days (1). Both sexes feed the young.

LOCAL RACE:
C.a. afer (Linnaeus), 1766: *Cape of Good Hope.* As illustrated; size above. South Africa. Other races in Central Africa and Angola.

759   See **760** *(b).*

760   Lesser Double-collared Sunbird
Klein Rooibors-suikerbekkie

Cinnyris chalybeus   (Linnaeus), 1766: *Cape of Good Hope.*

Native Name: Ingcungcu (X).

PLATE 63, ♂ AND ♀ (OPP. P. 529).
Length 12—13 cm (wing ♂ 52—55—58, ♀ 47—49—52; tail ♂ 41—47, ♀ 36—40; tarsus ♂ 16—17, ♀ 16; culmen ♂ 19—23, ♀ 18—20. 14 specimens, 10 ♂, 4 ♀). Iris dark brown; bill and legs black. Weight 7,4—10,2 g.

Identification: See under the last species. The grey to greenish belly avoids confusion with Nos. 757 and 761, which have black bellies. Females as illustrated. Young birds resemble females. No eclipse plumage in males but immature birds in intermediate dress have been mistakenly assumed to show it.

Distribution: Cape Province, Natal, Transvaal and Rhodesia northwards to Tanzania, south-eastern Zaïre and Angola.

Habits: A common species in our area, occurring wherever there are forests or scrub and commonly entering gardens and gum-tree plantations. May be found in quite dry country such as the Karoo and is commoner on flat country than in the mountains except in Southern Rhodesia where it occurs up to 2 000 metres. Flight rapid with much swerving and jinking.

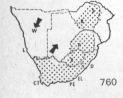

760

Food: Larvae, small beetles, flies and spiders; also the nectar of *Aloe, Salvia, Tecomaria, Erica, Plumbago* and many other flowers.

Voice: Call a slightly grating "cheep, cheep". Has a pleasant tinkling, scraping song.

Breeding: The nest, built by the female, is suspended from the branch of a bush or small tree, usually from 1—2 metres up but occasionally as high as 6 metres. It is roughly pear-shaped and made of grass, plant fibres, lichen and cobwebs, warmly lined with feathers and woolly plant-down which may also be incorporated in the framework. Breeds from April to November in the Cape but mainly in July and September, probably indicating two broods; September to November to November in Natal and year round in Rhodesia, but mainly during September and November. Eggs usually number 2, but 3 are found occasionally. Ground colour cream, almost obscured by spotting and mottling of brown and grey; some have hair-lines and pencillings of dark brown and blackish. Average (21) of race *(a)* 15,9 × 11,5 (14,6—17 × 10,9—12,4). Incubation 13—16 days (3). Nestling 15—19 days.

LOCAL RACES:
(a) C.c. chalybeus (Linnaeus), 1766: *Cape of Good Hope*. As illustrated, No. 760 *(a); size above. Western and central Cape Province.
(b) C.c. manoensis Reichenow, 1907: *Missale in Mano, Tanzania*. Rump grey, belly dark grey. Wing 59—63—67; tail 43—50; culmen 23—26 (39). Mashonaland and lower Zambesi Valley of Mozambique.
(c) C.c. subalaris Reichenow, 1899: *Pondoland*. Rump metallic blue, belly greenish yellow. Wing ♂ 55—58, ♀ 51—53; tail ♂ 43—46, ♀ 36—38; culmen ♂ 21—24, ♀ 17,5—18. 13 specimens, 11 ♂, 2 ♀. East Cape, Natal and Transvaal.

761 Neergaard's Sunbird   Neergaardse Suikerbekkie

Cinnyris neergaardi   C. Grant, 1908: *Coguno, Portuguese East Africa*.

PLATE 63, ♂ (OPP. P. 529).
Length about 10 cm (wing ♂ 54—56; tail 35—40; tarsus 15—16; culmen 13,5—15,5. 2 specimens). Iris dark brown; legs and bill black.

Identification: Very like the Black-bellied Sunbird but has a much shorter bill and a blue rump.
Distribution: Very restricted; from St. Lucia, Zululand, northwards to Panda and Inhambane.
Habits: Frequents the coastal bush and is not uncommon, although little has been recorded about it.
Breeding: Found breeding by Bell-Marley in Zululand in November. The nest is described as a beautifully compact affair, composed of feathers and down, covered with bright green lichens bound with remains of some larvae, and suspended from the tip of a thorn tree, 6 metres up. The eggs are slaty blue with dispersed spots of dark grey, and measure 16,1—16,7 × 11,0.

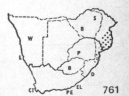

761

762 Yellow-bellied Sunbird   Geelbors-suikerbekkie

Cinnyris venustus   (Shaw and Nodder), 1799: *Sierra Leone*.

PLATE 64, ♂ AND ♀ (OPP. P. 544).
Length ♂ 11 cm, ♀ 10 cm (wing ♂ 50—51,5, ♀ 47; tail ♂ 37—40, ♀ 33—34; tarsus 14,5—15; culmen ♂ 20, ♀ 17). Iris dark brown; bill and legs black. Weight 6—8 g.

Identification: Has a longer bill, in both sexes, than both Blue-throated Little Sunbird, No. 769, and the Collared Sunbird, No. 771, while the broad purple

541

patch on the chest is distinctive in the male. Females, apart from the longer bill, lack the metallic green back of the female Collared Sunbird. Distinguishable from the White-bellied Sunbird, No. 763, by the yellow belly. Young birds resemble the female; males have dark throats.

Distribution: Senegal to Somalia, southwards to Angola and Rhodesian highlands. Records from the Kruger National Park doubtful.

Habits: A localized but common species in scrub-filled kloofs and on the borders of patches of forest but not actually *in* forest. Very restless and erratic in its actions, moving about a great deal. Hawks insects in the air.

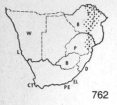

762

Food: Mainly spiders and small flies; also nectar, particularly from *Leonotis* and *Salvia* flowers.

Voice: Utters a low clicking note as it flies about; alarm call "cheer, cheer", rather drawn out; males have a short, rippling song in the breeding season.

Breeding: The nest is oval or pear-shaped with a well-defined porch and constructed of broad reed-strips and grass-blades, with some dead leaves, and bound on the outside with cobwebs; it is lined with vegetable-down and a few soft feathers. Nests are usually built only about a metre from the ground. Breeds from March to November, mainly from March to April and July to August. Eggs 2, white or cream, almost obscured with fine speckling and freckling of fawn and olive-fawn with underlying grey, sometimes forming a distinct ring or cap at the thick end. Average (35) 15,7 × 11,3 (13,9—17,3 × 10,4—12,1).

LOCAL RACE:
C.v. falkensteini Fischer and Reichenow, 1884: *Lake Naivasha, Kenya.* As illustrated; size above. Sudan to Rhodesia.

763   White-bellied Sunbird   Witbors-suikerbekkie

Cinnyris talatala   A. Smith, 1836: *Between Orange River and Kurri-chane.*

PLATE 63, ♂ AND ♀ (OPP. P. 529).
Length about 11 cm (wing ♂ 55—57,5—60, ♀ 50—52—55; tail ♂ 38—43, ♀ 32—38; tarsus 14,5—17; culmen ♂ 21,5—24, ♀ 19—20. 41 specimens, 31 ♂, 10 ♀. Iris dark brown; bill and legs black.

Identification: Rather like the last species, but male has *white* belly. Females whiter below than other similar species. Young resemble females.

Distribution: From Benguela and Damaraland eastwards to Natal and northwards to southern Tanzania.

Habits: Common in dry *Acacia,* poorly developed *Brachystegia* and other types of dry, open-wooded country. Also enters towns such as Pretoria, where the growth is more luxurious.

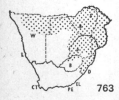

763

Food: The nectar of flowers, particularly *Loranthus,* a parasitic plant common in *Acacia* trees.

Voice: Normal call "tzick, tzick", sometimes running into a rattle of "tzicks". Alarm called by both sexes "chewy-chewy-chewy" uttered 4—7 times.

Breeding: The oval nest is slung, quite low down, from the branches of a thorn-tree or shrub, often imbedded in a mass of cobweb. It is built of grass and grass-stems which project over the entrance, mixed with cobweb, dead leaves and woolly plant-down. Breeds mainly from June to January. Two eggs are normally laid but three have been recorded, white with purplish grey and olive speckles and smudges, mainly at the thick end; another type is indistinctly speckled and finely freckled in pale fawn and light ash, sometimes with a few more distinct specks, sometimes concentrated at the thick end. Average (22) 15,9 × 11,3 (15—16,8 × 10,7—12,2). Incubation 13 days (3). Nestling 14—15 days (2).

764 Dusky Sunbird   Namakwa Suikerbekkie

Cinnyris fuscus Vieillot, 1819: *Great Namaqualand.*

PLATE 63, ♂ AND ♀ (OPP. P. 529).
Length about 11 cm (wing ♂ 54—57—59 (22), ♀ 48—50—52 (8); tail 38—41; tarsus 15,5—17; culmen 18—22. 8 specimens, 6 ♂, 2 ♀). Iris dark brown; bill and legs black.

Identification: The male is easily distinguished by his black throat and chest; in non-breeding dress (from about April to December) the black is restricted to a broad stripe from the throat over the head to the rump. The female resembles the female Lesser Double-collared Sunbird but is paler grey. Young birds resemble the female, but males have black throats.
Distribution: The Karoo, as far east as Colesberg, northwards to northern South West Africa.
Habits: Essentially a bird of dry or even very arid country; becomes concentrated at certain times in very large numbers where food is available, as in the valleys of dry rivers, extending along such rivers even into the Namib desert.
Food: Feeds commonly at the flowers of *Aloe dichotoma* and *Nicotiana glauca.*

764

Voice: Normal call a harsh "chrrrr, chek chek".
Breeding: The nest is slung from the branches of a bush or built against a prickly pear or euphorbia plant. It is made of plant-fibres, dry leaves and grass, lined with plant-down and occasionally a few feathers. Many preliminary nests are built. Eggs number 2 or 3, white with dark slate-blue, brown and purplish brown speckles and scattered spots, principally at the thick end. August to March. Average (7) 15,4 × 10,8 (15—15,9 × 10,7—10,9). Incubation by female.

765 Grey Sunbird   Grys Suikerbekkie

Cyanomitra veroxii (A. Smith), 1831: *Cafferland = Eastern Cape Province.*

PLATE 64 (OPP. P. 544).
Length about 17 cm (wing ♂ 62—63—66, ♀ 57,5—59—61,5; tail ♂ 48—52, ♀ 42—45; tarsus 15,5—18; culmen 24—26,5. 12 specimens, 7 ♂, 5 ♀). Iris dark brown; bill and legs black.

Identification: The male with metallic crown is immediately recognizable by his *red* pectoral tufts, if showing; otherwise rather resembles the Olive Sunbird, No, 766, but is *grey* below not greenish. Sexes alike; young birds are yellowish below.
Distribution: From just west of Port Elizabeth northwards to Somalia.

765

543

PLATE 64

762. *Cinnyris venustus falkensteini.* Yellow-bellied Sunbird. Geelbors-suikerbekkie. ♂ and ♀.

765. *Cyanomitra veroxii veroxii.* Grey Sunbird. Grys Suikerbekkie.

766 *(a). Cyanomitra olivacea olivacea.* Olive Sunbird. Olyf-suikerbekkie. ♂.

766 *(b). Cyanomitra olivacea olivacina.* Olive Sunbird. Olyf-suikerbekkie. ♂.

769. *Anthreptes reichenowi reichenowi.* Blue-throated Sunbird. Bloukeel-suikerbekkie. ♂ and ♀.

771. *Anthreptes collaris collaris.* Collared Sunbird. Kortbek-suikerbekkie. ♂ and ♀.

772 *(a). Chalcomitra amethystina amethystina.* Black Sunbird. Swart Suikerbekkie. ♂ and ♀.

772 *(b). Chalcomitra amethystina kirkii.* Black Sunbird. Swart Suikerbekkie. ♂ and ♀.

774. *Chalcomitra senegalensis gutturalis.* Scarlet-chested Sunbird. Rooikeel-suikerbekkie. ♂ and ♀.

775 *(a). Zosterops pallidus capensis.* Cape White-eye. Kaapse Witogie.

775 *(d). Zosterops pallidus pallidus.* Cape White-eye. Kaapse Witogie.

775 *(f). Zosterops pallidus virens.* Cape White-eye. Kaapse Witogie.

777. *Zosterops senegalensis anderssoni.* Yellow White-eye. Geel Witogie.

779

780

783

784 ♂ ♀

785 ♀

♂

796

786 ♂ ♀

804 ♂ ♀

787

788

Nlighton
'36

PLATE 65

779. *Bubalornis albirostris niger.* Buffalo Weaver. Buffelwewer. ♂ and ♀.
780. *Plocepasser mahali.* White-browed Sparrow-weaver. Koringvoël.
783. *Philetairus socius.* Social Weaver. Familievoël.
784. *Passer domesticus indicus.* House Sparrow. Huis Mossie. ♂ and ♀.
785. *Passer motitensis motitensis.* Great Sparrow. Groot Mossie. ♂ and ♀.
786. *Passer melanurus melanurus.* Cape Sparrow. Mossie. ♂ and ♀.
787. *Passer diffusus diffusus.* Southern Grey-headed Sparrow. Gryskop-mossie.
788. *Petronia superciliaris.* Yellow-throated Sparrow. Geelvlek-mossie.
796. *Ploceus rubiginosus.* Chestnut Weaver. Bruin Wewer.
804. *Amblyospiza albifrons albifrons.* Thick-billed Weaver. Dikbek-wewer.
                                                                    ♂ and ♀.

Habits: Quite a common bird of coastal bush and forest; tends to be overlooked because of its habit of keeping to the tops of the trees, seldom venturing down unless to a particularly tempting source of food. Is a loud and noisy species, however, and its distinctive call-note often reveals its presence. Has the habit, in common with the next species, of frequently flicking its wings when perched.

Food: Spiders; lepidopterous larvae; nectar especially from *Loranthus* flowers.

Voice: A loud "chik, chik" often followed by a ringing "cheep, choop".

Breeding: The nest is a rather untidy structure, oval in shape, made of grass and leaves bound with cobweb and usually unlined. It is placed at the ends of branches of trees or bushes up to 6 metres high. Breeds October to February. The eggs number 2 or 3 and are chocolate-coloured, often darker at the thick end. Average (30) 17,9 × 12,5 (16,5—19 × 12,2—13; one 19,9 × 12).

LOCAL RACES:
(a) C.v. veroxii (A. Smith), 1831: *Cafferland = Eastern Cape Province.* As illustrated; size above. Eastern Cape Province to Natal.
(b) C.v. fischeri (Reichenow), 1880: *Mozambique, Northern P.E.A.* Whiter breasted than *(a)* and slightly smaller. Wing ♂ 62 (5), ♀ 56 (1).

766 Olive Sunbird   Olyf-suikerbekkie

Cyanomitra olivacea (A. Smith), 1840: *Near Port Natal.*

PLATE 64, ♂ RACES *(a)* AND *(b)* (OPP. P. 544).
Length ♂ 15 cm, ♀ 13 cm (wing ♂ 65—66,5—69, ♀ 60—61,5—63; tail ♂ 53—61, ♀ 50—54; tarsus 16—18; culmen 25,5—30. 27 specimens, 18 ♂, 9 ♀. Iris dark brown; bill and legs black. Weight ♂ 9—12; ♀ 8—10,3 g.

Identification: More olive-green below than the last species; both sexes have *yellow* pectoral tufts. Young birds have brighter green under-parts, throat paler and no tufts.

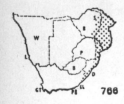

Distribution: From Pondoland eastwards along the coast to Kenya and across to West Africa, Zaïre, also Angola.

Habits: A locally common species which is essentially a bird of forests and thick coastal bush and banana trees. Spends most of its time at lower levels, where it darts about from shrub to shrub uttering a sharp "cip, cip". Hawks for insects from a perch quite often.

Food: Insects and the nectar of flowers such as *Leonotis, Achyrospermum,* bananas and *Loranthus.*

Voice: "Cip, cip" as it flies about. When alarmed a "chürr-chüwe-chüwe-chüwe-chüwe-chü-chü-chü". Males have a distinctive, fine, loud warbling song, uttered all the year round but more when breeding.

Breeding: The nest is an untidy structure of twigs, grass, moss, lichens and leaves. A long "tail" usually hangs down below. The nest is placed low down from 0,5 to 2 metres or so up. Breeds from September to January to March in Rhodesia. Eggs 2, very rarely 3, bluish or greyish white with scrolls, marks and spots of dark brown and underlying grey. Average (20) 18,5 × 12,6 (17,4—20,5 × 11,7—13,5).

LOCAL RACES:
(a) C.o. olivacea (A. Smith), 1840: *Near Port Natal.* Illustrated; size above. Pondoland, Natal and southern Zululand.

(b) C.o. olivacina (Peters), 1881: *Inhambane.* Illustrated. *(a).* Smaller than *(a).* Wing ♂ 58—59,5—63, ♀ 52,5—54—55,5. Northern Zululand northwards to northern Mozambique.
(c) C.o. sclateri Vincent, 1934: *Chirinda Forest.* Paler below, throat and breast "scalloped". Wing ♂ 63—66 (3), ♀ 55—58 (3). Females without pectoral tufts. Eastern districts of Rhodesia, above 600 metres.

767 = 766 *(b)*

768 = 766 extralim

769 Blue-throated Sunbird   Bloukeel-suikerbekkie

Anthreptes reichenowi   Gunning, 1909: *Mzimbiti, near Beira.*

PLATE 64, ♂ AND ♀ (OPP. P. 544).
Length about 10 cm (wing ♂ 55—56, ♀ 52—53; tail ♂ 40—41, ♀ 34—36; tarsus 15—17; culmen 15—16. 6 specimens, 3 ♂, 3 ♀).

Identification: Male most likely to be confused with the Collared Sunbird, No. 771, and Yellow-breasted Sunbird, No. 762; but note that yellow of breast extends up side of dark throat to eye; bill much shorter (than No. 762) and back dull. Female lacks green back and upper-parts of female Collared Sunbird, No. 771. Young resemble the female but are more olive above.
Distribution: From south of Inhambane, Chimonza northwards along the coast to Kenya. Two records from eastern Rhodesia.
Habits: Not a common species, which inhabits forest and thick coastal bush, spending its time searching the trees from the lower levels to the tops of the high trees. Quiet and unobtrusive, often a member of mixed bird parties; seldom visits flowers. Rather warbler-like in field appearance.

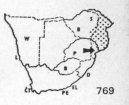
769

Food: Apparently mainly insects and spiders.
Voice: A rambling song. Call-note a double "tik".
Breeding: A nest from East Africa is described as oval with the entrance near the top under an overhanging porch and made of shredded grass, insect cocoons and bark, loosely woven with spiders' web. The only breeding records in our area consist of a sight record of large young being fed near Sinoia in November and eggs from Beira collected by P. A. Sheppard, two of which measure 15,1 × 10,4—11,1. Eggs are white, spotted and freckled with dull red, concentrated at the large end.

LOCAL RACE:
A.r. reichenowi Gunning, 1909: *Mzimbiti.* As illustrated; size above. Rhodesia and Mozambique.

770 Violet-backed Sunbird   Blou Suikerbekkie

Anthreptes longuemarei   (Lesson), 1831: *Senegal.*

PLATE 63, ♂ AND ♀ (OPP. P. 529).
Length about 13 cm (wing ♂ 79, ♀ 63,5; tail ♂ 52, ♀ 39; tarsus 15,5—18; culmen 15,5—16. 2 specimens). Iris dark brown; bill and legs black.

Identification: Sexes as illustrated. Young birds resemble the female but are yellower below and lack contrast of grey crown and nape and olive mantle.
Distribution: From Senegal across to Somalia, southwards to Angola on the west, eastern Rhodesia and Mozambique on the east.

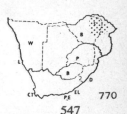
770

SUNBIRDS

Habits: Not common in our area. A bird of open forest and *Brachystegia* woodland. A quiet species which creeps about the branches and searches the leaves and bark of trees, often in company with "bird parties". May gather in some numbers where favoured flowers, particularly those of the *Erythrina* trees, are present. May assume all manner of postures, even hanging upside down.

Food: Largely insects, but also nectar.

Voice: Call note a loud single "tit"; alarm note "skeee".

Breeding: Nests fairly high up, from 4—20 metres from the ground, constructing an oval nest of dry leaves of lichen bound together with cobwebs and sometimes lined with grass. Breeds in August and October in Rhodesia. Eggs, normally 2, variable, ground-colour white to pale buff or blue, with scribblings and hair-lines of blackish brown and faint slate-grey, all over but concentrated at the thick end. Four from Zaïre measure 18,1—20,2 × 12,0—12,9.

LOCAL RACE:
A.l. nyassae Neumann, 1906: *Zomba, Nyasaland.* As illustrated; size above. Rhodesia and Mozambique to Malawi.

771 Collared Sunbird   Kortbek-suikerbekkie

Anthreptes collaris (Vieillot), 1819: *Gamtoos River, Cape.*

Native Names: Ingathane (X); i-Ntontso (Z).

PLATE 64, ♂ AND ♀ (OPP. P. 544).
Length about 10 cm (wing ♂ 50—51—54, ♀ 48—48,5—49,5; tail 34—41; tarsus ♂ 16—17, ♀ 14—15,5; culmen 13—15. 19 specimens, 12 ♂ 9 ♀). Iris brown; bill and legs blackish. Weight 7,6—8,9 g.

Identification: Unmistakable. Sexes as illustrated. Young birds resemble the female.

Distribution: From Knysna eastwards and northwards to Ethiopia and across to Gambia, Zaïre and Angola.

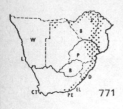

771

Habits: A widespread and common species in moist forests and thick coastal bush. Usually seen in pairs at the flowers on trees and creepers in the forest and seldom in the more open bush unless it is adjoining tangled forest. Creeps about quietly, more in the manner of a White-eye than a Sunbird. When alarmed has the habit of flicking the wings half open and then closing them again. Keeps mainly to the undergrowth at low levels.

Food: Mainly insectivorous; ants, flies, small beetles, larvae, spiders and snails. Also small fruits.

Voice: Normal call a quiet "tswee", rather like a Swee Waxbill; this is uttered louder to keep contact with one another. Also makes a trilling sound. Males sing prettily.

Breeding: The nest is placed about 1—4 metres up and is suspended from a hanging branch or trailing vine. It is pear-shaped, constructed of dry grass, plant-fibres, dead leaves, bark and lined with plant-down and feathers. Eggs 2 or 3, cream or pinky white, variably marked with olive and grey or reddish brown and purplish spots and streaks forming a cap round the large end. Average (42) of race *(a)* 16,3 × 11,3 (15—17,3 × 10,5—12; one 17,8 × 11,7). Breeds from October to March in Natal and Zululand. Incubation 17—19 days.

LOCAL RACES:
(a) A.c. collaris (Vieillot), 1819: *Gamtoos River, Cape.* As illustrated; size above. Knysna to Natal.
(b) A.c. zuluensis (Roberts), 1931: *Mkusi River, Zululand.* Margin of primaries and secondaries as in *(c)*; but coverts more metallic green, through only half as broad as in *(a)*; partly greenish on flanks; blue and purple band across throat broader. Wing ♂ 51—52—53 (7), ♀49 (1). Eggs smaller than *(a)*. Average (19) 15,2 × 10,9 (14,7—15,9 × 10—11,7). Zululand to Rhodesia.
(c) A.c. zambesiana (Shelley), 1880: *Shupanga, Zambesi.* Primaries and secondaries conspicuously margined with yellow, their coverts with only a trace of metallic green; below yellower on flanks; blue and purple band broadest. Wing ♂ 50—51,5—54 (5), ♀ 47—49 (2). The Zambesi valley northwards and west to the Chobe River and Mababe Flats.
(d) A.c. beverleyae Irwin, 1961: *Sentinel Ranch, Limpopo River, Rhodesia.* Areas adjacent to the Limpopo River. Under parts lighter and clearer lemon-yellow than *(b)* and *(e)*.
(e) A.c. patersonae Irwin, 1960: *Lower Pungwe, Rhodesia.* Highlands of Rhodesia and adjacent Mozambique. Larger and longer billed than *(b)*.

772 Black Sunbird   Swart Suikerbekkie

Chalcomitra amethystina   (Shaw), 1811: *Cape of Good Hope.*

Native Name: Ingcungcu (X).

PLATE 64, ♂ AND ♀ OF RACES *(a)* AND *(b)*(OPP. P. 544).
Length 15 cm (wing ♂ 70,5—72,5—76, ♀ 66—67—69; tail ♂ 45—54, ♀ 41—45; tarsus 15—18; culmen 25—30. 68 specimens, 50 ♂, 18 ♀. Iris dark brown; bill and legs black.

Identification: Lacks the red chest of the next species. Sexes as illustrated. Young birds resemble the female but are yellowish below; sub-adult males have iridescent throats, dark throat of female not as dark as in young.
Distribution: From Swellendam to Sudan and across to Zaïre, Angola and northern South West Africa.
Habits: A common species of open forest or almost any country where there are scattered trees and aloes. A very active and restless bird, continually on the move, with a loud persistent call. Comes into towns and in Pretoria is extremely common, having taken to exotic gum-trees where it chases insects visiting the flowers. Flies longer distances than most sunbirds, with rapid, undulating, direct but jinking flight. Sometimes sits for an hour or more inside a bush or creeper calling monotonously the whole time. Is subject to certain amount of local movement in search of favourable feeding localities. Forms parties of up to 20 when not breeding, many in juvenile plumage.

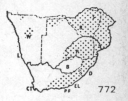

772

Food: Spiders, which may be taken from their webs, aphids, termites and other flying insects; also the nectar of *Aloe, Kniphofia* and other flowers.
Voice: Normal call a single, sharp "tseet"; also a stuttering "chichichi". Alarm call a very rapid, stuttering series "tit, tit, tit, tit". Males have a pleasant warbling song which they may utter for hours on end. Also call "chip-dew" loudly from a conspicuous perch (*cf.* next species).
Breeding: The nest is usually suspended from the branches of tall trees, 2—6 metres up. It is a pear-shaped structure, narrow and with the entrance at the top, made of grass, lichens, dead leaves and cobwebs with a porch over the entrance. Breeds during August to March in Natal; September to March in Transvaal and August to February in Rhodesia. Eggs number 2, very rarely 3, white or cream, clouded with elongate slate-grey and olive-brown markings; some eggs have fuzzy streaks and pencillings of chocolate, grey and blackish

brown. Average (34) 19,8 × 13,1 (17,8—21,4 × 12,4—13,6; one 17,0 × 12,0). Incubation by female only, 13—18 days. Nestling period 14—18 days; young are fed mainly by female.

LOCAL RACES:
(a) C.a. amethystina (Shaw), 1811: *Cape of Good Hope.* Illustrated; size above. Cape Province, Natal, eastern Transvaal and southern Mozambique.
(b) C.a. kirkii (Shelley), 1876: *Shupanga, Zambesi, Portuguese East Africa.* Illustrated. Smaller than *(a).* Wing ♂ 66,5—68—69 (5), ♀ 59,5—61—63 (5). Upper tail-coverts dull black. Rhodesia, Mozambique, north of the Incomati River to Malawi and southern Tanzania.
(c) C.a. deminuta (Cabanis), 1880: *Malandje, Angola.* Resembles *(b)* but has metallic upper tail-coverts. Ngamiland, Ovamboland, Angola and Zaïre; also Zambia meeting *(b).*

773 = 772 *(b)*

774　Scarlet-chested Sunbird　　　　　Rooikeel-suikerbekkie

Chalcomitra senegalensis (Linnaeus), 1766: *Senegal.*

PLATE 64, ♂ AND ♀ (OPP. P. 544).
Length 13—15 cm (wing ♂ 71—74—79, ♀ 64—68,5—70; tail ♂ 48—55, ♀ 42—48; tarsus 15—18,5; culmen 22—30. 42 specimens, 29 ♂, 13 ♀). Iris dark brown; bill and legs black.

Identification: Males unmistakable. Females may just be distinguished from females of the last species by being more heavily mottled, particulary above; in good view shows white edges to primaries and primary-coverts. Young birds resemble the female but have blackish chins. Immature males have throats like adults.

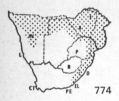

774

Distribution: Senegal to the Upper White Nile southwards to northern South West Africa, Ngamiland, eastern Transvaal and on the east coast as far as the Great Fish River. Scarce south of the Tugela River and modern status uncertain.

Habits: A fairly common species of the open forests and savannas of the moister parts of the continent. Is usually seen singly or in pairs, flying high overhead or visiting flowers on bushes or trees. Hawks flying insects.

Food: Insects such as crickets, ants, caterpillars; and spiders. Is very fond of *Leonotis, Erythrina* and *Aloe* flowers. Pierces flowers at the base.

Voice: In flight utters a sharp "zit". Males have a four-note piping call "tip, teeu, tip, tip", the second note lower than the others. May repeat this call every four seconds or so for more than an hour at a time.

Breeding: The nest is similar to that of the last species but is rather more bulky and nearly always covered with dead and skeleton leaves rather than lichen. It is very often built near hornet nests and frequently inside thick spiders' webs, from 2—10 metres up. Breeds October to January in Natal; August to March in Rhodesia; November to March in Damaraland. Eggs similar to those of the last species but markings usually more elongated. Clutch always two. Average (40) 19,2 × 13,2 (17,8—20,5 × 12,2—14). The female builds the nest, taking three to five days; the same site or nest is often used over and over again in succeeding years. Incubation 13½—15 days. Nestling 15½—19 days.

LOCAL RACES:
(a) *C.s. gutturalis* (Linnaeus), 1766: *Brazil = South Africa*. As illustrated; size above. Southern Africa to Zaïre and Tanzania.
(b) *C.s. saturatior* Reichenow, 1891: *Angola*. Angola and South West Africa. Darker and duller red on the mid-lower throat.

Family ZOSTEROPIDAE

The White-eyes are small, short-billed birds of a greenish or yellowish colour with a conspicuous white ring round the eyes. They feed on soft fruit and the nectar of flowers and insects and have the tongue partly grooved. The small outer primary has disappeared, so that there appear to be only nine primaries; in this respect they differ from all our other soft-billed birds such as the Warblers, Fly-catchers, etc. They are widely distributed over Africa and eastwards through the Indian Ocean Islands and southern Asia to Australia.

Humidity, food and probably other factors seem to influence the colour of white-eyes and what were formerly separate species now appear to be races or colour-varieties of one another; their classification is in a very fluid state. Some recognized forms apparently "hybridize" with other forms otherwise considered of another species. Current workers recognize from two to four species.

775   Cape White-eye   Kaapse Witogie

Zosterops pallidus   Swainson, 1838: *Southern Africa = Rustenburg, Transvaal.*

Native Name: Intukwane (X).

PLATE 64, RACES *(a)*, *(d)* AND *(f)* (OPP. P. 544).
Length 13 cm (wing 58—59,5—62; tail 46—50; tarsus 16,5—19; culmen 10,5—12. 9 specimens). Iris brown; bill black; legs greyish. Weight 10—13 g.

Identification: May be distinguished from the Yellow White-eye by its grey, green or whitish under-parts and green back. Sexes alike. Young birds are duller than adults and do not develop the white eye-ring until they are about five weeks old.
Distribution: Southern Africa to Ethiopia.
Habits: Extremely common and very well known. Is usually found in small loose flocks which keep on the move, the birds straggling after one another as they move from tree to tree and keeping in touch by constant calling and singing. Explores minutely the branches of trees and bushes, hedges, etc., and even comes on to the ground and clambers about small plants. These flocks break up during the breeding season.
Food: Soft fruit such as figs, insects, small berries and even the sugar in tea-room bowls. In winter searches for "honey-dew", a sugary substance exuded by aphids.
Voice: Normal call "cheep, cheep" or "peep, peep". Also sings beautifully, a long rambling song frequently breaking into repeated "cheeps", or imitations of other birds.
Breeding: Constructs a cup-shaped nest of fine straws, rootlets and fibres, covered externally with fine moss and cobwebs and slung on the outher twigs and leaves of projecting branches. Breeds from September to December. Eggs 2—3, pale blue or pure white. Average (17) 16,6 × 12,3 (15,3—17,6 × 11,2—13). Incubation 11—12 days; nestling 12—13 days.

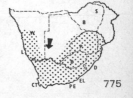

775

WHITE-EYES

LOCAL RACES:
(a) Z.p. capensis Sundevall, 1851: *Rondebosch, Cape Town.* Illustrated. Dull coloured, belly greyish; size above. Southern Cape Province northwards to Oliphants River, eastwards to Knysna.
(b) Z.p. atmorei Sharpe, 1877: *Grahamstown, Cape Province.* No yellow on lores. Brighter yellowish above and below; size as in *(a)*. Eastern Cape Province.
(c) Z.p. basuticus Roberts, 1936: *Mamathes, Basutoland.* Coloured as in *(b)* but larger. Wing 62—66; tail 46—51. Lesotho.
(d) Z.p. pallidus Swainson, 1838: *10 m. E. of Prieska.* With the flanks rufous and belly very pale. Wing 54; tail 43; tarsus 16; culmen 10. Orange River and Little Namaqualand to Damaraland. Illustrated.
(e) Z.p. sundevalli Hartlaub, 1865: *Cafraria superiore prope Vaal River.* Upper Vaal, south-western Transvaal and western Orange Free State. Less buffy on flanks.
(f) Z.p. virens Sundevall, 1851: *Caffraria = Durban, Natal.* This bird, formerly considered a full species has been found to breed in a natural state with No. 775 *(b) and appears to be a forest-haunting race of the Cape White-eye.* Illustrated.
(g) Z.p. caniviridis Clancey, 1962: *Pretoria, Transvaal.* Southern Botswana, Transvaal highveld, eastern Orange Free State and western Swaziland. Colder, greyer green above, flanks greyer.

776 This species, formerly *Z. vaalensis,* is considered a synonym of **775** *(d).*

777 Yellow White-eye — Geel Witogie

Zosterops senegalensis   Bonaparte, 1850: *Senegal.*

PLATE 64 (OPP. P. 544).
Length 12 cm (wing 59—60—62; tail 39—45; tarsus 14—16,5; culmen 9—11,5. 16 specimens). Iris brown; bill black; legs greyish. Weight 8—11 g.

Identification: Easily identified by its bright yellow belly and yellowish green upper-parts. Sexes alike. Young birds are darker above.
Distribution: Senegal to East Africa southwards to northern South West Africa, Ngamiland, Rhodesia, Mozambique, the low country of northern and eastern Transvaal and St. Lucia, Zululand.
Habits: A common bird which differs little in its habits from the preceding species.

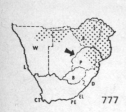

777

Food: Small insects, berries and soft fruit.
Breeding: The nest is typical and similar to that of the preceding species. Eggs 2—3, occasionally only 1, pure white, bluish white or blue, the shell without gloss. Average (7) 16,1 × 11,9 (15,6—16,7 × 11,7—12). Both sexes incubate.

LOCAL RACES:
(a) Z.s. anderssoni Shelley, 1892: *Damaraland.* Clearest and lightest yellow; size above.

778 See under **775** *(f).*

Family PLOCEIDAE

The Weavers comprise a large number of hard-billed birds, of which most species feed upon grain, with much variation between the extremes of both as regards structural appearance, colours and habits. They have been divided up into subfamilies which are dealt with here in the following order:

Subfamily **Bubalornithinae,** the Buffalo Weavers, large blackish birds which construct large nests of thorn sticks with two or more separate chambers and lay Sparrow-like eggs.

Subfamily **Plocepasserinae,** the Sparrow-Weavers, which construct nests of straw with two entrances, one of which is closed when eggs are laid; the eggs are white or pink, prettily marked. The Social Weaver builds one huge communal nest and lays Sparrowy eggs.

Subfamily **Passerinae,** the Sparrows, which either construct a large cosy nest in trees or use crevices or holes in trees, rocks or houses, the eggs more or less white and spotted or clouded.

Subfamily **Sporopipinae,** Scaly-feathered Weaver-Finches, construct a Waxbill-like nest but lay Sparrow-like eggs.

Subfamily **Ploceinae,** the true Weavers, which build woven nests either suspended or fastened to reeds. Eggs very variable.

Subfamily **Estrildinae,** the Waxbills, some of which make their own nests while others appear to be developing parasitic habits and always use old nests of other birds; all lay pure white eggs.

Subfamily **Viduinae,** the parasitic Whydahs, closely related to the Waxbills in whose nests they deposit their eggs, the young all being reared in harmony, unlike the cuckoos.

The family is widely dispersed over the Old World, most of the species being resident; though some in Europe and Asia are more or less migratory.

Subfamily BUBALORNITHINAE

779 Buffalo Weaver   Buffelwewer

Bubalornis albirostris (Vieillot), 1817: *Africa = Senegambia.*

Native Name: Pin (Ch).

PLATE 65, ♂ AND ♀ (OPP. P. 545).
Length about 24 cm (wing ♂ 121—124—126, ♀ 113—115—118; tail 96—113; tarsus 27—32; culmen 22—25, 15 specimens, 7 ♂, 8 ♀). Iris hazel; bill red; legs salmon colour.

Identification: Sexes as illustrated. Young birds resemble the female, but the breast-feathers are more broadly edged with white.

Distribution: From Senegal to Somalia, southwards to Damaraland, Botswana, western to eastern Transvaal and Swaziland. In the Kruger Park birds arrive in October, only odd birds are present in the winter.

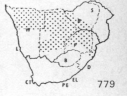

779

Habits: A fairly common species which is peculiar to the dry tropical savannas and is always found near large trees such as Baobabs or palms, in which it nests and roosts in small communities. It is therefore localized throughout the large area it covers. The birds roost in the nests, and if scattered during the day in search of food still foregather in the evenings.

Food: Insects, such as termites and locusts; also seeds and berries picked up on the ground. Chicks are fed on insects.

Voice: A variety of chattering, croaking and high-pitched noises.

Breeding: Nests are masses of thorny twigs, built by the males, placed in the branches of big trees, or on windmills, with chambers lined with grass-seeds and green leaves on the floor; each mass contains two or more entrances facing in different directions. Adult and immature males work in parties to construct these nests while the lining is added by the females. Breed from November to February in Transvaal; September to March in Rhodesia and South West Africa. Eggs number 3 or 4, dull white or greenish-tinged, more or less thickly and evenly speckled and mottled with grey and some olive. Average (19) 27,4 × 19,9 (26,1—29,4 × 18,9—20,8). Incubation starts with the first egg—11 days. Nestling period 20—23 days.

LOCAL RACE:
B.a. niger A. Smith, 1836: *Kurrichane.* From our area to Angola and eastern Zambia.

Subfamily PLOCEPASSERINAE

780   White-browed Sparrow-weaver   Koringvoël

> *Plocepasser mahali*   A. Smith, 1836: *Between Orange River and the Tropic.*

PLATE 65 (OPP. P. 545).
Length 17—19 cm (wing ♂ 95—103—109, ♀ 97—101—102; tail 57—66; tarsus 22—25; culmen 16—19. 24 specimens, 15 ♂, 9 ♀). Iris reddish brown; bill grey to blackish; legs pale brown. Weight 41—52 g.

Identification: The white eyebrow and rump and light brown back prevent confusion with the next species. Sexes alike. Young birds resemble adults but have paler bills.

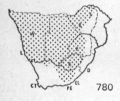

780

Distribution: From Middelburg, Cape, northwards through the Orange Free State as far east as Bloemfontein, the Transvaal and Rhodesia on the east and from the Orange River on the west to Angola. Beyond our limits to Kenya and Ethiopia.

Habits: A common and conspicuous species of the dry western acacia veld which occurs round large acacia trees, standing more or less isolated, in pairs or small parties. In the large trees a single pair of birds may construct as many as a dozen nests, in which they sleep separately. The nests used for roosting have two entrances facing downwards, the sleeping birds perching on a ridge across the centre. Seems to be entirely independent of water. Known to live for 10 years.

Food: Insects; also seeds.

Voice: Call-note a harsh "chick, chick". Also has a song of loud challenging liquid notes, uttered especially at dawn, of considerable volume and attraction.

Breeding: The nest is constructed of yellow or whitish grass-stems and is a round untidy structure looking like a bundle of straw thrown into a tree with the stalks projecting outwards at all angles. These stalks project forward to form an entrance tube which is very difficult to enter. Nests used for breeding are lined with feathery grass-tops and feathers. Nests are usually about 2—4 metres up and on the outside of a tree at the end of a branch. Breeds from September to January. Eggs 2 or 3, white to pink; sometimes merely speckled, with a ring at the thicker end, but more often beautifully marked with darker pink to red, brown or grey, the markings with a penumbra. The eggs are often elongate. Average (68) 24,3 × 16,0 (22,5—26,2 × 14,7—17,2).

LOCAL RACES:
(a) P.m. mahali A. Smith, 1836: *Between Orange River and the Tropic.* Illustrated; size above. Cape Province to Orange Free State.

(b) P.m. pectoralis (Peters), 1868: *Inhambane* in error = *Tete*. Wing ♂ 100—101 (2), ♀ 93. Eggs smaller than *(a)*. Average (9) 23,1 × 15,2 (22—24 × 14,9—15,5). Northern Botswana and the remainder of Rhodesia to Kenya; in Mozambique as far south as the Zambesi, not retaken at the type-locality.
(c) P.m. stentor Clancey, 1957: *Kenhardt*. Botswana, northern Cape and South West Africa. A paler rustier brown than *(a)*.

781 = 780 *(b)*

782 See page xxxii

783 Social Weaver   Familievoël

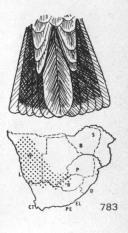

783

Philetairus socius (Latham), 1790: *Great Namaqualand.*

PLATE 65 (OPP. P. 545).
Length about 14 cm (wing ♂ 74—76—78, ♀ 71—73—74; tail 41—48; tarsus 18—21; culmen 15—17. 23 specimens, 10 ♂, 13 ♀). Iris dark brown; bill horn; legs light brown.

Identification: Unmistakable. Sexes alike. Young have feathers above edged with greyish brown, mottling on flanks less distinct.
Distribution: The area of the lower Vaal and Orange River valleys, northwards through South West Africa to Etosha Pan.
Habits: A common bird of dry areas, occurring in small flocks in the neighbourhood of their large communal nests, which are among the most remarkable in the world. First straws are laid on a strong branch of a large isolated kokerboom, camel-thorn or other large tree and these are gradually built up into a roof; under this a great number of nest-chambers are made with finer straw, the sharp ends of the stiff stalks being aligned along the entrance tunnel pointing slightly inwards, so that it is painful to try and insert a hand up the tunnel. At the top is a rounded nest-chamber. A pair or more sleeps in each chamber throughout the year and the nest is kept in repair in all seasons; one has been in use for 100 years. During the day the birds stream off into the veld uttering a clucking note, never going very far from the nest; after a short spell of feeding or gathering nesting material they all trail back again. They are very pugnacious, often falling from the nest locked in combat and fighting on the ground until exhausted. Rosy-faced Lovebirds, Pygmy Falcons, Scaly-feathered Finches and Red-headed Finches all take up their residence in empty compartments of these nests or eject the rightful owners, but not from the whole nest, all the species living at the same time under one roof. Giant Eagle Owls nest on top and Cape Cobras often raid the nests. When roosting but not breeding, the Social Weavers sleep in any compartment as one bird may be seen trying several different entrance holes before settling down.
Food: Grass-seeds and insects; seems to be quite independent of water, living on the edge of the Namib desert.
Voice: A rather nasal "klok, klok" sometimes as a quick stutter.
Breeding: Nest as above under Habits. Also recorded nesting under overhanging rocks. Breeds from August to February in the west and as late as April in Transvaal, stimulated by rain. Eggs 2—6, according to excellence of the rains, dull white thickly covered with pale olive-grey and slate-grey speckles, fairly evenly dispersed. Average (39) 21,2 × 15,2 (20—22,8 × 14,2—15,9). Up to 4 successive broods in a season. Incubation 13—14 days. Nestling period 21—24 days.

Subfamily PASSERINAE

784   House Sparrow   Huis Mossie

Passer domesticus   (Linnaeus), 1758: *Europe = Sweden.*

PLATE 65, ♂ AND ♀ (OPP. P. 545).
Length about 14—15 cm (wing 76—82,5; tail 54—56; tarsus 19; culmen 12—14). Iris hazel; bill black; legs pale brown. Weight 23 g.

Identification: Somewhat resembles the next species but is smaller and altogether duller, especially above. Female lacks the black line through eye of the next species. Young birds resemble the female.

Distribution: Introduced at Durban and East London whence it spread over the Cape Province, Orange Free State and towns of the southern Transvaal. Now extends into South West Africa (1968), eastern Botswana, and throughout Rhodesia. Also Beira.

Habits: Essentially a bird of towns and settlements, where it becomes tame and confiding, hopping about on pavements or chirping from the roof-tops. Is never found far from buildings.

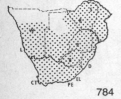
784

Voice: A loud penetrating "chee-ip", "cheep", "chissip", etc. A hard rattling twitter when excited.

Breeding: Either constructs a clumsy domed nest in trees, or more frequently occupies a hole in a tree or building, especially under the eaves or in an old swallow's nest. Breeds from September to March and may rear two or three broods in a season. Eggs 3—5, pale bluish white, more or less thickly blotched, spotted and speckled with dark brown, lilac and greyish brown. Average (14) 20,8 × 15 (19—22,1 × 13,9—15,5). Incubation chiefly by female, 12—14 days; nestling 15 days.

LOCAL RACES:
(a) P.d. domesticus (Linnaeus), 1758: *Europe = Sweden.* Introduced at East London whence it has spread to King William's Town, Fort Beaufort, Kokstad and Port Alfred.
(b) P.d. indicus Jardine and Selby, 1831: *India.* As illustrated; size above. Introduced at Durban, spreading to the Transvaal and Orange Free State.

785   Great Sparrow   Groot Mossie

Passer motitensis   A. Smith, 1836: *Old Latakoo, N. Cape.*

PLATE 65, ♂ AND ♀ (OPP. P. 545).
Length 15—16 cm (wing ♂ 83—84—85, ♀ 79—81—85; tail 56—67; tarsus 18—21; culmen 13—15. 18 specimens, 10 ♂, 8 ♀). Iris dark brown; bill brown; legs pale brown.

Identification: Altogether brighter coloured than the last species and very different in habitat preference. Sexes as illustrated. Young birds resemble adults of their respective sexes but are duller.

Distribution: Angola and South West Africa eastwards to Transvaal and Swaziland, northwards to Somalia and across to West Africa and the Cape Verde Islands.

Habits: A shy and unfamiliar species of the dry acacia savanna veld; it is found in the wilder parts, seldom in settlements and apparently never in towns.

785

Food: Grain and weed seeds.

Voice: A deeper-throated note than the Cape Sparrow.
Breeding: Constructs a large, thick-walled nest from 3—4 metres up in a thorn-tree, often using green wild asparagus leaves, besides other soft grass-tops, grass and feathers. Breeds from December to February. Eggs 5—6 in South West Africa, but usually 4 elsewhere, white marked with slate-grey spots and streaky blotches. Average (50) 20,5 × 15,1 (18,5—22,2 × 14—16,1).

LOCAL RACES:
(a) P.m. motitensis A. Smith, 1836: *Old Latakoo, Northern Cape.* Northern Cape, Botswana and adjacent territories to the east. As above.
(b) P.m. benguellensis Lynes, 1926: *Huxe, Angola.* South West Africa and Angola. Paler than *(a)*.

786 Cape Sparrow   Mossie

Passer melanurus   (Müller), 1776: *Cape of Good Hope.*

Native Names: Undlunkulu, Ungqobe (X); Tsiloane, Serobele (S); Tshiere (Ch).

PLATE 65, ♂ AND ♀ (OPP. P. 545).
Length 14—16 cm (wing ♂ 72—78—85, ♀ 73—76—80; tail 53—64; tarsus 17,5—21; culmen 12—14. 33 specimens, 22 ♂, 11 ♀). Iris brown; bill black; legs brown.

Identification: Males are unmistakable with their heavy pattern of black about the head. Females might be mistaken for the next species but are much greyer above. Young birds resemble the female.
Distribution: Confined to South Africa and South West Africa.
Habits: A very common species in some areas but unaccountably absent from other districts which appear suited to it; in general, likes fairly dry country and the drier suburbs of towns. A friendly and confiding bird that has attached itself to human settlements. Forms fair-sized flocks when not breeding, which are a common sight around farmyards, stock-pens and other spots where grain is scattered about. Roost in special nests throughout the year, and consequently may be seen building at any season.

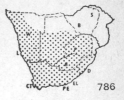

786

Food: Grain, seeds and soft shoots of plants; also insects and their larvae, which form the principal food given to the young.
Voice: Call a "chissip" or "Chirrup". Males have a jerky, chopping song, something like "chip, chollop, tlip, tlop", etc., etc.
Breeding: The nest is a large untidy mass of grass, dry weeds, string and old rags, cosily lined with feathers and other soft materials and with a somewhat elongated side entrance. It is placed in thorn bushes, trees, under the eaves of houses, in creepers, on telegraph poles, or it may use an old weaver-bird's or swallow's nest. Breeds throughout the year but mainly from September and October to March. May raise several broods in a season. Eggs number 3—6, white or greenish, more or less speckled or spotted, or even blotched; and others so heavily clouded and streaked with dark brown and grey-brown as almost to hide the ground colour. Average (100) 20,1 × 14,8 (18,2—23,5 × 13,4—15,7). Incubation period 12—14 days. Nestling period 16—25 days.

LOCAL RACES:
(a) P.m. melanurus (Müller), 1776: *Cape of Good Hope.* As illustrated; size above. Range as above except for *(b)* below.
(b) P.m. damarensis Reichenow, 1902: *Windhoek.* Paler on the hind-neck than *(a)*; South West Africa across to western Transvaal.

787   Southern Grey-headed Sparrow   Gryskop-mossie

Passer diffusus   (A. Smith), 1836: *North of the Orange River.*

PLATE 65 (OPP. P. 545).
Length about 15—16 cm (wing ♂ 79—82—87,5, ♀ 77—80—83; tail 58—65; tarsus 16—19; culmen 11—12,5. 21 specimens, 12 ♂, 9 ♀). Iris brown; bill brown; legs brown.

Identification: Both sexes might be mistaken for a female Cape Sparrow, but the reddish rump and wings should avoid confusion. Sexes alike, female duller. Young bird has mantle streaked.

Distribution: South West Africa, Griqualand West, Eastern Cape, Orange Free State, Lesotho, Natal and Transkei; as far north as Zambia.

Habits: A fairly common and wide-spread species of acacia savannas, usually found in trees of the thornveld, but not infrequently found in towns and villages as well. Is often overlooked as the hen of the Cape Sparrow. Occurs in pairs or small family parties.

 787

Food: Seeds and insects.

Voice: A quiet bird; normal call a chirp.

Breeding: Uses the old nests of Barbets and Woodpeckers, or holes under the eaves of buildings, lining them with some fibres and feathers for warmth. Breeds from October to February. Eggs 3—5, hardly distinguishable from those of the Cape Sparrow, though often darker. Average (24) 19,0 × 14,3 (18,1—20,3 × 13,9—15).

LOCAL RACES:
(a) P.d. diffusus (A. Smith), 1836: *North of Orange River.* As illustrated; size above. South Africa northwards to western Zambia.
(b) P.d. stygiceps Clancey, 1954: *Umzinyati Falls, Natal.* Eastern low lying moist coastal areas. Darker above.

788   Yellow-throated Sparrow   Geelvlek-mossie

Petronia superciliaris   (Blyth), 1845: *South Africa.*

PLATE 65 (OPP. P. 545).
Length 15—16 cm (wing ♂ 89—93—98, ♀ 86—88—91; tail ♂ 55—63, ♀ 52—59; tarsus 18—20; culmen 13,5—14,5. 41 specimens, 19 ♂, 22 ♀). Iris brown; bill horn; legs brown. Weight 27,2 g.

Identification: The yellow spot on the throat is not too obvious, but this is the only sparrow with a broad creamy white eyebrow. In the field appears rather like the Streaky-headed Seedeater, No. 867, but is darker below and has a white bar in the wing. Sexes alike. Young birds have no yellow throat-spot and are browner above. Displays yellow spot in courtship.

Distribution: From the southern end eastern Cape Province northwards to Tanzania on the east and from the Vaal and Orange River northwards to the borders of Zaïre on the west.

Habits: A fairly common but quiet and retiring bird which inhabits acacia savannas and tall trees along rivers and streams, usually near water. Spends

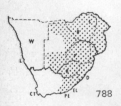 788

much of its time clambering around high in the trees, particularly along dead branches. May descend to the ground where it *walks* quite rapidly. Has the habit of flirting the tail at intervals, particularly when agitated. Usually seen in pairs.

Food: Insects and seeds.

Voice: A single or double sparrow-like, slightly nasal "chick, chick". Also quite a presentable song.

Breeding: Nests in old Woodpecker or Barbet holes, in natural holes or behind loose bark; the bottom of the nest is padded with fibres, feathers and grass. Breeds from October to January. Eggs, normally 3—4, are rather glossy and like darkest Cape Sparrow eggs, very dark brown over a barely discernible buffy ground-colour. Average (28) 18,5 × 14,2 (16,9—20 × 12,8—15,3). Nestling period 18—19 days (Skead). Only one bird, presumably the female, incubates and feeds the young.

Subfamily SPOROPIPINAE

789   Scaly-feathered Finch   Baardmannetjie

Sporopipes squamifrons   (A. Smith), 1836: *South Africa = Graaff-Reinet.*

Native Names: Sansakhane (S); Thluthlithane (Ch).

PLATE 68 (OPP. P. 576).

Length 10—11 cm (wing ♂ 57—57,5—58,5, ♀ 52—56—58; tail 34—40; tarsus 14—16; culmen 9—10. 24 specimens, 9 ♂, 15 ♀). Iris light brown; bill pink; legs flesh.

Identification: Unmistakable; sexes alike. Young birds have horn-coloured beaks, no scaling on foreheads and wing-feathers brownish not black, edged with dull white.

Distribution: From Beaufort West and Graaff-Reinet northwards through western Orange Free State, Transvaal and Rhodesia, South West Africa and southern Angola.

Habits: A common species, found in small parties frequenting the vicinity of tangled thorn bushes. Is very tame and confiding, coming into camps, gardens, fowl-runs and kraals, even in cities such as Bulawayo. Spends a lot of time fighting with other birds of its kind. Seems quite independent of water.

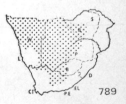

789

Food: Grass-seeds.

Voice: When disturbed flies off uttering a chattering note; also has a quaint guttural song, uttered with the feathers of the head standing out while the bird bobs up and down.

Breeding: Nests more or less colonially, several pairs nesting in close proximity in nearby trees or bushes. The nest is an untidy, round, sparrow-like structure of white grass-stems, with a pointed entrance, placed in the midst of thorny bushes and also under the eaves of houses. Breeds throughout the year, but mainly from September to December. Eggs number 3—5 or even 6, pale greenish, thickly clouded with markings of greyish brown. Average (100) 15,8 × 11,5 (13,9—17,5 × 10,3—12,7).

PLATE 66

790. *(a). Symplectes bicolor bicolor.* Forest Weaver. Bosmusikant.

790 *(d). Symplectes bicolor stictifrons.* Forest Weaver. Bosmusikant.

791. *Hyphanturgus ocularis.* Spectacled Weaver. Brilwewer. ♂ and ♀.

791X. *Hyphanturgus olivaceiceps.* Olive-headed Weaver. Olyfkop-wewer.

792. *Ploceus intermedius cabanisii.* Lesser Masked Weaver. Klein Swartkeel-geelvink. ♂ and ♀.

793 *(a). Anaplectes rubriceps rubriceps.* Red-headed Weaver. Rooikop-wewer. ♂ and ♀.

797 *(a). Ploceus cucullatus spilonotus.* Spotted-backed Weaver. Bontrug-wewer. ♂ and ♀.

797 *(b). Ploceus cucullatus nigriceps.* Spotted-backed Weaver. Bontrug-wewer. ♂ and ♀.

799 *(b). Ploceus capensis olivaceus.* Cape Weaver. Kaapse Wewer. ♂ and ♀.

800 *(a). Ploceus subaureus subaureus.* Yellow Weaver. Geel Wewer. ♂ and ♀.

801. *Ploceus xanthops.* Golden Weaver. Groot Goudwewer. ♂ and ♀.

802 *(a). Ploceus xanthopterus xanthopterus.* Brown-throated Golden Weaver. Bruinkeel-goudwewer. ♂ and ♀.

803 *(b). Ploceus velatus inustus.* Masked Weaver. Swartkeel-geelvink. ♂ and ♀.

790
D A

791 X
KN

791
♂ ♀

803 B
♂ ♀

792
♂ ♀

797 A
♀ ♂
♂ B

799 B
♂ ♀

800 A
♀ ♂

802 A
♂
♀

793
♂
♀

801
♂
♀

IGHTON
'36

♀
818

♂ Br

818 ♂ N-Br

♂ N-Br

♂ Br

816 ♀

♂ Br

815

810 D
♂ N-Br

810 A
♀

813 ♀

♂ Br

814 ♀

♂
Br

♂ Br

808 A

809

♂ Br

812

♂ Br

♀

♂ Imm

LIGHTON
'36

PLATE 67

808. *(a). Euplectes orix orix.* Red Bishop. Rooi Kaffervink. ♂ Br. and ♀.

809. *Euplectes hordeaceus hordeaceus.* Fire-crowned Bishop.
Vuurkop-rooivink. ♂ Br. adult and immature.

810 *(a). Euplectes capensis capensis.* Cape Widow. Kaapse Kaffervink.
♂ Br. and ♀.

810 *(d). Euplectes capensis crassirostris.* Cape Widow. Kaapse Kaffervink.
♂ Br. and N-Br.

812. *Euplectes afer taha.* Golden Bishop. Goudgeel-kaffervink. ♂ Br. and ♀.

813. *Euplectes ardens ardens.* Red-collared Widow.
Rooikeel-kaffervink. ♂ Br. and ♀.

814. *Euplectes albonotatus albonotatus.* White-winged Widow.
Witvlerk-kaffervink. ♂ Br. and ♀.

815. *Euplectes macrourus macrourus.* Yellow-backed Widow.
Geelrug-kaffervink. ♂ Br. and N-Br.

816. *Euplectes axillaris axillaris.* Red-shouldered Widow.
Kortstert-flap. ♂ Br. and ♀.

818. *Euplectes progne progne.* Long-tailed Widow. Flap.
♂ Br. and N-Br., ♀.

Subfamily PLOCEINAE

790 Forest Weaver

Bosmusikant

Symplectes bicolor (Vieillot), 1819: *Senegal = South Africa.*

Native Names: Ingilikingci (X); i-Tolongo, i-Qubushu (Z).

PLATE 66, RACES *(a)* AND *(d)* (OPP. P. 560).
Length about 18 cm (wing ♂ 86—89—92, ♀ 80—83—84; tail 57—60; tarsus 21—33; culmen 20—21. 11 specimens, 7 ♂, 4 ♀). Iris dark brown; bill brown, the edges whitish; legs flesh.

Identification: As illustrated. Sexes alike. Young birds have paler, more speckled throats. No seasonal change of plumage in adults.

Distribution: The coastal strip from eastern Cape Province eastwards to Natal, thence to eastern Transvaal, Mozambique, eastern Rhodesia and northwards over the wooded parts of tropical Africa from East to West Africa.

Food: Apparently insects only.

790

Voice: Call a "tseet, tseet" or "spink, spink". Alarm call a series of "tseets" run rapidly together. Song of southern birds sounds like the squeaking of a rusty hinge; more northerly birds have a more distinct five-note song rendered as "don't *please* do that-squeeze" in a creaking tone.

Habits: A common species occurring in pairs in forest, wooded kloofs, thick coastal bush or relict forest-patches. Spends most of its time quietly creeping about the branches of trees examining the bark for insects and hanging in all sorts of strange attitudes. Is rather quiet and easily overlooked unless its curious call is heard.

Breeding: The nest is a retort-shaped structure with a long entrance tunnel pointing downwards, rather like the nest of the next species but constructed of coarser material, the brownish vines of an epiphytic creeper, the ends of the stalks projecting in all directions. The male builds the nest; it is lined with *Usnea*. Several nests may be built spread over quite a large area but only one is used for breeding and almost exactly the same site, but not the same nest, is used year after year, the old nest often hanging next to the new one. Eggs 3—4, pinky white in colour with numerous spots of reddish to olive-brown and some slate-blue. Average (100) 22,8 × 15,3 (20,9—24,6 × 14—16,6); one 25,4 × 15,8). Breeds from September to December, rarely as late as February.

LOCAL RACES:
(a) S.b. bicolor (Vieillot), 1819: *Senegal = South Africa.* As illustrated; size above. Eastern Cape Province to Natal. No spots on forehead, dark spot in centre of chest.
(b) S.b. lebomboensis (Roberts), 1936: *Ingwavuma, Zululand.* Dark above as in *(a),* but forehead spotted. Forests of the Lebombo Mountains.
(c) S.b. sclateri (Roberts), 1931: *Mkusi River, Zululand.* More olive-tinged above, forehead spotted. Low country of north-eastern Zululand.
(d) S.b. stictifrons Fischer and Reichenow, 1885: *Lindi, Tanganyika.* More rufous ashy above, forehead spotted, size smaller. Wing ♂ 80—84,5—90, ♀ 80—86; tail 53—60; culmen 19—19,5. 12 specimens, 10 ♂, 2 ♀. Illustrated.

791 Spectacled Weaver   Brilwewer

Hyphanturgus ocularis (A. Smith), 1828: *South-east Coast of South Africa.*

Native Names: Ikreza (X); i-Gelekel (Z); Phorokhosa (Ch); i-Jekete (D).

PLATE 66, ♂ AND ♀ (OPP. P. 560).
Length 15—16 cm (wing ♂ 73—76,5—79, ♀ 70—73—76; tail 58—67; tarsus 23—26; culmen 18—22. 27 specimens, 10 ♂, 17 ♀). Iris brown; bill black; legs brown.

Identification: The black line through eye in both sexes and the black bib of male are distinctive. Sexes as illustrated. Young birds resemble the female, bill pale horn.

Distribution: Eastern Cape Province to Natal and northwards through eastern Transvaal and Rhodesia, Mozambique to Ethiopia and across to Cameroon.

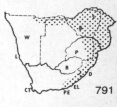

Habits: A common species of thick matted bush along streams and rivers but also well away from water; in general, occurs in lower bush than the previous species but the two may occur together. Is not a gregarious species and is usually seen alone or in pairs, perhaps with young. Spends most of its time in trees and may often be seen perched on the top of a bush calling to its mate.

791

Food: Almost entirely insects, including caterpillars, spiders and millipedes; seeds rarely.

Voice: A quiet species. Individuals keep in contact by a pretty, tripping, descending "tee-tee-tee-tee-tee-tee". Alarm note a harsh staccato "chit" or running series of "chits". Also a twanging noise like a watch-spring unwinding, but no song or prolonged swizzling.

Breeding: Both sexes construct a retort-shaped nest of neatly woven strips of sanseviera or other fibre plants, thin-walled but strong with a long protruding entrance, usually 30—60 cm long but rarely as much as 3 metres. Nests of pure horse-hair have been found. The nest is usually just out of reach up to about 6 metres from the ground, suspended from the ends of trailing thorny creepers at the edge of a ditch or bordering a river or stream. In the eastern Cape Province also nests on bushes miles from any water. Breeds from October to January or as late as March in Rhodesia. Eggs 2—3, are usually greenish white, sometimes pinky white with a variable quantity of speckles, spots and streaks of greyish olive. Average (100) 22,1 × 14,8 (20—24 × 13,4—16; one 25,3 × 15,2). Incubation by both sexes, 13½ days; nestling period 18—19 days. Both sexes feed the young.

LOCAL RACES:
(a) H.o. ocularis (A. Smith), 1828: *South-east Coast of South Africa.* As illustrated; size above. Eastern Cape Province to southern Mozambique.
(b) H.o. suahelicus (Neumann), 1905; *Lewa, Usambara, Tanganyika.* Bill shorter, culmen 19—20 and cheeks heavily washed with golden brown. Mashonaland and the lower Zambesi Valley northwards to Kenya.
(c) H.o. tenuirostris Traylor, 1964: *Sepopa, Ngamiland.* Confined to the Okavango Swamps. Bill noticeably more slender than any other form.
(d) H.o. crocatus (Hartlaub), 1881: *Victoria Nile.* Cameroon to Ethiopia south to Angola. Recorded within our area on the Cunene River. More golden yellow above and heavier bill than *(c)*.

791X   Olive-headed Weaver   Olyfkop-wewer

Hyphanturgus olivaceiceps Reichenow, 1899: *Songea, S.W. Tan-ganyika.*

PLATE 66 (OPP. P. 560).
Length 16 cm (wing ♂ 79—82,2—83,5, ♀ 76,5—77,6—78,5; tail ♂ 41,5—42,9—45. ♀ 39,5—41,2—42; bill ♂ 14—14,8—16, ♀ 14—14,6—15,5. 19 specimens, 11 ♂, 8 ♀). Iris ruby red; bill black; legs slightly blued, flesh-brown.

Identification: The forehead and crown golden yellow contrast with moss green upper parts, sides of face, chin and throat. Chestnut-tinged neck and chest. No eclipse plumage. Female lacks golden crown.
Distribution: Tanzania, Malawi and Mozambique. Recently found in numbers in Inhambane, district Sul do Save.
Habits: A canopy feeder with mixed bird parties in winter in Brachystegia forest. Feeds mainly in leaf clusters and especially in tufts of *Usnea*.
Voice: Distinctive call-notes and a short song.
Food: Small insects.

LOCAL RACE:
H.o. vicarius (Clancey and Lawson), 1966. 8 *miles west of Panda, Inhambane*. Southern range of the species. Smaller than nominate race; yellow forms a line up the back in male.

792   Lesser Masked Weaver   Klein Swartkeel-geelvink

Ploceus intermedius Rüppell, 1845: *Shoá, Abyssinia.*

PLATE 66, ♂ AND ♀ (OPP. P. 560).
Length about 15 cm (wing ♂ 72—74—75, ♀ 67—69,5—73; tail 46—56; tarsus 18—22; culmen 14—17. 29 specimens, 14 ♂, 15 ♀). Iris ♂ yellowish white, ♀ brown; bill ♂ black, ♀ horn; legs bluish. Weight 21,2—23 g.

Identification: Likely to be confused with the Masked Weaver, No. 803, but note that in male the black on crown goes *back* behind eye, not forward across forehead; eye is yellowish white, not red; and legs are bluish; the black of throat is rounded below, not pointed. Males in non-breeding dress resemble the female. Young birds are whitish below with yellow on chest, otherwise like females.
Distribution: From Ethiopia southwards to Natal, Transvaal, Botswana and Damaraland. Common in southern Mozambique.

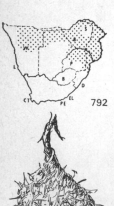

792

Habits: A common but localized species usually found along rivers and streams, frequenting the trees in savanna country. When not breeding forms small flocks of half a dozen birds or so and does not join big mixed flocks of weavers.
Food: Insects, particularly caterpillars; the flowers of aloes, pollen from which often gives the birds orange faces, and a few seeds.
Voice: Voice not as harsh or loud as the Masked Weaver, but while building nests a large colony makes a deafening noise.
Breeding: Weaves a thin-walled but strong, kidney-shaped nest from strips of reed or palm leaves; it is distinguishable from the Masked Weaver's nest by having a short, narrow entrance tunnel about 25 cm long and by short stiff, 25 cm lengths of building material which stick out at all angles. Nests are

suspended from trees, often over water but also well away from it at heights varying from a metre or so up to the top of high trees, 15—18 metres up. They are very often *inside* the tree. Breeds from October to March. Eggs 2 or more, usually 3, are pure immaculate white. Average (29) 21,7 × 14,7 (20,2—23,1 × 13,9—15,5). Both sexes feed the young.

LOCAL RACE:
P.i. cabanisii (Peters), 1868: *Inhambane.* As illustrated; size above. Southern Africa to southern Zaïre and Tanzania.

793 Red-headed Weaver   Rooikop-wewer

Anaplectes rubriceps (Sundevall), 1851: *Upper Caffraria = Mohapoani Mountains, W. Transvaal.*

PLATE 66 (OPP. P. 560). ♂ AND ♀.
Length 15 cm (wing ♂ 80—82—85, ♀ 76—77,5—79; tail 48—54; tarsus 18—20; culmen 16—18,5. 42 specimens, 23 ♂, 9 ♀). Iris red-brown; bill orange or yellowish; legs brown.

Identification: In summer plumage red *mantle* distinguishes male from Queleas. Males in non-breeding dress resemble the female; orange-yellow beak conspicuous. Young birds are similar to the female, but young males have some orange on the crown. Note yellowish edges to wing-feathers.

Distribution: From Botswana, eastern and northern Transvaal, Swaziland and southern Mozambique northward to Ethiopia and across to Ghana.

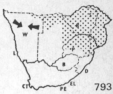

Habits: A not uncommon but localized species of the dry savannas, though always found near water. Said to be migratory. Also prefers areas in which large trees occur, in which it spends most of its time, creeping quietly about the branches in search of its food. Frequently joins "bird parties" while so occupied.

793

Food: Mainly insects such as spiders; also seeds.

Voice: Both sexes utter a high-pitched continuous squeaky chatter while at the nest.

Breeding: Constructs a remarkably neat and strong nest of woven twigs and a little grass, with broad leaves intertwined in the top to form a rainproof covering. The building is done by the male, although the female may work from the inside shaping the structure. Nests are usually slung at the ends of drooping branches high up in tall trees but may also be lower down on telegraph wires, and are often solitary or in small colonies; only occasionally are colonies of as many as 40 nests met with. The nest is retort-shaped with a short entrance spout. Polygamous. Breeds from October to December. Eggs, normally 3, are greenish blue, paler at the thin end and sometimes with cloudy zones of darker blue. Average (33) 20,6 × 14,5 (18,8—21,9 × 13,5—15).

LOCAL RACE:
A.r. rubriceps (Sundevall), 1850: *Upper Caffraria = Mohapoani Mountains, Western Transvaal.* Size above. Southern Africa to south-eastern Zaïre.

794 An unsatisfactory race of **793** with more or less black about face.

795 See page xxxii

796 Chestnut Weaver   Bruin Wewer

Ploceus rubiginosus   Rüppell, 1840: *Temben Province, Abyssinia.*
PLATE 65 (OPP. P. 545).
Length about 16 cm (wing ♂ 82—84—89, ♀ 72—79—83; tail 48—65; tarsus 21—23; culmen 18—21. 14 specimens, 8 ♂, 6 ♀). Iris reddish brown; bill bluish grey; legs pale grey.

Identification: The bird illustrated is a male. The female is buffy brown with a pale throat and belly; males in non-breeding dress probably resemble the female but are streaked with black on the mantle.
Distribution: From Ethiopia and East Africa to Angola and northern South West Africa.
Habits: Very little recorded in our area. Occurs in flocks; and many more females have been collected than males, so is probably polygamous. The males flock and desert the breeding colony, leaving the females feeding the young.

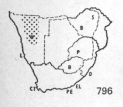

796

Breeding: Nests colonially. Builds retort-shaped nests thickly lined by female with grassheads and lays greenish blue eggs. Clutch 3—4. Average (20) 22,8 × 15,7 (21,5—24,5 × 14,5—16,8).

LOCAL RACE:
P.r. trothae Reichenow, 1905: *Windhoek.* As illustrated above. Angola and South West Africa.

797 Spotted-backed Weaver   Bontrug-wewer

Ploceus cucullatus   (Müller), 1776: *Senegal.*

Native Names: i-Hlokohloko (Z); Ihobohobo (X); i-Ngozha (D).

PLATE 66, RACE *(a)* ♂ AND ♀, *(b)* ♂ (OPP. P. 560).
Length about 17 cm (wing ♂ 85—89—92, ♀ 79—81—83; tail ♂ 53—62, ♀ 48—53; tarsus 19—23; culmen 18,5—22. 38 specimens, 29 ♂, 9 ♀). Iris red; bill black; legs flesh.

Identification: Both races may be distinguished by the heavily spotted back in the male. Males of the southern form are easily distinguished from the Masked Weavers by this and also by the fact that the forehead is *yellow,* not black. Males in non-breeding dress resemble the female.

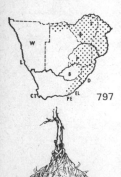

797

Distribution: Africa south of the Sahara, but not South West Africa or the western Cape Province.
Habits: A common species which frequents trees along rivers and streams in flocks throughout the year.
Food: Seeds, grain and insects.
Voice: A husky swizzling, not as prolonged or as harsh as the Cape Weaver. Alarm note "zit".
Breeding: Nests are suspended from the drooping branches of thorn-trees or tall exotics such as gums; occasionally from reeds. The leaves are stripped off the twigs holding the nests. The nests, built by the male, are woven of coarse strips of reed or grass blades as an outer shell, thickly lined with finer grass and soft flowery grass-tops. A short spout may, or may not be present. Males hang below the nest while building and sway from side to side, chattering and

fanning their wings exactly as in the Cape Weaver. Eggs, nearly always 3, are variable, usually greenish blue, plain or faintly speckled or finely spotted with brown or reddish. Average (100), race *(a)* 23,4 × 15,4 (21,5—26,4 × 14,1—16,7; one 21 × 14). Incubation by female only; female only, apparently, feeds the young.

LOCAL RACES:
(a) P.c. spilonotus Vigors, 1831: *Algoa Bay.* Illustrated as No. 797. Size above. Eastern Cape Province to Natal, southern Mozambique and Transvaal. Flocks in southern Mozambique may contain birds completely intermediate between this and the next race.
(b) P.c. nigriceps (Layard), 1867: *Kuruman.* Illustrated. Wing ♂ 87—90 (5), ♀ 78—83 (5). Eggs, average (26) 23,0 × 15,0 (21—25,8 × 12,8—16). From Botswana, Rhodesia and northern Mozambique to Tanzania. Not found recently at Type-locality, which is now considered to be *Bulawayo.*

798 = 797 (b)

799 Cape Weaver   Kaapse Wewer

Ploceus capensis (Linnaeus), 1766: *Cape of Good Hope.*

Native Names: Ihobohobo (X); Talane (S).

PLATE 66, ♂ AND ♀ (OPP. P. 560).
Length 18 cm (wing ♂ 89—93, ♀ 84—85; tail 53—61; tarsus 21—24; culmen 21—24). Iris ♂ cream, ♀ brown; bill black; legs flesh colour. Weight 38 g.

Identification: The only weaver in its area without black on the face, except for the Yellow Weaver, No. 800, which is bright canary-yellow, and Golden, No. 801, which has a yellow (not washed with chestnut) forehead. No. 802 is much smaller. Most males plain in winter. Female as illustrated.

Distribution: Cape Province, Natal, Orange Free State and the more temperate parts of Transvaal to Zoutpansberg. Inhabits almost any type of country where there are trees or bushes, usually near water.

Habits: Forms flocks in winter, often with Starlings (Pied, European and Wattled).

Food: Flowers and other soft parts of plants; also insects and seeds. Foreheads often become discoloured with pollen.

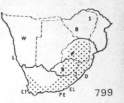

799

Voice: Alarm note an urgent "chuk, chuk". Male utters "a-zwit, a-zwit" rapidly repeated and a harsh guttural, chattering and swizzling song with some clear notes.

Breeding: Nests colonially, occasionally singly, July to October in Cape, midsummer in east and north. Polygamous. Large kidney-shaped nest is usually hung from trees over water, but sometimes far from water near farmhouses, hotels, etc. May be quite low or at the top of high trees. Reeds may be used, often in association with other Weavers and Bishop-birds. Male builds nest; female, after accepting, adds lining. Eggs 2—5, immaculate greenish blue; colour often unevenly distributed over egg, usually darker at thick end. Average (100) 24,8 × 16,5 (22,5—27 × 15,6—17,6). Incubation 13½ days; fledgling period 17 days.

LOCAL RACES:
(a) P.c. capensis (Linnaeus), 1766. *Cape of Good Hope.* Western and southern Cape Province. Head little, or not, washed with chestnut.
(b) P.c. olivaceus (Hahn), 1822. *Windvogelberg, Eastern Cape Province.* From Algoa Bay eastwards over the rest of the range. Yellow of head and throat washed with chestnut, as illustrated.

800 Yellow Weaver   Geel Wewer

Ploceus subaureus   A. Smith, 1839: *Algoa Bay.*

Native Name: Inthlethlekwane (X).

PLATE 66, ♂ (OPP. P. 560).
Length 18 cm (wing ♂ 81—83—86, ♀ 76—80; tail 53—61; tarsus 21—22,5; culmen 17,5—19,5. 13 specimens, 9 ♂, 4 ♀). Iris red, female and non-breeding male, brown; bill black; legs flesh.

Identification: The male is more canary-yellow than illustrated. In breeding dress may be distinguished from the Cape Weaver by its thick black beak, *red* eye and more yellow colour. Sexes as illustrated. Young bird resembles the female but has the mantle streaked.

Distribution: From Uitenhage eastwards to Natal and northwards to Kenya. In South Africa only found within about 50 km of the coast.

Habits: A locally common species of dams, reed-beds on rivers and lagoons along the coast and littoral.

Food: Seeds, small berries and insects.

Voice: Call a rather grating "tzik". Also a quiet, rolling swizzling.

800

Breeding: The nests are rounded structures suspended between upright reeds, sometimes from a reed on one side only, from palm fronds or from bushes standing in water. Palm leaves are stripped for a metre or so above the nest. The nests are made externally of coarse strips of reed blades and lined internally with softer grass-tops, the entrance below with no projecting tube. Breeds from September to December. Eggs 3, variable, white or pale blue; either plain or more usually sparingly speckled, mainly at the thick end, with brown, black or violet. Average (70) 23,2 × 15,2 (21—25,3 × 14,1—16,4).

LOCAL RACES:
(a) P.s. subaureus A. Smith, 1839: *Algoa Bay.* Yellower than illustrated. Size above. Eastern Cape to Natal. Eggs as above.
(b) P.s. tongensis (Roberts), 1931: *Sordwana Bay, Zululand.* Brighter yellow than *(a)*; rather smaller. Wing ♂ 79—80; tail 52; tarsus 21,5; culmen 17,5. Zululand and southern Mozambique.
(c) P.s. aureoflavus A. Smith, 1839: *West Africa = Zanzibar Island.* Much clearer and brighter yellow, size smaller. Wing ♂ 76—79, ♀ 70—71; tail 44—51; tarsus 18—20; culmen 17—19. Zanzibar southwards to the lower Zambesi Valley.

801 Golden Weaver   Groot Goudwewer

Ploceus xanthops   (Hartlaub), 1862: *Angola.*

Native Name: i-Hlokanhloka (G).

PLATE 66, ♂ AND ♀ (OPP. P. 560).
Length about 18 cm (wing ♂ 85—89,5—94, ♀ 83—83,5—85; tail ♂ 67—70, ♀ 62—66; tarsus 22—26; culmen 19—21,5. 19 specimens, 13 ♂, 6 ♀). Iris deep yellow; bill, breeding dress black, winter brown; legs brownish.

Identification: Males are distinguishable from the eastern races of the Yellow Weaver, No. 800, by having greenish, not yellow backs; from the eastern Cape Weaver, No. 799, by having no chestnut on forehead and chin. Females are much yellower below than the females of either of those two species. Males in non-breeding dress are fuller yellow, particularly on the forehead. Young birds are greener·above than the female and have the mantle streaked.

Distribution: Uganda to Kenya and southwards to Angola, Ngamiland, Zambia and Rhodesia, eastern Transvaal and to near Durban in Natal. Common in Ngamiland.

Habits: Not very common in our area; frequents the tangled bush and weeds on the borders of marshes and streams and is normally gregarious in habits except when nesting (see below).

Food: Insects, fruit and seeds.

Voice: A short harsh chirp and a prolonged swizzling "chee".

Breeding: Nests are often solitary, though a few may be found scattered about within a certain radius, not, however, in colonies like those of many other Weavers. The nest is a large structure of woven broad strips of reed blades, thickly lined with softer grasses and flowery grass-tops, with the entrance under a hood, below, but well to one side. Some of the flowery tops often project from the entrance. It is suspended from 1 to 6 metres above water from reeds, or from trees away from water. Breeds from October to May. Eggs 2 or 3, variable from plain white or pale blue to blue, freckled or spotted or blotched with light reddish brown, burnt umber or violet and charcoal-grey. Average (70) 24,2 × 16,3 (22,7—26,7 × 15,5—17,3).

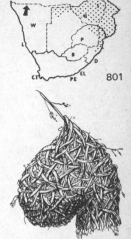

801

802 Brown-throated Golden Weaver
Bruinkeel-goudwewer

Ploceus xanthopterus   (Finsch and Hartlaub), 1870: *Shupanga*.

PLATE 66, ♂ AND ♀ (OPP. P. 560).
Length about 15 cm (wing ♂ 68—72—76, ♀ 62; tail ♂ 44—51, ♀ 42; tarsus 18—22; culmen 16—18. 6 specimens, 5 ♂, 1 ♀). Iris yellowish brown; bill black; legs flesh.

Identification: A small and very short-tailed species, the male easily identified by its brown throat, conspicuous even in flight. Note the very yellow wings and short rounded bill.

Distribution: From the coast of Natal northwards to Malawi and across Ngamiland, but not yet recorded from Rhodesia.

Habits: Very little recorded, a species which would repay study. Occurs in dense riverine growth and seems to be essentially a bird of water localities, frequenting the dense reedbeds of rivers or coastal lagoons.

Breeding: Nests are suspended from the tops of reeds or branches of bushes standing in marshes, are constructed of strips of reed blades and lined with softer grasses and flowery grass-tops, the entrance being below without a projection. Breeds in October and November. Eggs 3, rarely 4, are remarkable for being usually uniform olive-green to chocolate; sometimes evenly speckled all over with pale pinky grey on a buffy ground. Average (28) 21,1 × 14,5 (19,5—23 × 13,8—15,1).

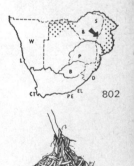

802

LOCAL RACES:
(a) *P.x. xanthopterus* (Finsch and Hartlaub), 1870: *Shupanga*. Upper-parts golden yellow; size above; height of bill at base about 8. Lower Zambesi Valley.
(b) *P.x. castaneigula* (Cabanis), 1884: *Impalera, north-eastern Bechuanaland.* Upper-parts more greenish; size larger. Wing ♂ 76—81—84, ♀ 67—68—69; tail ♂ 55—62, ♀ 50—52; tarsus ♂ 22—24, ♀ 19—21; culmen ♂ 17,5—19,5, ♀ 16,5—17. 12 specimens, 8 ♂, 4 ♀. Upper Zambesi Valley.

569

(c) P.x. marleyi (Roberts), 1929: *St. Lucia.* Upper-parts as in *(a)*, golden yellow; size large. Wing ♂ 78—79; tail 51; tarsus 22—23,5; culmen 19—19,5; height of bill at base about 10. The tip of the beak heavy and rather blunt as compared with the other two forms.

803 Masked Weaver   Swartkeel-geelvink

Ploceus velatus Vieillot, 1819: *Namaqualand.*

Native Name: Ihobohobo.

PLATE 66, ♂ AND ♀ (OPP. P. 560).
Length ♂ 15 cm, ♀ 14 cm (wing ♂ 75—77—79, ♂ 65—69—72; tail 49—53; tarsus 20—22; culmen 15,5—17. 13 specimens, 9 ♂, 4 ♀). Iris brown, red in breeding ♂ and ♀; bill black; legs flesh. Weight 23—35 g.

Identification: For differences between this and the Lesser Masked Weaver, see No. 792. The plain back avoids confusion with the Spotted-backed Weaver, No. 797, in breeding males. Note that both sexes have *red* eyes when breeding. In off-season dress males resemble the female but are slightly larger. Young birds are similar to the female in non-breeding garb.

Distribution: From South Africa northwards to Angola and Malawi. Appears to have arrived only recently in the south-west Cape.

Habits: A locally common species occurring usually in acacia country or open woodland and along streams and rivers of the interior plateaux. Is gregarious at all times but may live and breed in quite small colonies.

803

Food: Seeds, insects, the soft parts of flowers and fruit.

Voice: Normal call a "tick, tick". Also "swizzles", starting with a few preliminary stuttering notes and breaking into a chattering "swizzle".

Breeding: Builds in colonies of perhaps only one male and two females up to a dozen or more birds in the same tree or reed-bed. The nests are suspended from the ends of branches or placed between upright reeds and are built by the males in two forms. One is transparent below and has no entrance tube; this type is not lined and is used for roosting. The second type is better made, is lined by the female and decorated with leaves and grass-tops and has a short entrance tube about 8—12 cm long. Both types are rounded ovals with the entrance below and are made of a shell of woven strips of reed or grass blades. Polygamous, each male having two or three females. Eggs are extraordinarily variable in colour in different clutches, being pure white to pink, pale bluish white to dark greenish blue, immaculate at times but usually speckled, spotted or blotched in various shades of grey and brown, in varying intensity. They number 2 or 3 as a rule. Average (100) of race *(a)* 20,3 × 14,0 (18,5—22,4 × 13—15,8). Incubation by female, which also feeds the young.

LOCAL RACES:
(a) P.v. velatus Vieillot, 1819: *Namaqualand.* Northern Western Cape, southern South West Africa, Botswana, Mozambique north.
(b) P.v. inustus Clancey, 1959: *Lokenburg, Calvinia.* Western and south-western Cape. Paler yellow below and lacks rust-brown wash below the black mask.
(c) P.v. nigrifrons (Cabanis), 1851: *Eastern Cape Province.* Eastern and north-eastern Cape, Orange Free State, Lesotho, Transvaal highveld and southern Natal. Heavily washed rust-brown on crown and below black mask. Larger than other races. Wing ♂ 82—85—89, ♀ 77—78—80,5; tail ♂ 55—63, ♀ 52—56; tarsus 21—24; culmen ♂ 18—20, ♀ 16—18. 25 specimens, 18 ♂, 7 ♀.
(d) P.v. caurinus. Clancey, 1959: *Okahandja, S.W.A.* Dry areas of Damaraland, Ovamboland north to southern Angola. Paler and less rich in colour. The rust-brown on throat almost completely absent.

804 Thick-billed Weaver   Dikbek-wewer

Amblyospiza albifrons (Vigors), 1831: *Algoa Bay*.

PLATE 65, ♂ AND ♀ (OPP. P. 545).
Length about 18 cm (wing ♂ 94—95,5—99, ♀ 83—85—90; tail ♂ 65—71, ♀ 58—65, tarsus 21—24; culmen 23—25. 16 specimens, 9 ♂, 7 ♀). Iris brown; bill ♂ black, ♀ horn, lower mandible paler; legs greenish grey. Weight ♂ 45—61, ♀ 36—45 g.

Identification: The very heavy bill and white patches in the wings of the male are distinctive. Sexes as illustrated. Young birds are similar to the female but have yellowish bills.

Distribution: From the eastern Cape Province to Natal and thence northwards to Angola on the west and southern Ethiopia on the east across to Ghana.

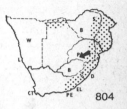

804

Habits: A fairly common species of mixed marshes and bush country; is usually seen in marshes or reed-beds during the breeding season, otherwise frequenting the trees of forest near by. Flight undulating and rather woodpecker-like, with alternating periods of flying and gliding.

Food: The soft inner portions of seeds, the large beak being used to remove any hard coating. Also berries of *Chaetacme aristata*. Eats a few insects and even mice in captivity!

Voice: A chattering while nest-building; normally rather silent.

Breeding: In suitable places where there are reeds and rushes it constructs an unusual type of nest, an oval slung between two upright reeds, composed throughout of woven strips of rushes, with thick walls, and a very narrow entrance at the side a third of the height from the top. It is started as a strip between the reeds, then added to behind like a basket, then upwards and over the top until the front is reached, where it is closed up close around the entrance, the thickness of the walls remaining as built. Both sexes build and a nest takes about 14 days to complete. Males also build nests with larger entrances but these nests never contain eggs and are probably used for roosting. Breeds in small colonies of about half a dozen pairs from November to March. Eggs 3—4, occasionally 5, pinky white to dark pink, more or less spotted with red and brown. Average (100) 23,8 × 16,4 (22,0—26,1 × 15,0—17,4).

LOCAL RACES:
(a) A.a. albifrons (Vigors), 1831: *Algoa Bay*. As illustrated. Size above. Eastern Cape Province to Malawi and the east coast as far north as northern Mozambique.
(b) A.a. maxima Roberts, 1932: *Kasane, Bechuanaland*. Larger than *(a)* and darker. Wing ♂ 108; tail 84; tarsus 24,5; culmen 26. Northern Botswana and Ngamiland.
(c) A.a. woltersi Clancey, 1956: *Manhica P.E.A*. Coastal Mozambique and eastern Rhodesia. Females paler than *(a)*.

805 Red-billed Quelea   Rooibek-vink

Quelea quelea (Linnaeus), 1758: *India = Senegal*.
Native Name: le-Rhakane (S).

PLATE 68, 3 VAR. ♂ AND ♀ (OPP. P. 576).
Length about 13 cm (wing ♂ 65—67—70, ♀ 63—65—67; tail 34—40; tarsus 17—19; culmen 13—14,5. 39 specimens, 27 ♂, 12 ♀). Iris brown; bill red, breeding female waxy yellow; legs pink. Weight 17,5—19,7 g.

Identification: Unmistakable. Males are variable as illustrated; females develop a waxy yellow bill when breeding. Males in winter resemble the females and both have red beaks. Young birds are similar to the female.

571

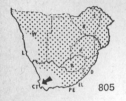

805

Distribution: From Senegal to Ethiopia southwards as far as Damaraland, Botswana, Orange Free State and Natal. Also occurs sporadically as far as Cradock, the Cape Peninsula, the eastern Cape and Pondoland.

Habits: A superabundant species, found in flocks of hundreds, thousands, hundreds of thousands and even millions—truly comparable with locusts, which they have replaced as the main plague of seed-growing farmers throughout Africa. Even during the breeding season occurs in vast flocks which from a distance appear like fast-moving clouds of smoke. Before roosting usually descend in a swarm to drink, often in flight, many being eaten by crocodiles, or drowning due to the numbers involved. May occur in such vast numbers as to break the trees in which they roost. Very fast-flying and subject to considerable local movement but probably not a long-distance migration.

Food: Almost entirely seeds and grain; some insects when young are fed.
Voice: A harsh "chack, chack". A noisy chatter when congregated.
Breeding: Breeds in huge flocks, usually in thorn-trees, every one of which is crowded with nests over several acres. Also breeds in small scattered colonies of perhaps a dozen nests during the period December to April. The nest is a small purse-shaped structure made of strips of grass blades with little lining and with a large entrance at the side, so that it appears as if the eggs will roll out; it is a roughly woven structure and is built by the male. Breeds from December to April. Eggs 3—4, sometimes 5, are pale greenish blue. Average (46) 18,9 × 13,9 (17,8—20 × 13—14,7). Incubation 12 days. Nestling period 13 days. When a large colony has young, numbers of hawks gather, while small carnivora, leguaans and even leopards, hyenas and vultures feed on young that have fallen to the ground.

LOCAL RACE:
Q.q. lathamii (A. Smith), 1836: *Near Kurrichane.* South Africa to Angola, southern Zaïre, Malawi and northern Mozambique.

806   Red-headed Quelea   Rooikop-rooibek-vink

Quelea erythrops (Hartlaub), 1848: *St. Thomé Island, West Africa.*
PLATE 68, ♂ AND ♀ (OPP. P. 576).
Length 13 cm (wing ♂ 63—65—66, ♀ 60—61—62; tail 31—36; tarsus 16—18; culmen 13,5—15. 13 specimens, 9 ♂, 4 ♀). Iris dark brown; bill ♂ black, ♀ horn; legs pinkish brown.

Identification: Likely to be mistaken for the next species but males have *blackish* throats. (See also under No. 793.) Males in non-breeding dress resemble the female but may have a wash of red on forehead and face. Young birds resemble the female with buffy edges to feathers of upper-parts.
Distribution: From Senegal to Ethiopia southwards to Angola on the west and Mozambique on the east and irregularly as far south as Natal and Pondoland.
Habits: A bird of open country such as marshy localities and grassy woodlands. Often forms flocks with other species such as weavers, other queleas and even mannikins.

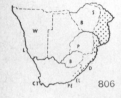

806

Food: Mainly grass seeds and cultivated rice.
Voice: A concerted twittering while building nests; males have a little buzzing song.

Breeding: Not recorded in our area; elsewhere nests colonially, usually in reed beds, both sexes constructing the small spherical nests with side entrances. Eggs nearly always 2, uniform pale greenish blue. Average (53) 18,9 × 13,4 (17,4—20,7 × 12,5—14,3). Incubation by female only.

807   See page xxxii

808   Red Bishop   Rooi Kaffervink

Euplectes orix   (Linnaeus), 1758: *Africa = Angola.*

Native Names: Intakomlilo (X); i-Bomvana (Z); Thaka (S).

PLATE 67, *(a)* BR. ♂ AND ♀ (OPP. P. 561).
Length about 14 cm (wing ♂ 74—76—79, ♀ 65—67—68; tail ♂ 40—45, ♀ 34—40; tarsus 20—23; culmen ♂ 15—16, ♀ 13,5—14. 29 specimens, 20 ♂, 9 ♀). Iris dark brown; bill ♂ black, ♀ pale brown; legs brown. Weight 15—30 g.

Identification: Males have *black* foreheads and thus cannot be mistaken for the next species. Undertail coverts bright red. In winter, males resemble the females but are larger and darker and lack streaking on breast and crown. Young birds resemble the female and young males do not assume the red-and-black plumage until the *second* breeding season.

Distribution: From Cape Town northwards to Somalia and Senegal.

Habits: A very common and well-known social species which occurs in small or very large flocks throughout the year. In grain-growing districts—such as Berg River in the Cape and Mooi River in the Transvaal—is looked upon as a great pest, and considerable expense is incurred annually in endeavouring to keep the flocks away from the ripening grain. When nesting, males fly airily about over the reeds, their plumes puffed out, in slow, bumble-bee-like flight, making a buzzing sound. May occur in isolated communities in patches of suitable reeds, many miles from the next colony. Also appears sporadically and disappears again suddenly, perhaps deserting young and eggs.

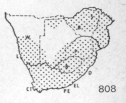
808

Food: Mainly seeds and grain but also insects, especially when feeding young.

Voice: Displaying males utter a "zik, zik, zik" note and a whining, wheezy "tay-zatzayzaay".

Breeding: Favoured nesting sites are patches of fluitjiesriet *(Phragmites)* standing in a marsh, river or donga; has also taken to nesting in standing corn. Polygamous, each male constructing several nests and having about three mates. The males construct an oval shell of a nest with the entrance at the top on one side. It is made of thin strips of reed blade, and at first is so open that the eggs can be seen from outside. As incubation progresses the female adds a lining of soft grass seed-heads. Breeds from August to November in the Cape, males losing their plumage by the end of December; in the eastern Cape and Transvaal from late November to March or even April. Thousands may nest in a single reed-bed. Eggs are pale greenish blue and nearly always number 3, but from 2—5 and even 7 have been recorded, the larger numbers perhaps due to two females laying in the same nest. Average (100) of race *(a)* 20,1 × 14,5 (17,8—21,6 × 13,7—15,7). Incubation by female only 11—14 days. Nestling period 13—16 days. Young fed by female.

LOCAL RACES:
(a) E.o. orix (Linnaeus), 1758: *Africa = Angola.* As illustrated. Size above. Distribution as shown on map.

809   Fire-crowned Bishop   Vuurkop-rooivink

Euplectes hordeaceus   (Linnaeus), 1758: *In Indiis* = *Senegal.*

PLATE 67, BR. ♂ AND ♂ IMM. (OPP. P. 561).
Length 13—15 cm (wing ♂ 71—76,5—79, ♀ 57—68; tail 41—49; tarsus 20—22; culmen 15—17. 10 ♂ specimens). Iris dark brown; bill breeding ♂ black, eclipse ♂ and ♀ brown, pale at base and below; legs brown.

Identification: Has blacker wings in the male than the last species and forehead *red,* except for a very narrow band of black. Undertail coverts brownish. The female has darker wings than the female of the Red Bishop. Otherwise it is similar to the immature male figured, but is smaller and paler above.

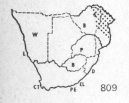

Distribution: From Senegal to Ethiopia southwards to Angola on the west and Rhodesia on the east along the Zambesi and in the Eastern Districts.
Habits: In general habits very similar to the last species, inhabiting reed-beds and bushes growing in long rank grass. These birds while being polygamous are not found in such large flocks as No. 808; usually occurring in pairs or family parties. Habitat similar to No. 812.
809
Food: Grass seeds, corn and rice; a few insects occasionally.
Breeding: Recorded January to March; otherwise like the last, but does not breed in such large colonies; each male has a territory and several females. Eggs, normally 3, pale blue. Average (17) 18,5 × 13,8 (17,4—19,9 × 12,9—14,4) in Zaïre.

LOCAL RACE:
E.h. hordeaceus (Linneaus), 1758: *In Indiis* = *Senegal.* From Senegal to the Sudan and southwards to Angola and Rhodesia. Another race in north-east Africa. As illustrated. Size above.

810   Cape Widow   Kaapse Kaffervink

Euplectes capensis   (Linnaeus), 1766: *Cape of Good Hope.*

Native Names: Isahomba (X).

PLATE 67, *(a)* BR. ♂ AND ♀, *(d)* BR. AND N-BR. (OPP. P. 561).
Length about 14 cm (wing ♂ 83—84,5—86, ♀ 72; tail ♂ 55—60, ♀ 47; tarsus ♂ 22—24; ♀ 21; culmen ♂ 17,5—19, ♀ 16,5. 6 specimens, 5 ♂, 1 ♀). Iris dark brown; bill black, but see under races; legs dark brown. Weight 16,5 g.

Identification: Note yellow *rump* and shorter tail than No. 815. Males in non-breeding dress retain the yellow shoulder and rump but otherwise are streaked like females, but with darker wings and tail. Young resemble females.

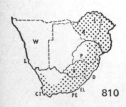

Distribution: From Cape Town northwards through eastern Africa to Ethiopia, westwards to Angola and north of Zaïre forests to Cameroon.
Habits: A common and conspicuous species found in the rank vegetation at the foot of mountains and hills where marshy ground or boggy streams occur in otherwise fairly dry scrub. When not breeding these birds form small flocks. In the breeding season males spend much of their time perched on top of a
810
bush, often quite high up, keeping watch all around and uttering a squeaky "skeek" or "chinsk". Known to live for nearly 19 years *(c)*.
Food: Mainly seeds but also insects.
Voice: As above. Males flying round their territories utter a swizzling, churring, buzzing sound.

Breeding: Constructs an oval, thick-walled nest of strips of grass, with the entrance at the side near the top, under a slight hood, in matted grass or weeds at no great height from the ground, usually 1 or 2 metres or so and sometimes in more or less of a bower. Is not really colonial when nesting, one male having a fairly large territory with three or four females nesting in it, perhaps 20 metres apart, although several males may have contiguous territories. Breeds during August to November in the Cape; January to February in Transvaal and a little later to April in Rhodesia. A lining of grass seeds or wool is added when the young are still quite small. Eggs number 2—4, normally 3, and are pale greenish, heavily streaked and blotched with dark olive and greyish slate. Average (31) of race *(a)* 21,1 × 15,7 (19,7—23,2 × 14,5—15,9). Incubation by female only, 13—16 days (21 also recorded). Nestling 14½ days.

LOCAL RACES:
(a) E.c. capensis (Linnaeus), 1766: *Cape of Good Hope.* Illustrated as No. 810A, ♂ & ♀. Size above. The lower mandibles usually white in full-plumaged males. From the Cape Peninsula eastwards throughout the southern Cape Province.
(b) E.c. macrorhynchus (Roberts), 1919: *Oliphants River, Cape Province.* Mandible white in full-plumaged males. Considerably larger than *(a),* with a much larger bill. Wing ♂ 87,5—88—90; tail ♂ 61—67; tarsus ♂ 23—25; culmen ♂ 20—21,5. 5 specimens. Piketberg to Little Namaqualand.
(c) E.c. approximans (Cabanis), 1851: *South Africa = Kaffirland = De Bruin's Drift, Fish River.* Mandible black in full-plumaged males. Smaller than *(a).* Wing ♂ 76—77,5—81; tail 52—57; tarsus 20—21,5; culmen 16—17,5. 16 ♂ specimens. Eastern Cape Province, Natal and southern Transvaal. Eggs smaller than *(a).* Average (11) 19,6 × 14,5 (18,9—20,1 × 14—15).
(d) E.c. crassirostris (Ogilvie-Grant), 1907: *north end of Ruwenzori Range, Uganda.* Distinctly smaller than *(a).* Illustrated. Wing ♂ 67—70—72, ♀ 60—63; tail ♂ 46—56, ♀ 39—44; tarsus ♂ 19,5—21, ♀ 17,5—19; culmen ♂ 13,5—15,5 ♀ 13—14. 15 specimens, 10 ♂, 5 ♀. Bill brown not black. Eggs small. Average (27) 19,0 × 13,9 (17,6—21,4 × 13—14,7). Northern Transvaal northwards.

811 = 810 *(d)*

812   Golden Bishop   Goudgeel-kaffervink

Euplectes afer   (Gmelin), 1789: *Africa = Senegal.*

Native Names: Rramakhatho, Thakha, Thapiniane (S).

PLATE 67, BR. ♂ AND ♀ (OPP. P. 561).
Length about 12 cm (wing ♂ 62—64—66, ♀ 61—62; tail 33—40; tarsus 16,5—18; culmen 12—13. 18 specimens, 16 ♂, 2 ♀). Iris brown; bill ♂ black, ♀ brown; legs brown.

Identification: A small unmistakable species in breeding dress. Crown yellow not black as in the last species. Male in non-breeding dress resembles the female. Young birds resemble the female but have buff edges to the feathers of the upper-parts.
Distribution: From Senegal to Ethiopia, southwards to Damaraland on the west and the eastern Cape Province on the east, to Cradock and Fort Beaufort.
Habits: A locally fairly common species of rank vegetation in open moist or marshy ground, even in large gardens in Pretoria and Johannesburg. During the breeding season the males are very conspicuous as they float about with their yellow plumes puffed out like a ball of gold and black. Forms flocks during the winter months often in company with other weavers; these flocks may range considerable distances.

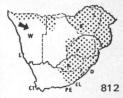

812

575

PLATE 68

789. *Sporopipes squamifrons.* Scaly-feathered Finch. Baardmannetjie.
805. *Quelea quelea lathamii.* Red-billed Quelea. Rooibek-vink. ♂ and ♀.
806. *Quelea erythrops.* Red-headed Quelea. Rooikop-rooibekvink. ♂ and ♀.
820. *Amadina erythrocephala.* Red-headed Finch. Rooikop-mossie. ♂ and ♀.
821. *Amadina fasciata meridionalis.* Cut-throat Finch. Bandkeel-vink.
♂ and ♀.
822. *Lonchura fringilloides.* Pied Mannikin. Dikbek-fret.
823. *Lonchura cucullata scutata.* Bronze Mannikin. Fret.
824. *Lonchura bicolor rufodorsalis.* Red-backed Mannikin. Rooirug-fret.
829. *Pytilia afra.* Golden-backed Pytilia. Geelrug-melba. ♂ and ♀.
830. *Pytilia melba melba.* Melba Finch. Melba-vink. ♂ and ♀.

805 ♂

805 ♀

♂

♂

806 ♂

789 ♀

820 ♀

♂

821 ♀

♂

822

829 ♂

♀

824

830 ♀

♂

823

NLIGHTON '36

827

828

831

832

819

833 A

833 B

835

836

837

NLIGHTON
'36

PLATE 69

819. *Pirenestes minor.* Nyasa Seedcracker. Niasa-saadbreker.
827. *Hypargos nitidulus.* Green Twinspot. Groen Robbin. ♂ and ♀.
828. *Cryptospiza reichenowii.* Nyasa Crimson-wing. Niasa Rooirug-robbin.
♂ and ♀.
831. *Hypargos margaritatus.* Pink-throated Twinspot. Rooskeel-robbin.
♂ and ♀.
832. *Hypargos niveoguttatus.* Red-throated Twinspot. Rooikeel-robbin.
♂ and ♀.
833. *(a). Lagonosticta rubricata rubricata.* Blue-billed Firefinch.
Kaapse Robbin. ♂ and ♀.
833 *(b). Lagonosticta rubricata haematocephala.* Blue-billed Firefinch.
Kaapse Robbin. ♂ and ♀.
835. *Lagonosticta rhodopareia jamesoni.* Jameson's Firefinch.
Jamesonse Robbin. ♂ and ♀.
836. *Lagonosticta nitidula plumbaria.* Brown Firefinch. Bruin Robbin. ♂.
837. *Lagonosticta senegala rendalli.* Red-billed Firefinch. Rooibek-robbin.
♂ and ♀.

Food: Grass seeds and insects; young are fed on caterpillars, etc.

Voice: Males make a harsh squealing sound as they chase each other and also have a short buzzing song, lasting about two to three seconds and sounding like a faulty small alarm clock with no bell. Goes "sip, sip" while "puff-balling" and "chee, chee" when landing.

Breeding: Constructs an oval, thin-walled, woven nest of strips of grass with the entrance placed at one side near the top under a hood; it is placed in short matted grass or weeds such as black-jacks (*Bidens*), the tops twisted over to hide the nest, in moist or marshy ground. Breeds from December to March. Eggs number 3—5 and are dull white with speckles and spots of blackish scattered over the surface, more concentrated at the thick end. Average (69) 17,9 × 12,8 (16,6—19,1 × 12—13,6; one 16 × 12,2).

LOCAL RACE:
E.a. taha A. Smith, 1836: *Near Kurrichane, South Africa.* As illustrated. Size above South Africa northwards as far as southern Angola and Zambia.

813   Red-collared Widow   Rooikeel-kaffervink

Euplectes ardens   (Boddaert), 1783: *Cape of Good Hope.*

Native Names: ♂ Ujobela; ♀ Intakazana (X); ♂ u-Joerjo, ♀ i-Ntaka (Z); le-Tzoo, Tjobolo (S); i-Sakabuya (G).

PLATE 67, BR. ♂ AND ♀ (OPP. P. 561).
Length ♂ about 24—40 cm (wing ♂ 74—76—78, ♀ 64—67—70; tail ♂ summer 210—287, ♀ 43—48; tarsus ♂ 21—23, ♀ 19—22; culmen 14—15. 29 specimens, 22 ♂, 7 ♀). Iris brown; bill ♂ summer black, ♀ brown; legs brownish. Weight 15,2—22 g.

Identification: Males in breeding dress are easily identified by their yellow or red "cut throats". In winter plumage they are also fairly easy to distinguish from other similar species by their heavy markings above and very distinct whitish eyebrows; wings and tail black. Young birds resemble the female but the feathers of the upper-parts are more broadly edged with buff.

Distribution: From the eastern Cape Province and Orange Free State northwards to Ethiopia and across to Gambia.

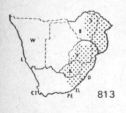

Habits: A species of grass-veld and bushveld districts, usually to be seen in the long grass and reeds near rivers and vleis but also spending much of its time among bushes and trees. During the breeding season males make display flights, taking off from conspicuous perches and flying with the long tail spread vertically.

813

Food: Mainly seeds but also insects, including ants.

Voice: Utters a weak "kizz, zizz, zizz, zizz" and "kee, kee, kee".

Breeding: Polygamous, up to three females per male recorded. Breeds from October to April, constructing an oval, woven nest of strips of dry coarse grass blades round an interior of finer softer grass, so arranged that the seed-heads protrude round the entrance and form a rough porch. There may also be a bower of living grass pulled over the nest. It is placed from one to two metres up in grass or reeds growing in ditches, etc. Eggs, usually 3 sometimes 4, pale greenish blue with rather scattered slate-grey speckles and some olive spotting or blotching, mostly at the thick end; rarely with a dense zone round the thickest part. Average (100) 19,0 × 13,7 (17,8—20,4 × 12,7—14,6; one 17,3 × 13,1, another 21,5 × 13,2). Incubation period 12—15 days.

LOCAL RACE:
E.a. ardens (Boddaert), 1783: *Cape of Good Hope*. As illustrated. Size above. South Africa to southern Zaïre and Tanzania.

814 White-winged Widow   Witvlerk-kaffervink

Euplectes albonotatus (Cassin), 1848: *Port Natal = Durban*.

PLATE 67, BR. ♂ AND ♀ (OPP. P. 561).
Length 15—19 cm (wing ♂ 73—78, ♀ 64—69; tail ♂ 67—90, ♀ 40—45; tarsus ♂ 19—22, ♀ 17—19; culmen 13—15). Iris dark brown; bill ♂ light bluish grey, ♀ brown above, whitish flesh below; legs ♂ blackish, ♀ dark flesh. Weight 18,9 g.

Identification: Breeding males resemble those of the next species but lack yellow backs. Note long squarish tail. In non-breeding plumage the male resembles the female but is larger and retains the wing and shoulder patches of the breeding dress. The female is streaked below and usually with yellow superciliary stripe. Young birds resemble the female but have chest and flanks darker.

Distribution: From Natal, Transvaal, Ngamiland and Ovamboland northwards to Zaïre, East Africa, Ethiopia and across to Darfur. Common north of Pretoria.

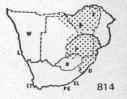

814

Habits: Quite a common species which frequents the rank grass and weeds in moist places in the dry acacia savannas. Is usually rather gregarious and may often be seen in numbers in the grass bordering cultivated fields or in old lands.

Food: Grass seeds. Nestlings fed regurgitated soft grass.

Voice: A rather quiet bird which utters a rustling sound followed by a throaty double chirp.

Breeding: Constructs an oval, woven nest with an entrance at the side near the top and covered by a distinct porch. The outer frame-work is of dry and semi-dry grass and incorporates some of the surrounding vegetation; the lining is of finer dry grass, some of the dry heads forming the porch. Polygamous up to a ratio of 1:4. Eggs number 2 or 3, greenish white with numerous dark olive and slate-grey indefinitely shaped speckles and spots, more concentrated at the thick end. Average (74) 18,6 × 13,5 (16,5—20,8 × 12,6—14,5). Incubation 12—14 days. Nestling 11—13½ days.

LOCAL RACES:
(a) E.a. albonotatus (Cassin), 1848: *Port Natal = Durban*. As illustrated. Size above. Natal northwards to Tanzania, Malawi, across to Ngamiland and northwards to Zambia and Lubumbashi Province.
(b) E.a. asymmetrurus (Reichenow), 1892: *S.W.A. = Angola*. Tail of breeding males longer than in *(a)*. Ovamboland to Zaïre and Gabon.

815 Yellow-backed Widow   Geelrug-kaffervink

Euplectes macrourus (Gmelin), 1789: *Whidah, Dahomey*.

PLATE 67, ♂ BR. AND N-BR. (OPP. P. 561).
Length ♂ 18—22 cm (wing ♂ 80—85, ♀ 71—73; tail ♂ 108—117, ♀ 51; tarsus ♂ 21,5—23,5, ♀ 19—20; culmen 15—16. 4 specimens). Iris dark brown; bill black, brownish in non-breeding dress; legs black, brownish in off-season.

Identification: In breeding dress males are easily distinguishable from the last species and No. 810 by their yellow backs. In non-breeding dress the yellow

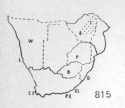

on the wings is retained but the white of the last species is absent. Shows a small white downy patch in the centre of the black breast.

Distribution: West to East Africa, southwards to Angola and Rhodesia, where it occurs above 900 metres.

Habits: A fairly common species which inhabits grassy localities usually near water. Is rather wild and difficult to approach. Forms small flocks with other species when not breeding. The males display with a jerky, ungainly flight working the tail up and down.

815

Food: Grass seeds and a few insects.

Voice: A thin buzzing sound.

Breeding: The nest is placed in damp spots about 15 to 60 cm above the ground; it is oval or pear-shaped and is constructed of fine dry grass without any lining material, and is so thin that it can easily be seen through; a lot of living material is built into the walls. There is no porch over the entrance which is at the side near the top. Breeds from December to March. Eggs 2—3, pale bluish green *finely* marked with numerous irregular small streaks and spots of brown and underlying ashy grey. Average (100) 18,6 × 13,7 (Pitman) from Zambia, (13) 19,2 × 14,1 (16,9—21 × 13,5—14,7) from Zaïre.

LOCAL RACE:
E.m. macrourus (Gmelin), 1789: *Whidah, Dahomey.* As illustrated. Size above. From Senegal to Uganda, southwards to Angola and Rhodesia. Other races in East Africa.

816   Red-shouldered Widow   Kortstert-flap

Euplectes axillaris   (A. Smith), 1838: *Caffreland = Eastern Cape Province.*

Native Names: Isakomba (X); i-Ntaka (Z).

PLATE 67, BR. ♂ AND ♀ (OPP. P. 561).
Length ♂ 19 cm (wing ♂ 83—87—95, ♀ 66—70,5—72; tail ♂ 55—81, ♀ 40—43; tarsus ♂ 23—24, ♀ 19—20; culmen 15—18. 16 specimens, 10 ♂, 6 ♀). Iris dark brown; bill ♂ bluish black, ♀ and winter ♂ horn; legs brown.

Identification: The only widow-bird with red shoulders and a *short* tail; in non-breeding dress males retain the red and cinnamon shoulder patches and the black primaries. Female as illustrated; note the cinnamon shoulder. Young birds resemble the female but young males are larger.

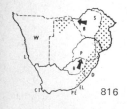

Distribution: From Cameroon to Ethiopia southwards to Angola, Ngamiland, eastern Rhodesia, Mozambique, eastern Transvaal, Zululand, Natal and eastern Cape Province.

Habits: A fairly common species of the coarse vegetation and grass in or near marshes also in reed and papyrus swamps. To a small extent gregarious, but not plentiful anywhere, though conspicuous where it does occur. Males often

816

fly about rather aimlessly just above the grass, bobbing up and down and suddenly twisting backwards and dropping down on to some conspicuous perch—hence the trivial name of "flap". Forms large flocks when not breeding.

Food: Mainly grass seeds, including rice, but also insects, termites, etc.

Voice: A husky, rolling, quiet "tseek, wirra, wirra, wirra, wirra".

Breeding: The nest is placed in a patch of longish grass in some ditch or hollow near marshes; it is usually very low, almost on the ground, and is a rather bulky oval of woven strips of grass with a large amount of the living grass woven into the walls and pulled over the top in a loose bower. Breeds from October to January, rarely as late as March. The normal clutch is 3 eggs, laid on successive days (Skead). They are pale bluish green, with a clouding and blotching of light to dark greyish olive. Average (74) 19,5 × 14,1 (17,7—21,6 × 13—15). Incubation, by female only, 12—13 days (Skead). Nestling period 15—16 days (Skead).

LOCAL RACES:
(a) E.a. axillaris (A. Smith), 1838: *Eastern Cape Province*. As illustrated. Size above.
(b) E.a. bocagei (Sharpe), 1871: *Huilla, Angola*. Lesser wing-coverts more orange than red; primary coverts cinnamon. Ngamiland and the upper Zambesi Valley to Angola and Lubumbashi Province.

817 = 816 *(b)*

818 Long-Tailed Widow   Flap

Euplectes progne   (Boddaert), 1783: *Cape of Good Hope.*

Native Names: ♂ Ibhaku, ♀ Intakazana (X); i-Sakabula (Z); ♂ Tjobolo, ♀ le-Pan, le-Phaka (S).

PLATE 67, BR. AND N-BR. ♀ (OPP. P. 561).
Length ♂ summer 48—60 cm, winter 20—24 cm, ♀ 15—19 cm (wing ♂ 124— 140—160, ♀ 89—94—103; tail ♂ summer 310—490, winter 88—140, ♀ 57—62; tarsus ♂ 25—29, ♀ 22,5—24; culmen 16—19. 28 specimens, 23 ♂, 5 ♀). Iris brown; bill blue-grey; legs brown. Weight 37 g.

Identification: Breeding males easily identified. In off-season, males retain wings as in summer dress and are larger than females. Young birds resemble the female but young males are larger. Males take at least two years to develop full plumage.
Distribution: From eastern Cape Province, Natal and Transvaal; Angola, Zaïre and Kenya.
Habits: A common species which frequents open grass-veld, particularly in valleys where the grass is more luxuriant, and in summer at once attracting attention by its conspicuous black plumage and long tail. When breeding the males keep a look-out for intruders and go from one nest to another, uttering a peculiar low churring note at each, to warn the hen. At this time the males frequent their territories round the nests only during daylight, proceeding in the evening to some roosting place in reeds and returning early in the morning. When making these flights the cocks fly high, and even in strong winds seem to make good headway in spite of the long feathers. In courtship the tail is bent downwards while the bird flies slowly just above the vegetation with slow deliberate wing-beats. Known to live 18 years in captivity.
Food: Seeds and termites.
Voice: Rather quiet but male has a quiet chuckling, swizzling song; normal note "zik". Warning note as above.
Breeding: The nests are very cunningly hidden in short tufts of grass, close to or on the ground, the growing grass being twisted over so as to hide them completely from sight, the entrance being hidden by a hood and the growing grass. The nest is spherical in shape with a side entrance, often concealed by seed-heads, and is made of grass with a lining of finer grass. The female only builds. Breeds from October to January, occasionally as late as March. Eggs

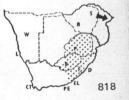

818

2—4, normally 3, are dull white heavily covered with fine specks of light olive and bluish grey and here and there overlying blotches of dark greyish olive. Average (100) 21,7 × 15,3 (20—24 × 14,1—16,2). Incubation period 14 days; female only broods and feeds.

LOCAL RACE:
E.p. progne (Boddaert), 1783: *Cape of Good Hope.* As illustrated. Size above. South Africa.

Subfamily ESTRILDINAE

819   Nyasa Seedcracker   Niasa-saadbreker

Pirenestes minor   Shelley, 1894: *near Zomba.*

PLATE 69 (OPP. P. 577).
Length about 14 cm (wing ♂ 58—60, ♀ 59—61; tail 50—56; tarsus 17,5—19,5; culmen 8,5—9,5. 7 specimens, 2 ♂, 5 ♀). Iris dark brown; bill black; legs dark brown.

Identification: Male illustrated (*cf.* No. 828); female similar but throat and chest brownish. Young has whole head brown.
Distribution: Tanzania and Malawi southwards to Beira; recorded once from eastern Rhodesia in the lower Pungwe area.
Habits: Not common in our area; frequents the tangles of bush along streams, usually in hilly country where the rainfall is heavy, and keeps low down in the bushes.
Food: Grass seeds.

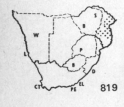

819

Voice: Vincent records that the only notes he heard were a nondescript and sharp, sparrow-like "zeet" and a sharp, clicked "quap". Also has a trilling song.
Breeding: The nest is a rather flimsy dome-shaped structure with entrance at the side, large for the size of the bird—up to 20 cm in length. Built of large leaves and ferns, lined with grasses. Eggs 3, white without gloss about 17 × 13. January. Both sexes incubate.

820   Red-headed Finch   Rooikop-mossie

Amadina erythrocephala   (Linnaeus), 1758: *Africa = Angola.*

PLATE 68, ♂ AND ♀ (OPP. P. 576).
Length about 14 cm (wing 70—72,5—75; tail 46—55; tarsus 14—17; culmen 11—12,5. 32 specimens, 24 ♂, 8 ♀). Iris brown; bill horn; legs flesh. Weight 24—24,4 g.

Identification: As illustrated. The female and young males have a faint pink wash on the head; the young otherwise resemble the female. More heavily built than the next species.
Distribution: Peculiar to South Africa and Angola; not found in the southern Cape Province and the moister east; mainly in the west, but extending over the Drakensberg into the acacia thornveld.

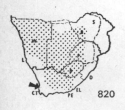

820

Habits: A common species which frequents dry open savannas in small flocks or pairs. Very common in the Kalahari Gemsbok Park, where it may gather in very large numbers at drinking places. Feeds on the ground but perches freely in trees and fences, often gathering around farm buildings.
Food: Mainly seeds.

582

Voice: Normal call a harsh "chuk, chuk". Males utter a typical mannikin-like, churring song with the feathers of the throat puffed out.
Breeding: Either occupies and warmly lines the nests of other birds such as Sparrows, Buffalo Weavers, Social Weavers and Masked Weavers, or uses holes in buildings. Breeds from March to September. Eggs number 4—6 and are pure white. Average (42) 18,3 × 14,7 (17—19,6 × 13,2—15,5; one 16,6 × 14,5). Both sexes incubate and brood.

821 Cut-throat Finch   Bandkeel-vink

Amadina fasciata (Gmelin), 1789: *Senegal.*

PLATE 68, ♂ AND ♀ (OPP. P. 576).
Length about 12 cm (wing 63—66—67,5; tail 39—42; tarsus 12,5—14; culmen 10,5—11. 11 specimens). Iris brown; bill bluish horn; legs pale flesh.

Identification: Females are rather like females of the last species but are more lightly built and browner. Young birds resemble the female, but males have a pale red band across the throat.
Distribution: West to East Africa southwards to Ngamiland, Rhodesia and Transvaal and Mozambique. Its appearance in Rhodesia, and later Transvaal, appears to be comparatively recent.
Habits: A fairly common species of dry acacia savannas or thinly wooded areas. It has much the same habits as the Red-headed Finch but is easily overlooked.
Food: Mainly seeds, also very fond of termites.
Voice: Similar to the last species.
Breeding: Usually uses the nest of other birds such as weavers. Eggs 4—6, pure white. February to April, June, August in Rhodesia. Average (23) 6,8 × 12,6 (16—18,1 × 12,1—13,4). Incubation period 12 days (Priest).

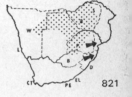

LOCAL RACE:
A.f. meridionalis Neunzig, 1910: *Northern Rhodesia.* As illustrated. Size above. Southern Africa, Zambia and Malawi.

822 Pied Mannikin   Dikbek-fret

Lonchura fringilloides (Lafresnaye), 1835: *India = Liberia.*

PLATE 68 (OPP. P. 576).
Length about 13 cm (wing 57,5—64; tail 33—39; tarsus 13,5—15,5; culmen 15—17. 5 specimens). Iris dark brownish red; bill blackish above, bluish grey below; legs blackish.

Identification: Not unlike the Red-backed Mannikin, No. 824, but much larger and with only the throat, not the chest, black, the back barred and with rufous on the flanks. Sexes alike. Young birds are brown above, buff below; rump and tail black.
Distribution: Senegal to Kenya, southwards to eastern Transvaal and Natal.
Habits: The rarest of our three mannikins, found in the bush along streams but shy. Is usually seen in flocks of about a dozen.
Food: Grass seeds and rice.
Voice: Quite a loud "pee-oo, pee-oo". Males execute a quiet, hopping song.
Breeding: The nest is a rounded structure of grass, with a porch and untidy additions of bark, leaves and grass stems on the outside, lined with the

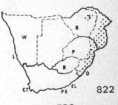

flowering tops of grasses. It is usually placed about 3—5 metres up in the branches of a tree. Breeds from October to April. Eggs 4—6 to the clutch, pure white. Average (25) 15,5 × 11,3 (14,6—16,4 × 10,8—11,9).

823   Bronze Mannikin   Fret

Lonchura cucullata   (Swainson), 1837: *Senegal.*

Native Names: se-Lyamoroka (S); Chinyamdzururu (D).

PLATE 68 (OPP. P. 576).
Length 9—10 cm (wing 47—50—51,5; tail 30—35; tarsus 11—12,5; culmen 9—10. 24 specimens). Iris brown; bill black above, mandible grey; legs brown.

Identification: Lacks the black head and red back of the next species. Sexes alike. Young birds are brown, paler below; tail black. In flight shows a paler rump than the other mannikins.
Distribution: From West to East Africa, southwards to Transvaal, Natal and the eastern Cape Province.
Habits: A very common species which is gregarious, being found in small flocks in moister areas where there is open bush and grass. They spend much of their time on the ground or clambering around on grass stems; when disturbed they all fly off to a nearby tree, drifting back singly or in small groups to continue feeding. The nests are kept in repair throughout the year and are used for roosting by parties of birds. Seems to be somewhat gregarious even when breeding.
Food: Grass seeds, mainly from growing grass, also rice and insects such as termites. Nestlings fed on seed.
Voice: A husky, "chik, chik, chikka". Song: "chi chu, chi chu che-ri-hit chu".
Breeding: The nest is placed conspicuously in a tree or bush and is rounded, untidy and made of dried grass and stems, warmly lined with flowering tops. May also use an old weaver or other bird's nest e.g. Blue Waxbill, adding a new lining. Breeds from November to April. Eggs 4—6, pure white. Average (50) 14,2 × 10,4 (13,3—15 × 9,6—11); one 14,4 × 11,5. Incubation by both sexes, 14—16 days. Nestling period 19½—23 days. Also 14—17 recorded.

LOCAL RACE:
L.c. scutata(Heuglin), 1863: *Dembae, Abyssinia.* As illustrated. Size above. From Ethiopia southwards to eastern Cape Province; westwards to Zaïre and Angola.

824   Red-backed Mannikin   Rooirug-fret

Lonchura bicolor   (Fraser), 1842: *Cape Palmas, Liberia.*

PLATE 68 (OPP. P. 576).
Length about 9½ cm (wing 47—48—51,5; tail 30—33; tarsus 12—13,5; culmen 9,5—10. 9 specimens). Iris brown with outer rim reddish; bill bluish grey; legs dark grey.

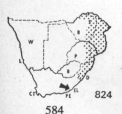

Identification: Smaller, with black on the chest and a redder back than the Pied Mannikin. Sexes alike. Young birds are more chestnut above than the young of the previous species; dirty white below, flanks brown.
Distribution: Portuguese Guinea to Ethiopia, southwards to eastern Rhodesia, Mozambique and Natal. Recorded also from Port Alfred.

Habits: A fairly common species which frequents grassy clearings in the bush; usually occurs in parties of about a dozen.
Food: Almost entirely grass seeds.
Voice: A clear whistling note uttered in flight.
Breeding: The nest is a rounded structure of dry grass with a side entrance and sometimes a porch of grass-heads. More than one pair of birds may construct it and perhaps lay in it. Breeds from October to March. Eggs 4—7, the larger clutches perhaps due to two females; white. Average (10) 14,0 × 10,2 (13—15 × 9,8—10,5).

LOCAL RACE:
L.b. rufodorsalis (Peters), 1863: *Inhambane.* As illustrated. Size above.

825   Swee Waxbill   Swie

Coccopygia melanotis   (Temminck), 1823: *Pays des Cafres = Eastern Cape Province.*
PLATE 70, ♂ AND ♀ (OPP. P. 592).
Length 9—10 cm (wing 46,5—48—49; tail 34—39; tarsus 12,5—13,5; culmen 8—9. 14 specimens). Iris red; bill upper mandible black, the lower red; legs dark brown.

Identification: Sexes as illustrated. The black tail and red rump combined with green back are distinctive. Young birds have black bills but otherwise resemble the female.
Distribution: From the Cape Peninsula (apparently arrived during the last 50 years or so) to Natal and thence to the Zoutpansberg; also Ovamboland.
Habits: A common species which frequents the borders of forest or thick bush near streams, in pairs or small flocks. Spends a lot of time feeding off growing grasses but is very quiet and easily overlooked.
Food: Grass seeds and small insects.
Voice: Normal call a gentle "swee, swee" and also a more urgent explosive "tzwee".

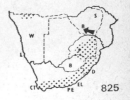

825

Breeding: Places its nest in the branches of trees, often in the gardens about houses, composed of dry grass-stems, recumbent pear-shaped with the entrance at the point—at one side—and lined with flowery grass-tops which may project over the entrance. Breeds from November to March but also recorded in June and July. Eggs 4—10, the large numbers probably due to two hens, pure white. Average (50) 13,9 × 10,5 (12,8—14,6 × 9,8—11,1).

LOCAL RACES:
(a) C.m. melanotis (Temminck), 1823: *Pays des Cafres = Eastern Cape Province.* As illustrated. Size above. From Cape Town to the Zoutpansberg.
(b) C.m. bocagei (Shelley), 1903: *Huilla, Benguella.* More yellow below than *(a)*. Ovamboland to Angola.

826   East African Swee   Tropiese Swie

Coccopygia quartinia   (Bonaparte), 1850: *Abyssinia.*

PLATE 70, ♂ (OPP. P. 592).
Length 9 cm (wing 42—45,5; tail 35—38; tarsus 12,5—13; culmen 8—9). Iris red; maxilla black, mandible red; legs brownish.

Identification: Males lack the black face of the previous species. Sexes alike. Young birds have more orange rumps and black bills. Is sometimes considered as a race of the last species.

585

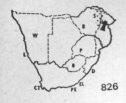

Distribution: From Ethiopia to Zaïre and East Africa southwards to eastern Rhodesia.
Habits: A species of forests and of bracken and grass-covered slopes round their margins. In general habits similar to the previous species.
Food: Seeds.
Voice: A weak "sree".
Breeding: As for the last species.

826

LOCAL RACE:
C.q. stuartirwini Clancey, 1969: *Gorongoza*. As illustrated. Size above. From Rhodesia and Gorongoza.

827 Green Twinspot   Groen Robbin

Hypargos nitidulus   (Hartlaub), 1865, *Natal*.

PLATE 69, ♂ AND ♀ (OPP. P. 577).
Length about 11 cm (wing 52—54; tail 34—35; tarsus 13,5—14,5; culmen 9—11). Iris brown; bill black, tip orange; legs brown. Weight 8—10 g.

Identification: The only greenish twinspot. Sexes as illustrated. Young birds are dull grey below and greenish above; they may breed in this plumage.
Distribution: From the Amatola Mountains northwards on the east coast to Ethiopia and across to Zaïre and Sierra Leone.

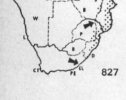

Habits: Reputedly rare but probably more common than is usually suspected. A retiring inhabitant of forests and thick coastal bush; easily overlooked. Emerges to feed in grassy clearings and is frequently found in the neighbourhood of thickets of palms.

827

Food: Seeds, including rice when available.
Voice: A small squeaking "tseet". Also a quiet song.
Breeding: The nest is a large untidy domed structure of grass, with a side entrance, placed some 3—5 metres up in the branches of a tree; reminiscent of that of the Bronze Mannikin. Eggs laid in captivity numbered 3, pure white. One measured 16,6 × 11,3.

LOCAL RACE:
H.n. nitidulus (Hartlaub), 1865: *Natal*. As illustrated. Size above. From Pondoland to northern Mozambique.

828 Nyasa Crimson-wing   Niasa Rooirug-robbin

Cryptospiza reichenowii   (Hartlaub), 1874: *Bondongo, Cameroon*.

PLATE 69, ♂ (OPP. P. 577).
Length 12 cm (wing 53—56; tail 37—42; tarsus 17—18; culmen 10,5—11,5. 5 specimens). Iris dark brown; bill black; legs brown. Weight 11,5—15 g.

Identification: Might be mistaken for the Nyasa Seedcracker but the male is red *only* around the eye, while the female has no red on the head at all (*cf.* No. 819). Note also that the wings and back are reddish. Sexes as illustrated. Young birds have brown on the upper-back and less red on the rump.
Distribution: From West to East Africa, coming within our limits in northern Mozambique and eastern Rhodesia above about 1 350 metres.

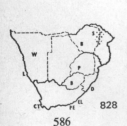

Habits: A rare species of evergreen forests which keeps low down and well hidden, emerging only at the forest edges. Prefers giant heaths when present. Is usually found in small parties which fly only a few yards if flushed.

828

Food: Grass seeds.

Voice: Rather silent. A sharp rasping chirp of "tzeet". Also a tiny song, very soft, consisting of four long-drawn notes descending in major thirds, each followed by the chirp (in a northern race).

Breeding: The nest is placed usually 4—6 metres from the ground in tree-ferns and sapling "forest papaw" (*Cycliomorpha parviflora*); in shape oblate spheroid with a wide-porched entrance pointing slightly upwards, composed of skeletonized leaves and lined with feathery seed-heads of a small *Panicum* and a rhizomorphic mycelium commonly known as "horse hair"; the eggs are white and measurements given by Sir Charles Belcher are 17,5 × 13, taken in Malawi.

LOCAL RACE:
C.r. australis Shelley, 1896: *Mount Chiradzulu, Nyasaland.* As illustrated. Size above. Eastern Rhodesia to Zaïre and Uganda.

829　Golden-backed Pytilia　　　　　　Geelrug-melba

Pytilia afra　(Gmelin), 1789: *Angola.*

PLATE 68, ♂ AND ♀ (OPP. P. 576).
Length 11 cm (wing 59—60—61; tail 34—38; tarsus 14—16; culmen 10—11,5. 6 specimens). Iris reddish brown; bill brown, with tip and lower mandible red; legs flesh.

Identification: Rather like the next species but in males there is less red on the face and neck and more on the tail and wings; the beak is shorter and not as red. Females have redder wings than the next species. Young birds resemble the female but the red rump is more orange.

Distribution: Ethiopia southwards to Mozambique and Zoutpansberg, westwards to Angola.

Habits: A bird of the tangled thorn-brakes near water, generally preferring damper situations than the next species. Is usually seen in pairs or in small scattered flocks when not breeding. Feeds on the ground.

Food: Small grass seeds.

Voice: A fairly high piping whistle of even notes uttered twice in quick succession.

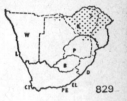

829

Breeding: The nest, usually placed about 2 metres up, is a loose, ragged, rather open ball of fine yellowish grass and weed stems with a few feathers as a lining. Breeds from January to April in Rhodesia, also in the winter in Malawi. Eggs 3—4, pure white. About 16 × 11,7. Males have been found brooding during the day.

830　Melba Finch　　　　　　　　　Melba-vink

Pytilia melba　(Linnaeus), 1758: *China = Angola.*

PLATE 68, ♂ AND ♀ (OPP. P. 576).
Length 13—14 cm (wing ♂ 57—59—62,5, ♀ 57—58,5—62; tail 46—53; tarsus 14—17; culmen 12—14. 40 specimens, 26 ♂, 14 ♀). Iris reddish brown; bill red; legs brownish.

Identification: See No. 829 for differences between this and the Yellow-backed Pytilia; markings on under-parts bolder and more sharply separated. Sexes as illustrated; young birds are uniform olive-grey, rump pale reddish, sometimes with a few markings below; bill brownish.

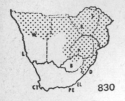

830

Distribution: East to West Africa, southwards to Angola and Damaraland on the west, Botswana, Transvaal, Mozambique and Natal on the east.

Habits: A fairly common species of the dry thorn brakes, especially in valleys near water, but nevertheless able to do without water, as is evidenced in its occurring in the dry Kalahari. Usually seen singly or in pairs, it is a rather restless bird, moving about a lot but coming out into clearings or roads to feed on the ground, particularly in the late afternoonn.

Food: Seeds and small insects, particularly termites.

Voice: Normal call a single "wick". Also utters a pretty but very quiet song, consisting of a long set phrase, repeated at intervals over and over again.

Breeding: The nest is a thin-walled, round structure of dry grass-stems placed in a tree from 2—4 metres up. The ends of the stems protrude all round like bristles and the entrance is at the side. Breeds in late summer and early winter, February to June. Eggs 4—5, pure white. Average (35) 16,4 × 12,5 (14,7—17,3 × 11,6—13,5). Both sexes incubate, the males apparently during the day. Period 12 days.

LOCAL RACE:
(a) P.m. melba (Linnaeus), 1758: *Angola.* As illustrated. Size above. Southern Africa to Angola, Zambia, southern Zaïre, Malawi, Mozambique and southern Tanzania.
(b) P.m. thamnophila Clancey, 1957: *Big Bend, Swaziland.* Mozambique to Natal. Mantle greener and throat peach rather than scarlet.

831   Pink-throated Twinspot   Rooskeel-robbin

Hypargos margaritatus (Strickland), 1844: *Cape Town = Inhambane.*

PLATE 69, ♂ AND ♀ (OPP. P. 577).
Length about 13 cm (wing ♂ 52—56; tail 50—54; tarsus 15,5—17; culmen 11—12. 8 specimens). Iris brown; bill black; legs blackish.

Identification: Resembles the next species. Males, however, are pink on the throat and chest. Sexes as illustrated. Young birds resemble the female.

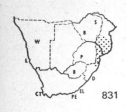

831

Distribution: Locally distributed from about St. Lucia, Zululand, northwards to Inhambane.

Habits: Quite a common species which frequents the coastal tangles of palms and bushes and also the forests of the Lebombo Mountains. Is usually found in pairs or small parties. When disturbed from the ground, where it searches for its food, it invariably darts into the thickets close by, sometimes, however, pausing on the edge to watch one and make sure danger threatens.

Food: Seeds and probably insects.

Voice: Rather like that of a Firefinch, a trilling "tit, tit tititit".

Breeding: Nothing appears to have been recorded.

832   Red-throated Twinspot   Rooikeel-robbin

Hypargos niveoguttatus (Peters), 1868: *Inhambane.*

PLATE 69, ♂ AND ♀ (OPP. P. 577).
Length about 13 cm (wing ♂ 54—56—58; tail 48—53; tarsus 16—17,5; culmen 12—13,5. 9 specimens). Iris dark brown; bill blue-black; legs slate-grey.

Identification: Redder on the throat than the previous species; females with some orange on the chest. Young birds have brownish back and breast, belly dark grey, head light grey.

Distribution: Kenya southwards to Zambia, Malawi, Beira and eastern and northern Rhodesia.
Habits: A locally common species, frequenting the dense bush and thorn tangles along streams and rivers but also in quite dry country. In the evenings comes out into clearings or onto roads to feed in small parties.
Food: Grass seeds.
Voice: A tinkling trill, a rather cricket-like "trrerreee".
Breeding: The nest is a domed structure of grass, fibres, rootlets and feathers, and is placed in a bush. Breeds from March to June in the north of its range. Eggs 3, white, 15,7—16 × 12,2—12,5.

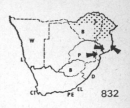

832

LOCAL RACE:
H.n. niveoguttatus (Peters), 1868: *Inhambane.* As above.

833   Blue-billed Firefinch   Kaapse Robbin

Lagonosticta rubricata   (Lichtenstein), 1823: *Kaffirland.*

Native Names: Isicibilili (X); mo-Salasopen (S).

PLATE 69, NOS. 833 *(a)* ♂ AND ♀; 833 *(b)* ♂ AND ♀ (OPP. P. 577).
Length about 12 cm (wing 46—48,5—50; tail 41—48; tarsus 13—16; culmen 10—12. 32 specimens). Iris brown; bill blue-black; legs slate.

Identification: Easily confused with the next species, except in the south where the latter does not occur. Southern birds, Race *(a)*, have blackish bellies; crown and hind-neck grey. In race *(b)*, these parts are washed with pinky red thus resembling the next species, but the *back* is brownish, *not* washed with pink as it is in No. 835; this applies to both sexes. In the hand it is easily shown that the species is distinct because the next bird, Jameson's Firefinch, does not have the second primary attenuated. Sexes as illustrated. Young birds are brownish, the belly dusky; bill blackish above, lower mandible horn.

Distribution: From Ethiopia to Portuguese Guinea, southwards to Angola, eastern Rhodesia, Transvaal, Natal and eastern Cape Province as far as Knysna.
Habits: A common species which frequents the grass and scrub on the borders of forest, thick bush along streams and bracken-briar. Is particularly fond of thick thorn-tree scrub with tall grass growing up underneath it. Usually found in pairs or small parties, not easily seen as they keep to the thick tangles and fly low down and unobtrusively from one patch to the next, showing a quick flash of the crimson rump. Is easily located by its characteristic call.
Food: Seeds and small insects.
Voice: Has a stuttering alarm-note; also a beautiful bell-like trill which may last for as long as ten seconds, followed by "wink, wink, wink".
Breeding: The nest is placed low down, from 60 cm—2 m up, usually well concealed. It is a round, ball-shaped structure, with a large entrance at the side, loosely built of dry yellowish grass with an external wrapping of coarser blades. Breeds from November to April. Eggs 3—5, pure white. Average (24) 15,2 × 11,7 (14,5—16,2 × 10,9—12,4).

833

LOCAL RACES:
(a) L.r. rubricata (Lichtenstein), 1823: *Kaffirland.* As illustrated. Size above. South Africa as far north as Transvaal and southern Mozambique.

(b) L.r. haematocephala Neumann, 1907: *Songea, Tanganyika.* Illustrated. Crown red, not grey as in *(a).* Wing 47—48—51; tail 40—42; tarsus 13,5—15; culmen 10—11,5. 13 specimens. Rhodesia northwards to western Zambia, Lubumbashi Province and Tanzania.

834 = 833 *(b)*

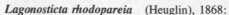

835 Jameson's Firefinch   Jamesonse Robbin

Lagonosticta rhodopareia (Heuglin), 1868:

PLATE 69, ♂ AND ♀ (OPP. P. 577).
Length about 12 cm (wing 46—48—50; tail 38—45; tarsus 12,5—14; clumen 9,5—11. 22 specimens). Iris brown; bill bluish grey; legs pinkish grey. Weight 9,4 g (9).

Identification: In the hand, adults may be differentiated from the preceding species by lacking an attenuated tip to the second primary. In the field, appears pinker and the upper-parts are washed with pink throughout so that there is little contrast between the back and the breast. Young birds resemble the female but lack the pink on lores and breast.
Distribution: From Zululand and the Transvaal northwards to Ethiopia and Zaïre.

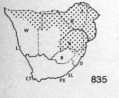

835

Habits: A common species whose habitat preference is much the same as that of the preceding species, but in general prefers similar conditions in *drier* country and greatly favours thick thorn scrub with grass. Habits otherwise very similar.
Food: Grass seeds.
Voice: The same as for the preceding species, including the trill.
Breeding: The nest is identical with that of the preceding species and is often placed in bushes which have grass growing up through them. Recorded nesting from November right through to June. Eggs 3—5, pure white. Average (14) 14,9 × 11,2 (13,5—15,9 × 10,5—11,9). Both sexes incubate.

LOCAL RACE:
L.r. jamesoni Shelly, 1882: *Tatin River, Matabeleland.* As illustrated. Size above. South Africa to Lubumbashi Province and Malawi.

836 Brown Firefinch   Bruin Robbin

Lagonosticta nitidula Hartlaub, 1886: *Mpala, Lake Tanganyika.*

PLATE 69, ♂ (OPP. P. 577).
Length about 10 cm (wing 52; tail 35; tarsus 16; culmen 9). Iris brown to reddish brown; bill purple at base, sides red, culmen steel-blue; legs slate-grey.

Identification: Likely to be mistaken for the Red-billed Firefinch but red confined to throat and upper chest and more freckled with white spots; *rump grey* not red, a useful distinguishing feature in flight. Sexes alike.
Distribution: From Angola to Tanzania, southwards to the upper Zambesi Valley. May be seen on the south bank near Victoria Falls and Okavango Swamps.

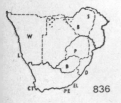

836

Habits: A rare bird in our area. Inhabits thickets and reeds along rivers, coming out to feed in clearings and on farm lands. Spends a lot of time on the ground in grass searching for seeds. Becomes quite tame. Apparently breeds in October. Its parasite, *Hypochera incognita* should be sought in Okavango.

Food: Grass seeds.
Voice: In flight "tsiep, tsiep"; also "chick, chick" on the ground. A deeper trill than No. 833, almost guttural, not at all bell-like.

LOCAL. RACE:
L.n. plumbaria Clancey, 1962: *Sepopa, Bechuanaland.* As above.

837   Red-billed Firefinch   Rooibek-robbin

Lagonosticta senegala   (Linnaeus), 1766: *Senegal.*

Native Name: i-Ncweeti (Z).

PLATE 69, ♂ AND ♀ (OPP. P. 577).
Length about 10 cm (wing ♂ 47—48,5—51, ♀ 46,5—47,5—50; tail 32—38; tarsus 11—12,5; culmen 8,5—9,5. 24 specimens, 16 ♂, 8 ♀. Iris red; bill red, darker above along the culmen; legs brownish.

Identification: Red bill prevents confusion with Nos. 833 and 835. For differences from the Brown Firefinch, see the preceding species. Sexes as illustrated; note lack of red on female, except rump. Young birds resemble the female but lack the red lores and white spots on flanks; bill grey.
Distribution: From Senegal to Arabia, southwards to the Kalahari, Orange River, Transvaal, Natal and Eastern Cape to Oudtshoorn.
Habits: A common, familiar and very tame little bird, often seen in camps and suburbs of towns (common in Salisbury). Frequents its haunts in pairs or small family parties and searches for its food on the ground, in clearings and on roads, taking refuge in the bushes when alarmed.

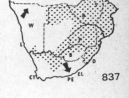

837

Food: Seeds and small insects.
Voice: A distinctive, slightly nasal "fweet, fweet", often uttered in flight. Does not trill like the two larger species.
Breeding: Constructs a round nest with a wide side entrance and lined with hair and feathers, on the ground amongst weeds or low down in palms or bushes. Breeds from November to April, also in August. Eggs 3—4, pure white. Average (16) 13,4 × 10,5 (12,5—14,1 × 9,9—11,4). Nestling 16½—19 days (4).

LOCAL RACES:
(a) L.s. rendalli Hartert, 1898: *Upper Shiré River, Nyasaland.* As illustrated. Size as above. From Cape, Transvaal and Ngamiland northwards to Lubumbashi Province and Malawi.

(b) L.s. pallidicrissa Zedlitz, 1910: *Humpata, Angola.* Ovamboland, Angola. Paler.

838   Orange-breasted Waxbill   Rooiassie

Amandava subflava   (Vieillot), 1819: *Senegal.*

PLATE 70, ♂ AND ♀ (OPP. P. 592).
Length 9—10 cm (wing 42—45—47; tail 31—36; tarsus 10—12; culmen 8—9. 12 specimens). Iris orange-red; bill red, with culmen and spot at base black; legs brownish.

Identification: Rather like the Quail Finch but easily distinguished even in flight by the red rump of the male. Sexes as illustrated. Young birds resemble the female but have blackish beaks.
Distribution: West to East Africa, southwards to Transvaal, Zululand and the eastern Cape Province.

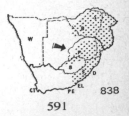

838

591

PLATE 70

825. *Coccopygia melanotis melanotis*. Swee Waxbill. Swie. ♂ and ♀.
826. *Coccopygia quartinia stuartirwini*. East African Swee.

Tropiese Swie. ♂.

838. *Amandava subflava clarkei*. Orange-breasted Waxbill. Rooiassie.

♂ and ♀.

839. *Uraeginthus angolensis angolensis*. Blue Waxbill. Blousysie. ♂ and ♀.
840. *Granatina granatina*. Violet-eared Waxbill. Koningblousysie. ♂ and ♀.
841. *Estrilda erythronotos erythronotos*. Black-cheeked Waxbill.

Swartwang-rooibekkie.

842. *Estrilda perreini incana*. Grey Waxbill. Grys Rooibekkie.
842X. *Estrilda thomensis*. Cinderella Waxbill.
843. *(a). Estrilda astrild astrild*. Common Waxbill. Rooibekkie.
844. *Ortygospiza fuscocrissa muelleri*. Quail Finch. Kwartelvinkie. ♂ and ♀.
845. *Ortygospiza locustella locustella*. Locust Finch.

Rooivlerk-kwartelvink. ♂ and ♀.

825 ♂

♀

838 ♂ ♀

843A

826 ♂

840 ♂

♀

839 ♂

♀

842

842 x

KN

841

844 ♂ ♀

845 ♂ ♀

NLIGHTON
'36

852

853

846

854

847

849

851

850

NLIGHTON '36

PLATE 71

846. *Vidua macroura.* Pin-tailed Whydah. Koning-rooibekkie. ♂ and ♀.
847. *Vidua regia.* Shaft-tailed Whydah. Pylstert. ♂ and ♀.
849. *Hypochera funerea funerea.* Black Widow-finch. Blouvinkie. ♂ and ♀.
850. *Hypochera purpurascens.* Purple Widow-finch.
851. *Hypochera chalybeata amauropteryx.* Steel-blue Widow-finch.
Staalblou Vinkie. ♂ and ♀.
852. *Steganura paradisaea.* Paradise Whydah. Paradysvink. ♂ and ♀.
853. *Steganura orientalis obtusa.* Broad-tailed Paradise Whydah.
Breëstert-paradysvink. ♂.
854. *Anomalospiza imberbis imberbis.* Cuckoo Finch. Koekoekvink. ♂ and ♀.

Habits: A common bird, never found far from the shelter of marshes or reed-beds along rivers, spreading on to the neighbouring grassy flats to feed, usually in small flocks. They are sprightly little birds, always on the move, wagging their tails laterally and climbing up and down reed-stems or hopping about on the ground; when disturbed they fly off in straggling parties at no great height and soon alight again.

Food: Small seeds and tiny insects.

Voice: A rather quiet metallic, tinkling note, often uttered in flight.

Breeding: Always occupies the nests of other birds such as weavers, widow and bishop-birds, warmly relining them with soft material and feathers. Breeds from January to May. Eggs 3—5 or 6, pure white. Average (100) 13,5 × 10,2 (12,3—14,9 × 9,5—10,8; one 11,8 × 9,7). Incubation by both sexes, 12—14 days (8). Nestling period 17—21 days (7).

LOCAL RACE:
A.s. clarkei (Shelley), 1903: *Richmond Road, Natal.* As illustrated. Size above. South Africa to Angola and across to Kenya.

839 Blue Waxbill   Blousysie

Uraeginthus angolensis   (Linnaeus), 1758: *Angola.*

Native Name: li-Vivi (Ch).

PLATE 70, ♂ AND ♀ (OPP. P. 592).
Length 12—13 cm (wing 50—52—56; tail 47—61; tarsus 13—15; culmen 9—11. 31 specimens). Iris red; bill lilac, tip blackish; legs pale brown.

839

Identification: The only waxbill with pale blue under-parts. Sexes as illustrated. Young birds resemble the female but are pale; bills blackish.

Distribution: From Angola to Tanzania, southwards to Damaraland, Botswana, Transvaal and Natal.

Habits: A very common and familiar bird which frequents the grass and bushes in drier thornveld along streams and rivers, usually in small parties, or as individuals scattered about within calling distance. May come into villages and even large towns.

Food: Small seeds and insects such as termites.

Voice: Contact call an urgent-sounding "weety-weet" or "weet-weet". Also a lively little song interspersed with "weety-weets". Alarm call a harsh stuttering rattle.

Breeding: Constructs a round nest, with a wide side entrance, of dry grass stems, in a bush, tree or palm, up to 3 metres from the ground; it is very frequently near a wasps' nest and seldom shows much attempt at concealment. Has been known to use old nests of other birds. Breeds mainly from December to March, but also as late as May and even in August. Eggs 3—5, pure white. Average (38) 14,2 × 10,7 (13,2—15,5 × 10,2—11,3). Incubation 11—12. Nestling 16 days.

LOCAL RACES:
(a) U.a. angolensis (Linnaeus), 1758: *Angola.* As illustrated. Size above. Angola to Ngamiland, western Rhodesia, Botswana and Transvaal.
(b) U.a. damarensis Reichenow, 1904: *Damaraland.* Lighter above than *(a).* Wing 50—51—53 (11). Northern South West Africa.
(c) U.a. niassensis Reichenow, 1911: *Songea, Nyasaland.* Darker above than *(a).* Size similar. Malawi southwards to Natal.

840 Violet-eared Waxbill   Koningblousysie

Granatina granatina   (Linnaeus), 1766: *Brazil = Angola.*

Native Names; le-Te, le-Bibe (Ch).

PLATE 70, ♂ AND ♀ (OPP. P. 592).
Length about 14 cm (wing ♂ 56—58—59, ♀ 55—56—59; tail 61—71; tarsus 15—17; culmen 10—12. 19 specimens, 14 ♂, 5 ♀). Iris red; bill red, base purple; legs purplish.

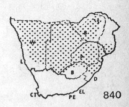

Identification: Unmistakable; sexes as illustrated. Young birds are dull editions of the female. In flight the tail appears broad and heavy.
Distribution: From Angola and South West Africa to Rhodesia, Transvaal, Botswana, Natal and southern Mozambique (rare).
Habits: A fairly common species which frequents the dry thorn scrub in pairs or small parties, but does not form large flocks like some waxbills; sometimes associates with the Blue Waxbill, but is also found in drier situations.
Food: Small seeds and insects.
Voice: Call a repeated "tiu-woo-wee"; also a pretty song.
Breeding: The nest is a rounded, loosely built structure of grass-stems lined with feathers, with a side entrance and a slight porch; it is placed from 0,5 to 2 metres up in a thorn bush or shrub. Breeds from January to May. Eggs 3—4, pure white. Average (35) 15,7 × 12,0 (14,6—17,3 × 11—31). Both sexes incubate; the male has been observed bringing feathers to the female when relieving her.

841 Black-cheeked Waxbill   Swartwang-rooibekkie

Estrilda erythronotos   (Vieillot), 1817: *India = Kurrichane.*

PLATE 70 (OPP. P. 592).
Length about 13 cm (wing 52—54—58; tail 53—60; tarsus 13—16; culmen 9—10,5. 27 specimens). Iris reddish; bill blue-black; legs black. Weight 9,1—9,3 g.

Identification: The black face, long tail and vinaceous flanks and rump are distinctive. The female is slightly duller and has less red below. Young birds resemble the female.
Distribution: From Damaraland, Rhodesia and Transvaal northwards to Mossamedes in the west and Ethiopia and Somalia in the east.
Habits: A common species of dry thorn bush country, usually seen in pairs in the thorn-bushes or feeding on the ground, flying into the bushes when alarmed. Forms flocks of as many as fifteen individuals when not breeding. Roosts in nests, sometimes unoccupied nests of Masked or Sparrow-weavers.
Food: Seeds and insects; also green vegetable matter.
Voice: Birds in a flock keep in contact by whistling a melodious, slightly quavering ascending and mournful "fwooee".
Breeding: Constructs a large round nest of dry grass-stems, high up in very thorny trees, the entrance facing downwards and protruding about 10 cm, and with a smaller "cock's nest" on the top; the same tree is often used year after year, so that old nests of the preceding three or four years may sometimes be seen near the new ones. Breeds from January to March. Eggs 3—6, white. Average (20) 15,2 × 11,0 (14,7—16,5 × 10,7—11,4).

LOCAL RACE:
E.e. erythronotos (Vieillot), 1817: *India = Kurrichane.* As illustrated. Size above. South Africa, Angola and Zambia.

842   Grey Waxbill   Grys Rooibekkie

Estrilda perreini   (Vieillot), 1817: *Malimbe, Portuguese Congo.*

PLATE 70 (OPP. P. 592).
Length about 11 cm (wing 48—49—50,5; tail 43—49; tarsus 14,5—15,5; culmen 8—9.
7 specimens). Iris red; bill tip grey, base blue; legs black.

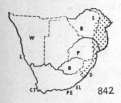

Identification: The only grey waxbill with a red rump in our area. Adults occasionally have white spots, or white spots on red feathers on flanks. Sexes alike. Young birds have no black streak through eye, rump duller red.
Distribution: From Angola to Tanzania and southwards east of the escarpment to the coast of Natal.
Habits: A species of thick, moist bush where there is grass; is seldom seen but is probably commoner than it appears to be. Spends most of its time in thick cover, perhaps venturing out into the grass near by and diving back into the bushes when alarmed, with a flash of its red rump.
Food: Grass seeds only recorded.
Voice: A thin, slightly explosive "pseeu, pseeu".
Breeding: Builds a roughly retort-shaped nest, with a short spout, of grass, lined with soft grass-heads or feathers and placed from 2—4 metres up in forks of shrubs or trees. Breeds from October to March. Eggs 4—5, pure white. Average (30) 14,6 × 11,4 (13,7—15,4 × 10,5—11,5). Both sexes incubate.

LOCAL RACES:

(a) E.p. incana (Sundevall), 1850: *Lower Caffraria = Durban.* As illustrated. Size above. Natal and southern Zululand.
(b) E.p. poliogastra (Reichenow), 1886: *Inhambane.* Paler than *(a).* Size similar. Wing 46—48—50 (10). Northern Zululand, the extreme east of Rhodesia and Mozambique.

842X   Cinderella Waxbill

Estrilda thomensis   Sousa, 1888: *Sao Thomé Island.*

PLATE 70 (OPP. P. 592).
Length 11 cm (wing 50; tail 40; tarsus 14; culmen 8). Iris red, bill red, black tip, legs black.

Identification: Similar to the Grey Waxbill but lacks black on chin of that species. Middle of belly sooty black merging to scarlet lower abdomen and black under tail coverts. General impression in the field is of a paler bird than No. 842.
Distribution: Angola to the Cunene River, where it was collected in October.
Habits: Collected in riverside cover along the Cunene where it is not uncommon. Occurs in small parties in low bushes of savanna and riverine scrub. Originally described in error from Sao Thomé Island.

843   Common Waxbill   Rooibekkie

Estrilda astrild   (Linnaeus), 1758: *"Canaries, America, Africa"* =
Cape Town.

Native Names: Intshiyane (X); in-Tiyane (Z); se-Tzetze, Borokhane (S);
Chiwanzaburi (D).

PLATE 70 (OPP. P. 592).
Length 13 cm (wing 48—49—51; tail 50—61; tarsus 14—16; culmen 9—9,5. 28
specimens). Iris brown; bill red; legs brown.

Identification: Too well known to require description. The female is not as
red below as the male. Young birds are indistinctly barred below and have
very little red on chest; bills blackish.

Distribution: The greater part of the continent south of the Sahara.

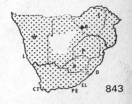

Habits: A common and very well-known bird, usually found in small flocks
and when not breeding may assemble in very large numbers. Frequents open
marshy country and reedy or grassy banks of rivers and streams. A very lively
bird, continually on the move, always flirting its tail from side to side and
when disturbed trailing off one behind the other.

843

Food: Grass seeds and small insects.

Voice: Call-note a loud "ping, ping". When excited a harsher, urgent
"dee-dee *dur* dit", descending on the "dur".

Breeding: Constructs a large round nest of dry grass-stems, on the ground or
in tufts of grass or small bushes often over water, the entrance protruding
as a spout of about 7—10 cm, closed by the converging ends of the grass-stems.
On top of the nest there is a more or less completed smaller nest known as a
"cock's nest", from the old idea that the male slept in it during the night. This
does not happen but nearly fully-fledged young have been found in it. There is
usually a bare patch of ground in front of the main nest. Breeds from
September to January in the Cape; November to April further north. Eggs
number 5—6 as a rule, larger numbers, such as 10, being probably due to two
females laying in the same nest. They are pure white. Average (100) 13,8 ×
10,7 (12,4—15,5 × 9,9—11,4) (odd larger eggs reported are considered as
those of some parasite). Both sexes incubate, period 11 days (Skead). Nestling
period 19—21 days (Skead). The nest is not kept clean when there are young
and becomes filthy inside. Parasitised by the Pintailed Whydah.

LOCAL RACES:

(a) E.a. astrild (Linnaeus), 1758: *Canaries, America, Africa = Cape Town.* As
illustrated. Size above. Cape Province, Orange Free State, Natal and Transvaal.

(b) E.a. damarensis Reichenow, 1902: *Rehoboth.* Much paler than *(a)* and even paler
than *(d).* Wing 49—51—53 (12). South West Africa.

(c) E.a. cavendishi Sharpe, 1900: *Mapicuti, Cheringoma District, Mozambique.* Paler
about the throat, sides of face and with narrower barring. Size smaller. Wing about 46.
Mozambique, eastern Rhodesia northwards to Kenya.

(d) E.a. ngamiensis Roberts, 1932: *Shorobe, north of Maun, Ngamiland.* As for *(c)* but
paler above as well. Wing 46—47,5—49,5; tail 46—50,5; tarsus 12,5—14; culmen 8—9
(12 specimens). Ngamiland.

844 Quail Finch — Kwartelvinkie

Ortygospiza fuscocrissa Heuglin, 1863: *Dembea and Tigré, Abyssinia.*

Native Names: u-Nonhwe (Z); le-Kolukotoane (S); Unonkxwe (X).

PLATE 70, ♂ AND ♀ (OPP. P. 592).
Length about 10 cm (wing 52—55—58; tail 25—31; tarsus 13—15; culmen 9—10. 15 specimens). Iris bright hazel; bill red; legs light brown. Weight 12 g.

Identification: The only waxbills which might be confused with this species are the next species (for differences see No. 845) and the Orange-breasted Waxbill, No. 838, but the latter has a red rump and eyebrow. Young birds are paler above and unbarred brownish below; bill blackish.

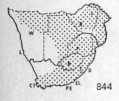

Distribution: From Damaraland and northern Kalahari on the west, southern Cape Province on the east, north to Uganda and Ethiopia. About 100 reported near Cape Town, 1952-53, now resident.

Habits: Frequents the open grasslands, especially on the borders of pans of water, around which grow certain weeds of which it is partial to the seeds. Usually in small parties which rise steeply at one's feet (a few usually remain till later) with whirring wings and characteristic call. They then circle overhead if no other pans are near, or if there are, fly off to them and settle again. They almost never perch even on grass-stalks. In particular, therefore, they like areas with bare ground between patches of grass.

Food: Mainly seeds, also spiders.

Voice: Characteristic call on the wing—"tirrilink", bell-like in quality.

Breeding: Nests in the latter part of summer, from December to April, constructing a round nest of grass, warmly lined with softer grasses and feathers, with a side entrance, placed on the ground and well hidden under a tuft of grass. Eggs 4—6, pure white. Average (100) 14,5 × 11,2 (12,7—15,5 × 10,5—11,8), incubated by both sexes. Apparently female only feeds the young. Nestling 17½ days.

LOCAL RACE:
(a) *O.f. muelleri* Zedlitz, 1911: *Simbiti, Tanganyika.* Southern and eastern race.
(b) *O.f. pallida* Roberts, 1932: *Nkate.* Botswana. More dusky brown than (a).
(c) *O.f. bradfieldi* Roberts, 1929: *Okahandja.* Northern S.W.A. Darker than (b).

845 Locust-finch — Rooivlerk-kwartelvink

Ortygospiza locustella (Neave), 1909: *Upper Luansenshi River, Lake Bangweulu, Northern Rhodesia.*

PLATE 70, ♂ AND ♀ (OPP. P. 592).
Length about 9½ cm (wing 43—46; tail 27; tarsus 13—14; culmen 8,5—9. 3 specimens). Iris yellow; bill red with black culmen; legs brown.

Identification: Likely to be confused with the preceding species due to their similar habits, but the spotted back in both sexes and red wings are distinctive. Sexes as illustrated. Young birds resemble the female, are browner below and on the wings, bill blackish.

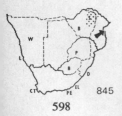

Distribution: From Zaïre and south-west Tanzania southwards to Malawi, Rhodesia and near Beira.

Habits: Its general habits are similar to those of the Quail Finch but its powers of flight are not so great. Forms flocks when not breeding.

Food: Small seeds.
Voice: Utters a squeaking, querulous "chip, chip" in the air. Calls less than the Quail Finch.
Breeding: Nests are placed on the ground between stems of wiry grass but not attached to them; they are ball-shaped and composed of fine, soft grasses, with a few feathers or grass-heads in the lining. The rounded entrance is lateral and high up. Breeds from January to May. Eggs 3—5, usually 4 or 5, pure white. Two measure 12,2 × 9,9 and 12,9 × 10.

LOCAL RACE:
O.l. locustella (Neave), 1909: *Upper Luansenshi River, Lake Bangweulu, Northern Rhodesia.* As illustrated. Size above. Range as above, but not Zaïre where another race occurs

Subfamily VIDUINAE

846 Pin-tailed Whydah   Koning-rooibekkie

Vidua macroura (Pallas), 1764: *East Indies = Angola.*

Native Names: Uhlakhwe (X); u-Hlegwane (Z); moLepe ♂, le-Helo ♀, Mma-monoke (S); Tahapietsi (Ch); Chinyampimbiri (D).

PLATE 71, ♂ AND ♀ (OPP. P. 593).
Length ♂ 26—34 cm, ♀ 12—13 cm (wing ♂ 69—73,5—79, ♀ 64—67—71; tail ♂ 47—52—longest feather 163—264, ♀ 43—50; tarsus ♂ 16—18, ♀ 15—16; culmen ♂ 9,5—11, ♀ 9—10,5. 43 specimens, 29 ♂, 14 ♀). Iris dark brown; bill adult ♂ red, ♀ brownish red; legs grey.

Identification: Breeding male with pied plumage and long tail unmistakable. Non-breeding males are slightly larger than females and rustier and more boldly striped with black on the head; their bills are also red. Immature birds resemble adults of their respective sexes in non-breeding dress. Young birds are not streaked for the first two months and have black bills.
Distribution: Africa south of the Sahara except thick forests and deserts.
Habits: A common and well-known species, often seen around homesteads in the country, in small parties consisting of perhaps only one male and half a dozen plainly coloured birds; these were considered by early observers to be all females but it has been found that many of them are immature males of the second year, so that males are probably not as polygamous as was previously thought. A very pugnacious species, males spending much of their time pursuing other small birds or courting their hens by hovering over them with quick mayfly-like dashes, moving in a circle in the vertical plane. When not breeding forms largish flocks. When seeking food gives a sudden forward and backward jump, scattering sand and seed in all directions; males on the ground may drag their tails or carry them gracefully arched in the air. Males sing from one perch for weeks on end.

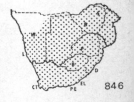

846

Food: Grass seeds and a few insects, occasionally hawked in the air.
Voice: In flight utters an aggressive "tseet, tseet" as it flaps its wings. The song of the male is a harsh, wispy, "peetzy, weetzy, weetzy" (Skead).
Breeding: Probably polygamous and certainly promiscuous. Parasitic on the Common Waxbill. An egg of the host is said to be destroyed to make room for each of those of this parasite, but thereafter the young grow up with the others

in amity and remain for a time with the flocks of the host. Eggs are pure white; reasonably authentic eggs measure 15,5—17 × 11—12,3. 5 from the Cape 16,2 × 12,2 (15,9—16,5 × 12,1—12,3). One or two may be laid in a nest. Any suspect eggs found should be measured and allowed to hatch. November to March in Rhodesia. Nestling period 20 days (Skead).

847 Shaft-tailed Whydah   Pylstert

Vidua regia (Linnaeus), 1766: *Africa = Angola.*

PLATE 71, ♂ AND ♀ (OPP. P. 593).
Length ♂ 30—34 cm, ♀ about 12 cm (wing ♂ 70—72,5—75, ♀ 68—70; tail ♂ 37—42—longest feather 210—243, ♀ 37—43; tarsus ♂ 14,5—16,5, ♀ 14—15; culmen 9—10. 20 specimens, 17 ♂, 3 ♀). Iris brown; bill orange-red; legs orange-red.

Identification: Breeding male with buff and black plumage and long spatulate tail is unmistakable. In non-breeding dress the male resembles the female but is a trifle larger. Young birds resemble the female.

Distribution: The dry west from Orange Free State and northern Cape Province to Rhodesia and westwards across the Kalahari and Ngamiland to Damaraland and Angola.

847

Habits: Frequents thorny scrub and is particularly attracted by open grassy, or bare areas round stockyards, etc. Is usually found in small parties with a preponderance of plainly coloured females and immature males. Flocks contain long-tailed males from November to June. Males are aggressive and spend a lot of time chasing each other and disturbing other small birds.

Food: Almost entirely small seeds.

Breeding: Known to parasitise the Violet-eared Waxbill and possibly also other small seed-eating birds, though eggs have not been positively identified as they are probably like those of the host. The young are almost exactly like those of the Violet-eared Waxbill, even to the colour of the mouth-spots, but have shorter tails and no blue on the rump.

LOCAL RACES:
(a) V.r. regia (Linnaeus), 1766: *Africa = Angola.* As above.
(b) V.r. woltersi Rosa Pinto, 1961: *Funhalouro, Portuguese East Africa.* Southern Mozambique; very local.

848 Purple Widow-bird. See page xxxii

849 Black Widow-finch   Blouvinkie

Hypochera funerea (de Tarragon), 1847: *Natal.*

PLATE 71, ♂ AND ♀ (OPP. P. 593).
Length about 12 cm (wing ♂ 67—70, ♀ 65—69; tail 37—40; tarsus 12—14; culmen 9—10). Iris brown; bill whitish; legs reddish.

Identification: Easily distinguished from the next species by its whitish bill and reddish legs which avoid confusion with the two preceding Whydahs. Males in non-breeding dress and young birds resemble the female.

Distribution: From Uitenhage to Natal, Zululand, Transvaal and northwards to Central Africa. Distribution much the same as its host's, No. 833.

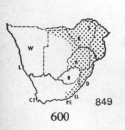

849

Habits: Quite a common bird, which inhabits a variety of country but is usually found in open bush and particularly in bare patches where it feeds on the ground in a characteristic fashion, giving little quick jumps and scattering the dust with its feet. Males perch on telegraph poles or the tops of bare trees and, when breeding, utter their grating song, returning to the same site for weeks at a time. They also bob up and down in flight in front of the females uttering a hoarse "cha, cha".

Food: Grass seeds.

Voice: As above. During song this species mimics the trills and phrases of its host breeding bird—namely No. 833 the Blue-billed Firefinch. Males also sing a hoarse, chattering choppy song well interspersed with "cha" notes. The males call from one perch for long intervals.

Breeding: Known to be parasitic on the Firefinch, No. 833, but data for our area are urgently needed.

LOCAL RACES:
(a) H.f. funerea (de Tarragon), 1847: *Natal.* Cape Province, Natal, Transvaal and western Rhodesia.
(b) H.f. codringtoni Neave, 1907: *Petauke, Northern Rhodesia.* Eastern Rhodesia. Greener than *(a).*

850 Purple Widow-finch

Hypochera purpurascens Reichenow, 1883: *Usegua, Tanzania.*

PLATE 71 ♂ AND ♀ (OPP. P. 593).
Length 12 cm (wing ♂ 67—70, ♀ 65—99; tail 37—40; tarsus 12—14; culmen 9—10). Iris brown; bill whitish; legs whitish.

Identification: These three blackish finches are distinguished from each other by the colour of the bill and legs and by which host species they mimic in their song. This bird should show whitish legs in the illustration. White bill and whitish legs are diagnostic, with song.

Distribution: As No. 835, Jameson's Firefinch.

Habits: Much as previous species.

Voice: Mimics the Jameson's Firefinch call.

Breeding: Parasitic on Jameson's Firefinch.

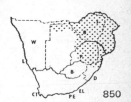

850

851 Steel-blue Widow-finch   Staalblou Vinkie

Hypochera chalybeata Müller, 1776: *Brazil = Senegal.*

PLATE 71, ♂ AND ♀ (OPP. P. 593).
Size as for No. 849. Iris brown; bill red; legs red.

Identification: Very similar to the last two species but has red bill and legs in both sexes. Female has buffy chest.

Distribution: Mozambique, Transvaal and Botswana to Damaraland, north to Senegal and Arabia.

Habits: Similar to those of the preceding species, inhabiting waste ground in open bush but also coming into towns, even Bulawayo. When not breeding, forms flocks which wander about.

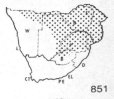

851

601

Voice: Mimics Red-billed Firefinch.
Breeding: Known to parasitise the Red-billed Firefinch, a young bird believed to be of this species seen being fed by a female near Pretoria.

LOCAL RACE:
H.c. amauropteryx Sharpe, 1890: *Rustenburg.* Throughout our area.

852   Paradise Whydah   Paradysvink

Steganura paradisaea   (Linnaeus), 1758: *Africa = Angola.*

PLATE 71, ♂ AND ♀ (OPP. P. 593).
Length ♂ 33—38 cm, ♀ 15 cm (wing ♂ 79—81—84, ♀ 78—82; tail ♂ 55—64—longest feather 255—315, ♀ 52—57; tarsus 16—18; culmen 10,5—12,5. 23 specimens, 20 ♂, 3 ♀). Iris brown; bill black; legs brown.

Identification: Breeding males have long *pointed* tail-feathers. Females and non-breeding males are larger and more heavily marked about the head than the other small Whydays in winter dress. Off-season males are slightly larger than the female and more boldly marked. Young birds are brownish above and whitish below.

Distribution: Angola to Somalia, southwards to Damaraland, Botswana, Transvaal and Natal.

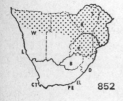

852

Habits: A fairly common species of dry thornveld savannas and open woodland. It is often seen in small flocks searching for seeds on the ground. In the breeding season, males execute display flights, cruising about quite high up with the two shorter, broad tail-feathers raised almost at right-angles to the others. They also hover over females, bobbing up and down with slow wing-beats, each beat causing the long tail to jerk and undulate. Males often sit on the tops of bare trees or on telegraph wires at this time of year and are then very conspicuous; they are in breeding plumage from January to July.

Food: Seeds and insects.
Voice: A sharp "chip"; males also sing, a rather sparrow-like succession of notes.

Breeding: Parasitic, laying its eggs in nests of the Melba Finch and possibly other small Finches and Waxbills. More data urgently required. Large eggs, found in Melba Finch nests and probably of this species, measure about 17,5—18 × 12—13.

LOCAL RACE:
S.p. paradisaea (Linnaeus), 1758: *Africa = Angola.* As illustrated. Size above. South Africa northwards to Angola and through East Africa to Sudan.

853   Broad-tailed Paradise-Whydah
Breëstert-paradysvink

Steganura orientalis   (Heuglin), 1871: *Keren, Eritrea.*

PLATE 71, ♂ (OPP. P. 593).
Length ♂ about 30 cm (wing 83—84; tail 54—58—longest feather 212—225; tarsus 16—17; culmen 11,5—13). Iris brown; bill black; legs brown.

Identification: Males have longest tail-feathers with rounded ends. Females and young similar to those of the Paradise Whydah.

Distribution: From West to East Africa, southwards to Angola and the Zambesi River, coming within our limits in northern Rhodesia, northern Transvaal and at Beira.
Habits: Very similar to those of the preceding species. Parasitises the Golden-backed Pytilia, *Pytilia afra*.

LOCAL RACE:
S.o. obtusa Chapin, 1922: *Luchenza, Nyasaland*. As illustrated. Size above. Angola to Kenya, southwards to the Zambesi and Beira.

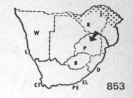
853

854 Cuckoo Finch   Koekoekvink

Anomalospiza imberbis (Cabanis), 1868: *East Africa = Zanzibar*.
PLATE 71, ♂ AND ♀ (OPP. P. 593).
Length about 13 cm (wing 66—73; tail 41—44; tarsus 18; culmen 12,5—14). Iris dark brown; bill blackish; legs grey-brown.

Identification: The deep bill should prevent confusion with any other similar-looking bird. Males are olive-yellow after moulting and become progressively brighter yellow as the feathers wear down. The female is browner above and whitish below. Young birds resemble the female but have the flanks buff, streaked with black; lower mandible yellowish.
Distribution: West to East Africa, southwards to Damaraland, Transvaal and northern Swaziland. Appears to be migratory in Rhodesia, being absent from April to August with one record in June.
Habits: An uncommon but widespread species. It has a considerable likeness to the canaries and seed-eaters in colour and for that reason has probably been overlooked. In South Africa it is a shy bird, making off at once when approached, with direct weaverlike flight. Is usually found in fairly open ground, such as the grass-veld around Pretoria, perching on the top of small bushes. Forms flocks even when in breeding condition.
Food: Grass seeds.
Voice: In flight utters various chattering sounds which may break into a garbled warble; male's song sounds like "tsileu, tsileu, tsileu"; in display makes a "swizzling".
Breeding: Parasitises Prinia and Cisticoline Warblers. There may be two parasites in a nest and the young of the host usually disappear. Eggs have been described as white or pale blue or pinkish, marked with brown, reddish brown and violet. November to March in Rhodesia. They measure 17—17,3 × 12,5—13 (3). Incubation 14 days. Nestling 18 days.

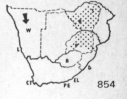
854

LOCAL RACE:
A.i. imberbis (Cabanis), 1868: *East Africa = Zanzibar*. As illustrated. Size above. Angola, Zaïre and Kenya southwards to Damaraland and Transvaal.

Family FRINGILLIDAE

The Canaries, Seed-eaters and Buntings, represented by eighteen indigenous species, are members of a world-wide family. The first of the ten primaries is rudimentary. In southern Africa two sub-families are recognised. The *Fringillinae* have the mandibles of equal length and with cutting edges meeting. They tend to be arboreal. The *Emberizinae* have a gap between mandibles about midway along the length, these are more terrestrial in habits.

855 Cape Siskin   Pietjie-kanarie

Serinus totta (Sparrman), 1786: *Hottentot Country = Cape Province.*
PLATE 72, ♂ AND ♀ (OPP. P. 608).
Length 13 cm (wing 68—72; tail 49—53; tarsus 14—15,5; culmen 9—10,5. 6 specimens). Iris brown; bill brown, mandible paler; legs brown.

Identification: Sexes as illustrated. The white spots on wing and tail are conspicuous in this southern species. Young birds resemble the female.
Distribution: The Cape mountains from Klaver southwards and eastwards to the Eastern Cape.
Habits: Frequents the scrub of the hills and mountains, in pairs or small parties. Is at home in exotic pine forests.
Food: Seeds, buds and insects.

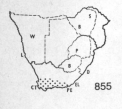

855

Voice: Normal call "peechee". Song, pleasant but weak.
Breeding: The nest is placed in a low bush or, more often, in a crevice in a rock and is composed of grass-stems, weed twigs and fine roots, lined with protea down, other soft material and hair. In the Cape, breeds September to December. Eggs 3—5, greenish blue sparingly and finely speckled with red-brown, brown and some slate-grey mainly as a cap at the thick end. Measurements: 18,7 × 13,1; 16,4 × 13,2; 18,2 × 13,0; 17,0 × 12,8.

856 Drakensberg Siskin   Drakensberg Pietjie-kanarie

Serinus symonsi (Roberts), 1916: *Sanqubetu Valley, Basutoland.*
PLATE 72, ♂ (OPP. P. 608).
Length 132—140 (wing 73—78; tail 54—59; tarsus 16—17; culmen 10,5—11). Iris brown; bill brown mandible paler; legs brown.

Identification: Male illustrated. Both sexes lack white tips to wing and tail feathers. Female duller and browner below than No. 855. Young like the female but more streaked.
Distribution: High mountain areas of the Eastern Cape, Griqualand East, Lesotho and Natal.
Habits: Frequents grass lands and riverine scrub; in winter descends to lower levels. Usually found in small parties but may form large flocks in winter.
Food: Buds, petals, seeds and insects.

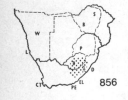

856

Voice: Described as a wonderful songster, singing all day long.
Breeding: The nest is a cup of grass, lined with horsehair and placed in a hollow rock or bush growing among rocks. Eggs, 3—4, white, with fine brown speckling and odd larger spots of brown and purplish. About 17 × 13,5 and laid December to January.

857 Cape Canary   Kaapse Kanarie

Serinus canicollis (Swainson), 1838: *Cape of Good Hope.*

Native Names: Ulonji, Umlonji (X); um-Zwilili (Z); Tale, Tsoere (S).
PLATE 72, ♂ (OPP. P. 608).
Length about 13 cm (wing ♂ 75—79—82, ♀ 72—75—79; tail 48—58; tarsus 14—16; culmen 9,5—11. 30 specimens). Iris brown; bill brown, mandible paler; legs grey-brown.

Identification: Yellow crown and grey nape distinctive. Females duller; young streaked.

Distribution: From the highlands of Ethiopia through East Africa to Angola and Southern Africa but not South West Africa.

Habits: A common bird which frequents the country adjacent to the scrub and forest of the mountains. Apparently a winter visitor only along Natal and Zululand coastal areas. Also fond of orchards in similar country, alighting on the high trees used for windbreaks and singing loudly. Usually found in small flocks during the day-time, gathering at dusk to common roosting places where hundreds and even thousands may be heard calling and singing in concert. These flocks break up during the breeding season.

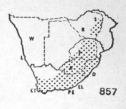

857

Food: Seeds, especially the soft green seeds of weeds and shrubs.

Voice: Normal call a loud ascending "tsweeët". Also sings well, a loud wild song, rather like an English Lark, usually preceded by "tsweet" notes.

Breeding: Nests during the months July to February, constructing a small basin-shaped nest of pliant grass and tendrils, warmly lined with woolly material, in the branches of a bush or tree at 2—20 metres from the ground, usually at about 6 metres. It is built entirely by the female, taking some two weeks. Eggs 3—4, rarely 5, greenish white, sparingly speckled, spotted and sometimes streaked at the thick end, with reddish brown and sometimes a little purplish grey. Average (40) 17,3 × 12,8 (16,0—18,5 × 12,1—13,5). Incubation, 12—14—16 days, by female only, the male feeding the female on the nest. Nestling period 15½—18½ days.

LOCAL RACE:
S.c. canicollis (Swainson), 1838: *Cape of Good Hope.* Throughout our region with other races to the north. Size above.

858 Forest Canary   Gestreepte Kanarie

Serinus scotops   (Sundevall), 1851: *Pietermaritzburg, Natal.*

Native Name: Unotswitswitswi (X).

PLATE 72, ♂ (OPP. P. 608).
Length 13 cm (wing 64—66—68; tail 48—53; tarsus 14—16; culmen 10—12. 17 specimens). Iris brown; bill horn; legs dusky.

Identification: The black chin and heavy streaking distinguish this bird from other canaries. The female resembles the male but the chin and lores are grey, not black. Young resemble females but are more streaked.

Distribution: From Caledon eastwards to Natal, eastern Transvaal and Zoutpansberg.

Habits: Peculiar to thick bush and forested areas, frequenting the glades and borders of the forests and never straying far from them or large trees.

Food: The green seeds of weeds and indigenous shrubs.

Voice: The normal note a quiet "tsik". Also sings well but with less vim than its congeners.

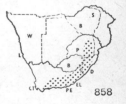

858

Breeding: Nests during the midsummer months, constructing a basin-shaped nest in a bush or small tree at no great height from the ground, 1—5 metres. Eggs 2—4, white with reddish speckles and spotting of reddish brown and some purplish grey, sparingly distributed, but more concentrated at the thick end. Measurements: 16,9 × 12,3; 16,9 × 12,6; 18,3 × 12,2; 17,3 × 12,6.

LOCAL RACES:
(a) S.s. scotops (Sundevall), 1851: *Pietermaritzburg, Natal.* As illustrated. Size above. Caledon to Natal.

CANARIES

(b) S.s. transvaalensis Roberts, 1940: *Woodbush, Transvaal.* More heavily striped below than *(a).* Size the same. Eastern and northern Transvaal.

859 Yellow-eye Canary   Geeloog-sysie

Serinus mozambicus (Müller), 1776: *Mozambique.*

Native Name: Unyilego (X).

PLATE 72 (OPP. P. 608).

Length 12 cm (wing 63—68—73; tail 39—49; tarsus 12—14; culmen 8—10. 31 specimens). Iris brown; bill horn; legs dusky brown.

Identification: Rather resembles the Yellow Canary, No. 866, but is smaller, has a yellow rump and is much paler yellow below. Sexes similar, but female duller. Young birds dull and streaked below, especially on the flanks.

Distribution: West to East Africa southwards to Uitenhage on the east and Botswana and N'gamiland on the west.

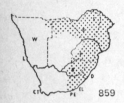

Habits: Occurs in the bushveld and savannas amongst trees where it may be found in small parties or flocks, spending much of its time in the upper branches. Males are often very pugnacious among themselves. A favourite cage bird among many native tribes. An erratic flyer, swerving and diving 859 frequently.

Voice: A melodious "tseeu". A lively song is uttered from the tops of tall trees.

Breeding: Constructs a basin-shaped nest in the branches of a tree 1—6 metres up, in the months September to March or even May. Eggs 3—4, white, sparsely speckled with pink or brown all over, more concentrated at the thick end. Average (33) 16,5 × 12,4 (15,2—18 × 11,2—13,1). Incubation 13—14½ days; nestling 16—24 days.

LOCAL RACES:

(a) S.m. granti Clancey, 1957: *Lusikisiki District, Pondoland.* Yellow below less bright than *(b),* averaging darker above. Eastern Cape Province, Natal, Zululand and the extreme south of Mozambique.

(b) S.m. mozambicus (Müller), 1776: *Mozambique.* As illustrated. Size above. Transvaal, Orange Free State, Swaziland and Mozambique northwards to Malawi and Tanzania.

(c) S.m. vansoni Roberts, 1932: *Zweizwei Waterhole, between Mababe Flats and Chobe River.* Paler above and less bright below. Northern South West Africa, south-eastern Angola, Barotseland and adjacent areas of Zambia.

860 Black-throated Canary   Bergkanarie

Serinus atrogularis A. Smith, 1836: *Kurrichane, W. Transvaal.*

PLATE 72, ♂ (OPP. P. 608).

Length 12 cm (wing 65—69—72; tail 41—47; tarsus 11—14; culmen 8—9. 11 specimens). Iris brown; bill brownish; legs flesh.

Identification: Sexes alike but female has less black on throat. Young have throats spotted with black.

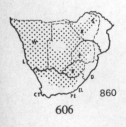

Distribution: The drier western districts from Angola south to Worcester, eastwards to Drakensberg, Transvaal, western Rhodesia, and Zambia to Ethiopia.

Habits: Usually found in small parties searching for food on the ground or 860 perching in trees. In very dry areas apparently dependent on water.

Food: Seeds of grasses and termites.
Voice: A melodious "tswee". Sings very well.
Breeding: Nests during the summer months, both sexes constructing basin-shaped nests in the branches of trees 1—15 metres up, but preferring to place them in the dry cones of protea flowers when these are available. Nests are lined with the down of these flowers. Eggs 3—5, white, faintly greenish at times, usually immaculate but sometimes speckled with purplish black or brown. Average (8) 16,6 × 12,0 (16—17,8 × 11,7—12,5). Incubation 12—13 days. Nestling 15½—17 days.

LOCAL RACES:
(a) S.a. atrogularis A. Smith, 1836: *Kurrichane, Western Transvaal.* Chin and throat heavily marked, below buffy white, above dark; tail with a fair amount of white. Size above. O.F.S., Western Transvaal and Botswana.
(b) S.a. ovambensis Roberts, 1937: *Ondonga, Ovamboland.* Only spotted with black on chin and throat, but on a white ground, above whiter than any others, tail not so extensively white as last; Ovamboland, Kaokoveld to Angola.
(c) S.a. deserti (Reichenow), 1918: *Windhoek.* Only spotted on chin and throat, on a buffy white ground, not so white above and below as *(b)*, outer tail-feathers about the same as in *(a)*. Wing ♂ 69 (3), ♀ 65—69 (4). Great Namaqualand and Damaraland.

860X   Lemon-breasted Canary

Serinus citrinipectus   Clancey and Lawson, 1960: *Panda, P.E.A.*

PLATE 72 ♂ AND ♀ (OPP. P. 608).
Length 12 cm (wing ♂ 62—64,9—67; tail 37,5—39,4—41,5; tarsus 13—13,6—14; culmen 11—11,5—12. 9 ♂ specimens). Iris dark brown; bill dark flesh to horn; legs brown.

Identification: As illustrated.
Distribution: Originally described from Inhambane area, Mozambique, now known also to extend to Beit Bridge, Birchenough Bridge, Rhodesia and southern Malawi. Also Zululand.
Habits: Apparently occurs in semi-rural cultivated areas in company with the Yellow-eye Canary. In non-breeding times it forms more compact flocks than other canaries.
Voice: Typical canary song with sparrow-like quality.
Food: Small seeds.
Breeding: Unknown. In captivity, incubation by ♀ 13—14 days. Egg 16 × 12, white with a few brown streaks.

861   Blackhead Canary   Swartkop-kanarie

Alario alario   (Linnaeus), 1766: *Cape of Good Hope.*

PLATE 72, ♂ AND ♀ (OPP. P. 608).
Length 12—15 cm (wing ♂ 62—67—71 (12), ♀ 63—64 (4); tail 42—49; tarsus 13—15; culmen 8—9. 10 specimens). Iris brown; bill grey, paler below; legs slate.

Identification: As figured, see also under race *(b)* below. Young resemble the female but duller and streaked above. Males vary in the amount of black on the breast.
Distribution: Cape Province, Orange Free State, Western Transvaal and South West Africa as far north as Swakopmund.

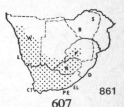

861

PLATE 72

855. *Serinus totta.* Cape Siskin. Pietjie-kanarie. ♂ and ♀.

856. *Serinus symonsi.* Drakensberg Siskin. Drakensberg Pietjie-kanarie. ♂.

857. *(a). Serinus canicollis canicollis.* Cape Canary. Kaapse Kanarie. ♂.

858. *(a). Serinus scotops scotops.* Forest Canary. Gestreepte Kanarie. ♂

859. *Serinus mozambicus mozambicus.* Yellow-eye Canary. Geeloog-sysie.

860. *Serinus atrogularis atrogularis.* Black-throated Canary. Bergkanarie. ♂.

860X. *Serinus citrinipectus.* Lemon-breasted Canary. ♂ and ♀.

861. *Alario alario alario.* Blackhead Canary. Swartkop-kanarie. ♂ and ♀.

863. *(a). Crithagra sulphurata sulphurata.* Bully Seed-eater. Geel Dikbek-sysie.

863. *(c). Crithagra sulphurata sharpei.* Bully Seed-eater. Geel Dikbek-sysie.

865. *(a). Crithagra albogularis albogularis.* White-throated Seed-eater. Witkeel-dikbek-sysie.

865. *(e). Crithagra albogularis crocopygia.* White-throated Seed-eater. Witkeel-dikbek-sysie.

866. *(a). Crithagra flaviventris flaviventris.* Yellow Canary. Geelsysie. ♂ and ♀.

866. *(c). Crithagra flaviventris marshalli.* Yellow Canary ♂. Geelsysie ♂.

867. *(a). Poliospiza gularis gularis.* Streaky-headed Seed-eater. Streepkop-sysie.

868. *Poliospiza mennelli.* Black-eared Seed-eater. Swartoor-sysie.

869. *Poliospiza leucoptera.* Protea Seed-eater. Witvlerk-sysie.

870. *Fringilla coelebs.* Chaffinch. De Vink. ♂ and ♀.

871. *Fringillaria impetuani.* Lark-like Bunting. Vaal Streepkoppie.

872. *Fringillaria tahapisi tahapisi.* Rock Bunting. Klipmossie. ♂ and ♀.

873. *(a). Fringillaria capensis capensis.* Cape Bunting. Streepkoppie.

874. *Emberiza flaviventris flaviventris.* Golden-breasted Bunting. Rooirug-geel-streepkoppie.

875. *Emberiza cabanisi orientalis.* Cabanis' Yellow Bunting. Geel Streepkoppie.

856

855 ♂

♀

858 A

857 A ♂

859

861 ♂

♀

860 X ♀ ♂

860 ♂

866 A ♀

866 C ♂

KN

865 E

863 A

863 C

867 A

868

865 A

871

870 ♀ ♂

KN

869

875

872 ♂

♀

873 A

874

NIGHTON '36

Habits: A common bird in dry karroid areas, usually found in parties, though also in pairs or single, searching for food on shrubs and on the ground. In some years wanders down into the coastal grassveld of the eastern Cape.

Food: Seeds taken mainly off the ground.

Voice: A gentle "tweet" or "sweea". Also sings well, rather more quietly and melodiously than most of our seed-eaters.

Breeding: Nests August to April, constructing a small cup-shaped nest of twigs lined with vegetable-down and placed in a bush or small tree, usually only a metre or so from the ground. Eggs 3—5, greenish white with a few scattered speckles and some spots of reddish to dark brown. Average (15) 16,7 × 12,5 (16,2—18,2 × 12,0—13,0).

LOCAL RACES:

(a) A.a. alario (Linnaeus), 1766: *Cape of Good Hope.* As figured on Plate 72. Confined to the Cape Province but not Namaqualand.

(b) A.a. leucolaema Sharpe, 1903: *Hountop River, Great Namaqualand.* Like *(a)* except that the forehead, eyebrow, face, chin and throat are white or show a variable amount of black. Female whiter on the throat than in *(a).* Found in South West Africa eastwards over the Orange Free State and western Transvaal and Namaqualand.

Both races may be found together in the western Cape Province.

862 = 861 *(b).*

863   Bully Seed-eater   Geel Dikbek-sysie

Crithagra sulphurata   (Linnaeus), 1766: *Cape of Good Hope.*

Native Name: Indweza eluhlaza (X).

PLATE 72, *(a)* AND *(c)* (OPP. P. 608).

Length 15—16 cm (150—160; wing 76—81—84; tail 58—64; tarsus 17—19; culmen 13—15. 18 specimens). Iris hazel; bill grey, mandible yellowish; legs brown.

Identification: The large bill and greenish chest differentiate the southern races from the Yellow Canary, No. 866, and there is no marked sexual difference as there is in that species. See also under No. 866.

Distribution: South Africa, except South West Africa and dry areas, north through Angola and Malawi to Central and East Africa.

Habits: A fairly common species, usually found singly or in pairs in open coastal bush, mountains or grassland with trees, particularly between the escarpment and the coast.

Food: Seeds and buds, particularly of tall euphorbias.

Voice: A deep "sqeerk". Song deep and rather undistinguished.

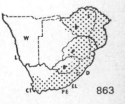

863

Breeding: Breeds July to November in the Cape, in midsummer further north. Nests are like those of the canaries: shallow basins lined with fibrous and woolly material. Situated usually 2—6 metres up. Eggs 2—4, pale greenish white, usually uniform, but sometimes with a few spots or lines of brown to dark brown at the thick end. Average (28) 19,5 × 14,2 (17,8—20,8 × 13,4—14,8); races *(a)* and *(b)* below. Incubation 12½—17 days. Nestling 15—21 days.

LOCAL RACES:

(a) C.s. sulphurata (Linnaeus), 1766: *Cape of Good Hope.* As figured. Size above. Cape Province.

(b) C.s. wilsoni Roberts, 1936: *Kloof, Natal.* More yellowish above and below than *(a).* Size similar. Natal to northern Transvaal and southern Mozambique.

(c) C.s. sharpei (Neumann), 1900: *Kilimanjaro, Tanganyika.* Smaller than the preceding races and with a lighter bill. Thus resembles No. 866 but there is not the great colour disparity in the sexes, the yellow of the forehead is broken by the green of the crown, and the chest shows some greenish and is not uniform bright yellow. Wing 72—77; tail 53—58; tarsus 16—17; culmen 12—13. 7 specimens. Eggs: Average (25) 18,4 × 13,4 (16,2—20,6 × 12,6—14). Rhodesia and northern Mozambique, Malawi northwards to Uganda.

864 = 863 *(c).*

865   White-throated Seed-eater   Witkeel-dikbek-sysie

Crithagra albogularis   A. Smith, 1833: *South Africa = Piquetberg, Cape.*

PLATE 72, RACES *(a)* AND *(e)* (OPP. P. 608).
Length 15 cm (wing 74—78—81; tail 53—61; tarsus 20—22; culmen 12—15. 9 specimens). Iris brown; bill horn; legs brown.

Identification: The heavy bill and dull colour combined with a yellow or greenish yellow rump make this bird unmistakable. Sexes alike; young resemble adults.

Distribution: The dry districts of Cape Province northwards through the Karoo to Transvaal, Griqualand West, Great Namaqualand and Damaraland.

Habits: Frequents the dry scrub, particularly along valleys or on hillsides. Usually found in pairs or small parties. May be found in desert country as well as regions of fair rainfall.

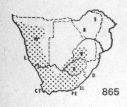 865

Food: Seeds and buds, particularly of euphorbias.

Voice: Call-note a deep "squee-yik". Song powerful and tuneful.

Breeding: Nest a shallow cup of rootlets and twigs lined with vegetable down, usually 1—3 metres up. Breeds from August to April. Eggs 2—4, pale greenish white, usually immaculate but occasionally scrolled with purplish black at the thick end. Average (50) 19,8 × 14,6 (17,2—22,1 × 13,5—16,6). Incubation by both sexes.

LOCAL RACES:
(a) C.a. albogularis A. Smith, 1833: *Berg River, Piquetberg, Cape Province.* As figured. Dimensions above. Western Cape to Little Namaqualand.
(b) C.a. hewitti Roberts, 1937: *Kleinpoort farm, Albany District, Cape Province.* Rump less yellow, eyebrows hardly perceptibly white, upper parts darker. Wing 77—79 (4). Eastern Cape Province.
(c) C.a. orangensis Roberts, 1937: *Fauresmith, Orange Free State.* Rump bright yellow in the middle. Otherwise like *hewitti.* Size as in *(a).*
(d) C.a. sordahlae (Friedmann), 1932: *Brukkaros Mountains, Great Namaqualand.* Middle of rump bright yellow in contrast to the sides, paler above and below, white eyebrows conspicuous. Wing 75—78—82 (15). Bushmanland and Great Namaqualand.
(e) C.a. crocopygia (Sharpe), 1871: *Daviljob, Otjimbingwe, Damaraland.* As illustrated. Darker above but paler below, yellow of rump extending right across. Size larger. Wing 78—86 (12).

866 Yellow Canary

Geelsysie

Crithagra flaviventris (Swainson), 1828: *Berg River, Cape.*

PLATE 72, ♂ AND ♀ (OPP. P. 608).
Length 13—14 cm (wing ♂ 69—71—73, ♀ 63—68—74; tail 47—57; tarsus 16—20; culmen 10—12. 22 specimens, 12 ♂, 10 ♀). Iris hazel; bill horn; legs dusky brown.

Identification: Resembles the Yellow-eye, No. 859, but is larger, lacks the yellow rump and the sexes are widely different. Also resembles the northern race of *C. sulphurata*, see No. 863, Plate 72, but lacks the greenish on the chest and the yellow of the forehead carries right across the base of the bill.
Distribution: Confined to Southern Africa, from Cape Town north to Damaraland and eastwards to eastern Cape Province, Orange Free State, southern Transvaal and Botswana.

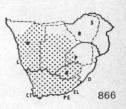

866

Habits: Frequents the scrub of the flats and coastal bush in the south and west and the open bush along streams in the east and dry northern areas. Also common in coastal scrub and may sometimes be seen right on the beach, even on rocks in the sea. Forms small flocks when not breeding.
Food: Seeds and termites.
Voice: A single rather deep "tzyee" or "tirriyip". Males are good singers.
Breeding: Builds a typical canary type of nest in a low bush or low in a bush or small tree 30 cm to 3 m up during July to November in the south-west Cape and later, midsummer to March in the north. Eggs 3—4, immaculate greenish white or more often boldly spotted or streaked at the thick end with dark chocolate or blackish. Average (80) 18,0 × 13,2 (16,1—20,6 × 12,5—14,6). Incubation by female, 12 days (Priest).

LOCAL RACES:
(a) C.f. flaviventris (Swainson), 1828: *Berg River, South-western Cape Province.* As figured. Size given above. South-western Cape, Little Namaqualand.
(b) C.f. guillarmodi (Roberts). 1936: *Sanqubetu Valley, Basutoland.* Darker above and about the face, the rump not very yellowish, ♀ heavily striped below. Size rather larger. Wing 76—77; tail 58—60; tarsus 19,5—20; culmen 10—10,5 (4 specimens, 2 ♂, 2 ♀). Lesotho mountains.
(c) C.f. marshalli (Shelley), 1902: *Potchefstroom.* More yellow especially on the rump, back paler in ♂, ♀ only slightly striped and yellowish below. Size as in *(a).* Wing ♂ 69—74—77 (12), ♀ 69—72 (4). Upper Orange and Vaal rivers and their tributaries, Griqualand West, Lesotho, southern and western Transvaal and eastern Botswana.
(d) C.f. damarensis Roberts, 1922: *Windhoek.* South West Africa and central Botswana. More yellow-green above.
(e) C.f. quintoni Winterbottom, 1959: *Hillmore, Beaufort West.* Karooid areas to the eastern Cape. Distinctly larger. Wing 71—82 mm.

867 Streaky-headed Seed-eater

Streepkop-sysie

Poliospiza gularis (A. Smith), 1836: *Latakoo = Kuruman, Northern Cape.*

Native Name: Indweza (X).

PLATE 72 (OPP. P. 608).
Length about 15 cm (wing 73—82; tail 58—68; tarsus 14,5—16,5; culmen 12—13,5. 34 specimens). Iris hazel; bill horn; legs pale brown.

Identification: See under No. 868. Sexes alike. Young birds are streaked on the mantle. Lacks the yellow or greenish rump of No. 865.

611

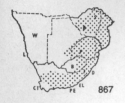

867

Distribution: The whole of Southern Africa except the extreme south-west Cape and South West Africa, northwards over the drier areas of Africa to Ethiopia and Cameroon.

Habits: A common and conspicuous species which frequents open woodland and tall scrub where it may be seen perched on the tops of bushes or trees.

Food: Seeds, very fond of sunflowers and kaffir-corn; also flower buds and petals. Termites and caterpillars also recorded.

Voice: Normal call "see-e-ee"; sings well in a quiet way.

Breeding: A neat cup of leaf-stems and grass, bound with cobwebs and lined with vegetable-down, is placed in a tree usually fairly high up (1—15 metres). September to April. Eggs 2—4, greenish white with a few speckles of pinky brown and dark brown at the thick end. Average (50) 18,4 × 13,9 (17—20,6 × 12,6—14,9). Incubation 12½—15 days. Nestling 12—17 days.

LOCAL RACES:

(a) P.g. gularis (A. Smith), 1836: *Latakoo = Kuruman, Northern Cape.* As illustrated. Size above. Northern Cape, Orange Free State, Transvaal and Matabeleland.

(b) P.g. humilis (Bonaparte), 1850: *Africa = Eastern Cape Province.* Darker and more buffy below. Smaller. Cape Province, except for *(a)* and *(c)*.

(c) P.g. endemion Clancey, 1952: *Town Bush, Pietermaritzburg.* Eastern Cape Province to Natal, Pondoland, East Griqualand, Natal and Zululand, southern Mozambique, Swaziland, eastern Orange Free State and south-western Transvaal.

868   Black-eared Seed-eater   Swartoor-sysie

Poliospiza mennelli   Chubb, 1908: *Tjoko's Kraal, Shangani River, Southern Rhodesia.*

PLATE 72 (OPP. P. 608).

Length 13—14 cm (wing 79—83; tail 48—56; tarsus 12,5—14,5; culmen 10—12,5. 5 specimens). Iris brown; bill brown; legs brown.

Identification: Very similar to the Streaky-headed Seed-eater, No. 867, but males have blacker cheeks while females, which have brown cheeks, are darker, particularly on the back, than females of the last species.

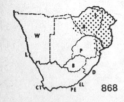

868

Distribution: From southern Mozambique northwards to Malawi, Rhodesia, Zambia and south-eastern Zaïre.

Habits: Found among trees in fairly open grassy country. Males spend a lot of time singing from the bare topmost branches of tall trees.

Food: Seeds and some fruit.

Voice: A nasal bunting-like bleat. Song consists of a series of uneven, twittering whistles—"teeu-twee-teu-twiddy-twee-twee", the second note much higher than the rest. This phrase is repeated over and over again.

Breeding: Recorded in September to March, the cup-shaped nest being constructed of lichen and placed fairly high, 1—9 metres up in a tree. Eggs 2—3, pale green, spotted and freckled with black and pale greyish lilac, usually in a zone at the larger end. 20,2 × 14,8 (17,2—22,0 × 13,2—16,0).

869   Protea Seed-eater   Witvlerk-sysie

Poliospiza leucoptera   (Sharpe), 1871: *Paarl, Cape Province.*

PLATE 72 (OPP. P. 608).
Length about 15 cm (wing 70; tail 58; tarsus 18; culmen 12,5). Iris brown; bill flesh-coloured and light; legs dark brown.

Identification: In Plate 72 the breast should appear darker. Can be distinguished from the White-throated Seed-eater, No. 865, by the *plain coloured rump*, faint white eyebrow and white bars in the wing. These are *not* conspicuous in flight but visible at rest. The white throat patch shows as a white bar.

Distribution: Confined to the mountains of the south-west Cape, from Niewoudtville southwards to Cape Hangklip and eastwards to the Baviaanskloof.

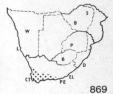

869

Habits: An uncommon and very retiring species, spending much of its time concealed in thick vegetation. When disturbed flies low over the scrub and soon takes cover again. Usually found scattered in pairs or as individuals in bushy kloofs in the mountains.

Food: Recorded eating the seeds of proteas, dried ericas, the plant *Othonna amplexicaulis* and *Rhus anacardia.*

Voice: Normal call a soft "tree-lee-loo". Also "sweet" like a Cape Canary. Males sing in typically Seed-eater fashion, rather like the Bully Seed-eater but softer and sweeter.

Breeding: A cup-shaped nest situated in a Protea or Pine tree, 3—5 metres up is well hidden in a fork. Made up of dried stems, protea fluff and grass. August to October. Eggs 2—4, ivory white or pale blue slightly glossy with black, purplish and reddish-brown spots and speckles mainly at thick end. Average (6) 20,6 × 14,6 (19—21,7 × 14,4—14,9). Incubation 17 days. Nestling 14 days.

870   Chaffinch   De Vink

Fringilla coelebs   Linnaeus, 1758: *Sweden.*

PLATE 72, ♂ AND ♀ (OPP. P. 608).
Length 15 cm (wing ♂ 83—90, ♀ 78—85; tail 58—67; tarsus 17—19; culmen 11,5—12,5. 12 specimens ex *Handbook British Birds*). Iris brown; bill lead-blue, brown in female and young; legs pale brown.

Identification: As illustrated. In flight both sexes show broad white shoulder-patch and conspicuous white on outer tail-feathers.

Distribution: Confined to the Cape Peninsula where it was introduced in 1898 by C. J. Rhodes. It has not spread far, being found from Sea Point to Plumstead and Tokai. Probably commonest in Newlands, Kenilworth and Kloof Nek.

Habits: A tame and confiding little bird which was often found in the Public Gardens, around the Zoo and similar places but has lately disappeared from the Gardens. Has declined in numbers in recent years. Seems to prefer areas of pine and oak woods. Does not form large flocks of one sex only in winter, as it does in Europe.

Food: Seeds, and in Europe insects. Will readily come to food put out for it.

613

Voice: Call-note "pink, pink", rather metallic. Song pleasant but always the same phrase, something like "chip, chip, chip, cherry-erry-erry, chip-pyooEEar", gradually increasing in tempo but falling, to rise with the final flourish.

Breeding: Builds a small compact, cup-shaped nest, covered with lichen, paper and spider webs, 8—12 metres up in a tree or bush. Eggs, laid in September and November, are greenish blue spotted with dark purplish brown. 19,7 × 14,0. Incubation almost entirely by female, 11—13 days (Europe). Nestling period 13—14 days (Europe).

LOCAL RACE:
F.c. gengleri Kleinschmidt, 1909: *Hampstead, England.* The birds introduced appear to be of this race.

871   Lark-like Bunting   Vaal Streepkoppie

Fringillaria impetuani   (A. Smith), 1836: *Between Nu Gariep and the Tropic.*

PLATE 72 (OPP. P. 608).
Length 13—14 cm (wing ♂ 72—75—80 (18), ♀ 70—72—75 (11); tail 52—61; tarsus 16—17,5; culmen 9—10,5. 14 specimens, 8 ♂, 6 ♀). Iris brown; bill horn; legs dusky flesh.

Identification: Sexes alike; young resemble adults. Seems to lack any diagnostic features in the field, the light-coloured bill and legs are noticeable. Call note (*q.v.*) very diagnostic.

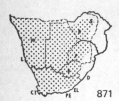

Distribution: Cape Province except the southern coastal belt, South West Africa, the Kalahari, Orange Free State, western Transvaal and beyond our limits, Angola and southern Zaïre.

Habits: Common in dry rocky country and thus particularly common in the Karoo. Rather lark-like in habits spending most of its time on the ground and only occasionally perching on bushes. In hot weather comes to water-holes in numbers towards evening.

Food: Seeds and insects.

Voice: Call a characteristic, plaintive, nasal "chut". Males sing during the breeding season from the tops of bushes or other slight eminences, a sprightly but guttural and monotonous song ending rather wheezily.

Breeding: Breeds during October and November in the Cape, to May in the north. The nest, apparently built by the female only, is a shallow basin composed of grass and roots, usually placed in the shelter of a patch of weeds or grass but also quite out in the open. Eggs 2—4, normally 3, are greenish white more or less spotted with brown. Average (31) 17,5 × 13,5 (16,0—19,6 × 12,5—15,3).

LOCAL RACES:
(a) *F.i. impetuani* (A. Smith), 1836: *Between Nu Gariep and the Tropic.* As above.
(b) *F.i. sloggetti* Macdonald, 1957: *Deelfontein, Cape Province.* Karooid areas. Pale above and below.

872   Rock Bunting   Klipmossie

Fringillaria tahapisi   (A. Smith), 1836: *Sources of the Vaal River*.

Native Names: Undenjenje, Undenzeni (X); Motoelitoeli (S).
PLATE 72, ♂ AND ♀ (OPP. P. 608).
Length about 14 cm (wing ♂ 76—79—83 (31), ♀ 72—75—79 (23); tail 55—66; tarsus
15—18; culmen 9—11. 49 specimens, 28 ♂, 21 ♀). Iris brown; bill brown; legs brown.

Identification: The cinnamon breast and striped head render this Bunting
unmistakable. Sexes differ as shown in Plate 72. Young birds resemble female
but pale stripes on head are buff, not white; throat dusky, and buff margins to
wing-feathers broader.
Distribution: Widely dispersed over the continent south of the Sahara and
also in Socotra and Arabia. In our area absent from the dry west and southern
Cape Province.
Habits: Frequents rocky areas and is very common in such places as the
foothills of the Drakensberg, particularly where the ground is open, grassy and
stony. A confiding species which will enter the streets and gardens of large
towns.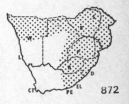
Food: Mainly seeds, also insects.
Voice: Call a quiet "pay-way" or "pee-wee" sometimes rendered as "be-
ware". Song, uttered by the male, is a short, soft skirl something like "per-pe,
pee-e-eter-cher".
Breeding: Constructs a basin-shaped nest of grass and fine roots in a tuft of
grass or shrub amongst the rocks, on the ground or on banks or ledges. Breeds
November to May. Eggs 2—4, normally 3, are dull white heavily obscured all
over with spots of reddish brown. Average (41) 17,5 × 13,2 (16,4—18,6 ×
11,9—14,4). Eggs from Zambia seem larger: (50) 19,4 × 13,5. Incubation
both sexes, 12—14 days. Nestling period, 14—16 days.

LOCAL RACE:
F.t. tahapisi (A. Smith), 1836: *Sources of the Vaal River*. Throughout our area and
Zambia. Other races to the north.

873   Cape Bunting   Streepkoppie

Fringillaria capensis   (Linnaeus), 1766: *Cape of Good Hope.*

Native Name: Mborokoane (S).
PLATE 72 (OPP. P. 608).
Length about 13 cm (wing ♂ 75—77—79, ♀ 71—73; tail 58—72; tarsus 19—20; culmen
10,5—12. 10 specimens, 7 ♂, 3 ♀).

Identification: The grey breast combined with black-and-white striped head
render this Bunting unmistakable. Sexes alike, young birds are duller.
Distribution: Throughout Southern Africa except the central Kalahari and
east coast, northwards to Malawi.
Habits: A common bird in localities where there are hills and mountains but
also in sandy coastal regions, particularly if rocks are present. Permanent
water is necessary to its existence. A tame and confiding bird which comes
round camp sites where it is often fed by campers. Usually seen in pairs
though several may live in close proximity.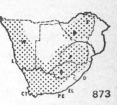

Food: Seeds and insects such as grasshoppers and beetles; also spiders.
Voice: Normal call a nasal chirp. Also a loud "cherowee" or "wheeoo whee". Song short, choppy and variable, something like "cheep, cheep, tip chiperee tip tipperee". Also described as "teedlee, teedlee, pip-pip-pip-pip".
Breeding: In the Cape breeds from July to January; to May in Rhodesia and the north later. The nest, of grass and fine roots, is bowl-shaped and placed inside a grass tuft or small bush. Eggs 2—4, normally 3, are white with pinky brown and purplish slate markings fairly evenly distributed all over, though more at the thick end. Average (44) 20,3 × 15,1 (17,9—24,5 × 13,6—16,2).

LOCAL RACES:
(a) F.c. capensis (Linnaeus), 1766: *Cape of Good Hope.* Above broadly striped on crown and back, chin and throat whitish, rest below greyish. Size above. Southern Cape districts.
(b) F.c. bradfieldi Roberts, 1928: *Waterberg, South West Africa.* Darkest rufous-toned above, very thinly striped, below lighter buffy olive. Wing ♂ 80—84. Waterberg and Otavi mountains.
(c) F.c. media Sharpe, 1904: *Deelfontein, Cape Province.* Above lighter than *(a)*, below lighter and clearer buffy, chin and throat buffy and not whitish. Wing ♂ 80—82 (3), ♀ 72—76 (5). Eastern Karoo districts from Port Elizabeth and Grahamstown to Griqualand West, Orange Free State and southern Botswana.
(d) F.c. basutoensis Vincent, 1950: *Source of Lekhalabaletsi River, eastern Basutoland.* Greyer below than *(c)* and *(e)*, less rufous above. Wing ♂ 83,5 (1). High mountain areas of Lesotho.
(e) F.c. reidi Shelley, 1902: *Ingagane River, Newcastle, Natal.* Above and below darker than *(c)*. Wing ♂ 81—87 (6), ♀ 77—79 (4). Highveld areas of East Griqualand, Natal, southern and south-eastern Transvaal.
(f) F.c. limpopoensis Roberts, 1924: *Pretoria, Transvaal.* Above dark, but more rufous, below as in *reidi*. Size similar. Wing ♂ 82—88 (7), ♀ 75—77—82 (9). Central, south-western and western Transvaal, north to Zoutpansberg.
(g) F.c. plowesi Vincent, 1950: *Matopos. Southern Rhodesia.* Matabeleland. Very pale.
(h) F.c. smithersii Plowes, 1951: *Chimanimani Mountains.* Very dark, below deep buffy grey, feathers of the back with broad dark centres. Wing ♀ 79 (1 = type). Mashonaland.

874 Golden-breasted Bunting
Rooirug-geel-streepkoppie

Emberiza flaviventris Stephens, 1815: *Cape of Good Hope.*

Native Names: Intsasa (X); Chiherehere (D).

PLATE 72 (OPP. P. 608).
Length 15—16 cm (wing ♂ 80—83,5—87, ♀ 77—80—81; tail 64—75; tarsus 16—19; culmen 12—13,5. 52 specimens, 37 ♂, 15 ♀). Iris brown; bill black, lower mandible brown; legs dull flesh.

Identification: Resembles the next species but has a white stripe above and below the eye. Female duller, back more brownish. Young has stripes of head buffy, back streaked.
Distribution: Throughout our area except Namaqualand and western Cape Province. Beyond our limits, all Africa south of the Sahara.
Habits: Frequents the trees of the savannas where it is quite a common bird; also found in open country and gardens. Spends much of its time on the ground walking about in search of food. Can apparently do without water for long periods.
Food: Mainly insects, particularly when breeding but also seeds.

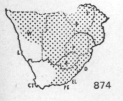

874

Voice: Call a low, hard, grating "zreede". Also a short song rendered "chwee, chi-it-twee". Alarm note a rather plaintive "chuck-a-cheer".

Breeding: Breeds in the months September to April, building a shallow bowl of rootlets and grass in the branches of a small tree or bush, from two to about seven feet above the ground. The eggs, 2 or 3, are glossy white, with a ring of scrawls, pencillings, hair lines and blobs of purplish, olive-brown and dark brown at the thicker end. Average (100) 19,7 × 14,3 (17,9—23,3 × 13,1—15,2; one 16,6). Incubation 12½ and 13 days. Nestling 16—17 days.

LOCAL RACES:
(a) *E.f. flaviventris* Stephens, 1815: *Cape of Good Hope.* Size above. Cape Province, Natal, southern and eastern Transvaal to eastern Rhodesia.
(b) *E.f. kalaharica* Roberts, 1932: *Tsotsoroga Pan, Bechuanaland.* Males uniform reddish on the back; females usually so, streaked in young and some females. Size larger. Western Transvaal to Botswana, Matabeleland and northern South West Africa.
(c) *E.f. princeps* Clancey and Winterbottom, 1960: 10 *miles east of Windhoek,* South West Africa. Paler than (b), tail longer.

875 Cabanis' Yellow Bunting Geel Streepkoppie

Emberiza cabanisi (Reichenow), 1875: *Cameroon.*

PLATE 72 (OPP. P. 608).
Length about 16 cm (wing 78—86; tail 68—75; tarsus 18,5—20,5; culmen 12—14. 6 specimens). Iris brown; bill dusky; legs brownish.

Identification: Lacks the white stripe below the eye of the last species; breast yellow without the reddish on the chest. Female has a less distinct streak on crown than male. Young birds have eyebrow-stripe brownish, yellower below; streaked with brown on flanks.

Distribution: Sierra Leone to Uganda, southwards to Angola, Mashonaland and Mozambique.

Habits: Very similar to those of the last species, usually noticed when disturbed while feeding on the ground and flying up into the branches of trees above. Occurs in rich Brachystegia in Rhodesia. Found in grass-covered country where there are trees and bushes, often on the borders of woods and other bushy areas.

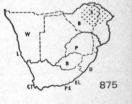

875

Food: Insects, particularly small grasshoppers; also small seeds.

Voice: The song consists of a piercing, sweet modulated whistle, varied but often resembling "wee, chidder-chidder-chidder, wee" or "her, ip, ip, ip . . . her, hee".

Breeding: Nests from September to January, building a somewhat bulky cup-shaped structure of grass, twiglets and dry weedy plant-stems, placed 1—5 metres up in a tree or bush, usually better hidden than the nest of the previous species. Eggs 2—3, white to light greenish, strikingly marked with a ring of twirls, pencillings and hair lines of chocolate-brown and sepia with underlying markings of lilac and slate-grey. Average (11) 20,0 × 14,7 (18—21,9 × 14,1—15,1).

LOCAL RACE:
E.c. orientalis (Shelley), 1882: *Morogoro, Eastern Tanganyika.* Tanzania, Zambia, Mashonaland and Mozambique.

617

Index to English Names

619

622

625

Index to Scientific Names

capensis, *Batis*, 672, pl. p. 480
capensis, *Botaurus s.*, 71, pl. p. 33
capensis, *Bubo*, 367, pl. p. 257
capensis, *Burhinus*, 275, pl. p. 161
capensis, *Euplectes*, 810, pl. p. 561
capensis, *Corvus*, 523, pl. p. 353
capensis, *Francolinus*, 181, pl. p. 129
capensis, *Fringillaria*, 873, pl. p. 608
capensis, *Macronyx*, 703, pl. p. 481
capensis, *Microparra*, 229, pl. p. 145
capensis, *Morus*, 44, pl. p. 32
capensis, *Motacilla*, 686, pl. p. 481
capensis, *Oena*, 318, pl. p. 225
capensis, *Phalacrocorax*, 48, pl. p. 32
capensis, *Podiceps r.*, 6, pl. p. 48
capensis, *Pycnonotus*, 543, pl. p. 369
capensis, *Smithornis*, 454, pl. p. 465
capensis, *Spatula*, 94, pl. p. 64
capensis, *Tyto*, 360, pl. p. 257
capicola, *Streptopelia*, 316, pl. p. 225
capricorni, *Campethera b.*, 446
Caprimulgus europaeus, 371, pl. p. 272
Caprimulgus fossii, 376, pl. p. 272
Caprimulgus natalensis, 375, pl. p. 272
Caprimulgus pectoralis, 373, pl. p. 272
Caprimulgus rufigena, 372, pl. p. 272
Caprimulgus tristigma, 374, pl. p. 272
cuprius, *Chrysococcyx*, 352, pl. p. 256
carbo, *Phalacrocorax*, 47, pl. p. 32
caroli, *Anthoscopus*, 530, pl. p. 368
carpi, *Caprimulgus n.*, 375
carpi, *Parus l.*, 528
carunculatus, *Grus*, 215, pl. p. 160
Casmerodius albus, 58, pl. p. 33
caspia, *Hydroprogne*, 290, pl. p. 224
castaneigula, *Ploceus x.*, 802
castaneiventer, *Pternistis a.*, 188, pl. p. 129
castro, *Oceanodroma*, xxxi
Catharacta skua, 286, pl. p. 209
cathkinensis, *Bradypterus b.*, 610
caudata, *Coracias*, 413, pl. p. 289
caurinus, *Ploceus v.*, 803
cavei, *Certhilauda a.*, 461
cavendishi, *Estrilda a.*, 843
Cecropis abyssinica, 503, pl. p. 352
Cecropis cucullata, 502, pl. p. 352
Cecropis senegalensis, 500, pl. p. 352
Cecropis semirufa, 501, pl. p. 352
Centropus cupreicaudus, 354, pl. p. 241
Centropus grillii, 353, pl. p. 241
Centropus senegalensis, 355, pl. p. 241
Centropus superciliosus, 356, pl. p. 241
Centropus toulou, 353, pl. p. 241
Cercococcyx montanus, 344X, pl. p. 241
Cercomela familiaris, 570, pl. p. 400

Cercomela schlegelii, 566, pl. p. 400
Cercomela sinuata, 572, pl. p. 400
Cercomela tractrac, 571, pl. p. 400
Certhilauda albescens, 461, pl. p. 320
Certhilauda albofasciata, 474, pl. p. 321
Certhilauda burra, 479, pl. p. 321
Certhilauda curvirostris, 475, pl. p. 321
Ceryle rudis, 394, pl. p. 288
Ceuthmochares aereus, 358, pl. p. 241
Chaetops frenatus, 540, pl. p. 368
Chaetura boehmi, 389, pl. p. 273
Chaetura ussheri, 388, pl. p. 273
Chalcomitra amethystina, 772, pl. p. 544
Chalcomitra senegalensis, 774, pl. p. 544
chalcopterus, *Rhinoptilus*, 280, pl. p. 208
chalcospilos, *Turtur*, 321, pl. p. 225
chalybeus, *Cinnyris*, 760, pl. p. 529
chalybeus, *Lamprotornis*, 738, pl. p. 528
changamwensis, *Bias m.*, 667
changamwensis, *Cyanomitra o.*, 768
chapini, *Dryoscopus c.*, 712
Charadrius asiaticus, 240, pl. p. 184
Charadrius hiaticula, 233, pl. p. 184
Charadrius leschenaultii, 239, pl. p. 184
Charadrius marginatus, 235, pl. p. 184
Charadrius mongolus, 234, pl. p. 184
Charadrius pallidus, 236, pl. p. 184
Charadrius pecuarius, 237, pl. p. 184
Charadrius tricollaris, 238, pl. p. 184
chelicuti, *Halcyon*, 403, pl. p. 288
cheniana, *Mirafra*, 456, pl. p. 320
chicquera, *Falco*, 117, pl. p. 73
chiniana, *Cisticola*, 642, pl. p. 449
chirindensis, *Apalis*, 623X, pl. p. 417
Chlidonias leucoptera, 304, pl. p. 224
Chlidonias hybrida, 305, pl. p. 224
Chlidonias nigra, 305X, pl. p. 224
chloris, *Anthus*, 701, pl. p. 481
chlorochlamys, *Tauraco p.*, 337
chlorocephalus, *Oriolus* 521X, pl. p. 353
Chlorocichla flaviventris, 550, pl. p. 369
Chloropeta natalensis, 666, pl. p. 465
Chlorophoneus nigrifrons, 720, pl. p. 512
Chlorophoneus olivaceus, 717, pl. p. 512
Chlorophoneus sulphureopectus, 719, pl. p. 512
chloropterus, *Lamprotornis*, 739, pl. p. 528
chloropus, *Gallinula*, 210, pl. p. 145
chlororhynchus, *Diomedea*, 10, pl. p. 16
chobiensis, *Corythaixoides c.*, 339
chobiensis, *Anthus v.*, 695
chobiensis, *Turdus l.*, 552
choragium, *Clamator g.*, 346
Chrysococcyx caprius, 352, pl. p. 256
Chrysococcyx cupreus, 350, pl. p. 256

633

635

638

hybrida, Chlidonias, 305, pl. p. 224
Hydrobates pelagicus, 30
Hydroprogne caspia, 290, pl. p. 224
Hyliota australis, 668, pl. p. 465
Hyliota flavigaster, 670, pl. p. 465
Hypargos margaritatus, 831, pl. p. 577
Hypargos nitidulus, 827, pl. p. 577
Hypargos niveoguttatus, 832, pl. p. 577
hypernephela, Cercomela s., 572
Hyphanturgus ocularis, 791, pl. p. 560
Hyphanturgus olivaceiceps, 791X, pl. p. 560
Hypochera chalybeata, 851, pl. p. 593
Hypochera funerea, 849, pl. p. 593
Hypochera purpurascens, 850, pl. p. 593
hypoleucos, Actitis, 258, pl. p. 185
hypopyrrhus, Malaconotus, 723, pl. p. 512
hypoxantha, Prinia, 651, pl. p. 464
hypoxanthus, Andropardus i., 551

Ibis ibis, 76, pl. p. 49
ibis Bubulcus, 61, pl. p. 33
ibis, Mycteria, 76, pl. p. 49
icterina, Hippolais, 596, pl. p. 464
icterops, Sylvia c., 594
icteropygialis, Eremomela, 600, pl. p. 464
imberbis, Anomalospiza, 854, pl. p. 593
impavida, Muscicapa c., 656
impetuani, Fringillaria, 871, pl. p. 608
importunus, Andropadus, 551, pl. p. 369
incana, Estrilda p., 842, pl. p. 592
incerta, Pterodroma, 18, pl. p. 17
Indicator indicator, 440, pl. p. 256
Indicator meliphilus, 442X, pl. p. 256
Indicator minor, 442, pl. p. 256
Indicator variegatus, 441, pl. p. 256
indicus, Colius, 392, pl. p. 272
indicus, Passer d., 784, pl. p. 545
infuscatus, Bradornis, 663, pl. p. 465
infuscatus, Podiceps c., 4, pl. p. 48
insignis, Parus n., 528
insignis, Prodotiscus, 444, pl. p. 256
intensa, Cossypha n., 579
intermedius, Dendropicos f., 450
intermedia, Egretta, 60, pl. p. 33
intermedius, Phyllastrephus t., 546
intermedius, Ploceus, 792, pl. p. 560
intermedius, Sphenoeacus a., 618
interna, Erythropygia q., 585
interpres, Arenaria, 232, pl. p. 184
inustus, Ploceus v., 803
iolema, Cossypha c., 581
irwini, Buccanodon w., 434
isabellina, Cisticola b., 636, pl. p. 448

Ispidina picta, 398, pl. p. 288
Ixobrychus minutus, 67, pl. p. 48
Ixobrychus sturmii, 66 pl. p. 48

jacobinus, Clamator, 348 pl. p. 241
jamesi, Cisticola s., 638
jamesoni, Lagonosticta, 835, pl. p. 577
jardineii, Turdoides, 533, pl. p. 368
johnstoni, Seicercus r., 671
juncidus, Cisticola, 629, pl. p. 448
Jynx ruficollis, 453, pl. p. 304

kalahari, Cisticola a., 630
kalahariae, Certhilauda a., 474
kalaharica, Afrotis a., 226
kalaharica, Emberiza f., 874
kalaharica, Mirafra a., 466
kalaharica, Francolinus l., 179, pl. p. 128
kalahari, Tchagra s., 715
kaokensis, Certhilauda c., 475
karasensis, Cisticola s., 638
karruensis, Certhilauda a., 461
Kaupifalco monogrammicus, 144, pl. p. 112
kennedyi, Batis c., 672
khama, Eremopterix v., 485
kilimensis, Nectarinia, 752, pl. p. 529
kirkii, Chalcomitra a., 772, pl. p. 544
kirkii, Turdoides j., 533
klaas, Chrysococcyx, 351, pl. p. 256
kolybini, Lanius c., 708
kori, Ardeotis, 217, pl. p. 160

lacteifrons, Urocolius i., 392
lacteus, Bubo, 369, pl. p. 257
Lagonosticta jamesoni, 835, pl. p. 577
Lagonosticta nitidula, 836, pl. p. 577
Lagonosticta rubricata, 833, pl. p. 577
Lagonosticta senegala, 837, pl. p. 577
lais, Cisticola, 639, pl. p. 449
lamelligerus, Anastomus, 74, pl. p. 49
Lamprotornis acuticaudus, 741
Lamprotornis chalybeus, 738, pl. p. 528
Lamprotornis chloropterus, 739, pl. p. 528
Lamprotornis corruscus, 740, pl. p. 528
Lamprotornis nitens, 737, pl. p. 528
Lamprotornis australis, 743, pl. p. 528
Lamprotornis mevesii, 742, pl. p. 528
langi, Francolinus l., 179, pl. p. 128
Laniarius atrococcineus, 711, pl. p. 512
Laniarius bicolor, 710, pl p. 513
Laniarius ferrugineus, 709, pl. p. 513

639

macrourus, Circus, 168, pl. p. 112
macrourus, Euplectes, 815, pl. p. 561
macrura, Sterna, 294, pl. p. 224
maculata, Cisticola l., 639
maculosa, Prinia 651, pl. p. 464
magnirostris, Calendula, 463, pl. p. 320
mahali, Plocepasser, 780, pl. p. 545
major, Cisticola t., 631
major, Nectarinia f., 751
makalaka, Erythropygia l., 588
makarikari, Mirafra a., 459
makarikari, Pterocles b., 308
makawa, Chlorophoneus o., 717
Malaconotus hypopyrrhus, 723, pl. p. 512
Malcorus pectoralis, 619, pl. p. 464
Mandingoa nitidula, 827, pl. p. 577
manoensis, Cinnyris c., 760
margaritatus, Hypargos, 831, pl. p. 577
marginalis, Porzana, 200, pl. p. 144
marginatus, Charadrius, 235, pl. p. 184
marina, Pelagodrqma, 34, p. xxxi
mariquensis, Bradornis, 661, pl. p. 465
mariquensis, Cinnyris, 755, pl. p. 529
marjoriae, Mirafra a., 466
marleyi, Cisticola t., 632
marleyi, Ploceus x., 802
marshalli Crithagra f., 866
marwitzi, Phoeniculus p., 419
marwitzi, Hirundo d., 498
mashona Cisticola l., 640
maurus, Circus, 169, pl. p. 112
maxima, Amblyospiza a., 804
maxima, Megaceryle, 395, pl. p. 288
mechowi, Melierax m., 163, pl. p. 112
media, Gallinago, 249, pl. p. 161
media, Fringillaria c., 873
Megaceryle maxima, 395, pl. p. 288
meinertzhageni, Certhilauda a., 474
Melaenornis pammelaina, 664, pl. p. 465
melanocephala, Apalis, 623, pl. p. 417
melanocephala, Ardea, 55, pl. p. 33
Melanocorypha bimaculata, 487, p. xxxii
melanogaster, Eupodotis, 227, pl. p. 160
melanoleucus, Accipiter, 159, pl. p. 113
melanoleucus, Urolestes, 724, pl. p. 513
Melanophoyx ardesiaca, 64, pl. p. 48
melanophris, Diomedea, 8, pl. p. 16
melanops, Turdoides, 534, pl. p. 368
melanopterus, Stephanibyx, 243, pl. p. 184
melanorhynchus, Casmerodius a., 58, pl. p. 33
melanotos, Calidris, 251X, pl. p. 185
melanotos, Sarkidiornis, 91, pl. p. 65
melanotis, Coccopygia, 825, pl. p. 592
melanurus, Passer, 786, pl. p. 545

melba, Apus, 386, pl. p. 273
melba, Pytilia, 830, pl. p. 576
meleagris, Numida, 192, pl. p. 129
Melierax canorus 165, pl. p. 112
Melierax metabates, 163, pl. p. 112
Melierax musicus, 165, pl. p. 112
Melittophagus bullockoides, 409, pl. p. 288
Melittophagus pusillus, 410, pl. p. 288
Melocichla mentalis, 617, pl. p. 416
menetriesi, Buteo b., 154
mennelli, Poliospiza, 868, pl. p. 608
mentalis, Melocichla, 617, pl. p. 416
meridionalis, Amadina f., 821, pl. p. 576
meridionalis, Gallinula c., 210, pl. p. 145
meridionalis, Gypaetus b., 150, pl. p. 72
meridionalis, Himantopus h., 270, pl. p. 161
meridionalis, Melittophagus p., 410, pl. p. 288
Merops apiaster, 404, pl. p. 288
Merops boehmi, 408, pl. p. 288
Merops n. nubicoides, 407, pl. p. 288
Merops nubicus 407, pl. p. 288
Merops superciliosus, 406, pl. p. 288
Mesophoyx intermedius, 60, pl. p. 33
Mesopicos griseocephalus, 452, pl. p. 305
metabates, Melierax, 163, pl. p. 112
mevesii, Lamprotornis, 742, pl. p. 528
meyeri, Poicephalus, 327, pl. p. 240
Micronisus gabar, 162, pl. p. 113
Microparra capensis, 229, pl. p. 145
microrhynchus, Cinnyris b., 756, pl. p. 529
microscelis, Dissoura e., 77, pl. p. 49
migrans, Milvus, 128, pl. p. 112
milanjensis, Andropadus, 549, pl. p. 369
millardi, Calandrella c., 488
Milvus aegyptius, 129, pl. p. 112
Milvus migrans, 128, pl. p. 112
minor, Cisticola a., 648
minor, Colius s., 390
minor, Falco p., 113, pl. p. 73
minor, Fregata, 53, pl. p. 32
minor, Indicator, 442, pl. p. 256
minor, Lanius, 706, pl. p. 513
minor, Myrmecocichla f., 575
minor, Phoeniconaias, 87, pl. p. 49
minor, Pirenestes, 819, pl. p. 577
minor, Stephanibyx m., 243, pl. p. 184
minor, Tchagra a., 714
minullus, Accipiter, 158, pl. p. 113
minuta, Calidris, 253, pl. p. 185
minutus, Anthoscopus, 531, pl. p. 368
minutus, Antichromus, 716, pl. p. 512

pallidior, Mirafra a., 458, pl. p. 320
pallidior, Francolinus l., 179, pl. p. 128
palliditergum, Batis m., 673
pallidiventris, Halcyon l., 401
pallidiventris, Parus r., 529
pallidus, Bradornis, 662, pl. p. 465
pallidus, Charadrius, 235, pl. p. 184
pallidus, Pycnonotus b., 545
pallidus, Urocolius i., 392
pallidus, Zosterops, 775, pl. p. 544
palpebrata, Phoebetria, 12X, pl. p. 16
paludicola, Riparia, 509, pl. p. 352
palustris, Acrocephalus, 607, pl. p. 416
pammelaina, Melaenornis, 664, pl. p. 465
Pandion haliaetus, 172, pl. p. 112
par, Sterna b., 297, pl. p. 224
paradisaea, Steganura, 852, pl. p. 593
paradisea, Anthropoides, 216, pl. p. 160
parasiticus, Stercorarius, 284, pl. p. 209
Parisoma layardi, 659, pl. p. 465
Parisoma subcaeruleum, 658, pl. p. 465
Parus afer, 525, pl. p. 368
Parus griseiventris, 526, pl. p. 368
Parus leucomelas, 528, pl. p. 368
Parus niger, 527, pl. p. 368
Parus rufiventris, 529, pl. p. 368
Passer diffusus, 787, pl. p. 545
Passer domesticus, 784, pl. p. 545
Passer melanurus, 786, pl. p. 545
Passer motitensis, 785, pl. p. 545
passerina, Mirafra, 457, pl. p. 320
patae, Certhilauda a., 461
patersonae, Anthreptes c., 771
payesi, Ixobrychus m., 67, pl. p. 48
pectoralis, Caprimulgus, 373, pl. p. 272
pectoralis, Circaetus, 146, pl. p. 97
pectoralis, Coracina, 515, pl. p. 353
pectoralis, Erythropygia l., 588
pectoralis, Malcorus, 619, pl. p. 464
pectoralis, Plocepasser s., 781, pl. p. 545
pecuarius, Charadrius, 237, pl. p. 184
pekinensis, Falco n., 125
pekinensis, Apus a., 378
pelagicus, Hydrobates, 30
Pelagodroma marina, 34
Pelecanoides urinatrix, 38, p. xxxi
Pelecanus onocrotalus, 42, pl. p. 32
Pelecanus refescens, 41, pl. p. 32
peli, Scotopelia, 370, pl. p. 257
peltata, Platysteira, 677, pl. p. 480
pennatus, Hieraaetus, 139, pl. p. 97
percnopterus, Neophron, 111, pl. p. 72
peregrinus, Falco, 113, pl. p. 73
perlatum, Glaucidium, 365, pl. p. 257
Pernis apivorus, 132, pl. p. 112
perreini, Estrilda, 842, pl. p. 592

persicus, Merops s., 405
petersi, Podica s., 213, pl. p. 145
petricolus, Anthus s., 693
Petrochelidon spilodera, 504, pl. p. 352
Petronia superciliaris, 788, pl. p. 545
phaeonota, Columba g., 311
phaeopus, Numenius, 268, pl. p. 161
Phaethon rubricauda, 39, pl. p. 32
Phaethon lepturus, 40, pl. p. 32
Phalacrocorax africanus, 50, pl. p. 32
Phalacrocorax capensis, 48, pl. p. 32
Phalacrocorax carbo, 47, pl. p. 32
Phalacrocorax coronatus, 51, pl. p. 32
Phalacrocorax neglectus, 49, pl. p. 32
Phalaropus fulicarius, 271, pl. p. 185
Phalaropus lobatus, 272, pl. p. 185
phanus, Telophorus z., 722
Phedina borbonica, 504X, pl. p. 352
Philetairus socius, 783, pl. p. 545
Philomachus pugnax, 256, pl. p. 185
Phoebetria fusca, 12, pl. p. 16
Phoebetria palpebrata, 12X, pl. p. 16
phoebus, Tauraco c., 336
phoenicea, Campephaga, 513, pl. p. 353
Phoeniconaias minor, 87, pl. p. 49
Phoenicopterus ruber, 86, pl. p. 49
phoenicopterus, Lamprotornis n., 737, pl. p. 528
Phoeniculus purpureus, 419, pl. p. 240
Phormoplectes angolensis, 795, p. xxxii
Phyllastrephus debilis, 548, pl. p. 369
Phyllastrephus flavostriatus, 547, pl. p. 369
Phyllastrephus terrestris, 546, pl. p. 369
Phylloscopus trochilus, 599, pl. p. 464
picta, Ispidina, 398, pl. p. 288
pileata, Oenanthe, 568, pl. p. 400
pileatus, Necrosyrtes m., 110, pl. p. 72
Pinarocorys nigricans, 464, pl. p. 320
Pinarornis plumosus, 538, pl. p. 368
pintoi, Camaroptera s., 615
pintoi, Mirafra r., 468
pipiens, Cisticola, 645X, pl. p. 449
Pirenestes minor, 819, pl. p. 577
Pitta angolensis, 455, pl. p. 240
placidus, Bradornis i., 663
Platalea alba, 85, pl. p. 49
Platysteira peltata, 677, pl. p. 480
Plectropterus gambensis, 88, pl. p. 65
Plegadis falcinellus, 83, pl. p. 49
Plocepasser mahali, 780, pl. p. 545
Plocepasser rufoscapulatus, 782, p. xxxii
Ploceus capensis, 799, pl. p. 560
Ploceus cucullatus, 797, pl. p. 560
Ploceus intermedius, 792, pl. p. 560
Ploceus rubiginosus, 796, pl. p. 545

645

Sarothrura lugens, 206X, pl. p. 144
Sarothrura rufa, 205, pl. p. 144
sarwensis, Mirafra a., 459
saturatior, Calandrella c., 488
saturatior, Chalcomitra s., 774
saturatior, Eremomela i., 600
saundersi, Sterna a., 299
savensis, Laniarius f., 709
Saxicola rubetra, 577, pl. p. 400
Saxicola torquata, 576, pl. p. 400
schalowi, Rhinopomastus c., 421
schalowi, Tauraco c., 334, pl. p. 240
schalowi, Treron a., 323
schlegelii, Cercomela, 566, pl. p. 400
Schoenicola brevirostris, 616, pl. p. 416
schoenobaenus, Acrocephalus, 608, pl. p. 416
Schoutedenapus myoptilus, 385X, pl. p. 273
scita, Stenostira, 678, pl. p. 480
sclateri, Childonias h., 305, pl. p. 224
sclateri, Cyanomitra o., 767, pl. p. 544
sclateri, Spizocorys, 491, pl. p. 321
sclateri, Symplectes b., 790
scopifrons, Sigmodus, 729, pl. p. 513
scops, Otus, 363, pl. p. 257
Scopus umbretta, 72, pl. p. 49
Scotopelia peli, 370, pl. p. 257
scotops, Eremomela, 602, pl. p. 464
scotops, Serinus, 858, pl. p. 608
scriptoricauda, Campethera, 446X, pl. p. 305
scutata, Lonchura c., 823, pl. p. 576
seebohmi, Rhinoptilus c., 279
Seicercus ruficapilla, 671, pl. p. 465
seimundi, Bradornis i., 663
semirufa, Cecropis, 501, pl. p. 352
semitorquata, Alcedo, 396, pl. p. 288
semitorquata, Certhilauda c., 475, pl. p. 321
semitorquata, Streptopelia, 314, pl. p. 225
semitorquatus, Poliochierax, 126, pl. p. 73
senegala, Lagonosticta, 837, pl. p. 577
senegala, Tchagra, 715, pl. p. 512
senegalensis, Centropus, 355, pl. p. 241
senegalensis, Cecropis, 500, pl. p. 352
senegalensis, Chalcomitra, 774, pl. p. 544
senegalensis, Ephippiorhynchus, 75, pl. p. 49
senegalensis, Halcyon, 399, pl. p. 288
senegalensis, Podica, 213, pl. p. 145
senegalensis, Stigmatopelia, 317, pl. p. 225
senegalensis, Zosterops, 777, pl. p. 544
senegaloides, Halcyon, 400, pl. p. 288
senegallus, Xiphidiopterus, 247, pl. p. 184

sephaena, Francolinus, 174, pl. p. 128
Serinus atrogularis, 860, pl. p. 608
Serinus canicollis, 857, pl. p. 608
Serinus citrinipectus, 860X, pl. p. 608
Serinus mozambicus, 859, pl. p. 608
Serinus scotops, 858, pl. p. 608
Serinus symonsi, 856, pl. p. 608
Serinus totta, 855, pl. p. 608
serpentarius, Sagittarius, 105, pl. p. 72
serratus, Clamator j., 348, pl. p. 241
sharpei, Camaroptera b., 628
sharpei, Chrysococcyx c., 350, pl. p. 256
sharpei, Crithagra a., 863
shelleyi, Cinnyris, 757, pl. p. 529
shelleyi, Francolinus, 177, pl. p. 128
Sheppardia gunningi, 591, pl. p. 401
Sigelus silens, 665, pl. p. 465
Sigmodus retzii, 728, pl. p. 513
Sigmodus scopifrons, 729, pl. p. 513
signata, tychaedon, 584, pl. p. 401
silberbaueri, Cisticola f., 637
silens, Sigelus, 665, pl. p. 465
similis, Chlorophoneus s., 719
simplicissima, Motacilla c., 687, pl. p. 481
simulator, Erythropygia l., 588
sinuata, Cercomela, 572, pl. p. 400
slogetti, Fringillaria i., 871
smithersi, Cisticola c., 642
smithersi, Fringillaria c., 873
smithersi, Mirafra r., 468
smithi, Eremopterix l., 484, pl. p. 321
smithi, Turdus o., 553, pl. p. 369
smithii, Campethera a., 447
smithii, Hirundo, 496, pl. p. 352
Smithornis capensis, 454, pl. p. 465
socius, Philetairus, 783, pl. p. 545
solitarius, Cuculus, 343, pl. p. 241
sordahlae, Crithagra a., 865
soror, Batis m., 675, pl. p. 480
sowerbyi, Buccanodon w., 434, pl. p. 304
sparsa, Anas, 95, pl. p. 64
sparsimfasciatus, Accipiter t., 160
Spatula capensis, 94, pl. p. 64
Spatula clypeata, 93, pl. p. 64
spatulata, Coracias, 414, pl. p. 289
spelonkensis, Apalis t., 622, pl. p. 417
Spheniscus demursus, 2, pl. p. 32
Sphenoeacus afer, 618, pl. p. 416
Sphenorhynchus abdimii, 78, pl. p. 49
spilodera, Petrochelidon, 504, pl. p. 352
spilogaster, Hieraaetus, 141, pl. p. 97
spilonotus, Ploceus, 797, pl. p. 560
spilonata, Salpornis, 532, pl. p. 368
Spizocorys conirostris, 490, pl. p. 321
Spizocorys sclateri, 491, pl. p. 321
Spizocorys starki, 492, pl. p. 321

647

649

Upupa africana, 418, pl. p. 240
Uraeginthus angolensis, 839, pl. p. 592
urbica, Delichon, 507, pl. p. 352
urinatrix, Pelecanoides, 38, p. xxxi
Urocolius indicus, 392, pl. p. 272
Urolestes melanoleucus, 724, pl. p. 513
ussheri, Telacanthura, 388, pl. p. 273
usticollis, Eremomela, 601, pl. p. 464
usheri, Pterocles b., 310

vaalensis, Anthus, 695, pl. p. 481
vaalensis, Zosterops, 776, pl. p. 544
vaillantii, Trachyphonus, 439, pl. p. 304
validus, Pachycoccyx a., 345, pl. p. 241
vansoni, Serinus m., 859
variegatus, Indicator, 441, pl. p. 256
velatus, Ploceus, 803, pl. p. 560
velox, Sterna b., 298
venusta, Apalis t., 622
venustus, Cinnyris, 762, pl. p. 544
vermiculatus Burhinus, 274, pl. p. 161
vernayi, Francolinus c., 173
verreauxi, Aquila, 133, pl. p. 96
verreauxi, Aviceda c., 127, pl. p. 73
verreauxi, Cinnyricinclus, 736, pl. p. 528
verreauxi, Turdus l., 552
veroxii, Cyanomitra, 765, pl. p. 544
verticalis, Eremopterix, 485, pl. p. 321
vespertinus, Falco, 120, pl. p. 73
vexillaria, Macrodipteryx, 377, pl. p. 272
vibrator, Campethera a., 447
victorini, Bradypterus, 612, pl. p. 416
Vidua macroura, 846, pl. p. 593
Vidua regia, 847, pl. p. 593
vidua, Motacilla a., 685
viduata, Dendrocygna, 100, pl. p. 65
vigorsii, Eupodotis, 220, pl. p. 160
vincenti, Mirafra a., 459
violacea, Anthobaphes, 753, pl. p. 529
virens, Zosterops, 778, pl. p. 544
Viridibucco simplex, 438X, pl. p. 304
viriditincta, Eremomela i., 600
vittata, Sterna, 292, pl. p. 224
vocifer, Haliaeetus, 149, pl. p. 96

voelckeri, Seicercus r., 671
volkmanni, Turtur c., 321
vulgaris, Sturnus, 733, pl. p. 528
vulpinus, Buteo b., 154, pl. p. 112
vulturnus, Macronyx c., 704, pl. p. 481
vylderi, Treron a., 323, pl. p. 225

wahlbergi, Aquila, 137, pl. p. 97
waibeli, Mirafra s., 460
watti, Francolinus l., 179
welwitschii, Caprimulgus f., 376
whytti, Buccanodon, 434, pl. p. 304
whytii, Sylvietta w., 621X
wilsoni, Crithagra s., 863
wilsoni, Erythropygia q., 585
witputzi, Calandrella c., 488
woltersi, Amblyospiza a., 804
woltersi, Vidua r., 847
woodfordii, Ciccaba, pl. p. 257
woodwardi, Buccanodon o., 435
woodwardi, Sylvia b., 595

xanthops, Ploceus, 801, pl. p. 560
xanthopterus, Ploceus, 802, pl. p. 560
Xenus cinereus, 257, pl. p. 185
Xiphidiopterus albiceps, 246, pl. p. 184
Xiphidiopterus senegallus, 247, pl. p. 184

yakutensis, Phylloscopus t., 599

zambesiae, Francolinus s., 174
zambesiae, Prodotiscus, 444, pl. p. 256
zambesiana, Anthreptes c., 771
zambesiana, Erythropygia l., 587, pl. p. 401
zeylonus, Telophorus, 722, pl. p. 512
zombae, Lybius t., 431
Zosterops pallidus, 775, pl. p. 544
Zosterops senegalensis, 777, pl. p. 544
zuluensis, Anthreptes c., 771
zuluensis, Francolinus s., 174
zuluensis, Mirafra a., 458
zuluensis, Tricholaema l., 432

Indeks tot Afrikaanse Name

A

Aasvoël, Egiptiese, 111, **pl. 10,** bl. 72 en **pl. 11**
  Krans, 106, **pl. 10,** bl. 72 en **pl. 11**
  Monnik, 110, **pl. 10,** bl. 72 en **pl. 11**
  Swart, 108, **pl. 10,** bl. 72 en **pl. 11**
  Wit, 112, **pl. 10,** bl. 72 en **pl. 11**
  Witkop, 109, **pl. 10,** bl. 72 en **pl. 11**
  Witrug, 107, **pl. 10,** bl. 72 en **pl. 11**
Albatros, Groot, 7, **pl. 2,** bl. 16
Arend, Breëkop-, 142, **pl. 12** en **pl. 14,** bl. 96
  Bruin Slang-, 145, **pl. 11** en **pl. 15,** bl. 97
  Dwerg-, 139, **pl. 12** en **pl. 15,** bl. 97
  Gebande Slang-, 148, **pl. 11** en **pl. 15,** bl. 97
  Klein Gevlekte, 136, **pl. 12** en **pl. 14,** bl. 96
  Kroon-, 143, **pl. 12** en **pl. 14,** bl. 96
  Langkuif-, 138, **pl. 12** en **pl. 15,** bl. 97
  Steppe-, 135, **pl. 12** en **pl. 14,** bl. 96
  Suidelike Gebande Slang-, 147, **pl. 11** en **pl. 15,** bl. 97
  Swartbors-slang-, 146, **pl. 11** en **pl. 15,** bl. 97
  Vis-, 149, **pl. 12** en **pl. 14,** bl. 96
  Wahlbergse, 137, **pl. 12** en **pl. 15,** bl. 97
  Witkruis-, 133, **pl. 12** en **pl. 14,** bl. 96

B

Baardmannetjie, 789, **pl. 68,** bl. 576
Bassiaan, 23, **pl. 3,** bl. 17
Bergeend, 90, **pl. 9,** bl. 65
Berghaan, 151, **pl. 11** en **pl. 14,** bl. 96
Bergkatlagter, 540, **pl. 48,** bl. 368
  Damara, 539, **pl. 48,** bl. 368.
Bleshoender, 212, **pl. 23,** bl. 145
Blou Kwartel, 191, **pl. 20,** bl. 128
Bokmakirie, 722, **pl. 60,** bl. 512
Bont Elsie, 269, **pl. 25,** bl. 161
Bontrokkie, 576, **pl. 50,** bl. 400
Boomkruiper, 532, **pl. 48,** bl. 368
Boompieper, 698, **pl. 59,** bl. 481
Boomvalk = 115
Bosbontrokkie, 672, **pl. 58,** bl. 480
  Beloog-, 677, **pl. 58,** bl. 480
  Mosambique-, 675, **pl. 58,** bl. 480
  Pririt-, 674, **pl. 58,** bl. 480

  Witsy-, 673, **pl. 58,** bl. 480
  Woobwardse, 676, **pl. 58,** bl. 480
Bosduif, 311, **pl. 33,** bl. 225
Boskraai, 422, **pl. 41,** bl. 289
  Kuifkop-, 423, **pl. 41,** bl. 289
Boskrapper, 546, **pl. 49,** bl. 369
Boskruiper, Geelstreep-, 547, **pl. 49,** bl. 369
  Klein Geelstreep, 548, **pl. 49,** bl. 369
Bosloerie, 393, **pl. 34,** bl. 240
Bosluisvoël, 61, **pl. 5,** bl. 33
Bosmusikant, 790, **pl. 66,** bl. 560
Bosuil, *sien* Uil
Breëbek, 454, **pl. 57,** bl. 465
Bromvoël = 430
Byvanger, Klein, 518, **pl. 47,** bl. 353
  Mikstert-, 517, **pl. 47,** bl. 353
Byvreter, Boehmse, 408, **pl. 40,** bl. 288
  Blouwang-, 406, **pl. 40,** bl. 288
  Europese, 404, **pl. 40,** bl. 288
  Klein, 410, **pl. 40,** bl. 288
  Mikstert-, 411, **pl. 40,** bl. 288
  Rooibors-, 407, **pl. 40,** bl. 288
  Rooikeel-, 409, **pl. 40,** bl. 288

D

Dagbrekertjie = 570
Dassievanger = 133
Dassievoël, 573, **pl. 50,** bl. 400
Diedrikkie, 352, **pl. 36,** bl. 256
Dikkop, 275, **pl. 25,** bl. 161
  Water-, 274, **pl. 25,** bl. 161
Doodvoël = 259
Dopertjie = 6
Draaihals, 453, **pl. 42,** bl. 304
Drawertjie, Bloukop-, 276, **pl. 30,** bl. 208
  Bronsvlerk-, 280, **pl. 30.** bl. 208
  Drieband-, 279, **pl. 30,** bl. 208
  Dubbelband-, 278, **pl. 30,** bl. 208
  Trek-, 277, **pl. 30,** bl. 208
Duif, Bos-, 311, **pl. 33,** bl. 225
  Geelbek-bos-, 312, **pl. 33,** bl. 225
  Groot Ring-, 314, **pl. 33,** bl. 225
  Klein Rooioog-tortel-, 315, **pl. 33,** bl. 225
  Papegaai-, 323, **pl. 33,** bl. 225
  Tortel-, 316, **pl. 33,** bl. 225
  Withals-bos-, 313, **pl. 33,** bl. 225
Duifie, Blouvlek, 320, **pl. 33,** bl. 225
  Groenvlek, 321, **pl. 33,** bl. 225

651

K

Kaffertjie, 486, **pl. 45,** bl. 321
  Grysrug, 485, **pl. 45,** bl. 321
  Rooirug, 484, **pl. 45,** bl. 321
Kaffervink, *sien* Vink
Kakelaar, 419, **pl. 34,** bl. 240
  Swartbek-, 421, **pl. 34,** bl. 240
Kalkoen, Wilde-, 82, **pl. 7,** bl. 49
Kalkoentjie, 703, **pl. 59,** bl. 481
  Geelkeel-, 704, **pl. 59,** bl. 481
  Rooskeel-, 705, **pl. 59,** bl. 481
Kanarie, Berg-, 860, **pl. 72,** bl. 608
  Gestreepte, 858, **pl. 72,** bl. 608
  Kaapse, 857, **pl. 72,** bl. 608
  Pietjie, 855, **pl. 72,** bl. 608
  Swartkop-, 861, **pl. 72,** bl. 608
Kapokvoël, Kaapse, 531, **pl. 48,** bl. 368
  Grys, 530, **pl. 48,** bl. 368
Katakoeroe, Blou, 516, **pl. 47,** bl. 353
  Swart, 513, **pl. 47,** bl. 353
  Witbors-, 515, **pl. 47,** bl. 353
Katlagter, Kaalwang, 537, **pl. 48,** bl. 368
  Pylvlek, 533, **pl. 48,** bl. 368
  Swart, 538, **pl. 48,** bl. 368
  Swartwang-, 534, **pl. 48,** bl. 368
  Wit, 536, **pl. 48,** bl. 368
  Witkruis, 535, **pl. 48,** bl. 368
Kelkiewyn, 307, **pl. 30,** bl. 208
Kemphaan, 256, **pl. 29,** bl. 185 en **pl. 27**
Kersogie = 775
Kiewiet, Lel-, 247, **pl. 26,** bl. 184
Kiewietjie, 242, **pl. 26,** bl. 184
  Bont-, 245, **pl. 26,** bl. 184
  Klein Swartvlerk-, 244, **pl. 26,** bl. 184
  Swartvlerk-, 243, **pl. 26,** bl. 184
  Witkop-, 246, **pl. 26,** bl. 184
  Witvlerk-, 248, **pl. 26,** bl. 184
Klappertjie, 466, **pl. 44,** bl. 320
  Laeveld-, 468, **pl. 44,** bl. 320
Kleinspringkaanvoël, Gewone, 281, **pl. 30,** bl. 208
  Swartvlerk-, 282, **pl. 30,** bl. 208
  Withals-, 283, **pl. 30,** bl. 208
Kleinjantjie, Bandkeel-, 622, **pl. 53,** bl. 417
  Chirinda-, 623X, **pl. 53,** bl. 417
  Geelbors-, 625, **pl. 53,** bl. 417
  Rooioor-, 619, **pl. 56,** bl. 464
  Ruddse, 624, **pl. 53,** bl. 417
  Swartkop, 623, **pl. 53,** bl. 417
Klipmossie, 872, **pl. 72,** bl. 608
Kliplyster, Angola-, 562, **pl. 49,** bl. 369
  Kaapse-, 559, **pl. 49,** bl. 369
  Korttoon-, 561, **pl. 49,** bl. 369
  Langtoon-, 560, **pl. 49,** bl. 369

Klipwagter, Berg, 569, **pl. 50,** bl. 400
Klopkloppie, Bleekkop-, 635, **pl. 54,** bl. 448
  Gevlekte, 631, **bl. 54,** pl. 448
  Kleinste, 634, **pl. 54,** bl. 448
  Kortvlerk-, 636, **pl. 54,** bl. 448
Knoet, 254, **pl. 27** en **pl. 29,** bl. 185
Koekoek, 340, **pl. 35,** bl. 241
  Afrikaanse, 341, **pl. 35,** bl. 241
  Dikbek-, 345, **pl. 35,** bl. 241
  Groot Gevlekte, 346, **pl. 35,** bl. 241
  Klein, 342
  Swart, 344, **pl. 35,** bl. 241
Koester, Bosveld-, 699, **pl. 59,** bl. 481
  Donker, 694, **pl. 59,** bl. 481
  Geelbors-, 701, **pl. 59,** bl. 481
  Gewone, 692, **pl. 59,** bl. 481
  Gestreepte, 696, **pl. 59,** bl. 481
  Klip-, 697, **pl. 59,** bl. 481
  Kortstert-, 700, **pl. 59,** bl. 481
  Nicholsonse, 693, **pl. 59,** bl. 481
  Vaal, 695, **pl. 59,** bl. 481
Koggelaar = 568
Kokkewiet = 709 en 722
Kolgans, 89, **pl. 9,** bl. 65
Kongkoit, 721, **pl. 60,** bl. 512
Koningblousysie = 840
Koningriethaan, 208, **pl. 23,** bl. 145
  Klein, 209, **pl. 23,** bl. 145
Koning-rooibek = 846
Korhaan, Blou, 223, **pl. 24,** bl. 160
  Bos-, 224, **pl. 24,** bl. 160
  Damara Vaal = 220(*e*), **pl. 24** bl. 160
  Langbeen, 227, **pl. 24,** bl. 160
  Natalse, 222, **pl. 24,** bl. 160
  Swart, 225, **pl. 24,** bl. 160
  Vaal, 220, **pl. 24,** bl. 160
Koringvoël, 780, **pl. 65,** bl. 545
Kouvoël, 134, **pl. 12** en **pl. 14,** bl. 96
Kraai, Bont = 522
  Huis, 523X, **pl. 47,** bl. 353
  Swart, 523, **pl. 47,** bl. 353
  Witbors-, 522, **pl. 47,** bl. 353
  Withals-, 524, **pl. 47,** bl. 353
Kraan, Blou-, 216, **pl. 24,** bl. 160
  Lel-, 215, **pl. 24,** bl. 160
Krabpluvier = 273
Krabstrandloper, 273, **pl. 25,** bl. 161
Krombek = 621, **pl. 56,** bl. 464
Kwartel, Afrikaanse, 189, **pl. 20,** bl. 128
  Blou, 191, **pl. 20,** bl. 128
  Bont, 190, **pl. 20,** bl. 128
Kwarteltjie, Bosveld-, 196, **pl. 22,** bl. 144
  Kaapse, 194, **pl. 22,** bl. 144
Kwartelkoning, 198, **pl. 22,** bl. 144
Kwartelvinkie, 844, **pl. 70,** bl. 592

653

656

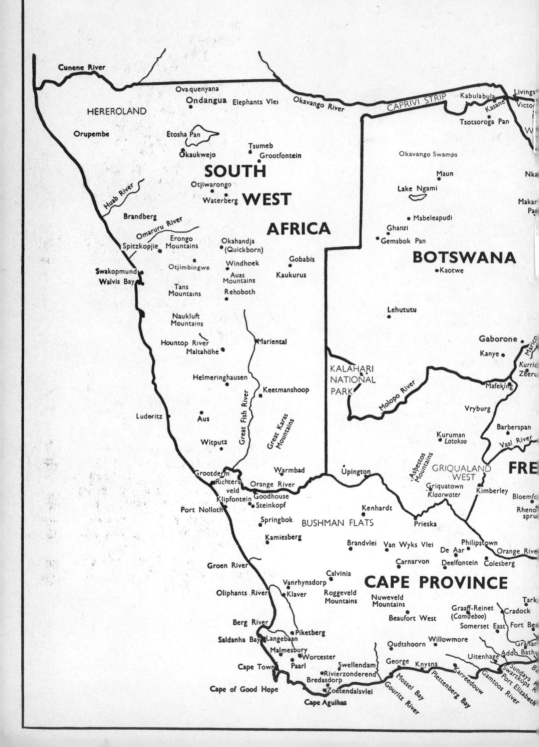

MAP SHOWING SOME PLAC[
NAMES USED BY EARLY TR[